RARE METALS HANDBOOK

RARE METALS HANDBOOK

Second Edition

EDITED BY

Clifford A. Hampel

Consulting Chemical Engineer
Skokie, Illinois

REINHOLD PUBLISHING CORPORATION

Chapman & Hall, Ltd., London

CONTRIBUTORS

ARCHER, R. S., Chief Metallurgist (Retired, 1960), Climax Molybdenum Co., 1270 Avenue of the Americas, New York 20, N.Y. *Molybdenum.*

BAREFOOT, R. R., Central Research Laboratory, Canadian Industries, Limited, McMasterville, Quebec, Canada. *Platinum Metals.*

BEAMISH, FRED E., Professor of Chemistry, Department of Chemistry, University of Toronto, Toronto 5, Ontario, Canada. *Platinum Metals.*

CARON, PETER E., Manager By-Product Sales, American Smelting and Refining Company, 120 Broadway, New York 5, N.Y. *Selenium, Tellurium.*

COFFINBERRY, A. S., Plutonium Physical Metallurgy Group (CMF–5), University of California, Los Alamos Scientific Laboratory, Los Alamos, New Mexico. *Plutonium.*

COOPER, HUGH S., Consulting Chemist and Metallurgist, 16401 South Woodland Road, Shaker Heights, Ohio. *Boron.*

DAANE, A. H., Professor of Chemistry, Iowa State University and Senior Chemist, Ames Laboratory, U.S. Atomic Energy Commission, Ames, Iowa. *Scandium, Yttrium.*

DUNN, H. E., Associate Technical Director, Vanadium Corporation of America, 420 Lexington Ave., New York 17, N.Y. *Vanadium.*

EDLUND, D. L. Associate Technical Director, Research Center, Vanadium Corporation of America, Cambridge, Ohio. *Vanadium.*

FIELD, JACK E., Research Chemist, Pigments Department, E. I. duPont de Nemours & Co., Inc., Edge Moor, Del. *Silicon.*

FOUNTAIN, R. W., Manager, Metals Research, Metals Research Laboratories, Union Carbide Metals Company, Niagara Falls, N.Y. *Chromium.*

HAMPEL, CLIFFORD A., Consulting Chemical Engineer, 8501 Harding Ave., Skokie, Ill. *The Rare Metals, Rubidium and Cesium, Tantalum, Physical Properties of Metals.*

HARNER, HAROLD R., Director of Research, Research Laboratory, Chemicals and Metals Division, The Eagle-Picher Company, Joplin, Mo. *Germanium.*

HOWE, HERBERT E., Research Metallurgist, Central Research Laboratories, American Smelting and Refining Company, South Plainfield, N.J. *Bismuth, Thallium.*

ISSEROW, SAUL, Project Manager, Nuclear Metals, Inc., Concord, Mass. *Uranium.*

KING, R. A., Research Engineer, Research and Development Division, The Consolidated Mining and Smelting Company of Canada, Limited, Trail, British Columbia, Canada. *Indium.*

KJELLGREN, BENGT R. F., Chairman of the Board, The Brush Beryllium Co., 5209 Euclid Ave., Cleveland 3, Ohio. *Beryllium.*

KREMERS, HOWARD E., District Manager, Market Development Department, American Potash & Chemical Corp., 99 Park Ave., New York 16, N.Y. *Rare Earth Metals.*

LANDOLT, PERCY E., Consulting Engineer, 598 Madison Ave., New York 22, N.Y. *Lithium.*

LI, K. C., Chairman, Wah Chang Corporation, Woolworth Building, New York 7, N.Y. *Tungsten.*

LYON, DONALD W., Technical Supervisor, Pigments Department, E. I. duPont de Nemours & Co., Inc., Edge Moor, Del. *Silicon.*

MANTELL, C. L., Consulting Chemical Engineer, 457 Washington St., New York 13, N.Y.; Chairman, Department of Chemical Engineering, Newark College of Engineering, Newark, N.J. *Calcium, Barium and Strontium; Manganese.*

MARTIN, DONALD R., Director of Research, Technical Center, Libbey-Owens-Ford Glass Company, 1701 East Broadway, Toledo 5, Ohio. *Hafnium.*

McBRYDE, W. A. E., Head, Department of Chemistry, University of Waterloo, Waterloo, Ontario, Canada. *Platinum Metals.*

McCUTCHEON, F. G., deceased, formerly Technical Director, Mining Smelting Division, The Eagle-Picher Company, Miami, Okla. *Cadmium.*

MELAVEN, A. D., Professor of Chemistry, Department of Chemistry, University of Tennessee, Knoxville 16, Tenn. *Rhenium.*

MILLS, J. R., Assistant Manager, Research and Development Department, The Consolidated Mining and Smelting Company of Canada, Limited, Trail, British Columbia, Canada. *Indium.*

MINER, W. R., Plutonium Physical Metallurgy Group (CMF–5), University of California, Los Alamos Scientific Laboratory, Los Alamos, New Mexico. *Plutonium.*

MULFORD, R. N. R., Plutonium Physical Metallurgy Group (CMF–5), University of California, Los Alamos Scientific Laboratory, Los Alamos, New Mexico. *Plutonium.*

MUSGRAVE, JOHN R., Chief, Service Section, Research Laboratories, Chemicals and Metals Division, The Eagle-Picher Company, Joplin, Mo. *Cadmium, Gallium.*

OGDEN, H. R., Chief, Nonferrous Metallurgy Division, Battelle Memorial Institute, 505 King Ave., Columbus 1, Ohio. *Titanium.*

PERKINS, M. F., Retired, formerly Superintendent of Pure Metal Development, American Smelting and Refining Company, Central Research Laboratories, South Plainfield, N.J. *Selenium, Tellurium.*

PIZZOLATO, PHILIP J., Research Division, New York University, New York, N.Y. *Hafnium.*

SCHLECHTEN, A. W., Chairman, Department of Metallurgical Engineering, University of Missouri, School of Mines and Metallurgy, Rolla, Mo. *Zirconium.*

SCHONFELD, F. W., Group Leader, Plutonium Physical Metallurgy Group (CMF–5), University of California, Los Alamos Scientific Laboratory, Los Alamos, New Mexico. *Plutonium.*

SHERWOOD, E. M., Consultant, Division of Inorganic Chemistry and Chemical Engineering, Battelle Memorial Institute, 505 King Ave., Columbus 1, Ohio. *Columbium.*

SITTIG, MARSHALL, Consultant, P.O. Box 549, Princeton, N.J. *Lithium.*

STONE, JOHN R., Research Investigator, American Smelting and Refining Company, 120 Broadway, New York 5, N.Y. *Selenium, Tellurium.*

TATE, R. E., Plutonium Physical Metallurgy Group (CMF–5), University of California, Los Alamos Scientific Laboratory, Los Alamos, New Mexico. *Plutonium.*

THOMPSON, A. P., Retired, formerly Director of Research, Research Laboratories, The Eagle-Picher Company, Joplin, Mo. *Gallium.*

WABER, J. T., Plutonium Physical Metallurgy Group (CMF–5), University of

California, Los Alamos Scientific Laboratory, Los Alamos, New Mexico. *Plutonium.*

WHITE, C. E. T., Research Engineer, Research and Development Department, The Consolidated Mining and Smelting Company of Canada, Limited, Trail, British Columbia, Canada, *Indium.*

WHITTEMORE, CARL R., Chief Metallurgist, Deloro Smelting & Refining Co., Limited, Deloro, Ontario, Canada, *Cobalt.*

WILHELM, H. A., Associate Director, Institute for Atomic Research and Ames Laboratory of the U.S. Atomic Energy Commission, Iowa State University, Ames, Iowa. *Thorium.*

In Appreciation of

COLIN GARFIELD FINK

1881–1953

Pioneer in the field of rare metals, distinguished contributor to knowledge of electrometallurgical techniques, and ingenious experimenter, his loss by the electrochemical profession is compensated only by the rich heritage he leaves as a teacher whose infectious curiosity and energetic enthusiasms inspired all who were his students, as a devoted servant and builder of The Electrochemical Society for which he was Secretary from 1921 to 1947, as a prolific producer of original research which made common many rare metals, and as an amiable, devoted friend. Truly his works and life will be perpetuated by the stimulus he gave to so many others by personal and scientific contacts; they will detail and expand the fields whose vistas he outlined.

PREFACE

To Second Edition

In the years which have passed since the material for the First Edition of the "Rare Metals Handbook" was prepared, a flood of new data has appeared about the metals included in this book. In content this additional material probably is more than equal to the amount known about these metals six years ago. This new information, the wider usage and interest in the rare metals, and the important advances in this field make this Second Edition necessary and valuable.

One evidence of the increasing importance of the rare metals in our technology is the multitude of symposia dealing with them presented before scores of technical societies during recent years in this and other countries. Another is the growing volume of data about the engineering properties of many of these metals, indicative of the desire for improved structural materials.

Typical of much of the surge of interest in and work on the rare metals is the expansion of knowledge about the rare earth metals, most of which have been virtually unknown in the pure form. The studies and production processes that have issued from the Ames Laboratory (Institute for Atomic Research) and other agencies working with the rare earth metals have resulted in the addition of essentially 16 new metals (including scandium and yttrium) to the roster of metals with valuable and unusual properties.

Although several of the metals included in this book can no longer be called "rare," inasmuch as they have reached tonnage production rates, they are still covered, simply because there is no real reason why they should be omitted. They are still uncommon to the vast majority of people in the metals field, and a convenient summary of information about them is worthwhile to users of the book if only for reference purposes within a single volume. In addition, on a price basis, they cannot be called the equivalent of the more common metals, with the exception of manganese, which sells for less than nickel and tin.

Several new metals have been added to the list included in this book: cesium, chromium, plutonium, rubidium, scandium, and yttrium, and separate chapters have been prepared on columbium and tantalum. A total of 55 metals is covered in the Second Edition. With few exceptions the chapters contain greatly enhanced presentations of information due not only to the additional data developed in the past several years, but to the release of large amounts of hitherto classified information.

The gratifying acceptance of the First Edition has led to the use of the same mode of presentation in each of the chapters with emphasis on the element itself rather than its compounds. No major change has been made in the purposes of the compilation, outlined in the Preface to the First Edition.

To each of the new contributors as well as those who readily accepted the task of revising their original contributions go the appreciation and thanks of the Editor. Without their cordial cooperation this Second Edition would have been virtually impossible for the Editor to undertake.

Special thanks are expressed to G. G. Hawley, Executive Editor of the Reinhold Book Division, and to his staff for handling of the manuscript, and for the new format being used for this edition.

Finally, thanks to my wife, Merrylyn, and my daughter, Beth, for undergoing curtailment of many outside activities so that the Editor could assume the host of time-consuming details associated with the preparation of this Edition.

CLIFFORD A. HAMPEL

Skokie, Illinois
February, 1961.

PREFACE

To First Edition

This book has been designed to accomplish the following purposes:

1. To bring together for the first time the available reference data on over 34 rare or uncommon metals—the latest methods of production from ores or other raw materials, the chemical and physical properties, fabrication techniques, and present and potential uses.

2. To offer an authoritative, concise and readily available background to the man who desires information about a specific metal or metals, and at the same time to give him selected bibliographical references to enable him to conduct a more detailed search if he so desires.

3. To provide a convenient source of data for the man who has a general question, such as "What metals have melting points over 1000°C and densities below that of steel?"

The treatment has been limited to emphasis upon the metallic or elemental form with only a minor presentation of material about compounds, interesting though these are in many instances. This has been dictated by space considerations as well as the desire to concentrate attention on the metals themselves, which often receive scanty treatment in most inorganic chemistry treatises.

The list of metals selected for inclusion is admittedly arbitrary, but it covers most of the less common metals about which there is an expanding interest. While there may be debate of an academic nature as to whether elements like boron and silicon are metals, they do exhibit some of the properties commonly regarded as characteristic of metals, and the growing interest in them in several fields of metallurgy warrants their inclusion in this book.

As pointed out in the final chapter, it so happens that cost alone is a worthy basis for regarding a given metal as rare or common. A classification of metals in order of increasing price per pound reveals that of the first 13 only one of the metals included in this book, manganese, appears among them. Also, of the metals not covered in this book, only mercury, silver, and gold appear further down the list. This is not surprising since cost is a good measure of the availability and scope of usage of a metal regardless of the relative rarity of raw materials, complexity of processing, etc., for the production of a metal in commercially attractive form.

The designation, "Rare Metals," was chosen as being simple and not misleading as compared with other names considered, i.e., "Less Common Metals" or "Unusual Metals" or even "Extraordinary Metals." It suffers from a certain amount of inaccuracy, of course, but the term is such that most people in the field will know exactly what group is meant to be covered by the phrase "Rare Metals." The long use of the term by such pioneers as Drs. John W. Marden and Colin G. Fink in the symposia of the Electrochemical Society, where many of the original reports of the isolation and properties of these metals have been presented, was a major factor in choosing the name for the "Rare Metals Handbook."

This book would not have been possible, of course, without the cordial cooperation of the contributors to it. To each of these busy men who generously gave the time required to prepare the individual chapters the Editor is deeply indebted, and to all of them his heartfelt thanks are given. He wishes especially to express his appreciation to those who, having completed their work at an early date, patiently awaited the slower submission of the chapters by others who were delayed for one reason or another in the completion of their contributions.

Deep appreciation is due to Dr. John R. Musgrave of The Eagle-Picher Company for his early assistance in selecting the elements included in the book and his enthusiasm for its purpose, to the late Francis M. Turner of Reinhold Publishing Corporation, to the late Dr. Colin G. Fink of Columbia University, to Dr. John W. Marden of Westinghouse Electric Corporation, and to A. A. Smith, Jr., of American Smelting and Refining Company. All supported the initiation of the work and generously drew upon their wide circles of friends to suggest contributors for the various chapters.

Special thanks are expressed for the continued stimulation and personal assistance given by Fred P. Peters, Vice President of the Reinhold Publishing Corporation, whose friendships in and knowledge of the metals field are only equalled by his stature in these respects in the field of technical literature. In a similar manner the cooperation of G. G. Hawley, Executive Editor of the Reinhold Book Division, has been most helpful in the completion of this work. To him and to Miss Jeanne Bergquist go sincere appreciation for their handling of the manuscript and their coordination of almost as many styles of usage as there are chapters in the book.

Acknowledgment is made of the valued assistance of Dr. Charles L. Mantell in supplying data and reviewing the chapter on "Manganese" by the Editor.

Without the help of these friends and many others who gave support and advice the completion of the work would have been much more difficult.

Finally, sincere thanks are given my wife, Merrylyn, for undergoing many lonely evenings so that the multitude of details associated with an activity of this sort could be handled, and for her candid advice and criticism.

CLIFFORD A. HAMPEL

Homewood, Ill.
  February, 1954.

CONTENTS

CONTENTS

1. THE RARE METALS

Clifford A. Hampel

Consulting Chemical Engineer
Skokie, Illinois

The last war not only affected profoundly major fields of science and technology, but it also stimulated the rate at which new developments were applied and widened the scope of their applications. These trends have continued since that time and no evidence of any slackening of steady progress has appeared.

New and widespread interest has been aroused with respect to materials by which the changing but ever-expanding demands of technology can be satisfied. Materials hitherto unknown, or if known, regarded as little more than scientific curiosities, have been demanded for the new techniques and developments.

In a prime position among such materials are the rare or uncommon metals. The accelerated rate of consolidation of the gains of science has placed new significance upon more than laboratory quantities of the rare metals. Whereas before the war only a few workers devoted their scientific activities to them, hundreds are now working with and expanding the knowledge about their procurement and utilization, as evidenced, for example, by the large number of research and development programs directed to the production and application of these metals.

The well-known story of uranium, and to a lesser extent of thorium, for atomic energy purposes hardly needs repeating, but it serves to illustrate the sudden and increasing demand for a metal so scarce that in 1940 only a few grams of good uranium were in existence. Information about it was so scanty that even the melting point was not known accurately. (For example, the "Handbook of Chemistry and Physics" in 1943 lists the melting point as less than 1850°C

(3362°F), while it is now known to be 1132°C (2070°F). At the same time a supply of high-purity beryllium had to be provided to serve as a source of neutrons for the uranium pile.

The nuclear energy program has since created an interest in other metals of specific properties, notably gallium, indium, and bismuth, to serve as possible heat transfer media; hafnium-free zirconium as a material of construction of high corrosion resistance and low neutron absorption cross section; elements such as gadolinium, hafnium, and boron, whose high thermal neutron absorption cross sections make them useful as control rods; and plutonium as a nuclear fuel.

The rapidly growing electronics industry has demanded a host of rare metals for a variety of purposes—germanium and silicon for transistors and other devices where semiconductors are needed, selenium for photoelectric cells and rectifiers, tungsten and beryllium for x-ray tubes, tantalum for transmitting tubes and capacitors, molybdenum for receiving tubes, platinum and tungsten for contacts, and tellurium as a semiconductor in thermoelectric devices, to cite a few examples.

The requirement for cobalt alloys to be used for high-temperature service and permanent magnets has created an acute demand for cobalt, whose production rate formerly was about equal to that of silver. Titanium, whose high strength and low weight are so interesting to the aircraft and marine industries, has received a phenomenal amount of attention. While it has had its ups and downs, due chiefly to changing demands by the military aircraft program, ti-

'ly become a major metal
truction. Beryllium is
easing amounts to meet
its unique properties in nu-
applications.

other fields likewise require one or
of the rare metals to satisfy the peculiar
operties needed for practical application of
new developments, but the above serve to indicate the varied and growing demand for these metals.

Why are these metals rare or uncommon? One or more of several reasons can be advanced to explain the situation. (1) The natural supply or abundance in the earth's crust may be small. (2) Even if a metal is fairly prevalent, the concentration in accessible deposits may be so low as to require the handling and processing of huge amounts of worthless material in order to extract even small quantities of the desired element in either compound or elemental form. Or, to put it another way, deposits of ore in economically desirable concentrations are few. (3) The chemical and physical properties of the element may be such that conversion to the elemental form is very difficult. (4) Even though available, the element may not have enough attractive properties or uses to create a demand for it in competition with other available materials on a cost basis.

The common denominator of all these reasons is, of course, economics. The ingenuity of chemists, engineers, and metallurgists is sufficient to find ways of providing the element in the desired form if cost is no barrier. However, the present or potential cost of the metal must be low enough to make its production and application worthwhile before the metal will take its place in the economy. The outstanding exceptions to the last statement are those metals vital to the national defense, notably uranium, where of course cost is no barrier.

The economic factor has another influence which has retarded the greater production and use of many of the rare metals. Markets are often not certain until the metal is available in assured supply; and vice versa, the metal often is not produced in appreciable quantity until the market is certain—a vicious cycle that can be broken by the courageous producer who deliberately sets out to find markets and

uses for a metal he knows he can produce. This, of course, is a common practice in the chemical industry, which develops many new products each year and then finds uses and outlets for them. This practice is being followed to an increasing degree by the producers of metals and is one reason for the widespread interest in the rare metals.

Of great import to the growing knowledge of the production, properties, and applications of the rare metals, and to their increasing use, are the research and development programs of the Atomic Energy Commission and the various defense agencies. When these programs have created a demand for a given metal, the government has often financed (in one way or another) the required production facility to supply its needs. In many instances, excess capacity has been provided in these plants so that peacetime uses can be evaluated and established on an economically attractive basis.

Natural Occurrence

While many other factors may also affect the availability of a metal as an item of commerce and use, the prevalence of it in the earth's crust is a most important factor, and a knowledge of the relative abundance of the metals in the crust of the earth points up the other reasons for the relative commonness or rareness of any one metal in our civilization.

One of the most recent compilations of the average amounts of the elements in the earth's crust is given by Mason;[6] it is based largely upon data developed by the late V. M. Goldschmidt of Norway and the late F. W. Clarke, for 41 years Chief Chemist of the U. S. Geological Survey until his retirement in 1925. Table 1.1 gives the order of occurrence of the elements in grams per ton or parts per million.

This assembly of the order of prevalence of the elements reveals a host of interesting relationships. The first eight elements—oxygen, silicon, aluminum, iron, calcium, sodium, potassium, and magnesium—comprise about 99 per cent of the crust, but only one, oxygen, is present extensively as an element, and only one, iron, is used chiefly in elemental form. However, aluminum also has become one of the more common commercial metals, and magnesium is also used to a considerable extent. It is of interest to note that the production

Table 1.1. The Average Amounts of the Elements in the Earth's Crust in Grams per Ton or Parts per Million*

(Omitting those present in less than 0.001 g/ton: Ne, Kr, Xe, Ra, and the short-lived radioactive elements)

O	466,000	Ge	7
Si	277,200	Be	6
Al	81,300	Sm	6.5
Fe	50,000	Gd	6.4
Ca	36,300	Pr	5.5
Na	28,300	Sc	5
K	25,900	As	5
Mg	20,900	Hf	4.5
Ti	4,400	Dy	4.5
H	1,400	U	4
P	1,180	B	3
Mn	1,000	Yb	2.7
S	520	Er	2.5
C	320	Ta	2.1
Cl	314	Br	1.6
Rb	310	Ho	1.2
F	300	Eu	1.1
Sr	300	Sb	1?
Ba	250	Tb	0.9
Zr	220	Lu	0.8
Cr	200	Tl	0.6
V	150	Hg	0.5
Zn	132	I	0.3
Ni	80	Bi	0.2
Cu	70	Tm	0.2
W	69	Cd	0.15
Li	65	Ag	0.1
N	46	In	0.1
Ce	46	Se	0.09
Sn	40	A	0.04
Y	28	Pd	0.01
Nd	24	Pt	0.005
Cb(Nb)	24	Au	0.005
Co	23	He	0.003
La	18	Te	0.002
Pb	16	Rh	0.001
Ga	15	Re	0.001
Mo	15	Ir	0.001
Th	12	Os	0.001?
Cs	7	Ru	0.001?

* From Brian Mason, "Principles of Geochemistry" (copyright 1952 by John Wiley & Sons, Inc., New York), p. 41. Reprinted by permission of the publisher.

rates of steel, aluminum, and magnesium in the United States at the present time are roughly in the ratio of 3000:50:1. Sodium is produced in much greater quantity than magnesium, and is used more as a chemical reducing agent than as a metal. One other of the eight, calcium, is

made commercially, but in relatively small amounts.

Two of the most commonly used elements that are naturally present and used in elemental form, sulfur and carbon, are 13th and 14th, respectively, in the list, and the next, chlorine, ranks second to iron in the tonnage converted to and used in the form of the element.

Thus, of the first 15 elements in order of abundance (through chlorine), only oxygen, sulfur, and carbon occur and are used widely in the native uncombined form. Also, iron, chlorine, aluminum, sodium, and magnesium are the leading elements, in that order, which are reduced to the elemental state for application. In our industrial civilization oxygen is the major element in tonnage use as an element, even if the biological consumption is disregarded; carbon is next; and iron is third.

Noteworthy is the relative abundance in the earth's crust of many elements which are not commonly used in large quantities, such as titanium, rubidium, zirconium, and vanadium. Conversely, elements that have long played important roles in our civilization really are quite scarce. Copper is about as abundant as tungsten and much less so than manganese, zirconium, and vanadium. Nitrogen is no more abundant than cerium, tin is less abundant than lithium, and lead and molybdenum are about equal to gallium. Thorium and uranium are both more abundant than boron, and vanadium is somewhat more prevalent than zinc. Mercury is much less abundant than the rare earths, beryllium, and tantalum.

It is rather startling to find that rubidium ranks 16th in order of prevalence, almost as abundant as chlorine, when it and its compounds are so little known in chemistry and are such uncommon articles of commerce.

The Oceans as Source of Metals

The oceans, which cover over 70 per cent of the earth's surface, contain an average of 3.5 per cent of dissolved solids—an insignificant quantity as compared with the weight of the earth's crust, but one of utmost importance in that the oceans are so accessible. Of more consequence, the constituents are in solution. As is well known, much effort and cost are often involved in dissolving solids prior to further processing and ultimate recovery of

TABLE 1.2. ELEMENTS PRESENT IN SOLUTION IN SEA WATER*

(excluding dissolved gases)

Element	Concentration (g/ton)	Element	Concentration (g/ton)
Cl	18,980	Mn	0.001–0.01
Na	10,561	Pb	0.004–0.005
Mg	1,272	Se	0.004
S	884	Sn	0.003
Ca	400	Cs	approx. 0.002
K	380	U	0.00015–0.0016
Br	65	Mo	0.0003–0.002
C (inorganic)	28	Ga	0.0005
Sr	13	Ni	0.0001–0.0005
(SiO$_2$)	0.01–7.0	Th	< 0.0005
B	4.6	Ce	0.0004
Si	0.02–4.0	V	0.0003
C (organic)	1.2–3.0	La	0.0003
Al	0.16–1.9	Y	0.0003
F	1.4	Hg	0.0003
N (as nitrate)	0.001–0.7	Ag	0.00015–0.0003
N (as organic		Bi	0.0002
nitrogen)	0.03–0.2	Co	0.0001
Rb	0.2	Sc	0.00004
Li	0.1	Au	0.000004–0.000008
P (as phosphate)	> 0.001–0.10	Fe (in true solution)	< 10^{-9}
Ba	0.05	Ra	$2 \times 10^{-11} - 3 \times 10^{-10}$
I	0.05	Ge	Present
N (as nitrite)	0.0001–0.05	Ti	Present
N (as ammonia)	> 0.005–0.05	W	Present
As (as arsenite)	0.003–0.024	Cd	Present in marine organisms
Fe	0.002–0.02	Cr	Present in marine organisms
P (as organic		Tl	Present in marine organisms
phosphorus)	0–0.016	Sb	Present in marine organisms
Zn	0.005–0.014	Zr	Present in marine organisms
Cu	0.001–0.09	Pt	Present in marine organisms

* Based on material from H. U. Sverdrup, Martin W. Johnson, Richard H. Fleming, *"The Oceans"* (Copyright 1942 by Prentice-Hall, Inc., New York) pp. 176–177. Reprinted by permission of the publisher.

desired products, so the fact that sea water is a solution, admittedly dilute, has definite technological importance.

Some 50 elements are known to be present in sea water, and undoubtedly others found in marine organisms were derived from sea water. Table 1.2 presents the concentrations of the elements in sea water as developed by Sverdrup, Johnson, and Fleming.[10] The concentration ratios are remarkably constant over the globe because of the homogeneity of the oceans. Ranges are given for many of the elements and represent variations in concentrations due to localized conditions and to biological activity which changes with depth.

The order of prevalence of elements in sea water differs markedly from that given in Table 1.1 for the earth's crust (which includes the oceans and other bodies of water making up the hydrosphere), for several reasons. The solubility relationships are different in aqueous systems than in the silicate systems which comprise such a major portion of the solid crust. Therefore, the ions formed by the leaching process that gave the sea its dissolved constituents vary radically in concentration from those found in the solid crust. Further, interaction in solution has altered the ratios of elements present in sea water. Also, marine organisms of all sorts have selectively removed certain elements, and this age-old process has served to change the ratios of abundance of many elements in sea water. Natural adsorption and ion exchange mechanisms have contributed to the removal and substitution of several elements. The low values for toxic elements like arsenic and selenium are due to the adsorption of them on freshly precipitated ferric hydroxide, according to Goldschmidt.[7] Many of the rare elements are present in deposits on the ocean bottom, as evidenced by their presence in deposits left by ancient seas now being mined.

The oceans have been referred to often as a veritable storehouse of chemicals, including metals; sodium and magnesium compounds, bromine, and magnesium metal are being profitably extracted from it at the present time.[11] It is of interest to note that magnesium made from a sea water source utilizes a raw material containing only 0.13 per cent magnesium, although vast deposits of ores containing 30 per cent or more are available, giving one case at least where a truly dispersed natural raw material is preferred to a more concentrated one as a source of a commercial product. Incidentally, the plants using sea water for magnesium production achieved lower production costs during the war period than did any others, and were the only ones which operated continuously during the postwar years when other plants were shut down.

The old story of gold from sea water may not be as absurd as it sounds. Some 40 years ago, a plant in France actually operated a sea water gold extraction process, and while it failed financially, the margin of failure was not a tremendous one. While gold has long been a lure, it is likely that not gold, but other valuable products, among them metals, will be recovered from the ocean. This likelihood is enhanced by the recent advances in ion exchange, porous membrane, adsorption, and electrochemical techniques.

Other Sources of Metals

In the future an even more important method of extracting metals from the sea may be the deliberate cultivation of specific marine organisms which concentrate one or more elements in their bodies by biological activity. It is common knowledge, of course, that coral and oyster shells concentrate calcium carbonate, diatoms concentrate silica, and oysters and lobsters concentrate copper. Organisms less well known do likewise with other elements

like iron, vanadium, cobalt, zinc, and manganese.[2]

Certain seaweeds like kelp have been sources of potassium and iodine for over a century, and other sea plants are known to concentrate a variety of specific elements in their bodies. All are potential sources of elements needed by man for industrial use.

It has long been recognized that land plants are often effective concentrators of certain elements. Notable examples, insofar as the rare metals are concerned, are the plants that concentrate selenium. *Astralagus,* a species of vetch, also known as locoweed, grows well only in soil containing selenium and builds up concentrations as high as 1.5 per cent of this valuable metal. Other plants are known to concentrate germanium, and the existence of germanium in many coals is due to the same ability on the part of some ancient plants which later became coal. Still other plants are recognized as being able to concentrate manganese, boron, barium, and the rare earths, to name a few examples.[1]

An interesting sidelight to this ability of plants to retain specific elements is prospecting for metals by the collection and deliberate analysis of such plants to determine if desirable mineral deposits are located in the ground below the growth. It has been established that high-selenium plants are good indicators of the location of uranium deposits.[3]

Still another potential raw material for many of the rare metals is provided by bacteria and other microorganisms which live upon dilute sources of specific elements and convert them to more concentrated deposits. The native sulfur found in the caprock of some salt domes very likely derived from bacterial conversion of the sulfate content of anhydrite to free sulfur; it is recognized that the anaerobic type species *Sporovibria desulfuricans (Beijerinck) Starkey* reduces sulfate to free sulfur or sulfide. Other bacteria are able to digest, convert, and concentrate iron, manganese, cobalt, and vanadium, to name a few metals so affected. Some geologists believe that the iron ore deposits were formed by bacterial action, as were those of many types of manganese dioxide-containing ores. Whether these deductions are true or not need not concern us now; the important fact is that the proper culture of specific microorganisms may provide a vital source of concentrated supplies of many of the rare metals in the future. The utilization of microorganisms to extract the minute amounts of many valuable metals from ash and slag piles, for example, as well as from low grade mineral deposits, opens up a whole new vista of possibilities for the scientist and engineer in their roles of satisfying the apparently insatiable demands of an industrial culture for greater supplies of metals at a time when the known deposits of the metals are becoming lower and lower in grade and quality.

Currently, one of the large copper companies is initiating the recovery, on a large scale, of copper from mine waste dumps by a process based on bacterial action.[12] The naturally occurring species *Thiobacillus ferrooxidans*, which has been bred to withstand 17,000 ppm zinc (originally 150 ppm was the limit), 12,000 copper, 6290 aluminum, 4975 calcium, 2400 magnesium, 3280 manganese, and 100 molybdenum, is used to oxidize ferrous iron in a leach solution to ferric iron. The ferric iron, in turn, oxidizes copper to the cupric state and builds up the concentration of the latter in the leach solution from which it can be recovered. The bacteria are autotrophic, and need oxygen and CO_2 for growth, but no organic materials. They exist in and are tolerant to sulfuric acid, and operate best at 15–40°C (59–104°F) and a pH of 1.5-2.5. Reactions in the presence of bacteria are:

$$2FeSO_4 + H_2SO_4 + \tfrac{1}{2}O_2 \rightarrow Fe_2(SO_4)_3 + H_2O$$

$$Fe_2(SO_4)_3 + 6H_2O \rightarrow 2Fe(OH)_3 + 3H_2SO_4$$

$$4FeS_2 + 15O_2 + 2H_2O \rightarrow 2Fe(SO_4)_3 + 2H_2SO_4$$

$$Fe_2(SO_4)_3 + Cu \rightarrow CuSO_4 + 2FeSO_4$$

A culture of this bacteria species has been deposited with the American Type Culture Collection, 2112 M St., N.W., Washington 7, D.C. and has Collection Catalog No. 12912.

Available Concentration of Metals

One of the reasons for the wide discrepancy in many instances between the natural prevalence and the commercial availability of some metals is the degree of concentration of any given metal in a mineral, an ore body, or some other industrial raw material.

Almost all of the metals long known and used by man—iron, zinc, copper, tin, lead,

mercury, and silver—are present in the earth as easily recognized minerals containing rather high percentages of the metal. This, plus the ease with which they are extracted from the minerals, accounts for their long usage. Conversely, many metals high on the prevalency list are widely dispersed in small amounts in common minerals and almost without exception never occur in any appreciable concentration. Examples of this type are rubidium and gallium. Rubidium forms no minerals of its own and is always incorporated in potassium minerals, and gallium is incorporated principally in aluminum minerals. Another, zirconium, forms specific minerals, chiefly zircon, which in turn are widely dispersed in small amounts throughout some of the commonest rocks.[8]

To be commercially attractive an ore must contain a concentration of the desired metal to make the extraction of it technically and economically feasible. This concentration varies greatly, as might be expected, from metal to metal owing to the chemical and physical properties of the metals and their compounds as they determine the extraction processes which can be used. For copper it may be 1 per cent or less, and for iron it should be 30 per cent or more; for magnesium it can be 0.13 per cent, the amount in sea water, and for aluminum it is 30 per cent or more, to cite a few contrasting examples. Changing technology and economic demand continuously alter the minimum concentrations required in an ore or other raw material source for the production of various metals. A prime illustration of this is the copper situation where residue piles of material discarded in previous years have been reworked as newer processes have made possible the recovery of copper contents formerly inaccessible.

Insofar as many of the metals covered in this book are concerned, the chief sources of such metals are the residues of operations for the recovery of other more common metals, whereby small quantities of the scarce metals are concentrated to values which permit their extraction. The platinum metals are derived principally from residues of the nickel extraction process; gallium, germanium, cadmium, and indium are recovered from by-product lines of lead and zinc operations, as are thallium and bismuth; while selenium, tellurium, cobalt, and rhenium are obtained from copper production residues. Most of these are exceedingly rare in natural deposits, but modern technology has improved upon geological processes and provided raw materials of relatively high concentrations from which these metals can be extracted.

Unusual Processing Problems

In most cases the rare metals are not extracted with ease from their ores or other raw materials, and further, their fabrication into desired forms often is not as simple as it is with the more common metals. These characteristics have required the application of many techniques that are greatly different from the more classical ones normally used for the more easily handled metals. In fact it has been necessary to develop the special techniques in some instances before certain of the rare metals could be prepared in anything approaching a pure form or a desired shape.

The relationship between the abundance and ease with which the metals may be converted to elemental state is indicated in Table 1.3 which lists the metals in four categories: abundant or scarce in nature, and easily or difficultly recoverable. While the location of some of the metals may be debated, the listings in Table 1.3 do reveal why the metals commonly used by man are in that status even though some are very scarce in nature. With the exception of aluminum and magnesium, all are easily reduced to and recoverable in elemental form, and only in comparatively recent times have the more refractory aluminum and magnesium become common. This follows from the fact that only recently have there been available the processes necessary for the production of aluminum, magnesium, and the other metals more difficult to recover.

In other words, the growing availability of the less familiar metals has gone hand in hand with the phenomenal development of knowledge of the physical sciences and their industrial applications which has characterized the last 50-year period and especially the last 20-year period. This is to be expected, of course, and augers well for the future, since a study of the individual chapters of this book shows that only a preliminary beginning has been made with respect to many of the metals and their

TABLE 1.3. RELATIONSHIP OF ABUNDANCE TO EASE OF CONVERSION TO ELEMENTAL FORM

Scarce Metals		Abundant Metals	
Easily Converted	Difficult to Convert	Easily Converted	Difficult to Convert
Antimony	Barium	Iron	Aluminum
Arsenic	Beryllium		Calcium
Bismuth	Boron		Magnesium
Cadmium	Cesium		Manganese
Cobalt	Chromium		Potassium
Copper	Columbium		Silicon
Gold	(Niobium)		Sodium
Lead	Gallium		Titanium
Mercury	Germanium		
Nickel	Hafnium		
Selenium	Indium		
Silver	Iridium		
Tellurium	Lithium		
Tin	Molybdenum		
Zinc	Osmium		
	Palladium		
	Platinum		
	Plutonium		
	Rare Earths		
	Rhenium		
	Rhodium		
	Rubidium		
	Ruthenium		
	Scandium		
	Strontium		
	Tantalum		
	Thallium		
	Thorium		
	Tungsten		
	Uranium		
	Vanadium		
	Yttrium		
	Zirconium		

properties, extraction, processing, fabrication, and use.

To emphasize the import of some of the unusual techniques which have been applied to the production of the rare metals, the following brief description of several is presented as they relate to the metals covered in this book.

Electrolytic Processes. Electrolysis offers one of the best means, and in some cases the only practical means, of producing the pure metals. The electrochemical industry as a whole is the major consumer of electric power in the United States, and the recovery, refining, and application of metals account for a sizable portion of this consumption.[4]

Deposition from aqueous solution is used to

produce cadmium, chromium, cobalt, gallium, indium, manganese, and thallium. It is also valuable for the application of many of the metals as electrodeposited coatings, among them cadmium, chromium, cobalt, palladium, platinum, rhodium, indium, and tungsten. The electrodeposition of germanium from non-aqueous solutions has been reported.

Figure 1.1 shows the cells used for the electrolytic refining of indium to produce metal of 99.98 per cent purity.

By taking advantage of the half-wave potentials of a whole series of metals in mercury, selective extraction of suitable metals can be made from even a dilute solution containing several of them if mercury is used as the cathode in a cell containing the solution. In reverse, metals of extremely high purity can be separately recovered by making an anode of the amalgam containing several metals, with an appropriate cathode in an electrolytic cell. In addition, the amalgam of a metal may be distilled to remove the mercury and leave behind the desired metal. These and other treatments comprise a new field of great potentiality aptly called "amalgam metallurgy,"[5] whose use may serve to delay the inevitable and in

Figure 1.1. Cells for the electrolytic refining of indium to produce metal of 99.98 per cent purity. (*Courtesy Consolidated Mining and Smelting Company of Canada, Ltd.*)

some instances current depletion of sources of strategic metals workable by presently used processes.

Deposition from molten salt baths has made possible the commercial production of aluminum, magnesium, and sodium, of course, and has been applied to the preparation of barium, beryllium, boron, calcium, cerium, columbium, lithium, the rare earths, strontium, tantalum, thorium, and uranium. The success of the commercial molten salt electrolysis for aluminum and magnesium has led to intensive search for similar processes for the large-scale low-cost production of titanium and zirconium. It is likely, however, that powdered metals will result, with associated problems of attaining high purity and of obtaining massive metal from cell products.

Metal Replacement. The principle of the well-known Goldschmidt or thermite reduction of metal oxides with aluminum has been applied to the use of calcium, sodium, and magnesium for the production of several of the rare metals from their oxides and halogen compounds.

Titanium, hafnium, and zirconium are being made by the Kroll process, which reduces the tetrachlorides of these metals with molten magnesium. Uranium and beryllium are produced by the reduction of their fluorides with magnesium.

Sodium is used to prepare columbium, hafnium, tantalum, titanium, and zirconium from the halides of these elements. Figure 1.2 shows the large reaction vessel used for the production of titanium by the reaction of sodium on titanium tetrachloride to make sponge metal.

Calcium is used to produce the rare earth metals, scandium, yttrium, thorium, plutonium, and vanadium, chiefly by reduction of the fluorides of these metals. All of the above processes are operated under carefully maintained inert atmospheres to ensure high purity metal products.

Sodium amalgam can also be used for the reduction of many metals from their halides under anhydrous conditions and at much lower temperatures, the active agent being the sodium dissolved in the mercury. In a manner similar to that whereby iron will displace and plate out copper from a copper solution, amalgams of certain metals, for example zinc, will chloride, but its production is not confined to this process. Many of the platinum metals are recovered by a final hydrogen reduction of oxides or ammonium chloro compounds.

Halide Decomposition. In addition to the production of metals by reduction of metal halides, which incidentally are very attractive intermediates owing to the high purity attainable in their formation, their relative ease of reduction, and the rather low melting and boiling points that characterize them in general, many of the metal halides decompose thermally to yield the metal. Thus, the iodides of titanium, hafnium, chromium, zirconium, vanadium, thorium, and uranium can be decomposed on a heated surface, such as an electrically heated tungsten wire, in an evacuated container to form the corresponding massive metals in a state of very high purity. Commercially, this iodide process is to be regarded more as a purification step than as a primary production process, but several of the pure metals have been prepared initially if not solely by it.

Some of the metal halides decompose thermally by disproportionation to yield a subhalide plus the metal or a mixture of halides. For example, titanium dichloride changes when heated to a mixture of titanium metal and titanium tetrachloride, while titanium trichloride

Figure 1.2. Titanium sponge is made by the reduction of titanium tetrachloride with sodium under an inert atmosphere. In the above photograph, the reaction vessel is being withdrawn from the reaction furnace after completion of the reaction. The sponge will be removed from it, consolidated into an electrode, and melted into massive form in the furnace illustrated in Figures 1.5 and 1.6. (*Courtesy Union Carbide Metals Co.*)

displace a series of metals from solution, the series being defined by the relation of the half-wave potentials to that of zinc. The amalgam formed by this displacement may be treated in a variety of ways to recover the pure metal contained therein, another aspect of "amalgam metallurgy."

Silicon is being prepared by the reduction of silicon tetrachloride with zinc vapor, the purity of the product being controlled by the purity of the tetrachloride if pure zinc is used.

Hydrogen Reduction. Germanium, molybdenum, and tungsten are made commercially by the reduction of their oxides with hydrogen, and rhenium by the reduction of either potassium or ammonium perrhenate. Cobalt is prepared by hydrogen reduction of its oxide or

Figure 1.3. Die arrangement of the 2,000 ton press used to prepare bars of compacted tantalum powder which are subsequently sintered. Powder of proper size distribution is being poured into the die cavity. (*Courtesy Wah Chang Corp.*)

Figure 1.4. High vacuum sintering vessels used for the sintering of green bars of tantalum from the press shown in Figure 1.3. The sintered bars are used to make sheet, tubing, etc., or are melted into ingot form in arc or electron beam furnaces. (*Courtesy Wah Chang Corp.*)

when heated can form a mixture of the di- and tetrachlorides. While these disproportionation reactions are not used at the present for metal production, so far as is known, they may become useful in the future.

Inert Atmosphere Arc Melting. The great avidity of many of the rare metals toward oxygen, nitrogen, hydrogen, and carbon, plus the fact that many of them are obtained from the initial reduction stage in the form of finely divided powders of great surface area and reactivity, requires the use of special techniques for the formation of massive metal forms. Tungsten, molybdenum, tantalum, and columbium have long been fabricated by powder metallurgy operations involving the sintering of a bar (compacted under high pressure) in an atmosphere of hydrogen for the first two and under a high vacuum for the last two. Figure 1.3 illustrates the 2,000 ton press used to prepare bars of compacted tantalum powder which are subsequently sintered in high vacuum sintering furnaces of the type shown in Figure 1.4. These sintered bars are suitable for processing into sheet, tubing, etc., or for melting in arc or electron beam furnaces.

The above metals, as well as titanium, zirconium, and hafnium, are now being melted in arc furnaces to form massive ingots. A compacted bar of the metal powder or sponge is

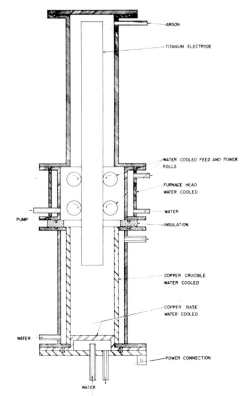

Figure 1.5. Sketch showing components of elementary inert atmosphere, consumable electrode arc melting furnace for titanium ingot preparation. (*Courtesy Republic Steel Corporation.*)

fed as a consumable electrode into a furnace maintained under a vacuum or an inert atmosphere of helium or argon, the molten metal being collected in a water-cooled copper crucible which serves as the second electrical terminal. In essence the container for the molten metal is a solidified shell of the metal itself, and the pickup of impurities from a ceramic crucible is eliminated. A nonconsumable tungsten electrode can also be used to strike the arc for melting, in which case the metal is fed directly into the molten pool on the lower electrode; however, the trend is toward the consumable electrode type of furnace to avoid contamination of the metal by the nonconsumable electrode material. Alloys can also be prepared in these furnaces by feeding the alloying elements in appropriate fashion to the molten pool.

Figure 1.5 is a sketch of the components of an elementary inert atmosphere, consumable electrode arc melting furnace for titanium ingot preparation. An arc is struck between the upper electrode and some pieces of titanium on the base of the water cooled copper mold, and the upper electrode is advanced as it is melted until the mold is filled. In Figure 1.6, an arc

Figure 1.6. Furnace for consumable electrode arc melting of titanium sponge under vacuum or inert atmosphere. Here the copper mold has been lifted off the titanium ingot after the mold and its ingot have been removed from the lower part of the furnace assembly in the background. The mold (above the ingot) is positioned in the furnace between the base plate and the cylindrical upper portion of the furnace (immediately behind the man at the left). The sponge feed electrode is lowered through the upper part of the furnace as it melts, the feed continuing until the mold is filled. Before further processing, the ingot is machined to remove surface roughness. (*Courtesy Titanium Metals Corp. of America.*)

melted titanium ingot weighing 4,000 pounds is being withdrawn from a commercial arc melting furnace. Ingots weighing as much as 10,000 pounds have been made in similar apparatus.

The use of high vacuum systems is also applied to the processing and melting of the rare metals as a method of preventing or reducing contamination.

Electron Beam Melting. A new means for the direct melting of high melting point metals into ingots of high purity is the electron beam process. The process consists of using a beam of high-velocity electrons which act as a heat source. The electrons from an electron gun are accelerated and focused onto the metal to be melted by a high voltage potential between the gun and the metal in a high vacuum chamber. Molten metal is collected and solidified in a water cooled copper mold.*

This form of melting not only consolidates metals of high melting points into ingots, but also causes a great decrease in impurity content. Many impurities are vaporized from the metal by the combination of high temperature and low pressure. The degree of impurity removal is controlled by the vapor pressure of the impurity elements and compounds, relative to the vapor pressure of the metal being treated, at the temperature of the molten metal.

Depending on the metal, ingots several inches in diameter and several feet long can be produced. In any one unit, the ingot diameter is usually proportional to the melting point of the metal.

The same technique can be applied to the fusion welding of reactive metals of high melting point, such as tantalum, tungsten, molybdenum, titanium, zirconium, and columbium. Consistently high quality welds are obtained because of the extremely pure atmospheres which can be maintained. The ability to focus accurately the electron beam permits very precise welds to be made.

Zone Refining. Impurities in a bar of metal can be segregated by zone refining. This technique consists of melting a small zone of the bar by induction heating or by use of an electron beam, and then moving the melted zone along the length of the bar by a corresponding movement of the source of heat. The result is a sweeping of impurities toward one end of the

* Chapter 9, "Columbium" contains a detailed description of the apparatus and method.

bar due to the greater solubility in the liquid phase of most of the impurities.

In practice, the rod is supported at both ends in a horizontal or vertical quartz tube under an inert atmosphere while being heated in one zone. The molten material is maintained by the surface tension of the liquid and a combination of magnetic and electrical levitation effects. As applied as a production step in the preparation of ultrapure silicon and germanium for semiconductor uses, a single crystal rod of these elements can be made by "seeding" the original molten zone with a single crystal and sweeping the zone slowly along the bar, usually from bottom to top. Single crystal germanium is shown in Figure 1.7.

Zone refining can be applied to the production of a large number of metals in very pure form. It prevents the pickup of impurities from a container which usually occurs in other purification methods.

In general the preparation of the rare metals has been characterized by the requirement that the products be in a state of purity much higher than has ever been the case with the more common metals. Only as very pure metals were derived have the true properties been appreciated. The influence on the hardness of titanium and zirconium, for example, caused by a few hundredths of a per cent of oxygen or nitrogen is so great that these metals were long thought to be nonductile until metals of very low oxygen and nitrogen content were made. It is recognized that much of the work done on alloy systems with impure metals must be reviewed now that the pure metals are available. Many other data have been or will be revised as pure metal is available for the evaluation of properties.

The details of the current status of the rare metals as well as data and information on derivation, properties, fabrication, and application given in the individual chapters of this book reveal a host of relationships which should stimulate the wider usage and understanding of the rare metals, materials that will contribute greatly to the expansion of the benefits of our technological era.

It should be emphasized that the whole story of the development of the rare or uncommon metals is the result of the utilization of the techniques of physics, inorganic chemistry, physical chemistry, and chemical engineering,

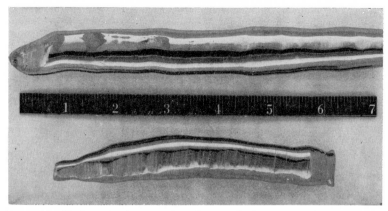

Figure 1.7. Single crystal germanium bar made by zone refining to attain ultrapure germanium for semiconductor devices. (*Courtesy Eagle-Picher Co.*)

as well as those of metallurgy, to achieve our present state of knowledge and progress. The future can only be one of greater achievement as these skills are blended more thoroughly to ultimately reach full exploitation of the possibilities of these unique materials.

An example is offered by the recent discovery of Stern of the increased corrosion resistance imparted to titanium by the addition of 0.1 per cent palladium or other noble metals. During basic work on corrosion phenomena, Stern developed an electrochemical theory which describes how passivity-type corrosion inhibitors function. From this he predicted that alloying with noble metals would create a similar electrochemical situation on titanium. Subsequent work confirmed this prediction.[9] The platinum group additive creates galvanic couples at the surface of the alloy. These provide a mixed potential at the surface higher than the critical potential for passivity of the titanium. Incidentally, the mechanical properties of the alloy are identical with those of unalloyed titanium.

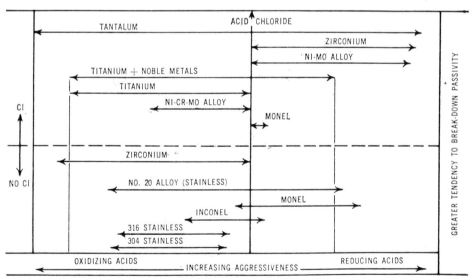

Figure 1.8. Titanium alloyed with noble metals, like palladium, has its useful corrosion range extended beyond that of unalloyed titanium. The corrosion resistance of these, and other metals and alloys, is indicated in this diagrammatic sketch which shows the general corrosive effects of oxidizing and reducing acids, and of the presence of chloride ion. (*Courtesy Union Carbide Metals Co., Metals Research Laboratories.*)

As shown in Figure 1.8, the corrosion resistance of titanium, which is fine in oxidizing reagents, is extended to the range of reducing reagents by the presence of palladium. This graphic summary also indicates the useful ranges of other metals and alloys in oxidizing and reducing corrosive media in the presence or absence of chlorides. Oxidizing-type environments include nitric acid, ferric chloride, aqua regia, cupric chloride, hydrogen peroxide, and sodium hypochlorite. Reducing-type or nonoxidizing environments include hydrochloric acid, sulfuric acid, phosphoric acid, oxalic acid, acetic acid, and aluminum chloride.

Tantalum has the greatest area of resistance to all conditions. The titanium-palladium alloy approaches, but does not equal, tantalum as the second best material. Zirconium is suitable in reducing media in the presence of acid chlorides and in oxidizing media in the absence of acid chlorides. The stainless steels are affected adversely by the chloride ion, and certain nickel-base alloys are useful under various limited conditions.

The 0.1 per cent palladium alloy is made by first mixing palladium and titanium powders in a high palladium ratio, pressing them into a consumable electrode, and arc melting the electrode under an inert atmosphere. The master alloy so prepared is then used by titanium mill product producers to prepare the final dilute alloy from titanium sponge.

As can be appreciated, many branches of science and technology contributed to attain the end product, a new corrosion resistant material of construction.

References

1. Anon., *Battelle Memorial Rev.*, **2**, No. 9, 101 (1953).
2. Armstrong, E. F., and Niall, L. M., "Raw Materials from the Sea," Constructive Publications, Ltd., Leicester, Eng., 1945.
3. Cannon, Helen, *U. S. Geol. Survey Circ. 264* (1953).
4. Faust, C. L., *J. Electrochem. Soc.*, **98**, No. 10, 133c–137c (1951).
5. Hohn, H., *Research*, **3**, 407–417 (1950).
6. Mason, B., "Principles of Geochemistry," p. 41 New York, John Wiley & Sons, Inc., 1952.
7. *Ibid.*, p. 173.
8. *Ibid.*, p. 42.
9. Stern, M., and Wissenberg, H., *J. Electrochem Soc.*, **106**, 759–764 (1959); Stern, M., and Bishop, C. R., paper presented at American Society for Metals meeting, Chicago, Nov. 2 1959; *Chem. Eng. News*, **37**, No. 15, 26 (April 13, 1959); *Modern Metals*, **15**, 32 (1959).
10. Sverdrup, H. U., Johnson, M. W., and Fleming R. H., "The Oceans," pp. 176–177, New York Prentice-Hall, Inc., 1942.
11. Tressler, D. K., and Lemon, J. MacW., "Marine Products of Commerce," 2nd ed., New York, Reinhold Publishing Corp., 1951.
12. Zimmerley, S. R., Wilson, D. G., and Brater J. D., U. S. Patent 2,829,964, April 8, 1958 (to Kennecott Copper Corp.). This patent gives a good description of the problems of breeding and using this species of bacteria for copper recovery. See also Kennecott Copper Corp 1959 Annual Report.

2. THE ALKALINE EARTH METALS— CALCIUM, BARIUM, AND STRONTIUM

CHARLES L. MANTELL

Consulting Engineer
New York, New York

Group IIA of the periodic table contains the alkaline earth metals, calcium, strontium, barium, and radium. The last is known primarily in the form of its salts and, to date, has no metal application.

In the older chemistries, all the nonmetallic substances that were insoluble in water and unchanged by fire were called *earths*. Lime and magnesia showed alkaline reactions, hence they were termed *alkaline* earths. Calcium is derived from the Latin *calx* (lime); barium from the Greek *barys* (heavy); and strontium from Strontian, a town in Scotland. All three metals were first isolated by Davy, in 1808, by electrolysis of the fused chlorides.

Of the alkaline earth group, calcium has achieved the greatest use and tonnage. Calcium ranks fifth in the order of abundance of elements in the earth's crust, the percentage being estimated at 3.64; strontium is eighteenth, with a percentage of 0.03; and barium is nineteenth, with a percentage of 0.025.

In general, the metals are white and differ from each other by shades of color or casts. They are malleable, extrudable, and machinable, and may be made into rods, wire, or plate. They are less reactive than sodium and potassium, and they have higher melting and boiling points. Their common ores are the sulfates and carbonates, and they form analogous chlorides, peroxides, nitrates, chlorates (in all of which they are bivalent), true carbides, and acetylides. A typical acetylide is calcium carbide (CaC_2), which, upon reaction with water, gives acetylene. The volatilizable salts give intense flame colors, that of barium being green, calcium a brilliant crimson with a yellowish shade, and strontium a brilliant crimson without the yellow component. The nitrates, chlorides, and chlorates of strontium and barium compounds are used in pyrotechnics in the form of signals, flares, and fuses.

Calcium is more reactive chemically than barium or strontium, but considerably less reactive than sodium. Calcium is the cheapest of the alkaline earth metals but is more expensive than sodium; sodium is a fraction of the price of calcium, and the production of sodium is more than 100 times that of calcium. In organic synthesis, sodium is in a better competitive position; in metallurgical work, however, the low melting point and high vapor pressure of sodium are disadvantages in deoxidizing, reducing, degasifying, and alloying, and the less volatile calcium is preferred. In addition, the end products of the sodium reactions are more volatile and of lower melting point than the corresponding end products of the calcium reactions. Calcium metal itself competes, even in metallurgical work, with some of its own compounds, examples of which are calcium silicide, calcium boride, and calcium carbide, all of which are used as degasifiers, reductants, and sources of calcium for alloys. Often, however, in highly specialized alloy work, examples of which are the nickel-chromium and nickel-chromium-iron materials for high-temperature service, these compounds may introduce undesirable materials from which the metallic calcium is free.

The metallurgical applications of these metals depend upon their reactivity at high temperatures with the formation of nitrides, silicides, and carbides such as Ca_2C (in contrast to acetylides like CaC_2), which are quite stable. At lower temperatures, stable hydrides, of which calcium hydride is typical, are formed. In the manufacture of electronic tubes the ability to fix residual gases as oxides, nitrides, and, to a lesser extent, hydrides, makes these metals important as getters.

CALCIUM

Freshly cut surfaces of calcium are white, approximately the color of silver. Fractured surfaces are more brilliant than steel. At relative humidities above 30 per cent the metal tarnishes, with the formation of thin, bluish-gray films of oxide which are protective against further attack. Commercial calcium in the form of a cast slab 2 in. (5.08 cm) thick, exposed to the atmosphere under average conditions, corrodes to depths of ¼ in. (0.635 cm) in 6 months' time. Cubicciotti[29] has studied the oxidation of calcium.

Calcium cannot be cast by the usual foundry methods, owing to exceedingly rapid oxidation at the melting point, but melting and casting procedures employing protective fluxes give cast forms of the metal. Homer and Whitacre[58] propose to coat calcium powder by metals decomposed from their carbonyl compounds.

Calcium metal may be handled in a manner similar to magnesium and aluminum. It may be touched and may come in contact with the skin without danger. It can be machined in a lathe, turned into shapes, drilled, threaded, sawed, extruded, drawn into wire, pressed, and hammered into plates.

Commercial forms include in the 99 per cent

TABLE 2.1. ANALYSIS OF CALCIUM METAL

	Commercial				Distilled	
	Crystalline (Ethyl Corp.)	"Domal"* grade 4	"Nelco"†	"Domal" grade 3	"Nelco"	"Domal" grade 2
Ca	94–97	98–99	99+	99–99.5	99.5	99.9 + Mg
Ag	< 0.0005					(Mg 0.5 max)
Al	0.002	0.35	0.03–0.30	0.30	0.0010	0.0007–0.010
B	0.001	—	—	—	< 0.0001	0.00002 max
Ba	0.002					
Be	0.001	—	—	—	< 0.0001	
CaO	2–5					
Cd	—		—		—	0.00002 max
Cl$_2$	0.0–0.5					
Co	—	—	—	—	< 0.0002	
Cr	—	—	—	—	< 0.0002	
Cu	0.001					
Fe	0.04	—	< 0.010	—	0.0010	0.001–0.005 max
K	< 0.001					
Li	—	—	—	—	< 0.0001	0.001 max
Mg	0.25–1.0	0.5–1.5	0.2–0.5	0.75 max	0.5000	
Mn	0.001	—	< 0.010	—	0.0020	0.0005–0.004 max
N$_2$	0.0015	1.0	0.01–0.1	0.15 max	0.0200	0.01–0.025 max
Na	0.5–0.8					
Na + K	—	—	—	—	—	0.001 max
Ni	< 0.005					
Ni + Cu + Cr	—	—	—	—	—	0.001–0.005 max
Pb	0.01					
Si	0.004					
Sn	0.001					
Sr	< 0.001					

* Dominion Magnesium Ltd., Haley, Ont., Canada.
† Nelco Metals, Inc., Canaan, Conn.

Figure 2.1. Redistilled crystals of metallic calcium.

grade: crowns or crude condensed metal in full or broken forms; nodules in ½-in. and 6-mesh sizes; ingots 2¾ by 1¾ by 23 in.; billets 11 in. in diameter by 23 in. long cast in argon; cast slabs 25 by 16 by 2½ in.; extruded forms 0.92 in. in diameter by 12 in. long; pieces 1 by 3 by 8 in.; cylinders 7 in. in diameter by 25 in. long; and turnings. In the redistilled or 99.5+ per cent grade, commercial forms include broken crowns, lump 1 in. in diameter by 3 in., or crushed ⅜ in. by 20 mesh; 6-mesh nodules and ⅛-in. nodules. Table 2.1 gives analyses of commercial and distilled forms. For reference only, the analysis of Ethyl Corporation's experimental product is included. The highly crystalline character of distilled calcium is shown in Figure 2.1.

Calcium in ton lots sells for $2.05/lb in cast form, $2.95/lb for turnings, and $3.75/lb for distilled (99.9 per cent) material.

Large-scale use of metallic calcium in the United States is comparatively recent. Prior to 1939 the domestic market was satisfied with the importation from France of about 22 tons/year. By the end of World War II, however, annual consumption had risen to many times that figure.

Derivation

During World War II the United States obtained its supply of calcium by the electrolysis of fused calcium chloride as a primary source, and in later years by thermal processes under high vacuum from lime reduced with aluminum. In operations involving the preparation of lead-calcium alloys, calcium carbide may serve as the source of calcium metal. Silicon has not been found useful as a reducing agent at 1200°C (2192°F), the temperature limit of the retorts employed. Operating details for the electrolytic production of calcium in Europe are given by Mantell[86] in Table 2.2. At the Bitterfeld plant of I. G. Farbenindustrie, metallic calcium was produced in 10 cells at 1,400 amp., 25 volts per cell with an ampere efficiency of 50 per cent, which gave 13 kg/cell/day. Pure molten calcium chloride served as the electrolyte. The metal froze as deposited. Graphite anodes were used, and a small amount of potassium chloride was added to the bath to lower the melting point.

In 1939 the Electro Metallurgical Company started operating 2,000-amp. cells at Sault Ste. Marie, Michigan, and later operated 10,000-amp. units. Distilled and purified cast forms of the metal were produced in purities up to 99.5 per cent, and higher, calcium content. Currently, there is no electrochemical production in North America.

Pidgeon and Atkinson[105] report the vapor pressure of calcium, above a reaction mass of calcium oxide and aluminum which form calcium and $CaO.Al_2O_3$, to vary from 1.0 to 1.3 mm Hg from 1150–1200°C (2102–2192°F). It is suggested that the reaction proceeds by reduction of calcium oxide with aluminum vapor.

A method for the production of metallic cal-

TABLE 2.2. OPERATING DETAILS FOR THE
ELECTROLYTIC PRODUCTION OF CALCIUM IN
EUROPE

Electrolyte	Pure calcium chloride
Temperature (°C)	780–800 (1436–1472°F)
Current	
Current per cell	1,400 amp
Current density	650 amp/sq in.
(cathode)	100 amp/sq cm
Current efficiency (%)	50
Theoretical decomposi-tion voltage of $CaCl_2$ at 800°C (1472°F)	3.2
Voltage per cell	25
Energy consumption	26 kwhr/lb
Melting point of $CaCl_2$ (°C)	780 (1436°F)
Specific conductivity of $CaCl_2$ at 800°C (1472°F)	1.9 mhos/cc
Pounds $CaCl_2$ per lb Ca	
Theoretical	2.76
Actual	4.5
Anodes	Graphite
Cathodes	
Material	Iron or graphite coated with calcium
Type	Vertical, with surface contact
Cells	
Lining	Carbon
Casing	Sheet steel

cium by thermal reduction of lime has been patented by Pidgeon and McCatty.[106] Finely ground lime, containing not more than 3 per cent impurities and not more than 1 per cent magnesium oxide, is briquetted with a 5 to 20 per cent excess of powdered aluminum as a reducing agent. The briquettes are heated in a vacuum of 10 μ or better to about 1170°C (2138°F). A retort is used, so designed that the calcium vapor is condensed in a zone maintained at 740–680°C (1364–1256°F). The magnesium vapor is condensed in a zone maintained in the range of 350–275°C (662–527°F). A mixture of the two metals condenses in an intermediate zone where the temperature is 485–400°C (965–752°F). The apparatus is described with a diagram, and the following equations represent the reactions which take place when the briquettes are heated as described.

$$5CaO + 2Al \rightarrow 3Ca + (CaO)_2Al_2O_3$$
$$3MgO + 2CaO + 2Al \rightarrow 3Mg + (CaO)_2Al_2O_3$$

Manufacturing details of the production of calcium by the aluminum process are given in Table 2.3.[81]

TABLE 2.3. THERMAL REDUCTION BY ALUMINUM

Raw material	Calcined pure limestone (CaO), 200 mesh
Reducing agent	96 to 99% aluminum, 20 mesh
Temperature	1200°C (2192°F)
Pressure	20 μ
Retort materials	28% Cr, 15% Ni, balance Fe
Retort size	10 in. diameter, 10 ft long, 1.1 in. thick
Calcium purity	Mg 0.50 to 1.0; Al 0.01 to 0.2; Mn 0.005 to 0.02; N under 0.02%; chlorides none; alkalies none; Ca 98–99%
Time of cycle	12 hr
Reaction	$6CaO + 2Al \rightarrow 3Ca + 3CaO \cdot Al_2O_3$

In the United States Nelco Metals, Inc., Canaan, Connecticut, a subsidiary of New England Lime Co., and Union Carbide Metals Co., Niagara Falls, N. Y., produced calcium metal in 1959. Dominion Magnesium, Ltd., of Haley, Ontario, is the only producer in Canada, where 70,259 lb were made in 1959. Nelco Metals and Dominion Magnesium operate vacuum retorts in which lime is reduced to calcium metal by aluminum.

Warrington and McPhail[140] describe the retorts for thermal reduction of the alkaline earth metals under pressure. They are centrifugally cast, elongated cylinders with a dross-free internal surface, the ratio of the outside diameter to the wall thickness being 10.2–13.0:1. The reducing portion of the retort is kept between 90 and 120 in. in length. The best outside diameter of the retort may vary slightly, depending on the particular alkaline earth being produced; thus, for magnesium and barium, it is 12 to 14 in.; for calcium and strontium, 12.5 to 16 in. The walls are of stainless steel, such as 40 nickel–18 chromium, 20 nickel–25 chromium, or 17 nickel–27 chromium.

Bassereau[15] describes reduction by ferrosilicon or aluminum with subsequent distillation, Warrington[139] is specific as to briquette shapes in the Pidgeon process, and Wehner[141] gives details as to purification of electrolytic calcium by distillation. Jaffe and Parks[61] propose the decomposition of calcium carbide to the metal, and Miller[92] describes the ferrosilicon process for magnesium and the adaptation of the equipment to calcium production. Orman[102] has reported on European experimental production. Andrieux and Bonnier[11] discuss the production of metal from calcium-silicon and calcium-aluminum alloys by distillation.

Alexander[8] describes the production of calcium by sodium reduction of calcium chloride.

The Downs cell for the electrolysis of fused salt[85] produces a sodium metal containing calcium. The calcium crystallizes out of solution and is filtered from the liquid sodium. This is a third source of calcium metal and calcium-sodium material.

Wehner[141] has reviewed the electrolytic method.

Fujita et al.[40,41,43] have studied the production of calcium by various methods, as well as the purification processes for commercial manufacture.

The Ethyl Corporation has produced a crystalline calcium as a free-flowing crystalline powder of metallic luster by alcohol leaching of sodium-calcium sludges from Downs type fused salt cells making sodium metal. The resultant product has small dark crystals and a purity of about 94 to 96 per cent, and, since the preparation is at low temperature in the absence of gases, the calcium contains nitrogen impurity in not more than 15 ppm. Sales were expected of the order of 300,000 lb annually at a price of $1.25 to $1.50/lb. Unfortunately, the market for crystalline calcium was very small, and it could not compete with bulk calcium, which had a potential price of less than $1.00/lb. As a result, production of crystalline calcium was discontinued.

The Ethyl Corporation has developed procedures for the recovery of calcium from sludges containing calcium and sodium and formed in electrolytic processes for the manufacture of sodium from a mixture of sodium chloride and calcium chloride, while simultaneously producing a higher alcohol from a lower one, by treatment with a lower aliphatic alcohol. The calcium freed by this process is recovered, washed, and dried.[23, 56, 57]

Metal Hydrides, Inc., has patented a distillation method for sodium-calcium sludge separation.[50]

Betcherman and Pidgeon[19] give the details of calcium purification by distillation.

Nishida[98] has outlined Japanese practice, Burnett[22] the British methods in an argon atmosphere at 1 mm Hg pressure, and Barton[14] has patented a two-stage procedure.

Alexander[7] discloses the recovery of calcium from calcium hydride and magnesium oxide by the addition of alloying metals from which the calcium is distilled.

Physical Properties

The tensile properties of calcium metal are greatly affected by impurities, and, in the pure forms, by methods of fabrication. Calcium metal work-hardens upon mechanical processing, as is shown by the values for yield point and ultimate strength as well as elongation and reduction in area in the as-rolled and annealed condition.

Bulk calcium is a soft, crystalline metal which is both ductile and malleable. It may readily be extruded on heating to 420–460°C (788–860°F). It exists in two allotropic crystalline forms—the alpha form below 464°C (867°F) and the beta form above 464°C.

The physical properties of massive calcium are presented in Table 2.4. There is some uncertainty as to their accuracy, however, because of the effect of certain impurities which are difficult to remove from the bulk metal. For example, less than 1 weight per cent of combined nitrogen reduces the melting point of calcium from its normal value of 851°C (1564°F) to as low as 780°C (1436°F). Other properties are also affected.

The heat capacity of the low-temperature (alpha) form of calcium is given in terms of calories per gram atom per degree centigrade by the following equation (T in °K)[67]:

$$C_p = 5.24 + 3.50 \times 10^{-3}\ T$$

For the high-temperature (beta) form, the corresponding equation is[67]

$$C_p = 6.29 + 1.40 \times 10^{-3}\ T$$

Douglas[34] and Tomlin[132] have studied the vapor pressure from 800–900°K. The vapor pressure of calcium, in atmospheres, may be

TABLE 2.4. PHYSICAL PROPERTIES OF CALCIUM

Atomic number	20
Atomic volume (cc/g-atom)	25.9
Atomic weight	40.08
Boiling point	1482°C (2700°F)[131]
Color	White, approximating silver
Compressibility	
At 30°C (86°F)	
0 atm pressure	5.885×10^{-6}
11,600 atm pressure	5.300×10^{-6}
At 20°C (68°F)	
99–493 atm pressure	5.8×10^{-6}
100–500 megabars/sq cm	5.7×10^{-6}

$$\text{Compressibility} = -\frac{1}{\text{vol (cc)}} \times \frac{\Delta \text{ vol (cc)}}{\Delta \text{ pressure (atm)}}$$

Crystal structure	Face-centered cubic, a = 5.56 kX
Density (g/cc)	
At 20°C (68°F)	1.54 (0.056 lb/cu in.)[131]
At 450°C (842°F) alpha phase in extruded wire	1.48
At 480°C (896°F) beta phase	1.52
Elastic limit (psi)	1,470
Electrical resistivity (microhm–cm)	
At 0°C (32°F)	3.43
At 20°C (68°F)	4.6[129]
At 21°C (70°F)	
As rolled	4.24–4.50
Annealed	4.04–4.11
Electrochemical equivalent (valence two)	
mg/coulomb	0.20762
coulomb/mg	4.81640
Electrolytic solution potential versus hydrogen (volts)	−2.76
Electron configuration	2-8-8-2
Entropy (cal/°C/g-atom)	
Solid [25°C (77°F)]	9.95[68]
Gas [25°C (77°F)]	37.00[65]
Erichsen value on 1/32-in. sheet	
As rolled	3.55–3.6
Annealed	11.1
Hardness number, cast slab	
Brinell (500-kg load)	17
Rockwell (15-kg load, 1/16-in. ball)	42 as rolled
Moh	2[90]
Heat capacity (cal/g/°C) (specific heat)	
Alpha phase [0–460°C (32–860°F)]	0.17[67]
Beta phase [460–851°C (860–1564°F)]	0.19[67]
liquid [851–1200°C (1564–2192°F)]	0.19[65]
Heat of combustion (cal/g)	151.9
Heat of fusion (kcal/g-atom)	2.23[66]
Heat of transition (kcal/g-atom)	0.115[67]
Heat of vaporization (kcal/g-atom) [1482°C (2700°F)]	36.7[131]
Isotopes (stable)	40, 42, 43, 44, 46, 48
Mass magnetic susceptibility (cgs)	$+1.10 \times 10^{-6}$ [60]
Melting point	
°C	851[135]
°F	1564
Minimum interatomic distance (kX)	3.93
Modulus of elasticity (psi)	$3–4 \times 10^{6}$

TABLE 2.4. PHYSICAL PROPERTIES OF CALCIUM (cont.)

Specific heat (cal/g/°C)	
−185–20°C (−301–68°F)	0.157
0–100°C (32–212°F)	0.149
460–851°C (752–1564°F)	0.19[67]
Surface tension (dynes/cm)	255[130]
Temperature coefficient of electrical resistivity	
[per °C at 20°C (68°F)]	0.00457
Tensile properties	
Yield strength (psi)	
As rolled	12,300
Annealed	1,990
Ultimate strength (psi)	
As rolled	16,700
Annealed	6,960
Elongation in 1 in. (%)	
As rolled	7
Annealed	51
Reduction in area (%)	
As rolled	35
Annealed	58
Thermal conductivity [cal/sec/cm/°C (20°)]	0.3, same order as that of sodium and other alkali metals
Thermal expansion (per °C)	
Linear [0°–300°C (32–570°F)]	0.0000220
Cubic [0–21°C (32–70°F)]	0.000717
Thermal neutron absorption cross section (barns/atom)	0.43
Transition temperature (°C) (alpha to beta)	464 ± 4[120]
Valence	2
Volume conductivity referred to standard copper (%)	48.7

represented by the following equations,[131] where t is in degree centigrade:

Alpha form (0–460°C) (32–860°F)
$$\log p \ (\text{atm}) = 5.502 - 9018/(t + 267.7)$$

Beta form (460–851°C) (860–1564°F)
$$\log p \ (\text{atm}) = 5.107 - 8512/(t + 249.1)$$

Liquid (851–1482°C) (1564–2700°F)
$$\log p \ (\text{atm}) = 4.392 - 7406/(t + 203.5)$$

These equations are based on the thermodynamically consistent experimental data of Pilling[107] on solid calcium and of Hartmann and Schneider[54] on the molten metal. The data of Rudberg[112] on the solid metal have been rejected as inconsistent.

Priselkov and Nesmeyanov[108] represent the vapor pressure of calcium between 475–670°C (887–1238°F) as

$$\log p_{\text{Ca}} = 7.790 - 8524/T$$

Debye-Scherrer photographs are interpreted[91] as showing that calcium exists in three allotropic modifications, viz., alpha calcium, face-centered cubic; beta calcium, hexagonal close-packed; and gamma calcium, body-centered cubic, the transition points lying at about 250 and 450°C (482 and 842°F). The observed lattice constants of the three modifications are closely related to those of the analogous modifications of strontium.

Smith et al.[120] show, by x-ray diffraction patterns of calcium samples of different purities, that 99.9+ per cent calcium exists in only two allotropic forms: face-centered cubic to 464°C (867°F) and body-centered cubic from 464°C to the melting point. These results for the high-temperature allotrope differ from the widely accepted structure; handbooks and tables currently list the high-temperature allotrope as hexagonal close-packed. It is further shown that a previously reported intermediate allotrope of complex structure is the result of contamination. The temperature dependence of the electrical resistivity of the 99.9+ per cent calcium is linear for both the face-centered cubic allotrope and for the body-centered cubic allotrope. Calcium is self-annealing at room temperature.

Huber and Holley[59] have made calorimetric combustions of calcium metal at an initial temperature of 25°C (77°F) under an oxygen pressure of 50 atm. The energy of combustion is 15,806 joules/g. The corresponding standard heat of formation of the oxide (CaO) from the elements is calculated to be −635.09 ± 0.89 kjoules/mole. X-ray examination of the combustion products shows only the lines of CaO.

Collins *et al.*[26] have studied the masses of the calcium isotopes, and Kline and Zaffarano[72] their half lives.

Culler *et al.*[30] have investigated the neutron scattering by calcium.

Taylor[130] estimates the surface tension values of the alkaline earth metals at their respective melting points, in ergs per square centimeter, as 195 for barium, 255 for calcium, and 165 for strontium.

MacDonald and Mendelssohn[82] have studied the resistivity of the alkaline earth metals (calcium, barium, strontium) down to 20°K.

For equal dimensions, the specific and relative resistances of calcium, in comparison with copper, aluminum, and sodium, follow:

	Specific Resistance	Relative Resistance
International annealed copper standard	1.724	1.00
Calcium	4.53	2.63
Aluminum	2.83	1.64
Sodium	4.8	2.79

For equal weights and lengths, the relative resistance values are:

	Density	Relative Resistance
Copper	8.92	1.00
Calcium	1.55	0.46
Aluminum	2.70	0.50
Sodium	0.97	0.30

Mechanical Properties

Calcium metal is much harder than sodium but softer than aluminum and magnesium. In hardness characteristics it is much closer to aluminum and magnesium than to sodium. Under a 500-kg load, sections machined out of the impure calcium "cabbage," as obtained from electrolysis, show a Brinell hardness of 17. Under the same conditions, sodium is so soft that measurement cannot be made, the hardness being less than 1 on the Brinell scale. Pure aluminum has a Brinell hardness of 25; magnesium shows a Brinell hardness of 30, and Dow magnesium shows 32. On the Rockwell B scale, calcium in machined sections shows hardnesses from 36 to 40. On the Shore scleroscope, calcium shows hardnesses from 7 to 9 when the normal hammer is used, and from 11 to 12 when the magnifying hammer is employed, as compared to values of 20 to 23 for magnesium.

Distilled calcium shows an elongation of 53 per cent, whereas extruded wire gives 61 per cent, 98.5 per cent calcium gives 30.5 per cent, and impure materials (94 to 96 per cent) show no elongation.[16] With a loading speed of 4 mm/min., distilled calcium is more ductile than aluminum of 99.6 per cent purity and less ductile than lead, but it has a greater elongation than either. The modulus of elasticity of distilled calcium varies between 32×10^5 and 38×10^5 psi. No creep is observed on loading calcium with less than 570 psi at room temperature. Crushing tests show complete recrystallization of calcium at 300°C (572°F), and above, during deformation. The pressure required for deformation decreases with the temperature and has a sharp break at 440°C (824°F), a little below the transformation temperature. Above 460°C (860°F), calcium deforms plastically under very small loads. Calcium wire can be easily extruded between 420 and 460°C (788 and 860°F).

Applications

Calcium metal is employed as an alloying agent for aluminum and for bearing metals of the lead-calcium or lead-barium-calcium type; as a reducing agent for beryllium production; as an alloying agent and a deoxidizer for copper; as an alloying agent for the production of the age-hardening lead alloys for cable sheaths, battery plates, and related uses; as a modifying agent for magnesium and aluminum; as a debismuthizer for lead; as a controller for graphitic carbon in cast iron; as a carburizer and desulfurizer as well as a deoxidizer for numerous alloys, such as chromium-nickel, copper, iron, iron-nickel, nickel, nickel-cobalt, nickel-chromium-iron, nickel bronzes, steel, and tin bronzes; as an evacuating agent; as a reducing agent in the preparation of chromium metal powder, rare earth metals, thorium, uranium, and zirconium; and as a separator for argon from nitrogen. Typical of these applications is the addition of 0.25 per cent calcium to magnesium alloys to refine the grain structure, to reduce the tendency to take fire, and to modify the strengthening heat treatments. Other examples of the use of calcium are the precipitation-hardening lead-calcium alloys. The solid solubility of calcium in lead is of the order of 0.1 per cent at the melting point and decreases rapidly with reduction of temperature so that precipitation hardening takes place, since at ordinary temperatures the solid solubility is of the order of 0.01 per cent.

As discussed in the other chapters in this book, calcium has been employed as a reductant for the preparation of a number of refractory metals, e.g., to reduce beryllium oxide in the presence of copper to form beryllium-calcium alloys;[122] to reduce molybdenum from its oxides, employing magnesium oxide as a lining in a bomb in which pressures reach 1,200 psi at temperatures of 3000°C (5432°F);[47] to reduce fluorides, particularly those of beryllium and thorium in the presence of sulfur to give alloys;[124] and to reduce cerium halides in the presence of iodine.[126] The metals contain calcium and are refined by vacuum distillation.

Anselin et al.[12] obtained an 85–90 per cent yield in the reduction of plutonium fluoride by calcium to plutonium metal, which was produced in gram amounts.

Achard, Cara, and Loriers[1] mixed scandium fluoride with an equal weight of pure calcium and added barium fluoride (15 to 10 g scandium fluoride) to increase the mass of the flux. The mixture was heated in a tantalum crucible in argon at 1500–1600°C (2732–2912°F) for 5 to 6 min. After cooling and removal of the flux, the ingot of scandium was easily removed from the crucible.

For the reduction of thorium chlorides by calcium to metallic thorium, Lilliendahl[78] used lighter bombs than are needed when sodium is the reducing agent. Spedding et al.[127] state that the reaction requires excess calcium and a booster to produce additional heat to fuse the slag and the metal. Keller et al.[64] describe the casting and shaping of such thorium.

In the production of ductile titanium,[74] cal-

cium has been used as the reducing agent. The similar production of ductile vanadium[83] by reducing vanadium pentoxide with powdered calcium is practiced currently.

Schwarz and Koster[117] have attempted to reduce TiS_2 and Ti_2S_3 with calcium.

Johnston[63] has mixed titanium and titanium alloys with calcium chips to form consumable electrodes that give arc melted ingots which are ductile.

Kubaschewski and Dench[76] show that titanium in equilibrium with calcium and calcium oxide at 1000°C (1832°F) contains less than 0.1 per cent oxygen. When titania is reduced, either by calcium, or by magnesium and then by calcium, the titanium contains much more than 0.1 per cent oxygen. It is found that the products of the magnesium and calcium reductions contain unleachable amounts of magnesium and calcium. If the titania is reduced by molten magnesium and the magnesium removed in an intermediate stage by a vacuum treatment at 1200°C (2192°F) or above, the product of the subsequent calcium reduction is virtually free from calcium, and the low percentage of oxygen indicated by the equilibrium data is approached. A related method is claimed earlier by Dominion Magnesium.[33] Titanium, 99.7 per cent pure, is produced by the reduction of TiO_2 to TiO and (or) Ti_2O_3 with magnesium in an inert atmosphere at 550–565°C (1022–1049°F). The magnesium and magnesium oxide are removed with 5 to 10 per cent hydrochloric acid. Ti_2O_3 and TiO are reduced to titanium with calcium in an inert atmosphere at a temperature not exceeding 1000°C (1832°F). The reduction of titanium in two stages avoids the presence of oxygen, nitrogen, and hydrogen in the metal, which affects the properties.

De Hollander[32] states that a reducing atmosphere of calcium with a flux such as fused barium chloride is useful in the melting of small pieces of uranium.

An Atomic Energy Commission report[89] reveals that calcium might have been extensively used in early 1942 to prepare uranium from either uranium oxide or uranium fluoride, except that "when these materials were needed it was found that there was no quantity of high-purity calcium metal available." Foster and Magel[38] have found increased yields in the presence of manganese halides. Lemmon et al.[77]

have studied the thermodynamics of the reaction.

Beard and Crooks,[17] as did McKechnie and Seybolt,[83] have made kilogram buttons of massive ductile vanadium by reduction of vanadium pentoxide with calcium. Wilhelm and Long[143] disclose the addition of sulfur as a booster for the reaction.

Kelly[69] has reduced vanadium pentoxide to vanadium trioxide by hydrogen and has converted this to metal by reaction with calcium, and Long[80] also has made the metal from fluorides and sulfides.

Daane and Spedding[31] have prepared massive yttrium, thulium, terbium, holmium, and erbium in high purity and yields by reducing the fluorides of these rare earths with calcium metal in tantalum containers held in an inert atmosphere and heated by high-frequency current. Ytterbium can be reduced only to the bivalent state, as its fluoride is volatile at the operating temperature, 1500–1600°C (2732–2912°F).

Spedding and Daane[123] have also reviewed the calcium reduction of compounds of the rare earth metals and the properties of the products. Ahmann[4] has described work with samarium, cerium, and neodymium.

Lilliendahl and Rentschler,[79] Winter,[146] and Carlson, Schmidt, and Wilhelm[27] have studied the application of calcium for the preparation of zirconium and hafnium from their fluorides, and Spedding et al.[125] have added boosters such as sulfur or iodine to accelerate the reaction. Walsh[138] has prepared massive zirconium by calcium reduction of zirconium chlorides or fluorides in the presence of sulfur or iodine and describes the preparation of pure starting materials.

Winter[147] has patented the production of refractory metals, especially titanium or zirconium, by reduction of a volatile halide of the desired metal with a reducing metal, especially magnesium, in a reactor. The claims also specify manufacture of columbium, hafnium, molybdenum, tantalum, and tungsten, and the use of calcium, barium, strontium, sodium, potassium, and lithium as reducing agents.

Gibbs, Svec, and Harrington[46] have studied the action of the alkaline earth metals in the purification of the rare gases. Barium, calcium, calcium–10 per cent magnesium alloy, lanthanum, magnesium, thorium, and zirconium are effective for removing oxygen from argon; and

barium, calcium, calcium–10 per cent magnesium alloy, magnesium, thorium, and zirconium remove nitrogen from argon. Calcium, thorium, and zirconium have been studied only in the solid state. The calcium–10 per cent magnesium alloy is effective only after it has melted. Barium reacts so vigorously with the impurities in the argon that it melts despite a furnace temperature 350°C (630°F) below its melting point. Extensive results have not been obtained for either the calcium–10 per cent magnesium alloy or barium, but the results indicate that these metals are very effective in removing oxygen and nitrogen from rare gases at relatively low temperatures.

Field and Feller[37] have studied the catalytic activity of calcium in the formation of solid polymers.

The National Research Council of Canada has patented[96] a catalyst (for the oxidation of ethylene to ethylene oxide) which is deposited upon a metal base to give improved heat transfer and temperature control. The reaction temperature is 240–320°C (464–608°F), and the catalyst is an alloy of silver with calcium, magnesium, barium, or strontium, from which the alkaline earth metal has been leached to give an active silver surface. The preferred concentration of the alkaline earth metal in the alloy is 5 to 10 per cent, and the preferred mesh size of the ground alloy is 220 to 830 μ.

Cambron and Alexander[24] have prepared skeletal silver catalysts of high specific activity by the removal of calcium from calcium-silver alloys. Catalysts prepared from calcium-silver alloys show a higher specific activity, are more stable, and more conveniently prepared than are those from other silver alloys.

Calcium Hydride

Calcium combines with hydrogen gas to form calcium hydride. The reaction is reversible, and the hydrogen can be released by heating the hydride. Calcium hydride is stable at room temperature and is a useful source of hydrogen, since twice the volume of hydrogen is released when the hydride is slaked in water, as compared to that produced by a substantially equivalent weight of calcium metal. For hydrogen generation in isolated locations, calcium hydride offers attractive possibilities.

Calcium hydride production during World

War II demanded 10 tons of calcium metal/day. Consumption is of the order of 250,000 lb annually.

During World War II at least 500,000 lb of metallic calcium were converted to calcium hydride for use in generating hydrogen for inflating balloons.

Meerson and Kolchin[88] have studied the mechanism of reduction of metallic oxides by calcium hydride.

Alexander[6] states that lithium hydride is formed by mixing a lithium halide with reducing agents selected from the group of magnesium, calcium, and barium, and the hydrides of calcium and barium, heating in an atmosphere of hydrogen to 800°C (1472°F) to form a molten mass, and exposing this mass as a thin film to the action of hydrogen.

Calcium Alloys

Among the alloys of calcium that are of commercial importance is calcium-silicon, made as an electric furnace product from lime, silica, and a carbonaceous reducing agent.

Calcium-silicon alloy is used as a deoxidizer and degasifier in the production of steel. It is also used in making high-tensile-strength gray irons.

In steelmaking, calcium-silicon alloy is used both as a furnace and a ladle addition. Both calcium and silicon are active deoxidizers, and their reaction products form a low-melting-point slag which frees itself readily from the metal, thus producing a clean steel. Calcium-silicon alloy also improves the fluidity of liquid steel. In open-hearth practice this alloy is added in the ladle; in electric-furnace practice it may be added either in the furnace or in the ladle.

In basic electric-furnace practice the calcium-silicon alloy finds wide application for quick deoxidation of both metal bath and slag. It is usually used in crushed form, 2 in. or less in size.

In acid electric steelmaking, final additions of deoxidizing alloys are made primarily to prevent the evolution of gas and the formation of blowholes during solidification, although other effects, such as improved toughness, may also be obtained.

The amounts of calcium-silicon commonly used range from 1 to 6 lb/ton of steel, with 2 to 4 lb being the average.

Calcium-manganese-silicon alloy is sometimes used by steelmakers in place of calcium-silicon because it provides three active elements in proper balance to produce low-melting-point-reaction products which coalesce and become liberated easily from the molten metal. This alloy is a cleanser for oxides, gases, and nonmetallic impurities in steel. In addition to improving the cleanliness of steel, calcium-manganese-silicon alloy promotes fluidity, improves ductility, and helps prevent pinholes in steel castings.

The analyses of these alloys are given in Table 2.5. If the manufacturer of steel can use these materials without introduction of undesirable additions to the melts, the prices per pound of calcium show that the use of elemental calcium is entirely noncompetitive with these calcium alloys in the production of iron and steel or related metal products.

The constitutional diagrams of the alloys of calcium with aluminum, copper, hydrogen, gold, lead, magnesium, nickel, silicon, silver, tin, or zinc have been well studied and almost completely worked out, whereas those for the alloys with antimony, beryllium, bismuth, boron, cadmium, lithium, mercury, nitrogen, platinum, sodium, or thallium are either incomplete or fragmentary.

TABLE 2.5. ANALYSES AND PRICES OF CALCIUM-SILICON AND CALCIUM-MANGANESE-SILICON ALLOYS

	Ca–Si	Ca–Mn–Si
Calcium (%)	30–33	16–20
Silicon (%)	60–65	53–59
Manganese (%)	—	14–18
Iron (%)	1.5–3	
Weight (lb/cu ft)	110	130
Price (per ton)	$25–$30	$24–$28
Price (per lb contained calcium)	$0.005	$0.002–$0.003

Asai[13] has investigated electrical-contact properties of alloys of silver, copper, cadmium, tin, and zinc containing 1 to 7 per cent calcium. Calcium additions increase the contact properties of silver.

BARIUM

Barium melts at 710°C (1310°F) and boils at 1500°C (2732°F).[134] It is the least volatile of the alkaline earth metals. Its vapor pressure at 1200°C (2192°F) (the temperature of its reduction from the oxide) is about 50 mm Hg.

Metallic magnesium,[71] calcium,[145] barium, and strontium[39] reduce each other's oxides. The reduction of alkaline earth metal oxides with aluminum was observed by Mallet[84] in 1877, but other investigations have shown that the end product of the reaction is an alloy of aluminum with the alkaline earth metal.[5,10,27] Fujita and Yokomizo[42] have reduced barium oxide with aluminum at 1000–2000°C (1832–3632°F) at 10^{-3} mm Hg. The reduction starts at 1040°C (1904°F) to yield about 50 per cent of barium. Besides barium, barium aluminates of various compositions are formed, but the reaction proceeds mainly according to: $6BaO + 2Al \rightarrow 3Ba + 3BaO \cdot Al_2O_3$. Orman and Zembala[103] describe the process whereby barium oxide and aluminum are mixed in the proportion 10:1 by weight, and batches of up to 715 g are distilled in the apparatus at 10^{-4} mm Hg and at 1125°C (2057°F) for 6 to 7 hr. At 700°C (1292°F), the reaction is completed: $4BaO + 2Al \rightarrow BaO \cdot Al_2O_3 + 3Ba + 488$ kcal; a higher temperature, however, is needed to distill off liquid barium. Side reactions producing intermediate $BaAl_4$ decrease the yields of barium. At 925°C (1697°F) the yields are only 27.4; at 1025°C (1877°F), 28.2; at 1075°C (1967°F), 32.3; and at 1125°C (2057°F), 34.0 per cent of the total batch by weight. High vacuum (10^{-4} mm Hg) is necessary. Silicon also has been suggested as a reducing agent, and the results obtained are the same.[148,149]

The Guntz[52,53] process consists of heating 3 parts of barium oxide with 2 parts aluminum in a vacuum at about 1200°C (2192°F) and condensing the barium vapor in a cool end of the tube. Matignon[87] later suggested using silicon instead of aluminum, or a 90 per cent ferrosilicon, which is cheaper but requires a temperature of operation 50°C (122°F) higher than that necessary with aluminum.

Barium oxide can readily be reduced by aluminum, and alloys containing 36.0 per cent barium have been made in this way.[5,10] Barium peroxide can be flashed with aluminum powder, yielding alloys with up to 60 per cent barium.[128]

Guntz[51] states that the electrolysis of fused barium chloride does not yield any metal but only subchloride. Agladze and Avaliani[2] confirm this.

Barium is noncompetitive with calcium in that its production is only a fractional percentage of that of calcium and its price is higher. Table 2.6 gives analyses, shapes, and small-lot prices of commercial barium metal.

TABLE 2.6. CHEMICAL ANALYSES AND PRICES OF BARIUM AND STRONTIUM

	Barium	Strontium
Ba	98.0	0.1
Sr	1.0	98.5
N_2	0.1	0.05
Mg	0.4	0.5
Ca	0.4	0.8
Price (per/lb)		
Extruded rod 0.92 in. in diameter	$6.00	$8.00
Crystalline lumps	$5.00	$6.50

Fusion electrolysis with a heavy metal cathode, in which the heavy metal may be introduced also as salt or taken from a subsidiary soluble anode, has frequently been employed for making barium alloys. In this way, Kornilow[73] obtained an 11 per cent barium-zinc alloy. Frary metal,[28] which contains about 2 per cent barium, some calcium, and the balance lead, is made in a similar way. Ray[110] has made barium alloys with 73 per cent antimony, 72 per cent tin, 84 per cent bismuth, and 97 per cent aluminum, respectively, by fusion electrolysis with a heavy metal cathode.

Guntz[51] and Gautier[45] have shown that cadmium-barium, made by fusion electrolysis, yields a fairly pure barium in a vacuum at high temperature.

Calcium is also a suitable reducing agent for barium chloride. Muthmann, Weiss, and Metzger[95] have carried out this reaction and obtained a barium-calcium alloy.

Kroll[75] has studied the processes for making barium and its alloys.

Sawamoto and Asai[114] have studied the production of barium from barium oxide and calcium carbide.

Barium metal readily reacts with water and most acids. Upon heating barium in hydrogen gas at about 200°C (392°F), a violent reaction takes place, forming a hydride of barium (BaH_2). This is a solid, gray compound readily decomposed by water and acids. The nitride of barium (BaN_6) decomposes with explosive violence upon heating. Barium will unite with

TABLE 2.7. PHYSICAL PROPERTIES OF BARIUM AND STRONTIUM

	Barium	Strontium
Atomic number	56	38
Atomic volume (cc/g-atom)	39	34
Atomic weight	137.36	87.63
Boiling point		
°C	1500	1380
°F	2732	2516
Crystal structure	Body-centered cubic	Face-centered cubic
Density [g/cc at 20°C (68°F)]	3.5 (0.126 lb/cu in.)	2.6 (0.094 lb/cu in.)
Electrical resistivity [microhms–cm at 20°C (68°F)]	—	23
Electrochemical equivalent		
mg/coulomb	0.71171	0.45404
coulomb/mg	1.40507	2.20244
Electron configuration	2-8-18-18-8-2	2-8-18-8-2
Heat of fusion		
cal/g	13.3	25
Btu/lb	23.9	45
Isotopes (stable)	130, 132, 134, 135 136, 137, 138	84, 86, 87, 88
Latent heat of vaporization at boiling point (cal/g)	262	383
Melting point		
°C	710	770 ± 10
°F	1310	1418 ± 18
Specific gravity (g/cc)	3.74	2.54
Specific heat at 20°C (68°F) (cal/g/°C)	0.068	0.176
Surface tension (dynes/cm)	195	165
Thermal neutron absorption cross section (barns/atom)	1.17	1.16
Valence	2	2

carbon and nitrogen to form barium cyanide, which is thermally a stable compound. Barium metal is a good deoxidizer for copper, according to Schumacher and Ellis.[116] The physical properties of barium and strontium are given in Table 2.7. Barium metal does not show superconductivity down to 0.15°K.[35, 49] The masses of barium isotopes are: barium 136, 135.9488 ± 0.0010; barium 137, 136.9502 ± 0.0010; barium 138, 137.9498 ± 0.009.

Barium alloys with aluminum and magnesium are getters in evacuated electronic tubes. Jeffries[62] states that thin films of barium on special steel balls greatly improve the life and reduce the friction of rotating anodes in highly evacuated x-ray tubes and make possible the operation of these anodes at relatively high temperatures. Many forms and getter arrangements are found in the patent and other literature.[44, 70, 101, 115, 119] Bloomer[20] and Wagener[136] have analyzed the specific application of barium as a getter for nitrogen, hydrogen, carbon mon-

oxide, carbon dioxide, and water vapor. Anderko[9] has measured the liquidus temperature of magnesium-barium alloys used for getters. Oda[100] and Morrison and Zetterstrom[94] have studied the adsorption of carbon monoxide at low pressures, and Wagener[137] has reported on the decay of gathering rates of barium getters.

Duffendack, Wolfe, and Randolph[36] have developed a nickel-barium alloy for spark plugs to ensure regular performance and a constant voltage through the spark gap. Randolph[109] has reported on the performance of nickel-barium and nickel-barium-copper alloys.

Westrum and Eyring[142] have prepared americium metal in microquantities by reduction of AmF_3 by barium in a high-vacuum furnace at 1100°C (2012°F).

Barium and strontium have long-lived isotopes which are among the fission products from thermal neutron bombardment of uranium 233.[144]

Moore and Allison[93] have studied the adsorption of strontium and barium on tungsten. The work function for a monolayer of strontium is approximately 2.2 volts and for barium approximately 1.9 volts. The adsorption is physical rather than chemical, even though the mean activation energies for desorption are 77.4 for strontium and 80.7 kcal/mole for barium.

Agladze and Avaliani[3] have prepared barium and cadmium alloys in a fused medium by electrolysis of a fused mixture of 40 to 73 per cent barium chloride and 27 to 60 per cent potassium chloride at 700–720°C (1292–1328°F) with a liquid cadmium cathode. Alloys are obtained containing up to 40 per cent barium. The alloys are very friable and chemically active. The activity increases with an increase in temperature and content of barium. The current efficiency is 88 to 95 per cent for alloys with 25 to 30 per cent barium.

STRONTIUM

Strontium metal may be produced by methods similar to those employed for calcium and barium, e.g., by electrolysis of the fused chloride mixed with potassium chloride.[97, 133]

The Guntz process has been applied successfully to the reduction of other alkaline-earth metal oxides. It is easier to make strontium[52] than barium by this method.

Snyder and Lipkin[121] have reported the technique for strontium distillation.

Rinck[111] has studied the existence of three allotropic forms with transition points at 235 and 540°C (455 and 1004°F) by thermal analysis, electrical resistivity, differential thermal electrical effect, and expansion of a specimen of redistilled strontium.

Bridgman[21] has measured the electrical resistance of strontium under pressures up to 7,000 kg/sq cm at temperatures up to 200°C (392°F). The curves of resistance versus pressure at 0, 100, and 200°C (32, 212, and 392°F) are parallel, with resistance increasing with pressure. The mean temperature coefficient of strontium between 0 and 100°C (32 and 212°F) is 0.00283 at atmospheric pressure.

Bell *et al.*[18] have studied the electromagnetic concentration of the four isotopes of strontium.

Sheldon and King[118] have found that strontium crystallizes below 215° ± 10°C (419 ±

180°F) as face-centered cubic (α) [a = 6.0726 ± 0.0005 kX, 25°C (77°F)]; between 215° and 605 ± 10°C (419 and 1121 ± 18°F) as hexagonal close-packed (β) [a = 4.31 ± 0.01, c = 7.05 ± 0.01 kX, 248°C (478°F)]; and above 605°C (1121°F) as body-centered cubic (γ) [a = 4.84 ± 0.01 kX, 614°C (1137°F)].

Nottorf[99] has found strontium in uranium fission materials: strontium[90], half life 17 years, β-ray 0.04 mev; and yttrium 90, daughter of strontium 90.

Priselkov and Nesmeyanov[108] represented the vapor pressure of strontium between 400 and 600°C (752 and 1112°F) as

$$\log P_{Sr} = 7.435 - 7{,}548/T$$

The potential applications of strontium are similar to those of calcium and barium. The relative nonavailability of the metal has resulted in a situation in which too little is known of its alloys and their properties. In commercial applications it offers no advantages over calcium; it is also much higher in price.

Table 2.6 gives analyses of commercial strontium metal and prices for extruded rod and crystalline lumps in small lots.

References

1. Achard, J. C., Cara, P., and Loriers, J., *Compt. rend.*, **243**, 493 (1956).
2. Agladze, R. I., and Avaliani, A. Sh., *Trudy Gruzin. Politekh. Inst.*, No. 5, 147 (1955); *Referat. Zhur., Met.*, (1956).
3. Agladze, R. I., and Avaliani, A. Sh., *Trudy Inst. Metal. i Gornogo Dela, Akad. Nauk Gruzin. S. S. R.*, **2**, 89 (1949).
4. Ahmann, D. H., *Iowa State Coll. J. Sci.*, **27**, 120 (1953).
5. Alberti, E., *Z. Metallk.*, **26**, 6 (1934).
6. Alexander, P. P., U.S. Patent 2,606,100 (1952).
7. Alexander, P. P., U.S. Patent 2,656,268 (1953).
8. Alexander, P. P., U.S. Patent 2,794,732 (1957).
9. Anderko, K. P., *J. Metals*, 9, *Trans. AIME*, **209**, 612 (1957).
10. Andress, K. R., and Alberti, E., *Z. Metallk.*, **27**, 126 (1935).
11. Andrieux, J. L., and Bonnier, E., *Compt. rend.*, **243**, 1259 (1956).
12. Anselin, F., Faugeras, P., and Grison, E., *Compt. rend.*, **242**, 1996 (1956).
13. Asai, H., *Nippon Kinzoku Gakkaishi*, **16**, 464 (1952).
14. Barton, J., U.S. Patent 2,684,898 (1954).

15. Bassereau, G. J. A., French Patent 1,004,466 (Mar. 31, 1952).

16. Bastien, P., *Rev. mét.*, **32**, 120 (1935).

17. Beard, A. P., and Crooks, D. D., *J. Electrochem. Soc.*, **101**, 597 (1954).

18. Bell, W. A., Buttram, H. J., and Love, L. O., *U.S. Atomic Energy Comm., Rept. No. Y-692* (1950).

19. Betcherman, I. I., and Pidgeon, L. M., *Trans. Can. Inst. Mining Met. Engrs.*, **54**, in *Can. Mining Met. Bull.*, No. 468, 253 (1951).

20. Bloomer, R. N., *Brit. J. Appl. Phys.*, **8**, 40 (1957).

21. Bridgman, P. W., *Proc. Am. Acad. Arts Sci.*, **84**, 111 (1955).

22. Burnett, R. L., U.S. Patent 2,650,085; British Patent 698,861 (1953).

23. Calingaert, G., U.S. Patent 2,543,390 (1951).

24. Cambron, A., and Alexander, W. A., *Can. J. Chem.*, **34**, 665 (1956).

25. Carlson, O. N., Schmidt, F. A., and Wilhelm, H. A., *J. Electrochem. Soc.*, **104**, 51 (1957).

26. Collins, T. L., Nier, A. O., and Johnson, W. H., *Phys. Rev.*, **84**, 717 (1951).

27. Compagnie de produits chimiques et electro-metallurgiques Alais, Froges et Camargue, French Patent 935,324 (June 16, 1949).

28. Cowan, W. A., Simpkins, L. D., and Hiers, G. O., *Trans. Electrochem. Soc.*, **40**, 27 (1921).

29. Cubicciotti, D., *J. Am. Chem. Soc.*, **74**, 557 (1952).

30. Culler, G., Fernbach, S., and Sherman, N., *Phys. Rev.*, **101**, 1047 (1956).

31. Daane, A. H., and Spedding, F. H., *J. Electrochem. Soc.*, **100**, 442 (1953).

32. De Hollander, W. R., *U.S. Atomic Energy Comm., Rept. No. HW-38912* (1955).

33. Dominion Magnesium, Ltd., British Patent 664,061 (Jan. 2, 1952).

34. Douglas, I. P. E., *Proc. Phys. Soc. (London)*, **67B**, 783 (1954).

35. Duckworth, H. E., Kegley, C. L., Olson, J. M., and Stanford, G. S., *Phys. Rev.*, **83**, 1114 (1951).

36. Duffendack, O. S., Wolfe, R. A., and Randolph, D. W., *Trans. Electrochem. Soc.*, **59**, 181 (1931).

37. Field, E., and Feller, M., U.S. Patent 2,726,234 (1955).

38. Foster, L. S., and Magel, T. T., U.S. Patent 2,834,672 (1958).

39. French Patent 366,761 (Oct. 11, 1906).

40. Fujita, E., *Repts. Govt. Chem. Ind. Research Inst. Tokyo*, **45**, 378 (1950); *ibid.*, **49**, 233 (1954); *J. Electrochem. Soc. Japan*, **22**, 528 (1954).

41. Fujita, E., and Yokomizo, H., *J. Electrochem. Soc. Japan*, **19**, 148 (1951); *ibid.*, **22**, 413 (1954).

42. Fujita, E., and Yokomizo, H., *Repts. Govt. Chem. Ind. Research Inst. Tokyo*, **47**, 291 (1952).

43. Fujita, E., Yokomizo, H., and Kurozaki, Y., *J. Electrochem. Soc. Japan*, **19**, 196 (1951).

44. Gabbrielli, E., Italian Patent 537,699 (Jan. 2, 1956).

45. Gautier, H., *Compt. rend.*, **134**, 1054 (1902).

46. Gibbs, D. S., Svec, H. J., and Harrington, R. E., *Ind. Eng. Chem.*, **48**, 289 (1956).

47. Gilbert, H. L., and Block, F. E., *J. Electrochem. Soc.*, **102**, 394 (1955).

48. Giraitis, A. P., U.S. Patent 2,756,141 (1956).

49. Goodman, B. B., *Proc. NBS Semicentennial Symposium Low-Temp. Phys., Natl. Bur. Standards*, **519**, 71 (1952); *Nature*, **167**, 111 (1951).

50. Gruber, B. A., Gordon, E., and Jermain, R. A., U.S. Patent 2,735,668 (1956).

51. Guntz, A., *Chim. & ind. (Paris)*, Special No. 461 (February, 1929).

52. Guntz, A., *Compt. rend.*, **143**, 339 (1906).

53. Guntz, A., and Galliot, *Compt. rend.*, **151**, 813 (1910).

54. Hartmann, H., and Schneider, R., *Z. anorg. u. allgem. Chem.*, **180**, 275 (1929).

55. Hawkes, A. S., and Krohn, I. T., U.S. Patent 2,759,896 (1956).

56. Hill, E. F., U.S. Patent 2,543,406 (1951).

57. Hill, E. F., and Soroos, H., U.S. Patent 2,543,407 (1951).

58. Homer, H. J., and Whitacre, J. R., U.S. Patent 2,839,423 (1958).

59. Huber, E. J., Jr., and Holley, C. E., Jr., *J. Phys. Chem.*, **60**, 498 (1956).

60. Hume-Rothary, W., "Atomic Theory for Students of Metallurgy," Inst. Metals (London), 1945.

61. Jaffe, S., and Parks, J. M., U.S. Patent 2,839,380 (1958).

62. Jeffries, Z., *Mining and Met.*, **22**, 82 (1941).

63. Johnston, J. H., U.S. Patent 2,819,158 (1958).

64. Keller, W. H., Lyon, W. L., Svec, H. J., and Thompson, R., *U.S. Atomic Energy Comm., Rept. No. TID-5223*, 446 (1952).

65. Kelley, K. K., *U.S. Bur. Mines, Bull. No. 383* (1935).

66. Kelley, K. K., *U.S. Bur. Mines, Bull. No. 393* (1936).

67. Kelley, K. K., *U.S. Bur. Mines, Bull. No. 476* (1949).

68. Kelley, K. K., *U.S. Bur. Mines, Bull. No. 477* (1950).

69. Kelly, J. C. R., Jr., U.S. Patent 2,702,739 (1955).

70. King, A. J., U.S. Patent 2,437,097 (1948).

71. Kirsebom, G. N., U.S. Patent 2,111,367 (1938).

72. Kline, R. M., and Zaffarano, D. J., *U.S. Atomic Energy Comm., Rept. No. ISC-510* (1954).

73. Kornilow, I. I., *J. Inst. Metals*, **4**, 385 (1939).

74. Kroll, W. J., *Trans. Electrochem. Soc.*, **78**, 35 (1940).

75. Kroll, W. J., *U.S. Bur. Mines, Inform. Circ. No. 7327* (1945).

76. Kubaschewski, O., and Dench, W. A., *Bull. Inst. Mining Met.*, **599**, 1 (1956).

77. Lemmon, A. W., Ward, J. J., Fischer, S. M., Geankoplis, C. J., and Clegg, J. W., *U.S. Atomic Energy Comm., Rept. No. BMI-550* (1952).

78. Lilliendahl, W. C., U.S. Patent 2,537,067 (1951).

79. Lilliendahl, W. C., and Rentschler, H. C., U.S. Patent 2,537,068 (1951).

80. Long, J. R., *Iowa State Coll. J. Sci.*, **27**, 213 (1953).

81. Loomis, C. C., *Trans. Electrochem. Soc.*, **89**, 207 (1946).

82. MacDonald, D. K. C., and Mendelssohn, K., *Proc. Roy. Soc. (London)*, **A202**, 523 (1950).

83. McKechnie, R. K., and Seybolt, A. U., *J. Electrochem. Soc.*, **97**, 311 (1950).

84. Mallet, J. W., *Liebig's Ann. Chem.*, **190**, 62 (1878).

85. Mantell, C. L., "Industrial Electrochemistry," 3rd Ed., p. 535, New York, McGraw-Hill Book Company, Inc., 1950.

86. Mantell, C. L., and Hardy, C., "Calcium Metallurgy and Technology," New York, Reinhold Publishing Corp., 1945.

87. Matignon, *Compt. rend.*, **156**, 1378 (1913).

88. Meerson, G. A., and Kolchin, O. P., *Soviet J. Atomic Energy*, **2**, 305 (1957); *Atomnaya Energ.*, **2**, 253 (0000); *Sbornik Nauch. Trudov Moskov. Inst. Tsvetnykh Metal. i Zolota*, No. 25, 195 (1955); *Referat. Zhur. Met.*, No. 1012 (1956).

89. Meister, G., *U.S. Atomic Energy Comm., Rept. No. MDDC-1673* (1948).

90. Mellor, J. W., "A Comprehensive Treatise on Inorganic and Theoretical Chemistry," Vol. 3, New York, Longmans, Green & Co., Inc., 1946.

91. Melsert, H., Tiedema, T. J., and Burgers, W. G., *Acta Cryst.*, **9**, 525 (1956).

92. Miller, G. L., *Vacuum*, **2**, 19 (1952).

93. Moore, G. E., and Allison, H. W., *J. Chem. Phys.*, **23**, 1609 (1955).

94. Morrison, J., and Zetterstrom, R. B., *J. Appl. Phys.*, **26**, 437 (1955).

95. Muthmann, W., Weiss, L., and Metzger, J., *Liebig's Ann. Chem.*, **355**, 144 (1907).

96. National Research Council of Canada, British Patent 728,821 (Apr. 27, 1955).

97. Neumann, B., and Bergve, E., *Z. Elektrochem.*, **20**, 187 (1914).

98. Nishida, K., Japan Patent 3,102 (July 3, 1953).

99. Nottorf, R. W., *Iowa State Coll. J. Sci.*, **26**, 255 (1952).

100. Oda, Z., *Ôyô Butsuri*, **25**, 234 (1956).

101. Oda, Z., Arata, H., and Yoshida, S., *Ôyô Butsuri*, **25**, 240 (1956).

102. Orman, M., *Prace Inst. Ministerstwa Hutnictwa*, **5**, 129 (1953).

103. Orman, M., and Zembala, E., *Prace Inst. Met.*, **4**, 437 (1952).

104. Padgitt, F. L., Smith, M. B., and Thomas, W. H., U.S. Patent 2,761,777 (1956).

105. Pidgeon, L. M., and Atkinson, J. T. N., *Can. Mining Met. Bull.*, No. 429, 14 (1948).

106. Pidgeon, L. M., and McCatty, S. A., U.S. Patent 2,464,767 (1949).

107. Pilling, N. B., *Phys. Rev.*, **18**, 362 (1921).

108. Priselkov, Yu. A., and Nesmeyanov, An. N., *Doklady Akad. Nauk S.S.S.R.*, **95**, 1207 (1954).

109. Randolph, D. W., *Trans. Electrochem. Soc.*, **66**, 85 (1934).

110. Ray, K. W., *Metals & Alloys*, **1**, 112 (1929).

111. Rinck, E., *Compt. rend.*, **234**, 845 (1952).

112. Rudberg, E., *Phys. Rev.*, **46**, 763 (1934).

113. Saller, H. A., and Rough, F. A., *Chem. Eng. Progr., Symposium Ser.*, **50**, No. 11, 63 (1954).

114. Sawamoto, H., and Asai, M., *Research Repts. Fac. Eng. Nagoya Univ.*, **4**, 41 (1951).

115. Schultink, L., and van Zanten, P. G., *Philips Tech. Rev.*, **18**, 222 (1956–57).

116. Schumacher, E. E., and Ellis, W. C., *Trans. Electrochem. Soc.*, **61**, 91 (1932).

117. Schwarz, R., and Koster, A., *Z. anorg. u. allgem. Chem.*, **285**, 1 (1956).

118. Sheldon, E. A., and King, A. J., *Acta Cryst.*, **6**, 100 (1953).

119. Siemens & Halske A.-G. (H. Katz, inventor), German Patents 895,478 (Nov. 2, 1953); 905,517 (Mar. 4, 1954).

120. Smith, J. F., Carlson, O. N., and Vest, R. W., *J. Electrochem. Soc.*, **103**, 409 (1956).

121. Snyder, T., and Lipkin, D., *Natl. Nuclear Energy Ser., Div. V, 3, Misc. Phys. and Chem. Techniques*, 252 (1952).

122. Société anon. des manufactures des glaces et produits chimiques de Saint-Gobain, Chauny & Cirey, French Patent 973,654 (Feb. 13, 1951).

123. Spedding, F. H., and Daane, A. H., *J. Metals*, **6**, 504 (1954).

124. Spedding, F. H., Wilhelm, H. A., and Keller, W. H., U.S. Patent 2,785,065 (1957).

125. Spedding, F. H., Wilhelm, H. A., and Keller, W. H., U.S. Patent 2,797,160 (1957).

126. Spedding, F. H., Wilhelm, H. A., Keller, W. H., Ahmann, D. H., Daane, A. H., Hach, C. C., and Ericson, R. P., *Ind. Eng. Chem.*, **44**, 553 (1952).

127. Spedding, F. H., Wilhelm, H. A., Keller, W. H., Iliff, J. E., and Neher, C., *U.S. Atomic Energy Comm., Rept. No. TID-5232*, 428 (1952).

128. Stansfield, E., *Mem. Proc. Manchester Lit. & Phil. Soc.*, **48**, Pt. I, Sec. IV, 1 (1901–02).

129. Swisher, C. L., *Phys. Rev.*, **10**, 601 (1917).

130. Taylor, J. W., *Metallurgia*, **50**, 161 (1954).

131. Thomson, G. W., and Garelis, E., Ethyl Corporation (1952).

132. Tomlin, D. H., *Proc. Phys. Soc. (London)*, **67B**, 787 (1954).

133. Trautz, M., *Z. Elektrochem.*, **21**, 130 (1915).

134. van Arkel, A. E., "Reine Metale," Herstellung-Eigenschaften-Verwendung (Appendix), Berlin, J. Springer, 1939.

135. von Antropoff, A., and Falk, E., *Z. anorg. u. allgem. Chem.*, **187**, 405 (1930).

136. Wagener, S., *Brit. J. Appl. Phys.*, **1**, 225 (1950); **2**, 132 (1951).

137. Wagener, S., *Vacuum*, **3**, 11 (1953); *Proc. Inst. Elec. Engrs. (London)*, **99**, Pt. III, 135 (1952).

138. Walsh, K. A., *U.S. Atomic Energy Comm., Rept. No. AECD-3640* (1950).

139. Warrington, H. G., Canadian Patent 534,279 (Dec. 11, 1956).

140. Warrington, H. G., and McPhail, D. J., U.S. Patent 2,829,878 (1958).

141. Wehner, G., *Freiberger Forschungsh.*, **B17**, 18 (1956).

142. Westrum, E. F., Jr., and Eyring, L., *J. Am. Chem. Soc.*, **73**, 3396 (1951).

143. Wilhelm, H. A., and Long, J. R., U.S. Patent 2,700,606 (1955).

144. Wilkinson, G., and Grummitt, W. E., *Nucleonics*, **9**, 52 (1951).

145. Winkler, C., *Ber.*, **23**, 2647 (1890).

146. Winter, C. H., Jr., U.S. Patent 2,586,134 (1952).

147. Winter, C. H., Jr., U.S. Patent 2,763,542 (1956).

148. Woehler, L., and Muller, F., *Z. anorg. u. allgem. Chem.*, **120**, 49 (1921).

149. Woehler, L., and Schuff, W., *Z. anorg. u. allgem. Chem.*, **209**, 33 (1932).

3. BERYLLIUM

Bengt R. F. Kjellgren

The Brush Beryllium Company
Cleveland, Ohio

INTRODUCTION

In 1797 Vauquelin discovered the element beryllium as a constituent of the mineral beryl. In the French language the element is referred to as glucinium (Gl). This name is derived from the sweetish taste of many of its compounds.

The first metallic beryllium was produced by Wöhler and Bussy in 1828. They obtained beryllium in the form of an impure powder by reducing beryllium chloride with metallic potassium.

During the nineteenth century numerous other investigators contributed to the development of the chemistry of beryllium. Of particular interest is the work of the French scientist Lebeau,[8] published in 1899, which includes descriptions of the electrolysis of sodium beryllium fluoride resulting in the production of small, hexagonal beryllium crystals, and the preparation of beryllium-copper alloys by direct reduction of beryllium oxide with carbon in the presence of copper. Also of interest is the work by the German scientist Oesterheld,[10] who, in 1916, published the equilibrium diagrams of beryllium with copper, aluminum, silver, and iron, and the investigations by Wilhelm Kroll, W. B. Donahue, and C. Adomali, who all worked on methods of producing pure beryllium by reducing mixtures of beryllium fluoride and alkaline earth and alkali fluorides with alkaline earth metals and magnesium.[28]

Commercial development of beryllium in the United States was begun in 1916 by Hugh S. Cooper, who produced the first significant beryllium metal ingot, and by the Brush Laboratories Company, which started their development work under the direction of C. B. Sawyer in the early 1920's. In Germany the Siemens-Halske Konzern began their commercial development work in 1923.

Beryllium alloys made their commercial appearance in the United States in 1932, when the American Brass Company, using beryllium-copper master alloy produced by the Beryllium Corporation of America, made available the first rolled beryllium copper. The developments of the Brush Laboratories Company were taken over by the Brush Beryllium Company in 1931. This company entered the beryllium-copper field in the early 1930's and was the first company to develop a commercial process to produce and market metallic beryllium in solid form.

Beryllium is the first element in Group II of the periodic system of elements. Its atomic number is 4, its atomic weight 9.013, and it has a valence of two corresponding to 2s electrons in the L-shell. No isotopes have been found in beryllium occurring in nature. Radioactive isotopes of mass numbers 6, 7, 8, 10, and 11, however, have been artificially produced.

Metallic beryllium is grayish in color. Large crystals of bright metallic luster are usually discernible. It is a very light metal (specific gravity 1.845) and is known as the only such metal combining good physical strength with a high melting point [1285°C (2345°F)].

OCCURRENCE

There are some 30 recognized minerals containing beryllium; only 3 are of significance, viz., beryl ($3BeO \cdot Al_2O_3 \cdot 6SiO_2$), phenacite ($2BeO \cdot SiO_2$), and bertrandite ($4BeO \cdot 2SiO_2 \cdot$

H_2O). Of these three, only beryl is now of industrial importance. However, substantial low grade deposits of the other two minerals have now been found. The recovery of beryllium from these low grade ores is now under investigation. In pure form this mineral is a beryllium aluminum silicate containing approximately 14 per cent beryllium oxide (BeO), 19 per cent aluminum oxide (Al_2O_3), and 67 per cent silicon dioxide (SiO_2). The pure composition is approached in the precious forms of beryl—emerald and aquamarine.

Industrial grades of beryl ore now reaching the market contain approximately 10 to 12 per cent beryllium oxide. Rarely is ore of more than 12 per cent beryllium oxide available, and the trend is toward a supply ranging from 11 per cent downward to the marginal ores containing less than 9 per cent. Other constituents of the ore are aluminum oxide, 17 to 19 per cent; silicon dioxide, 64 to 70 per cent; alkali metal oxides, 1 to 2 per cent; iron, 1 to 2 per cent; and minor amounts of other oxides. Feldspar, quartz, and mica are the principal mineral contaminants of commercial grades of beryl ore.

Occurrences of beryllium in the earth's crust are widely distributed and are estimated to amount to approximately 0.001 per cent.[2] Beryl ore containing 10 to 12 per cent beryllium oxide, however, has not as yet, with one or two exceptions, been found anywhere concentrated in large enough quantities to be mined economically for its own sake. The supply is, therefore, generally obtained as a by-product of mining feldspar, lithium, or mica in pegmatite dikes, and only those crystals which are large enough to be hand-sorted and cobbed are recovered. The best producing pegmatites, suitable for hand sorting and cobbing, contain 1 to 2 per cent beryl ore. The by-products from these operations and low-grade beryl ore containing about 0.1 per cent beryl will require beneficiation processes to recover the beryl. According to the Bureau of Mines, reserves of such low-grade ores in the United States amount to over 1,000,000 tons of beryl-ore content.

Recently, privately owned facilities for concentrating low-grade beryl ores have been constructed in Colorado. The feasibility of operating these mills on an economic basis has not yet been established.

The principal producers of beryl ore are the Union of South Africa, Argentina, Brazil, and India. Small amounts are produced in British East Africa, French Morocco, Mozambique, Portugal, and Canada. In the United States the principal sources are found in Colorado, Maine, New Hampshire, and South Dakota. Many undeveloped deposits are located in Canada, particularly in the Great Slave Lake area of the Northwest Territories. Most of the beryl ore consumed by the beryllium industry in the United States is imported. Up to this time, the supply of hand-sorted and cobbed ore has been more than sufficient to meet the industrial demand.

PRODUCTION AND ECONOMIC STATISTICS

As beryl ore is the mainstay of the beryllium industry, beryl-ore statistics offer an accurate measure of the size and activity of the industry. Table 3.1 shows in detail, for the years 1940 through 1959, the total new supply of beryl, from both domestic and foreign sources, the total consumption of beryl in the United States, and the approximate stocks remaining at the end of the year. As a matter of additional interest, the approximate prevailing prices paid for beryl ore during this period are also listed.

In spite of the substantial increase in prices of beryl ore as shown in Table 3.1, the price of pure beryllium metal is now only about 20 per cent higher than in 1940, illustrating the counteracting effects of greater volume and steadily improving technology. The volume effect on prices of beryllium in beryllium-copper master alloy has not been so great as for pure beryllium. Even in this case, however, the price of the beryllium content in beryllium copper has only doubled, while the cost of the beryllium content in beryl ore increased about 15 times.

Prices for beryllium in vacuum-cast billet form ranged in 1959 from $47 to $85/lb, depending on quantities ordered, whereas the price of beryllium content in beryllium-copper master alloy (4 per cent Be) remained steady at $43/lb.

Only limited amounts of beryl ore are obtained from domestic sources, over 90 per cent of our new supply coming from abroad. It may be of interest to observe just where this ore is produced. Tables 3.2 and 3.3 describe this in detail. Table 3.2 shows the beryl shipments

TABLE 3.1. UNITED STATES BERYL SUPPLY, CONSUMPTION, STOCKS, AND PRICES, 1940 TO 1959 BY YEARS
(Short Tons)

Year	Domestic mine production*	Imports†	Total new supply	Consumption (estimated)*	Stocks at end of year (estimated)‡	Approximate price per unit§
1940	121	805	926	600	700	$ 2.50
1941	158	2,666	2,824	1,200	1,700	3.85– 4.50
1942	269	2,050	2,319	2,352	2,000	5.60– 7.50
1943	356	4,840	5,196	3,058	3,600	6.50–10.40
1944	388	3,115	3,503	2,176	4,800	9.00–14.50
1945	39	1,201	1,240	1,738	4,600	9.00–14.50
1946	100	1,188	1,288	1,013	5,000	9.00–14.50
1947	145	767	912	1,735	4,200	16.00–18.00
1948	99	1,720	1,819	1,970	3,600	16.00–26.00
1949	475	3,811	4,286	1,029	6,800	26.00–28.00
1950	559	4,887	5,446	3,007	9,400	28.00
1951	484	4,316	4,800	3,388	10,800	28.00–35.00
1952	515	5,978	6,493	3,476	14,800	39.00
1953	751	7,998	8,749	2,661	20,900	47.00
1954	669	5,816	6,485	1,948	25,400	43.00–47.00
1955	500	6,037	6,537	3,860	28,100	38.00–50.00
1956	460	12,371	12,831	4,431	36,500	36.00–38.00
1957	521	7,290	7,811	4,309	40,000	36.00–38.00
1958	463	4,599	5,062	6,002	39,060	30.00–33.00
1959	328	8,038	8,366	8,178	38,500	31.00–34.00

* United States Bureau of Mines.

† Department of Commerce.

‡ Estimate by author.

§ Estimate by author. (One unit equals 1 per cent BeO content in beryl ore. Thus, beryl containing 11 per cent BeO contains 11 units.)

TABLE 3.2. BERYLLIUM CONCENTRATES (BERYL) SHIPPED FROM MINES IN THE UNITED STATES, 1952–1959, BY STATES (Short Tons) (United States Bureau of Mines)

State	1952	1953	1954	1955	1956	1957	1958	1959
Colorado	54	75	59	46	179	182	134	124
New Hampshire	*	57	12	20	*	4	14	20
New Mexico	101	89	117	106	31	29	27	11
South Dakota	334	392	337	294	195	268	240	156
Other†	26	138	144	34	55	38	48	17
Total	515	751	669	500	460	521	463	328
Value	$233,257	$354,487	$303,649	$267,927	$236,748	$275,855	$238,017	$170,523
Average value per ton	$452.93	$472.02	$453.88	$535.85	$514.25	$529.00	$514.00	$520.00

* Included with "Other" to avoid disclosing individual-company confidential data.

† Arizona, 1953–1958; Connecticut, 1953–1959; Georgia, 1952–1957; Idaho, 1953–1954, 1957; Maine, 1952–1959; Maryland, 1954, 1957; New Hampshire, 1956–1957; New York, 1954; North Carolina, 1953–1958; Virginia, 1954–1956; and Wyoming, 1956–1959.

TABLE 3.3. BERYLLIUM ORE (BERYL CONCENTRATES) IMPORTED FOR CONSUMPTION IN THE UNITED STATES, BY COUNTRIES, 1953–1959 (Short Tons) (United States Department of Commerce)

Country	1953	1954	1955	1956	1957	1958	1959
Afghanistan	—	11					
Argentina	1,459	—	441	2,330	1,545	772	2,480
Belgian Congo	—	11	128	992	222	1,188	395
Brazil	2,614	1,828	1,735	2,607	2,165	888	2,833
British East Africa	22	23	93	264	56	30	15
British Somaliland	—	—	—	29			
British West Africa	—	—	—	22			
Hong Kong	—	—	—	1			
India	199	392	845	3,360	1,256	600	
Korea	8	4	6				
Madagascar	330	77	28	212	43		329
Morocco, French	23	—	—	26			
Mozambique	392	1,295	620	1,110	965	284	1,382
Nigeria	—	—	3				
Norway	—	—	—	—	—	—	4
Pakistan	—	—		15	69		
Portugal	332	338	283	242	33		77
Rhodesia and Nyasaland	1,296	957	861	559	266	135	151
Surinam	—	10					
Sweden	—	5					41
Union of South Africa	1,323	865	994	602	670	699	331
Total	7,998	5,816	6,037	12,371	7,290	4,599	8,038
Value	$3,752,718	$2,574,061	$2,226,068	$4,459,387	$2,526,068	$1,547,466	

from mines in the United States, 1952 to 1959, by states, in short tons. Table 3.3 shows the beryl imported into the United States, by countries, 1953 to 1959, in short tons.

DERIVATION

In the industrial processes now in use, the beryllium content in beryl ore is, as a first step, converted into a water-soluble beryllium salt, which is extracted by leaching; beryllium hydroxide or beryllium oxide is then recovered from the beryllium-containing solutions. The beryllium hydroxide and beryllium oxide so produced serve as raw materials for the production of beryllium metal and beryllium alloys.

Two industrial processes for the recovery of beryllium oxide from beryl ore are now in active use in the United States.

Copeaux-Kawecki Process

This process is used by the Beryllium Corporation, Reading, Pennsylvania. It is based on a reaction discovered by Copeaux.[3] He found that when beryl ore is mixed and sintered with sodium fluosilicate at approximately 750°C (1382°F), sodium beryllium fluoride and sodium aluminum fluoride are formed. The reaction is accompanied by the volatilization of silicon fluoride. Kawecki[16] improved the Copeaux process by using sodium ferric fluoride instead of sodium fluosilicate. The Kawecki reaction results in the formation of sodium beryllium fluoride, aluminum oxide, silicon dioxide, and iron oxide, with only very minor evolution of silicon fluoride.

After extracting the water-soluble sodium beryllium fluoride from the sintered material remaining after the Kawecki reaction, the solution is treated with caustic soda.

The beryllium hydroxide formed is filtered off, washed, dried, and ignited to beryllium oxide at a temperature of about 800°C (1472°F). This type of beryllium oxide contains some sodium fluoride but is sufficiently pure to serve as a raw material for the production of beryllium copper and other beryllium alloys.

The sodium fluoride which is formed in addition to beryllium hydroxide when the so-

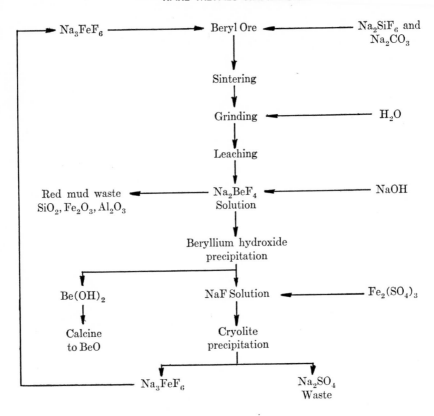

FIGURE 3.1. Beryllium hydroxide or oxide production.
Beryllium Corporation process.

dium beryllium fluoride solution is precipitated with sodium hydroxide is recovered from the dilute filtrate remaining after separation of the hydroxide by the addition of a concentrated solution of ferric sulfate. Sodium ferric fluoride is then precipitated, separated by filtration, and used again for sintering beryl ore. The Kawecki process, therefore, not only prevents the loss of fluorine, by eliminating the volatilization of silicon fluoride, but also allows recycling of the sodium fluoride needed to convert the beryl ore into sodium beryllium fluoride. Losses of sodium ferric fluoride in the process are replaced by additions of sodium fluosilicate and sodium carbonate.

A flow sheet of the Beryllium Corporation process for recovering beryllium hydroxide or beryllium oxide from beryl ore is shown in Figure 3.1.

Sawyer-Kjellgren Process

This process[17,18] is used by The Brush Beryllium Company, Cleveland, Ohio. It is based on

the discovery that if beryl ore is first completely melted and then quenched in cold water, the resulting glassy beryl frit becomes reactive to sulfuric acid. Beryl ore is otherwise very resistant to acid attack except by hydrofluoric acid, which is not economical to use in practice, owing to the large amount of silica present in beryl ore.

The solution of aluminum and beryllium sulfates which is obtained after treating the finely ground, glassy beryl frit with sulfuric acid is treated with ammonium sulfate in order to crystallize and separate the bulk of aluminum as ammonium alum. The beryllium sulfate-rich mother liquor is then treated with chelating reagents to prevent impurities from precipitating at the subsequent addition of sodium hydroxide, which results in the production of a pure precipitated grade of beryllium hydroxide containing small amounts of sodium sulfate as the major impurity. The hydroxide is ignited to beryllium oxide by heating to a temperature of about 750–850°C (1382–1594°F).

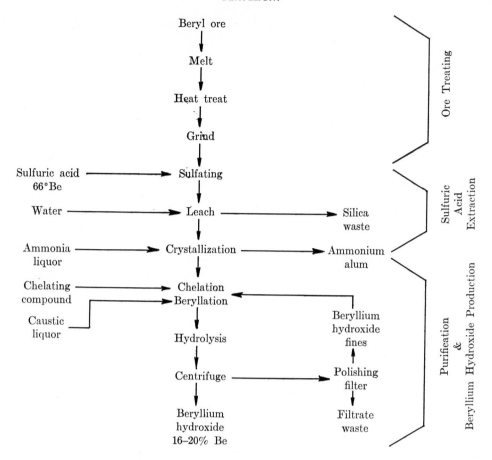

FIGURE 3.2. Beryllium hydroxide production.
Brush Beryllium Company process.

A flow sheet of The Brush Beryllium Company process for recovering beryllium hydroxide (or beryllium oxide) from beryl ore is shown in Figure 3.2.

PRODUCTION

Pure Beryllium Oxide

The technical grades of beryllium hydroxide or beryllium oxide produced as intermediate products in the production of beryllium metal and beryllium-copper master alloy contain, as a major impurity, salts of sodium and also minor amounts of elements occurring in commercial grades of beryl ore (Si, Fe, Al, Cu, Mg, Li, Mn, etc.).

These impurities are generally removed or substantially reduced by dissolving the technical grade hydroxide in sulfuric acid and purifying the formed beryllium sulfate by re-crystallization. The pure beryllium sulfate crystals obtained in this manner are then heated in gas-fired firebrick furnaces to drive off sulfur trioxide (as SO_2), leaving a pure grade of beryllium oxide as a residue. To remove all sulfur in the oxide, temperatures of 1000–1200°C (1832–2192°F) are required in a reducing atmosphere.

An extremely pure but very expensive grade of beryllium oxide can also be produced by converting the technical grade beryllium hydroxide into beryllium base acetate [BeO·3Be$(C_2H_3O_2)_2$]. The impurities remaining in this salt are separated by extracting the basic acetate with chloroform, filtering the solution to remove the insoluble impurities, evaporating the chloroform, and subliming the residue. The pure basic acetate so obtained is subsequently fumed down with chemically pure sulfuric acid. The resulting pure beryllium sulfate is then decomposed as noted above.

Beryllium Metal

All pure beryllium metal now produced in the United States is made by the reduction of beryllium fluoride with magnesium metal. The beryllium fluoride used is produced from beryllium hydroxide.

In this process, developed by Kjellgren[19] and used by The Brush Beryllium Company, an excess of beryllium fluoride is used in relation to the amount of magnesium added.

The reaction, which is carried out in a graphite-lined furnace, is kept under control by gradually charging magnesium metal and beryllium fluoride in solid form at a furnace temperature of about 900°C (1652°F). The heat generated by the reaction is absorbed as fast as it is liberated and serves to supply part of the heat required to melt the solid magnesium and the beryllium fluoride. Since the reaction is carried out below the melting point of beryllium, the metal is produced as very fine particles dispersed in a slag consisting of the magnesium fluoride formed by the reaction and the excess beryllium fluoride used.

The beryllium particles are melted and coalesced by raising the furnace temperature to somewhat above the melting point of beryllium. At this temperature the slag is very liquid, because of the presence of the excess beryllium fluoride, and the molten beryllium separates well and floats on the molten slag. As soon as this occurs, the molten metal and the slag are poured out together into a cold graphite crucible and solidified. In the process of pouring, the molten beryllium metal is broken up into pebbles so that the solid mixture obtained in the graphite crucible consists of beryllium pebbles embedded in solid slag. This mixture is broken up, and the beryllium pebbles and the excess beryllium fluoride present in the slag are recovered in the process which is used for producing the beryllium fluoride from beryllium oxide.

In this process the beryllium oxide is dissolved in a solution of ammonium hydrogen fluoride. The ammonium beryllium fluoride solution produced in this manner, and the ammonium beryllium fluoride solution recovered from leaching out the excess beryllium fluoride present in the mixture of the pebbles and slag resulting from the reduction, are mixed together and treated with lead peroxide, calcium carbonate, and ammonium polysulfide to precipitate impurities. After filtration, extremely pure ammonium beryllium fluoride is recovered from the filtrate by evaporation and crystallization.

In this manner the pure ammonium beryllium fluoride crystals produced in the process are derived both from beryllium oxide, the raw material, and from the beryllium fluoride present in the recycled slag.

The crystals obtained are then decomposed by heat into ammonium fluoride vapor, which is absorbed in water and recycled to the step of leaching the beryllium fluoride-containing slag, and into molten beryllium fluoride, which is collected in the form of small clear droplets or lumps.

After leaching the mixture of pebbles and slag resulting from the metal reduction step in order to recover the soluble beryllium fluoride, the beryllium pebbles are easily separated from the remaining insoluble small crystals of magnesium fluoride.

Beryllium pebbles obtained in this manner are remelted in a beryllium oxide crucible heated in a vacuum furnace.

The purity of the metal is controlled by the purity of the beryllium fluoride and the purity of the magnesium used.

A flow sheet of the Brush Beryllium Company process for recovering beryllium metal from beryllium hydroxide is shown in Figure 3.3.

Processes for producing beryllium in flake form by electrolysis of molten mixtures of beryllium and alkali chlorides have been worked out by Cooper,[24] Sawyer and Kjellgren,[25] and Morana.[26] These processes have, so far, not been used in industrial practice in the United States. The Pechiney Company in France has, however, over a period of years, produced beryllium flake by chloride electrolysis, although it is reported that their production is minor in comparison with the production in the United States.

Beryllium-Copper Master Alloy

Beryllium-copper alloys may be produced in the usual way of melting two metals together. These alloys, however, are, at the present time, made by direct reduction of beryllium oxide with carbon in the presence of copper, as this method has so far proved to be cheaper than direct alloying.

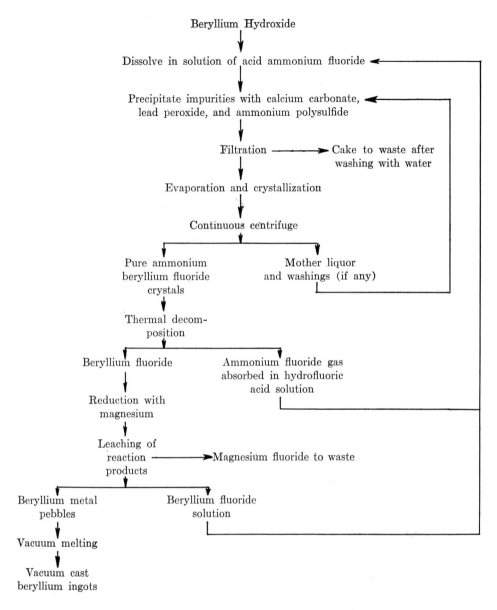

FIGURE 3.3. Beryllium metal production from hydroxide.
Brush Beryllium Company process.

Commercial processes for the production of beryllium copper were developed and patented by Sawyer and Kjellgren[20] and by Gahagan.[21] These processes use similar techniques and are based on the reduction of a mixture of beryllium oxide, carbon, copper, and by-product drosses and scrap alloys recycled in the process. The mixture is charged into an electric arc furnace operated at temperatures from 1800–2000°C (3272–3632°F). At these temperatures beryllium oxide is reduced with carbon. The carbon monoxide is given off as a by-product. The reaction is complicated by the formation of beryllium carbide, especially when the beryllium concentration in the copper alloy formed is increased. Practical experience has demonstrated that the best yields are obtained when an alloy containing 4 to 4.25 per cent beryllium is formed. At higher percentages the amount of beryllium carbide formed is excessive, and at lower percentages the production capacity of the furnace becomes less economical.

The electric power consumption is approximately 2.75 KWH/kg of 4 per cent alloy. The beryllium-copper master alloy produced by this process usually contains less than 0.10 per cent iron, 0.08 per cent silicon, and 0.06 per cent aluminum.

PHYSICAL PROPERTIES

Beryllium

Table 3.4 summarizes the values of the physical constants of beryllium obtained by Losano[9] and Sawyer and Kjellgren,[13] and the values published in the 1948 "Metals Handbook" of the American Society for Metals, as well as more recent results by others.

The extreme hardness frequently attributed

to beryllium in the literature is localized in a thin film of beryllium oxide on the surface of the metal. This hard oxide film is often strong enough to scratch glass.

Beryllium has a high permeability to x-rays, owing to its low atomic weight. Its permeability is approximately 17 times greater than that of aluminum.

Beryllium (isotope beryllium 9) has a small capture cross section for thermal neutrons and is a source of neutrons which are formed when beryllium is bombarded with other neutrons, alpha particles, deuterons, and gamma rays. A bombardment with alpha particles, for example, causes the following nuclear reaction:

$$_{4}^{9}Be + _{2}^{4}He \rightarrow _{6}^{12}C + _{0}^{1}n$$

The small mass of the beryllium nucleus, the small tendency of the nucleus to absorb

TABLE 3.4. PHYSICAL PROPERTIES OF BERYLLIUM

Atomic number	4
Atomic weight	9.013
Specific gravity (x-ray)	1.8445
Melting point	1285°C (2345°F)
Boiling point (vapor pressure 1 atm)	2507°C (4545°F)
(vapor pressure 0.1 atm)	2100°C (3812°F)
(vapor pressure 0.01 atm)	1797°C (3267°F)
(vapor pressure 0.001 atm)	1557°C (2835°F)
Specific heat [30–100°C (86–212°F)] (cal/g)	0.425
Latent heat of fusion (cal/g)	250–275
Latent heat of vaporization (cal/g)	5,917
Linear coefficient of thermal expansion [20–200°C/68–392°F)]	
Parallel hexagonal axis	12×10^{-6}
Perpendicular hexagonal axis	9×10^{-6}
Thermal conductivity at 20°C (68°F)	0.35 cgs
Electrical conductivity (% of Cu*)	38.9–43.1
Reflectivity (white light) (%)	50–55
Hardness (Brinell), 1,000-kg load	90–120
Velocity of sound (m/sec)	12,600
Type of crystal lattice at 20°C (68°F)	Close-packed hexagonal
Lattice constant (Å–10^{-8}cm) 20°C (68°F)	$a_0 = 2.2854$, $C_0 = 3.5829$, $C_0/a_0 = 1.5677$
Minimum interatomic distance (Å)	2.22
Electrochemical equivalent (mg/coulomb)	0.04674
Atomic radius (Å)	1.123
Thermal neutron cross section (barns/atom)	0.0090 ± 0.005
Coordination number	12
Allotropy	None
Magnetic mass susceptibility (cgs) electromagnetic units [20°C (68°F)]	-1.0×10^{-6}
Hall coefficient (cgs emu)	0.0024 ± 0.0001
Thermoelectric power (platinum) (mv)	0.16
Electrode potential (volts)	+1.69–1.9

* International Annealed Copper Standard = 100%.

neutrons, and particularly its low affinity for slow neutrons make it possible to reduce the neutron velocity without significant loss of energy. These properties make beryllium more efficient than graphite in moderating the velocity of neutrons in nuclear energy devices.

The radioactive beryllium isotopes are short-lived except for beryllium 10 which has a half life of about 2,700,000 years. Particularly unstable is isotope beryllium 8, which splits into two alpha particles in less than 10^{-15} sec after formation in nuclear reactions.

Beryllium Oxide

The values in Table 3.5 are recorded from "The Reactor Handbook," Volume 3, "Materials,"

AECD–3647, a publication by the United States Atomic Energy Commission (1955).

Beryllium oxide crystallizes in the hexagonal system with a zincite (ZnO) type of structure. It is prismatic, with a definite 1010 cleavage. Beryllia is an ionic crystal consisting of a close-packed array of oxygen atoms with beryllium atoms in the interstices, also close packed.

As seen from Table 3.5, the most outstanding properties of beryllium oxide for refractory uses are its high melting point, high electrical resistivity, and high thermal conductivity in the crystalline state. In addition, its stability at high temperatures and general thermal chemical inertness make it a remarkable refractory, and it often provides the only solution for some high-temperature problems.

TABLE 3.5. PHYSICAL PROPERTIES OF BERYLLIUM OXIDE

Density (g/cc)	
Single crystal	3.025
Hot-pressed	2.6–2.95
Slip castings after firing	2.2–2.8
Dust pressings after firing	2.2–2.8
Melting point (°C)	2550 ± 25 (4622 ± 77°F)
Boiling point (°C)	4260 ± 160 (7700 ± 320°F)
Heat of fusion (cal/mole)	17,000 ± 1400
Entropy of fusion [cal/(mole) (°C)]	6.0 ± 0.5
Heat of vaporization (cal/mole)	117,000 ± 10,500
Entropy of vaporization [cal/(mole) (°C)]	25.8 ± 2.3
Heat of sublimation (cal/mole) 600–3000°C (1112–5432°F)	152,000 ± 10,000
Heat of formation [$\Delta H°$ f25°C (kcal)]	−149.0
Thermal conductivity [cal/(sec) (cm) (°C)] of hot-pressed beryllia, density 2.87 g/cc	
200°C (392°F)	0.190
600°C (1112°F)	0.095
1000°C (1832°F)	0.056
1400°C (2552°F)	0.037
Specific heat [cal/(mole) (°C)]	
−273°C (−459°F)	0
−100°C (−148°F)	0.3
0°C (32°F)	5.5
100°C (212°F)	7.7
400°C (752°F)	10.5
800°C (1472°F)	12.3
Allotropy	No allotropic transformations of beryllia are known
Electrical resistivity (ohm–cm)	
Sintered beryllia, density 2.25 g/cc	
1000°C (1832°F)	80,000,000
1200°C (2192°F)	4,000,000
1400°C (2552°F)	250,000
1600°C (2912°F)	35,000
1800°C (3272°F)	6,500
2000°C (3632°F)	1,600

TABLE 3.5. PHYSICAL PROPERTIES OF BERYLLIUM OXIDE (*cont.*)

Mean coefficient of linear thermal expansion per °C:	
25–100°C (77–212°F)	$(5.5 \pm 1) \times 10^{-6}$
25–300°C (77–572°F)	$(8.0 \pm 0.6) \times 10^{-6}$
25–600°C (77–1112°F)	$(9.6 \pm 0.8) \times 10^{-6}$
25–800°C (77–1472°F)	$(10.3 \pm 0.9) \times 10^{-6}$
25–1000°C (77–1832°F)	$(10.8 \pm 1) \times 10^{-6}$

Lattice constants (Angstroms)

	Room Temperature	1025°C (1877°F)
a_0	2.69	2.72
c_0	4.39	4.43
c_0/a_0	1.63	1.63

Refractive indices

$$\alpha D = 1.719$$
$$\beta D = 1.733$$

Beryllium oxide, in addition to its other unique properties, has, like beryllium, a low capture cross section for thermal neutrons and high moderating ability. For this reason, it is playing an increasingly significant role in the nuclear energy field, as the need for high-temperature materials of good nuclear characteristics in many cases is becoming essential.

CHEMICAL PROPERTIES OF BERYLLIUM

Beryllium is a very active element at high temperatures, making the production of pure beryllium a difficult technical problem. At ordinary temperatures beryllium is quite resistant to oxidation in air. Highly polished surfaces of the pure metal retain their brilliance for years. At 700°C (1292°F) the oxidation is noticeable, and at 1000°C (1832°F) it is quite rapid. Finely divided beryllium reacts slowly with oxygen in the air and burns brilliantly when ignited. Nitrogen attacks beryllium at temperatures above 900°C (1652°F), forming beryllium nitride (Be_3N_2). Carbon forms beryllium carbide (Be_2C) at temperatures above the melting point of the metal. The reaction is exothermic.

Beryllium reacts readily with sulfuric and hydrochloric acids. Diluted nitric acid attacks the metal slowly, whereas concentrated nitric acid has little effect. Alkaline solutions react with beryllium with the evolution of hydrogen.

Beryllium metal reacts with fused alkali halides, releasing the alkali metal until an equilibrium is established. It does not react with fused halides of the alkaline earth metals, or magnesium, but it will reduce aluminum halides and halides of heavier elements. Alkaline earth metals and magnesium can be used effectively to produce beryllium from its halides.

Chemically speaking, beryllium is quite closely related to aluminum, and its complete separation from this element is difficult.

Aqueous corrosion of beryllium is not well understood but relates to its history of fabrication. Beryllium metal produced by powder metallurgy techniques is much more consistent in behavior than is cast metal, probably because of the difference in grain size. Ions of chloride, sulphate, copper, and iron in the water increase the pitting rate to some extent. Commercial vacuum hot-pressed beryllium powder compacts readily pass tests involving exposure to 250°C (482°F) water for 96 hrs. Some samples of the same material have been found to be more corrosion resistant than zirconium in 350°C (662°F) water, but other samples disintegrate completely. There is some evidence that the amount of impurities present in metallic beryllium affects its resistance to corrosion in high-temperature water, with higher-than-normal iron contents being beneficial and higher-than-normal aluminum and silicon contents being harmful.

Beryllium is not attacked by pure molten sodium at 500°C (932°F), an important property for nuclear applications. It has been found that if the molten sodium contains more than about 0.01 per cent oxygen, beryllium oxide is formed at the above temperature.

There is no evidence of stress corrosion of beryllium either in high-temperature water or in sodium.

TOXICITY

The toxicity of any element depends upon many factors, such as the type of compound in which the element occurs, the amount and concentration of the element or compound involved, the time of contact or exposure, and the manner in which the body is exposed, such as skin contact, exposure of the lungs by inhalation, or ingestion through the mouth.

During recent years, medical research groups have devoted much time to the study of the effect of beryllium and its compounds on the human body. The exact role played by the beryllium atom itself is not clearly understood, especially since the intensity of the attack on the skin or mucous membranes varies greatly, depending on the element or elements combined with the beryllium atom and on the individual who has been exposed.

Recent research indicates that beryllium compounds given in food to animals cause no toxic effects in concentrations which would be very toxic for compounds of many other elements. As far as is known, no cases of digestive poisoning caused by ingestion of beryllium have been recorded in the beryllium industry, and furthermore, no cases of dermatitis or pneumonitis have been reported as the result of the mining of beryl ore, or the mechanical working or handling of low-beryllium alloys, such as the beryllium-copper alloys now in use.

Soluble compounds of beryllium, however, may cause dermatitis, and acute pneumonitis may be encountered when mists, dust, or fumes of these compounds, or those resulting from melting the metal and its alloys, are inhaled. The sensitivity of individuals varies greatly. A few individuals are supersensitive and therefore cannot be employed in the beryllium industry. This is especially true in the production of beryllium halides, which are much more active than, for example, beryllium sulfate.

Medical authorities assert also that mists, dust, or fumes containing beryllium or its compounds may be instrumental in causing a delayed type of pneumonitis which develops relatively slowly and may extend over a period of years. The delayed type of pneumonitis, resulting in a number of fatalities, first appeared in 1943 in the fluorescent-lamp industry, in which beryllium zinc silicate is used. This health hazard is less understood than are dermatitis and acute pneumonitis; it has been the subject of extended investigation by the United States health authorities and other medical groups attempting to determine whether beryllium, or its compounds, plays a role in the development of this disease.

The beryllium health hazard is effectively reduced by proper ventilation; frequent washing of the hands, arms, face, and neck; and showers at the close of each shift. Personal cleanliness should be emphasized, and the operator should be provided with a clean set of working clothes at the beginning of each shift in order to combat dermatitis.

It is also advisable to have the plant physician check the chest of every employee at frequent intervals and to x-ray all employees at least once a year. An employee showing signs of lung irritation should immediately be given a period free from work long enough for recovery to take place, thus reducing the danger of acute pneumonitis that might end fatally. It is, of course, also advisable to take measures to control the volume of mists, dust, or fumes containing beryllium or its compounds; such measures include enclosing and ventilating the equipment involved in their production or use, and monitoring the air, both in the plant and in the vicinity of the plant, for the purpose of maintaining a safe level of beryllium content in the air.

Many years of industrial experience clearly indicate that beryllium, its alloys, and compounds can be safely produced and handled when there is close cooperation between the engineering staff, the production management, and the plant physician.

In this connection it should be of interest to note that the capital expenditure of installing modern ventilation and dust-collecting equipment is not excessive if sound engineering principles are applied, and, in fact, will generally be a profitable investment because of resulting higher process yields and improved employee morale.

Figure 3.4. Milling machine equipped with vacuum chip pickup around cutter and "Aerotec" chip collector which exhausts fine dust into precipitron system. (*Courtesy Brush Beryllium Company*.)

An example of the equipment needed to collect chips and fine dusts from the machining operation is shown in Figure 3.4.

MECHANICAL PROPERTIES

Beryllium

The mechanical properties of beryllium relate to its history of fabrication but depend fundamentally on its close-packed hexagonal crystal structure, which is characterized by high directionality. At room temperature the fracture stress on the basal plane is lower than the slip stresses on the 1010 prism planes.[23] Beryllium, therefore, fractures along the basal plane at room temperature, although it has substantial elongation in the prismatic planes for all degrees of purity up to about 2 per cent nonberyllium additives.

On the other hand, beryllium metal, which exhibits a tensile elongation of 0.5 to 3 per cent at room temperature, develops elongations from 25–50 per cent at 400–450°C (752–842°F). This change in tensile properties is due to a brittle-ductile transition, which takes place at about 200–300°C (392–572°F). The metal becomes hot short at about 850°C (1562°F), when failure takes place principally in the grain boundaries.

When beryllium is worked along preferential planes, for example, by extrusion, substantial elongation can be obtained in the direction of extrusion at room temperature. Uniaxial ductility in the plane of a sheet can also be obtained by cross rolling. Unless the metal is worked in all directions, however, at least one plane remains brittle at room temperature.

The mechanical properties of hot extruded flake and cast metal, and of compacts of vacuum hot-pressed beryllium powder (Brush QMV), and extrusions of this material are shown in Tables 3.6 and 3.7.

As seen from Table 3.7, the mechanically deformed metal, which is structurally anisotropic, has appreciably better mechanical properties in the direction of working than has the vacuum hot-pressed metal which has an isotropic structure.

As pure beryllium undergoes no known allo-

TABLE 3.6. SOME ROOM TEMPERATURE DIRECTIONAL PROPERTIES
OF EXTRUDED BERYLLIUM

Material	Condition	Longitudinal to extrusion		Transverse to extrusion	
		Ultimate strength (psi)	Elongation (%)	Ultimate strength (psi)	Elongation (%)
Cast and extruded	As extruded	32,700	0.36	19,400	0.30
Cast and extruded	Annealed 800°C (1472°F)	40,000	1.82	16,600	0.18
Extruded flake	As extruded	46,600	0.55	29,100	0.30
Extruded flake	Annealed 800°C (1472°F)	63,700	5.0	25,500	0.30

TABLE 3.7. TYPICAL VALUES OF ROOM TEMPERATURE MECHANICAL PROPERTIES OF
BERYLLIUM FABRICATED FROM POWDER

	Vacuum* hot-pressed powder	Hot extruded† from powder
Ultimate tensile strength (psi)	45,200	81,800
Tensile yield (0.2%) (psi)	32,100	39,500
Tensile elongation (%)	2.3	15.8
Tensile modulus of elasticity (psi)	44.4×10^6	41.4×10^6
Compression yield (0.2%) (psi)	24,600	38,000
Compression modulus (psi)	44.2×10^6	41.8×10^6
Poisson's ratio	0.024	0.032
Ultimate torsion strength (psi)	38,900	81,000
Torsion yield (psi)	18,300	14,200
Torsion modulus (psi)	21.5×10^6	21.0×10^6
Twist to failure (deg)	145	390
Ultimate strength (double shear) (psi)	36,800	61,300
Unnotched Charpy impact (ft–lb)	0.8	4.1
Tensile impact (ft–lb)	1.4	4.5

* Properties independent of direction of pressing.
† Direction of tensile testing same as direction of extrusion; transverse properties similar to hot-pressed values.

TABLE 3.8. THE EFFECT OF TEMPERATURE OF EXTRUSION AND HEAT TREATMENT
ON THE MECHANICAL PROPERTIES OF BERYLLIUM CASTINGS[7]

Extrusion temperature	As extruded and machined		As extruded, machined, and annealed at 800°C (1472°F)	
	Ultimate strength (psi)	Elongation (%)	Ultimate strength (psi)	Elongation (%)
500°C (952°F)	73,100	0.28	51,600	3.30
700°C (1292°F)	60,200	0.30	47,600	2.74
900°C (1652°F)	44,500	0.45	45,100	2.47
1060°C (1948°F)	36,500	0.39	52,100	3.38
1208°C (2206°F)	34,800	0.44	50,200	3.80

tropic changes relative to temperature, the only method of heat treatment utilized is by recrystallization of the worked metal at 704–900°C (1300–1650°F). The effect of heat treatment and extrusion temperatures on extruded cast beryllium is shown in Table 3.8.

The mechanical properties at elevated tem-peratures of fabricated beryllium made from flake, powder, and cast ingots which have been hot-extruded, are shown in Table 3.9. The tests shown in this table were performed from room temperature to 800°C (60–1472°F). It should be noted that at 400°C (752°F) the tensile elongation values are optimum, falling off at

TABLE 3.9. PROPERTIES OF EXTRUDED BERYLLIUM

Test temperature	Condition	Direction of test	Flake[7]		Cast[7]		Powder	
			Ultimate strength (psi)	Elongation (%)	Ultimate strength (psi)	Elongation (%)	Ultimate strength (psi)	Elongation (%)
Room	As extruded	Long.	46,600	0.55	32,700	0.36	85,000	16.0
		Trans.	29,100	0.30	19,400	0.30	63,000	1.5
	Annealed at 800°C (1472°F)	Long.	63,700	5.0	40,000	1.82		
			25,500	0.3	16,600	0.18		
200°C (392°F)	As extruded	Long.			39,900	13.2	62,000	23.5
		Trans.			16,600	1.1	44,000	2.2
	Annealed at 800°C (1472°F)	Long.			37,900	13.4		
		Trans.			14,300	1.4		
400°C (752°F)	As extruded	Long.	30,600	14.8	27,700	29.0	43,000	29.0
		Trans.	27,800	1.9	14,500	3.0	41,000	6.5
600°C (1112°F)	As extruded	Long.	13,600	10.6	25,900	20.8	23,000	8.5
		Trans.	11,200	2.5	16,000	1.2	22,500	4.5
800°C (1472°F)	As extruded	Long.	4,800	9.1	9,300	25.6	5,200	10.5
		Trans.	5,900	0.3	6,900	9.6	5,000	6.0

higher temperatures. The best transverse structural values are found for extruded flake and powder.

Creep properties and stress rupture data at elevated temperatures are shown in Tables 3.10 and 3.11.

TABLE 3.10. CREEP PROPERTIES OF VACUUM HOT PRESSED BERYLLIUM BLOCK
Tensile Stress versus Creep Rate

Stress (psi)	Minimum creep rate (%/hr)
at 427°C (800°F)	
8,290	0.00028
10,090	0.00056
12,490	0.0048
15,000	0.052
18,000	0.142
at 538°C (1000°F)	
4,190	0.001
4,930	0.01
5,290	0.06
at 677°C (1250°F)	
2,000	0.0009
2,220	0.018
2,700	0.07
3,190	0.28
at 732°C (1350°F)	
650	0.00036
970	0.0072
1,090	0.051
1,390	0.3

TABLE 3.11. STRESS RUPTURE DATA VACUUM HOT PRESSED BERYLLIUM BLOCK
Stress (psi)

Temperature		Stress (psi)			
°C	°F	10 hr	100 hr	1,000 hr	2,500 hr
427	800	22,000	18,000	13,000	10,500
538	1000	7,500	5,000	4,300	4,000
649	1200	3,500	2,500	2,150	2,000
732	1350	1,200	950	800	720
816	1500	310	230		

Beryllium Alloys

Beryllium alloyed with various heavy metals, such as copper and nickel, produces alloys with a capacity for precipitation hardening. Copper or nickel alloys relying on beryllium as the precipitation-hardening agent are characterized by an ability to dissolve beryllium in solid solution over a range from approximately 0.1 per cent to over 3.0 per cent. More beryllium is dissolved at high temperatures than at room temperature. When such an alloy is heated into the range of higher solubility for beryllium and quickly cooled from this temperature to room temperature as by quenching in water, the portion of the beryllium not soluble at room temperature forms a supersaturated solution. The alloy in this form is soft and workable at room temperature. Upon reheating, however, to a relatively low temperature, below red heat, the supersaturated solution of beryllium in the alloy gradually breaks down into crystals which

TABLE 3.12. MECHANICAL PROPERTIES OF BERYLLIUM COPPER*

Annealing quench temperature (°C)	Cold rolling	Aging Temperature (°C)	Time (hr)	Proportional limit† (psi)	Tensile strength (psi)	Elongation in 2 in. (%)	Electrical conductivity (% of Cu)‡	Brinell hardness (3,000 kg, 10 mm)
800 (1472° F)				8,000	70,000	45.0	17	110
800		300	2	46,000	175,000	6.3	22	340
800	B. & S. No. 4			39,000	118,000	4.3	16	220
800	B. & S.	300	2	55,000	193,000	2.0	21	365

* Contains 2–2.25% Be, 0.25–0.50% Ni, balance Cu. (Determined on 0.050-in. sheet.)
† Based on rigorous determinations.
‡ International annealed copper standard = 100%.
Source: Reference 12.

perhaps are submicroscopic particles of very hard beryllium compounds. These particles become densely scattered through the grains of the metal and thus function to harden it greatly. The reheating process producing the precipitation-hardening effect may be accurately controlled so that a wide range of properties can be obtained, from the softest state with high ductility to the hardest state of minimum, perhaps zero, ductility.

The properties of these alloys are further improved if the soft-annealed alloy is hardened by cold working before the low-temperature hardening heat treatment. Properties characteristic of beryllium-copper-nickel alloys are illustrated in Table 3.12. Nickel or cobalt is added mostly to prevent grain coarsening in cold-working operations, such as rolling and drawing.

Binary beryllium-copper alloys cannot be precipitation-hardened if the beryllium content is less than 1 per cent. If approximately 1.5 per cent nickel or cobalt is added, however, considerable precipitation hardening may be obtained with beryllium contents as low as 0.20 per cent. These low-beryllium alloys require 100–200°C higher temperatures, both for the solution and for the precipitation-hardening treatments. Properties characteristic of these low-beryllium–copper alloys are illustrated in Table 3.13.

The low-beryllium–copper alloys are characterized by their high electrical conductivity. It is remarkable that the proportional limit for these low-beryllium–copper alloys is practically the same as for the high-beryllium alloys.

Beryllium nickel is heat-treatable and has properties generally similar to those of beryllium copper and stainless steels. It has no outstanding property, such as the high electrical conductivity of beryllium copper.

After annealing and cold working, however, nickel alloys containing approximately 2 per cent beryllium can be heat-treated to give very high tensile properties, such as 260,000 psi with an elongation in 4 in. of 8.3 per cent and a Brinell hardness of 480. The use of beryllium

TABLE 3.13. MECHANICAL PROPERTIES OF LOW-BERYLLIUM COPPER*

Annealing Quench temperature (°C)	Time (hr)	Aging Temperature (°C)	Time (hr)	Proportional limit† (psi)	Yield point 0.50% (psi)	Tensile strength (psi)	Elongation in 10 in. (%)	Electrical conductivity (% of Cu)‡	Brinell hardness (3,000 kg, 10 mm)
900 (1652° F)	1			4,700	17,200	39,150	24.4	46.1	55
900	1	475	2	56,000	65,950	96,850	5.7	65.2	210
900	1			23,800	67,100	72,300	1.0	38.9	
900	1	425	2	55,000	86,500	127,500	8.3	59.3	220

* Contains 0.25% Be, 1.33% Ni, 0.08% Fe, balance Cu. (Determined on 0.08-in.-diameter wire.)
† Based on rigorous determinations.
‡ International annealed copper standard = 100%.
Source: Reference 12.

nickel is indicated in industry for high-temperature springs and for special parts in instruments, but beryllium-nickel alloys have not yet been produced in large quantities.

Binary beryllium-iron alloys have too coarse a grain structure for commercial applications. Beryllium steels containing nickel and chromium exhibit high strength and hardness at elevated temperatures. It is possible that beryllium may be used to modify steels where special properties not producible with carbon are desired.

Magnesium, which has a lower boiling point [1120°C (2048°F)] than the melting point of beryllium [1284°C (2343°F)], forms alloys with beryllium containing a maximum of 0.5 to 1 per cent magnesium. These alloys have no commercial applications, and their properties have not been determined. Beryllium, when alloyed with magnesium or magnesium alloys in quantities as small as 0.005 per cent, however, greatly reduces the flammability of magnesium and retards its oxidation at the melting point. This small addition of beryllium tends to coarsen the grain of the magnesium alloys, which, at present, limits this application to those magnesium alloys in which grain coarsening is of no practical consequence.

Aluminum alloys in all proportions with beryllium, but there is very little solid solubility of beryllium in aluminum, or vice versa. The eutectic contains only small amounts of beryllium. Beryllium-aluminum alloys solidify over a very extended temperature range, from the melting point of beryllium [1284°C (2343°F)] to the melting point of the eutectic [644°C (1191°F)]. Large-size sound castings are, therefore, difficult to produce, because of excessive segregation. Although beryllium-aluminum alloys made on the laboratory scale exhibit good properties, especially at elevated temperatures, the commercial applications are limited by segregation difficulties.

FABRICATION

Beryllium

Experimental processes for fabricating beryllium by vacuum casting followed by hot working, wherein the metal is protected by a steel envelope, have been discussed in detail in articles published by Kaufmann, Gordon, and Lillie.[6, 7] Ingots up to 8 in. in diameter have been made in beryllium oxide crucibles under vacuum at about 100 to 500 μ pressure, using

Figure 3.5. Multiple tool turning operation for chipping beryllium vacuum cast ingot. (*Courtesy Brush Beryllium Company*.)

induction heating. The metal is poured through an opening in the crucible bottom which is closed during melting by a beryllia stopper rod. The ingot solidifies in a graphite mold containing an insulated hot top. The rate of cooling in the mold is important, as too rapid cooling promotes cracking; cooling the ingot too slowly results in a coarse-grained structure and partial reaction with the graphite mold. Forging, rolling, and extruding can be carried out on cast beryllium in the temperature range of 317–1093°C (700–2000°F), provided that the metal is encased in a protecting jacket, e.g., SAE 1020. The extrusion process can be used to produce bar, rod, plates, or tubing. The billet is jacketed and usually extruded at 816–1093°C (1500–2000°F) through a conical or bell-mouthed die. The leading end of the billet is in the form of a truncated cone over which is placed a soft steel cone.[7] Beryllium in the form of flake or powder can be also converted to bar, plates, rod, and tubing by compacting the particles into a steel can and extruding as with cast metal.

Beryllium is, however, as a rule not fabricated by casting techniques, because very coarse grains tend to develop in the castings, causing brittleness and low tensile strength.

Generally, therefore, beryllium is fabricated by powder metallurgy techniques. The metal is first cast in vacuum to obtain clean ingots, which subsequently are converted into chips by machining. (See Figure 3.5). The chips are then ground to powder in an inert atmosphere, and the powder is compacted into dense, fine-grained bodies by any one of the following powder metallurgy processes[27]: (1) vacuum hot pressing; (2) hot pressing (in air or inert gas); (3) vacuum sintering to shape (no compaction during sintering); (4) cold and/or warm compaction, followed by sintering and coining; (5) cold and/or warm compaction, followed by hot extrusion or hot pressing.

Of these processes, only the vacuum hot pressing [see Reference 27 (c)] developed by H. W. Dodds is used extensively in the beryllium industry. This process is carried out in practice by loading beryllium powder in steel

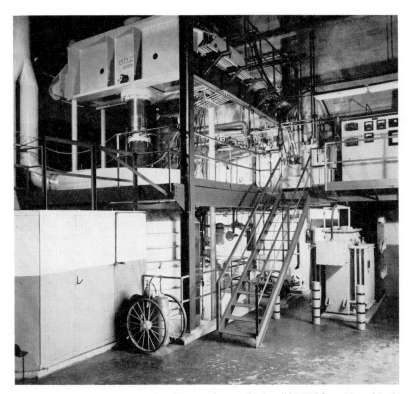

Figure 3.6. Vacuum hot pressing furnace for producing "QMV" beryllium block up to 65 inches in diameter. "QMV" is a trademark of the Brush Beryllium Company. (*Courtesy Brush Beryllium Company.*)

or graphite dies and compacting the powder with pressures of 50–250 psi under a vacuum of about 50 μ at temperatures of 1052–1093°C (1925–2000°F) to essentially theoretical density (1.8445).

A vacuum hot-pressing furnace for producing beryllium blocks up to 65 in. in diameter is shown in Figure 3.6.

The strength of the metal so produced is generally about twice that of similar products fabricated from cast metal. Also, the fine-grained metal produced by powder metallurgy methods is readily machined to extremely high tolerances, in contrast to the fabricated cast metal which is difficult to machine.

Vacuum hot-pressed blocks of high density weighing up to 2,000 lb have been made successfully. Hot pressings generally contain 0.6 to 2 per cent beryllium oxide, depending on particle size, conditions of oxidation, and the use of slightly oxidized chips recycled into the attritive step from machining operations.

The beryllium oxide helps to retain fine grains at elevated temperatures, the oxide film acting as a barrier at the grain boundaries. As a result of the random mixing and packing of the powder loaded into the dies before sintering and the limited grain growth owing to the presence of beryllium oxide, the structure of the sintered compacts is substantially isotropic, exhibiting ultimate strengths up to 50,000 psi with elongations up to 3 per cent.

Beryllium metal can be machined, rolled, extruded, forged, brazed, and soldered, and the surface finished by electroplating or chemical treatment.

An example of the machining operation is shown in Figure 3.7.

It is possible to work beryllium plastically substantially at temperatures above 455°C (850°F). Since the metal can recrystallize as low as 749–760°C (1380–1400°F), the range of 454–760°C (850–1400°F) is called the warm working range, and 760°C (1400°F) and above is the hot working range. In hot working it is usually not desirable to exceed 843°C (1550°F), although so-called "hot" extrusions are carried out at 900–1150°C (1650–2100°F). In the "hot" extrusion range the beryllium must be protected with a steel jacket for oxidation protection and to prevent galling of the dies. Rolling sheet of beryllium is performed between 455 and 843°C (850 and 1550°F). The sintered

Figure 3.7. Cutting a large block of beryllium. (*Courtesy Brush Beryllium Company.*)

blocks are jacketed in heavy steel assemblies and rolled down to about ⅛ in. From this thickness beryllium is rolled bare to thickness as thin as a few mils.

Since beryllium is notch sensitive, precautions must also be taken to avoid surface scratching. Also in annealing, overheating must be avoided, particularly after working the metal, to prevent excessive grain growth resulting from the breaking down of the oxide barrier in the grain boundaries.

Beryllium-Copper Alloys

The subject of beryllium copper has been surveyed rather extensively.[11] The types of alloys commercially available and their fabricated forms are given in Table 3.14.

Beryllium-copper alloys can be readily melted in any commercial-type furnace. Because of its good fluidity in the molten state, the alloy can be used to fill intricate molds by sand casting, investment casting, or pressure casting. The pouring range of the high-strength alloys is 1010–1177°C (1850–2050°F), while for the high-conductivity alloys, it is 1177–1232°C (2050–2250°F). In order to prevent bubbles by gas absorption or oxide formation, the lowest temperature consistent with good flow should be used.

Hot and cold working are extensively used

TABLE 3.14. AVAILABLE FORMS OF FABRICATED BERYLLIUM COPPER*

	Wrought (composition %)						Cast (composition %)				
	High strength		High conductivity				High strength			High conductivity	
Be	1.80–2.05	1.60–1.80	1.80–2.05	0.45–0.60	0.25–0.50	0.35–0.50	2.00–2.25	2.60–2.85	2.50–2.60	0.55–0.70	0.35–0.50
Co	0.25–0.35	0.25–0.35		2.35–2.60	1.40–1.70		0.35–0.60	0.35–0.65		2.35–2.60	0.35–0.50
Ni			0.35			1.50			1.10		1.50
Ag						0.90–1.10					
Cu	Balance	Balance	Balance	Balance	Balance	Balance	Balance	Balance	Balance	Balance	Balance
Cold-rolled strip	X	X				X					
Flat wire	X	X									
Square or rectangular bar	X	X	X	X	X						
Cold-drawn rod (round, square, hex.)	X		X	X	X						
Wire	X	X		X	X						
Hot-rolled bar (round, square, hex.)	X	X		X	X	X					
Turned rod	X		X	X	X						
Billets	X	X	X	X	X						
Forgings	X		X	X	X						
Welded tubing	X		X								
Seamless tubing	X		X								
Castings, pigs							X	X	X	X	X
Sand castings							X	X	X	X	X
Pressure castings							X	X	X	X	X
Plaster-mold castings							X	X	X	X	X
Investment castings							X	X	X	X	X

* Available fabricated forms designated as X.

TABLE 3.15. SPECIFICATIONS FOR WROUGHT BERYLLIUM-COPPER ALLOYS[15]

(a) Composition

Be	1.80–2.05%
Ni or Co	0.20% min
Ni + Co + Fe	0.60% max
Cu + Be + additives	99.50% min

(b) Temper of BeCu alloy strip

Treatment	Minimum tensile strength before heat treatment (psi)	Minimum tensile strength after heat treatment* (psi)
Cold rolled and solution treated	60,000	160,000†
Cold rolled, solution treated, and rolled quarter hard	75,000	170,000†
Cold rolled, solution treated, and rolled half hard	85,000	180,000†
Cold rolled, solution treated, and rolled full hard	100,000	185,000‡

* Test specimens heated to 316°C (600°F) for 2–3 hr for specification test.
† For special-grade alloy strip,[16] add 10,000 psi.
‡ For special-grade alloy strip,[16] add 5,000 psi.

to form the wrought alloys. The hot-working range is 788–802°C (1450–1475°F) for the high-strength alloys and 900–927°C (1650–1700°F) for the high-conductivity materials. Beryllium copper can be cold-rolled similar to other copper-base alloys, although it work-hardens to a higher strength than most. As it can be hardened by heat treatment, however, it is not necessary to cold-work as severely as other copper-base materials to obtain hardness, and the absence of this severe, directionally worked grain structure allows formability in all directions. Although the beryllium-copper alloys are not free machining, they can be fabricated by this method, similar to other copper alloys.

The properties of fabricated beryllium copper depend on the amount of cold working and heat treatment, as can be seen from the specification limits for structural properties of high-strength material which are shown in Table 3.15.[15] Solution annealing is carried out at 788°C (1450°F) for the high-strength alloys, with age hardening being performed at 316–343°C (600–650°F); for the high-conductivity materials, the solution annealing is done at 927°C (1700°F), with the hardening at 454–482°C (850–900°F).

Beryllium copper can be joined by metal, carbon, inert arc, and resistance welding as well as silver brazing and soft soldering. Gas fusion welding methods and hard soldering (bronze brazing) are not satisfactory, however. As the temperatures of all joining treatments, except soft soldering, are above the heat treatment temperatures, joining should not be done on heat treated material. Scaling during joining or heat treatment may be avoided by carrying out the operation under cracked ammonia, city gas, or hydrogen. Oxide scale can be removed, however, by pickling in a 20 to 30 per cent sulfuric acid solution at 71–320°C (160–180°F), followed by immersing in 30 per cent nitric acid.

APPLICATIONS

Beryllium

The oldest use of beryllium relates to its high penetrability by x-rays. Beryllium windows in x-ray tubes transmit the rays 17 times better than aluminum and are particularly useful when longer and more easily absorbed x-rays are present. A beryllium x-ray window also serves to filter out electrons. Beryllium in x-ray tubes made possible the use of long-wave rays of greater intensity for applications both in x-ray therapy and in x-ray diffraction studies.

Later, nuclear applications requiring machined parts of nuclear-grade beryllium for moderators and reflectors in compact high-flux atomic reactors and test reactors were developed. The USAEC Materials Testing and Engineering Testing Reactors and the nuclear reactor in the submarine *Seawolf* all use such parts. Recently, testing reactors in Europe have been built with beryllium reflectors. At the present time, beryllium is also being seriously considered as a canning material for fuel elements, particularly where natural or slightly enriched uranium is desired as fuel. In addition, beryllium is used as a neutron source resulting from exposing beryllium to radiations from radium, from deuterons in cyclotrons, or from the neutrons produced in nuclear reactors.

An example of a machined nuclear reactor part is shown in Figure 3.8.

Figure 3.9. Spherical gyroscope part machined from hot pressed beryllium. (*Courtesy Brush Beryllium Company*.)

Figure 3.8. Hexagonal nuclear reactor shape machined from hot pressed beryllium. (*Courtesy Brush Beryllium Company*.)

Lately, the unique physical, chemical, and mechanical properties of beryllium have aroused great interest in its use in structural and thermal applications. The most important of these properties are its low density, high melting point, very high modulus of elasticity, high heat absorption, resistance to oxidation, good mechanical properties at elevated temperatures, and the ease of machining powder metallurgy processed beryllium metal to extremely close tolerances. It is the combination of these properties which is the basis for presently active developments aimed at the manufacture of rolled, forged, extruded, and machined products for missile, aircraft, and space vehicle structures. These properties also make beryllium an ideal metal for gyroscopes, accelerometers, and computer parts and for inertial guidance instruments as well as other components where light-

ness, stiffness, and stable dimensions are required. A spherical beryllium gyroscope part is shown in Figure 3.9.

Beryllium Oxide

Beryllium oxide is used to a minor extent in the lighting industry. The luminous mixture of oxides in Welsbach mantles contains beryllium oxide. It may also be converted to beryllium zinc silicate, which is used in certain fluorescent lamps as a material producing an ivory-colored type of light.

Because of its high melting point, chemical inertness, strength, resistance to thermal shock, and high thermal conductivity (about 10 times that of alumina), beryllium oxide crucibles made from fused or highly sintered oxide are used for special high-temperature (up to 2000°C or 3632°F) melting applications, particularly where a minimum or no attack on the crucible material is required to preserve the purity of the melt. Also, since beryllium oxide well retains its electrical insulation at high temperatures, beryllia crucibles are well suited for high frequency electric heating of metals with high melting points.

High density beryllium oxide has one of the best combinations of thermal, electrical, and nuclear properties found in ceramic oxides. Since it has about the same nuclear properties as beryllium metal, it can be used for the same applications. It is of interest, however, mainly for nuclear applications requiring temperatures higher than the maximum temperatures applicable to the use of beryllium metal.

Other uses of beryllium oxide are found in electronics, such as low-loss dielectrics and wave-guide windows, and as a component in high modulus structural glass fibers.

Beryllium-Copper Alloys

Beryllium-copper alloys are fabricated into strip, rod, wire, sheet, and tube. The mills usually furnish these materials in fully annealed condition, or with varying degrees of cold rolling or work hardening to fit the specified applications. Forgings and castings are available, including sand, pressure, investment, plaster, permanent mold, and centrifugal castings.

Beryllium-copper alloys can be classified as (1) high strength or (2) high conductivity. High-strength alloys (over 1.5 per cent beryllium) offer maximum strength and hardness, whereas high-conductivity alloys (under 0.75 per cent beryllium) are preferred where electrical or thermal conductivity is more essential than maximum strength or hardness.

A few of the uses of the high strength–high hardness beryllium-copper alloys follow:

Springs	Safety tools
Bellows	Valve parts
Electrical contacts	Bearing retainer rings
Diaphragms	Resistance welding
Bearings	electrodes
Cams	(RWMA Class 4)
Aircraft engine parts	Flash welding
Shell-loading equipment	Cowl flap hinges
Plastic molds	Spring shims and
Bushings	washers
Marine propellers	Precision castings
Pump parts	Rollers
Gears	Gun-mount parts

The widespread use of beryllium-copper springs is shown in Table 3.16, which lists some of their applications in military equipment and related devices.

The high electrical conductivity beryllium-copper alloys contain 0.25 to 0.7 per cent beryllium and from 1.5 to 2.5 per cent cobalt or nickel as the grain refiner and stabilizer. Silver and/or chromium is also sometimes added in special alloys. Some of the applications of this group of high conductivity alloys include:

Resistance welding	Resistance welding dies
electrodes	Electrode holders
(RWMA Class 3)	Marine diesel brake
Spot, seam, flash, and	and clutch drums
projection welding	Pinions
dies, and electrodes	Sliding contacts
Switches	Electrical control heads
Circuit breakers	Current carrying
Switchgear	terminals
Welding jaws	

The applications listed in Table 3.16 are based on the unique advantages of beryllium copper, which may be summarized as follows:

(1) Excellent formability before heat treatment or precipitation hardening.

(2) Remarkable increase in physical properties after simple heat treatment.

(3) High electrical and thermal conductivity.

(4) Unusual resistance to fatigue and impact.

(5) Corrosion resistance comparable to pure copper.

(6) Stability under load, or freedom from elastic drift.

(7) Readily machinable in annealed or semi-hard state.

(8) Broad variations in properties possible through changes in beryllium content or heat-treatment procedure.

(9) Excellent castability properties.

(10) Special properties, nonmagnetic, antisparking, etc.

(11) Stability at elevated temperatures.

Beryllium-Nickel Alloys

This group of heat-treatable beryllium alloys has received considerable attention because of its excellent strength and hardness, but, for various reasons, it has not assumed a significant place in terms of volume applications.

Beryllium-nickel alloys closely resemble the stainless steels with respect to density and resistance to corrosion, and their strength, hardness, and elastic modulus compare with the high-strength alloy steels. The fact that beryllium nickel is castable, and can be formed in the soft or annealed state followed by precipitation hardening, commends it over many of these steels.

Some applications for the beryllium-nickel alloys include precision springs, hypodermic

TABLE 3.16. APPLICATIONS FOR BERYLLIUM-COPPER SPRINGS IN MILITARY EQUIPMENT AND RELATED DEVICES[1]

Electrical connectors for aircraft engine mounts	Diesel fuel injection units
Aircraft fuel gauge instruments	Aircraft carburetor metering springs
Aircraft engine tachometers	Signal Corps telegraph sets
Crystal clips for aircraft radio	Aircraft oil pressure controls
Bearing support springs for gyro rotors in aircraft flight control devices	Radio receiver headset bands
Brush springs for aircraft generators	Brush springs for electric propeller motors
Contact springs for aircraft relays	Diaphragm springs for aircraft carburetors
Nonmagnetic springs for radio transmitters	Control springs for oxygen regulators
Electrical instrument moving element supports	Breaker springs for aircraft ignition equipment
Brush springs for aircraft dynamotors	Solenoid guides for aircraft control equipment
Contact blades for radio jacks	Machine gun synchronizers for aircraft
Spring contacts for radio tube sockets	Hand grenade springs
Electrical connectors for aircraft radio sets	Radio transmitter relay contact blades
Operating springs for small bomb release switches	Relay blades for Signal Corps generators
Contact springs for automatic teletype aircraft	Release springs for fire extinguishers
Brush springs for tank turret motors	Bearing seals for aircraft auxiliary power plant
Solenoid springs for sensitive relays	Automatic searchlight control equipment
Contact springs for airport lighting switches	Machine gun firing pin springs
Contact springs for automatic paging equipment	Self-powered telephone transmitters
Friction springs on radio trimmer condensers	Radio transmitting diaphragms

needles, and surgical instruments. Their possible use, as strip, in lightweight "honeycomb" structures for airborne applications is under investigation. In cast form they find use as the matrix in diamond drill bits, as hot pressed molds for molding plastics, and in a multitude of precision-cast shapes for use in airplane fuel pumps and similar applications, business machine parts, etc.

Beryllium-Iron Alloys

Like beryllium nickel, the beryllium-iron alloys have aroused considerable interest in the past, but no commercial applications of significant volume have developed. The binary beryllium-iron alloys are too coarse-grained. Additions of nickel refine the grain and improve the alloy considerably. A 1 per cent beryllium alloy with 6 per cent nickel can be hardened by quenching and aging to around 600 Brinell. Beryllium steels containing 1 per cent beryllium, 12 per cent chromium, and 11 per cent nickel exhibit high strength and hardness at elevated temperatures, and this alloy was reported by the Germans in 1931 to retain its spring properties at red heat.

The approximate composition of some of the alloys in this group are listed below:

Beryllium "Elinvar" is used widely in Swiss watch factories, under the name of "Nivarox," in the form of springs. "Elinvar" was especially developed for the manufacture of spiral springs for watchmakers, and is characterized by a ratio of expansion to temperature that is nil. The beryllium addition preserves these compensatory thermoelastic properties, at the same time ensuring a structural hardening which gives the springs a hardness and elasticity equal to those of spiral springs made from carbon steel. The beryllium "Elinvar" springs are also amagnetic.

Beryllium "Contracid" is used primarily in Europe in surgical instruments, springs, and

	Be	Ni	Cr	Mo	W	Co	Mn	Fe
				(Per Cent)				
Beryllium "Invar"	1.0	38	—	—	—	—	—	Balance
Beryllium "Elinvar" ("Nivarox")	0.5	30	—	—	8	—	—	Balance
Beryllium "Contracid"	0.6	60	15.0	7	—	—	—	Balance
"Ticonium"	1.5	36	29.5	6	—	27		
"Elgiloy"	0.04	15	20.0	7	—	40	2	Balance

similar applications involving high strength coupled with excellent resistance to corrosion.

"Ticonium" is used in the dental field, in the form of cast dentures, etc., combining excellent castability and corrosion resistance with good properties after heat-treatment. It is produced by the Consolidated Car Heating Company, Albany, New York.

"Elgiloy" is produced by the Elgin Watch Company. It is reported to combine excellent corrosion resistance with superior physical properties for use in watches, springs, hypodermic needles, and similar applications.

Miscellaneous Beryllium Alloys

A new beryllium alloy investigated is a zinc-base alloy developed by the General Electric Research Laboratory, and known as "Zncube." It contains 0.1 per cent beryllium, 2 to 2.5 per cent copper, balance zinc.

Small additions, such as 0.1 to 0.5 per cent, of beryllium to aluminum have found considerable use in casting aluminum alloys. The beryllium promotes the fluidity of these alloys and tends to refine the grain.

FUTURE PROSPECTS OF THE BERYLLIUM INDUSTRY

Looking ahead, it can safely be said that the beryllium industry will be as large as its ore supply will permit. The current ore supply (hand-cobbed beryl) has, during the last 2 years, been in excess of industrial demands. The prices of per BeO unit (see Table 3.1) reached a peak of $50 in 1955 but dropped to $36–$38 in 1956 and 1957 and to $30–$33 in the fall of 1958, in spite of a considerable increase in industrial demand for beryl ore during 1958. In 1959 the price range varied between $31.75 and $34.00.

The Bureau of Mines has developed a method of concentrating low grade beryl ore. Intensive development work in this field is also being done by private industry. These methods have not yet been economically evaluated in commercial practice. There are, however, most encouraging prospects, that, if needed, the supply of hand-cobbed beryl could be augmented by beryl-ore concentrates from beneficiation of low-grade beryl and other beryllium bearing ores.

Methods of exploration for beryllium bearing minerals have lately been greatly enhanced by use of an instrument which detects the presence of beryllium in ore samples by gamma ray bombardment. The intensity of the neutron emission (see Physical Properties) produced by the presence of beryllium is measured by the instrument.

Since interest in the use of pure beryllium now includes not only nuclear devices but also structural applications in the field of aircraft and missiles, it is not unlikely that the use of pure beryllium will, within the foreseeable future, exceed the use of beryllium in beryllium copper and other alloys.

References

1. Carson, R. W., Vice President, Instrument Specialties Co., Little Falls, New Jersey, July 8, 1942.
2. Clarke, F. W., and Washington, H. S., *U. S. Geol. Survey, Profess. Paper 127* (1924).
3. Copeaux, H., *Compt. rend.*, **168**, 610 (1919).
4. Emeleus, H. J., and Anderson, J. S., "Modern Aspects of Inorganic Chemistry," p. 503, New York, D. Van Nostrand Co., Inc., 1939.
5. Hausner, H. H., and Pinto, N. P., "The Powder Metallurgy of Beryllium," *Steel*, **127**, 93 (Dec. 11, 1950).
6. Kaufmann, A. R., and Gordon, E., "Vacuum Melting and Casting of Beryllium," *Metal Progress*, 387 (Sept. 1947).
7. Kaufmann, A. R., Gordon, P., and Lillie, D. W., "The Metallurgy of Beryllium," *Trans. Am. Soc. Metals*, **42**, 785 (1950).
8. Lebeau, P., *Ann. chim. et phys. 7*, **16**, 457–503 (1899).
9. Losano, L., *Alluminio (Milan)*, **8**, 67–75 (1939).
10. Oesterheld, G., *Z. anorg. u. allgem. Chem.*, **97**, 6 (1916).
11. Richards, J. T., "Beryllium Copper," in "Engineering Materials Manual," T. C. du Mond, editor, p. 173, New York, Reinhold Publishing Corp., 1951.
12. Sawyer, C. B., *Metals & Alloys*, **14**, 37–39 (1941).
13. Sawyer, C. B., and Kjellgren, B. R. F., *Metals & Alloys*, **11**, 163–67 (1940).
14. Stanley, W. A., "The Resistance Welding of Beryllium," *Product Eng.*, **21**, 88 (Feb. 1950).
15. "Standard Specifications for Beryllium-Copper Alloy Plate, Sheet and Strip," *ASTM B-194-55*, 1955, p. 330.
16. U.S. Patent 2,312,297 (Feb. 23, 1943), H. S. Kawecki (to Reconstruction Finance Corp.).

17. U.S. Patent 2,018,473 (Oct. 22, 1935), C. B. Sawyer and B. R. F. Kjellgren (to Brush Beryllium Co.).
18. U.S. Patent (reissue) 20,214 (Dec. 22, 1936), C. B. Sawyer and B. R. F. Kjellgren (to Brush Beryllium Co.).
19. U.S. Patent 2,381,291 (Aug. 7, 1945), B. R. F. Kjellgren (to Brush Beryllium Co.).
20. U.S. Patent 2,176,906 (Oct. 24, 1939), B. R. F. Kjellgren and C. B. Sawyer (to Brush Beryllium Co.).
21. U.S. Patent 2,193,482 (March 12, 1940), A. J. Gahagan (to Beryllium Corp. of America).
22. Udy, M. C., Shaw, H. L., and Boulger, F. W., Nucleonics, 11, No. 5, 52–59 (1953).
23. Tuer and Kaufman, Chapter VII (B), "The Metal Beryllium," Cleveland, Ohio, The American Society for Metals, 1955.
24. U.S. Patent 1,775,589 (Sept. 9, 1930), H. S. Cooper.
25. U.S. Patent 2,188,904 (Feb. 6, 1940), and U.S. Patent 2,311,257 (Feb. 16, 1943), C. B. Sawyer and B. R. F. Kjellgren (to Brush Beryllium Co.).
26. U.S. Patent 2,843,544 (July 15, 1958), S. J. Morana (Beryllium Corporation).
27. a) U.S. Patent 2,725,288 (Nov. 29, 1955), C. B. Sawyer and H. W. Dodds,
    b) U.S. Patent 2,794,241 (June 4, 1957), C. B. Sawyer and H. W. Dodds,
    c) U.S. Patent 2,818,339 (Dec. 31, 1957), H. W. Dodds.
28. a) U.S. Patents 1,359,813 and 1,740,857, W. J. Kroll,
    b) U.S. Patent 2,072,067, W. B. Donahue,
    c) U.S. Patents 2,193,363 and 2,193,364, C. Adomali.

Special acknowledgment for the use of material is made to:

(1) Kirk-Othmer, "Encyclopedia of Chemical Technology," Vol. 2, article on "Beryllium and Beryllium Alloys," by B. R. F. Kjellgren, New York, Interscience Publishers, Inc., 1948.

(2) Transactions of the Electrochemical Society, article on "The Production of Beryllium Oxide and Beryllium Copper," 89, 247 (1946) and "The Production of Beryllium," 93, 122 (1948), by B. R. F. Kjellgren.

(3) Bureau of Mines, Bulletin 556 on "Beryllium, A Chapter from Mineral Facts and Problems," 1956.

(4) The Metal Beryllium, by D. W. White, Jr., and J. E. Burke, The American Society for Metals, Cleveland, Ohio, 1955.

(5) Encyclopedia Britannica, "Beryllium" (new edition in preparation 1959).

(6) "Beryllium Fabrication," Reprint No. 34, by K. G. Wikle, The Brush Beryllium Company, 1958.

4. BISMUTH

HERBERT E. HOWE

American Smelting & Refining Company
South Plainfield, New Jersey

INTRODUCTION

Bismuth was probably not recognized as a specific metal by the early Orientals, Greeks, or Romans. By the Middle Ages, Europeans were becoming aware of its specific nature, and in the fifteenth century Basil Valentine referred to it as *wismut*. The early mineralogist Georgus Agricola, at the end of the sixteenth century, latinized *wismuth* to *bisemutum*. But the origin of the name has not been definitely determined, and opinions range from *bleuweiss*, white lead; *wismat*, white mass or metal; to *wiesen mute* (meadow mines), alluding to the mines in the meadows around Schneeberg, Saxony.[14, 28]

Because bismuth was always found associated with other ores, it was often confused with known metals of the time and sometimes was referred to as imperfect tin or silver, female antimony, or a form of lead. Not until the middle of the eighteenth century, through the research of J. Pott, C. Geoffroy, and T. Bergman, was bismuth definitely recognized as a specific metal.

OCCURRENCE

The abundance of bismuth in the earth's crust has been estimated to be 0.00002 weight per cent, about the same order of plentifulness as silver, less than tin, but more than gold.

Bismuth occurs both as native bismuth and in ores. The native bismuth is not abundant but is found in veins associated with silver, lead, zinc, and tin ores in localities such as Saxony, Bolivia, Canada, and England.

The most important ores are bismite, or bismuth ocher (Bi_2O_3); bismuthinite, or bismuth glance (Bi_2S_3); and bismutite and bismutosphaerite (carbonates). The ores are widely distributed on all the continents, but they occur in small quantities. The principal source of bismuth ores is Bolivia. Although bismuth ores have been found in various sections of the United States, no ores are mined.

PRODUCTION

Bismuth is generally obtained as a by-product in the smelting and refining of lead, copper, tin, silver, and gold ores.[16] For the last decade, world production has varied between an estimated 2 and 4.8 million pounds. The figure for 1959 was 5.2 million pounds. Although production figures for the United States are not published, it can be estimated that between 40 and 50 per cent of the total is refined in this country.

The leading bismuth-producing countries, in approximate order of amount produced, are the following.

United States

Almost all the refined bismuth produced in the United States is as a by-product in refining domestic lead and imported lead bullion, and from smelting and refining copper. The major producers are:

58

1. American Smelting and Refining Company.
2. Cerro de Pasco Copper Co.
3. American Metals Climax Co.
4. United States Smelting, Refining and Mining Co.
5. International Smelting and Refining Co.

It should be noted that these plants are primarily lead refineries, but the Cerro de Pasco Copper Co. produces bismuth alloys at its Brooklyn, New York, plant.

Peru

The Cerro de Pasco Copper Company is the largest producer in Peru, recovering bismuth as a by-product of its copper- and lead-smelting operations at Oroya.

Mexico

The production of bismuth in Mexico also is largely as a by-product of copper- and lead-smelting operations such as at the Monterrey plant of the American Smelting and Refining Company. Most of its output is exported to the United States as bismuth lead bars.

South Korea

In South Korea, bismuth is being recovered in large quantities from mines southeast of Seoul, where it is found as bismuthinite in tungsten ores.

Canada

The Consolidated Mining and Smelting Company of Canada, Ltd., Trail, B.C., is the major Canadian producer of bismuth. The bismuth is recovered from the treatment of lead-silver ores.

CONSUMPTION AND PRICES[16]

The principal consumers of bismuth are the manufacturers of pharmaceutical chemicals and low-melting alloys. Bismuth compounds, both organic and inorganic, are used in indigestion remedies, cosmetics, and antisyphilitic drugs. Prior to World War II, the fusible alloys containing bismuth were used in limited amounts for fire alarms, sprinklers, and other safety devices. The total metallurgical uses represented only 25 per cent of the bismuth consumed. This amount increased to about 55 per cent during the war, when the aircraft industry found a number of ingenious time-saving methods which employed fusible alloys of bismuth, e.g., for bending thin-wall tubing, anchoring parts and tools during machining or punching, and in patternmaking. In the postwar period these applications have been extended into other industry so that, by 1959, 60 per cent of the bismuth was consumed as a metal or in alloys.

The present quoted price on bismuth is $2.25 per pound. It has been quoted at this price since September, 1950.

RECOVERY[2, 12, 20]

At the present time, only a small portion of the bismuth recovered comes from mines worked specifically for their bismuth ore content. But bismuth can be recovered from the concentrates of high-grade sulfide and carbonate ores by smelting in small reverberatory furnaces, with carbon for reduction, iron to decompose any bismuth sulfide present, and an alkaline flux to produce a fusible slag.

If bismuth occurs as an oxide or carbonate in ores such as those found in Bolivia and Peru, or in other metallurgical products, the most satisfactory recovery is made by leaching with hydrochloric acid. The separation depends on the precipitation of bismuth oxychloride from the chloride solution by diluting. By repeated dissolution, precipitation, and use of scrap iron to remove copper, the oxychloride is purified. The dry filtrate is smelted with lime and charcoal to crude metallic bismuth.

The primary sources of bismuth in the world and particularly in the Western Hemisphere are as by-products of copper and lead smelting and refining. Bismuth is often found in these ores and will remain with the metals after smelting.

Bismuth is partially volatilized by the high temperature of the copper converter, and is caught as a dust in the bag house or Cottrell systems, along with other elements such as lead, arsenic, antimony, etc., which are then transferred to the lead-smelting and -refining operation. The major portion of the bismuth remains with the metallic copper, however, and, during the electrolytic refining, bismuth accumulates in the anode slimes with the other impurities, i.e., lead, selenium, tellurium, arsenic, antimony, and the precious metals. The procedure for handling the slimes is such that the bismuth is collected in the lead.

Bismuth is found in most lead ores and will accompany the lead through the smelting and refining operations. Refineries that treat bullion by the furnace-kettle process will practice de-bismuthizing only when the bismuth content is above 0.05 per cent. The Missouri ores containing negligible amounts of bismuth are not treated. The two most important methods for removing bismuth from lead are the Betts and the Betterton-Kroll processes.

Betts Electrolytic Process

In the Betts process, anodes of lead bullion are electrolytically refined in a solution of lead fluosilicate and free fluosilicic acid. Thin sheets of pure lead form the cathodes. The impurities, including bismuth, are collected in the anode slimes which are filtered, dried, and smelted. The metal from this smelting is cupeled, and bismuth goes into the lead-antimony slag and the litharge. These slags are reduced to metal containing 20 per cent or higher bismuth and are transferred to the bismuth plant for refining.

Betterton-Kroll Process

The basic reactions of this process are the formation of high-melting compounds, such as Ca_3Bi_2 and Mg_3Bi_2, which liquate from the bath and are removed as dross. Enriched calcium and magnesium lead from a previous charge is added to softened and desilverized lead, containing bismuth (>0.05 per cent). The resulting dross is skimmed, and then the required amounts of calcium (as a lead alloy) and magnesium metal are stirred into the molten metal. The charge is cooled, and the liquating bismuth dross is skimmed. This removes bismuth to 0.02 per cent. If it is to be removed more completely, excess calcium and magnesium plus a small amount of antimony are added.

The enriched bismuth dross is melted in small 25-ton kettles, and the dross is separated from the entrapped lead by liquation. This dross is treated with lead chloride or chlorine to remove the calcium and magnesium, and, after desilverizing the bismuth by the Parkes process, further chlorination removes the lead. Final treatments with caustic soda produce a high-purity bismuth (>99.995 per cent bismuth).

The Sperry process for making white lead in electrolytic cells recovers bismuth as a by-product in the anode slimes.

Crystallization Process

The crystallization process for concentrating bismuth in lead by squeezing the eutectic liquid (high in bismuth) out of the solidified high-lead portion at a temperature within the melting range is seldom used.

PHYSICAL PROPERTIES

Bismuth will fracture as a brittle, crystalline metal having a high metallic luster with a pinkish tinge. Rhombohedral crystals of bismuth are shown in Figure 4.1. As a member of Group VA of the periodic table, it is in the same subgroup as phosphorus, arsenic, and antimony.

Bismuth is one of the few metals (antimony and gallium the others) which increases in volume on solidification, this expansion being 3.32 per cent.

Figure 4.1. Rhombohedral crystals of bismuth.

TABLE 4.1. PHYSICAL PROPERTIES OF BISMUTH

Atomic number	83
Atomic weight (one stable isotope)	209
Atomic volume (cc/gram-atom)	21.3
Density	
lb/cu in. at 20°C (68°F)	0.354
g/cc " 20°C (68°F)	9.8
" " 271°C (520°F) (solid)	9.74
" " 271°C (liquid)	10.07
" " 300°C (572°F)	10.03
" " 400°C (752°F)	9.91
" " 600°C (1112°F)	9.66
" " 800°C (1472°F)	9.40
" " 960°C (1760°F)	9.20
Melting point	271°C (520°F)
Latent heat of fusion (cal/g)	12.5
Specific heat (cal/g/°C)	
20°C (68°F)	0.0294
271°C (520°F) (liquid)	0.0340
400°C (752°F)	0.0354
600°C (1112°F)	0.0376
800°C (1472°F)	0.0397
1000°C (1832°F)	0.0419
Boiling point	1627°C (2960°F)
Latent heat of vaporization [cal/g at 1627°C (2960°F)]	204.3
Vapor pressure (mm Hg)	
920°C (1683°F)	1
1120°C (2048°F)	10
1325°C (2417°F)	100
1425°C (2597°F)	200
1500°C (2732°F)	400
Thermal conductivity (cal/sq cm/cm/°C/sec)	
20°C (68°F)	0.020
250°C (482°F)	0.018
300°C (572°F)	0.041
400°C (752°F)	0.037
700°C (1292°F)	0.037
Coefficient of linear thermal expansion (μ in./°C)	13.3
Volume expansion on solidification (%)	3.32
Surface tension (dynes/cm)	
300°C (572°F)	376
500°C (932°F)	363
780°C (1436°F)	344
Electrical resistivity (microhms-cm)	
−100°C (−148°F)	75.6
0°C (32°F)	106.8
100°C (212°F)	160.2
300°C (572°F) (liquid)	128.9
400°C (752°F)	134.2
600°C (1112°F)	145.2
750°C (1382°F)	153.5
Crystallography	Rhombohedral $a_0 = 4.7457$ Å Axial angle 57° 14.2'
Thermal neutron absorption cross section (barns/atom)	0.034 ± 0.002

TABLE 4.1. PHYSICAL PROPERTIES OF BISMUTH (*cont.*)

Thermal neutron activation cross section (barns/atom)	0.019 ± 0.002
Mechanical properties	
Modulus of elasticity in tension (psi)	4.6×10^6
Shear modulus (psi)	1.8×10^6
Poisson's ratio	0.33
Brinell hardness (100-kg 10-m ball–30 sec)	7
Impact strength unnotched Charpy (ft–lb)	
18°C (65°F)	0.097
66°C (150°F)	0.147
93°C (200°F)	0.294
149°C (300°F)	0.514
204°C (400°F)	0.441
232°C (450°F)	0.441
Creep psi (load for deflection rate of 0.001 in./in./hr)	
66°C (150°F)	600
121°C (250°F)	450
177°C (350°F)	350
204°C (400°F)	300

Resistance of metals to attack by bismuth			
Molybdenum	Good resistance to at least 1110°C (2030°F)		
Tantalum	" " " " " 900°C (1652°F)		
Chromium	" " " " " 732°C (1350°F)		
Beryllium	" " " " " 500°C (930°F)		
Columbium	" " " " " 482°C (900°F)		
Aluminum	" " " " " 300°C (570°F)		
Nickel and nickel alloys	Poor " above 271°C (520°F)		
Copper	Eutectic at 270°C (519°F)	Solubility (%)	0.2
Manganese	" " 268°C (514°F)	" "	0.6
Magnesium	" " 260°C (500°F)	" "	0.54
Zinc	" " 254°C (490°F)	" "	2.7
Platinum	" " 266°C (511°F)	" "	1.0
Tin	" " 139°C (282°F)	" "	42.0

Reference 13 gives the literature of many of the data listed. See also References 7, 9, 22, 23, 26, and 28.

The thermal conductivity of bismuth is lower than any metal with the exception of mercury.

The most diamagnetic of all metals, bismuth has a mass susceptibility of -1.35×10^6.

Bismuth displays the greatest increase in resistance when influenced by a magnetic field (Hall effect) of any of the metals. The thermal conductivity decreases in a magnetic field.

The high electrical resistance of bismuth has recently been employed by making molten bismuth, enclosed in a vitreous silica tube, the resistance-heating unit for a furnace. Temperatures as high as 1350°C (2462°F) have been obtained. It is one of the metals in which the electrical resistance is greater in the solid than in the liquid state. The ratio of liquid to solid resistivity is 0.5 for most metals, but is approximately 2 for bismuth.

High thermoelectric effects are produced when bismuth is coupled with certain other materials. Bismuth can be extruded as wire and sheet, making the practical applications of this thermoelectric effect possible.

Because of its low absorption cross section for thermal neutrons, bismuth has attracted attention as a fuel carrier and coolant for nuclear reactors and as windows for neutron transparency in medical reactors.

Bismuth forms a number of binary, ternary, quarternary, and quinary alloys which have low melting points, and the more common ones are often referred to as "fusible alloys."[7, 8, 15, 18] Table 4.2 gives the eutectic composition and temperature of these alloys.

The applications for the fusible alloys are not limited to the eutectic composition, for a range of melting temperatures and physical properties may be obtained by varying composition from the eutectic. For example, an alloy of 48 per cent bismuth, 28.5 per cent lead, 14.5 per

TABLE 4.2

System	Composition	Eutectic temperature
Ag-Bi	97.5 Bi	262°C (503.6°F)
Au-Bi	82.0 Bi	240°C (464°F)
Cd-Bi	60.0 Bi	144°C (291°F)
In-Bi	33.7 Bi	72°C (161.6°F)
	67.0 Bi	109°C (228°F)
Li-Bi	99.0 Bi	243°C (469°F)
Mg-Bi	59.0 Bi	551°C (1024°F)
Na-Bi	97.0 Bi	218°C (424°F)
Pb-Bi	56.5 Bi	125°C (257°F)
Sb-Bi	Miscible in liquid and solid state	
Sn-Bi	57.0 Bi	139°C (282°F)
Tl-Bi	76.5 Bi	198°C (388°F)
	47.5 Bi	188°C (370°F)
Zn-Bi	97.3 Bi	254°C (489°F)
Pb-Sn-Bi	52 Bi-16 Sn-32 Pb	96°C (205°F)
Pb-Cd-Bi	52 Bi-8 Cd-40 Pb	92°C (198°F)
Sn-Cd-Bi	54 Bi-20 Cd-26 Sn	102°C (216°F)
Sn-Zn-Bi	56 Bi-4 Bn-40 Sn	130°C (266°F)
In-Sn-Bi	58 B-17 In-25 Sn	79°C (174°F)
Tl-Pb-Bi	55.2 Bi-33.3 Pb-11.5 Tl	91°C (196°F)
	42.2 Bi-9.8 Pb-48 Tl	186°C (367°F)
Tl-Sn-Bi	50 Bi-35.7 Sn-14.3 Tl	124°C (255°F)
	44 Bi-31 Sn-25 Tl	167°C (333°F)
Pb-Sn-Cd-Bi	50 Bi-10 Cd-13.3 Sn-26.7 Pb	70°C (158°F)
In-Pb-Sn-Bi	49.4 Bi-11.6 Sn-18 Pb-21 In	57°C (135°F)
Tl-Sn-Cd-Bi	49.1 Bi-18.2 Cd-23.4 Sn-9.2 Tl	94.6°C (202°F)
In-Cd-Pb-Sn-Bi	44.7 Bi-5.3 Cd-8.3 Sn-22.6 Pb-19.1 In	47°C (117°F)

cent tin, and 9 per cent antimony is a noneutectic alloy [melting range 103–263°C (217–506°F)] which is used extensively for anchoring dies, punches, and magnets, and for holding irregular parts for machining.

Since fusible alloys are used in a number of safety devices, e.g., safety plugs for compressed gas cylinders and tanks, automatic sprinkler systems, and fire-door releases, ranges of freezing temperatures and yield points are possible from noneutectic alloys. Table 4.3 gives a few such alloys.

In addition to their extremely low melting points, alloys of bismuth often exhibit unusual expansion and contraction characteristics. When a metal is cast, the following volume changes take place: (1) volume change from liquid to solid, and (2) volume change owing to thermal contraction.

Alloys of bismuth-lead and particularly

TABLE 4.3. FREEZING TEMPERATURE RANGES AND YIELD TEMPERATURES OF NONEUTECTIC ALLOYS

Composition					Freezing range,		Yield* temp.,	
Bi	Pb	Sn	Cd	Others	(°C)	(°F)	(°C)	(°F)
14.0	43.0	43.0	—	—	163–143	325–289	154	309
21.0	42.0	37.0	—	—	152–120	306–248	142	288
5.0	32.0	45.0	18.0	—	139–132	282–270	135	275
48.0	28.5	14.5	—	9.0 Sb	263–103	505–217	116	241
59.4	14.8	25.8	—	—	114–95	198–181	100	212
52.0	31.7	15.3	1	—	92–83	194–158	90	194
42.5	37.7	11.3	8.5	—	90–70	149–142	72	161
48.0	25.6	12.8	9.6	4.0 In	65–61		64	147

* Temperature at which fusible alloy will yield, as prescribed by Compressed Gas Manufacturers Association.

bismuth-lead-tin exhibit another volume change which occurs when the alloys are solidified. This is an increase in volume owing to a change in the solid structure of the alloy. This transformation is accompanied by heat evolution which is readily detected. The expansion can be as high as a 1 per cent linear increase. The composition for the maximum expansion is about 56 per cent bismuth, 20 per cent tin, and 24 per cent lead, and it will decrease as the contents of the constituents are changed or as other elements, such as cadmium, antimony, or indium, are added. For example, the linear expansion of the ternary eutectic compositions is 0.8 per cent. The reaction in the solid state is such that the rate is related to the magnitude of the expansion; i.e., the greater the expansion, the faster it occurs. At the higher magnitudes of expansion, most of it takes place in 20 to 30 min. Such an expansion also occurs in the bismuth-lead system with a linear increase of 0.3 per cent, but it requires several hundred hours to reach its maximum. Contraction due to cooling would be canceled by this expansion, and various practical uses have been made of this phenomenon to grip tools, punches, and parts to be machined.

Since bismuth is one of the three metals which expands on solidification, it is not unusual that the various alloys of bismuth-lead and bismuth-tin have different liquid-to-solid volume changes. This volume change is zero at about 50 per cent bismuth in the bismuth-tin alloy and at about 70 per cent bismuth in the bismuth-lead alloy.

The dimensional changes which usually take place in castings can be controlled by selecting a composition where volume changes (liquid-to-solid and solid transformation) are such that an accurate dimensional casting results.

CHEMICAL PROPERTIES[14, 21]

Bismuth, like the other members of its family, arsenic and antimony, forms two sets of compounds in which it is trivalent and quinquevalent. The trivalent compounds are the more common.

Bismuth Oxides

Bismuth does not readily oxidize at ordinary temperature in dry or moist air. The silver-white luster is retained for long periods of time. Rapid oxidation at the boiling point produces the trioxide.

Bismuth trioxide, Bi_2O_3, is the best defined of the oxides, the existence of others being questioned. Other oxides which may be found are the tetroxide, Bi_2O_4, and pentoxide, Bi_2O_5. The oxide mineral, bismite, is a bismuth trioxide.

The trioxide may be formed by ignition of bismuth hydroxide or by heating the basic nitrate in air. The latter method is used for the commercial production of bismuth trioxide. Bismuth is dissolved in hot nitric acid, and an excess of sodium hydroxide is added. Continued heating of the mixture precipitates a heavy yellow powder of bismuth trioxide. It is sold for use in enameling for cast iron, and in porcelain painting. Although the trioxide is a basic anhydride, it will act as a weak acid in warm, very concentrated potassium hydroxide.

Bismuth tetroxide may be prepared by oxidizing bismuth trioxide, using agents such as potassium ferricyanide with concentrated potassium hydroxide or ammonium persulfate with dilute sodium hydroxide.

Bismuth pentoxide is an acid anhydride, although salts of this acid have not been prepared in the pure state. This oxide can be prepared by oxidation of bismuth trioxide, using either chlorine or an electrolytic oxidation in hot concentrated alkali, forming a scarlet red precipitate.

Bismuth hydroxide is prepared in a manner similar to that for the trioxide, with the exception that it is precipitated cold from the nitrate solution with sodium hydroxide.

Halides

The compounds of bismuth with the halogens are of the form BiX_3. They are usually formed by dissolving bismuth in nitric acid and adding a soluble halogen salt. Since the salts of trivalent bismuth hydrolyze in water to insoluble basic salts, dilution of the above solution will precipitate the oxysalt:

$$BiCl_3 + 2H_2O \rightleftharpoons Bi(OH)_2Cl + 2HCl.$$

This reversible reaction shows that the relative amounts of hydrochloric acid and water that are present will determine which way the reaction will go. If water is added, a white precipitate of basic chloride forms, and if hydrochloric acid is added, the precipitate dissolves. When this precipitate is dried, it gives up a molecule of water, forming BiOCl. Most other halogen salts of bismuth act as the chloride. Bismuth chloride is used for pigment and cosmetics. Bismuth bromide is employed in veterinary medicine.

Bismuth Nitrates

The best solvent for bismuth is nitric acid. From the concentrated solution bismuth nitrate pentahydrate $[Bi(NO_3)_3 5H_2O]$ is formed. But, like other salts of bismuth, with the addition of water an oxysalt $(Bi_2O_3N_2O_5 \cdot 2H_2O)$ will precipitate.

The bismuth nitrate $[Bi(NO_3)_3 \cdot 5H_2O]$ is prepared by evaporation of the concentrated solution and then cooling to form the crystals.

Bismuth subnitrate is prepared by the hydrolysis of bismuth nitrate at a given nitric acid content between temperatures of 30 and 70°C (86 and 158°F). In commercial production the hydrolysis is carried out using sodium bicarbonate to maintain the proper acidity. The quantity of water used is controlled, and the subnitrate is formed by stirring at 40–50°C (104–122°F).

Bismuth subcarbonate is prepared from bismuth subnitrate. By adding sodium bicarbonate to a suspension of the subnitrate in water, the bicarbonate is precipitated. The product obtained depends on the nature of the subnitrate suspension, the amount of water, and the temperature.

Both of these compounds, i.e., bismuth subcarbonate and bismuth subnitrate, are used in pharmacology for the treatment of diarrhea, enteritis, and gastric ulcers, and for making the alimentary canal opaque in x-ray diagnosis.

Sulfur Compounds

Bismuth trisulfide occurs in nature as bismuthinite (bismuth glance). It may be prepared by the reaction of hydrogen sulfide on a solution of bismuth salts. The trisulfide is insoluble in cold dilute mineral acids and soluble in hot dilute nitric acid or boiling concentrated hydrochloric.

Bismuth sulfate is not precipitated from an acid solution of the salt, but, if the solution is evaporated to give off fumes, a bismuth acid sulfate $[Bi_2(SO_4)_3H_2SO_4 \cdot 6H_2O]$ is formed. By heating at 350°C (662°F), the normal sulfate $[Bi_2(SO_4)_3]$ can be formed.

Organic Compounds

A number of organic bismuth preparations have been used for the treatment of syphilis. Bismuth potassium tartrate, bismuth sodium tartrate, sodium potassium bismuth, and iodobismuthite sodium are water-soluble preparations. The oil-soluble compounds are bismuth camphorcarboxylate and bismuth ethyl camphorate.[10]

Bismuth subgallate is a water-insoluble organic compound of bismuth which is also used in the treatment of irritations of the alimentary canal.[10]

FABRICATION

The melting of bismuth may be handled in the same manner as lead. Its low melting point and the extremely low solubility of iron in bismuth permits the use of steel or cast-iron vessels. Within the range of 300–400°C (572–752°F), the rate of oxidation is low, and fluxes are not generally used.

Bismuth, being a brittle metal at ordinary temperatures, is usually cast to the desired form. The liquid-to-solid expansion produces either a swelling or exudations on the open end as the casting freezes.

Bismuth at ordinary temperatures is too brittle to roll, draw, or extrude; however, above 225°C (437°F), it becomes more plastic, permitting extrusion in various shapes. Rods of 1-in. diameter to fine wires (0.010-in. diameter) have been successfully extruded. The fine wires have a reasonable ductility if bent slowly around diameters equal to their own or larger.

For protective and ornamental coatings the electrodeposition of bismuth from strongly acid solution of perchlorate has been suggested as the most satisfactory. The chloride bath is considered superior for the preparation of high-purity bismuth.

In the electroplating of bismuth on iron, a solution of $NaBiCl_4$ has been found by one investigator to be stable and capable of giving a dense, finely crystalline deposit. The conditions for best results are a cathodic current density of 2–2.7 amp/sq dm for a solution containing 20–100 g/liter of bismuth salt, 200–300 cc/liter of HCl, and small amounts of glue.

TOXICITY[24]

Toxicity is not a problem in the handling of bismuth. It is one of the least toxic of the heavy metals, and cases of bismuth poisoning in industrial use have not been recorded.

APPLICATIONS

The applications of bismuth may be divided into the following groups: pharmaceutical (about 30 per cent); fabricating alloys (about 60 per cent); and others, e.g., ammunition solders, fuse alloys, aluminum alloys, and nuclear (about 10 per cent).

The pharmaceutical uses are principally in indigestion remedies, cosmetics, and antisyphilitic drugs.

The fabricating alloys, commonly referred to as fusible alloys, have low melting temperatures and controllable dimensional changes, and are finding increasing application for such uses as forming and stretching dies in aircraft construction; spotting, erecting, and checking fixtures for automobile and aircraft construction; filling thin-wall tubing and molding for bending; anchoring dies, punches, and machine, magnetic, and ceramic parts; holding irregular or delicate parts during machining; making cores on which copper, iron, nickel, and other metals are electroformed; coating wood patterns; proof casting; making molds for wax models in precision casting; and producing accurate patterns.

A recent use for a fusible alloy has been found in the rubber industry for vulcanizing in neoprene. Neoprene extrusions are continuously vulcanized in a fusible metal (42 per cent tin and 58 per cent bismuth) bath at 205–315°C (400–600°F).

The uses of the fusible alloys for safety fuses (fire-detection and alarm systems, automatic-sprinkler heads, fire-door releases, and safety plugs for tanks and cylinders of compressed gases) are well known.

Low-melting solders of bismuth are used where high-temperature soldering would affect the base metal, e.g., soldering caps to armor-piercing shells.

Small additions of bismuth are added to aluminum alloys and to malleable irons and steels to improve machinability. Bismuth (~0.01 per cent) in cast steels improves the mechanical properties, permitting the casting of automotive crankshafts, connecting rods, etc., which were formerly produced by forging.

The eutectic alloys of bismuth-tin and bismuth-cadmium are sprayed as coatings against selenium to form the barrier layer (counterelectrode) in selenium rectifiers.

The availability of bismuth as a ductile wire offers opportunities for taking advantage of such properties as resistance changes in magnetic fields, voltage change owing to the Hall effect, and high negativity in thermocouples (highest known).

Intermetallic compounds of bismuth with tellurium or selenium have been found to be effective thermoelectric materials for making use of the Peltier effect for refrigeration.[25] The Peltier effect, whereby heat can be absorbed at one junction of a thermocouple and emitted at the other when an electric current is passed through it, has been extensively investigated as a means of refrigeration. Good Peltier thermocouple materials should exhibit high thermoelectric power, low thermal conductivity, and low electrical resistivity. The semiconductor compounds Bi_2Te_3 and Bi_2Se_3 have excellent combinations of these properties. A temperature difference of 29°C (85°F) between an inner chamber and outside conducting fins has been produced experimentally with 20 watts. It is estimated that the present values for coefficients of performance must be increased by a factor of 2 to be comparable to compressor-type refrigerators in home appliances.

Bismuth is playing an increasingly important part in nuclear energy. The liquid metal fuel reactor[3] (LMFR) (see Figure 4.2) being developed in the United States uses liquid bismuth as the carrier for the fuel (U_{235} or U_{233}) and as the coolant. The fissionable uranium is dissolved to a 0.15 per cent concentration in the liquid bismuth. The reactor has a moderator of unclad graphite. The solvent bismuth containing the solute (U_{235} or U_{233}) is pumped through the graphite moderator. The design

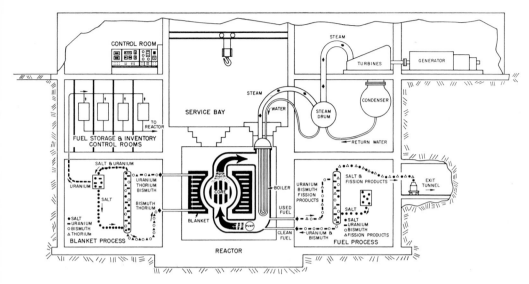

Figure 4.2. Diagram of liquid metal fuel nuclear power reactor using bismuth as the carrier for the uranium fuel and the liquid metal coolant for the reactor.

parameters are such that criticality is reached, and self-sustained fission takes place. The heat generated by the fission reactions is transmitted to the liquid bismuth which is pumped through the heat exchangers.

A typical power reactor would have the following operating conditions:

1. Total heat   500 Mw
2. Electric power   200 Mw
3. Total uranium-bismuth fuel
    (0.15 per cent uranium,
    99.8 per cent bismuth)   300 tons
4. Fuel temperature   Inlet 400°C (752°F)
                   Outlet 500°C (932°F)
5. Breeding blanket
    Thorium-bismuth intermetallic
    dispersion in molten bismuth,
    approximately 10 per cent thorium

The advantages of this type of reactor are:

1. No solid fuel elements are required to be removed, processed, or fabricated.

2. The fission products can be removed by continuous processing.

3. The uranium used up during fission is replaced by breeding U_{233} from thorium.

A permanent magnet[1] (named "Bismanol") of high coercive force and maximum energy products has been produced from MnBi by the United States Naval Ordnance Laboratory.

The powdered MnBi is compressed at low temperatures [300°C (572°F)] and pressures (100–200 psi) in a magnetic field to orient the easy direction of magnetization. An energy product of 4.3×10^6 gauss-oersteds, a coercive force of 3,400 oersteds, and a residual flux density of 4,200 gausses have been reported for this magnet.

Fusible alloys have been used to produce short-life dies. By cooling the alloys in liquid nitrogen [−195.6°C (−320°F)] a technique has been developed to produce experimental sheet-metal stampings in 24 to 48 hr. The Brinell hardness of about 9.2 is increased to 45 by cooling at −195.6°C (−320°F).

References

1. Adams, E., Hubbard, W., and Syeles, A., *Navord Report No. 2440,* May 20, 1952.
2. Betterton, J. O., and Lebedeff, Y. E., *Trans. AIME,* **121,** 205 (1936).
3. Brookhaven National Laboratory, Nuclear Engineering Dept., *Nucleonics,* **12,** No. 7, 11 (1954).
4. Cullity, B. D., *Trans. AIME,* **175,** 757 (1948).
5. Goodman, C., "The Science and Engineering of Nuclear Power," Vol. 2, pp. 158, 286, Reading, Mass., Addison-Wesley Publishing Company, 1949.
6. Gruzensky, P. M., and Crawford, W. J., *U.S. Bur. Mines, Inform. Circ. No. 7681* (May, 1954).

7. Hansen, M., "Constitution of Binary Alloys," 2nd Ed., New York, McGraw-Hill Book Company, Inc., 1958.

8. Haughton, J. L., "Bibliography of the Literature Relating to Constitutional Diagrams of Alloys," London, Institute of Metals, 1942.

9. "International Critical Tables," New York, McGraw-Hill Book Company, Inc., 1926.

10. Jenkins, G. L., and Hartling, W. H., "The Chemistry of Organic Medicinal Products," New York, John Wiley & Sons, Inc., 1941.

11. Levin, A. I., *J. Appl. Chem. (U.S.S.R.)*, **17**, 613 (1944).

12. Liddell, D. M., "Handbook of Nonferrous Metallurgy, Recovery of the Metals," pp. 193, 143, New York, McGraw-Hill Book Company, Inc., 1945.

13. Lyon, R. N. (Ed.), "Liquid-Metals Handbook," Washington, D.C., Atomic Energy Commission, 1952.

14. Mellor, J. W., "A Comprehensive Treatise on Inorganic and Theoretical Chemistry," Vol. 9, p. 587, New York, Longmans, Green & Co., Inc., 1929.

15. "Metals Handbook," pp. 744–745, Cleveland, American Society for Metals, 1948.

16. "Minerals Yearbook, (U.S. Bur. Mines)," Washington, D.C., Government Printing Office, 1930–1957.

17. Patton, W. G., *Iron Age*, **161**, 84, 86 (1948).

18. Peters, F. P., *Sci. American*, **170**, 16 (Jan. 1944).

19. Piontelli, R., *Atti congr. intern. chim., 10th Congr., Rome, 1938*, **3**, 609 (1939).

20. Powell, A. R., "The Refining of Bismuth," in "Symposium, The Refining of Non-ferrous Metals," pp. 245, 257, London, The Institution of Mining and Metallurgy, 1950.

21. Prescott, A. B., and Johnson, C. E., "Qualitative Chemical Analysis," 7th Ed., pp. 243, 254, Princeton, N.J., D. Van Nostrand Company, Inc., 1924.

22. Quill, L. L., "Chemistry and Metallurgy of Miscellaneous Materials: Thermodynamics Nuclear Energy Series," New York, McGraw-Hill Book Company, Inc., 1950.

23. "Reactor Handbook," Vol. 3, Sec. 1, "General Properties of Material," AECD-3647, Washington, D.C., Office of Technical Services, U.S. Atomic Energy Commission, 1955.

24. Sax, N. Irving, "Dangerous Properties of Industrial Materials," New York, Reinhold Publishing Corp., 1957.

25. Shilliday, Theodore, *J. Appl. Phys.*, **28**, No. 9, 1035 (1957).

26. Smithells, C. J., "Metals Reference Book," London, Butterworth & Co. (Publishers) Ltd., 1949.

27. Thompson, J. G., *Natl. Bur. Standards (U.S.)*, *Circ. No. 388* (1930).

28. Thompson, J. G., *Natl. Bur. Standards (U.S.)*, *Circ. No. 382* (1950).

5. BORON

HUGH S. COOPER

Consulting Chemist and Metallurgist
Shaker Heights, Ohio

INTRODUCTION

Boron, in one form or another, has been known for at least 400 years. The word "borax" is said to be of Arabian or Persian origin, derived from the "borak" which means white. At a very early period the Arabs used the general expression "baurach" for a number of various salts, presumably thinking that these minerals were of common origin. When it was learned, however, that these salts differed from each other, the term "baurach" was finally restricted to one particular compound from Tibet and India. This salt is now the familiar borax of general household use.

The very early workers, Gay-Lussac and Thenard[37] and Sir Humphry Davy, prepared impure boron by reduction of boron trioxide with potassium in an iron tube, and by electrolysis of boracic acid. About 50 years later, Wöhler and Sainte-Claire Deville[107] describes two varieties of boron which they made—one resembling the diamond, the other graphite. The work of Hampe,[46] however, and later that of Joly,[51] showed that adamantine boron is largely aluminum boride (AlB_{12}), and that the graphitoidal variety is essentially a borocarbide ($B_{48}C_2Al_3$). Heinrich Biltz[12] made a study to clear up this question and concluded that the crystalline boron of previous workers was actually aluminum boride corresponding to the formula AlB_{12}. The chestnut-brown powder, resulting from the reaction between magnesium and boron trioxide and thought to be amorphous boron by all of the early workers, has been shown by Weintraub[93] and Kahlenberg[53]

to be a suboxide. At any rate, the reduction of boron trioxide with magnesium never yields even a pure suboxide, the product being always contaminated with magnesium, carbon, silica, iron, and the like.

Boron is classed as a metalloid. Its atomic weight is 10.82, and it is listed as element 5, in Group III, of the periodic table. Natural boron consists of 19.57 per cent boron 10 and 80.43 per cent boron 11.

OCCURRENCE

Boron is far from being a rare element. It makes up 0.001 per cent of the earth's crust. In nature, the metalloid is never found in the uncombined or elementary state. Most of the native abundant forms are boric acid and borate compounds of sodium and of calcium. Natural boric acid (sassolite, H_3BO_3) has the composition B_2O_3, 56.4 per cent, and H_2O, 43.6 per cent. Sassolite occurs chiefly in solution or in vapors near volcanoes or hot springs. The main source of this compound is Italy.

Colemanite is calcium borate ($Ca_2B_6O_{11} \cdot 5H_2O$, or $2CaO \cdot 3B_2O_3 \cdot 5H_2O$); its composition is B_2O_3, 50.9 per cent; CaO, 27.2 per cent; H_2O, 21.9 per cent. This mineral is found in important quantities in the United States.

Ulexite is a boron atrocalcite or a borate of sodium and calcium ($CaNaB_5O_9 \cdot 8H_2O$, or $2CaO Na_2O \cdot 5B_2O_3 \cdot 16H_2O$); this has the composition B_2O_3, 43 per cent; CaO, 13.8 per cent; Na_2O, 7.7 per cent; H_2O, 35.5 per cent. The main sources of ulexite are the United States, Chile, Bolivia, and Peru.

By far the most important source of boron is now the mineral kernite, also called rasorite. Great quantities of this mineral are mined in California. Massive beds of nearly pure borax and kernite are found in the Kramer area. These deposits are estimated to be about ½ mile wide with a thickness of more than 200 ft. Formerly, the borax was recovered from underground mines, but in January, 1956, a start was made to convert the operation to open-pit stripping, and in 1957 the borax was reached after the removal of about 10,000,000 tons of overburden. Borax mining is now greatly simplified and is proceeding currently at a rate of about 800,000 tons a year. On such a basis it has been stated that known reserves would be sufficient to last at least 100 years. Household borax is sodium tetraborate—$Na_2B_4O_7$ plus 10 molecules of water. Kernite is also sodium tetraborate of this same formula, but it contains only 4 molecules of water. Kernite, as mined, contains about 75 per cent of sodium tetraborate and 25 per cent of clay. To prepare pure borax, it is necessary only to dissolve the soluble tetraborate away from the clay with water, from which solution the salt is readily crystallized.

HISTORICAL REVIEW

To give a brief review of the borax industry,[69] in 1864, which was the first year of recorded domestic production, only 12 tons were produced. At that time the price of borax was about $780/ton. Up to about 1925, the greater part of the borax produced in this country was taken from ulexite and colemanite. Mule teams were used, in this early period, to haul these native compounds. It was from this crude means of transportation that the name "20 Mule Team" originated—a household term for borax even today. These minerals were obtained from deposits located in Death Valley, or from brines from Searles Lake, California. During 1925, a new deposit of sodium tetraborate mineral was discovered at Boron (at that time Kramer), California. This is the mineral referred to as kernite.

The discovery and development of these deposits had a far-reaching effect on the domestic and foreign market. Several mines were opened; the production of borax from this source was more economical than from conversion of ulexite and colemanite, and, following the year 1930, imports of boron minerals virtually ceased. With the exception of the years 1940 and 1948, domestic production has steadily increased. In 1949, for example, the production was 467,592 tons at a per ton price of $66.46. In 1956 it was 944,950 tons having a B_2O_3 content of 315,000 tons, and in 1959 borax production amounted to 619,946 tons containing 314,286 tons of B_2O_3. The product for 1959 was valued at $46,150,000. These figures indicate a resumption of the rise interrupted by the 1958 decline. The development of new uses for boron compounds accounts for this great increase. Now, with the advent of boron steels and other alloys, high-energy fuels, anti-knock additives to gasoline,[7] and many other uses too numerous to mention, further substantial increases can be expected.

PROCESSES FOR MAKING BORON

Weintraub[93] was the first research worker to make pure boron. Moissan[64] selected the reduction of boron oxide with magnesium as being the most suitable process, but, as previously stated, this method yields only an impure boron suboxide. After a thorough study of this process, the best material made by Weintraub analyzed 84 per cent boron, 0.6 per cent magnesium, 0.2 per cent iron, with traces of boron nitride and 14.45 per cent oxygen. Weintraub finally concluded that pure boron could not be made by this process and ascribed the formula B_7O to the product. Later, Kahlenberg[53] gave the formula B_3O to the compound and claimed that Weintraub's material was a mixture of B_3O and free boron. Kroll claims that the main oxygen contaminant of magnesium-reduced B_2O_3 is boron monoxide.[57] This same oxide has been prepared by Wartik and Apple at Pennsylvania State University,[92] and by Kanda, King, Russell, and Katz.[54] Low-grade boron made by the magnesium-reduction process is currently being produced by a number of companies. An analysis, made on one of these products in the writer's laboratory, gave boron, 89.11 per cent; magnesium, 3.98 per cent; carbon, 0.22 per cent; iron, 0.18 per cent; and silicon, 0.47 per cent. The balance can be assumed to be oxygen. It has been stated that the oxygen and magnesium can be largely expelled by arc fusion in an inert atmosphere,[57] or by high-temperature vacuum treatment of commercial boron.[73]

In the process of making pure boron, as finally developed by Weintraub,[94] boron trichloride was reduced by hydrogen between water-cooled copper electrodes in a high-tension arc. This boron was in the form of powder and in fused pellets, and had a purity in excess of 99.80 per cent. In later work A. H. Warth[91] (a fellow worker with Weintraub) modified this process. In the Warth method the same reaction was employed, but the boron was deposited on a heated tungsten wire or rod. Weintraub also made alloys of carbon and boron by co-deposition of the elements from these compounds on a heated surface.[103]

Boron has also been made by the reduction of boron trichloride with hydrogen, using an arc between electrodes of tungsten or molybdenum.[45] Van Arkel[88] prepared boron by dissociation of boron bromide (BBr_3) on a heated tungsten wire. A similar process is described by Laubengayer, Hurd, Newkirk, and Hoard,[58] but, in this instance, hydrogen is used along with the boron bromide. Kiessling[55] also employed this same method. Kiessling discusses the yields of the element obtained at different temperatures, as well as the purity. McCarty and Carpenter have reported recently on the synthesis of boron triiodide and its decomposition on tantalum at 800–1000°C (1472–1832°F) to yield a new crystalline modification of boron.[61a] Boron has also been made by reduction of diborane.[65, 76] Crystalline boron is also formed when a mixture of hydrogen and BCl_3 is passed over a heated filament of tungsten-tantalum alloy wire,[11] or titanium wire.[82] It can also be deposited from the same mixture on graphite or on individual wires of tungsten, tantalum, or molybdenum.[2, 72] In another process, impure boron has been obtained by reduction of potassium or sodium fluoborate, with potassium, sodium, or lithium.[81] In still another method, it is claimed that BF_3 can be reduced with an alkali metal, the latter in a gaseous state.[80]

Although it is true that boron of high purity can be obtained by thermal decomposition or by hydrogen reduction of boron chloride or bromide or from diborane, in general, the yields are small and the cost is so high as to make such methods useful only in special instances where cost is a negligible factor. There has been a major effort, however, by Fetterley,[33] of the Norton Company, to produce boron on a pilot scale from boron chloride and hydrogen. In this process the boron is deposited on carbon resistor rods heated to about 1400°C (2552°F). Apparently, boron carbide is formed first adjacent to the graphite; next a layer of boron is deposited which contains, however, about 3 per cent of carbon. Production in such a unit proceeds at a rate of about 1 lb/hr.

Concerning other processes, Andrieux[4] claims to have made boron of "Moissan purity" by the electrolysis of a molten mixture of boron oxide, magnesium oxide, and magnesium fluoride. Bath temperatures are 1000–1100°C (1832–2012°F)), the anode is carbon, and the cathode is an iron rod. This same investigator describes another process[3] in which the electrolysis is performed in baths containing Na_2O and B_2O_3, with and without MgF_2. A British patent[13] and a United States patent[67] disclose a fused-salt process in which the initial components of the fused system are KCl, KF, and B_2O_3. This process was discussed by Nies, McIntyre, and Fajans at a meeting of the Electrochemical Society in 1958.[66] Newkirk has reviewed very thoroughly the methods for the preparation of elemental boron.[65a]

The writer has developed two patented processes for making boron, either of which can be used for making industrial quantities of the element. In the first method, described by Cooper,[17] potassium fluoborate is electrolyzed in a fused bath of potassium chloride. In the second process[18] boron is obtained by electrolysis from a molten mixture of potassium chloride, potassium fluoborate and boron oxide.

In the first process the anode is a graphite-lined pot of heat-resisting alloy, and the cathode is preferably a low-carbon iron plate or cylinder. To prevent disintegration of the graphite anode at the top, it is water-cooled. The cathode is bolted to a water-cooled copper terminal around which some salt solidifies at the surface of the bath, thereby preventing contamination of the boron with copper. A cell of this type operates for extended periods at currents as high as 3,000 amp at voltages of 6 to 12. Current efficiency is about 75 per cent.

In this process, chlorine is evolved at the anode, and so it can be assumed that potassium is set free from the potassium chloride, which, in turn, reduces the potassium fluoborate to form elemental boron. There is a progressive build-up of potassium fluoride in the bath, coupled with a corresponding rise in voltage. The boron, after removal from the cathode and washing and drying, is predominantly coarsely crystalline, greatly resembling coke. A typical analysis is boron, 99.41 per cent; carbon, 0.29 per cent; and iron, 0.20 per cent.

Details of the operation of the above process in the Atomic Energy Commission plant of Hooker Chemical Corp. are given by Miller.[63a]

In the second process the cell construction is

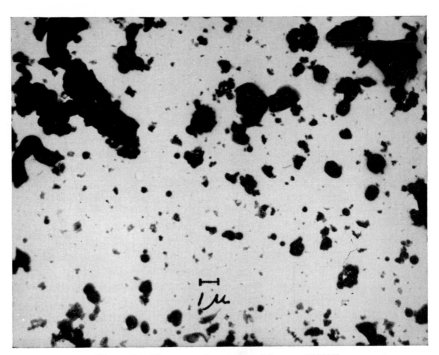

Figure 5.1. Electron micrograph of boron (5000X).

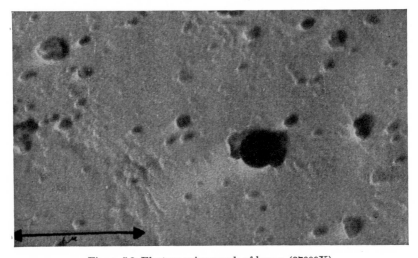

Figure 5.2. Electron micrograph of boron (37000X).

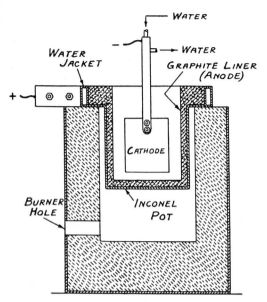

Figure 5.3. A schematic diagram of boron cell.

quite similar, but in this instance oxygen is liberated at the anode where it combines with the carbon. The boron from this process consists predominantly of fine material which readily passes through a −325-mesh sieve. An electron micrograph (Figure 5.1), magnification X5,000, of this fine boron shows particle sizes down to less than 1/10 μ with above 5 μ for

Figure 5.4. Electrolytic boron cell.

the largest particles. Some of the larger particles are believed to be agglomerates of the very small particles, however. Figure 5.2 shows a magnification of X37,000 of a similar specimen of boron. The purity of this metal is quite the same as that made by the other process mentioned. By special grading and purification, boron can be obtained showing a purity of 99.70 per cent, with carbon 0.05 per cent and iron 0.15 per cent. A schematic diagram of a boron cell is shown in Figure 5.3 and an actual photograph of a cell in Figure 5.4.

PRODUCTION OF BORON 10

As already mentioned, natural boron is a mixture of the isotopes boron 10 and boron 11 in a 19.57:80.43 ratio.

The United States Atomic Energy Commission is interested in producing boron 10 because of its high neutron-capture cross section of 3,850 barns, as compared with 38 barns for boron 11 and 755 barns for natural boron. Boron 10 has become important for control of nuclear reactors, as a shield for nuclear radiation, and for instruments for detecting neutrons. Because of its low neutron-capture properties, boron 11 is of interest in other ways.

In 1953 the United States Atomic Energy Commission authorized the building of a plant for making boron 10. This plant began production in June, 1954, and was operated by Hooker Chemical Corp. for the United States Atomic Energy Commission until about July, 1958, when it was placed on stand-by. The plant has a capacity of 500 kg/yr of elemental boron enriched to 90 to 95 per cent boron 10 per total.[63] To separate the boron 10 from boron 11, a boron fluoride–dimethyl ether complex is employed, the separation being accomplished in large fractionation columns.[16] Following a period of initial operations using the "hot-wire" process,[2, 11, 72] the process was altered to substitute fused salt electrolysis for final boron recovery. In the altered process the boron-10 complex from the fractionation columns is reacted with potassium fluoride[30] to produce KBF_4 in which the boron content consists largely of boron 10. stand-by. Using the Cooper process of U.S. Patent 2,572,248, boron 10 is deposited on a metal cathode from a bath consisting of KCl and the $KB^{10}F_4$ produced as described.[15]

PHYSICAL PROPERTIES

Since, up to a recent date, only relatively small amounts of pure boron have been available, many of the properties of this interesting element are still unknown, and, indeed, many of the published properties must doubtless be revised.

According to Warth,[91] the density of boron deposited on a tungsten filament is very close to 2.30. The Formstecher and Ryskevec[35] determination is more recent and probably more accurate. They give a density of 2.34 ± 0.01 for boron made from diborane.

The true melting point of boron is still somewhat in doubt. Guertler and Pirani[43] apparently have accepted Weintraub's value of around 2400°C (4352°F). Cueilleron,[21] on the other hand, determined the melting point of boron to be between 2000 and 2075°C (3632 and 3767°F). This determination was made on boron prepared by reduction of the chloride with hydrogen in a high-frequency arc. The specimen was melted with an atomic hydrogen torch. This latter figure would seem more nearly correct, although there is some evidence that the true melting point may be somewhat higher than that given by Cueilleron. In certain experiments performed by the writer, boron was heated under a pressure of 9,000 psi in argon. Under these conditions, boron readily assumed the form of the mold, and the finished product had a density of 2.24. Readings with an optical pyrometer indicated the temperature of plasticity to be about 2000°C (3620°F). In other experiments a briquette of boron was heated in a carbon resistor furnace in argon at atmospheric pressure. At 2200°C (3992°F) there was considerable vaporization of the material, which made it difficult to obtain precise temperature readings. At this point the current was cut off, and, after cooling, a black, well-fused, crystalline mass was obtained. From these experiments one can estimate the melting point of boron to be somewhere between 2100 and 2200°C (3812 and 3992°F). A later value[49] places the melting point at 2300°C (4172°F) and the boiling point at 2550°C (4622°F).

The modulus of elasticity of boron is approximately 64×10^6, and the tensile strength is between 230,000 and 350,000 psi.[85]

The heat of combustion of boron with oxygen is reported by Johnston, Hersh, and Kerr[50] to be 13.95 kcal/g of boron, or 25.120 Btu/lb.

The coefficient of expansion of boron, according to Warth, is greater than that of quartz but less than that of tungsten. This value is not in agreement with that of Dupuy and Hackspill,[29] who state that the linear coefficient of expansion between temperatures of 20 and 750°C (68 and 1382°F) is 8.3×10^{-6}, with an accuracy of 3 per cent. A brochure published by Hooker Electrochemical Company[49] gives the coefficient of linear expansion as 1.1 to 8.3×10^{-6}/°C in the 20 to 750°C range. The specific heat of boron is given in the following table:

Temperature (°C)	Specific heat (cal/g)
−191 to −78 (−311.8–108.4°F)	0.071
− 76 to 0 (−104.8–32°F)	0.180
0 to 100 (32–212°F)	0.307
100 (212°F)	0.387
500 (932°F)	0.472
900 (1652°F)	0.510

The electrical properties of boron are interesting and probably unprecedented among the elements. It is feebly conductive at room temperatures but quite conductive at high temperatures. Weintraub[95] states that the "cold" resistance of boron is 9,000,000 ohms and that ther esistance above 1000°C (1832°F) is but a fractional part of an ohm. The following table indicates the remarkable change which takes place with rise in temperature. Column 3 of the table gives the early values determined by Weintraub,[95] and column 2 gives approximate values read from a graph recently published by Greiner and Gutowski,[42] which are surprisingly close to the early Weintraub determinations. Electrical properties of boron have

RESISTIVITY OF BORON (OHM-CM)

Temperature (°C)	Greiner and Gutowski	Weintraub
−150 (−238°F)	40,000,000,000	
− 10 (14°F)	4,000,000	
0 (32°F)	3,000,000	
27 (81°F)	650,000	775,000
100 (212°F)	40,000	66,000
170 (338°F)	3,000	7,700
320 (608°F)	40	180
520 (968°F)	1.2	7
600 (1112°F)	0.2	4

also been reported by Bruce and Hickling;[14] Ryoser Uno, Taizo Irie, Sanae Yoshida, and Kenechi Shinohara;[87] and Shaw, Hudson, and Danielson.[78]

The influence of carbon dissolved in boron is no less interesting. This influence is of extraordinary magnitude, so that even as small an amount as 0.1 per cent, for instance, will increase the conductivity manyfold. With 7 to 8 per cent of carbon dissolved in boron, the remarkable characteristics disappear altogether, and the material has a conductivity comparable to that of carbon.

Freymann[36] has determined the effect of temperature and of visible and infrared radiation on the electrical resistance of boron.

Norton Company[32] gives the bending strength of boron as 76,000 psi and places the Knoop hardness (100-g load) at 2,500. This hardness value would seem to be on the low side, because silicon carbide, with a Knoop hardness of about 2,500 in a cutting operation, makes only a slight marking on boron. On the other hand, the value 5,000, as given by Formstecher and Ryskevec,[35] is undoubtedly much too high. The Knoop hardness (100-g load) of arc-melted boron produced in the writer's laboratory and having a purity greater than 99.5 per cent was 3,300. Since this measurement was made on dense, arc melted boron, this hardness value is probably close to the true hardness of boron.

Information on the crystal structure of boron is somewhat confusing. Samples of boron, prepared in the writer's laboratory by electrolysis, were examined by x-ray diffraction. The diffraction lines of these specimens, though faint, matched those obtained from crystalline boron deposited on a hot filament during hydrogen reduction of boron tribromide.[58] This reference reports needlelike single crystals of deposited boron as tetragonal space group $D_4^b = 4/m$ with a = 8.93 Å and C = 5.06 Å. This same reference also reports that a second type of single crystal was found in the hydrogen-reduced deposits. These are plate crystals with an orthorhombic structure having a = 10.13 Å, b = 8.93 Å, and c = 17.86 Å. Szabo and Tobias[84] give powder x-ray data on boron prepared by thermal decomposition of the bromide. These data, although agreeing with each other as to the number of forms and temperature range, disagree as to crystal structure. Warren

and Godfrey[90] give a powder pattern which does not agree with that given by Laubengayer et al.[58] Newkirk has reviewed recently the factors relating to the physical forms of boron.[65a]

CHEMICAL PROPERTIES

Boron readily combines with fluorine, chlorine, bromine, and iodine. Pure boron is resistant to chlorine up to 500°C (932°F), but there is rapid combination at 550°C (1022°F), giving boron trichloride. The element is unaffected by boiling in hydrochloric or hydrofluoric acids. It is oxidized by hot concentrated nitric acid, but, unless the boron is in finely powdered condition, the reaction proceeds only at a very slow rate. Hot concentrated sulfuric acid, or a hot solution of chromic acid in sulfuric acid, attacks boron only to a barely appreciable extent. As will be noted in the analytical procedure outlines, boron is soluble in a mixture of nitric, hydrochloric, and sulfuric acids.

Concentrated hydrogen peroxide slowly oxidizes the powdered element, but a hot solution of ammonium persulfate has only slight action. Boiling concentrated aqueous sodium hydroxide gives no reaction. Boron reacts vigorously with fused sodium peroxide, or with a fusion mixture of sodium carbonate and potassium nitrate. In molten sodium hydroxide there is no apparent reaction below 500°C (932°F), but at higher temperatures boron crystals are slowly etched.[58]

When the pressed metal is heated in air, there is no apparent oxidation up to about 750°C (1382°F), but at 800°C (1472°F) the surface begins to show a black glaze. This coating is apparently completely protective up to about 1000°C (1832°F). In pure oxygen at 1000°C, the attack is quite rapid. Pure boron of small particle size, of the order of 1/10 to about 10 μ, oxidizes slowly at room temperature. For example, a sample of 99 per cent material, after some months in the laboratory, was reanalyzed and found to contain only 92 per cent of the element. As the particle size increases, the resistance to oxidation is also increased, and it has been found that, when a size is reached around 40 mesh and above, no changes in composition are noted. For this reason the finely divided pure element should be kept in airtight containers that are completely filled.

Some new properties of boron have been established by Cueilleron.[22] A mixture of boron with potassium permanganate, lead oxide (Pb_3O_4), antimony oxide (Sb_2O_3), or lead nitrate ignites on shock or friction but without detonation. Boron explodes with hydrogen iodide.

Boron forms many useful metallic and inorganic compounds. Outstanding among these are the borides, carbide, silicides, nitride, and hydrides. Because of the difficulty of obtaining the borides in pure form by reduction methods, very little has been known about their properties until recently. Now that ample high-purity boron is available in quantity by the Cooper process, these compounds can be made in pure form by direct combination of the elements. The borides of the refractory metals could become of great industrial importance and are being intensively studied.[8, 40, 70, 77] In general, they are characterized by high melting points —in excess of 2000°C (3632°F)—and great hardness, and in the case of borides of aluminum (AlB_{12}), silicon (SiB_6), titanium (TiB_2), zirconium (ZrB_2), and chromium (CrB_2), the resistance to scaling above 1000°C (1832°F) is quite good. The borides of tungsten, molybdenum, tantalum, and columbium, though not so resistant to high temperature in an oxidizing atmosphere, are exceedingly refractory, are extremely hard, and may find a place in high-speed cutting tools. Chromium boride is currently being used in hard facing operations for improving wear resistance, also for coating steel to render steel sections resistant to molten aluminum. Aluminum boride (AlB_{12}) and silicon boride (SiB_6), now produced in pure form in the writer's laboratory, may form the basis for a new abrasives industry. In this connection the Knoop hardnesses (100-g load) of aluminum boride and silicon boride have been recently determined here to be 3,700 and 3,400, respectively. Boron carbide (2800 K_{100}) has been produced in quantity for a number of years; it has found extensive use as a polishing agent, for sandblast nozzles, etc. An impure form of calcium boride has also been marketed over a considerable period of time as a deoxidizing agent for copper. Pure calcium boride (CaB_6) is now being made and could be of interest in other directions. This compound is quite stable. It has a melting point of 2235°C (4055°F) and a Knoop hardness (100-g load) of about 2,500.[74]

The metallic borides of Group-IV metals, surprisingly, are better electrical conductors than their respective components, and it is to be expected that their thermal conductivities will follow much the same pattern. Some of these compounds respond to conventional sintering and hot-pressing procedures, and, in certain instances, the resulting shapes have considerable strength.

Boron forms a nitride having quite remarkable properties.[39, 68] This compound is a white powder having an average particle size of about 1 μ. The melting point of boron nitride is said to be 3000°C (5432°F), and it withstands oxidation at temperatures up to about 650°C (1202°F). The true density is 2.20 g/cc, and the apparent density is 0.11 g/cc or 7 lb/cu ft. Electrical resistance is extremely high at all temperatures up to 2400°C (4352°F), at which point the material is not heated by high-frequency current. Boron nitride has a hexagonal plate structure like graphite and has been suggested as a lubricant.[19] It has also been patented as a paint pigment.[20] Boron nitride can be hot-pressed into various forms such as crucibles, etc.[86] It has recently been subjected to pressures in excess of 1,000,000 psi at temperatures above 1650°C (3002°F) to yield a material as hard as diamond.[5]

The hydrides of boron are colorless solids, liquids, or gases and are easily oxidized, with consequent large energy liberation. These compounds have been extensively studied by government agencies[60] because of desirable characteristics as rocket fuels. The highest jet velocities are attained with elements of low atomic weight, and, although hydrogen is probably the "tops" theoretically as a propellent fuel, it is extremely difficult to contain, and so must be combined with other elements, such as boron or lithium. It is generally agreed that, for many reasons, boron is the likeliest candidate for this role. For a propellent fuel of reasonably high bulk density, very high jet velocities may be expected from reacting boron hydride with fluorine oxide[60] of water; boron hydride is a water-reaction fuel, being highly explosive when exposed to moist air or traces of water.[10]

It is interesting to compare the energy release of boron with other fuels: 1 cu ft of boron releases 3,603,986 Btu upon combustion; the same amount of kerosene, 946,000 Btu;

and gasoline, 790,000 Btu.[52] Boron-derived fuels to be used in reaction motors of jets and rockets yield half again as much heat per pound as the best hydrocarbon fuels, and it has been said that such boron fuels will develop into a billion-dollar industry in a decade. These fuels, in a general way, are conveniently made by reacting lithium hydride with boron trichloride or boron trifluoride. Such reactions, when modified in various ways, can yield diborane (B_2H_6), pentaborane (B_5H_9), and decaborane ($B_{10}H_{14}$).

Although there still remains much to be learned about these various boron compounds, it appears obvious that, as far as the investigations have proceeded, new industries are in the making in which boron, in some form or other, will play an important role.

METHODS OF ANALYSIS

The determination of boron in iron and steel is covered very completely by the *Bureau of Mines Information Circular 7363*,[24] and so need not be dwelt upon here. An analytical procedure for boron can also be found in a circular published by the National Bureau of Standards.[71] When the boron content is well above 90 per cent and more frequently above 99 per cent, the following method has proved extremely reliable:

Chemicals:
Mannitol
Sulfuric acid (CP)
Nitric acid (CP)

Solutions required:

NaOH–0.2 N solution
Preparation: usual

Methyl Red
Dissolve 1.0 g into 100 ml ethyl alcohol

Brom Cresol Green
Dissolve 1.0 g into 100 ml ethyl alcohol

Phenolphthalein
Dissolve 2.0 g into 100 ml ethyl alcohol

Standard HCl
300 cc 1-1 HCl in distilling flask w/condenser
Temperature: 108–108.5°C (226.4–227.3°F)
Distill approximately 150 cc

Calculate density and specific gravity, check tables for HCl % value
Example: Barometric pressure
29.80 = 760 mm Hg
760 mm = 180.1939 density
1.09 sp gr = 20.22% HCl
18.019 g HCl diluted to 100 ml = N HCl
This example is elaborated upon in ASTM, E50 (1946).

Equipment: A small Bunsen with a low flame is best. Avoid over 2 in. of distilling at all times. Water must be kept running while the sample is being digested and cooled.

Procedure: Weigh a 200-mg sample into a 300-cc flask. Wash sample down and place under condenser with water running.
Add:
50 cc H_2O
10 cc HNO_3
5 cc HCl
2 cc H_2SO_4

Acids and H_2O are added through top of condenser. After reaction is completed light Bunsen. Heat to slow boil and slowly boil until sample is in solution. This takes from 1 to 2 hr. Cool to room temperature under condenser, wash down, and remove from same.

Bring solution in flask to just basic with 0.1 N standard NaOH, using methyl red to pH of 7.0. Do this with sample being held in cooling trough and with slow additions of the NaOH. Add pulp and filter through Whatmans 41. Wash five times with hot water.

Return filtrate to original flask. Add N HCl until solution is just acid, add 3 drops over. Place back under condenser and boil for 5 min. Cool and remove.

Add 1 ml brom cresol green and slowly add 0.1 N standard NaOH dropwise until HCl is neutral—indicator will turn pale green. Add 1 drop 0.1 N HCl to check and 1 drop 0.1 N NaOH to bring it back.

Add 1 ml phenolphthalein and 1 g mannitol. Titrate with the 0.2 N NaOH. Add mannitol and titrate until permanent pink shows which will hold. Mannitol is added in

1-g portions. 1 cc of NaOH = 0.30% of boron. 200-mg sample = 66.20 cc titration. 66.20 × 0.30 = 19.86%, × 5 = 99.30% boron in the sample.

NaOH is standardized against a solution of previously fused B_2O_3 CP. A blank from this solution is run with the sample.

FABRICATION TECHNIQUES

Boron can be produced in various shapes either by hot pressing or cold pressing, followed by sintering. In the hot pressing of boron conventional equipment for making carbide shapes can be used, but the temperatures employed are naturally much higher because no binders, such as cobalt or nickel, are used. Boron begins to show plastic flow at about 1800°C (3272°F), and pressing temperatures need not exceed 2000°C (3632°F). Induction heating is preferable, and the heating time to consolidate the boron should be as brief as possible. Graphite molds are employed, preferably coated with boron nitride. A protective atmosphere of inert gas, such as argon, is also desirable. As an example, with a mold cavity about 0.35 in. in diameter, the optimum condition would be 25 kw as power input, time of heating about 1½ to 2 min, temperature about 1800°C (3272°F), and pressures of about 5,000–9,000 psi.

In another process[62] the boron powder, after pressing, is sintered on a BeO support in a hydrogen atmosphere at 1800–2200°C (3272–3992°F). Other methods for the consolidation of boron are dwelt upon by F. G. Stroke[83] and by Hays and Burke.[47] Boron shapes can also be made by mixing boron with 1 to 10 per cent of boron oxide, then consolidating the powder by pressing at about 50 tons/sq in., followed by sintering at 800°C (1475°F). Such pieces will show a compressive strength in excess of 36,000 psi.[104] Boron has been deposited as thin films[28] and used as ion-chamber coatings[65] and for other purposes.

APPLICATIONS

The uses of boron for motor-starting devices, gramophone needles,[26] lightning arrestors, and thermal cutouts for transformers have been patented.[96] The element has also been used as a sealing material for vacuum vessels. A eutectic alloy, with 96 per cent iron, nickel, or cobalt, is recommended.[59] Electric contacts of silver and boron have also been claimed in another patent.[48]

Boron has also been suggested as a thermoelectric couple,[97] a pivot bearing,[98] an electrical resistor,[99] and a variable-resistance device.[100] An important and growing use for fairly substantial amounts of boron is in the manufacture of "ignitors" in ignitron rectifier and control tubes.[61, 79, 89] This ignitor consists of a mixture of boron and other materials, sintered at very high temperatures to form semiconductors with good mechanical properties. One of these ignitors is shown in Figure 5.5.[38]

Figure 5.5. Ignitor as used in G-E sealed ignitors. (*Courtesy General Electric Company.*)

Boron is also of value in atomic work as a neutron absorber and for applications in neutron thermometers and high-temperature-coefficient resistors.[76] The use of boron and boron compounds for nuclear purposes has been reported by Finlay.[34] For neutron absorption, the isotope boron 10 is naturally preferred because of its much higher value—above five times that of natural boron. Boron 11, on the other hand, would be useful for applications requiring a low neutron-capture cross section, e.g., for reactor linings or fuel cladding.

Boron is probably the best medium known for the treatment of copper to free it from gas and produce a metal of extremely high conductivity.[101, 102] In this same connection, copper-boron alloys carrying other metals have been patented by the American Brass Company.[1] Copper-boron alloys of high purity, carrying up to about 6 per cent boron, are currently being made by Cooper Metallurgical Associates. These alloys offer means for introducing precise amounts of boron into copper for deoxidation purposes and as master alloys for producing various copper-boron alloys by conventional foundry practices; they have also been employed with great success in brazing certain metals which normally do not unite readily.

Boron is an important component in many alloys. It is used, e.g., in cutting tools,[25, 106] high-temperature alloys,[44] and in hard facing[31, 75] and cementing[56] of softer base metals to provide hard wear-resisting surfaces. Boron is alloyed with aluminum[105] to improve the strength without impairment of electrical conductivity. Because of the great affinity of boron for oxygen, its high efficiency, and the fusibility of the slags formed, it has been suggested as a reducing agent[9] in much the same way as aluminum and silicon are employed.

Referring to the production of boron steels, the boron is usually added as a master alloy,[23] e.g., ferroboron and manganese boron. The main purpose of this addition is to increase the hardenability.[6, 24, 26, 41] The boron content is exceedingly small, about 0.0005 to 0.005 per cent. The steels are thoroughly deoxidized before these additions. The consumption of boron steel is on a steady upward trend because of the desire to conserve the more costly and scarce metals such as chromium, molybdenum, and nickel. It has been stated that the output of these steels could easily reach 2,000,000 tons/year in the near future. This would call for the employment of about 200,000 lb of contained boron per annum. For making boron steels there are indications that pure ferroboron, corresponding to the compound Fe_2B, produces much better results than the various complex boron alloys now used and may remove the need for critical control of boron content. From this brief outline on boron, boron compounds, and alloys, it seems quite apparent that this element will ultimately take its place on an equal footing with its sister elements carbon and silicon, and become just as indispensable to the metallurgical, chemical, and electrical industries.

References

1. American Brass Co., British Patent 536,893, (May 30, 1941).
2. Anderson, R. D., "Operating Instructions for Production of Product 891-A at Stamford Research Laboratories," U. S. Army Engineering Corps., Vol. 1, 2, 3, LC, M-356 (1944–1946).
3. Andrieux, L., and Deiss, W. J., *Bull. soc. chim. France*, 6, 838–841, (1955).
4. Andrieux, L., *Compt. rend.*, 185, 119–120 (1927).
5. Anonymous, *Materials & Methods*, pp. 194–196, May 1957.
6. Archer, R. S., *Metal Progr.*, pp. 677–686, Oct. 1946.
7. Bartleson, J. D., U.S. Patents 2,725,856 (1956); 2,751,285 (1956); Darling, S. M., U.S. Patents 2,710,251 (1956); 2,710,252 (1956); 2,741,548 (1956); Fay, P. S., U.S. Patent 2,767,069 (1957); Hughes, E. G., U.S. Patent 2,725,857 (1956).
8. Battelle Memorial Institute, "The Formation of Refractory Coatings by Vapor-Deposition Methods," *Rand report R-137* (1949).
9. Becket, F. M., U.S. Patent 924,130 (June 8, 1909).
10. Bell, R. P., and Emeleus, H. J., *Quart. Revs. (London)*, 2, 132–51 (1948).
11. Belmore, E. A., and Teller, A. M., "The Hydrogen Reduction of Boron Trichloride on Alloy Wires," *AEC Report NYO-1269* (1956).
12. Biltz, H., *Ber.*, 41, 2634–35 (1908).
13. Borax Consolidated, Ltd., British Patent 781,813 (Aug. 28, 1957).
14. Bruce, J. H., and Hickling, A., *Trans. Faraday Soc.*, 35, 1436–1439 (1939).
15. Chilton, C. H., *Chem. Eng.*, pp. 148–150 (May 1957).
16. Christ, R. H., et al., U.S. Patent 2,796,330 (June 18, 1957 to AEC).
17. Cooper, H. S., U.S. Patent 2,572,248 (Oct. 23, 1951).
18. Cooper, H. S., U.S. Patent 2,572,249 (Oct. 23, 1951).
19. Cooper, H. S., U.S. Patent 2,156,803 (May 2, 1939).
20. Cooper, H. S., U.S. Patent 2,152,536 (March 28, 1939).
21. Cueilleron, J., *Compt. rend.*, 221, 698–99 (1945).
22. Cueilleron, J., *Ann. chim.*, 19, 459–86 (1944).
23. Dawe, C. N., U.S. Patent 2,579,369 (Dec. 8, 1951).
24. Dean, R. S., and Silkes, B., *U.S. Bur. Mines Inform. Circ. No. 7363* (1946).
25. DeGolyer, A. G., U.S. Patent 1,493,191 (March 6, 1924).
26. Dicker, S. G., British Patent 326,899 (Jan. 1, 1929).
27. Diggs, T. G., Irish, C. R., and Carwile, N. L., *J. Research Nat. Bur. Standards*, 41, (6), 545–574 (1948).

28. Dodson, R. W., and Russell, H., "Preparation of Boron Films," *L. C., PB 52,418* (1944).

29. Dupuy, E., and Hackspill, L., *Compt. rend.*, **197**, 229–30 (1933).

30. Eberle, A. R., U.S. Patent 2,796,323 (June 18, 1957 to AEC).

31. Edmonds, W. H., and Cole, N. W., U.S. Patent 2,088,838 (Aug. 3, 1937).

32. Fetterley, G. H., Norton Company, Private Communication (1951).

33. Fetterley, G. H., U.S. Patent 2,542,916 (April, 1951).

34. Finlay, G. R., *Am. Ceram. Soc. Bull.*, **36**, (3), 109–111 (1957).

35. Formstecher, M., and Ryskevec, E., *Compt. rend.*, **221**, 747–749 (1945).

36. Freymann, R., *Compt. rend.*, **199**, 1109–1110 (1934).

37. Gay-Lussac, J., and Thenard, L., "Recherches Physico-Chem.," p. 276 (1811).

38. General Electric Company (Courtesy of).

39. Giardini, A. A., *U.S. Bur. Mines Inform. Circ. No. 7664* (1953).

40. Glaser, F. W., "Physical Properties of Cemented Borides," Summary, Progress Report, American Electro Metals Corp., *L.C. PB-117-522* (1954).

41. Grange, R. A., Seems, W. B., Holt, W. S., and Garvey, T. M., "Effect of Boron and Kind of Boron Additions Upon Properties of Steel," *Am. Soc. Metals, Preprint No. 5* (1949).

42. Greiner, E. S., and Gutowski, J. A., *J. Appl. Phy.*, **28**, (11), 1364–5 (1957).

43. Guertler, W., and Pirani, M., *Z. Metallk.*, **11**, 1–7 (1919).

44. Guy, A. G., U.S. Patent 2,575,915 (Nov. 20, 1951).

45. Hackspill, L., Stieber, A., and Hocart, R., *Compt. rend.*, **193**, 776–778 (1931).

46. Hampe, W., *Liebig's Ann.*, **183**, 75 (1876).

47. Hays, L., and Burke, J. E., "Plastic Bonding of Boron Powder," *AECD-2279* (1944).

48. Heusel, F. R., Emmert, K. L., and Wiggs, J. W., U.S. Patent 2,221,286 (May 23, 1939).

49. Hooker Electrochemical Co., "Boron and Its Isotopes," (Brochure complied for the U.S. Atomic Energy Commission) (1957).

50. Johnston, H. L., Hersh, H. N., Kerr, E. C., *J. Am. Chem. Soc.*, **73**, 1112–1117 (1951).

51. Joly, *Compt. rend.*, **97**, 456 (1883).

52. Joseph, James, Science and Mechanics Publishing Co., Chicago, Ill. (April 1957 Issue).

53. Kahlenberg, H. H., *Trans. Am. Electrochem. Soc.*, **47**, 23–55 (1925).

54. Kanda, F. A., King, A. J., Russell, V. A., and Katz, W., *J. Am. Chem. Soc.*, **78**, 1509–10 (1956).

55. Kiessling, R., *Acta Chem. Scand.*, **2**, 707–712 (1948).

56. Kontorovich, I., and L'vovski, M., *Metallurg.*, **14**, 89–98 (1939).

57. Kroll, W. J., Bur. of Mines; *Met. Ind.*, **22**, (73–17 wkly) 323–325 (Oct. 1948).

58. Laubengayer, A. J., Hurd, D. T., Newkirk, A. E., and Hoard, J. L., *J. Am. Chem. Soc.*, **65**, 1924 (1943).

59. Lenz, K., and Woekel, E., U.S. Patent 2,159,-808 (May 23, 1939).

60. Leonard, A. S., *J. Am. Rocket Soc.*, No. 68 (1946).

61. Marshall, D. E., and Rigrod, W. W., *Electronics*, **20**, 122–126 (May 1947).

61a. McCarty, L. V., and Carpenter, D. R., *J. Electrochem. Soc.*, **107**, 38 (1960).

62. McKinley, T. D., U.S. Patent 2,463,404 (Mar. 1, 1949).

63. Miller, G. T., Kralik, R. J., Belmore, E. A., and Drury, J. S., *AEC Report A/Conf. 15/P/1836* (June 27, 1958).

63a. Miller, G. T., *J. Electrochem. Soc.*, **106**, 815 (1959).

64. Moissan, H., *Ann. chim. et phys.*, **6**, (7), 296 (1895).

65. Moss, N., "Preparation of Boron Coated Ion Chambers," *L. C., PB91841* (1947).

65a. Newkirk, A. E., "Preparation and Chemistry of Elementary Boron," presented at Am. Chem. Soc. Meeting, Boston, April 1959.

66. Nies, N. P., *J. Electrochem. Soc.*, **107**, 817–20 1960.

67. Nies, N. P., et al., U.S. Patent 2,832,730 (April 29, 1958).

68. Norton Company, Tech. Bull. (1958).

69. Pickard, M. H., *Chem. Eng.*, pp. 269–72, Feb. 1950.

70. Pollack, W., "Cemented Boride Composites for Tool Bits," *Armour Research Foundation, Project No. B687* (1958).

71. Richmond, M. S., and Telford, R. E., *Nat. Bur. of Standards, T.I.D.* **5241**, Nov. 1954.

72. Rochow, T. G., "Production of 891 (Crystalline Boron)" *AEC Report, A-1791* (1944).

73. Russell, V. A., Swift, R., King, A. J., and Kanda, E. A., "Methods of Preparation of Pure Boron," *Armed Services Tech. Inf. Agency*, MCC-1023-TR-149, June 1955.

74. Samsonov, G. V., Markovski, L. Ya., "The Chemistry of Borides," *Upsekhi Khim.*, **25**, No. 2, 190–237 (1956).

75. Sanderson, L., *Can. Mining J.*, 139–141 (March 1937).

76. Schlesinger, H. I., Schaeffer, G. W., Barbaras, G. D., and Wartick, T., "Deposition of Pure Boron," *AEC, MDDC 1339* (Aug. 15, 1944).

77. Schwarzkopf, P., Glaser, F. W., *Iron Age*, pp. 138–139, Apr. 1954.

78. Shaw, W. C., Hudson, D. E., and Danielson, G. C., "Electrical Properties of Crystalline Boron," *Iowa State College, 380* (1953).

79. Slepian, I., and Ludwig, L. R., *Trans. AIEE,* **52,** 693–8 (1937).

80. Spevack, J., U.S. Patent 2,685,501 (Aug. 3, 1954 to AEC).

81. Starck, H. C., German Patent Appl. No. S/5856 and German Patent 936,745 (Dec. 22, 1955), and Sowa, F. J., U.S. Patent 2,465,989 (Apr. 5, 1949) and Canadian Patent 493,996 (June 30, 1953).

82. Stern, D. R., and Lynds, L., *J. Electrochem. Soc.,* **105,** 676 (1958).

83. Stroke, F. G., "The Consolidation of Boron," *AECD-2291* (1944).

84. St. V. Nery Szabo, and Tobias, C. W., *J. Am. Chem. Soc.,* **71,** 1882 (1949).

85. Talley, C., (Experiment, Inc.), *Metals Rev.,* p. 13, May 1958.

86. Taylor, K. M., *Ind. Eng. Chem.,* **47,** (12), 2506–2509 (1955).

87. Uno, Iric, Yoshida, and Shinohara, *J. Sci. Research Inst. (Tokyo),* **47,** 216–22 (1953).

88. Van Arkel, A., U.S. Patent 1,774,410 (Aug. 6, 1930).

89. Warmaltz, N., *Philips Research Repts.,* **6,** (5) (Oct. 1951).

90. Warren, B. E., and Godfrey, T. N., *J. Am. Phys.,* **18,** 1121 (1950).

91. Warth, A. H., "The Element Boron," *Bull. Maryland Acad. Sci.,* **3,** (3), 8–9 (1923).

92. Wartik, T., and Apple, E. F., *J. Am. Chem. Soc.,* **77,** 6400–1 (1955).

93. Weintraub, E., *Trans. Am. Electrochem. Soc.,* **16,** 165–184 (1909).

94. Weintraub, E., U.S. Patents 1,046,043 (Dec. 3, 1912) and 1,074,672 (Oct. 7, 1913).

95. Weintraub, E., *J. Ind. Eng. Chem.,* **5,** 106–115 (1913).

96. Weintraub, E., U.S. Patent 1,019,568 (March 5, 1912).

97. Weintraub, E., U.S. Patent 1,079,621 (Nov. 23, 1913).

98. Weintraub, E., U.S. Patent 1,088,858 (March 3, 1914).

99. Weintraub, E., U.S. Patent 1,415,748 (May 9, 1922).

100. Weintraub, E., U.S. Patent 1,110,848 (Sept. 15, 1914).

101. Weintraub, E., *Trans. Am. Electrochem. Soc.,* **18,** 207–210 (1910).

102. Weintraub, E., *Bull. soc. franc. electriciens,* **4,** 229–230 (1924).

103. Weintraub, E., U.S. Patents 1,019,569 and 1,019,394 (March 5, 1912).

104. Wellborn, W. W., "Preparation of High Strength Shapes from Crystalline Boron," *Atomic Energy Comm. Doc. 2732* (Oct. 26, 1949).

105. Wetzel, R. T., and King, W. E., U.S. Patent 2,545,866 (March 20, 1951).

106. Wissler, W. A., U.S. Patent 1,602,995 (Oct. 12, 1926); Field, B. E., and Franks, R., U.S. Patent 1,626,726 (May 3, 1927); Field, B. E., U.S. Patent 1,750,796 (March 18, 1930); Wissler, W. A., U.S. Patent 1,774,862 (Sept. 2, 1930); DeGolyer, A. G., U.S. Patent 2,135,494 (Nov. 8, 1939).

107. Wöhler, F., and Deville, H. St. C., *Ann. chim. et phys.,* **52,** [3], 62 (1858).

6. CADMIUM

F. G. McCutcheon*

The Eagle-Picher Company
Henryetta, Oklahoma

and

John R. Musgrave

Research Laboratories
The Eagle-Picher Company
Joplin, Missouri

INTRODUCTION

In 1817 Strohmeyer[71] undertook the investigation of some zinc carbonate, from Salzgitter, Germany, which was being used for pharmaceutical preparations. This compound, upon heating, was yellow in color instead of white (as would be expected from pure zinc oxide). It was at first thought that the contaminant was iron or arsenic; however, further tests did not indicate the presence of either of these elements. Strohmeyer concluded that the contaminant was a metallic oxide not previously known. He separated some of this metallic oxide from the zinc carbonate by careful precipitation with hydrogen sulfide and subsequently reduced it to the metal, the first known preparation of the new element. He named the metal cadmium, from cadmia, a term for calamine (zinc carbonate), because it was found associated with zinc.

Hermann,[25] at about the same time, separated a similar sulfide from some Silesian zinc ore and sent it to Strohmeyer, who identified it as the sulfide of the same metal which he had just discovered. Meissner[48] and Karsten[35] also detected the new element shortly after Strohmeyer's announcement.

* Deceased.

Cadmium was first produced in the United States in 1906[13, 27] by the Grasselli Chemical Company, from blue powder, a by-product of zinc smelting.

Cadmium is in Group II, Period 5 of the periodic table. Its atomic number is 48; its atomic weight is 112.41.

OCCURRENCE

Cadmium is a relatively rare element; its abundance in the lithosphere is estimated at only 0.5 g/ton of the earth's crust.[2] Greenockite (CdS) is apparently the only true cadmium mineral known, and it has been found only in very small quantities, usually in association with sphalerite (ZnS). Cadmium oxide is, in a few instances, detected as a coating on hemimorphite crystals.[59]

Zinc and cadmium are closely associated; most zinc ores contain some cadmium. Practically all of the cadmium recovered is from such zinc ores, which may contain as much as 0.5 per cent cadmium. Small amounts of zinc minerals containing greater proportions of cadmium are sometimes found, but they are not of commercial importance. Lead and copper ores containing zinc may also have sufficient cadmium to allow its economic recovery, but it is generally agreed that the cadmium in such ores is associated with the zinc rather than the other metals.

Cadmium was first recovered from the zinc ores of Upper Silesia; there is still some production from these ores. At present,[49] the major sources are:

Australia—zinc ores
Tasmania—zinc ores
Belgian Congo—zinc ores
Canada—zinc-lead ores (British Columbia)
       zinc-copper ores
             (Manitoba, Saskatchewan)
Mexico—zinc and zinc-lead ores
Peru—zinc ores
Southwest Africa—zinc-copper-lead ore (Tsumeb)
Western United States—zinc and zinc-lead ores
Tri-State (Missouri-Oklahoma-Kansas)—zinc ores
Poland—zinc ores
U.S.S.R.—zinc and zinc-copper ores

Other countries also have some cadmium-bearing zinc ores. Mexico is probably the largest primary source of cadmium-bearing ores on the basis of quantities mined.

PRODUCTION AND STATISTICS

World production of cadmium in 1957 was estimated at 20,000,000 lb, of which about 10,000,000 lb were made in the United States.[53] Since primary cadmium is recovered entirely as a by-product from residues obtained during the reduction of zinc, zinc-lead, zinc-copper, or complex ores containing these metals, the volume of such ores smelted controls the amount of cadmium produced. Secondary cadmium recovery is relatively small.

The previous section details the more important *sources* of cadmium-bearing ores; however, processing of the smelting by-products for recovery of cadmium (and subsequent purification) is frequently done elsewhere. Only a small proportion of the cadmium in Mexican ores is actually smelted and refined in Mexico; the bulk (as either ore concentrate or by-product) is shipped to the United States for treatment. Similarly, concentrates from the Southwest Africa ores are smelted in other countries. The Tasmanian ores are treated in Australia. Particularly, the United States production figures do not reflect correctly the amount of cadmium originating from ores mined in the United States.

At the end of 1950, cadmium was quoted at $2.50/lb in the United States. The price of cadmium has risen from $1.00/lb in 1945 to this high figure; it has since declined to $1.30/lb (1959).

Increase in cadmium production appears to be based on better recovery from present sources or on the discovery (and commercial utilization) of other cadmium-bearing ores.[49] It is likely, from past experience, that these ores will be in zinc or zinc-containing deposits. Some additional cadmium could be recovered as secondary metal from bearing metals, alloys, and, possibly, from discarded cadmium-plated articles.

DERIVATION

Cadmium and its compounds have generally lower melting and boiling points than do the analogous zinc compounds; further, cadmium oxide can be more easily reduced than the corresponding zinc oxide. These conditions are the basis for recovery of cadmium in by-products of zinc smelting or from lead or copper smelting operations where zinc (and cadmium) are present.[41]

The first commercial process (now of only historical interest) was essentially a crude separation during the reduction of zinc in a retort. Roasted zinc ore mixed with coal or coke was charged to a retort. The retort was connected to a primary condenser and a "prolong" (really a secondary condenser). As the roasted zinc ore was reduced by externally applied heat, the zinc and cadmium were vaporized, and the bulk of the zinc and some of the cadmium were condensed in the primary condenser. Because of its lower boiling point, most of the cadmium was not caught in the primary condenser, but (together with some zinc) was condensed in the prolongs as "blue powder." This blue powder, containing 3 to 5 per cent cadmium, was again reduced with coal or coke and carefully redistilled to obtain a fairly pure cadmium metal and a partially oxidized cadmium powder. The cadmium powder was returned for reduction and distillation. Losses by this method were high; only 25 per cent of the cadmium was recovered. As knowledge of the metallurgy of zinc and cadmium improved, the process was discarded in favor of better recovery methods.

In present practice a wide variety of processes are used, but they are all essentially combinations of the basic methods outlined below:

Initial Recovery

(1) As fumes from roasting of zinc ore, sintering of roasted zinc ore, copper smelting, or lead blast-furnace smelting. The cadmium in these fumes is sometimes further concentrated by pyrometallurgy.

(2) As sludges in purification of zinc sulfate solutions (from roasted ore). The zinc sulfate solutions are used in manufacture of lithopone or as feed for electrolytic zinc cells.

Purification

(1) By solution of fumes or sludges (usually in sulfuric acid), removal of impurities by chemical means, and precipitation of the cadmium (as a sponge) with zinc dust. The cadmium is then melted and distilled; usually, careful redistillation is employed to obtain a purer product.

(2) Solution of fumes or sludges and purification of the solutions (as above) followed by electrowinning of the cadmium from the purified solution. The electrodeposited cadmium is generally of high purity.

(3) Distillation of cadmium-bearing zinc metal.

Recovery

Complete descriptions of specific processes appear in the literature;[10,27,29,41,43] only the general methods are described here.

In roasting zinc ores to oxidize the zinc and sulfur, some of the cadmium is volatilized, particularly if careful control of temperature is not exercised. This fume can be recovered by suitable collection devices (e.g., baghouses, electrostatic precipitators) and is usually combined with other dusts for recovery of cadmium. This roaster fume *normally* contains only 3 to 5 per cent of cadmium. After roasting, the zinc ore (containing most of the cadmium) is further processed by either pyrometallurgical or wet methods to recover the metals.

In the conventional fire process, the roasted zinc ore is mixed with coal or coke and sodium or zinc chloride and passed over a sintering machine. Combustion of the coal provides the necessary temperature in the bed to allow reaction of the chlorides with cadmium, lead, and some other impurities; these impurities are volatilized and collected, usually in an electrostatic precipitator. The zinc, however, is not appreciably attacked by the chlorides at the sintering temperature[10] and remains with the sinter. The by-product fumes so obtained, depending on the amount of cadmium in the original sinter, may contain as high as 25 per cent cadmium.

A variation of this procedure is employed in some plants. When all of the cadmium is not volatilized in one pass over the sintering machine, that remaining tends to collect in the lower part of the sinter bed. To recover this cadmium, this lower part of the sinter bed is separated from the upper part (containing little cadmium) and returned to the sinter feed; the upper layer is passed on to the reduction operation.[11] The zinc sinter is mixed with coal or coke and sent to the retorts for reduction and distillation of the metals by any of the conventional methods (horizontal retorts, electrothermic process, etc.)

In some lead blast-furnace operations, where zinc and cadmium are present in the original ore, the fumes from the furnaces contain the oxides of these two metals. Similarly, some copper smelting operations produce a cadmium-bearing fume. In some cases this fume is collected in bagrooms as it is produced; in others[29] the fume is allowed to recirculate and thereby increase the cadmium concentration before collection. Such fumes are usually low (5 per cent or less) in cadmium.

It is desirable to increase the cadmium content of these low-cadmium fumes before the purification step. Generally, this is done by refuming the dusts under controlled conditions in order to volatilize the cadmium selectively. This can be done in either a kiln or a reverberatory furnace.[29] Some lead blast-furnace dusts are reacted with a siliceous flux, and the cadmium is fumed off while the lead silicate so formed is returned to the blast furnace.[74] Further treatment of fumes to recover and purify the cadmium is described later in this section.

Hydrometallurgy is also employed to recover cadmium from roasted zinc ore. In the preparation of zinc sulfate solution for the manufacture of lithopone or for use in electrowinning of zinc, it is necessary to remove all metals (in solution) which have a detrimental effect upon the operations. In the manufacture of lithopone, any metals producing colored sulfides or sulfates are undesirable; in the electrolysis of zinc, some metals interfere with the electrodeposition.

In making a zinc sulfate solution, roasted zinc ore (crude zinc oxide) is leached with sulfuric acid; the insoluble portion is filtered off, and the zinc sulfate is purified by chemical means. One step of this purification involves the addition of excess zinc dust to precipitate copper and cadmium.[41] This copper-cadmium sludge is further treated as described in the purification steps.

Purification

The fumes or sludges described above may contain from 5 to 50 per cent of cadmium and are usually reacted with sulfuric acid. If reducing agents are present (such as SO_2), it is necessary to counteract them with an oxidizing agent. Any lead is precipitated as lead sulfate. Some of the other impurities are separated by chemical means, leaving mainly copper and cadmium (and sometimes arsenic) in the solution. The copper and cadmium are fractionally precipitated as sponges with zinc dust; the quantity of zinc dust used is somewhat dependent on the final purification step (whether melting of cadmium sponge or electrolytic deposition of cadmium from solution). The spent liquor is returned to the zinc circuit for recovery of the zinc.

One variation of the above method of concentrating the cadmium-bearing residue involves direct treatment with chlorine gas.[40] A water slurry of the residue is chlorinated, whereupon the cadmium goes into solution. The solution is filtered and acidified, and the cadmium is precipitated with zinc dust (as above).

The presence of arsenic in many of the flue dusts or residues necessitates extreme care and adequate ventilation, especially where acid is used. Arsine can easily be produced, and, when zinc dust is used with an acid solution, conditions are very favorable for its formation. Inhalation of even small amounts of this gas can result in death, making complete safety measures mandatory.

If the cadmium is to be treated by pyro-metallurgical means, the addition of zinc dust to the liquor is controlled to give a nearly pure cadmium sponge; this is done by incomplete precipitation of the cadmium. The remaining cadmium in the liquor is recovered by recycling of the liquor. The cadmium sponge is briquetted to reduce oxidation losses and charged to a retort. If necessary, a little coke is added for reduction of any oxide. The cadmium is distilled from the retort and subsequently redistilled under carefully controlled conditions to obtain pure cadmium. This pure cadmium is remelted under a layer of caustic soda and cast into appropriate shapes.

Where the cadmium is to be recovered by electrolytic methods, a certain amount of zinc can be tolerated in the electrolytic cells. Hence excess zinc dust is added to the cadmium-bearing solution to precipitate all of the cadmium, and the purified zinc-cadmium sponge is used for the raw feed to the electrolytic cells. This sponge is oxidized and dissolved in dilute sulfuric acid and electrolyzed at 2.6 to 2.7 volts and 4 to 10 amp/sq ft,[43] using aluminum cathodes and lead or "Duriron" anodes. An excess of cadmium over zinc must be maintained in the electrolyte; milk of lime is added to precipitate the zinc where necessary. Glue is used to reduce the tendency of cadmium to deposit in irregular shapes.

Some cadmium is recovered directly from cadmium-bearing zinc metals by direct distillation. The process is, in effect, an adaptation of the standard chemical engineering principles of rectification. Zinc boils at $907°C$ ($1664.6°F$), cadmium at $767°C$ ($1412.6°F$), and lead at $1750°C$ ($3182°F$).[61] The zinc, which contains both lead and cadmium, is melted and fed to a rectifying column in which it is separated into a lead-zinc alloy (liquid) and zinc and cadmium vapors. These vapors are condensed and fed to a second rectifying column; zinc liquid is collected from the bottom of the column, and the cadmium vapors are collected in a condenser. The cadmium is then purified and cast into shapes.

PHYSICAL PROPERTIES

Cadmium, in many respects, is similar to zinc. The good adherence to metals (particularly ferrous) of electrodeposited cadmium and the corrosion resistance and physical characteristics of such coatings[41] have led to their widespread use.

Physical constants of cadmium are given in Table 6.1.

TABLE 6.1. PHYSICAL CONSTANTS OF CADMIUM
(Superscript numbers refer to references)

Atomic number	48.0[19]
Atomic weight	112.41[19]
Isotopes and abundance (%)	
Mass No. 106	1.4[7]
Mass No. 108	1.0[7]
Mass No. 110	12.8[7]
Mass No. 111	13.0[7]
Mass No. 112	24.2[7]
Mass No. 113	12.3[7]
Mass No. 114	28.0[7]
Mass No. 116	7.3[7]
Color	Silver-white
Crystal structure	Hexagonal pyramids[13]
Index of refraction	
(l) 4360 Å	0.39[55]
(l) 5460 Å	0.546[55]
(l) 5790 Å	0.82[55]
(s) 5890 Å	1.13[55]
(s) 6300 Å	1.31[55]
Hardness (cast Cd), Mohs scale	2.0[62]
Ductility	Considerable[71]
Density (g/cc)	
20°C (68°F) (s)	8.65[19]
330°C (626°F) (l)	8.01[7]
400°C (752°F) (l)	7.93[7]
600°C (1112°F) (l)	7.72[7]
Specific volume (cc/g)	
20°C (68°F) (s)	0.1156
330°C (626°F) (l)	0.1248
Melting point	321°C (609.8°F)[19]
Boiling point	767°C (1412.6°F)[61]
Latent heat of fusion (cal/g)	13.2[19]
Latent heat of vaporization (cal/g)	286.4[7]
Vapor pressure (mm Hg)	
394°C (741°F)	1.0[72]
484°C (903°F)	10.0[72]
578°C (1072°F)	60.0[72]
611°C (1132°F)	100.0[72]
711°C (1312°F)	400.0[72]
767°C (1413°F)	760.0[72]
Viscosity (centipoises)	
350°C (662°F)	2.37[7]
400°C (752°F)	2.16[7]
500°C (932°F)	1.84[7]
600°C (1112°F)	1.54[7]

Surface tension (dynes/cm)	
330°C (626°F)	564.0[7]
370°C (698°F)	608.0[7]
420°C (788°F)	598.0[7]
450°C (842°F)	611.0[7]
500°C (932°F)	600.0[7]
Specific heat (g-cal/g)	
321–700°C (610–1292°F) (l)	0.0632[7]
25°C (77°F) (s)	0.055[19]
Thermal conductivity (cal/sec/sq cm/°C/cm)	
358°C (676°F)	0.105[7]
435°C (815°F)	0.119[7]
Linear thermal coefficient of expansion (cm/cm/°C)	
25°C (77°F) (s)	29.8×10^{-6} [19]
320–540°C (608–1004°F), approx.	150×10^{-6} [55]
Volume resistivity (microhm-cm)	
(s) 0°C (32°F)	6.83[19]
(l) 400°C (752°F)	33.7[7]
(l) 700°C (1292°F)	35.8[7]
Electrochemical equivalent Cd++ (mg/coulomb)	0.582[43]
Electrode potential Cd++ (H$_2$ = 0.0 volts)*	−0.40 volt[9]
Thermal neutron absorption cross section (barns/atom)	2,900[7]

* National Bureau of Standards nomenclature.

CHEMICAL PROPERTIES

Cadmium is almost always divalent; certainly it exhibits this valence in all of its stable compounds.

In moist air, a thin coat of cadmium oxide is slowly formed on the metal at room temperature. At higher temperatures, cadmium oxidizes to CdO, forming a brown powder. Cadmium does not react with water at room temperature, but cadmium vapor and steam will form cadmium oxide and hydrogen; the reaction is reversible.

Cadmium reacts with solutions of the halogens to form the corresponding halides, chlorine being the most reactive. Most inorganic acids and some organic acids will dissolve cadmium; nitric acid is the best of the acid solvents. Unlike zinc, cadmium is not soluble in alkalis; hence it is not amphoteric. Cadmium is, however, soluble in ammonium nitrate solution, forming a cadmium-ammonium complex.

In detecting cadmium qualitatively, it is precipitated with other Group II metals as the sulfide, which is bright yellow. If other metals in Group II are present, the sulfide precipitate is redissolved, excess ammonium hydroxide is added (any precipitate is filtered off), potassium cyanide solution is added to discharge any color from copper ions, and the cadmium sulfide is reprecipitated with H_2S.[69]

Quantitatively, cadmium is determined by dissolving the material to be analyzed, removing interfering ions, and precipitating the cadmium as sulfide. This sulfide can then be converted to the sulfate by reaction with sulfuric acid, evaporation of the solution, and weighing as $CdSO_4$.[3] As an alternative, the sulfide can be dissolved in hydrochloric acid, the solution neutralized with sodium hydroxide, potassium or sodium cyanide added to the solution, and the cadmium electrolyzed from this cyanide solution.[3,4]

Wet methods for determination of cadmium, as discussed in the previous paragraphs, are usually difficult and time consuming in the presence of other materials. Where a large number of cadmium determinations are routinely made, polarographic analyses are quick and reasonably accurate. Cadmium has a half-wave potential (vs. SCE) of approximately -0.6 to -0.8, depending upon the supporting medium. The actual details of analysis will depend upon the material being analyzed.[36]

In the determination of cadmium in ores, a preferred method is to dissolve the ore by conventional methods, evaporate the solution to dryness, dissolve cadmium and other soluble materials in hydrochloric acid, and filter off the insoluble material. The cadmium-bearing solution is then adjusted to $1 N$ in hydrochloric acid, and the cadmium is determined by conventional polarographic methods.

For the determination of cadmium (and lead) in zinc metal, standard polarographic methods are available.[5]

Cadmium gives good results by spectrographic methods both in a solid matrix and in a solution.[6] The more commonly used spectrographic lines are 2288.02 and 3261.06 Å. With care and adequate standards, quantitative determinations of cadmium can be made. The accuracy is dependent on the precision of the spectrographic equipment available and should be, with good equipment, ± 5 per cent.

Iron and steel have good resistance to cadmium up to 700°C (1292°F), but stainless steel is attacked at the melting point of cadmium.[7] Many metals are appreciably soluble in liquid cadmium; included in this category are gold, silver, cobalt, copper, magnesium, mercury, nickel, lead, platinum, antimony, tin, and zinc. Some of the more refractory metals (columbium, chromium, wolfram, and molybdenum) are thought to have some resistance to attack by cadmium.

The corrosion resistance of cadmium is exhaustively covered in "The Corrosion Handbook."[76] In rural atmospheres the resistance is good, but in industrial atmospheres (particularly where SO_2 or SO_3 is present), corrosion is rapid. Cadmium plate is attacked by moist ammonia fumes when residues from cyanide plate baths have not been cleaned from the surface; removal of such residues eliminates the corrosion action. Unsaturated oils will react with cadmium, presumably because of the acid constituents in such oils. Hydrogen sulfide (in high concentrations) and moisture rapidly corrode cadmium plating; the usual atmospheric concentrations do not affect such plate. Sulfur dioxide, as has been previously mentioned, is quite corrosive in the presence of moisture. Most acids will attack cadmium; a careful study of pH (using solutions of HCl and NaOH) shows that attack begins as soon as there is an acid reaction in the solution, the corrosion increasing rapidly as the acid concentration rises. Oxygen increases the rate of corrosion in aqueous solutions; when cadmium is partly immersed in a solution, the attack at the water line is very pronounced.

TOXICITY

The fumes of cadmium and its compounds, as well as solutions of its compounds, are poisonous. Johnstone[32] discusses the toxicology of cadmium at length; his opening paragraph is decidedly pertinent:

Cadmium has probably more lethal potentialities than any other of the metals. Lead, mercury, manganese, and many others may bring about an acute or chronic illness, but rarely do any of these cause sudden death from an acute exposure. Failure to appreciate the toxic properties of this metal (cadmium) has caused workers to be unwittingly exposed to its fume and has furthermore allowed manufacturers to incorporate this metal in products without due warning of its presence.

The most common form of poisoning is from inhalations of fumes of cadmium or of its compounds. The initial symptoms from such exposure are a dry or sore throat, followed by cough, headache, and dizziness. This is followed by fever and shortness of breath. Apparently, there is acute inflammation of the lungs which produces edema; the fluid progressively reduces the lung area until the blood cannot obtain oxygen, and death ensues. Where there is any likelihood of cadmium fumes, protective masks should be worn by the workmen.

Some cases of cadmium poisoning have been reported where foods or drinks have been prepared or stored in cadmium-plated containers. If such foods or drinks are taken into the stomach, severe stomach pains occur quickly, accompanied by vomiting; the immediate rejection of the poison by the stomach is probably responsible for the fact that no fatalities have been reported from such cases. Many health services now forbid the use of cadmium-coated articles for food use.

A lucid discussion of cadmium toxicity symptoms and treatment is given by Princie in a recent government report.[49]

ALLOYS

Data on the binary systems are reproduced below. Budgen[13] has summarized this information, and much of the following is taken from his book. Many ternary and quaternary alloys are also discussed by Budgen; few details are presented here on these systems because of space limitations.

Binary Systems

Aluminum. Aluminum and cadmium are insoluble in each other in the solid state. Neither solid solutions nor chemical compounds are formed.[23]

Antimony. One stable compound is formed (SbCd); a second compound is unstable (Sb$_2$Cd$_3$). Two eutectics are formed, one melting at 292°C (557.6°F) and containing 92 per cent cadmium by weight, the other melting at 453°C (847.4°F) and containing 40 per cent by weight of cadmium.[1, 75] Antimony and cad-

mium are both soluble in each other in the solid state.[54]

Arsenic. Two compounds are formed, Cd$_3$As$_2$ and CdAs$_2$. The stable eutectic melts at 526°C (978.8°F) and contains 47 per cent of cadmium.[64]

Bismuth. Neither bismuth nor cadmium is soluble in each other in the solid state.[34] Only one eutectic is formed; it melts at 140°C (284°F) and contains 40 per cent by weight of cadmium.

Calcium. Two eutectics are formed; the first, melting at 319°C (606.2°F), contains 99 per cent by weight of cadmium, the other melts at 415°C (779°F) and has 29 per cent by weight of cadmium.[18]

Copper. Two compounds are formed, Cu$_2$Cd and Cu$_2$Cd$_3$.[63, 65] Eutectics are formed at 60 per cent by weight of cadmium [melting at 542°C (1007.6°F)] and at 99 per cent by weight of cadmium [melting at 314°C (597°F)]. Cadmium is slightly soluble in solid copper.[57]

Gallium. Cadmium is nearly insoluble in gallium at 30°C (86°F). Cadmium will dissolve 12 to 13 per cent of gallium to form an alloy which freezes at 258°C (496.4°F).[79]

Gold. Gold and cadmium form two compounds, AuCd and AuCd$_3$.[77] A eutectic is formed at 303°C (577.4°F) and contains 87 per cent by weight of cadmium.

Indium. Cadmium and indium are completely miscible in the liquid state.[81] A eutectic is formed, melting at 122.5°C (252.5°F), which contains 25 per cent cadmium by weight. Indium is not very soluble in cadmium in the solid state; however, it retains 15 per cent cadmium in solid solution at 25°C (77°F).

Iron. Cadmium and iron appear to be insoluble in each other in the solid state.[31]

Lead. Lead and cadmium are practically insoluble in each other in the solid state. A eutectic is formed at 249°C (480.2°F) containing 17.4 per cent by weight of cadmium.[1,8,16,33,70]

Lithium. A compound LiCd is formed; LiCd$_3$ and Li$_3$Cd have been reported present.[21] Lithium is rather soluble in solid cadmium.[44]

Magnesium. A compound is formed which is soluble in both magnesium and cadmium in the solid state. The composition of the compound is disputed.[28, 66]

Mercury. Cadmium and mercury are completely soluble in one another in the liquid state, but only partially soluble in the solid state.[22, 47]

Nickel. Nickel is insoluble in solid cadmium.[73, 78] A compound NiCd is formed. A eutectic is formed containing 99.75 per cent cadmium and melting at 318°C (604.4°F).

Selenium. A compound CdSe is reported.[15]

Silver. Two compounds of silver and cadmium are formed, AgCd and $AgCd_4$, which form solid solutions with silver; there are no eutectics.[20] The 7.5 per cent cadmium–92.5 per cent silver alloy can be electrodeposited on steel from cyanide solutions.[30]

Sodium. A complex binary system is formed with numerous compounds of sodium and cadmium reported. Three eutectics are also reported, at 95°C (203°F) (28 per cent by weight of cadmium), 346°C (654.8°F) (95 per cent by weight of cadmium), and 285°C (555°F) (98.5 per cent by weight of cadmium).[37, 38, 45, 60]

Thallium. A eutectic is formed, melting at 203°C (397.4°F), containing 17 per cent by weight of cadmium.[58] Thallium will dissolve about 10 per cent cadmium in the solid phase; cadmium, however, does not dissolve thallium.

Tin. A eutectic is formed at 29 per cent by weight of cadmium, melting at 176°C (348.8°F); solid solutions exist on either side of the eutectic.[24]

Zinc. Zinc and cadmium are slightly soluble in each other in the solid state. The only eutectic melts at 270°C (518°F) and contains 83 per cent by weight of cadmium.[26, 39]

Ternary Systems

Bismuth-Lead. A ternary eutectic is formed with 8.15 per cent by weight of cadmium, 40.2 per cent lead, and 51.65 per cent bismuth, and melting at 91.5°C (196.7°F).[8]

Bismuth-Tin. A ternary eutectic is formed containing 31.2 per cent by weight of cadmium, 27.9 per cent tin, and 40.9 per cent bismuth, melting at 103°C (217.4°F).[22]

Lead-Tin. A ternary eutectic is formed which melts at 145°C (293°F) and contains 18 per cent by weight of cadmium, 32 per cent lead, and 50 per cent tin.[22]

Magnesium-Zinc. The ternary eutectic contains 82.9 per cent by weight of cadmium, 16.6 per cent zinc, and 0.5 per cent magnesium. It melts at 250°C (482°F).[12]

Tin-Zinc. The ternary eutectic contains 24.8 per cent by weight of cadmium, 73.1 per cent tin, and 2.1 per cent zinc. It melts at 164°C (327.2°F).[42]

Note: Many quaternary alloys are used as solders and for low-temperature fusion; they are discussed under the heading "Applications."

FABRICATION TECHNIQUES

The major use of cadmium is for plating articles to give a protective coating (mainly for iron and steel); most of this plating is done by electrodeposition. Although cadmium can be deposited from acid baths, such as sulfate or fluoborate, practically all commercial plating is done from cyanide baths. The plating of cadmium has been described in detail in the literature.[9, 68]

Acid baths do not give good deposits without effective addition agents and also have poor throwing power. Sulfate baths are used in electrowinning (see under the heading "Derivation") where smoothness of deposition is not an important factor.

Cyanide baths are essentially a solution of cadmium oxide and sodium cyanide in water; it is thought that a sodium cadmium cyanide and free sodium hydroxide are present in the solution. A typical formula is:

Cadmium oxide   32 g/liter
Sodium cyanide   75 g/liter

The cadmium concentration of commercial baths may be as much as 50 per cent higher or lower than the above formula. Also, brighteners are usually added to the bath (furfural, some sulfonic acids, sulfite pulp by-products, etc., for low bath concentrations; nickel or cobalt for higher concentrations). Plating is done at room temperature with high-purity cadmium anodes; current densities at the anodes do not exceed 20 amp/sq ft; at the cathode they may vary from 5 to 50 amp/sq ft.

Electroplated cadmium coatings are usually dipped in dilute solutions of oxidizing agents (nitric acid, chromic acid, or hydrogen peroxide) to brighten and passivate the surface of the deposits. Only a quick dip is given; a longer time of dipping would reduce the thickness of the cadmium coating and thereby decrease the protective value. In some processes certain organic materials are used as brighteners.

The alloys of cadmium which are in commercial use apparently can be manufactured without difficulty; there are no indications that any but normal precautions must be taken in melting or casting such alloys. The ease of oxidation of cadmium in air might involve some additional care in the preparation of the alloys.

Cadmium is rarely used alone, and fabrication of the pure metal is not discussed here. Bearing metals containing cadmium are poured by conventional methods; casting of other alloys involves no particular problems.

APPLICATIONS

The majority of the cadmium metal produced is used as a protective coating for iron and steel and, to a much smaller extent, for copper.[52] Although the properties of zinc and cadmium are similar, cadmium is much easier to deposit evenly and smoothly, and such cadmium coatings have greater resistance to atmospheric and galvanic corrosion than do similar zinc coatings. Further, cadmium is resistant to alkalies, whereas zinc is attacked by caustic solutions. Neither zinc nor cadmium has much resistance to acid attack.

A wide variety of both small and large parts for many uses are cadmium-plated for such protection. However, cadmium is almost never used in equipment or containers for food or drinks, since cadmium is poisonous. (See under the heading "Chemical Properties.")

A very small amount of cadmium is plated by dipping the article in molten cadmium, but the process is not presently used to any extent; electroplating has supplanted it almost entirely.

Approximately 10 per cent of the cadmium is used in alloys. These alloys are employed as bearing metals, solders, electrical conductors, and in jewelry.

Cadmium-base bearing metals are used for high-speed automotive, aircraft, and marine engines that operate at high temperatures. There are two types: one containing about 1 per cent nickel and the remainder cadmium, the other containing 0.7 per cent silver and 0.6 per cent copper with 98 per cent or more of cadmium. Because of the low acid resistance of cadmium and consequent attack by organic acids in lubricants, a coating of indium is sometimes applied to the cadmium bearing to reduce the acid attack.[67] Some lead-antimony-tin bearing metals also contain small amounts of cadmium for increased strength.

Cadmium is a constituent of many solders. Zinc-tin alloys are used for high-temperature solders. At times when tin was scarce, owing to war or other disruptions, cadmium has been substituted in whole or in part for tin in many of the soft solders, particularly in lead-tin and lead-tin-copper alloys. Alloys of silver and cadmium, along with varying proportions of copper, zinc, and sometimes other metals, are widely used for brazing. This series of alloys can be used to make satisfactory joints with both ferrous and nonferrous metals. Some of them have been successfully used with such difficult materials as tungsten, tungsten carbide, and molybdenum. Certain of these solders are used, with or without gold, in the jewelry trade.[50]

Low-melting alloys, containing varying quantities of bismuth, lead, tin, and cadmium, are used in sprinkler systems, fire-detection units, and similar applications, as well as for low-temperature brazing and soldering. Some of these alloys are used for proof casting of materials where accurate casting is important.

The addition of cadmium in small amounts to copper gives an alloy with almost as high electrical conductivity as pure copper, and it has the added advantage of better strength and hardness.

Cadmium sulfide and sulfoselenide are used as colored pigments. The cadmium halides are used in photography.

High-purity, crystalline cadmium sulfide is being used in photovoltaic cells, radiation detection devices, infrared windows, and photosensitive elements. One description of the manufacture of these high-purity crystals has been published.[46] One of the intriguing uses is in solar cells for conversion of sunlight into electrical energy. Experimental devices have been made which have better conversion efficiency than those made with other materials.

A small but important scientific use of cadmium is in the Weston standard cell, which is the working standard for the United States in maintaining the value of the volt.[14] The absolute standard cell is composed of 12.5 per cent cadmium—87.5 per cent mercury (by weight) amalgam, with cadmium sulfate crystals and saturated cadmium sulfate solution as the negative half and mercury, mercurous sulfate, cadmium sulfate crystals, and saturated cadmium sulfate solution as the positive half. A "working" standard cell, which is portable, has no cadmium sulfate crystals, and the cadmium sulfate solutions are saturated at 4°C (39.2°F), giving an unsaturated solution at room temperature. The "working" cell has an emf of very close to 1.0186 volts.[17]

Another use of cadmium is in the nickel-cadmium storage battery. In this cell the negative plates comprise iron grids with sponge cadmium (and iron) as the active agent and the positive plates (also of iron grids) have a nickel oxide as the active ingredient. The electrolyte is an aqueous solution of potassium hydroxide; sometimes lithium hydroxide is added. A careful study of the comparative behavior of lead-acid and nickel-cadmium storage cells[80] shows only minor advantages over the lead-acid type. For heavy-duty use, however, these batteries have given excellent service.

Special purpose nickel-cadmium batteries of a design different from those described in the previous paragraph have found acceptance, particularly in smaller sizes. These batteries have as their negative plates sponge cadmium on a nickel grid; the positive plates are of nickel oxide on a nickel grid. The electrolyte is an aqueous solution of potassium hydroxide. This cell has certain specific advantages and is being manufactured for use as a power component in guided missiles.

Although nuclear reactors do not rate as a major consumer of cadmium, their use of this metal is important. Cadmium has the ability to filter out low energy (thermal) neutrons, and, when rods of cadmium are inserted in a reactor, this absorption of thermal neutrons provides a method for controlling the chain reaction. With proper adjustment of the cadmium rods, the rate of nuclear fission and production of heat can be controlled to provide the desired energy or, if necessary, to stop the reaction.[53] Cadmium can also be used as a container for the uranium elements, because of the same properties described for its use in the atomic reactor.

References

1. Abel, E., Redlich, O., and Adler, J., *Z. anorg. u. allgem. Chem.*, **174**, 269 (1928).
2. Ahrens, L. H., *S. African J. Sci.*, **41**, 152 (1945).
3. ASTM, "Methods for Chemical Analysis of Metals," pp. 411–412, Philadelphia, 1950.
4. ASTM, "Methods for Chemical Analysis of Metals," p. 431, Philadelphia, 1956.
5. ASTM, *ibid.*, p. 521.
6. ASTM, *ibid.*, p. 554.
7. Atomic Energy Commission, "Liquid-Metals Handbook," 2nd Ed., p. 40, Washington, D.C., Government Printing Office, 1952.
8. Barlow, E., *J. Am. Chem. Soc.*, **32**, 1390 (1910).
9. Blum, W., and Hogaboom, G. B., "Principles of Electroplating and Electroforming," New York, McGraw-Hill Book Company, Inc., 1949.
10. Bray, J. L., "Non-Ferrous Production Metallurgy," New York, John Wiley & Sons, Inc., 1941.
11. Bruderlin, E. J., U.S. Patent 2,178,366 (Oct. 31, 1939).
12. Bruni, G., Sandonini, C., and Quereigh, E., *Z. anorg. Chem.*, **68**, 73 (1910).
13. Budgen, N. F., "Cadmium: Its Metallurgy, Properties and Uses," London, Charles Griffin & Co., Ltd., 1924.
14. *Bur. Standards Bull.*, **4**, p. 1 (1907); *Bur. Standards Circ. 29.*
15. Chikashige-Hitosaka, *Mem. Coll. Sci. Univ. Kyoto*, **2**, 233 (1917).
16. Clara Di Capera, *Atti reale accad. Lincei*, (5), **31**, 1 (1922).
17. Dole, M., "Principles of Experimental and Theoretical Electrochemistry," New York, McGraw-Hill Book Company, Inc., 1935.
18. Donski, L., *Z. anorg. Chem.*, **57**, 185 (1908).
19. Everhart, J. L., Lindlief, W. E., Kanegis, J., Weissler, P. G., and Siegel, F., *Natl. Bur. Standards (U.S.), Circ. No. C447*, p. 459 (1943).
20. Gautier, H., *Bull. soc. encour. ind. natl.*, **5**, 1315 (1896).
21. Grube, G., Vosskukler, H., and Vogt, H., *Z. Elektrochem.*, **38**, 869–80 (1932).
22. Gulliver, G. H., "Metallic Alloys," London, Charles Griffith & Co., Ltd., 1921.
23. Gwyer, A. G. C., *Z. anorg. Chem.*, **57**, 113 (1908).
24. Hanson, D., and Pell-Walpole, W. T., *J. Inst. Metals*, **56**, advance copy No. 686, 449–70 (1935).
25. Herman, K. S. L., *Gilbert's Ann.*, **59**, 95, 113 (1818).
26. Hirdicks, G., *Z. anorg. Chem.*, **55**, 415 (1907).
27. Hofman, H. O., "Metallurgy of Zinc and Cadmium," New York, McGraw-Hill Book Company, Inc., 1922.
28. Hume-Rothery, W., and Rowell, S. W., *J. Inst. Metals*, **445**, advance copy, 18 pp. (1927).
29. Huttl, J. B., *Eng. Mining J.*, **147**, 82–85 (1946).
30. Ingalls, W. R., "The Metallurgy of Zinc and Cadmium," *Eng. Mining J.* (1906).

31. Isaac, E., and Tamman, G., *Z. anorg. Chem.*, **55**, 58 (1907).

32. Johnstone, R. T., "Occupational Medicine and Industrial Hygiene," pp. 265–276, St. Louis, The C. V. Mosby Company, 1948.

33. Kapp, A., *Ann. phys.*, **6**, 754 (1901).

34. Kapp, A., *Drudes. Ann.*, 6754 (1901) Dissert., Konigsberg.

35. Karsten, C. J. B., *Archiv. Berg. Hutt.*, **1**, 209 (1819).

36. Kolthoff, I. M., and Lingane, J. J., "Polarography," 2nd Ed., New York, Interscience Publishers, Inc., 1952.

37. Kurnakoff, N. S., *Z. anorg. chem.*, **23**, 439 (1900).

38. Kurnakoff, N. S., *ibid.*, **52**, 173 (1907).

39. LeBlanc, M., and Schopel, H., *Z. Elektrochem.*, **39**, 695–701 (1953).

40. Leverett, W. H., U.S. Patent 2,138, 281 (Nov. 29, 1938).

41. Liddell, D. M., "Handbook of Nonferrous Metallurgy. Recovery of the Metals," New York, McGraw-Hill Book Company, Inc., 1945.

42. Lorenz, R., and Plumbridge, D., *Z. anorg. Chem.*, **83**, 228 (1913).

43. Mantell, C. L., "Industrial Electrochemistry," New York, McGraw-Hill Book Company, Inc., 1940.

44. Masing, G., and Tamman, G., *Z. anorg. Chem.*, **67**, 183 (1910).

45. Matthewson, C. H., *Z. anorg. Chem.*, **50**, 180 (1906).

46. Medcalf, W. E., and Fahrig, R. H., *J. Electrochem. Soc.*, **105**, 719 (1958).

47. Mehl, R. F., and Barrett, C. S., *Am. Inst. Mining Met. Engrs., Tech. Publ. No. 225*, 16 pp. (1929).

48. Meissner, W., *Gilbert's Ann.*, **59**, 99 (1818).

49. Mentch, R. L., and Lansche, A. M., *U.S. Bur. Mines, Inform. Circ. No. 7881* (1958).

50. "Minerals Yearbook (U.S. Bur. Mines)," Washington, D.C., Government Printing Office, 1944.

51. "Minerals Yearbook (U.S. Bur. Mines)," Washington, D.C., Government Printing Office, 1945.

52. "Minerals Yearbook (U.S. Bur. Mines)," Washington, D.C., Government Printing Office, 1950.

53. "Minerals Yearbook (U.S. Bur. Mines)," Washington, D.C., Government Printing Office, 1957.

54. Murakami, T., and Shinagawa, T., *Kinzoku-no-Kenkyu*, **5**, 283–96 (1928).

55. National Research Council, "International Critical Tables of Numerical Data, Physics, Chemistry and Technology," Vol. V, p. 249, New York, McGraw-Hill Book Company, Inc., 1926.

56. Peirce, W. M., and Waring, R. K., *Trans. Am. Inst. Mining Met. Engrs.*, **121**, 445–52 (1936).

57. Pozodin, S. A., Mikheeva, V. I., and Kagan, G. A., *Ann. inst. anal. phys. chim. (U.S.S.R.)*, **7**, 39–47 (1935).

58. Puschin, N. A., *Z. anorg. Chem.*, **30**, 101 (1902).

59. Rankama, Kalervo, and Sahama, Th. G., "Geochemistry," p. 712, Chicago, University of Chicago Press, 1949.

60. Reiningham, P., and Kremmann, R., *Z. Metallk.*, **12**, 273 (1920).

61. Rossini, F. D., Wagman, D. D., Evans, W. H., Levine, S., and Jaffe, I., *Natl. Bur. Standards (U.S.), Circ. No. 500*, pp. 653, 667, 670 (1952).

62. Rydberg, J. R., *Z. physik. Chem.*, **33**, 353 (1900).

63. Sahmen, R., *Z. anorg. Chem.*, **49**, 301 (1906).

64. Schemtschusehny, *J. Soc. Chem. Ind.*, 1209 (1911).

65. Schoofs, J., *Rev. universelle mines*, **6**, 278–84 (1950).

66. Schulze, G. E. R., *Z. Metallk.*, **32**, 252 (1940); *Met. Abstr.* (in *J. Inst. Metals*), **8**, 326 (1941).

67. Smart, C. F., *Trans. Am. Inst. Mining Met. Engr.*, **128**, 295–310 (1938).

68. Soderberg, G., and Westbrook, L. R., *Trans. Electrochem. Soc.*, **80**, 429 (1941).

69. Stieglitz, Julius, "The Elements of Qualitative Chemical Analysis," Vol. 2, New York, Century Company, 1911.

70. Stoffel, A., *Z. anorg. Chem.*, **53**, 137 (1907).

71. Strohmeyer, F., *Schweigger's Journal*, **22**, 362 (1818).

72. Stull, D. R., *Ind. Eng. Chem.*, **39**, 540 (1947).

73. Swartz, C. E., and Phillips, A. J., *Am. Inst. Mining Met. Engrs., Inst. Metals Div., Contrib. No. 55* (1933).

74. Teats, R., U.S. Patent 1,727,492 (Sept. 10, 1929).

75. Treitschke, W., *Z. anorg. Chem.*, **50**, 217 (1906).

76. Uhlig, H. H., "The Corrosion Handbook," New York, John Wiley & Sons, Inc., 1948.

77. Vogel, R., *Z. anorg. Chem.*, **48**, 333 (1906).

78. Voss, G., *Z. anorg. Chem.*, **57**, 34 (1908).

79. Wilkinson, W. D., "Properties of Gallium," ANL-4109, Chicago, Argonne National Laboratory, 1948.

80. Willihnganz, E., "Is There a Lifetime Battery?" paper presented at the convention of the Association of American Battery Manufacturers, Inc., Chicago (November, 1948).

81. Wilson, C. L., and Wick, O. J., *Ind. Eng. Chem.*, **29**, 1164 (1937).

7. CHROMIUM

R. W. FOUNTAIN

Metals Research Laboratories
Union Carbide Metals Company
Niagara Falls, New York

The element chromium was first isolated in 1797 by Vauquelin from the mineral crocoite, which was discovered in 1765 in Russia by Pallas. Its name was derived from the Greek word *chromos,* meaning color, because of the varied colors of its compounds. The green color of emerald, serpentine, and chrome mica and the red color of ruby are caused by chromium.

Chromium ores were first used to make chromium chemicals about 1800 and were first employed as a refractory in 1879. Although a patent was granted on a chromium steel in 1865, it was not until about 1910 that chromium became important metallurgically.

OCCURRENCE AND CHARACTERISTICS

Chromium is widely distributed in the rocks of the earth's crust, and ranks in abundance as the twenty-first element. Its average percentage is very small, 0.035.

Although chromium is widely dispersed in natural deposits, it is never found in the uncombined state. Virtually all ores of chromium are made up of the mineral chromite, which is composed primarily of iron oxide and chromium oxide and corresponds ideally to the formula $FeO \cdot Cr_2O_3$, containing 68 per cent Cr_2O_3 and 32 per cent FeO. The chemical composition of the better grades of chrome ore varies between 42 to 56 per cent Cr_2O_3 and 10 to 26 per cent FeO. The ore, as mined, also contains varying amounts of magnesia, alumina, and silica. The major producing countries are Southern Rho-desia, U.S.S.R., Union of South Africa, Turkey, Cuba, New Caledonia, and the Philippines.

Chromite, the most important source of chromium, is an insoluble mineral which crystallizes, in the isometric system, in octahedrons. It is brittle, fractures unevenly, and has a hardness of about 5.5 on Mohs scale. Its specific gravity ranges from 4.1 to 4.9. The color of chromite varies from jet black to brownish black. In thin sections it is translucent to opaque; the high-chrome varieties are red brown, and the high-alumina varieties are more coffee-colored. Chromite may be weakly magnetic.

Chromite deposits are associated with peridotites and pyroxenites or with the serpentine resulting from the alteration of those two rocks. The chromite occurs as disseminated grains, or as lenses and tabular masses. Thayer[81] finds a correlation between the composition of the chromite and the associated rocks. He says, "High-alumina chromites occur in peridotitic masses which contain feldspathic members, and high-chrome chromites occur in feldspar-free peridotites low in alumina and iron. The high-iron chromites of the Bushveld type apparently resulted from crystallization in pyroxenic environments deficient in alumina and relatively rich in iron."

Most of the ores are of a sufficiently high grade to be marketed without dressing except for hand picking. With disseminated ores, however, table concentration can frequently be used to produce a concentrate with about 50 per cent Cr_2O_3. It is not common practice to beneficiate chrome ores; although it may improve the Cr_2O_3 content, it does not generally improve the chromium-to-iron ratio. The total production of chromite in various countries from 1948 to 1958 is given in Table 7.1.[56]

The softening point of chrome ore varies from 1260–1425°C (2300–2597°F), depending largely on the impurity content. Chromite is chemically neutral and almost insoluble in most slags, but its reactivity increases and its refractoriness decreases with increase in the amount of iron it contains.

TABLE 7.1. WORLD PRODUCTION OF CHROMITE, BY COUNTRIES
1948 to 1952 (Average) and 1953 to 1958 (Short Tons)[56]*

Country	1948–52 (average)	1953	1954	1955	1956	1957	1958
North America							
Canada	415						
Cuba	92,745	77,205	80,011	85,107	59,248	127,126	82,801
Guatemala	477	441	146	320	979	1,200	
United States	6,563	58,817	163,365	153,253	207,662	166,157	143,795
Total	100,200	136,463	243,522	238,680	267,889	294,483	227,696
South America							
Brazil	2,187	3,942	2,108	4,546	4,536	4,000	2,899
Europe							
Albania	48,600	51,800	110,200	135,000	147,000	184,400	221,800
Greece	16.612	40,520	29,508	27,902	53,581	49,135	25,550
Portugal	99	6	23				
U.S.S.R. (est.)	580,000	600,000	600,000	600,000	600,000	600,000	880,000
Yugoslavia	108,760	139,950	137,216	139,119	130,913	132,570	125,188
Total (est.)	765,000	900,000	900,000	900,000	1,000,000	1,000,000	1,274,538
Asia							
Afghanistan	448						
Cyprus (exports)	14,629	9,115	10,080	9,599	6,526	5,678	13,260
India	24,996	72,543	50,968	100,071	59,009	87,968	67,668
Iran	6,355	23,657	23,406	38,504	29,700	27,600	27,558
Japan	34,767	41,418	36,138	29,269	43,947	51,050	46,078
Pakistan	19,756	26,255	24,527	31,808	25,487	20,000	26,935
Philippines	359,837	614,086	442,230	655,882	781,598	799,744	458,903
Turkey	566,038	1,005,883	619,001	710,253	918,308	772,368	524,000
Total	1,026,826	1,792,957	1,206,350	1,575,386	1,864,575	1,764,408	1,564,402
Africa							
Egypt	61	231	584	926	281		110
Rhodesia and Nyasaland, Federation of Southern Rhodesia	306,149	463,028	442,506	449,202	448,965	654,072	618,841
Sierra Leone	17,159	27,277	21,011	23,231	21,900	18,344	12,556
Union of South Africa	537,593	798,562	706,935	597,368	690,851	722,588	696,057
Total	860,962	1,289,098	1,171,036	1,070,727	1,161,997	1,395,004	1,327,564
Oceania							
Australia	1,088	3,070	5,536		6,828	3,650	660
New Caledonia	98,175	134,032	93,645	50,790	53,932	71,100	52,249
Total	99,263	137,102	99,181	50,790	60,760	74,750	52,909
World total estimate	2,855,000	4,300,000	3,600,000	3,800,000	4,400,000	4,500,000	4,050,000

* Compiled by Pearl J. Thompson and Berenice B. Mitchell.

USES OF CHROMIUM ORE

Chrome ores or concentrates are generally classified into three main groups: (1) metallurgical, (2) refractory, and (3) chemical.

Metallurgical chromite normally requires a minimum of 48 per cent Cr_2O_3 with a chromium-to-iron ratio of 3:1. Generally, a hard, lumpy ore is preferred, but, for certain metallurgical applications, a soft ore or chromite concentrate can be used.

Refractory ores, used in making chrome brick, chrome-magnesite brick, plastic cement, and other refractory products, are high in Cr_2O_3 plus Al_2O_3 and relatively low in iron and silica. The refractoriness of chrome brick is limited principally by the silicate binding rather than the chrome itself, requiring that the amount of silica and fluxes be kept to a minimum. In practice, an excess of magnesium oxide is added to all chrome ore to combine with all the silica to form the magnesium silicate, forsterite, during firing.

Chemical-grade ore should be as high in Cr_2O_3 and as low in SiO_2 and Al_2O_3 as possible. Specifications are more variable than for the metallurgical and refractory grade and usually are determined for each ore on a basis of price, availability, and past experience.

Of the total chromite consumed in the United States, approximately 65 per cent is for metallurgical use, about 25 per cent for refractories, and the balance chemical. The consumption of chromite and tenor of ore used by these primary consumer groups in the United States from 1948 to 1957 is given in Table 7.2.[56]

CHROMIUM METAL

Two broad classes of chromium available to industry are ferrochromium and chromium metal. Ferrochromium can be produced by the direct reduction of ore without the removal of iron, whereas chromium metal can be produced electrolytically, or by the reduction of chromium salts, oxides, or iodides, only after a previous chemical treatment to remove iron and other elements. A discussion of the various grades of ferrochromium and their production is beyond the scope of this chapter. For information on ferrochromium, the reader is referred to the reviews by Udy[83] and Sully.[79]

Chromium metal of various degrees of purity is produced by several processes which will be described.

Alumino- and Silicothermic Chromium

Commercially pure chromium metal has been produced in large amounts by the Goldschmidt[29] process which is based on the following reaction:

$$Cr_2O_3 + 2Al \rightarrow 2Cr + Al_2O_3$$

The charge of Cr_2O_3 and aluminum powder is placed in a refractory-lined container and ignited. The container is generally preheated, and the mix is ignited with barium peroxide and powdered magnesium. As the reaction is highly exothermic, once started, it is self-sustaining. Chromium metal of about 97 to 99 per cent purity can be made in this manner. The principal impurities are aluminum, iron,

TABLE 7.2. CONSUMPTION OF CHROMITE AND TENOR OF ORE USED BY PRIMARY CONSUMER GROUPS IN THE UNITED STATES[56]

Years	Metallurgical		Refractory		Chemical		Total	
	Gross weight (short tons)	Average Cr_2O_3 (%)	Gross weight (short tons)	Average Cr_2O_3 (%)	Gross weight (short tons)	Average Cr_2O_3 (%)	Gross weight (short tons)	Average Cr_2O_3 (%)
1948 to 1952 (average)	485,064	47.8	355,643	34.0	144,516	44.6	985,223	42.4
1953	742,822	46.3	441,155	33.6	151,778	44.5	1,335,755	42.7
1954	502,278	46.3	278,324	34.3	133,371	44.6	913,973	42.4
1955	993,653	46.5	431,407	34.4	158,923	44.8	1,583,983	43.0
1956	1,211,914	46.8	474,562	34.4	160,124	45.4	1,846,600	43.5
1957	1,117,073	47.1	434,922	34.8	148,474	45.0	1,760,469	43.9
1958	777,682	46.9	311,911	35.2	131,156	45.6	1,220,749	43.8
1959	795,971	46.7	379,300	34.6	161,625	44.5	1,336,896	43.1

and silicon. The carbon, sulfur, and nitrogen content may be of the order of 0.03, 0.02, and 0.045 per cent, respectively.

Commercially pure chromium metal is also made by the reduction of chromic oxide with silicon. This process is performed in an electric arc furnace, as it is not sufficiently exothermic for the reaction to be self-sustaining. The equation for the reaction is:

$$2Cr_2O_3 + 3Si \rightarrow 4Cr + 3SiO_2$$

This product is similar to that made by the aluminothermic process, except that the aluminum content is much lower, and the silicon may be present in amounts as high as 0.8 per cent.

Carbon-Reduced Chromium

In addition to the above processes, chromium metal is also produced by the reduction of the oxide with carbon.[20] This process, performed at low pressure, is based on the reaction

$$Cr_2O_3 + 3C \rightarrow 2Cr + 3CO$$

A mixture of Cr_2O_3 and finely divided carbon is briquetted, placed in a suitable refractory container, and heated to temperatures in the range of 1275–1400°C (2327–2552°F). The pressure maintained during the process is dependent upon the temperature. The minimum pressure for a reduction temperature of 1400°C (2552°F) is about 280 to 315 μ. Pressures lower than this result in unnecessary loss of chromium by volatilization. The carbon, nitrogen, and oxygen contents of this product are reported to be 0.015, 0.001, and 0.04 per cent, respectively, the silicon content is about 0.02 per cent, and the iron is less than 0.03 per cent.

Electrolytic Chromium

The electrowinning of chromium has been studied for many years.[2, 13, 18, 52, 53, 54, 71] The present two commercial processes are based on: (1) chromium-alum electrolytes,[16, 17] or (2) chromic acid electrolytes.[33, 87]

Chromium-Alum Process. A typical chromium-alum electrolyte process is that used by the Union Carbide Metals Company at its Marietta, Ohio, plant.[16] The capacity of this plant is about 2,000 net tons/year of chromium metal. The flow sheet for this process for the

production of chromium from ferrochromium is shown diagrammatically in Figure 7.1.[16] High-carbon ferrochromium, sized to pass through a 20-mesh screen, is treated with a mixture of reduced anolyte, chromium-alum mother liquor, and make-up sulfuric acid at a temperature near the boiling point. After leaching, the slurry is cooled to 80°C (176°F), or lower, with cold mother liquor from the ferrous ammonium sulfate crystallization. The undissolved solids, mostly silica, are separated and discarded. The chromium in the filtrate is converted to the nonalum-forming modification by holding at an elevated temperature for several hours.

This conditioned liquor is pumped into a batch-type crystallizer, and the temperature is reduced to 5°C (41°F) in order to separate the iron as ferrous ammonium sulfate crystals. After this separation, the mother liquor is clarified and sent to the aging circuit. Aging and crystallization are carried on at approximately 30°C (86°F), and about 80 per cent of the chromium is precipitated as ammonium chrome alum. The crystal slurry is filtered and washed; the filtrate is returned to the leach circuit, and the washed chromium-alum crystals are dissolved in hot water to produce cell feed. Typical analyses of the various solutions and crystals from the chemical circuit are shown in Tables 7.3 and 7.4.[16]

Successful electrodeposition of chromium requires control of the pH of the catholyte between relatively narrow limits and preservation of the divalent chromium formed at the cathode. Sulfuric and chromic acids formed at the anode must be prevented from mixing with the catholyte, in order to prevent oxidation of the divalent chromium and to maintain pH control. Cell feed is supplied continuously to the operating cells to maintain the chromium concentration within optimum limits. The pH of the catholyte in each cell is controlled by adjusting the amount of catholyte flowing through the diaphragms into the anolyte chambers. Typical analyses of the solutions in the electrolytic circuit and cell-operating data are given in Tables 7.5 and 7.6.[16]

A general view of the cell room at the Marietta Plant is given in Figure 7.2.

The chromium stripped from the cathodes varies between 1/8 and 1/4 in. in thickness. The appearance of the metal is shown in Figure

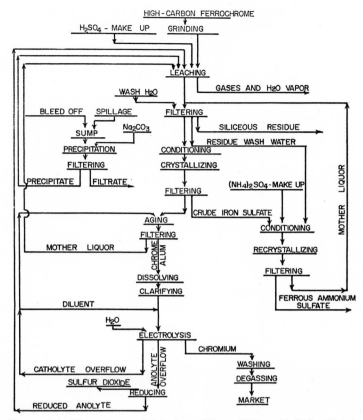

Figure 7.1. Flow sheet of Marietta Plant, Union Carbide Metals Company, for production of electrolytic chromium. (*Courtesy M. C. Carosella and J. D. Mettler.*)

TABLE 7.3. TYPICAL ANALYSIS OF SOLUTIONS IN CHEMICAL CIRCUIT (CHROMIUM-ALUM PROCESS)[16]

Solution	Composition (g/liter)			
	Cr	Fe	NH₃	Free H₂SO₄
Leach filtrate	72	19.0	75	85
Residue wash water	4	2.0	2	4
Crude iron mother liquor	73	4.0	80	87
Ferrous ammonium sulfate mother liquor	35	7.0	80	5
Chromium-alum mother liquor	20	5.0	64	95
Cell feed	130	0.2	43	3

TABLE 7.4. TYPICAL ANALYSIS OF CRYSTALS PRODUCED IN CHEMICAL CIRCUIT (CHROMIUM-ALUM PROCESS)[16]

Type crystals	Composition (%)		
	Cr	Fe	NH₃
Crude iron sulfate	3.4	6.5	6.7
Ferrous ammonium sulfate	0.4	10.0	7.0
Chromium-alum	9.1	0.01	3.0

TABLE 7.5. TYPICAL ANALYSES OF SOLUTIONS IN ELECTROLYTIC CIRCUIT (CHROMIUM-ALUM PROCESS)[16]

	Chromium (g/liter)						
	Total	+6	+3	+2	Fe	NH₃	H₂SO₄
Cell feed	130	0	130.0	0.0	0.200	43	3
Circulating mixture	65	0	63.0	2.0	0.100	68	1
Catholyte	23	0	11.5	12.5	0.035	84	
Anolyte	15	13	2.0	0.0	0.023	24	280

TABLE 7.6. CELL-OPERATING DATA
(CHROMIUM-ALUM PROCESS)[16]

Cathode current density	70 amp/sq ft
Cell potential	4.2 volts
Current efficiency	45%
Electrical consumption	8.4*
pH	2.1 to 2.4
Catholyte temperature	53° ± 1°C
	(125.5–129.2° F)
Time of deposition	72 hr
Cathode material	Type 316 stainless
Anode material	1–99 silver-lead

* KWH of alternating current to motor generators per pound of metal produced.

TABLE 7.7. AERONAUTICAL RESEARCH LABORATORIES
PRACTICE FOR ELECTRODEPOSITION OF CHROMIUM
(CHROMIC ACID PROCESS)[87]

Condition	A.R.L. practice
Bath composition	300 g/liter chromic acid;
	4 g/liter sulfate ion
Temperature	84–85°C (183–185° F)
Current density	880 amp/sq ft
Current efficiency	6–7%
Plating time	80–90 hr
Production rate	1,000 g/week

Figure 7.2. General view of cell room at Marietta Plant, Union Carbide Metals Co., for the production of electrolytic chromium. The type 316 stainless steel cathodes, on which the chromium is deposited, are being removed from a cell. They are withdrawn on a 72-hour cycle, and the brittle chromium deposit is then stripped from them with air hammers.

Figure 7.3. Chromium metal, after being stripped from the cathodes, is between ⅛ and ¼ inch thick. The smooth side of the chips was that against the cathode, the rough side that facing the electrolyte. (*Courtesy Union Carbide Metals Co.*)

7.3. Its typical analysis is chromium, 99.8 per cent;* iron, 0.14 per cent; carbon, 0.01 per cent; silicon, nil; phosphorus, nil; sulfur, 0.025 per cent; aluminum, nil; manganese, nil; copper, 0.001 per cent; and lead, 0.002 per cent. The metal will contain about 0.5 per cent oxygen, 0.004 per cent hydrogen, and < 0.01 per cent nitrogen.

Chromic Acid Process. Chromium is also produced by the electrolysis of chromic acid.[33, 87] The cell used at the Aeronautical Research Laboratories in Australia for this process is shown in Figure 7.4.[87] The cell conditions employed are shown in Table 7.7.[87]

The effect of the plating variables on the electrodeposition of chromium from the chromic acid bath has been the subject of a detailed study which may be summarized as follows:

1. With higher operating temperatures [87°C (189°F)], it is possible to reduce the oxygen content of the deposited metal to 0.01 per cent.

2. The CrO_3 to SO_4 ratio should be kept below 100 to obtain low-oxygen metal.

* Metallic basis.

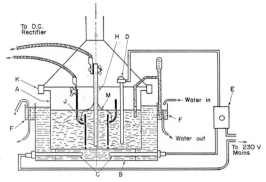

Figure 7.4. Apparatus for producing electrolytic chromium by electrolysis of chromic acid. (A) Lead-lined plating bath; (B) water jacket; (C) immersion heaters; (D) glass-sheathed thermostat; (E) hot-wire vacuum switch; (F) constant head devices; (H) copper cathode; (J) pure lead anode; (K) suction duct; (M) glass belt. (*Courtesy H. L. Wain.*)

3. Current efficiencies above about 8 per cent do not appear to be associated with low oxygen contents.

4. Low current densities favor better current efficiencies.

As can be seen in Table 7.8,[87] the purity of the chromium produced by electrolysis of chromic acid is considerably better than that resulting from the chrome-alum bath.

Oxygen Removal. Although the purity of the chromium resulting from the electrolysis of either chrome-alum or chromic acid electrolytes is superior to that produced by smelting techniques, it still has a high oxygen content. In studying the mechanical properties of electrolytic chromium, the generally accepted hypothesis has been that oxygen contamination was the principal cause of room-temperature brittleness. Therefore, techniques to remove oxygen have been considered, and three processes— hydrogen reduction,[28, 43, 50] the iodide process,[3, 8, 30, 86] and calcium refining[42]—will be discussed.

HYDROGEN-REDUCTION PROCESS. The hydrogen-reduction technique consists primarily of heating electrolytic chromium in a stream of purified dry hydrogen in the temperature range of 1200–1500°C (2192–2732°F). Although this process is effective in reducing the oxygen and also the nitrogen content, it has little effect on the metallic impurities. The results obtained on hydrogen reduction of electrolytic

TABLE 7.8. ANALYSIS OF ELECTRODEPOSITED CHROMIUM (CHROMIC ACID PROCESS)[87]

Element	Concentration*	Method of analysis
O_2	0.02	Chemical and vacuum fusion
N_2	0.0025	Chemical and vacuum fusion
H_2	0.009	Vacuum fusion
Cu	F.T. (0.002–0.003)	Spectroscopic
Ag	F.T. ($<$ 0.0005)	Spectroscopic
Mg	F.T. ($<$ 0.005)	Spectroscopic
B	F.T.? ($<$ 0.005)	Spectroscopic
Si	V.F.T. ($<$ 0.0005)	Spectroscopic
Ca	V.F.T. ($<$ 0.001)	Spectroscopic
Sb	N.D. ($<$ 0.003)	Spectroscopic
Co	N.D. ($<$ 0.01)	Spectroscopic
Ni	N.D. ($<$ 0.001)	Spectroscopic
Sn	N.D. ($<$ 0.0005)	Spectroscopic
Pb, Al, Fe, Zn, Ti	N.D.	Spectroscopic

* Concentration is in weight per cent. F.T. means faint trace; N.D. means not detected.

TABLE 7.9. PURIFICATION OBTAINED BY HYDROGEN REDUCTION OF CHROMIC ACID CHROMIUM[33]

Starting material		Treatment [hours at 1500°C (2732°F)]	Product	
O_2 (wt %)	N_2 (wt %)		O_2 (wt %)	N_2 (wt %)
0.11	0.002	3.5	0.020	$<$ 0.001
0.11	0.002	4.0	$<$ 0.005	0.001
0.12	—	3.0	0.020	$<$ 0.001
0.12	—	4.0	$<$ 0.005	$<$ 0.001
0.05	—	3.0	$<$ 0.005	$<$ 0.001

chromium from the chromic acid process are shown in Table 7.9.[33]

THE IODIDE PROCESS. The iodide process for preparing high-purity chromium from electrolytic chromium is based on the thermal decomposition of chromous iodide.

Cyclic Process. In the original van Arkel-deBoer apparatus, the impure chromium and iodine were sealed in an evacuated bulb containing a hot deposition surface, usually an electrically heated wire. The entire assembly was heated to a temperature at which iodine vapor reacts with chromium to form chromous iodide vapor. This diffuses to the hot surface where it dissociates to deposit chromium and release free iodine. The iodine then returns to form more chromous iodide, and the process continues. In the original process some gaseous and metallic impurities were carried over and deposited with the chromium. For this reason the cyclic process has been modified into a straight-flow process.

Straight-Flow Process. In this modified process the iodination and deposition steps are carried out separately.[8] The chromous iodide is separated from the residue of impurities and any unreacted chromium. The purified chromous iodide is then vaporized and passed over a hot surface where metallic chromium is deposited and the iodine is liberated. The chromous iodide is generally prepared at temperatures of about 900°C (1652°F), whereas the filament temperatures during deposition may vary from 1000–1300°C (1832–2372°F).

TABLE 7.10. REPRESENTATIVE ANALYSES FOR ELECTROLYTIC FEED CHROMIUM AND AS-DEPOSITED IODIDE CHROMIUM FROM WHICH IT WAS PREPARED[59]

Element	Composition (wt %)	
	Electrolytic feed material	As deposited*
O	0.380	0.0044
N	0.006	0.0013
H	0.0056†	0.00008
C	0.004	0.002
S	0.019	0.011
Al	0.005	N.D.‡
Ca	0.001	0.005
Cu	0.002	$<$ 0.001
Fe	N.D.	0.003
Mg	0.002	0.002
Mn	N.D.	
Mo	0.010	0.005
Ni	0.003	N.D.
Si	0.010	$<$ 0.005

* Prepared in "Vycor" unit.
† After degassing.
‡ N.D. designates not detected.

The efficiency of the straight-flow process is quite low; only about 10 per cent of the chromous iodide used is recovered as chromium per pass over the hot surface. In the van Arkel-deBoer process the recovery of the chromium is much higher, but, since it takes place in a sealed system, there is a greater probability of impurity transfer.

Representative analyses for iodide chromium made by the straight-flow process and the electrolytic chromium from which it was deposited are given in Table 7.10.[59]

CALCIUM-REFINING PROCESS. The calcium-refining technique consists of reacting chromium with calcium vapor at a temperature of about 1000°C (1832°F) in a titanium-lined bomb, the titanium acting as a getter to prevent nitrogen contamination.[42] Calcium metal, about 3 per cent of the total charge weight, is placed in one end of the reduction bomb, and chromium metal powder is placed above the calcium and separated from it by a 200-mesh stainless-steel screen. The sealed bomb is evacuated and then heated to the reaction temperature. During heating and outgassing, a pressure of about 20 μ is maintained until the calcium vapor sweeps up the bomb into the cold stem and condenses. This effectively seals off the vacuum line and allows the pressure of calcium vapor in the bomb to rise until the reaction temperature is reached. The total reaction time is about 14 hr. A representative analysis of the chromium produced by this technique is oxygen, 0.027 per

cent; nitrogen, 0.0018 per cent; carbon, 0.008 per cent; sulfur, 0.012 per cent; and iron, about 0.15 per cent.

The present costs of various grades of chromium metal are given in Table 7.11. The increase in purity is reflected in the price of the product.

PHYSICAL PROPERTIES OF CHROMIUM

Chromium is one of the transition elements in Group VIA of the periodic table with an atomic number of 24[62] and an atomic weight of 52.01.[62] The general physical properties of chromium are given in Table 7.12.

Electronic Structure

In the solid or gas phase, chromium has the following electronic structure:[41]

$$(1s)^2 \ (2s)^2 \ (2p)^6 \ (3s)^2 \ (3p)^6 \ (3d)^5 \ (4s)^1$$

Values of the electronic radii of the various orbits as well as their ionization potentials have also been obtained.[75]

Thermal Properties

Latent heat of vaporization at the boiling point is 76,635 cal/mole.[46, 72] The temperature variation is given by[46]

$$\Delta H = 89,450 - 4.66 \ T \ (T, \ °K).$$

Latent heat of sublimation at 298°K is given as 89,368 cal/mole,[46] and the temperature variation is

$$\Delta H = 89,400 + 0.20 \ T - 1.48 \times 10^{-3} \ T^2 \ (T, \ °K).$$

The *vapor pressure* of chromium in atmospheres is given as a function of temperature (°K), as follows:[21]

10^{-6} atm	10^{-5} atm	10^{-4} atm	10^{-3} atm
1350 (solid)	1465	1600	1755

10^{-2} atm	1 atm
1960	2495 (liquid)

The *coefficient of thermal expansion* as a function of temperature in the range of −100 to 700°C (−148 to 1292°F) is given as:[39,40]

$$\alpha_t = 5.88 \times 10^{-6} + 1.548 \times 10^{-8}t - 1.163 \times 10^{-11}t^2 \ (t, \ °C).$$

TABLE 7.11. REPRESENTATIVE PRICES OF VARIOUS GRADES OF CHROMIUM METAL COMMERCIALLY AVAILABLE

	Present price/pound
Aluminothermic chromium	$1.00–$1.29
Electrolytic chromium	$1.15–$1.19*
Vacuum-grade electrolytic chromium	$1.19–$1.23†
Laboratory-grade electrolytic chromium	$4.50‡
High-purity chromium	$28.00
Calcium-refined chromium	$40.00–$50.00 (depending on amount)
Iodide chromium	$85.00–$125.00 (depending on amount)

* 99.8% chromium metallic base, 0.2% maximum iron.
† Low oxygen.
‡ Low oxygen, low nitrogen, 0.03% maximum iron.

TABLE 7.12. PHYSICAL PROPERTIES OF CHROMIUM

Property	Reported values	Reference	Preferred value	Reference
Atomic weight	52.01			
Atomic number	24			
Crystal structure [20°C (68°F)]	Body-centered cubic $a_0 = 2.8844$–2.8848 Å	24, 64, 80	2.8845 Å	64
Valence	2, 3, 6	62		
Density [20°C (68°F)]	7.18–7.20 g/cc	11	7.19	11
Specific heat [25°C (77°F)]	5.55 cal/mole/°C or 0.11 cal/g/°C	48		
Melting point	1845–1903°C (3353–3457°F)	9, 35, 91	1875°C	91
Boiling point (760 mm Hg)	2199–2660°C (3990–4820°F)	4, 34, 46, 77	2199°C	34
Linear coefficient of thermal expansion [20°C (68°F)]	6.2×10^{-6}/°C	39, 40		
Electrical resistivity {microhm-cm [20°C (68°F)]}	12.8–12.9	11, 24		
Modulus of elasticity [20°C (68°F)]	42×10^6 psi	58		
Isotopes	Cr^{50}–4.49% Cr^{53}–9.43% Cr^{52}–83.78% Cr^{54}–2.30%	72		
Thermal conductivity [20°C (68°F)]	0.16 cgs units	61		
Latent heat of fusion	3.2–3.64 kcal/mole	48, 57, 85	3.2 kcal/mole	48
Latent heat of vaporization	76.635 kcal/mole	46, 72		
Emissivity at 6690 Å	Solid 0.34; liquid 0.39	89		
Total emissivity at 100°C (212°F) (nonoxidizing atm)	0.08	26		
Reflectivity (silver = 100%)	λ, Å R% 1,300 14 2,000 37 3,000 67 5,000 70 10,000 63 40,000 88	19, 45		
Refractive index	$\mu = 1.64$ to 3.28 $\lambda = 2{,}570$ to 6,080	26		
Electrochemical equivalents (mg/coulomb)	Valence 6; 0.08983 Valence 3; 0.17965 Valence 2; 0.26949			
Standard electrode potential [25°C (77°F)]	Valence 0 to +3; 0.71 volt	51		

The *heat content, entropy,* and *free energy function* of chromium for various temperatures have also been reported.[47, 48]

Bridgman[12] has given the relationship between the *compressibility* and *pressure* (p, is in kg/sq cm) as follows:

$$\text{At } 30°\text{C}; \frac{\Delta V}{V_0} = -5.187 \times 10^{-7}p + 2.19 \times 10^{-12}p^2.$$

$$\text{At } 75°\text{C}; \frac{\Delta V}{V_0} = -5.310 \times 10^{-7}p + 2.19 \times 10^{-12}p^2.$$

It has been found that various physical properties of chromium show, as a function of temperature, certain anomalies which have not been satisfactorily explained. The most striking of these are the discontinuous changes which occur at almost the same temperature, 37°C (98.6°F), in Young's modulus,[11, 24, 67, 68] internal friction,[24, 69] resistivity,[24, 66] thermoelectric power,[24] and coefficient of thermal expansion[24] (Figure 7.5). These changes were originally thought to result from impurities in chromium but are now attributed to the properties of chromium itself. There are no indications of an allotropic transformation of chromium at the temperatures at which abnormal behavior takes place; the crystal structure remains body-centered cubic above

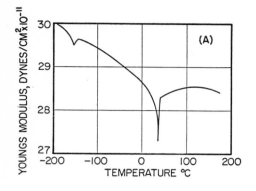

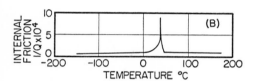

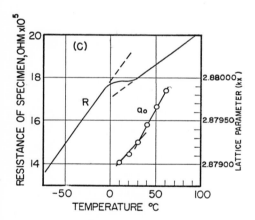

Figure 7.5. Thermal dependence of some physical properties of chromium. (A) Young's modulus: 1 dyne/sq cm = 1.4504 × 10⁻⁵ psi; (B) internal friction; (C) electrical resistance and lattice parameter. (*Courtesy M. E. Fine, et al.; A. H. Sully, et al.; M. E. Straumanis and C. C. Weng.*)

and below the transition,[24] and the lattice parameter shows only a slight break.[78] The difference between the variation of the lattice constant with temperature and the linear expansion data suggests, however, that there is a deviation from the ideal body-centered cubic arrangement, on passing through the transition, corresponding to a denser packing above the transition than below.

There also appears to be a relationship be-

tween the anomaly in Young's modulus and that in the volume expansivity of the material. The temperature at which the anomalies occur has been found to decrease with both compressive stress and the amount of impurities. If the anomalous volume change takes place in a compression test, there will be an apparent increase in strain parallel to the compression axis and a decrease normal to this axis, so that Young's modulus and Poisson's ratio will be simultaneously reduced. Direct experimental evidence of this phenomenon has been obtained, showing that, for certain chromium samples, the Poisson ratio may even become negative.[67]

Careful measurements have revealed that the lattice component of the thermal conductivity of chromium is surprisingly high, accounting for about one-third of the total thermal conductivity.[66] In this respect chromium differs from all other transition metals, a similar behavior being observed only in beryllium.[65] Chromium also exhibits, unlike other transition elements, a definite antiferromagnetic behavior, the Néel temperature being about 200°C (392°F).[90] The antiferromagnetism of chromium was detected only recently by neutron-diffraction studies and was not revealed earlier by measurements of the paramagnetic susceptibility.[24, 55]

CHEMICAL PROPERTIES

The chemical properties of chromium have been treated extensively elsewhere.[22, 60, 73, 82] The general corrosion characteristics of chromium in selected aqueous solutions are given in Table 7.13.[84]

Chromium reacts with the anhydrous halogens, hydrogen chloride, and hydrogen fluoride. Aqueous hydrofluoric acid, hydrochloric acid, hydrogen bromide, and hydrogen iodide will dissolve chromium, as will dilute sulfuric acid. Hydrogen is evolved during the dissolution of chromium in dilute sulfuric acid, whereas in boiling concentrated sulfuric acid, sulfur dioxide is liberated. When exposed to fuming nitric acid or aqua regia at room temperature, chromium is not affected.

Certain acids, such as concentrated nitric, phosphoric, chloric, and perchloric, form a thin oxide layer on chromium, resulting in passivity. In this condition chromium displays quite outstanding corrosion resistance and is

TABLE 7.13. RESISTANCE OF ELECTRODEPOSITED CHROMIUM TO ACIDS, SALTS,
AND VARIOUS ORGANIC SUBSTANCES*[84]

	Penetration [inches per year (IPY)]	
Simple immersion test	12°C (54°F)	58°C (136°F)
Acids		
Acetic	0.000	0.015
Acetic (100% glacial)	0.000	0.008
Citric	0.000	0.007
Formic	0.000	1.200
Glycolic	0.000	0.023
Hydrobromic	0.001	0.186
Hydrofluoric	1.000	
Hydriodic	0.000	0.015
Nitric	0.000	0.012
Nitric (100% fuming)	0.000	0.005
Oxalic	0.000	0.001
Perchloric	0.001	0.042
Phenolsulfonic (ortho)	0.000	0.026
Phosphoric	0.001	0.034
Phosphoric (85%)	0.000	0.002
Sulfuric	0.011	10.000
Sulfuric (100%)	0.030	0.069
Tartaric	0.000	0.004
Trichloroacetic	0.001	0.103
Salts		
Aluminum chloride	0.000	0.003
Ammonium chloride	0.000	0.004
Barium chloride	0.000	0.001
Calcium chloride	0.000	0.000
Calcium hypochlorite	0.002	0.035
Chromic chloride	0.000	0.003
Cupric chloride	0.015	
Cupric nitrate	0.002	0.007
Ferric chloride	0.000	0.016
Magnesium chloride	0.000	0.000
Manganese chloride	0.000	0.000
Mercuric chloride	0.079	
Potassium chloride	0.000	0.000
Sodium chloride	0.000	0.000
Stannous chloride	0.000	0.035
Strontium chloride	0.000	0.000
Zinc chloride	0.000	0.001
Others		
Carbon tetrachloride (saturated solution)	0.000	0.000
Chlorobenzene (saturated solution)	0.000	0.000
Chlorobenzene (100%)	0.000	0.000
Chloroform (saturated solution)	0.000	0.000
Chloroform (100%)	0.000	0.000

* Concentrations 10% by weight for solid solutes or 10% by volume for liquids, unless otherwise stated.

TABLE 7.14. RATE OF ATTACK OF CHROMIUM EXPOSED TO HOT GASES
Milligrams/Square Decimeters/Day[38]

Gas	700°C (1290°F)	800°C (1470°F)	900°C (1650°F)	1000°C (1830°F)
Oxygen	47	97	220	630
Steam	5	37	117	210
Carbon dioxide	27	34	130	308
Sulfur dioxide	16	39	320	360

not attacked by dilute mineral acids. Dissolved oxygen is sufficiently oxidizing to maintain passivity in neutral solutions, but in solutions of low pH, stronger oxidizing agents must be present and the halogen acids absent to maintain the passive condition. The general corrosion resistance of chromium resembles that of the more highly alloyed stainless steels. Generally, chromium is cathodic to the common metals and alloys and, if galvanically coupled to them, tends to accelerate their rates of corrosion.

When exposed to elevated temperatures, about 600–700°C (1112–1292°F), chromium is attacked by alkali hydroxides but is unaffected by fused alkali carbonates. Sulfides are formed when chromium is reacted at 600–700°C (1112–1292°F) with sulfur vapor or hydrogen sulfide. It also reacts with sulfur dioxide in this temperature range. Oxidation of the metal takes place at about 1000°C (1832°F) in carbon monoxide, and it is attacked by phosphorus at about 800°C (1472°F). Ammonia reacts with chromium at 850°C (1562°F) to form a nitride, and hot nitric oxide forms both nitride and oxide with chromium. Calcium vapor has little effect on the metal at red heat.

When heated in air, chromium will form an oxide layer of Cr_2O_3, although it is relatively unaffected at room temperature by wet or dry air. At temperatures above its melting point, chromium will burn in oxygen.

Some data on the rate of attack of various atmospheres on cast chromium at elevated temperatures are given in Table 7.14.[38]

The valencies exhibited by chromium are: 6, which is very stable; 5, fairly certain, but unstable and rare; 4, probably nonexistent unless in the chromium phenyl compounds; 3, the most stable of all; 2, quite definite but unstable in air; 1, very improbable; and 0, in the carbonyl compound, $Cr(CO)_6$.

The first and second ionization potentials for chromium have been given as 6.74 and 16.6

volts, respectively. A value of 73 volts has been given for the fifth ionization potential, but this value is open to question.

ANALYSIS OF CHROMIUM

Chromium can be detected in compounds by the formation of a green borax bead, by the yellow color of chromates formed on fusion with potassium nitrate, and by the red-violet color produced by the reaction of hexavalent chromium with S-diphenylcarbazide. Qualitative spectrographic, x-ray, and polarographic techniques have also been used to detect the presence of chromium. Chromium is usually determined quantitatively by oxidation to dichromate followed by titration with a ferrous iron solution of known strength.

Analysis of chromium metal for impurities is readily performed using conventional analytical procedures. The analytical chemistry of chromium has been discussed in detail by Serfass and Muraca.[74]

CHROMIUM TOXICOLOGY

Pure metallic chromium, chromite, and trivalent compounds do not produce any serious damage to body tissue. The toxic action of chromium is confined to the hexavalent compounds.[23] These compounds exert an irritative, corrosive, and possibly toxic action on the human body. Under certain conditions the hexavalent compounds cause denaturation and precipitation of tissue proteins. Intimate contact, as in industrial exposure, will affect primarily the skin and respiratory tract. Skin contact may result in chrome ulcers and dermatitis. Inhalation of chromate dust or chromic acid mist may cause ulceration and perforation of the nasal septum as well as chronic irritation or congestion of the respiratory passages. There is increasing evidence that the incidence of cancer of the respiratory tract is abnormally high among workmen exposed to hexavalent chromium dusts in chromium refining. The maximum allowable concentration of dusts and mists in the air measured as CrO_3 has been stated to be 0.1 mg/cu m of air for daily 8-hr exposure.

MELTING AND FABRICATION

Because of the high melting point of chromium and its reactivity in the molten state, special precautions must be taken during the melting of chromium and chromium-base alloys. In the molten state chromium and its alloys react with atmospheric nitrogen and with carbon, and undesirable networks of nitride and carbide then form during casting. It is also necessary to take positive steps to eliminate oxygen, which is always present in chromium prepared by conventional methods unless it has been subjected to purification treatments prior to melting. Several of these difficulties can be overcome by the use of vacuum melting, either induction or arc. Under suitable conditions the nitrogen content of chromium-base alloys can be reduced to about 0.01 per cent or less, and with proper control carbon can be used as a deoxidizer to produce alloys with carbon and oxygen contents in the range of 0.01 per cent or less.[25] However, vacuum melting is hampered by the high vapor pressure of chromium and its reactivity with most crucible materials. Crucibles for melting chromium must be very refractory, and only the pure, sintered refractory oxides have sufficiently high softening temperatures. Zirconia[63] and beryllia[32] crucibles have been used, as well as alumina crucibles lined with thoria.[15]

Arc melting in a water-cooled mold under an inert atmosphere has been successfully applied to the melting of chromium as well as other refractory metals.[5, 27, 36] This method has the primary advantage that no refractory crucible is in contact with the molten metal. To obtain low-oxygen materials, however, the chromium must be subjected to an oxygen purification prior to melting.

Many of the difficulties associated with normal melting procedures can be overcome by powder metallurgy techniques. Usually, the chromium powder is pressed at about 40,000 to 60,000 psi, and frequently a binder is employed which is removed by heating the compacts to a temperature of about 300°C (572°F) prior to sintering at high temperatures. The vacuum sintering is frequently performed in two steps: first, sintering at about 1300°C (2372°F) to promote the removal of occluded and adsorbed gases, and then treating at 1500–1700°C (2372–3092°F) to obtain densification. If the chromium was purified prior to compacting, sintering can be performed in an atmosphere of purified hydrogen, helium, or argon.

If sufficiently pure, chromium possesses enough ductility at elevated temperatures to allow it to be hot-worked by most conventional techniques, such as forging, rolling, or extrusion. During furnacing for working, however, an inert atmosphere should be employed in order to prevent contamination. Arc-melted ingots have been forged and swaged in the temperature range of 800–850°C (1472–1562°F) after an initial anneal at 1200–1250°C (2192–2282°F) to relieve strains set up in the ingots during solidification.[27, 59, 70] The initial working should be done carefully until the original cast structure is broken down; heavier reductions can then be made. Rolling can also be employed after the initial breakdown, and rolling temperatures as low as 500°C (932°F) appear feasible. The original breakdown of the cast structure can also be performed by extrusion at about the same temperatures as forging.[10]

MECHANICAL PROPERTIES

Efforts to develop alloys consisting predominantly of chromium have been marked within the last 15 years. This interest was originally stimulated in the early days of World War II, since, at that time, cobalt and nickel were in limited supply and only small quantities were stockpiled. The selection of chromium appeared quite obvious for several reasons. On the surface, at least, chromium possesses many of the properties generally considered to be important for high-temperature applications. Its melting point is considerably in excess of that of iron, cobalt, and nickel; its specific gravity is slightly less; and chromium shows better resistance to deformation at elevated temperatures. It was also one of the first high-melting-point transition metals available in fairly large quantities. Although chromium has sufficient ductility to be worked at elevated temperatures, it generally

TABLE 7.15. ROOM-TEMPERATURE TENSILE PROPERTIES OF SWAGED IODIDE CHROMIUM ROD[58]

Condition	0.2% offset yield strength (psi)	Ultimate strength (psi)	Elongation, (% in ¾ in.)	Reduction in area (%)
Wrought [swaged at 800°C (1472°F) plus stress-relief annealed]	52,500	60,000	44	78
Recrystallized [heated to 816°C (1511°F) after swaging]	—	41,000	0	0

displays very limited, if any, ductility at room temperature. This fact, more than any other, has prevented the widespread practical utilization of chromium and chromium-base alloys. As a result, the mechanical properties of chromium have received considerable study, with particular attention being given to the ductile-to-brittle transition temperature.

The mechanical properties of chromium depend strongly on many factors, such as purity, prior mechanical history, grain size, strain rate, and surface condition. Carbon, sulfur, and nitrogen in very small amounts can destroy the ductility of the metal. Specimens containing more than 0.01 per cent carbon,[59] 0.015 per cent sulfur,[59] or about 0.02 per cent nitrogen[43] are brittle at room temperature. For this reason, the elimination of impurities is very important before determining the various mechanical properties of chromium.

TENSILE PROPERTIES

The room-temperature tensile properties of swaged iodide-chromium rod prepared from a tungsten arc-melted ingot are given in Table 7.15.[58] Both of these tests were performed using an extremely low rate of straining of 0.005 in./min.

The highest value of ductility reported prior to the data on the iodide chromium was from the work of Johansen and Asai.[43] These investigators, who studied the mechanical properties of electropolished, wrought-chromium wire prepared from hydrogen-reduced electrolytic chromium, obtained an elongation of 25 per cent with an ultimate strength of 70,000 psi, using an appreciably higher rate of straining (0.02 in./min). Wain et al.,[88] reported an elongation of 15 per cent, with yield and ultimate strengths of 55,000 and 74,000 psi, respectively, for hydrogen-reduced electrolytic chromium in the form of cold-rolled, electropolished sheet.

The tensile properties of fully recrystallized chromium have been determined at temperatures up to 800°C (1472°F) by Johansen et al.,[44] and their results are shown in Figure 7.6. Virtually no ductility was obtained below 350°C (662°F); above this temperature, the ductility increased abruptly, reaching a maximum of approximately 50 per cent elongation at 400°C (752°F). At 500°C (932°F) the elongation dropped to about 30 per cent, but subsequently increased with a further increase in test temperature. The ultimate tensile strength tended to increase with temperature, reaching a maximum of 40,000 psi at 500°C (932°F).

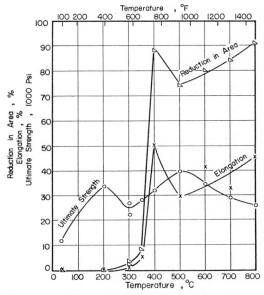

Figure 7.6. Effect of temperature on the strength and ductility of chromium rods. (*Courtesy Johansen, Gilbert, Nelson, and Carpenter.*)

TRANSITION TEMPERATURE

Chromium, similar to other body-centered cubic metals, displays a transition from ductile to brittle behavior. In the case of chromium the transition, which occurs continuously over a temperature range of perhaps 50–150°C (122–302°F) depending on the type of test employed and the other factors mentioned earlier, is from considerable ductility to complete brittleness. This behavior has received considerable study to determine the influence of impurities.

The ductile-to-brittle transition temperature of iodide chromium has been determined in a bend test on wrought sheet (0.015 to 0.030 in. thick), the bending stress being applied at a constant deflection rate of 0.05 in./min. The transition temperature was found to range from 0 to −20°C (32 to −4°F).[8] A transition temperature of cold-worked wire of −66°C (−87°F) has been reported by Johansen and Asai[43] in bending with a ram speed of 0.079 in./min. These results on the bend transition temperature of iodide and hydrogen-reduced chromium are substantially lower than the transition temperature of about 200°C (392°F) reported for less pure sintered chromium.[80] Sully has reported chromium to be sensitive to strain rate, the transition temperature being raised about 50°C (90°F) when the rate of straining is increased from about 0.003 to 0.77 in./min.[80]

The ductility of chromium has frequently been found to be affected by the surface condition, optimum results being obtained only after the removal of a thin layer by electropolishing.[43, 88] This effect has been attributed to elimination either of surface imperfections or of material which has been severely contaminated by nitrogen during processing.

It has been found that up to 0.34 per cent oxygen does not have an appreciable effect on the brittle-to-ductile transition of as-cast chromium.[76] Similar observations have been made on wrought samples; within the range from 0.006 to 0.37 per cent, oxygen has little effect on bend ductility.[8] It has been speculated that a pronounced increase in ductility should occur at some much lower oxygen content, as is observed in molybdenum.[8]

Studies of the influence of nitrogen on the transition temperature of chromium appear to indicate that nitrogen may be the most detrimental impurity,[76, 88] the critical content being as low as 0.002 to 0.003 per cent, or even less (Figure 7.7).[76] Nitrogen in solid solution is more detrimental to ductility than when pre-

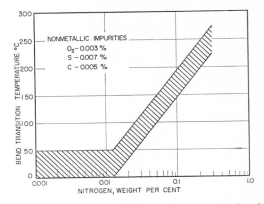

Figure 7.7. Effect of nitrogen content on the bend transition temperature of hydrogen reduced electrolytic chromium. (*Courtesy W. H. Smith and A. U. Seybolt.*)

cipitated as chromium nitride. A fast cooling rate tends to keep nitrogen in solution and to raise the transition temperature, whereas a very slow cooling rate allows a more complete precipitation of nitride. For example, the bend transition temperature of chromium containing 0.029 per cent nitrogen was found to be from 150–200°C (302–392°F) after water quenching from 1200°C (2192°F), and about 50°C (122°F) after furnace cooling from the same temperature.[76] In addition, it has been observed that the minimum nitrogen content to produce brittleness is much lower for the recrystallized material than for cold-worked specimens.[44] Attempts have been made to rationalize this effect of nitrogen in terms of dislocation locking by Cottrell atmospheres.[44] This theory involves the interaction between dislocations and certain specific solute atoms in a metal, and it has been shown to be responsible for yield-point and strain-aging phenomena. Annealing for recrystallization would provide a greater opportunity for diffusion of impurity atoms and, perhaps more significantly, would reduce the dislocation density. A smaller number of nitrogen atoms, therefore, will be required to form atmospheres of a given concentration in a recrystallized than in a cold-worked material.

Similar investigations have established the detrimental level for carbon as about 0.015 per cent.[8, 59, 76] The embrittling effect of carbon appears to result primarily from the formation of a brittle carbide network at grain boundaries. The effect of sulfur has not been studied in sufficient detail, but it has been reported that sulfur contents as high as 0.1 per cent do not have a significant effect on ductility.[76]

Attempts to minimize the harmful effects of these nonmetallic impurities by the addition of scavenging elements, such as aluminum, tantalum, titanium, or zirconium, have been quite disappointing.[28] Partial success has been achieved by cerium additions; about 2 per cent of this element has been found to lower the bend-transition temperature of chromium containing 0.02 to 0.07 per cent nitrogen by about 80°C (144°F)[76] (Figure 7.8). This improvement has been attributed to the removal of nitrogen from the chromium by the formation of cerium nitride. Furthermore, since cerium has a limited solid solubility in chromium, it has little effect in raising the transition temperature.

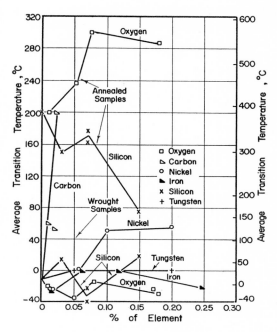

Figure 7.9. Effect of various alloy additions on the bend transition temperature of wrought and annealed iodide chromium sheet. (*Courtesy D. J. Maykuth, W. D. Klopp, R. I. Jaffee, and H. B. Goodwin.*)

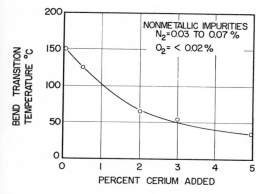

Figure 7.8. Effect of cerium additions on the slow bend transition temperature of as-cast chromium containing approximately 0.03 to 0.07 per cent nitrogen. (*Courtesy W. H. Smith and A. U. Seybolt.*)

The results of systematic investigations of the role of alloying additions on the brittle-to-ductile transition temperature have been reported by several investigators.[1, 59, 80] The effect of various alloy additions on the bend-transition temperature of wrought and annealed iodide chromium are shown in Figure 7.9.[59] An attempt has been made to correlate the increase in transition temperature with the localized strain produced by the substitutional atoms. This correlation was not entirely satisfactory, but a general correlation has been observed between the hardness and transition temperature, the harder alloys having the higher transi-

tion temperatures. The effect of an increasing total amount of metallic impurities on the bend transition temperature of sheet samples of iodide chromium is plotted in Figure 7.10.[8]

Before leaving the subject of transition temperature, it may be interesting to point out an

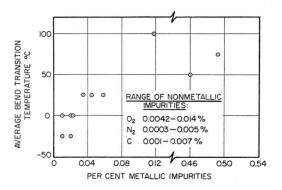

Figure 7.10. Effect of metallic impurities on the bend transition temperature of iodide chromium. (*Courtesy J. M. Blocher, Jr. et al.*)

observation which is unexpected and difficult to comprehend. Investigators at the Bureau of Mines[28] found that arc-melted chromium which could not be worked below 500°C (932°F) could, nevertheless, be cold-worked up to 60 per cent by intermittent refrigeration to liquid-air temperature, −190°C (−310°F), after each 5 per cent reduction. Suggestions made to explain this phenomenon postulated the existence of a low-temperature, ductile modification of chromium. There is, however, no evidence of any such transformation to substantiate this hypothesis.

ELECTROPLATING AND CHROMIZING

Chromium electroplating is generally of two types: (1) decorative and (2) "hard." The decorative finish is generally extremely thin, using only 0.00001 to 0.00002 in. thick. This plate is normally deposited over another electro-deposited layer, which is frequently nickel. The "hard" chromium coatings are relatively thick, usually from 0.003 to 0.010 in. and are applied directly to the base metal, generally steel.

Both types of electrodeposits are made using a standard plating bath consisting of chromic and sulfuric acids, the ratio of chromic to sulfuric being about 100:1. The temperature and current density should be so related as to give a cathode efficiency of about 12 per cent for bright deposits and 16 per cent for "hard" deposits. In general, the current density must be increased as the temperature is raised and must be slightly higher for hard deposits than for decorative coatings.

The thin decorative platings are generally applied to a nonnoble metal to protect it from corrosion and thus maintain a bright, attractive finish. The "hard," relatively thick chromium plates are used to take advantage of the high hardness and wear resistance or the low co-efficient of friction of such deposits. In both applications, however, the chromium usually has a hardness of 850 to 900 Brinell. More detailed information on chromium plating, including theories of deposition, structure of chromium plate, and methods of analyzing chromium-plating solutions, has been presented concisely elsewhere.[31]

Electroplates have certain disadvantages. The deposits are not free from porosity and thus must depend upon the undercoat for part of their corrosion resistance. Because of this porosity, they are not suitable for high-temperature oxidation resistance, and because there is a sharp interface with the base metal, differential thermal stresses frequently result in spalling.

In addition to the electrodeposited chromium layers, surfaces of chromium can also be obtained by chromizing. A widely used process has been described by Kelly.[49] In this process the metal to be treated is packed in a mixture of powdered chromium and alumina and heated for 3 to 4 hr at temperatures ranging from 1300–1400°C (2372–2552°F) to allow the chromium to diffuse into the base metal. The thickness of the chromized layer will depend on both time and temperature. A protective atmosphere is required to prevent oxidation of the chromium.

Other processes, such as chromizing with chromous chloride[6, 7] or salt-bath chromizing, have also been employed.[14]

CHROMIUM ALLOY SYSTEMS

A discussion of the alloy systems formed between chromium and the other metals as well as the nonmetals is beyond the scope of this chapter. An excellent compilation of the phase diagrams of systems involving chromium, as well as crystallographic data, has been prepared by Hansen and Anderko.[37] A discussion of the properties of many chromium-base alloy systems is given by Sully.[79]

APPLICATIONS

Chromium, chromium alloys, and chromium chemicals find a wide range of application, from simple alloy additions in the metallurgical industry to the production of pigments.

In the metallurgical industry chromium up to about 3 per cent is added to low-alloy steel for improved mechanical properties and increased hardenability. The steels of this type, which may also contain other elements such as molybdenum, nickel, manganese, and vanadium, are used for high-strength applications such as springs, roller and ball bearings, dies, and rails. Steels containing 5 to 6 per cent chromium have increased resistance to corrosion and oxidation and find many applications in the oil industry.

Steels containing above 10 per cent chromium are known as "stainless" for their superior resistance to oxidation and atmospheric corrosion. The stainless steels containing only chromium as a major alloy addition can be divided into two main groups: (1) the martensitic grades, which are hardenable, and (2) the ferritic grades, which are single phase at all temperatures and thus nonhardenable by transformation. The other major classification of stainless steels, also nonhardenable, are the austenitic steels which are alloyed to stabilize the high-temperature, face-centered cubic form of iron to room temperature and below.

The high-chromium, martensitic grades may contain up to about 2 per cent carbon, and the susceptibility to heat-treatment will depend on the carbon content. The high-carbon grades (1 to 2 per cent) are used when hardness and abrasive resistance are important in applications such as special tool and die steels. The lower-carbon heat-treatable grades (0.3 per cent carbon) are used in the manufacture of cutlery.

The excellent corrosion resistance of the ferritic stainless steels containing about 13 per cent chromium and 0.1 per cent carbon make them useful for automotive trim and in the chemical industry. Steels containing 25 to 30 per cent chromium have excellent oxidation resistance and are used in many elevated-temperature furnace applications.

Nickel and manganese can be added to steel in conjunction with chromium to produce the austenitic stainless steels of which the 18 per cent chromium–8 per cent nickel is probably the most widely used. These steels display a good combination of strength at room and elevated temperatures, as well as corrosion and oxidation resistance. They are generally employed where a combination of the above properties are required.

There are many other metallurgical applications of chromium. In cobalt- and nickel-base high-temperature alloys, chromium is added in amounts up to about 25 per cent for improved strength and oxidation resistance. Chromium is added to cast iron to improve its tensile strength and resistance to wear or heat. Cutting tools and some electrical-resistance materials also contain considerable quantities of chromium.

In addition to the beneficial effects that chromium imparts as an alloy addition, the growing success being obtained in increasing the purity and, as a result, the ductility of chromium metal may open a new area of interesting possibilities and engineering uses. Perhaps the most promising area of future application of chromium metal is the development of chromium-base alloys which have outstanding combinations of oxidation resistance and strength at elevated temperatures. Based on the recent advances in chromium technology, the prospects for a ductile high-temperature alloy based on chromium are much brighter than appeared possible a few years ago.

In the refractory industry the usefulness of chromite is based upon its high melting point, moderate thermal expansion, stability of crystalline form at elevated temperatures, and neutral chemical behavior. Chromite refractories are available in the form of molded bricks and shapes; plastic mixtures consisting of moistened aggregates which are rammed in place; castables composed of dry aggregates and a binder which, after being mixed with water, can be poured like concrete; and mortars and cement for laying bricks. Bricks made entirely of chromite have been largely replaced by bricks composed of mixtures of chromite and magnesia which have greater refractoriness, volume stability, and resistance to spalling.

One of the primary applications of chromium chemicals is for the manufacture of pigments. Various colors can be attained by the proper mixtures of chromium chemicals and other metals and compounds. Pigments account for about one third of the primary production of chromium chemicals.

In the textile industry chromium chemicals are used as mordants in the production of fast colors on wool and in oxidizing and after-treating dyes on cotton and other textiles. Both trivalent and hexavalent compounds, such as basic chromic acetates and chlorides, chromic fluorides, bisulfates, lactates, bromates, oxalates, and thiocyanates, are employed. Practically all types of leather now tanned use chrome reagents in the form of basic chromic sulfates which are produced from the dichromate.

Metal surface treatments and corrosion control use a large volume of chromium chemicals. Applications are chromium plating; chromizing; anodizing aluminum; treatment of zinc and magnesium; dips for iron, steel, brass, and tin; inhibitors for brines and recirculating water systems; and for a large number of combinations in the oil and gas industries.

Chromium chemicals also find application for oxidation in synthetic organic chemistry, such as the production of dyes, camphor, and synthetic fibers, and in bleaching, to mention only a few.[82]

References

1. Abrahamson, E. P., and Grant, N. J., "Proc. Regional Conf. on High-Temp. Alloys," Cleveland (1956).

2. Adcock, F. J., *J. Iron Steel Inst. (London),* **115, 369** (1927).

3. Ageyev, N. V., and Trapeznikov, "Investigation on High-Temperature Alloys," A.N.U.S. S.R., Moscow, 17 (1956).

4. Baur, E., and Brunner, R., *Helv. Chim. Acta,* **17, 958** (1934).

5. Beall, R. A., Asai, G., and Roberson, A. H., "Ductile Chromium and Its Alloys," p. 110, Cleveland, American Society for Metals, 1957.

6. Becker, G., Daeves, K., and Steinberg, F., *Z. physik. Chem.,* **A187, 354** (1940).

7. Becker, G., Daeves, K., *et al.,* U.S. Patents 2,236,209 (Mar. 25, 1941); 2,255,482 (Sept. 9, 1941); 2,257,668 (Sept. 30, 1941); 2,219,004–5 (Mar. 3, 1942); 2,399,848 (May 7, 1946); 2,-415,078 (Feb. 4, 1947).

8. Blocher, J. M., Campbell, I. E., Maykuth, D. J., Jaffee, R. I., and Goodwin, H. C., *WADC Tech. Rept. No. 53/470* (January, 1954).

9. Bloom, D. S., and Grant, N. J., *Trans. AIME,* **194, 524** (1952).

10. Brandes, E. A., and Stone, H. E. N., *J. Inst. Metals,* **87, 42** (1958).

11. Brenner, A., Buckhead, P., and Jennings, G., *J. Research NBS,* **40, 31** (1948).

12. Bridgman, P. W., *Proc. Am. Acad. Sci.,* **68, 33** (1933).

13. Bunsen, W., *Ann. Physik u. Chemie,* **1, 619** (1854).

14. Campbell, I. E., Burth, V. D., Hoeckelman, R., and Gonser, B. W., *Trans. Electrochem. Soc.,* **96, 262** (1949).

15. Carlile, S. J., Christian, J. W., and Hume-Rothery, W., *J. Inst. Metals,* **76, 169** (1949).

16. Carosella, M. C., and Mettler, J. D., "Ductile Chromium and Its Alloys," p. 75, Cleveland, American Society for Metals, 1957.

17. Carosella, M. C., and Mettler, J. D., *Metal Progr.,* **69, 51** (1956).

18. Carveth, H. R., and Curry, B. E., *Trans. Am. Electrochem. Soc.,* **7, 115** (1905).

19. Coblentz, W. W., and Stair, R., *Natl. Bur.*

Standards (U.S.), Research Paper No. 39, 352 (1928).

20. Cooper, H. S., U.S. Patent 2,850,378 (Sept. 2, 1958).

21. Darken, L. S., and Gurry, R. W., "Physical Chemistry of Metals," p. 304, New York, McGraw-Hill Book Company, Inc., 1953.

22. Ephriam, F., "Inorganic Chemistry," 4th Ed., New York, Interscience Publishers, Inc., 1946.

23. Fairhall, L. T., "Industrial Toxicology," Baltimore, The Williams & Wilkins Company, 1949.

24. Fine, M. E., Greiner, E. S., and Ellis, W. C., *Trans. AIME,* **191, 56** (1951).

25. Fountain, R. W., and Lamont, J. L., "Ductile Chromium and Its Alloys," p. 255, Cleveland, American Society for Metals, 1957.

26. Fréedericksz, V., *Ann. Phys.,* **34, 780** (1911).

27. Gilbert, H. L., Johansen, H. A., and Nelson, R. G., *J. Metals,* **5, 63** (1953).

28. Gilbert, H. L., Johansen, H. A., and Nelson, R. G., *U.S. Bur. Mines, Rept. Invest. No. 4905* (September, 1952).

29. Goldschmidt, H., German Patent 96,317 (Mar. 3, 1895); U.S. Patents 578,686 (Mar. 16, 1897); 895,628 (Aug. 11, 1908).

30. Goodwin, H. B., Gilbert, R. A., Schwartz, C. M., and Greenidge, C. T., *J. Electrochem. Soc.,* **100, 152** (1953).

31. Gray, A. G., "Modern Electroplating," New York, John Wiley & Sons, Inc., (1952).

32. Greenaway, H. T., *Aeronaut. Res. Lab. Austral. Struc. and Mat. Note No. 163* (1951).

33. Greenaway, H. T., *J. Inst. Metals,* **83, 121** (1954).

34. Greenwood, H. C., *Proc. Roy. Soc. London,* **A82, 356** (1905).

35. Grube, G., and Knabe, R., *J. Electrochem. Soc.,* **42, 793** (1936).

36. Ham, J. L., and Sibley, C. B., *J. Metals,* p. 976 (July, 1957).

37. Hansen, M., and Anderko, K., "Constitution of Binary Alloys," 2nd Ed. New York, McGraw-Hill Book Company, Inc., 1958.

38. Hatfield, W. H., *Engineer,* **134, 639** (1922).

39. Hindert, P., *J. Research NBS,* **26, 81** (1941).

40. Hindert, P., *J. Research NBS,* **27, 113** (1941).

41. Hume-Rothery, W., "The Structure of Metals and Alloys," p. 14, London, Institute of Metals 1956.

42. Isenberg, O. F., private communication, Lunex Company (Feb. 5, 1959).

43. Johansen, H. A., and Asai, G., *J. Electrochem. Soc.,* **101, 604** (1954); discussion: *ibid.,* **102,** 362 (1955).

44. Johansen, H. A., Gilbert, H. L., Nelson, R. G., and Carpenter, R. L., *U.S. Bur. Mines, Rept. Invest. No. 5058* (May, 1954).

45. Johnson, B. K., *Proc. Phys. Soc. (London),* **53,** 258 (1941).

46. Kelley, K. K., *U. S. Bur. Mines, Bull. No. 383* (1936).

47. Kelley, K. K., *U.S. Bur. Mines, Bull. No. 434,* 38 (1941).

48. Kelley, K. K., *U.S. Bur. Mines. Bull. No. 476* (1949).

49. Kelly, F. C., U.S. Patent 1,365,499 (1921).

50. Kroll, W. J., Hergert, W. F., and Yerkes, L. A., *J. Electrochem. Soc.,* **97,** 258 (1950); discussion: *ibid.,* **98,** 252 (1951).

51. Latimer, W. M., "Oxidation Potentials," Englewood Cliffs, N.J., Prentice-Hall, Inc., 1952.

52. Lloyd, R. R., Rawles, W. T., and Feeney, R. G., *Trans. Electrochem. Soc.,* **89,** 443 (1946).

53. Lloyd, R. R., Rosenbaum, J. B., Homme, V. E., and Davis, L. P., *Trans. Electrochem. Soc.,* **94,** 122 (1948).

54. Lloyd, R. R., Rosenbaum, J. B., Homme, V. E., Davis, L. P., and Merrill, C. C., *J. Electrochem. Soc.,* **97,** 227 (1950).

55. McGuire, T. R., and Kriessman, C. J., *Phys. Rev.,* **85,** 452 (1952).

56. McInnis, W., and Heidrich, H. V., "Chromium," preprint, "Minerals Yearbook (U.S. Bur. Mines)," Washington, D.C., Government Printing Office, 1957.

57. Maier, C. G., *U.S. Bur. Mines, Bull. No. 436,* 7 (1942).

58. Maykuth, D. J., and Jaffee, R. I., *Trans. ASM,* **49,** 948 (1957).

59. Maykuth, D. J., Klopp, W. D., Jaffee, R. I., and Goodwin, H. B., *J. Electrochem. Soc.,* **102,** 316 (1955).

60. Mellor, J. W., "A Comprehensive Treatise on Inorganic and Theoretical Chemistry," Vol. XI, London, Longmans, 1931.

61. "Metals Handbook," p. 1136, Cleveland, American Society for Metals, 1948.

62. "Metals Reference Book," New York, Interscience Publishers, Inc., 1955.

63. Parke, R. M., and Bens, F. P., "Symp. Materials for Aircraft Gas Turbines," 80, ASTM (1946).

64. Pearson, W. B., and Hume-Rothery, W., *J. Inst. Metals,* **81,** 311 (1953).

65. Powell, R. W., *Phil. Mag.,* **44,** 645 (1953).

66. Powell, R. W., and Tye, R. P., *J. Inst. Metals,* **85,** 185 (1956–57).

67. Pursey, H., *J. Inst. Metals,* **86,** 362 (1958).

68. Pursey, H., *Nature,* **169,** 150 (1952).

69. Pursey, H., *Nature,* **172,** 864 (1953).

70. Runck, R. J., Feainside, T. E., Blocher, J. M., and Campbell, I. E., "Ductile Chromium and Its Alloys," p. 129, Cleveland, American Society for Metals, 1957.

71. Sargent, G. J., *Trans. Am. Electrochem. Soc.,* **37,** 479 (1920).

72. Seaborg, G. T., and Perlman, I., *Rev. Mod. Phys.,* **20,** 565 (1948).

73. Segerblom, W., "Properties of Inorganic Substances," New York, Reinhold Publishing Corp., 1927.

74. Serfass, E. J., and Muraca, R. F., in "Chromium," M. J. Udy (Ed.), Vol. 1, p. 53, New York, Reinhold Publishing Corp., 1956.

75. Slater, J. C., "Introduction to Chemical Physics," p. 349, New York, McGraw-Hill Book Company, Inc., 1939.

76. Smith, W. H., and Seybolt, A. U., *J. Electrochem. Soc.,* **103,** 347 (1956).

77. Speiser, R., Johnston, H. L., and Blackburn, P., *J. Am. Chem. Soc.,* **72,** 4142 (1950).

78. Stramanis, M. E., and Weng, C. C., *Acta Cryst.,* **8,** 367 (1955).

79. Sully, A. H., "Chromium," London, Butterworth's Scientific Publications, 1954.

80. Sully, A. H., Brandes, E. A., and Mitchell, K. W., *J. Inst. Metals,* **81,** 585 (1953).

81. Thayer, T. P., *Econ. Geol.,* **41,** 202 (1946).

82. Udy, M. J., "Chromium," Vol. 1, New York, Reinhold Publishing Corp., 1956.

83. Udy, M. J., *op. cit.,* Vol. 2.

84. Uhlig, H. H., "The Corrosion Handbook," New York, John Wiley & Sons, Inc., 1948.

85. Umino, S., *Sci. Repts. Tôhoku Univ.,* **15,** 597 (1926).

86. van Arkel, A. E., Koogman, W., and deBoer, J. A., German Patent 562,616 (1932); U.S. Patent 1,891,132 (1923).

87. Wain, H. L., "Ductile Chromium and Its Alloys," p. 27, Cleveland, American Society for Metals, 1957.

88. Wain, H. L., Henderson, F., and Johnstone, S. T. M., *J. Inst. Metals,* **83,** 133 (1954–55).

89. Waklin, H. B., *Phys. Rev.,* **73,** 1458 (1948).

90. Weiss, R. J., "Ductile Chromium and Its Alloys," p. 163, Cleveland, American Society for Metals, 1957.

91. Wyman, L. L., and Sterling, J. T., *ibid.,* p. 180.

8. COBALT

C. R. W<small>HITTEMORE</small>

Deloro Smelting & Refining Co., Ltd.
Deloro, Ontario

INTRODUCTION

H. C. Hoover records in his translation of "De Re Metallica" by Agricola that the word "cobalt" (German *Kobalt*) is from the Greek word *cobalos,* mine. Its German form signified a mischievous spirit (gnomes and goblins) and was applied by the German miners in Saxony to certain ores which injured their hands and feet; in Europe the designation became widely used.[1]* These minerals were later found to be arsenical cobalt.

The chemistry and metallurgy of cobalt dates from the middle of the sixteenth century, although earlier use of cobalt is found in Egyptian and Babylonian pottery as far back as 1450 B.C. Cobalt salts impart a blue color to ceramics, and, when combined with nickel, chromium, or manganese compounds, all shades of blue to green are obtained.

Brandt in 1735 discovered the element cobalt, and in 1780 Bergman studied the properties of this new metal.

Prior to the close of the nineteenth century, the world output of cobalt was derived from Germany, Hungary, and Norway. In 1864 Garnier discovered the oxidized ores of New Caledonia which were developed in 1874. The next discoverey in 1903 was the rich silver-cobalt ores of Ontario, Canada, which produced 16 tons of cobalt in 1904.[4]

Union Minière du Haut Katanga in the

* The superscript numbers refer to references listed at the end of the chapter under headings corresponding to those used to divide the textual material.

Belgian Congo initiated in 1920 the extraction of cobalt from copper-cobalt ores and in a few years became the leading producer. The Belgian Congo is still the chief source of cobalt.

Table 8.1 shows the free-world production of cobalt in short tons of contained cobalt.

T<small>ABLE</small> 8.1. W<small>ORLD</small> P<small>RODUCTION OF</small>
C<small>OBALT</small>—S<small>HORT</small> T<small>ONS</small>

Country	1956*	1957*	1958*	1959*
Australia	13	14	17	15
Belgian Congo	10,019	8,945	7,166	9,374
Canada	1,758	1,961	1,355	1,649
Germany, West	990	1,100	1,219	1,620†
Morocco, French	716	500	1,021	1,391
Rhodesia and Nyasaland	1,271	1,583	1,792	2,372
United States	1,272	1,649	2,012	1,165
Total	16,039	15,852	14,582	17,686

* Bureau of Mines, Minerals Yearbook, 1959.
† Centre D'Information du Cobalt.

The current price quotation for cobalt is $1.50/lb, FOB carrier, New York, for metal 98 to 99 per cent cobalt content.

OCCURRENCE

Cobalt[2] is widely diffused in the igneous rocks of the earth's crust, making up only 0.0023 per cent, as compared with 0.008 per cent for nickel, and ranks thirty-fourth in order of prevalence. The amount of cobalt estimated to be in the earth's crust, as described in Chapter 1, is more than that of lead, and about one-third that of copper, yet its com-

114

TABLE 8.2. OCCURRENCE AND SOME PROPERTIES OF COBALT MINERALS

Mineral	Formula	Per cent element				Sp gr	Occurrence
		Co	Cu	S	As		
Carrollite	$CuS \cdot Co_2S_3$	38.0	20.5	41.5	—	4.84	N'Kana, Rhodesia
Linnaeite	Co_3S_4	57.9	—	42.1	—	4.90	Cobalt varies from 31–40% depending on iron, nickel, or copper present; Belgian Congo and Missouri
Smaltite	$CoAs_2$	28.2	—	—	71.8	6.50	Germany, Canada, French Morocco
Skutterudite	$CoAs_3$	20.8	—	—	79.2	6.79	Morocco, Norway
Cobaltite	$CoAsS$	35.5	—	19.3	45.2	6.3	Canada, Burma, Australia
Asbolite	$CoO_2 \cdot MnO_2 \cdot 4H_2O$	35.0	—	—	—	1.1	New Caledonia, Northern Rhodesia; cobalt varies from 4–35%
Heterogenite	$CoO \cdot 2Co_2O_3 \cdot 6H_2O$	57.3	—	—	—	—	Belgian Congo
Erythrite	$3CoO \cdot As_2O_5 \cdot 8H_2O$	29.5	—	—	25.0	3.0	Canada, Germany, Morocco

mercial production ranks with that of silver, an element far less abundant. Relatively little cobalt ore is mined chiefly for the cobalt content, and most of this metal is recovered as a by-product of ores treated for their copper or nickel content.

The principal cobalt minerals are the sulfides, arsenides, and oxidized compounds.[2,3,5,6,7] Table 8.2 lists some of their properties and occurrence.

CONCENTRATION

The ores of cobalt all contain very low concentrations of cobalt associated with other metals and, therefore, must be treated by concentrating processes to derive a material suitable for metal-extraction operations. Each of the several types of ore currently being processed requires a somewhat different concentration treatment, as described in the following section for typical ores.

Chalcopyrite-Cobaltite Ores

These sulfide ores are exemplified by the deposits in the Blackbird district, Lemhi County, Idaho, which contain 0.4 to 1 per cent cobalt.[8] The cobaltite is mainly associated with and as inclusions in the chalcopyrite, pyrite,

or pyrrhotite and in the cleavage planes of the mica-chlorite schist. In addition to cobalt, the ore typically contains 1 to 2 per cent copper, 10 to 15 per cent iron, 0.5 to 1.5 per cent arsenic, and 3 to 13 per cent sulfur.

In 1943 the Calera Mining Company initiated the development of the deposits and process for the recovery of the copper and cobalt.

Concentration of the mine-run ore is effected by crushing and fine grinding to 65 per cent —200 mesh for subsequent differential flotation.[1,6] A copper concentrate is floated at pH 9, and the underflow containing the depressed iron and cobalt is first activated for the separation of the iron and then for flotation of the cobalt. The cobalt concentrate, after cleaning, averages 17.5 per cent cobalt, 20 per cent iron, 1.0 per cent nickel, and 0.50 per cent copper, and comprises the raw material to the Garfield Refinery of Calera Mining Company, Garfield, Utah.

Copper-Lead-Cobalt-Nickel Sulfide Ores[2,6,11]

Complex copper-lead-cobalt-nickel sulfide ores associated with pyrite occur at Fredericktown in Madison County, Missouri. The source of the cobalt and nickel is siegenite [$(CoNi)_3S_4$] with iron and copper replacing in part the cobalt and nickel. Typical ore analysis is 1.28 per cent lead, 2.03 per cent copper, 1.08 per cent nickel, 0.87 per cent cobalt, 3.57 per cent iron, 15.4 per cent calcium oxide, and 23.9 per cent silica.

The intimate association and complexity of the minerals make flotation the logical method of beneficiation whereby the cobalt is concentrated tenfold. The ore is ground to −100 mesh in a lime-cyanide circuit and conditioned with "Aerofloat 31" to promote the copper and lead minerals which are removed in flotation cells as a bulk concentrate, the lead and copper being separated subsequently. The pulp from the copper-lead circuit flows to a separate bank of cells to which "Xanthate Z-8" and a frother are added for recovery of the siegenite. Over two-thirds of the cobalt in the ore is recovered in the cobalt-nickel concentrate, which typically contains 9.3 per cent cobalt, 14.4 per cent nickel, and 5.5 per cent copper.

Copper-Cobalt Oxidized and Sulfide Ores[3-11]

The cobalt-bearing ores of Union Minière du Haut Katanga in the Belgian Congo occur as complex minerals in the oxidized and sulfide state. To date, the differential concentration of copper and cobalt has not been achieved.

Three types of ore are treated separately at the Kolwezi concentrator:[3,11] (1) oxide copper containing a minor amount of cobalt; (2) cobalt-copper oxide ore, approximately equal in cobalt and copper content; and (3) mixed ore which contains both copper-cobalt oxides and copper-cobalt sulfides.

The mineralization of the upper deposits is predominately malachite [$Cu_2(OH)_2CO_3$], pseudo-malachite, chrysocolla ($CuO·SiO_2·H_2O$), and heterogenite ($CoO·2Co_2O_3·6H_2O$) and cobaltiferous wad.

The oxide ores containing 5 to 6 per cent copper and 0.2 to 0.3 per cent cobalt are wet ground to −65 mesh, conditioned with sodium carbonate, sodium silicate, and palm oil fatty acids for flotation of the copper. The concentrate assays 26 to 27 per cent copper and 1 per cent cobalt.

In the lower deposits the mineralization is composed of chalcocite (Cu_2S), bornite (Cu_5FeS_4), chalcopyrite ($CuFeS_2$), and carrollite ($CuS·Co_2S_3$). The gangue is a siliceous-dolomitic rock. The ore, containing 5 per cent copper and 0.1 to 0.2 per cent cobalt, is easily concentrated by flotation in an alkaline circuit using xanthate and a frothing agent. The concentrate assays 45 to 60 per cent copper and 0.5 to 2 per cent cobalt.

The mixed ores (sulfides and oxides) contain 4 to 6 per cent copper and 0.2 to 0.3 per cent cobalt, usually in the oxide form. Beneficiation is effected by the following operations: (1) grinding to moderate fineness, 70 per cent −200 mesh; (2) flotation of the chalcocite by amyl xanthate and frothing agents; (3) flotation of the malachite by superficial sulfidization with alkaline sulphydrate sulfide and collection with a xanthate; and (4) regrinding and reflotation of the sulfide middlings.

The sulfide concentrate is subjected to a sulfate roast and leaching treatment at the Kolwezi electrolytic plant. The oxide concentrate is sintered and electrically smelted to yield a rough copper-cobalt metal which is processed to copper anode metal and a cobalt slag for retreatment.

Copper-Cobalt Sulfide Ores

The Rhokana Corporation, Ltd., Northern Rhodesia obtains cobalt from the copper ores at N'Kana, the minerals being in the sulfide forms as chalcopyrite, chalcocite, and carrollite.[5]

The ore fed to the concentrator averages (by per cent) 3 copper, 0.14 cobalt, 2.5 iron, 1.5 sulfur, 45 silica, 12 aluminum oxide, 7 magnesium oxide, and 7 calcium oxide, and is ground to 90 per cent −200 mesh for flotation. The concentrates are thickened, filtered, and shipped to the smelter for separate processing. Typical analyses of the concentrator products are as follows:

| | Per Cent by Weight | | | | | |
	Cu	Co	Fe	S	SiO₂	Al₂O₃
Feed	3.2	0.14	2.5	1.5	45.0	12.0
Copper concentrate	56.8	0.65	10.4	24.0	4.2	1.2
Cobalt concentrate	25.0	3.50	17.0	17.5	21.0	5.0
Tailing	0.4	0.05				

TABLE 8.3

Per cent	Feed	Copper concentrate	Cobalt concentrate	Tailing	% Recovery in concentrate	
					Copper	Cobalt
Copper	4.77	34.6	3.1	0.14	93.0	13.9
Cobalt	0.37	0.4	4.2	0.025	4.6	80.7
Iron	—	25.3	33.2			
Sulfur	—	31.8	41.6			
Insoluble	—	6.2	14.9			
Moisture	—	6.8	8.8			

Chibuluma Mines Limited[9] is 9 miles west of Kitwe in Northern Rhodesia and is owned by Rhodesian Selection Trust.

Ore reserves are estimated at 7,300,000 tons, containing 5.23 per cent copper and 0.25 per cent cobalt.

The economic minerals in the Chibuluma ore body are chalcopyrite ($CuFeS_2$), linnaeite (Co_3S_4), and cobaltiferous pyrite. The gangue is mostly quartzite.

Copper minerals are selectively recovered after depressing the cobalt minerals by lime-sodium cyanide.

The cobalt minerals are recovered by activation with copper sulfate and the addition of sulfuric acid to bring the pH to 9.0.

Analyses of typical products and recoveries are shown in Table 8.3.

Canadian Silver-Cobalt Arsenide Ores

The concentration of Ontario cobalt silver ores still presents a problem as the various minerals respond differently. Fine leaf-silver, argentite, and ruby silver float readily, but antimonial silver, dyscrasite, and silver in the high-grade slimes from oxidized veins are recovered less readily, as are also the arsenides.

A typical flowsheet of mills using gravity concentration followed by flotation is shown in Figure 8.1.

The points essential for highest recovery of

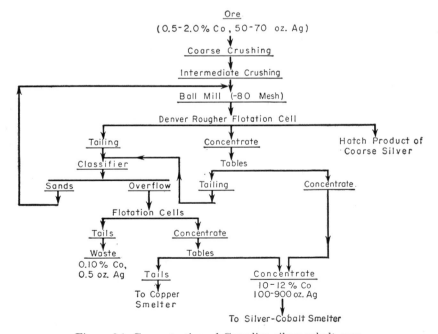

Figure 8.1. Concentration of Canadian silver-cobalt ores.

values from the cobalt ores are: (1) as coarse a grind as possible for cobalt recovery, and (2) removal of as much silver and cobalt as possible at the flotation cell in circuit with the ball mill. Flotation reagent additions consist of sodium carbonate and "Aerofloat" to the ball mill, and pine oil and "Pentasol Xanthate" to the rougher cell. Oxidized ores require additions of copper sulfate to the mill.

METALLURGY OF COBALT

Cobalt is recovered in metallic form from cobalt-bearing materials chiefly by two processes: (1) thermal reduction and purification and (2) electrowinning. A third process, recently introduced, utilizes leaching and reduction under pressure to yield metal by hydrometallurgical operations. The principal features of the extraction processes used by various metal producers are outlined in this section.

Cobalt from Oxidized Ores[1, 18, 20, 30, 38]

Union Minière du Haut Katanga, in the Belgian Congo, derives its cobalt from copper deposits, such as that at Musonoi, containing 0.5 to 10 per cent cobalt. The cobalt minerals are heterogenite, spherocobaltite, cornetite, and asbolite.

The richer cobalt ores and the sintered cobalt concentrates from the Kolwezi concentrator are processed at the Panda Smelter in three triphase furnaces. By difference in density the liquid metals, when tapped into a ladle, separate in two layers. One, the "white alloy," which is the lighter, contains percentagewise 15 copper, 44 cobalt, 1.5 silicon, and 39 iron; and the other, the heavy "red alloy," contains 89 per cent copper and 4.5 per cent cobalt. They are poured separately from the ladle. The white alloy is poured from the ladle lip into ingots or shotted in water for processing in Belgium. The red alloy is poured from the bottom and furnace-refined for copper. The 98.5 per cent pure copper is refined and cast into anodes at the Shituru plant. The refining slag (15 per cent cobalt) reverts to the electric furnace. The treatment of the white alloy is described by Young.[30]

Katanga produces electrolytic cobalt at the Jadotville-Shituru plant from the leaching of copper concentrates from Panda, Kolwezi, and other sources. The concentrates that form the feed to the copper-leaching plant also contains the cobalt in oxide form. Cobalt oxide is only slightly soluble in sulfuric acid and is made soluble by the reducing agent, ferrous sulfate, which is present in the solutions returned to the leaching circuit from the electrolysis of copper where a ferrous-ferric ion equilibrium is maintained. This makes possible a solution of 200 to 300 tons of cobalt/month. As the cobalt is not deposited with the copper, the solution increases in cobalt until an equilibrium concentration is reached. Volumetric balance is maintained by a solution bleed at the exit of the copper electrolysis which is used to dissolve low-grade copper-cobalt ores, thus permitting control of the amount of cobalt added to the circuit.

The cobalt-bearing solutions from (1) the leach-plant washing section, and (2) the copper electrolyte enriched with cobalt are treated with milk of lime for the removal of iron and copper at pH 5.8. Complete copper removal is effected by cementation on granulated annealed cobalt metal at pH 2.5. The cobalt is precipitated with milk of lime at a pH of 8.0 to 8.2, and the cobalt hydroxide precipitate, containing 15 per cent cobalt and 45 per cent calcium sulfate, is dissolved in the cobalt-spent electrolyte to give a neutral solution.

The prime electrolyte at a pH of 7.0 contains 70 g/liter of solids in suspension, 24 g/liter cobalt, and 120 g/liter magnesium sulfate in solution. Electrolysis is carried out using mild steel cathodes and lead (6 per cent antimony) anodes at a current density of 37 amp/sq ft. The cathode deposit stripped from the plates and the cobalt recovered by magnetic separation from the tank sludge, containing 3 to 4 per cent zinc and entrained basic sulfate, are refined in a 1,600 kva Héroult type furnace. Sulfur is eliminated by a high lime slag and the zinc is volatilized by poling. The liquid cobalt at 1600°C (2912°F) is granulated in water, dried and polished for market.

The finished cobalt analyzes (by per cent) 99 cobalt, 0.5 nickel, 0.1 silicon, 0.1 carbon, 0.15 iron, 0.02 copper, and 0.02 manganese.

Copper-Cobalt Sulfide Ores[1,18,25]

Treatment of copper-cobalt sulfide ores is illustrated by the processing of the Rhokana

Corporation's copper ores containing carrollite at N'kana. The cobalt concentrate, containing 32 per cent copper, 3.2 per cent cobalt, 13 per cent iron, and 23 per cent sulfur, is given a sulfatizing roast to convert the cobalt to cobalt sulfate under controlled temperature and furnace atmosphere conditions. The cobalt sulfate is water-leached at 80–85°C (176–185°F) to yield a solution containing 20 to 25 g/liter cobalt, 7 to 10 g/liter copper, and 0.3 to 0.4 g/liter iron. The residue is treated at the smelter for copper recovery.

The iron and copper are reduced to 0.2 and 0.02 g/liter, respectively, in the solution by air oxidation and milk of lime treatment at a pH up to 5.5. The clarified solution is passed over ¼-in. annealed cobalt granules to remove copper by cementation to a content of less than 0.001 g/liter. The solution containing 15 g/liter cobalt is treated with milk of lime to precipitate cobalt as $Co(OH)_2$ at a pH of 8.2. The cobalt hydroxide, 40 to 45 per cent solids, is added to the spent electrolyte circuit.

The purified electrolyte is heated to 70°C (158°F) and passed through the cells at a rate to give a discharge acidity of 1.8 pH. Cell anodes are made of antimonial lead, grid form, and carry 20 amp/sq ft, while the cathodes are mild steel carrying 15 amp/sq ft.

The cobalt metal stripped from the cathodes is melted in an electric furnace and granulated in water. The metal analyzes, by per cent, 99.89 cobalt, 0.041 copper, 0.032 iron, 0.019 sulfur, and 0.006 calcium.

Arsenical Cobalt Ores

Modern treatment of Ontario and Moroccan cobalt ores is represented at Deloro Smelting and Refining Company, Deloro, Ontario. Typical analyses of cobalt-bearing materials processed are as listed below.

Ore or concentrate with coke, iron scrap or ore, limestone, or silica, as required, are smelted in a Traylor blast furnace. Arsenic fume and dust are collected in a Cottrell precipitator and baghouse and furnace refined to yield a 99 per cent arsenic trioxide and a residue of silver, cobalt, lead, and nickel returnable to the blast furnace.

Speiss, matte, and bullion are tapped together into pots to separate into layers. On cooling, the layers can be broken apart and separated. The bullion is fluxed and air-blown in an oil-fired Schwartz furnace to remove arsenic, sulfur, lead, and copper and yield silver, 998 fine, or silver-gold bullion suitable for electrolytic separation of silver and gold.

The speiss and small amount of matte are ground to −100 mesh for roasting, to eliminate arsenic and sulfur and to oxidize the iron. The roasted speiss is mixed with water and sulfuric acid to convert the cobalt, nickel, copper, silver, and iron to water-soluble sulfates. The solids are returned to the smelter while the solution is first treated for silver removal; it then passes to the iron-arsenic removal tanks for oxidation of the iron by sodium chlorate followed by neutralization with lime to precipitate ferric arsenate, ferric hydroxide, and calcium sulfate, which are removed by countercurrent decantation. Copper is next removed by scrap iron treatment or by electrolysis. In either case the residual iron and copper in solution are removed by lime precipitation. The pulp is filtered, and the filter cake reprocessed for cobalt. The solution, containing cobalt and nickel, passes to the final stages of cobalt precipitation.

Oxidation and precipitation are effected by sodium hypochlorite to yield first, pure cobaltic hydroxide, $Co(OH)_3$, and then mixed cobaltic and nickelic hydroxides, $Co(OH)_3$ and $Ni(OH)_3$, which are recirculated. The cobalt precipitate is filter-pressed, the solution going to the nickel recovery plant, and the cobaltic hydroxide is heated to convert it to oxide. The washed oxide is mixed with charcoal and reduced to metal fines at 1000°C (1832°F). The metal fines are then melted in an electric furnace and granu-

| Material | Ag (oz/ton) | Percentage | | | | | | | |
		Co	Ni	Cu	Fe	As	S	SiO₂	CaO
Canadian cobalt concentrate	100–900	11.3	9.0	0.9	6.0	31	10.0	10.7	3.5
French Moroccan ore	6.7	9.6	0.33	0.11	1.8	43	1.7	27.5	4.5
Canadian silver-cobalt concentrate	1,200–2,500	5.56	0.92	0.13	20.8	11	3.0	19.4	9.3

lated in water. The metal analyzes, by per cent, 98.6 cobalt, 0.7 nickel, 0.37 iron, 0.12 silicon, 0.12 manganese, 0.03 copper, and 0.04 sulfur (maximum).

Pressure Leach Process[2, 7, 8, 14, 17, 33, 34, 35, 37]

The original basis of the process for the treatment of nickel-copper-cobalt ore or concentrates by leaching under pressure was initiated by F. A. Forward, C. S. Samis, and V. Kudryk, in 1947, at the University of British Columbia on behalf of Sherritt Gordon Mines, Ltd., which has large nickel ore deposits at Iynn Lake, Manitoba. Pilot plant engineering and design were handled by the Chemical Construction Company, which was investigating pressure leaching of sulfide ores with acid solutions and the precipitation of nickel from ammoniacal solutions by hydrogen reduction under pressure.

The combining of the ammonia leach as developed by Sherritt Gordon with Chemico's pressure hydrogen reduction and precipitation of nickel and cobalt from solution resulted in a hydrometallurgical process, replacing the conventional roasting, smelting, electrolytic, and fire refining operations.

Although variations in the basic steps make the process adaptable to the extraction from low-grade ores of a series of metals, such as nickel, copper, cobalt, and manganese, as applied to production of cobalt the process involves the preparation of concentrates of cobalt by conventional flotation treatment of the cobalt-bearing ore, and the leaching of a concentrate slurry in an autoclave under elevated pressure and temperature with either ammonia or acid. The leach solution is then oxidized by injecting air or oxygen into the autoclave. After leaching and oxidation, the autoclave contents are filtered, and the filtrate is purified to remove copper and iron. The cobalt and nickel in the resulting solution are reduced by hydrogen under pressure in separate steps. The metals are recovered in finely divided form which can be fabricated by powder metallurgy techniques or by melting and casting. The pressures involved in the general process are moderate. Leaching is carried out in agitator-equipped autoclaves at 77–82°C (170–180°F) and 100 to 110 psig. total pressure. Oxydrolysis is

also an autoclaving operation at 177–246°C (350–475°F) and a pressure of 700 psig. Nickel reduction autoclaves operate at 177–204°C (350–400°F) and 350 to 400 psig. total pressure.

Sherritt Gordon Mines, Ltd., mine and concentrate the ore at Lynn Lake, Manitoba. The ore is a massive pyrrhotite and disseminated sulfide with pentlandite, chalcopyrite, pyrrhotite, pyrite, and small amounts of cobalt-nickel pyrite. Two concentrates are produded: (1) low-nickel high-copper containing 28 to 30 per cent copper, and (2) low-copper high-nickel concentrate containing, by per cent, 12.0 nickel, 0.7 cobalt, 1.50 copper, 30.0 iron, 28.0 sulfur, and 28.0 insoluble.

The reduction feed solution contains 48 g/liter of nickel and 0.8 g/liter of cobalt in the form of diammine sulfates, and is reduced to 0.8 g/liter of nickel. At this stage about 8 per cent of the cobalt has been reduced. This dilute nickel-cobalt solution is treated with hydrogen sulfide to yield a nickel-cobalt sulfide precipitate.

The sulfides are washed and leached under oxidizing conditions at 122°C (250°F) and a total pressure of 100 psig. to yield a solution of 50 to 60 g/liter of cobalt plus nickel. The solution is purified to remove iron, unleached nickel, and cobalt sulfides (5.0 per cent) at pH 4.9 to 5.1, 82°C (180°F), and atmospheric pressure.

Nickel preferential reduction is carried out in an autoclave at 177°C (350°F) and 500 psig hydrogen pressure to yield a cobalt solution, nickel free, and a nickel metal powder containing 20 per cent cobalt which may be recycled to the refinery leach circuit or sold as a finished product.

The cobalt reduction is performed in similar equipment and the same operating conditions except for the presence of (1) a small quantity of a mixture of sodium sulfide and sodium cyanide as catalyst for the nucleation and (2) an excess of ammonia to ensure complete reduction of the cobalt. The metal powder is washed and dried in a nitrogen atmosphere. It analyzes 0.39 per cent nickel, 0.03 per cent iron, 0.02 per cent sulfur, and 99.3 per cent cobalt.

The Calera Mining Company, a subsidiary of Howe Sound Mining Company, processes (Fig. 8.2) the cobalt concentrate from the Blackbird Mine at its refinery near Garfield, Utah. The

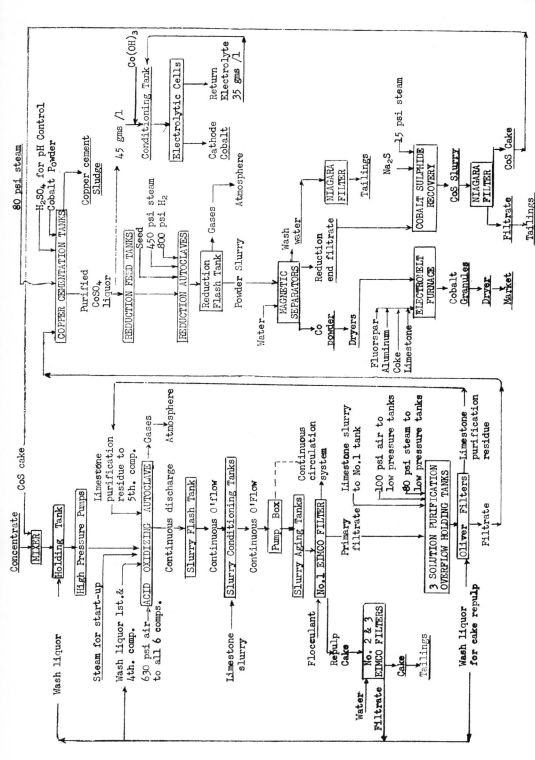

Figure 8.2. Flow sheet, Garfield Cobalt Refinery, Calera Mining Co., Garfield, Utah.

shipments are blended to give an arsenic-to-iron ratio of 1.20:1.00 which results in the following analysis in per cent.

Cobalt	17.50	Nickel	1.00
Iron	20.00	Copper	0.50
Arsenic	24.00	Insoluble	5.00
Sulfur	29.00	Moisture	12.00

The concentrate is mixed with process liquor to a density of 25 per cent solids. The slurry is then autoclaved under oxidizing conditions at 190°C (375°F) and 500 psig to yield a sulfate solution of nickel, iron, and copper and an insoluble residue of iron arsenate and calcium sulfate which is filtered off.

The acid slurry is partially neutralized with lime for the removal of iron, and filtered. The filtrate is given a final purification to remove residual iron, arsenic, copper, and some cobalt. The slurry is filtered, the residue recycled to the autoclave, and the filtrate treated with cobalt powder for cementation of the copper.

A portion of the purified cobalt–nickel sulfate solution is rigidly purified for the 8,000 lb/day electrolytic plant.

To the balance of the purified cobalt–nickel solution the required anhydrous ammonia is added to give a complex cobalt amine, and is subjected to reduction to metal in 450 gal autoclaves fitted with agitators, hydrogen spargers, and steam jackets. Reduction to metal is effected at 190°C (375°F) in the presence of hydrogen and a catalyst. Operating pressure is 700 to 800 psig.

The cobalt metal powder contains appreciable sulfur (0.15 per cent) and is processed in a Lectromelt furnace in the presence of a high lime slag, coke, and aluminum for degassing the metal. The physical characteristics of the granules are influenced by the metal temperature, deoxidation, and rate of pour. Subsequently, they are dried, polished, and packed.

The cobalt metal analyzes as follows:

	%		%
Cobalt	95.60	Arsenic	0.03
Nickel	3.90	Copper	0.02
Sulfur	0.03	Carbon	0.15
Iron	0.20		

Cobalt from Pyrites[13, 16, 18, 28]

The recovery of cobalt, copper, and zinc from cobaltiferrous pyrite conforms to the fol-lowing procedure. The pyrite ore or concentrate is first roasted for the recovery of sulfur for sulfuric acid manufacture. The roasted pyrite is mixed with 6 to 12 per cent sodium chloride, and in some cases, with 10 per cent pyrite, and is submitted to a chloridizing roast at 550–750°C (1022–1382°F) to render all metals, except iron, soluble in water or dilute hydrochloric or sulfuric acids. The iron residue is sintered with 1 per cent sodium chloride for the iron blast furnace.

The solution, containing iron, copper, zinc, manganese, cobalt, and nickel, is oxidized with air to convert iron to the ferric state, which with copper, zinc, and manganese are precipitated with lime solution. The precipitate is re-treated according to the metals to be recovered. To the cobalt solution sodium carbonate and chlorine are added at a controlled pH to precipitate cobalt hydroxide but leave nickel and zinc in solution. The cobalt hydroxide is dried and calcined at 750°C (1382°F), followed by a water wash to remove soluble salts, and then dried at a red heat to form cobalt oxide. The latter may then be sold as such or reduced with charcoal in a batch kiln at 1000°C (1832°F) to yield the metal.

Cobaltiferous pyrite ranges from 0.025 to 1.25 per cent cobalt, and extraction efficiency varies from 50 to 60 per cent.

The Bethlehem Steel Company recovers about 375 tons of metal/year from the iron pyrites that accompany the magnetite mined at Cornwall, Pennsylvania. The pyrites are processed to yield cobalt metal and oxide by the Pyrites Company, Wilmington, Delaware.

PHYSICAL PROPERTIES

Cobalt is a hard, magnetic metal, silvery-white on fracture, and closely resembling nickel and iron in appearance. Its atomic number is 27 and its atomic weight is 58.94. An isotope, cobalt 60, formed by atomic irradiation, is competing with radium as a gamma-ray source. The naturally occurring element is composed of 0.2 per cent of isotope 57 and 99.8 per cent of isotope 59.

Cobalt is one of the three ferromagnetic elements, along with iron and nickel, with a permeability approximately two-thirds that of iron, but, when alloyed with iron, nickel, and other metals, exceptional magnetic properties have been developed, as will be described in a subsequent section.

The properties of cobalt are more structure sensitive than those of most other elements, because, in addition to the usual effects of impurities, cobalt tends to exist as a mixture of two allotropes over a wide range of temperatures, the beta form predominating below about 400°C (752°F) and the alpha above that temperature. However, the transformation of beta to alpha and vice versa is sluggish and probably accounts for most of the wide variation in the reported data on physical properties. Additionally, it is now known that a great deal of the early work on precise determination of properties was conducted on samples whose cobalt content was no more than 93 per cent.

After the discovery[21] of the transformation from beta (hexagonal close packed, a = 2.5017 kx, c = 4.0614 kx) to alpha cobalt (face-centered cubic, a = 3.5370 kx),[36, 66] investigations placed the transformation temperature between 360–500°C (680–932°F).[15,29, 30,41,57,58,62,64,65,70,72,75,76] Subsequent investigations into the cause of this transformation range[11,67] revealed that the transformation was martensitic for specimens of a certain grain size, occurring at 388°C (730°F) on cooling and at 430°C (806°F) on heating.[67] Recently, the temperature has been determined to be 417 ± 7°C (783 ± 13°F) for the transformation in worked samples of 99.9+ per cent cobalt.[16]

There has been much controversy with regard to the existence of a second allotropic transformation in cobalt,[6,15,29,41,57,59,64,65,67,72,75] the more reliable results favoring the loss of ferromagnetism as the cause of the breaks in the values of various physical properties. However, recent evidence[38] has supported an allotropic transformation, probably back to hexagonal cobalt, overlapping the Curie point—the temperature at which cobalt loses its ferromagnetism—about 1120°C (2048°F). Further evidence has been supplied by a study of some cobalt alloys in which the Curie point and allotropic transformation begin to be separated.[37]

The dual effect of impurities both on the properties directly, and indirectly by their effect on the allotropic transformation, have made it difficult to obtain reliable data on properties at room temperature. For this reason, values have been preferred which are known to refer to either hexagonal or cubic cobalt rather than to the more usual mixture of the two forms. Even when cobalt metal of better than 99.9 per cent purity has been used, considerable variation has been found, e.g., 6.36 to 8.96 × 10⁻⁶ ohm-cm for the electrical resistance.

Battelle[86] zone-refined cobalt from 99.95 to 99.98 per cent purity and, using this material, determined the lattice constants and density which are compared with those by Taylor and Floyd[68] in Table 8.4.

The specific gravities of cubic and hexagonal cobalt, determined from x-ray diffraction data, are 8.90 and 8.94, respectively. For cobalt of better than 99.9 per cent purity, the highest observed values are 8.92 for wrought cobalt[24] (probably completely hexagonal) and 8.87 for cast cobalt.[38] It is possible that cobalt has a defective lattice, particularly in the powder form.[66]

The melting point of cobalt is 1493°C

TABLE 8.4. X-RAY AND DENSITY DATA OF HEXAGONAL CLOSE-PACKED COBALT

Reference	Condition	Lattice Constants, Å		
		a_0	c_0	c/a
Taylor and Floyd	Quenched from 400°C (752°F)	2.5074	4.0699	1.623
Battelle	Zone refined‡	2.5059	4.0695	1.624
Calculated density* (g/cc)	Remarks†			
8.832	Considerable f-c-c β cobalt present $a_0 = 3.561$			
8.844	Some f-c-c cobalt			

* Using the following constants: At wt = 58.94; Avogadro's No. = 6.0228 × 10²³.
† Presence of β cobalt determined by x-ray diffraction using Fe-K radiation.
‡ Material annealed.

(2719°F),[73] and the boiling point is 3100°C (5610°F). The latent heat of fusion has been found to be between 58 and 68 cal/g, 62 being the preferred value.[46, 48, 71, 72] The latent heat of vaporization is about 1,500 cal/g.

The heat of transformation at the Curie point has been reported to be between 0 and 14.7 cal/g,[61, 74, 77] but the most reliable value is probably 1.6 cal/g.[22] The coincidence of an allotropic transformation and the Curie point may account for some of this divergence.[38] At the lower allotropic transformation around 400°C (752°F), similar discrepancies exist,[22, 62, 72] but the best value is thought to be that determined by an adiabatic method[1] of 60 cal/mole.

The specific heat at elevated temperatures has been determined by both the adiabatic[1] and the drop methods.[21, 72, 77] Although the adiabatic method is to be preferred for cobalt in view of the martensitic-type transformation, these values do not extend beyond 800°C (1472°F). The determinations by the drop method[72, 77] agree fairly well up to the transformation above 1100°C (2012°F) when considerable divergence appears, but the difference in purity has led to the use of the more recent values[77] on 99.9 per cent cobalt. These weighted values, given in Table 8.5, are for the true specific heat. The specific heat of liquid cobalt has been found to be constant,[72] at 0.265 cal/g,

but this value may be too high. Atomic heats (Cp) have been calculated,[22, 77] as well as for constant volume (Cv), but, since the latter calculation depends on the extrapolation of Bridgman's values[5] for the compressibility at 30°C (86°F) (0.733 × 10⁻⁵) and at 75°C (167°F) (0.744 × 10⁻⁵) over a wide range of temperature, the results have not been included. The difference between Cp and Cv is small, however. Below room temperature, several determinations have been made,[10, 49, 54, 55] and the best values seem to be 0.0207 cal/g between −253 and 196°C (−423 and 385°F);[10] 0.0329 at −201.8°C (−331°F); 0.0672 at −150°C (−238°F); 0.0810 at −100°C (−148°F); 0.0915 at −50°C (−58°F); 0.0991 at 0°C (32°F), and 0.1032 at 50°C (122°F).[54] These values are in excellent agreement with the determinations at higher temperatures (Table 8.5).

No reliable figures exist for the thermal conductivity of cobalt, values ranging from 0.1299 to 0.172 cal/°C/cm/sec at 30°C (86°F).[2, 19, 32] Cobalt becomes superconducting at low temperatures.[35]

There are few reliable determinations of thermal expansion of pure cobalt.[12, 29, 32, 41, 57, 60, 70, 75, 76] Shinoda[60] had found that the coefficients for hexagonal cobalt are $\alpha_{11} = 16.1 × 10^{-6}$ and $\alpha_1 = 12.6 × 10^{-6}$ with a mean value of

TABLE 8.5. SPECIFIC HEAT, ELECTRICAL RESISTIVITY, AND THERMOELECTRIC DATA FOR COBALT

Temperature		Specific heat (cal/g)		Electrical resistance		Thermoelectric emf versus platinum (mv)
°C	°F	True	Mean	Microhm-cm ($\sigma × 10^6$)	Temperature coefficient of resistance ($\alpha × 10^3$)	
0	32	0.099	—	5.68	5.31	0.00
100	212	0.106	0.102	9.30	7.36	2.51
200	392	0.113	0.105	13.88	9.63	5.51
300	572	0.120	0.109	19.78	11.0	9.03
400	752	0.125	0.113	26.56	12.6	12.81
500	932	0.126	0.121	32.20	13.8	16.18
600	1112	0.136	0.123	40.2	15.0	18.80
700	1292	0.147	0.125	49.2	16.6	21.13
800	1472	0.159	0.128	58.6	16.6	22.81
900	1652	0.172	0.133	68.0	16.6	23.70
1000	1832	0.187	0.138	77.4	16.6	23.75
1100	2012	0.204	0.143	86.7	16.6	23.00
1200	2192	0.166	0.147	91.9	6.7	21.75
1300	2372	0.167	0.148	95.7	6.7	
1400	2552	0.168	0.149			

Note: The mean specific heat is measured between room temperature [ca. 25°C (77°F) and the temperature stated].

13.8 × 10⁻⁶ at room temperature. This is higher than other values. Table 8.6 gives values of the coefficient of expansion.

TABLE 8.6. COEFFICIENT OF THERMAL EXPANSION OF COBALT

Temperature		Schulze[57] 99.2% (× 10⁻⁶)	Fine and Ellis[12] 99.9% (× 10⁻⁶)	Masumoto and Nara[32] (× 10⁻⁶)
°C	°F			
20–100	68–212	12.5	—	12.55
100–200	212–392	13.6	(14.2)	13.57
200	392	—	14.2	—
200–300	392–572	14.4	(14.2)	14.37
300–400	572–752	15.1	(14.8)	15.4
400	752	—	15.7	—
450–500	842–932	14.0	—	—
600	1112	—	16.0	—
750	1382	—	16.8	—
$\frac{\Delta V}{V}$ (%)		0.30	0.24	0.27–0.36

Note: $\frac{\Delta V}{V}$ is the expansion on transforming from hexagonal to cubic close-packed cobalt.

Marick[29] and Meyer[41] took high-temperature x-ray diffraction photographs of cobalt, and Marick found a volume increase of 2 per cent between 1100–1500°C (2012–2102°F) which he attributed to the loss of ferromagnetism. Dilatometric measurements between 1000–1300°C (1832–2372°F) have revealed an expansion of 0.027 per cent between 1119–1145°C (2046–2093°F) occurring in two stages, because of the Curie point and an allotropic transformation.[37, 38]

The electrical resistance has been measured on many occasions,[7,14,17,19,22,24,26,27,29,30,31,33, 47,51,53,56,57,59,68] but only results for cobalt of known purity have been considered. High-purity cobalt was used by Schulze,[56] Jaeger, Rosenbohm, and Zuithoff,[22] and Marick,[29] but the latter's results are not believed to be reliable on account of the inconsistency in the position of the Curie point, compared with the x-ray results. Table 8.5 gives the weighted mean of these results for 99.95 per cent cobalt. Below room temperature, Tuijn and Onnes[68] found that cobalt did not show superconductivity, but Meissner and co-workers[33] estimated that pure cobalt would show superconductivity at 19°K for vacuum cast metal.

The Curie point has been determined by many investigators by indirect methods such as electrical resistance, thermoelectric emf, spe-

cific heat, and x-ray diffraction[22,29,30,52,56,61, 72,74] with few direct observations on pure cobalt.[14,40,42,63] Myers and Sucksmith determined it at 1121 ± 3°C (2050 ± 5°F),[42] whereas Meyer and Taglang found it to be 1131°C (2068°F),[40] but the former is believed to be preferable. In comparison, the Curie point of iron is 788°C (1450°F). The Curie point for hexagonal cobalt has been determined by extrapolation of the low-temperature data to be 1070[40] and 1150°K.[53]

The spontaneous magnetization at the absolute zero for single crystals of hexagonal cobalt has been found to be 160.9[14] and 162.55.[42] The saturation intensity for unit volume at the absolute zero has been found to be 1446[20,25] and 1437[42] for hexagonal cobalt single crystals. Myers and Sucksmith[42] have found that the magnetization of single crystals of cobalt increased with each cycle through the lower transformation up to the fifth cycle, with a somewhat smaller increase in the magnetization of cubic cobalt decreasing on heating. Surveys of the magnetic properties of cobalt have been published.[18,34]

The thermoelectric properties have been investigated for cobalt with platinum,[26,44,47,56,61] nickel,[8,22,45] iron,[8] and copper.[45,47] Table 8.5 gives the best value for the cobalt-platinum couple, calculated from results by Jaeger, Rosenbohm, and Zuithoff,[22] using Schulze's values for the temperature coefficient at higher temperatures. Bridgman[3] has determined the Peltier and Thomson effects.

Room temperature hardness[86] was found to vary from 81 to 249 Bhn, depending on the orientation of the hardness impressions within a crystal. Hot hardness ranged from 253 Brinell at room temperature to 17 Brinell at 900°C (1652°F), which difference from the original of 253 Brinell is due to impurities, and relative amounts of alpha and beta cobalt phases present.

The hardness of cast cobalt has been reported as 124 Brinell for 99.9 per cent purity,[24] whereas electrodeposited cobalt is about 300.[28] The properties are greatly affected by traces of other elements; e.g., carbon, sulfur, silicon, and manganese are harmful to the ductility of cobalt. Cast cobalt is reported to have a tensile strength of 35,000 psi, increased to 40,000 psi on annealing.[9,13] The strength increases rapidly on working and may attain 100,000 psi in the

TABLE 8.7. PHYSICAL PROPERTIES OF COBALT
(Most Accepted Values)

Atomic number	27
Atomic weight	58.94
Isotopes	57, 59, 60 (artificial)
Density (g/cc)	8.90 (0.321 lb/cu in.)
Melting point	1493°C (2720°F)
Boiling point at 760 mm Hg	3100°C (5610°F)
Latent heat of fusion (cal/g)	62
Latent heat of vaporization (cal/g)	1,500
Lattice constants	
Alpha, face-centered cubic	$a_0 = 3.5370$ Å
Beta, hexagonal close packed	$a_0 = 2.5017$ Å
	$c = 4.0614$ Å
Transformation temperature, beta to alpha	$417° \pm 7°C$ ($783° \pm 13°F$)
Volume expansion on transformation from	
hexagonal close packed to face-centered cubic	approx. 0.3%
Heat of transformation (cal/mole)	60
Curie point	1121°C (2050°F)
Specific heat (cal/g/°C)	
15–100°C (59–212°F)	0.1056
Liquid	0.141
Coefficient of thermal expansion [40°C (104°F)]	(see Table 8.6) 13.36×10^{-6}
Electrical resistance	(see Table 8.5)
Volume conductivity at 20°C (reference copper)	27.6%
Velocity of sound	
m/sec	4,724
ft/sec	15,500
Thermal conductivity	
0–100°C (cal/sec/sq cm/°C/cm)	0.165
32–212°F (Btu/hr/sq ft/°F/in.)	479
Hardness	
Cast, Brinell	124
Electrodeposited, Brinell	300
Tensile strength (psi)	
Cast	35,000
Annealed	40,000
Wire	100,000
Compressive strength, cast (psi)	120,000
Yield point (psi)	42,000
Young's modulus (psi), tension	30,000,000
Modulus of elasticity in shear	11,100,000

HIGH TEMPERATURE PROPERTIES

Rupture strength, 100 hr at 649°C (1200°F)	12,500 psi
at 816°C (1500°F)	3,000 psi
Creep 99.6% cobalt, 100 hr at 500°C (930°F); 12,000 psi, 2.7% elongation	
Creep at 1000°C (1832°F) for 1% strain in 24 hr:	
99.97% cobalt sintered and swaged	13,900 psi
Vacuum melted	6,700 psi

Tensile properties	Ultimate (psi)	Yield (psi)	Red. of Area (%)
Arc melted electrolytic			
At room temperature	57,500	43,000	3
At 927°C (1700°F)	12,400	8,100	12

form of wire.[28] The compressive strength of cast cobalt is 120,000 psi with a yield point at 42,000 psi.[28] Young's modulus is about 30,000,000 psi.

The self-diffusion in cobalt has been measured with divergent results.[33,43,50,88] The constant in the Arrhenius equation has been found to be 0.37 and 0.032, respectively, with the activation energies of 67,000 and 61,900 cal, respectively.

Mead and Birchenall,[85] by a method not sensitive to surface preparation, have obtained the equation $D = 0.83e^{(-67,700/RT)}$ sq cm/sec for self-diffusion in 99.9+ per cent cobalt; for dilute cobalt diffusing in nickel, $D_{Ni}^{Co} = 1.46e^{-68,300/RT}$ sq cm/sec.

Carter and Richardson[80] have measured the self-diffusion of cobalt in cobaltous oxide over a range of compositions and established the following diffusion coefficients:

At 1000°C (1832°F) $D = 2.6 \times 10^{-9} (PO_2)^{0.35}$ sq cm/sec^{-1}

At 1150°C (2102°F) $D = 9.0 \times 10^{-9}(PO_2)^{0.30}$ sq cm/sec^{-1}

At 1350°C (2462°F) $D = 5.1 \times 10^{-8} (PO_2)^{0.28}$ sq cm/sec^{-1}

Turnbull[69] has calculated the surface energy to be 234 ergs/sq cm for the liquid-to-solid interface.

The velocity of sound in cobalt is 4,724 m/sec or 15,500 ft/sec.[16a]

CHEMICAL PROPERTIES

Cobalt is very similar to iron and nickel in its chemical properties, as might be expected from its close proximity to those elements in the periodic table as the iron-cobalt-nickel triad of Group VIII. It forms both divalent and trivalent compounds, but the latter are much less stable than the divalent ones.

Cobalt in powder form is readily oxidized at room temperature, but in solid form it is not attacked by oxygen or water below about 300°C (572°F), being quite different from iron in this respect. The metal powder occludes 50 to 100 volumes of hydrogen and forms a small amount of hydride.

Carter and Richardson,[7,7a] investigating the oxidation of cobalt metal by means of inert markers of radio-platinum, concluded that oxidation occurs by cation diffusion across the growing oxide film. Oxidation rates at various temperatures and oxygen pressures agree with the rates calculated from the Wagner equation.

Above 950°C (1742°F) cobalt oxidizes in accordance with the parabolic law and forms cobaltous oxide (CoO) above 900°C (1652°F). Pressure increase accelerates the rate of oxidation to a point where it levels out below 1150°C (2102°F).

Cobalt decomposes ammonia gas at about 500°C (932°F), the nitrogen uniting with the metal to form a nitride, Co_4N_2; in the presence of air a nitrite is formed.

Cobalt combines with the halogens to form the respective halides, and it readily dissolves in sulfuric, hydrochloric, and nitric acids.

Cobalt chloride, $CoCl_2$, is used for preparing very fine cobalt powder[1] by reduction with hydrogen in the presence of 0.1 per cent (by weight of cobalt chloride) of metallic cobalt as a catalyst at temperatures in the range of 265–305°C (510–690°F). Davis describes the use of cobalt chloride as an indicator of humidity.[3]

Cobalt is slowly attacked by sodium and ammonium hydroxides.

Cobalt powder and carbon monoxide, under pressure of 100 atm and 200°C (392°F), react to form cobalt carbonyl, $Co_2(CO)_8$, which decomposes above 60°C (140°F) in the air to form cobalt and carbon monoxide. McKeever[4] describes the manufacture of cobalt carbonyl by suspending cobalt carbonate, basic cobalt carbonate, and cobalt hydroxide in a neutral organic liquid (alcohols and ketones) which is a solvent for cobalt carbonyl, and reacting with carbon monoxide at 140–300°C (284–572°F) under a pressure of 500 to 5,000 psi.

Cobalt carbide, Co_2C, is formed at 226–230°C (439–446°F) by reacting cobalt powder with carbon monoxide at atmospheric pressure.

Heyding and Calvert,[7] in their investigation of the compounds of cobalt and arsenic up to 60 per cent arsenic by weight, found the compounds Co_2As and $CoAs$ to exist at room temperature. Co_3As_2 is probably formed by the reaction of Co_2As with $CoAs$ above 940°C (1724°F). There are marked similarities between the iron-arsenic and cobalt-arsenic systems.

Cobaltous carbonate, $CoCO_3$, is made by the action of alkali carbonates on cobaltous salts and occurs in nature as sphaerocobaltite.

Cobaltic carbonate, $Co_2(CO_3)_2$, is produced by the oxidation of cobaltous carbonate.

Cobaltous fluoride, CoF_2, is a red crystalline solid, usually in a hydrated form. The free energy of cobaltous fluoride at various temperatures is as follows:

25°C	227°C	727°C	1227°C	kcal/mole
−147.9	−141.0	−125	−108.5	of fluorine

Cobaltic fluoride, CoF_3, forms brown crystals in the anhydrous state and red cobaltous fluoride on heating in air.

Cobaltous nitrate, $Co(NO_3)_2 \cdot 6H_2O$, is formed by the action of dilute nitric acid on cobalt metal, oxide, hydroxide, or carbonate.

Cobaltous oxide, CoO,[6] is slowly formed by heating cobalt metal to redness without free access of air, or by heating cobaltic oxide, Co_2O_3, or cobalto-cobaltic oxide, Co_3O_4, at a high temperature. It is a catalyst for the oxidation of ammonia and drying oils. Cobaltous oxide is dark gray, insoluble in water, soluble in acids and in alkali hydroxides, and slightly soluble in ammonia. It is the gray oxide of commerce.

Cobaltic oxide, Co_2O_3,[6] is prepared by heating cobalt compounds at a low temperature in the presence of air. Upon heating to 850°C (1562°F), cobaltic oxide is transformed into black cobalto-cobaltic oxide, Co_3O_4. Cobaltic oxide forms cobaltites when it unites with oxides of other metals, e.g., $ZnO \cdot Co_2O_3$.

Cobalto-cobaltic oxide, Co_3O_4, is formed on heating salts to 850°C (1562°F) and can be reduced to metal by carbon, carbon monoxide, or hydrogen.

Cobaltous phosphates are prepared in several forms by heating a cobaltous salt with phosphoric acid or alkaline phosphate.

Cobaltous orthosilicate, Co_2SiO_4, a violet crystalline compound, is found in slags and glazes.

Cobaltous sulfate, $CoSO_4 \cdot 7H_2O$,[2] is prepared by dissolving cobalt oxide, hydroxide, or carbonate in dilute sulfuric acid and crystallizing out as the pink heptahydrate.

Cobaltic sulfate, $Co_2(SO_4)_3$,[2] can be prepared by the electrolysis of a standard solution of cobalt sulfate in dilute sulfuric acid in a platinum dish as anode and with a platinum wire in a porous cell containing dilute sulfuric acid as cathode. It is an unstable salt.

Cobaltous sulfide, CoS,[2] is a black powder formed by passing hydrogen sulfide into an alkaline cobalt solution. It occurs as the natural sulfide, jaipurite, found in India.

Cobaltosic sulfide, Co_2S_4, cobaltic sulfide, Co_2S_3, and cobalt disulfide, CoS_2, have been prepared by heating together compounds of cobalt and sulfur under varying conditions. In nature, cobalt sulfides occur as the minerals carrollite, linnaeite, polydymite, siegenite, etc.

APPLICATIONS AND FABRICATION

Very little cobalt metal is used as such, other than the relatively small quantity as radioactive cobalt 60 which is used in radiotherapy, industrial radiography, and measuring instruments. Eighty-five per cent of the metallic cobalt consumption is used in manufacturing high-temperature alloys, permanent magnets, and tool and wear-resisting alloys.

The consumption data for the years 1957 to 1959, given in Table 8.8, stress the changing modes of application for cobalt.

TABLE 8.8. COBALT CONSUMED IN THE UNITED STATES BY USES* (Percentage Basis)

	1957	1958	1959
High-speed and other steels	3.8	2.6	8.4
Permanent and soft magnets	31.6	31.0	30.1
Cobalt-chromium-tungsten-molybdenum alloys	33.2	31.1	24.2
Alloy hard facing alloys and cemented carbides	8.3	6.8	7.5
Other metallic uses	2.5	3.3	8.1
Ground coat frit	5.2	6.1	5.5
Pigments	2.3	3.3	2.2
Salts and driers, etc.	11.0	13.7	11.5
Other nonmetallic uses	2.0	2.1	2.5
Total pounds	9,156,617	7,542,000	9,899,000

* Data based on U.S. Bureau of Mines statistics.

The United States is the largest consumer of cobalt in the world and is largely dependent upon imported supplies to satisfy its demand.

The applications and fabrication of cobalt and cobalt alloys are presented under four categories: ferrous alloys, nonferrous alloys, cobalt powder metallurgy, and electrodeposition.

Cobalt 60 characteristics are discussed under the heading "Biological Effects of Cobalt."

Cobalt in Ferrous Alloys

The iron-cobalt equilibrium diagram shows that cobalt is entirely miscible with gamma iron and forms solid solutions with alpha iron to about 80 per cent cobalt.[8] In general, the solid solubility of any element in ferrite produces increased strength and hardness while decreasing elongation and reduction of area.

The tendency for cobalt to form carbides is slightly less than that of iron. Cobalt is the only alloying element that reduces the hardenability of steel. Its principal function is to resist softening at elevated temperature when dissolved in ferrite.

High-Speed Steels.[1,2,3,4,5,6,7,9] Cobalt is an essential constituent of a group of tungsten tool steels capable of heavy cuts and feeds at high speeds in the machining of steels and nonferrous metals. These steels consist basically of 18 per cent tungsten, 4 per cent chromium, 1 per cent vanadium, 5 to 12 per cent cobalt, and 0.5 to 0.8 per cent carbon. In general, the cutting ability is proportional to the cobalt content up to 13 per cent cobalt. Cobalt dissolves in tungsten in amounts up to 30 per cent, and a tungsten-cobalt compound is precipitated upon reheating, thus improving the plain tungsten tool steels.

The addition of cobalt to molybdenum high-speed steels also improves their properties.

Magnets. The criteria used in the evaluation of permanent magnets is the maximum product of the magnetic flux density in the material multiplied by the magnetizing force. This is denoted by $(BH)_{max}$, where B is the flux density in gausses and H is the corresponding magnetizing force in oersteds. $(BH)_{max}$ represents a measure of the maximum amount of magnetic energy that can be stored in a unit volume of magnetic material. It is a measure of the "performance" of a permanent magnet, and the higher the $(BH)_{max}$ value, the more efficient the magnet. The value of remanence (Br) multiplied by the coercive force (Hc) is approximately proportional to $(BH)_{max}$. Since the shape of the magnet determines the flux density in a fully magnetized bar, $(BrHc)$ is not the only criterion. Too high coercive force with too low residual induction may give a satisfactory $(BrHc)$ but may not permit substitution of one material for another without redesigning the magnet.

Commercial cobalt magnet steels range from 6 to 50 per cent cobalt and 0.8 to 1.0 per cent carbon with $(BrHc)$ values of 0.90×10^6 gauss-oersteds.

In 1920 Honda and Saito developed the "K.S." steels, containing 0.4 to 0.8 per cent carbon, 30 to 50 per cent cobalt, 5 to 9 per cent tungsten, and 1.5 to 3 per cent chromium. Their $(BrHc)$ values range from 2.0 to 2.6×10^6 gauss-oersteds. The coercive force and performance products are, in general, directly proportional to the cobalt content. United States Patent 2,596,705 (1952), granted to D. L. Martin, discloses a magnetic alloy containing 5 to 7 per cent nickel, 4 to 6 per cent vanadium, 43 to 47 per cent cobalt, balance iron, having a coercive force of 50 to 100 oersteds and a Br of 12,000 gauss, minimum.

In the ternary system, iron-cobalt-nickel, there is a region which exhibits constant permeability in low fields. These alloys have been named "Perminvars," and a typical alloy contains 45 per cent nickel, 25 per cent cobalt, and 30 per cent iron. Magnetization properties are affected by air quenching, annealing, and low temperature tempering.

The precipitation-hardening magnet alloys contain little or no carbon and are not magnetic as cast, but obtain their properties by precipitation of one or more alloying constituents from a solid solution under controlled conditions. In 1931 Mishima discovered a number of iron-nickel-aluminum (16 to 32 per cent nickel, 5 to 12 per cent aluminum, balance iron) alloys of high coercive force. The addition of 0.5 to 40 per cent cobalt was found to decrease the grain size, with consequent increase of coercive force and residual magnetism. The commercial alloys known as the "Alnico"-type magnets are now made within the limits of nickel 14 to 30 per cent, aluminum 6 to 12 per cent, cobalt 5 to 35 per cent, balance iron; some grades also contain copper and titanium.

The "Alnico" alloys have high coercive force and high magnetic energy. Each of the grades exhibits certain advantages and limitations. Grades V and VI have directional characteristics obtainable by cooling the magnet from the normalizing temperature [about 1300°C (2372°F)] to black in a strong magnetic field.

TABLE 8.9. DATA FOR COBALT-BEARING MAGNETIC MATERIALS

High-permeability materials

Material	Form	Approximate composition (%)	Typical heat treatment "C"	Permeability at B=20 (gauss)	Maximum permeability	Saturation flux density B_s (Gauss)	Hysteresis loss* W_h (ergs/cc)	Coercive force* H_c (oersteds)	Resistivity (microhm-cm)	Density (g/cc)
"Permendur"	Sheet	4.97 Fe, 50.0 Co, 0.3 Mn	800 Anneal	800	5,000	24,500	12,000	2.0	7	8.3
"2 V Permendur"	Sheet	4.90 Fe, 49.0 Co, 2.0 V	800 Anneal	800	4,500	24,000	6,000	2.0	26	8.2
"Hiperco"	Sheet	6.40 Fe, 35.0 Co, 1.0 Cr	850 Anneal	650	10,000	24,200	—	1.0	25	8.0

Permanent-magnet alloys

Material	% Composition, Bal. Fe	Heat treatment [temperature† (°C)]	Magnetizing force H max. (oersteds)	Coercive force, H_c (oersteds)	Residual induction B_r (gauss)	Energy product, (BH) max. $\times 10^6$	Fabrication‡	Mechanical properties§	Weight (lb/cu in.)
17% cobalt steel	17 Co, 0.75 C, 2.5 Cr, 8 W	—	1,000	150	9,500	0.65	HR, M, P	H, S	0.296
36% cobalt steel	36 Co, 0.70 C, 4 Cr, 5 W	Q 950	1,000	240	9,500	0.97	HR, M, P	H, S	0.295
"Remalloy" or "Comol"	17 Mo, 12 Co	Q 1200, B 700	1,000	250	10,500	1.10	HR, M, P	H	0.295
"Alnico I"	12 Al, 20 Ni, 5 Co	A 1200, B 700	2,000	440	7,200	1.4	C, G	H, B	0.249
"Alnico II"	10 Al, 17 Ni, 2.5 Co, 6 Cu	A 1200, B 600	2,000	550	7,200	1.6	C, G	H, B	0.256
"Alnico II" sintered	10 Al, 17 Ni, 2.5 Co, 6 Cu	A 1300	2,000	520	6,900	1.4	Sn, G	H	0.249
"Alnico IV"	12 Al, 28 Ni, 5 Co	Q 1200, B 650	3,000	700	5,500	1.3	Sn, C, G	H	0.253
"Alnico V"	8 Al, 14 Ni, 24 Co, 3 Cu	AF 1300, B 600	2,000	550	12,500	4.5	C, G	H, B	0.264
"Alnico VI"	8 Al, 15 Ni, 24 Co, 3 Cu, 1 Ti	—	3,000	750	10,000	3.5	C, G	H, B	0.268
"Alnico XII"	6 Al, 18 Ni, 35 Co, 8 Ti	—	3,000	950	5,800	1.5	C, G	H, B	0.260
"Vicalloy I"	52 Co, 9.5 V	B 600	1,000	300	8,800	1.0	C, CR, M, P	D	0.295
"Vicalloy II" (wire)	52 Co, 14 V	CW + B 600	2,000	510	10,000	3.5	C, CR, M, P	D	0.292
"Cunico"	50 Cu, 21 Ni, 29 Co	—	3,200	660	3,400	0.80	C, CR, M, P	D, M	0.300
Platinum-cobalt	77 Pt, 23 Co	Q 1200, B 650	—	2,600	4,500	3.80	C, CR, M	D	
Platinax II	76.7 Pt, 23.3 Co	—	—	4,800	6,400	9.2			
Ticonal XXX	34.0 Co, 15 No, 7 Al, 4 Cu, 5 Ti, 35 Fe					11.0			
Ticonal G	24 Co, 3 Cu, 14 Ni, 8 Al, 50 Fe					5.0			

* At saturation.

† Q = quenched in oil or water; A = air-cooled; B = baked; F = cooled in magnetic field; CW = cold-worked.

‡ HR = hot-rolled or forged; CR = cold-rolled or drawn; C = cast; M = machined; G = must be ground; P = punched; Sn = sintered.

§ H = hard; B = brittle; S = strong; D = ductile; M = malleable.

All grades may be cast to the desired shape, and Grades II, IV, V, and VI can also be made by sintering in vacuum or in an atmosphere of dry hydrogen.

"Supermendur" (Western Electric) is nominally 49 per cent iron, 49 per cent cobalt, and 2 per cent vanadium. It can be rolled from 0.090 to 0.0003 in. without intermediate anneals or loss of ductility. Maximum permeability is 66,000 at 20,000 gauss, remanence of 21,500 gauss, coercive force of 0.26 oersted, saturation of 24,000 gauss, and low hysteresis loss.

Cobalt-platinum magnetic alloys in the range of 30 to 72.5 atomic per cent cobalt, prepared by sintering metal powders or by melting and casting, give a satisfactory product. The general treatment consists of heating to 900–1000°C (1652–1832°F) to disorder, and cooling to room temperature, followed by isothermal ordering at 600°C (1112°F). Alloys around 50 per cent atomic per cent have the best magnetic properties. The highest coercive force, 4,700 oersted and $(BH)_{max}$, 9×10^6 gauss-oersted, are obtained at 49.3 atomic per cent cobalt by controlled cooling [100°C (212°F)/min] from disordering treatment prior to aging at 600°C (1112°F).

Table 8.9 lists some of the common magnetic alloys and their properties.

Permanent magnets may be made by pressing and sintering metal oxide powders and then magnetizing at a low temperature. Magnets are made from Fe_3O_4 and $CoFe_2O_4$ by pressing, sintering at 1000°C (1832°F), and magnetizing at 300°C (572°F). At room temperature they have Br values of 3,000 to 5,000 gauss and Hc values of 600 to 400 oersteds.

General Electric "Vectolite" is made from iron oxide and cobalt oxide. It has high electrical resistance, a coercive force of 6,000 oersteds, and low eddy current loss, and is used in high-frequency magnetic fields.

Ferromagnetic crystalline oxides of manganese and cobalt having an ilmenite type crystal structure are used for recording tapes and as magnetic core materials in electronic equipment. The chemical composition may be represented by the formula $CoMnO_3$ which is formed by blending 3.35 parts of finely divided cobaltous-cobaltic oxide (Co_3O_4) with 3.5 parts manganese dioxide (MnO_2) and water 1½ times the weight of the oxide. This mixture is placed in a platinum tube, sealed, and subjected to 625°C (1157°F) at 3,000 atm.

Glass-to-Metal Seals.[1,2,3,4] The iron-nickel-cobalt alloys extensively used for glass-to-metal seals have low expansivity at temperatures less than their characteristic inflection temperatures and greater expansivity at higher temperatures. Hence, by blending, the inflection temperature of iron-nickel-cobalt materials can be made to coincide with the annealing range of certain glass compositions, and expansion properties can be made to equal or approach those of the glasses.

Nominal chemical compositions of such alloys are 54 per cent iron, 28 per cent nickel, and 18 per cent cobalt. They have transition temperatures at about 435°C (815°F) and expansivities between 25–325°C (77–617°F) of 4.0 × 10^{-6}/°C. Above the transition temperature, the expansivity may be as much as 12.0 × 10^{-6}/°C.

Alloys for Corrosion and Oxidation Resistance. The development of the gas turbine gave impetus to investigations on the effect of alloying elements in steel to improve performance at elevated temperatures. Bollenrath, Cornelius, and Bungardt in 1938 described a range of iron-nickel-chromium-cobalt-tungsten-molybdenum alloys for gas turbine blading. These alloys contain, by per cent, 10 to 18 chromium, 25 to 40 nickel, 20 to 35 cobalt, 0 to 8 tungsten, 0 to 8 molybdenum, and 0 to 3 titanium or 2 to 8 columbium.[6]

Bardgett and Bolsover[4] investigated a forgeable alloy steel, referred to as "Multi-Alloy," containing, percentagewise, 0.25 carbon, 1.63 manganese, 1.03 silicon, 46.52 nickel, 20.5 chromium, 2.73 molybdenum, 3.33 cobalt, 2.92 columbium, 3.52 tungsten, and 1.2 titanium. At 800°C (1472°F) and a stress of 5,000 psi, the creep strain at 300 hr was 0.20 per cent. Steels containing, by per cent, 6 to 7 cobalt, 0.2 to 0.43 carbon, 14.3 chromium, 18 nickel, 3.85 molybdenum, 3.85 copper, and 0.75 titanium were used with air-gas ratios of 2:1, 4:1, and 6:1 at temperatures up to 750°C (1382°F) with satisfactory scaling rates.

Valve stem tips for aero engines contain 1.27 to 1.43 per cent carbon, 11.75 to 13.75 per cent chromium, 2.7 to 3.3 per cent cobalt, 0.6 per cent nickel, and 0.5 to 0.85 per cent molybdenum with a hardness of Rockwell C52.

In the field of hardfacing alloys[3,8,12] for resistance to corrosion, abrasion, and oxidation

| Number | Composition (%) | | | | | | Vickers hardness number |
	C	Cr	W	Mo	Co	Others	
1	1.31	5.67	3.98	6.86	10.2	V 1.63	900
2	4.84	32.4	—	—	1.36	Mn 3.42	710
3	3.42	18.52	1.02	11.86	9.36	Ni 0.6	870
4	2.74	24.54	13.25	0.58	14.81	V 1.50	608

at high temperatures, the above compositions are typical of cast welding rods.

Where there is a combination of abrasion, oxidation at high temperature, and corrosion, the cobalt-base welding rods are required as listed subsequently under the heading "Cast Alloys" on page 133.

It is now practical to metal spray cobalt-base alloys finely powdered and formulated for applying by means of a spray gun or pistol onto carbon and low-alloy steel components. The sprayed metal is held in contact with the metal surface by a mechanical bond which is acceptable for some applications. In other applications the sprayed metal is subsequently fused and metallurgically bonded with the base metal. To effect such a bond the alloy must be at the fusion temperature which is indicated by the ability of the alloy to glisten or glaze. This property depends on surface tension, a wide plastic range, and freedom from oxide.

Applications comprise pump shafts, sleeves, pump plungers, pyrometer sheaths, edges of fan blades, etc.

Cobalt in Nonferrous Alloys

Alloys containing 20 to 65 per cent cobalt have excellent wear resistance and are oxidation and corrosion resistant under extreme corrosive media and elevated temperature conditions. These properties find application on the high-temperature side of jet engines, in valves operating under corrosive and high-temperature conditions, in sheet form for searchlight reflectors, and in castings for surgical and dental applications and cutting tools.

Such alloys may be classified on the basis of their alloy content as cobalt-chromium-tungsten and as cobalt-chromium-nickel-tungsten, with molybdenum replacing all or part of the tungsten. Numerous modifications may be obtained by the addition of small amounts of vanadium, columbium, tantalum, boron, titanium, and carbon.

Stellites. Elwood Haynes in 1899 developed an alloy of cobalt and chromium which resisted chemical fumes and possessed great hardness up to visible redness. It could not be cold worked, but was malleable at a bright orange heat. By 1908 he had developed a cutting alloy with an edge equal to that of tempered steel. To the cobalt-chromium base alloy, tungsten, molybdenum, and carbon were added to produce cutting tools superior to high-speed steel tools. This gave the cobalt-chromium tungsten alloys a field of their own, and they were termed "stellites" from the Latin word *stella,* star.

Processing. The cobalt-base alloys are produced from prime metals and master alloys in indirect-arc or induction melting furnaces without the use of slags but with the addition of deoxidants. They are cast at pouring temperatures of 1450–1600°C (2642–2912°F). Cast structures have proved capable of standing stresses at high temperature.

Vacuum melting is the most recent technique directed toward improving the physical properties of alloys. Mechanical properties are consistently at a higher level as oxidation and contained gases are eliminated. Chemical composition is capable of closer control, and elements such as manganese and silicon, which are used as deoxidants in standard melting, may be eliminated with improvement in ductility. The readily oxidizable elements boron, aluminum, titanium, zirconium, etc., can be used more effectively as alloying elements. Thus the temperature ratings and physical properties of cobalt-bearing alloys may be significantly improved.

The techniques of forging and rolling require close temperature control of the range for hot working, and also the degree of reduction. In pressing or forming, the number of anneals usually equals the number of draws.

Cobalt high temperature alloys are not difficult to machine when in the solution-treated, partially aged, or fully aged condition. They work harden like the austenitic stainless steels,

CAST ALLOYS

| Designation | Per Cent by Weight | | | | | | Rockwell C hardness |
	Co	Cr	W	Fe	C	Si	
No. 1 welding rod	50.0	33.0	13.0	2.0	2.0	1.0	54–56
No. 6 welding rod	64.0	25.5	4.75	2.5	1.0	1.75	39–42
No. 12 welding rod	58.0	29.0	9.0	1.5	1.85	1.50	48–51
Cutting alloys	42–48	30.5–35.5	15–19	1.5	1.75–2.7	1.50	59–68
Battery castings	50–65	28–32	5–15	1.5	0.75–1.25	1.00	40–50
Valve inserts	45–48	30.5	12.5	2.0	2.40	0.50	55–60
Wear	51–53	30–32	10–11	2.0	1.70	0.60	53–58

WROUGHT ALLOYS

| Designation | Per Cent by Weight | | | | | | | Rockwell C hardness |
	Co	Cr	W	Fe	C	Si	Ni	
Haynes 6B	59.0	30.0	4.5	1.5	1.10	0.70	1.0	42–45
Haynes 6K	58.0	31.0	4.5	1.5	1.60	0.70	1.0	46–49
Haynes 25	49.0	20.0	15.0	2.0	0.10	0.70	10.0	30–38

and the machining techniques for stainless are applicable. Cutting tools must have sharp edges and rigid mountings. Feeds and speeds are lower than those for austenitic stainless, but the depth of cut should be sufficient to avoid glazing. An efficient coolant is required.

Applications. Prior to 1939 the various cobalt-chromium-tungsten alloys found application chiefly for cutting tools, hardfacing, and corrosion-resistant castings. Modifications of these alloys furnished suitable high-strength alloys at elevated temperatures for jet engines and ordnance requirements.

The above tables show the composition and hardness of typical stellites.

Dental and Surgical Alloys. The cobalt–chromium-base alloys for dental and surgical applications are not attacked by body fluids, and hence do not set up an emf in the body to cause irritation of the tissues.

Typical dental and surgical alloys are as follows:

High-Temperature Alloys. Tables 8.10, 8.11, and 8.12 summarize the chemical compositions and physical properties of present-day cobalt-bearing alloys for high-temperature service.

The hardening of cobalt-base alloys low in carbon is based upon solution treatment and precipitation at temperatures from 538–871°C (1000–1600°F) and times from 8 to 100 hr. Impact values of all cast cobalt-base alloys are lower at room temperature than they are at 816°C (1500°F), but the impact values of wrought alloys are higher. Hot fatigue tests at 649°C (1200°F) indicate that the cast alloys are somewhat inferior to wrought alloys.

Cobalt Powder

Cobalt powder[1,8,12,14,17,23] is widely used for the production of sintered hard metals, sintered magnets, and sintered iron-nickel-cobalt master alloys ("Sivar"). Pure sintered cobalt has found little or no practical application. It is produced

| Alloy | Per Cent by Weight | | | | | | | | | |
	C	Co	Cr	Mo	Fe	Si	Mn	Ni	V	Be
A	0.46	62.7	29.3	5.6	0.80	0.30	0.60	—	2.0	—
B	0.55	61.0	30.0	5.8	1.00	0.50	0.75	—	—	—
C	0.20	57.8	18.0	2.0	0.50	0.50	—	14.0	7.0	—
D	0.50	63.7	27.5	5.3	1.80	0.10	0.10	—	—	—
E	0.20	27.5	27.5	5.3	1.60	0.40	0.70	35.7	—	1.20
F	0.40	67.9	24.0	5.3	1.50	0.30	0.60	1.4	—	—

TABLE 8.10. SUMMARY OF COMMERCIAL COBALT-BEARING ALLOYS FOR HIGH TEMPERATURE SERVICE

°C	°F	Tensile psi	Elongation %	Stress-rupture 10 hr	100 hr	1,000 hr	Creep data			

S–816 (NDRC 76)
42 Co, 20 Cr, 20 Ni, 4 W, 4 Cb, 4 Mo, 3 Fe, 1.3 Mn, 0.60 Si, 0.40 C

°C	°F	Tensile psi	Elong. %	10 hr	100 hr	1,000 hr	Creep data		
649	1200	112,000	22.0	75,000	62,000	48,000	29,000(a)	42,000(b)	
732	1350	98,000	23.0	49,000	37,000	29,000	19,000(a)	26,000(b)	
816	1500	73,000	23.0	30,000	24,000	18,000	12,000(a)	16,000(b)	
871	1600	51,000	17.0	20,000	14,500	10,500	5,000(a)	9,800(b)	
927	1700	44,500	15.0	—	10,000	5,800			
982	1800	25,500	20.0	8,800	5,300	3,000			

Cast Haynes Stellite No. 21 (NDRC 10 or Modified Vitallium)
60 Co, 27.5 Cr, 5.5 Mo, 2.5 Ni, <2.0 Fe, 1.0 Mn, 0.60 Si, <0.35 C

°C	°F	Tensile psi	Elong. %	10 hr	100 hr	1,000 hr	Creep data			
649	1200	71,000	18.4	70,000	51,000	42,000	10,000(c)	0.0_313 (d)	0.0_31 (e)	0.0_48 (f)
732	1350	68,600	9.5	—	36,000	27,500	15,000(c)	0.0_33 (d)	0.0_319(e)	0.0_31 (f)
816	1500	65,700	17.4	—	24,000	14,200	7,000(c)	0.0_322 (d)	0.0_31 (e)	0.0_465(f)
871	1600	41,600	19.3	—	16,700	13,200	7,000(c)	0.0_3125(d)	0.0_444(e)	0.0_444(f)
							10,000(c)	0.0_333 (d)	0.0_313(e)	0.0_313(f)
982	1800	33,300	35.0	12,500	9,400	6,500				

N–155 (Haynes Multimet, or NDRC 21 or NDRC 66 with 0.16% C)
27 Fe, 21 Cr, 21 Co, 21 Ni, 3.2 Mo, 2.5 W, 1.5 Mn, 1.2 Cb, 0.7 Si, 0.33 C, 0.14 N

°C	°F	Tensile psi	Elong. %	10 hr	100 hr	1,000 hr	Creep data			
538	1000	94,000	—	—	78,000					
649	1200	80,000	—	70,000	53,000	42,000				
732	1350	60,000	14.5	40,000	31,000	24,500	12,000(c)	0.0_442(d)	0.0_425(e)	0.0_413(f)
							15,000(c)	0.0_312(d)	0.0_479(e)	0.0_438(f)
816	1500	45,000	24.5	23,000	18,000	13,000	7,000(c)	0.0_48 (d)	0.0_442(e)	—
							10,000(c)	0.0_49 (d)	0.0_49 (e)	0.0_317(f)
982	1800	—	—	—	6,400	4,200				

Haynes No. 25 (L–605)
50 Co, 20 Cr, 15 W, 10 Ni, <2 Fe, 1.5 Mn, 0.50 Si, 0.10 C

°C	°F	Tensile psi	Elong. %	10 hr	100 hr	1,000 hr	Creep data		
816	1500	50,000	15.0	30,000	22,500	17,000	9,000(c)	0.0_348(d)	0.0_337(e)
							12,000(c)	0.0_21 (d)	0.0_46 (e)
871	1600	—	—	23,000	16,500	12,000	8,000(c)	0.0_38 (d)	0.0_333(e)
927	1700	30,000	—	17,500	11,000	7,200	6,000(c)	0.0_343(d)	0.0_333(e)
982	1800	21,000	16.0	11,500	7,200	4,500	4,000(c)	0.0_388(d)	0.0_276(e)

Haynes No. 23 (NDRC 63; AMS 5375)
64.5 Co, 26 Cr, 1.5 Ni, 5.5 W, <2 Fe, 0.40 C

°C	°F	Tensile psi	Elong. %	10 hr	100 hr	1,000 hr	Creep data			
—	Room	111,000	8.7	—	—	—				
538	1000	77,100	14.8	—	—	—				
649	1200	66,500	11.5	—	58,000	47,000				
816	1500	64,000	19.4	—	27,200*	21,800	12,000(c)	0.0_3285(d)	0.0_311(e)	0.0_435(f)
927	1700	37,500	7.0	17,000	14,000	11,500				
982	1800	33,100	32.0	12,500	8,600	5,400				

TABLE 8.10. (*cont.*)

| Temperature | | Tensile | Elongation | Stress-rupture | | | Creep data |
°C	°F	psi	%	10 hr	100 hr	1,000 hr	

Haynes No. 27 (NDRC 60; AMS 5378)
>30.0 Co, 26.0 Cr, 6.0 Mo, <2.0 Fe, 0.40 C, bal. Ni

°C	°F	psi	%	10 hr	100 hr	1,000 hr	Creep data
—	Room	90,000	12.7	—	—	—	
538	1000	63,600	16.0	—	—	—	
649	1200	63,400	14.0	58,000	55,000	46,000	
816	1500	55,400	21.3	29,200*	23,400	18,400	12,000(c) 0.0_319(d) 0.0_318(e) 0.0_48(f) Aged 50 hr at 816°C (1500°F).
927	1700	43,000	23.0	16,000	12,000	8,600	
982	1800	33,400	24.0	12,500	9,300	6,800	

K–42–B (NDRC 77)
42 Ni, 22 Co, 18 Cr, 13 Fe, 2.6 Ti, 0.7 Mn, 0.7 Si, 0.2–0.6 Al, 0.05 C

°C	°F	psi	%	10 hr	100 hr	1,000 hr	Creep data	
649	1200	117,000	9.0	76,000	65,000	39,000		
732	1350	97,000	4.0	50,000	37,000	26,000	24,000(a)	33,000(b)
816	1500	54,000	10.0	22,000	16,000	10,000	7,500(a)	13,500(b)
871	1600	29,000	45.0	—	—	—		

G–32–B
45.5 Co, 18.8 Cr, 12.5 Ni, 2.00 Mo, 1.30 Cb, 2.80 V, 0.30 C, 0.40 Mn, 0.40 Si, bal. Fe
Solution treated at 1280°C (2336°F), 10 min. and oil-quenched. Aged 46 hr at 750°C (1382°F)

°C	°F	psi	%	30 hr	100 hr	1,000 hr	Stress (creep rate 10^{-5}/hr)
—	Room	143,360	10.0	—	—	—	
700	1292	—	—	50,880	46,640	39,220	38,160
750	1382	—	—	44,520	38,160	31,800	30,740
800	1472	—	—	33,920	27,560	21,200	21,200
850	1562	—	—	25,440	21,200	14,840	15,900

Nimonic 90
62% Ni, 18 Co, 18 Cr, 1.0 Fe, 0.10 C, 2.0 Ti, 1.5 Al

°C	°F	psi	%	100 hr	300 hr	1,000 hr	
—	Room	156,880	39.0	—	—	—	
649	1200	—	—	72,080	66,780	60,420	
704	1300	110,240	20.0	58,300	51,940	45,580	
749	1380	97,520	15.0	42,400	37,100	31,800	
816	1500	72,080	8.0	26,500	22,260	16,960	

Physicals on hot-rolled bar, in fully heat-treated condition. Heat treatment consists of heating to 1052–1179°C (1925–2155°F) for 8–12 hr followed by air cooling, reheating to 704°C (1300°F) for 12–16 hr, and cooling in air.

* Aged 50 hr at 816°C (1500°F).

Symbols:

(a) Stress for creep rate of 0.0001%/hr
(b) Stress for creep rate of 0.001%/hr
(c) Stress for 1,800 to 2,000 hr

(d) Creep rate/hr at 500 hr
(e) Creep rate/hr at 1,000 hr
(f) Creep rate/hr at 2,000 hr

TABLE 8.11. COMPOSITION OF COMMERCIAL HIGH-TEMPERATURE COBALT-BEARING ALLOYS

Alloy	Maker	Per cent by weight										
		Co	Ni	Cr	Fe	Mn	Si	Mo	W	Cb	C	
"G-18-B"	Jessop	10.0	13.0	13.0	54.0	0.8	1.0	2.0	2.5	3.0	0.4	
"S-590"	Allegheny	20.0	20.0	20.0	27.0	1.5	0.6	4.0	4.0	4.0	0.43	
"H.S. 30"	Haynes-Stellite	51.0	15.0	26.0	1.0	0.5	0.4	6.0	—	—	0.42	
"Refractalloy 26"	Westinghouse	20.0	38.0	18.0	16.0	0.8	1.0	3.2	—	—	0.03	3.0 Ti, 0.2 Al
"X-40"	General Electric	55.0	10.0	25.0	0.6	0.6	0.7	—	7.0	—	0.50	
"X-50"	General Electric	40.0	20.0	23.0	3.0	0.6	0.50	—	12.0	—	0.80	
"René 41"	General Electric	11.0	Bal.	19.0	5.0	0.50	0.50	9.7	—	—	0.09	{ 0.010 B, 3.15 Ti, 1.60 Al
"J-1570"	General Electric	37.5	28.0	20.0	2.0	—	—	—	7.0	—	0.2	4.2 Ti
"V-36"	Allegheny	42.0	20.0	25.0	3.0	0.9	0.5	4.0	2.0	2.0	0.3	
"WI-52"	Tungsten Institute	68.0	1.0	19.5	0.5	0.3	0.3	—	11.0	1.5	0.4	0.09 B

TABLE 8.12. MECHANICAL PROPERTIES OF HIGH-TEMPERATURE COBALT-BEARING ALLOYS

Alloy	Tensile psi	Elongation (%)	1,000 hr rupture stress				Form
			649°C (1200°F)	732°C (1350°F)	749°C (1380°F)	815°C (1500°F)	
"G-18-B"	99,350	46.0	35,000	—	15,500	—	Wrought
"S-590"	160,000	10.0	42,000	24,000	—	15,000	Wrought
"H.S. 30"	96,600	10.0	—	35,000	—	21,700	Cast
"Refractalloy 26"	150,000	75.0	—	—	—	18,000	Wrought
"X-40"	101,000	11.0	46,000	34,000	—	23,200	Cast
"X-50"	—	—	—	—	—	22,500	Cast
"René 41"*	195,000	31.0	100,000	—	59,000	42,000	Wrought
"J-1570"	150,000	—	78,000	52,000	—	23,000	Wrought
"V-36"	—	—	43,000	26,500	—	18,000	Cast
"WI-52"	—	—	—	—	—	15,000 (1700°F)	Cast

* Heat treated and 100 hr stress rupture.

from finely divided oxide which is reduced by hydrogen, carbon monoxide, or other reducing gases at low temperatures [800°C (1472°F)] to yield soft, plastic, and spongy particles. Cobalt powder for cemented carbides is required to pass 325 mesh and contain 98 per cent cobalt, minimum. Cobalt powder has a specific gravity of 8.9 and an apparent density of 1.5 to 3.

One process for the manufacture of cobalt metal powder commences with cobalt hydroxide which is dissolved in sulfuric acid to form cobalt sulfate. To the purified cobalt sulfate solution, oxalic acid is added in excess to precipitate cobalt oxalate which is converted to oxide at 800–900°C (1472–1652°F). The cobalt oxide is reduced with hydrogen to metal contain-

ing, percentagewise, 98.8 cobalt, 1 nickel maximum, 0.05 manganese, 0.1 sodium oxide, and 0.5 ferric oxide. Grain size distribution is 50 to 60 per cent in the range of 0.1 to 5 μ.

Another method for obtaining cobalt metal powder is to digest cobalt oxide with hot hydrochloric acid. After purification the solution is treated with sodium hydroxide to precipitate cobalt hydroxide, which is heated to 400°C (752°F) to convert it to the oxide. This is reduced by dry hydrogen at 700°C (1292°F), yielding 99.0 per cent cobalt metal.

Cobalt–chromium alloy powders are produced by the hydride process by joint reduction of their respective oxides, and find application in sintered articles of high strength and hardness. Tungsten carbide–cobalt alloy powders[4,8,10,]

[11,12,15,16,19] are milled, pressed, and sintered in a purified hydrogen atmosphere in a temperature range of 1450–1550°C (2640–2820°F). At somewhat over 1400°C (2550°F) the pure cobalt becomes enriched with tungsten carbide and the sinter body consists of 97 to 87 per cent tungsten carbide and 3 to 13 per cent of the liquid phase. With increased temperature, an increasing amount of tungsten carbide is dissolved in the melt. Upon cooling, the tungsten carbide is precipitated because of its decreasing solubility in the cobalt. Less than 1 per cent tungsten carbide remains dissolved in the cobalt at room temperature.

The hardness of sintered tungsten carbide-cobalt alloys[26] varies with the interparticle distance according to an exponential relation. Impact strength increases with binder content, and transverse-rupture strength reaches a maximum for values of the mean free path between 0.3 and 0.6 μ. If the film binder becomes very thin, the strength is reduced by the brittle phase and incomplete dispersion of the carbide grains.

Steinitz,[21] describes a nonferrous permanent magnet, "Permet," containing 30 per cent cobalt, 45 per cent copper, and 25 per cent nickel, made from metal powders. "Fernico," made by General Electric Company[5] from metal powders of iron, nickel, and cobalt in a 50:30:15 ratio, is superior to the cast alloy in vacuum technique applications. Rostoker[18] investigated the iron-cobalt alloys containing 30, 40, and 50 per cent cobalt and found their saturation magnetizations to be about 10 per cent higher than that of pure iron.

Goetzel[11] describes the sintering of cobalt powder with iron, nickel, chromium, tungsten, molybdenum, aluminum, boron, and zinc.

Canadian Patent 559,409 (Goetzel, Grant, and Yoblin assignors to Sintercast Corporation) discloses powder metallurgical methods applicable to the manufacture of a heat-resisting matrix-hardened alloy containing 5 to 30 per cent chromium, up to 25 per cent iron, and up to 90 per cent of nickel and/or up to 70 per cent of cobalt. The alloy is hardened by random dispersion throughout the matrix of a slip (and recovery) inhibiting phase consisting of carbides, borides, silicides, and nitrides of titanium, zirconium, niobium, tantalum, and vanadium. The alloys have a high resistance to creep in the range 800–1050°C (1472–1922°F).

Warren and Libsch[27] investigated the influence of pressing and sintering conditions upon the permeability, density, and percentage of pores connected to the surface of iron-cobalt powder compacts. It was found that density does not always afford a reliable means of following the sintering process, but liquid-permeability measurements have indicated changes occurring in the sintering process not revealed by density measurements. The hydrogen reduction of the powder prior to sintering and control of the sintering cycle enable the theoretical density to be closely approached.

The combination of refractory metal oxides (alumina, zirconia)[3,9,22] with refractory metals and alloys, such as tungsten, molybdenum, cobalt, nickel, and chromium, offers possible high-temperature applications for turbine buckets and jet engine parts ("Ceramel" or cermet development).

Plating of Cobalt and Cobalt Alloys

Cobalt. Cobalt electroplating[11,14,19,20,21,23,24,28,30,34,35] has, to date, been limited in use owing to its price and its lower resistance than nickel or chromium to corrosive attack and to oxidation at elevated temperatures.

Cast or rolled anodes are used with various types of electrolytes, of which the following is typical:

Cobalt sulfate ($CoSO_4$)	278 g/liter
Sodium fluoride (NaF)	14 g/liter
Boric acid (H_3BO_3)	45 g/liter
Temperature, room and higher	
Current density, 28–47 amp/sq ft	

Cobalt deposits have a hardness of 270 to 311 Brinell, compared to 180 to 240 for nickel.

The electrical resistance of cobalt is 8.96 x 10^{-6} ohm-cm at 18°C (64°F), and the temperature coefficient of the resistance is about 0.0036 between 0–100°C (32–212°F). Impurities increase the specific resistance of cobalt. The standard electrode potential for Co→Co^{++} at 25°C (77°F) is +0.278 volt.

Cobalt-Nickel Electroplating. The codeposition of cobalt and nickel[11,18,25,26,32] from the sulfate-chloride bath has attained a significant commercial position owing to the fact that the deposits of the alloy are bright, ductile, and adherent. A widely used bath has the following composition:

	Oz/(US) gal
Nickel sulfate crystals	32
Nickel chloride crystals	6
Nickel formate	6
Boric acid	4
Cobalt sulfate	0.2–2.0
Ammonium sulfate	up to 0.3
Formaldehyde	0.3
Temperature, 60–70°C (140–158°F)	
pH, 2.0–4.0	
Current density, 40 amp/sq ft	
Bath agitation, mechanical	

The anode is an alloy of nickel with 1 to 18 per cent cobalt, according to the cobalt content of the bath; the higher the cobalt content of the anode and bath, the brighter the deposit. The formate acts as a buffer and the formaldehyde acts solely as a brightener.

Electrodeposition of cobalt or nickel alloyed with phosphorus[2,3,5,6,25] in amounts up to 15 per cent gives a deposit which is hard, corrosion resistant, and bright. Commercial applications are gauges, cylinder walls, piston rings, and valve stems. The plating bath consists of cobalt sulfate or chloride, to which are added phosphorous and phosphoric acids as buffers. Bath temperature is 75°C (165°F) with a current density of 0.1 amp/sq cm. Hardness of the deposit varies from 350 to 720 Vickers. On heat-treating at 400°C (750°F), the deposit becomes harder; a 10 per cent phosphorus-cobalt hardens to 1,100 Vickers.

Electrodeposited cobalt-tungsten alloys[1,15,16,18] are of commercial interest because of their hardness and, in particular, the hot hardness which approaches that of stellite. A suitable plating solution is as follows:

Cobalt (as chloride or sulfate)	25 g/liter
Tungsten (as sodium tungstate)	25 g/liter
Rochelle salt	400 g/liter
Ammonium chloride or sulfate	50 g/liter
Ammonium hydroxide to a pH of 8.5	
Temperature, 90°C (194°F)	
Current density, 2–5 amp/sq dm	
Anodes: tungsten, cobalt, or	
cobalt-tungsten alloy	

Plating by Chemical Reduction. Plating of cobalt may be accomplished by an autocatalytic chemical reduction reaction.[4,7,29] The bath is an aqueous solution of the cobalt salt containing a low concentration of hypophosphite, and cobalt is produced by the following reaction:

$$CoCl_2 + NaH_2PO_2 + H_2O \rightarrow Co + 2HCl + NaH_2PO_3.$$

The reduction of cobalt ion, shown above, is catalyzed by certain metals including cobalt, and, as cobalt is produced by the reaction, the effect is autocatalytic. Thus, the reaction, slow in starting, proceeds rapidly once it begins.

BIOLOGICAL AND BIOCHEMICAL ASPECTS OF COBALT

Animal Nutrition[2,3,4,5,6,7,8,10]

In animal nutrition, cobalt in the form of chloride, acetate, sulfate, or nitrate has been found effective in correcting mineral deficiency diseases such as bush sickness (enzootic marasmus), Mairoa dopiness, nutritional anemia, and Morton Mains disease.

Additions of cobalt to the soil naturally must vary with the area. A soil containing 0.02 to 0.07 ppm of cobalt is deficient, whereas healthy areas contain 0.13 to 0.30 ppm of cobalt. Additions of 0.5 to 10 lb of cobalt acetate/acre provide a healthy soil. In feeds and salt licks, 1.5 to 2.0 oz of cobalt nitrate added to a 150 lb mixture of bone meal and salt, or 1 oz of cobaltous sulfate $(CoSO_4 \cdot 7H_2O)/100$ pounds of salt, ensures healthy cattle. One per cent of salt in the feed provides 3 mg of cobalt/5 lb of grain.

Ecologists' studies have proved that early attempts to introduce cattle in Florida failed because there was no cobalt in the hay. Microscopic organisms inside the bodies of cattle require cobalt to effect digestion.

In Australia the sheep and cattle are being dosed with "cobalt bullets" to correct cobalt deficiency. The bullets lodge in the reticulum, dissolving slowly to give between 0.10 to 1.0 mg cobalt/day. One bullet will last the life of the animal.

It has been reported that cows give cobalt-containing antianemia vitamin B_{12} in their milk, provided their diet has sufficient cobalt.

Cobalt is not yet proved to be essential to plant growth, although it is found in minute amounts in many plants. Although cobalt has been effective in correcting deficiency diseases in animals, reports of its applications to human disorders are conflicting; however, investigators, in general, believe it to be essential in human nutrition. As to toxicity, Harding[4] states that cobalt metal powder suspended in saline solutions or in air produces acute damage to capillaries. In the lungs of experimental animals, it leads to severe, usually fatal, edema and hemorrhage. In the peritoneal cavity it leads to ascites and oligemic shock that may prove fatal.

Cobalt 60[1]

Cobalt 60 is eminently practical for use as a radiotherapeutic agent, since it is readily accessible and easily processed.

Cobalt 60 emits two gamma rays accompanied by beta radiation. The gamma rays, with intensities of 1.17 and 1.33 mev, comprise practically monochromatic radiation of approximately 1.25 mev intensity, which compares closely with that obtained from a well-shielded radium source. Beta radiation is soft enough to be filtered out by 0.3 mm of steel. This thickness provides adequate wall strength for needles and tubes and does not reduce the intensity of gamma radiation. The isotope's half life is 5.3 years, and the strength of cobalt 60 depends on the time of irradiation and the neutron density in the nuclear reactor. These factors are controllable, therefore a wide range of source strengths may be produced. Single compact sources are obtainable equivalent in gamma ray output to thousands of grams of radium.

As an indication of the growing use of cobalt 60,[14] the sales of Co-60 as metal by the Oak Ridge National Laboratory have increased from 25,493 curies in 1954 to 93,618 in 1956 and 173,235 in 1958. The list prices for Co-60 on the basis of specific activity are:

Specific activity, curies/g	List price, $/curie
1–10	2.00
11–25	3.00
26–40	4.00
greater than 40	5.00

Cobalt 60 is available from private companies as well as Oak Ridge National Laboratories, Brookhaven National Laboratories and Atomic Energy of Canada, Ltd. The Atomic Energy Commission ceased to provide encapsulation service for sources of Co-60 in 1958, and private companies now handle that service.

As to forms available, Atomic Energy of Canada, Ltd. prepares as standard items, needle and tube sources with linear intensities from 0.1 to 50 millicuries/cm active length, and wire sources of 0.1 to 8 millicuries.[1] It also supplies slugs of Co-60 $\frac{3}{8}$" x 1" in size, as well as small pellets. Oak Ridge National Laboratory can offer small pellets as well as wafers 1 and 2 cm in diameter and 1 mm thick. Brookhaven National Laboratory supply pipes $2\frac{1}{2}$" O.D. x 13" long and sheets $\frac{1}{8}$" x 2" x 13" in size.

For use in therapy applications special devices for holding the Co-60 source with radiation protection provisions and suitable focusing means are available. As of September 1959 there were 271 licensed Co-60 teletherapy installations in the United States and nine private companies making such machines.[14] The first unit was made in 1950 by General Electric Company. The active source for one such machine, a cobalt beam therapy unit, has a number of right cylinder cobalt pellets, of height and diameter equal to 1 mm, encased in a metal cylinder 1.25 inches in diameter and 9/16 inch high, which is encased in solid lead. The equipment weighs 3 tons.

In addition to therapy applications, cobalt 60 is finding use in feed sterilization, food preservation, analysis, metal technology, physical and chemical research, thickness determination, biological research, medical research, genetics studies, insect eradication, and the initiation of chemical reactions of all sorts. As a convenient, low cost, and powerful source of gamma radiation this valuable radioactive isotope offers great scope for studies and applications of a wide variety.

References

Introduction and Occurrence

1. Agricola, G., "De Re Metallica," translated from the first Latin edition of 1556 by H. C. Hoover and L. H. Hoover, London, 1912.
2. Clarke, F. W., "The Data of Geochemistry," *U.S. Geol. Survey, Bull. 770* (1924).
3. Drury, C. W., *Rept. Ontario Bur. Mines*, **27**, Pt. III (1918).

4. Harris, A. C., "Metallurgy of the Ores from Cobalt, Ontario," *Eng. Mining J.* (Apr. 8, 1916).
5. Kraut, K., *Z. angew. Chem.*, 19, 1793 (1906).
6. Young, R. S., "Cobalt," pp. 6–23, New York, Reinhold Publishing Corp., 1948 (Revised edition to appear in 1961).

New References for Second Edition

7. Bowie, S. H., and Taylor, K., *Mining Mag. (London)*, 49, 265 (1958).
8. *J. Metals*, 191, 17 (1951).
9. Perrault, R., "Le Cobalt," Paris, Dunod, 1946.

Concentration

1. Allen, C. F., and Kentro, D. M., Canadian Patent 461,396 (Nov. 29, 1949).
2. Cunningham, J. R., Canadian Patent 464,960 (May 9, 1950).
3. Denver Equipment Staff, "Union Minière du Haut-Katanga, Kolwezi Concentrating Plant," *Deco Trefoil*, November–December, 1952.
4. Fine, M. M., and Brown, W. E., *Trans. AIME*, p. 602 (July, 1951).
5. Hepker, H. N., personal communication.
6. Mayer, S. P., U.S. Patent 2,573,865 (Nov. 6, 1951).
7. Salzman, G., *Z. Erzbergbau u. Metallhüttenw.*, 4, 222 (1951).
8. *U.S. Bur. Mines, Rept. Invest. 4279* (May, 1948).

New References for Second Edition

9. Harper, J. E., *Mining World*, p. 34 (October, 1958).
10. Sengier, Edgar, *Mining World*, p. 38 (February, 1957).
11. *U.S. Bur. Mines, Rept. Invest. 5388* (February, 1958).

Metallurgy

1. AIME, *J. Metals*, 191, 17 (January, 1951).
2. AIME, *J. Metals*, 5, 775 (1953).
3. Brogdon, H. Vas, U.S. Patent 2,400,098 (May 14, 1946).
4. Churchward, R. E., and Shelton, F. K., U.S. Patents 2,476,284 (July 19, 1949); 2,577,739 (Dec. 11, 1951).
5. *Combined Intelligence Objectives Sub-Committee, Item No. 21, File No. XXI-20*, "Refining of Cobalt in Germany," London, H. M. Stationery Office, 1946.
6. *F.I.A.T., Final Rept. No. 829*, "Non-Ferrous Production Processes in the Hamburg District" (November, 1945) (cobalt from pyrite).
7. Forward, F. A. (to Sherritt Gordon Mines, Ltd.) Canadian Patents 492,486 and 492,487

(Apr. 28, 1953); U.S. Patents 2,647,820 (Aug. 4, 1953); 2,576,314 (Nov. 27, 1951).
8. Forward, F. A., Samis, C. S., and Kudryk, V., *Can. Mining Met. Bull.*, p. 350 (June, 1948).
9. Gill, A. S., *Proc. Australasian Inst. Mining & Met.*, No. 152/153, 73 (1949).
10. Hilgers, L. W., "Investigation of the Reduction of Cobalt Mixed Oxide and Refining Crude Cobalt," Aachen, Inst. für Metallhüttenwesen und Electrometallurgic. Communication, 1950.
11. Hills, R. C., and Dufour, M. F., U.S. Patents 2,400,115 (May 14, 1946); 2,531,336 (Nov. 21, 1950).
12. Johnusen, F., and Schwartz, W., *Z. Erzbergbau u. Metallhüttenw.*, 3, 138 (1950).
13. MacFarlane, T., "Extraction of Cobalt Oxide from the Iron Pyrites, near Brockville," *Ontario Dept. Mines, Article 18* (1863).
14. McGauley, P. J. (to Chemical Construction Corp.) U.S. Patent 2,647,819 (Aug. 4, 1953).
15. Mantell, C. L., U.S. Patent 2,506,159 (May 2, 1950).
16. Nakabe, Sanai, *Trans. AIME, J. Metals*, 3, 445 (1951).
17. O'Connor, J., *Chem. Eng.*, 59, 164 (1952).
18. Perrault, R., "Le Cobalt," Paris, Dunod, 1946.
19. Schaal, R. B. (to Ferro Enamel Corp.) U.S. Patent 2,379,659 (July 3, 1945).
20. Senger, E. B., *Eng. Mining J.*, (December, 1951).
21. Shelton, F. K., U.S. Patent 2,508,427 (May 23, 1950).
22. Shelton, F. K., Churchward, R. E., Stahl, J. C., and Livingston, G. F. *U.S. Bur. Mines, Rept. Invest. 3832* (November, 1945).
23. Société Générale Métallurgique de Hoboken, British Patent 650,595 (Feb. 21, 1951); French Patent 496,159 (Oct. 2, 1950).
24. Stahl, J. C., and Shelton, F. K., U.S. Patent 2,526,707 (Oct. 24, 1950).
25. Talbot, H. L., and Hepker, H. N., *Bull. Inst. Mining & Met.*, 514 (October, 1949).
26. Triggs, W. W., (to Société Générale Métallurgique de Hoboken), British Patent 655,149 (July 11, 1951).
27. Wallis, E. A., and West, DeWitt H., British Patent 672,993 (May 28, 1952); U.S. Patents 2,377,832 (June 5, 1945); 2,415,665 (Feb. 11, 1947).
28. Watanabe, Toshio, "On the Recovery of Cobalt in Cupriferous Pyrite," *Paper No. 477, Mem. Coll. Sci., Kyoto Imperial University* (1939).
29. Westcott, E. W., U.S. Patent 1,406,595 (Feb. 14, 1922).
30. Young, R. S., "Cobalt," New York, Reinhold Publishing Corp., 1948.

New References for Second Edition

31. Caron, M. H., *Trans. AIME*, **188**, 91 (1950); **188**, 67 (1950).
32. Ferrante, K. J., Good, P. C., and Gruzensky, P. M., *U.S. Bur. Mines, Rept. Invest. 5394* (May, 1958).
33. Forward, F. A., *Trans. Can. Inst. Mining Met.* **56**, 373 (1953).
34. Forward, F. A. and Mackiw, V. N., *Trans. AIME*, **203**, 457 (1955).
35. Forward, F. A., Samis, C. S., and Kudryk, V., *Trans. Can. Inst. Mining Met.*, **51**, 181 (1948).
36. Mitchell, J. S., *J. Metals*, p. 343 (March, 1957).
37. Nasher, S., *Can. Mining Met. Bull.*, **58**, No. 519, 396–410 (1955).
38. Senger, Edgar, *Mining World*, p. 38 (February, 1957).

Physical Properties

1. Armstrong, L. D., and Grayson-Smith, H., *Can. J. Research*, **28A**, 51 (1950).
2. Barrett, W. F., *Chem. News*, **33**, 266 (1876).
3. Bridgman, P. W., *Proc. Am. Acad. Arts Sci.*, **53**, 269 (1918).
4. Bridgman, P. W., *Metallwirtschaft*, **8**, 229 (1929).
5. Bridgman, P. W., *Proc. Am. Acad. Arts Sci.*, **70**, 285 (1935).
6. Cardwell, A. B., *Phys. Rev.*, **38**, 2033 (1931).
7. Copaux, H., *Compt. rend.*, **140**, 659 (1905).
8. Danreeker, C., *Ann. phys.*, **42**, 1504 (1913).
9. Deville, H. St. C., *Ann. chim. et phys.*, **46**, 202 (1856).
10. Dewar, J., *Proc. Roy. Soc. (London)*, **89A**, 158 (1913).
11. Edwards, O. S., and Lipson, H., *J. Inst. Metals*, **69**, 177 (1943).
12. Fine, M. E., and Ellis, W. C., *Trans. AIME*, **175**, 742 (1948).
13. Gant, T. H., *Metal Ind.*, **26**, 131 (1925).
14. Guillaud, G., and Roux, M., *Compt. rend.*, **229**, 1062 (1949).
15. Hendricks, S. B., Jefferson, M. E., and Schultz, J. E., *Z. Krist.*, **73**, 376 (1930).
16. Hess, J. B., and Barrett, C. S., *J. Metals*, **4**, 645 (1952).
16a. Hodgman, C. D. (Ed.), "Handbook of Chemistry and Physics," p. 2149, Cleveland, Chemical Rubber Publishing Co., 1952.
17. Holborn, L., *Z. Physik*, **8**, 58 (1921).
18. Honda, K., "Magnetic Properties of Matter," p. 82, Tokyo, Syokwabo & Co., 1928.
19. Honda, K., *Sci. Repts. Tôhoku Imp. Univ.*, **8**, 51 (1919).
20. Honda, K., and Masumoto, H., *Sci. Repts. Tôhoku Imp. Univ.*, **20**, 323 (1931).
21. Hull, A. W., *Phys. Rev.*, **17**, 571 (1921).
22. Jaeger, F. M., Rosenbohm, E., and Zuithoff, A. J., *Rec. trav. chim.*, **59**, 831 (1940).
23. Kalmus, H. T., and Harper, C. H., *Can. Bur. Mines, Rept. 309* (1914).
24. Kalmus, H. T., and Harper, C. H., *J. Ind. Eng. Chem.*, **7**, 6 (1915).
25. Kaya, S., *Sci. Repts. Tôhoku Imp. Univ.*, **17**, 1157 (1928).
26. Knott, C. G., *Proc. Roy. Soc. Edinburgh*, **18**, 310 (1891).
27. McLennan, J. C., Niven, C. D., and Wilhelm, J. O., *Phil. Mag.*, **6**, 672 (1932).
28. McNaughton, D. J., and Hotherstall, A. W., *J. Electrodepositors' Tech. Soc.*, **5**, 63 (1950).
29. Marick, L., *Phys. Rev.*, **49**, 831 (1936); *Z. Physik*, **307** (1935).
30. Masumoto, H., *Sci. Repts. Tôhoku Imp. Univ.*, **15**, 449 (1926).
31. Masumoto, H., *ibid.*, **16**, 321 (1927).
32. Masumoto, H., and Nara, S., *Kinzoku-no-Kenkyu*, **2**, 1023 (1926).
33. Meissner, W., Voight, B., and Adelsberger, V., *Ann. Physik*, **7**, 892 (1930).
34. Mellor, J. W., "Treatise on Inorganic and Theoretical Chemistry," Vol. 14, p. 486, New York, Longmans, Green & Co., Inc., 1935.
35. Mendelssohn, K., and Olsen, J. L., *Proc. Phys. Soc.*, **63A**, 2 (1950).
36. "Metals Handbook," p. 1137, Cleveland, American Society for Metals, 1948.
37. Metcalfe, A. G., AIME, annual meeting (Oct. 20, 1952).
38. Metcalfe, A. G., Proc. World Metallurgical Congress, Detroit, 1951.
40. Meyer, A. J. P., and Taglang, P., *Compt. rend.* **231**, 612 (1950).
41. Meyer, W. F., *Z. Krist*, **97**, 145 (1937).
42. Myers, H. P., and Sucksmith, W., *Proc. Roy. Soc. (London)*, **207A**, 427 (1951).
43. Nix, F. C., and Jaumot, F. E., Jr., *Phys. Rev.*, **82**, 72 (1951).
44. Noll, K., *Ann. Physik u. Chem.*, **53**, 874 (1894).
45. Pechaux, H., *Compt. rend.*, **147**, 532 (1908).
46. Rabinowitsch, E., and Thilo, E., *Z. physik. Chem.*, **6B**, 284 (1929).
47. Reichardt, G., *Ann. phys.*, **6**, 832 (1901).
48. Richards, J. W., *Chem. News*, **75**, 278 (1897).
49. Richards, T. W., and Jackson, F. G., *Z. physik. Chem.*, **70**, 414 (1910).
49a. Richardson, D., "Spectroscopy in Science and Industry. Proceedings of the Fifth Summer Conference on Spectroscopy and Its Applications," pp. 64–70, New York, John Wiley & Sons, Inc., 1938.
50. Ruder, R. C., and Birchenall, C. E., *Trans. AIME*, **191**, 142 (1951).

51. Ruer, R., and Kaneko, K., *Ferrum*, **10**, 257 (1913).

52. Ruer, R., and Kaneko, K., *Metall. u. Erz*, **9**, 421 (1921).

53. Schimank, H., *Ann. phys.*, **45**, 706 (1914).

54. Schimpff, H., *Z. physik. Chem.*, **71**, 257 (1910).

55. Schmitz, H. E., *Proc. Roy. Soc. (London)*, **72**, 177 (1903).

56. Schulze, A., *Z. Metallkunde*, **23**, 308 (1930).

57. Schulze, A., *Z. tech. Physik.*, **8**, 365 (1927).

58. Sekito, S., *Sci. Rept. Tôhoku Imp. Univ.*, **16**, 545 (1927).

59. Seybolt, A. U., and Mathewson, C. H., *Trans. AIME*, **117**, 156 (1935).

60. Shinoda, G., *Mem. Coll. Sci. Kyoto Imp. Univ.* **17A**, 27 (1934).

61. Shukov, S., *J. Russ. Phys. Chem. Soc.*, **40**, 1748 (1909).

62. Steinwehr, H. Von, and Schulze, A., *Z. Metallk.* **27**, 90 (1935).

63. Sucksmith, W., *J. phys. radium*, **12**, 430 (1951).

64. Sykes, W. P., *Trans. Am. Soc. Steel Treating*, **21**, 385 (1933).

65. Sykes, W. P., and Graff, H. F., *Trans. Am. Soc. Metals*, **23**, 50 (1935).

66. Taylor, A., *J. Inst. Metals*, **77**, 585 (1940).

67. Troiano, A. R., and Tokich, J. L., *Trans. AIME*, **175**, 728 (1948).

68. Tuijn, W., and Onnes, H. K., *Arch. néerl.*, **10**, 5 (1927).

69. Turnbull, D., *J. Chem. Phys.*, **18**, 769 (1950).

70. Uffelman, F. L., *Phil. Mag.*, **10**, 633 (1930).

71. Umino, S., *Sci. Repts. Tôhoku Imp. Univ.*, **15**, 597 (1925).

72. Umino, S., *Seitetsu Kenkyu*, **89**, 290 (1925).

73. Van Dusen, M. S., and Dahl, A. I., *J. Research NBS*, **39**, 291, *Research Paper No. 1828* (1947).

74. Wahl, W., *Z. Anorg. u. allgem. Chem.*, **66**, 60 (1910).

75. Wasserman, G., *Metallwirtschaft*, **11**, 61 (1932).

76. Wever, F., and Hashimoto, V., *Mitt. Kaiser-Wilhelm-Inst. Eisenforsch., Düsseldorf*, **11**, 293 (1929).

77. Wust, F., Meuthen, A., and Durrer, R., *Forsch. Ver. Deut. Ing.*, 204 (1918).

New References for Second Edition

78. Bibring, Herve, Sebilleau, François, and Buckle, Charlotte (Mme), *J. Inst. Metals*, **11**, 71 (1958).

79. Bridges, D. W., Baur, J. P., and Fassell, W. M. *J. Electrochem. Soc.*, **103**, 614 (1956).

80. Carter, R. E., and Richardson, F. D., *J. Metals*, **6**, 1244 (1954).

81. Carter, R. E., and Richardson, F. D., *J. Metals*, **7**, 336 (1955).

82. Fine, M. E., and Greener, E. H., *J. Metals*, **212**, 476 (1958).

83. Johns, C. R., and Baldwin, W. M., *J. Metals*, **185**, 720 (1949).

84. Martin, D. L., *J. Metals*, **206**, 578 (1956).

85. Mead, H. W., and Birchenall, C. E., *J. Metals*, **7**, 994 (1955).

86. Morral, F. R., *J. Metals*, **10**, 662 (1958).

87. Newkirk, J. B., and Martin, W. G., *J. Metals*, **212**, 398 (1958).

88. Ruder, R. C., and Birchenall, C. E., *J. Metals*, **191**, 142 (1951).

89. Shewmon, Paul, *Ind. Eng. Chem.*, **50**, 492 (1958).

90. Smeltzer, W. W., and Everett, L. H., *Ind. Eng. Chem.*, **50**, 496 (1958).

91. Taylor, A., and Floyd, R. W., *Acta Cryst.*, **3**, 285 (1950).

Chemical Properties

1. Beidler, E. A., U.S. Patent 2,642,357 (June 16, 1953).

2. Bourgoin, L., "Cours de Chimie—Metaux," L'Ecole Polytechnique, Montreal, 1940.

3. Davis, P. B., U.S. Patent 2,580,737 (Jan. 1, 1952).

4. McKeever, C. H., U.S. Patents 2,476,263 (July 12, 1949); 2,477,554 (July 26, 1949).

5. Mellor, J. W., "A Comprehensive Treatise on Inorganic and Theoretical Chemistry," Vol. 14, "Cobalt," London, Longmans, Green & Co., Ltd., 1935.

6. Weiser, H. B., "The Hydrous Oxides," New York, McGraw-Hill Book Company, Inc., 1927.

New References for Second Edition

7. Carter, R. E., and Richardson, F. D., *J. Metals*, **7**, 336 (1955).

8. Heyding, R. D., and Calvert, L. D., *Can. J. Chem.*, **35**, 449 (1957).

9. Kellog, H. H., *Trans. AIME*, **191**, 157 (1951).

10. Schachner, H., *Cobalt*, 37 (1959).

Cobalt in Ferrous Alloys

1. Climax Molybdenum Co., "Molybdenum in Steel and Iron Alloys," New York, Climax Molybdenum Co., 1948.

2. Das, D. K., Rideout, S. P., and Beck, Paul A., *Trans. AIME*, **194**, 1071 (1952).

3. Duwez, Pol, and Martens, H., *Trans. Am. Soc. Metals*, **44**, 484 (1952).

4. Gill, J. P., "Tool Steels," Cleveland, American Society for Metals, 1944.

5. Grossman, M. A., and Bain, E. C., "High Speed Steel," New York, John Wiley & Sons, Inc., 1931.

6. Habraken, L., and Coutsourads, D., *Cobalt*, No. 2, 11 (1959).

7. Martin, D. L., and Geisler, A. H., *Trans. Am Soc. Metals*, **44**, 461 (1952).

8. "Metals Handbook," Cleveland, American Society for Metals, 1948.

9. "Vanadium Steels & Irons," pp. 140-147, New York, Vanadium Corporation of America, 1937.

Magnets

Allec, M., "Magnets" (in French), *Metallurgie et Construction Mécanique*, **83**, 881, (1951).

Bates, L. F., "The Magnets-Resistance of High Coercivity Alloys," *Proc. Phys. Soc. (London)*, **58**, 153 (1946).

Bates, L. F., and Edmondson, A. S., "The Adiabatic Temperature Changes Accompanying the Magnetization of Cobalt in Low and Moderate Fields," *Proc. Phys. Soc. (London)*, **59**, 329 (1947).

Boggs, A., "Magnetic Materials," *Western Union Tech. Rev.*, **4**, 79–85 (1950).

Carr, W. J., "Intrinsic Magnetization in Alloys (Co-Fe.)," *Phys. Rev.*, **85**, 590 (1952).

Chegwidden, R. A., "Rectangular Hysteresis Loops of Co-Ni-Fe Alloys," *J. Metals (Tech. Sect.)*, **1** *(Metals Trans.)* **185**, 570 (1949).

Chegwidden, R. A., "A Review of Magnetic Materials for Communication Systems," *Metal Progr.*, **54**, 705–714 (November, 1948).

Ebeling, D. G., "Method of Making Cast Alnico Magnets," U.S. Patent 2,578,407 (Dec. 11, 1951).

Fallot, M., "The Magnetic Properties and the Constitutional Diagram of Iron-Cobalt Alloys," *Métaux, corrosion, usure*, **18**, 214 (1943).

Finke, H. E., "Modern Magnetic Materials," *Materials & Methods*, **25**, 72 (1947).

Garvin, S. J., "Production of Sintered Permanent Magnets," *Iron Steel Inst. (London), Spec. Rept. No. 38*, Ed. 2 (Rev.). "Symposium on Powder Metallurgy," pp. 67–72 (December, 1947).

Gaugler, E. A., "Soft Magnet Materials," *Prod. Eng.*, **20**, 84 (1949). Composition and heat-treatment and properties of magnetic Fe-Co alloys, and Fe-Ni-Co alloys.

Geisler, A. H., "Structure of Permanent Magnet Alloys," *Trans. Am. Soc. Metals*, **43**, 70 (1951).

Geisler, A. H., and Newkerk, J. B., "Mechanism of Precipitation in a Permanent Magnet Alloy," *Metals Technol.*, **15**, 20 (1948).

Geisler, A. H., "Structure and Properties of the Permanent Magnet Alloys," *Elec. Eng.*, **69**, 37 (1950).

Geisler, A. H., and Steigert, F. E., "Precipitation and Diffuse Scattering in an Fe-Mo-Co (17% Mo, 12% Co, bal. Fe) Alloy," *J. Metals*, **3**, 259 (1951).

Goldman, J. E., and Smoluchowski, "Magnetostriction and Order-Disorder," *J. Appl. Phys.*, **20**, 1 (1949). Alloys Fe-Co.

Goss, J. H., "Permanent Magnetic Material," *Mech. Eng.*, **70**, 671 (1948).

Harris, S., "The Production and Properties of Pressed Permanent Magnets," *Plastics (London)*, **10**, 534 (1946).

Hoselitz, K., "Modern Hard Magnetic Materials," *Metal Treatment*, **13**, 213 (1946).

Hotap, W., "The Particular Situation of Powder Metallurgy in the Manufacture of Permanent Magnets" (German), 4th International Mechanical Eng. Congress, 25 pp. (June, 1952).

Kittel, C., Nesbitt, E. A., and Shockley, W., "Theory of Magnetic Properties of Alnico V," *Phys. Rev.*, **77**, 839 (1950); discussion, Nov. 15, 757 (1950).

Knorr, W., "Study of the Most Suitable Chemical Composition of 4% Cr, 2% Co, 0.5% W Permanent Magnet Steel," *Arch. Eisenhüttenw.*, **23**, 53 (1952).

Lee, E. W., "Magnetostriction of Some Ferromagnetic Alloys," *J. Iron Steel Inst. (London)*, **171**, 160 (1952).

Martin, D. L., and Geisler, A. H., "Heat Treating Cobalt-Platinum Magnets," U.S. Patent 2,622,050 (Dec. 16, 1952).

Merill, F. W., "Performance of the New Alnico Permanent Magnet Materials," *Elec. Mfg.*, **39**, 72 (1947).

Myers, H. P., and Sucksmith, H., "The Spontaneous Magnetization of Cobalt," *Proc. Roy. Soc. (London)*, **207**, 427 (1951).

Nesbitt, E. A., "Vicalloy—A Workable Alloy for Permanent Magnets," *Metals Technol.*, **13** (February, 1946), and *Trans. AIME (Metals)*, 415 (1946).

Newkirk, J. B., Geisler, A. H., and Martin, D. L., "The Ordering Reaction in Co-Pt (50–50 At. %) Alloys," *J. Appl. Phys.*, **20**, 816 (1949).

Schneider, A., and Wunderlich, W., "Solid Solutions in Co-Mn Systems," *Z. Metallk.*, **40**, 260 (1949).

Stanley, J. K., "Metallurgical Factors Affecting the Magnetic & Mechanical Properties of Iron-Cobalt Alloys," *Trans. Am. Soc. Metals*, **42**, 150 (1950).

Stark, J. H., "Low Cost Processing of Alnico Rotors and Stators," *Elec. Mfg.*, **48**, 125 (1951).

Steinitz, R., "Permet, a Non-ferrous Permanent Magnet Made from Powders," *Powder Met. Bull.*, **1**, 45 (1946). Permet contains 30% Co, 45% Cu, 25% Ni.

Studders, R. J., "Permanent Magnets of Sintered Oxides," *Prod. Eng.*, **19**, 120 (1948).

Studders, R. J., "Permanent Magnet Stability," *Prod. Eng.*, **19**, 129 (1948).

Taglang, P., "Relation Between Moments and Curie Points of 'Isoelectronic' Alloys of the

Fe-Co-Ni Group," *Compt. rend.*, **229**, 704 (1949).

Torry, Allan, "The Structure of Nickel-Aluminum Magnet Alloys and the Control of Brittleness," *Metallurgie*, **34**, 147 (1946).

Turner, R. S., "Use of Synthetic Sand for Cast Magnets," *Foundry Trade J.*, **85**, 153 (1948).

Underhill, E. M., "Permanent Magnet Alloys," *Electronics*, **21**, 122 (1948).

Walker, J. G., and Williams, J. H., "Growing and Processing of Single Crystals of Magnetic Metals," *Rev. Sci. Instr.*, **20**, 947 (1949).

Weil, Louis, and Galley, M., "A New Method for Determination of Magnetostriction. Application to Cobalt Ferrite," *Compt. rend.*, **231**, 224 (1950).

Werner, Jellinghaus, "Permanent Magnets," *Iron and Steel*, **17** (1944). Quinternary alloys of Fe, Ni, Al, Co, and Cu with magnetic orientation.

Wilson, M. S., and Whittenton, J. M., "Influence of Improved Magnetic Alloys on Design Trends of Electrical Instruments," *Elec. Eng.*, **63**, 100 (1944). Use of a Co-Me-Fe alloy as a permanent magnet material.

Wohlfarth, E. P., "Magnetic Properties of Nickel-Cobalt and Related Alloys," *Phil. Mag.*, **40**, 1095 (1949).

New References for Second Edition

Anselin, F., "Permanent Magnetic Materials," *Cobalt*, No. 3, 17 (1959); No. 4, 29 (1959).

Arnold, H. D., and Elmen, G. W., "Permalloy, an Alloy of Remarkable Magnetic Properties," *J. Franklin Inst.* **195**, 621 (1923).

Backlund, N., "Electrical Resistance of Some Noble-Metal Alloys at Liquid Helium Temperatures," *J. Physics Chem. Solids*, **7**, 94 (1958).

Becker, J. J., "Magnetic Method for the Measurement of Precipitate Particle Sizes in a Cu-Co Alloy," *J. Metals*, **9**, 59 (1957).

Bumann, H., "Permanent Magnetic Alloys," *Arch. Eisenhüttenw.*, **15**, 547 (1942).

Ellis, W. C., "A Study of the Physical Properties of Electrolytic Cobalt and Its Alloys with Iron," *Rensselaer Polytech. Inst. Bull., Eng. Sci. Ser. No. 16* (1927).

Ellis, W. C., and Schumacher, E. E., "Magnetic Materials," *Metals & Alloys*, p. 269 (December, 1934).

Fountain, R. W., and Libsch, J. F., "Development of Mechanical and Magnetic Hardness in a 10 Pct. V-Co-Fe Alloy," *J. Metals*, **5**, 349 (1953).

Gerstenberg, D., "Magnetic Investigations on Solid Solutions of Palladium with Transition Elements (Cobalt)," *Ann. Physik*, **2**, 236 (1953).

Hall, R. C., Conrad, G. P., and Libsch, J. F., "Ordering and Magnetic Treatment of the 50 Pct. Fe—50 Pct. Co Alloy," *J. Metals*, **7**, 985 (1955).

Martin, D. L., "Processing and Properties of Cobalt-Platinum Permanent-Magnet Alloys," *J. Metals*, **212**, 478 (1958).

Toole, R. C., "Ferromagnetic Cobalt and Nickel Manganese Oxides Having the Ilmenite-Type Crystal Structure," Canadian Patent 546,593 (1957).

Glass-to-Metal Seals

1. Anonymous, *Metal Ind.*, **75**, p. 263 (Sept. 30); p. 292 (Oct. 7, 1949).
2. Mairs, K. H., *J. Metals*, **4**, 460 (1952).
3. Redston, G. D., and Stanworth, J. E., *J. Sci. Instr.*, **23**, 53 (1946).
4. Went, J. J., Canadian Patent 486,768 (Sept. 23, 1952).

Alloys for Corrosion and Oxidation Resistance

1. Anonymous, *Metal Progr.*, p. 116 (February, 1953).
2. ASTM, "Symposium on Materials for Gas Turbines," *Bull. Am. Soc. Testing Materials*, 199 (1946).
3. Avery, H. S., *Iron Steel Engr.*, p. 26 (September, 1951).
4. Bardgett, W. E., and Bolsover, G. R., *Iron Steel Inst. (London)*, p. 135 (July, 1952).
5. Binder, W. O., and Franks, R., U.S. Patent 2,624,671 (January 6, 1953).
6. Bollenrath, F., Cornelius, H., and Bungardt, W., *Metallwirtschaft*, **1**, 755 (1938).
7. Clarke, W. C., U.S. Patent 2,536,033 (Jan. 2, 1951).
8. Cornelius, H., *Arch. Eisenhüttenw.*, **15**, 47 (1941).
9. Franks, R., and Binder, W. O., Canadian Patents 460,262; 460,263; 460,274; 460,275 (October 11, 1949).
10. Lardge, H. E., *Iron Steel Inst. (London)*, Spec. Rept. No. 43 (July, 1952).
11. Ocott, E. L., U.S. Patent 2,462,665 (Feb. 22, 1949).
12. Riddihough, M., "Hardfacing by Welding," London, The Louis Cassier Co., Ltd., 1949.
13. Rose, K., *Materials & Methods*, **32**, 54 (1950).
14. Schmidt, M., U.S. Patent 2,553,600 (May 22, 1951).
15. Skues, C., Giffard, J. A., and Stokes, C., British Patent 616,207 (Jan. 18, 1949).
16. Sykes, C., and Shirley, H. T., *Iron Steel Inst. (London)*, Spec. Rept. No. 43, p. 153 (July, 1952).
17. Waindle, R. F., *Metal Progr.*, **56**, 808 (1949).

Cobalt in Nonferrous Alloys

ASM Staff, "Approximate Strength of Important Jet Engine Alloys (Round Test Bars)," *Metal Progr.*, **60**, 80B (1951).

Beattie, H. J., and Versnyder, F. L., "Microconstituents in High Temperature Alloys," *Am. Soc. Metals, Preprint 1*, 27 pp. (October, 1952).

Bieber, C. G., "Cast or Wrought Alloy, Age-hardenable," U.S. Patent 2,570,193 (Oct. 9, 1951).

Binder, W. O., and Spendelow, H. R., "New Cobalt-Base Alloy for High-Temperature Sheet," *Metal Progr.* **57**, 321 (1950).

Binder, W. O., and Weisert, E. D., "Some Notes on the Oxidation-Resistance of Boron-containing Cr-Ni-Co-Fe Alloys," *Corrosion*, **9**, 329 (February, 1953).

Buswell, R. W., Jenkins, I., and Pitkin, W. R., "Sintered Alloys for High Temperature Service in Gas Turbines," *Powder Met. Bull.* **6**, 110 (1952).

Cameron, J. M., and Youden, W. J., "Statistical Analysis of Stress-Rupture Data on S-816 Alloy (20% Co)," *Am. Soc. Testing Materials Proc.*, **50**, 951 (1950).

Chaston, J. C., and Child, F. C., "Some Cobalt Rich Alloys for High Temperature Service," *Iron Steel Inst. (London), Spec. Rept. No. 43*, pp. 246-8 (July, 1952).

Clark, F. H., "Metals at High Temperatures," New York, Reinhold Publishing Corp., 1950.

Comstock, G. J., and Shaw, J. D., "Properties of Cobalt-Nickel-Chromium Alloys Made by Powder Metallurgy," from "Physics of Powder Metallurgy," pp. 372-386; New York, McGraw-Hill Book Company, Inc., 1951.

Davis, E. A., and Manjoine, M. J., "Effect of Shape of Notch on Rupture Strength of High-Temperature Alloys," *Am. Soc. Testing Materials, Preprint 78*, 21 pp. (June, 1952).

Deloro Stellite, Ltd., "Hardfacing with Stellite," *Machinery (London)*, **80**, 179 (1952).

Dym, J. B., and Badger, T., "Cast Alloys Vary in Cutting Efficiency," *Am. Machinist*, p. 109 (Nov. 20, 1947).

Edwards, A. R., "New High Temperature Alloys," *Australasian Engr.*, p. 42 (June 7, 1952).

Foley, F. B., "Metal Alloy for High Temperatures (Ni-Cr-Co)," U.S. Patent 2,543,841 (Mar. 6, 1951).

Freeman, J. W., Ewing, J. F., and White, A. E., "Influence of Chemical Composition on Rupture Properties at 1500°F of forged Cr-Co-Ni-Fe Base Alloys," *Natl. Advisory Comm. Aeronautics, Tech. Note 2745*, 69 pp. (July, 1952).

Frey, D. N., Freeman, J. W., and White, A. E., "Fundamental Effects of Cold-Work on Some Cobalt-Chromium-Nickel-Iron base Creep-Resistant Alloys," *Natl. Advisory Comm. Aeronautics, Tech. Note No. 2586*, 12 pp. (July, 1952).

Gadd, E. R., "Precision Casting Turbine Blades," High Temperature Steels and Alloys for Gas Turbines, *Iron Steel Inst. (London), Spec. Rept. No. 43* (July, 1952).

Grant, N. J., Kates, L. W., and Hamilton, N. E., "Development and Evaluation of Cast Turbine Rotors," *Foundry*, **78**, 86 (1950).

Gresham, H. E., and Dunlop, A., "Investment-Casting Nozzle Guide Vanes," *Iron Steel Inst. (London), Spec. Rept. No. 43* (July, 1952).

Harder, O. E., and Roberts, D. A., "Cobalt-Chromium-Nickel Base Alloy," Canadian Patents 480,487; 480,488; 480,489 (Jan. 22, 1952).

Harkins, F. G., "Process Control for Resistance Welding Under Government Specifications (Co-base alloys)," *Welding J.*, (N.Y.), **31**, 567 (July, 1952).

Haynes, Elwood, "Alloys of Cobalt with Chromium and Other Metals," *Ind. Eng. Chem.*, **5**, 189 (1913).

Haynes, Elwood, "Stellite and Stainless Steel," *J. Western Soc. Engrs.*, **35**, 467 (1919–20).

Haynes Stellite Co., "Haynes Alloys for High Temperature," booklet, Kokomo, Ind.

Henry Wiggin & Co., Ltd., "The Nimonic Alloys," brochure, Birmingham, 16 England.

Jessop, Wm. & Sons, Ltd., "Alloy for High Temperature Service," British Patents 670,560 (April 23, 1952); 674,023 (June 18, 1952).

Kamen, E. L., and Beck, P. A., "Survey of Portions of the Cobalt-Chromium-Iron-Nickel Quaternary System," *Natl. Advisory Comm. Aeronautics, Tech. Notes No. 2603*, 62 pp. (February, 1952), and *2683*, 81 pp. (April, 1952).

Kinsey, H. V., "High Temperature Alloys for Gas Turbines," *Can. Metals*, p. 28 (October, 1952); p. 20 (December, 1952).

Lane, J. R., and Grant, N. J., "Carbide Reactions in High Temperature Alloys," *Trans. Am. Soc. Metals*, **44**, 113 (1952).

MacKenzie, B. J., "Industrial Applications of Stellite," *Can. Metals*, **15**, 48 (1952).

Manjoine, M. J., "Effect of Rate of Strain on the Flow Stress of Gas Turbine Alloys at 1200° and 1500°F," *Am. Soc. Testing Materials Proc.*, **50**, 931 (1950).

Manly, W. D., and Beck, P. A., "Survey of the Chromium-Cobalt-Nickel Phase Diagram at 1200°C," *Natl. Advisory Comm. Aeronautics, Tech. Note 2602*, 45 pp. (February, 1952).

Martin, D. L., and Geisler, A. H., "Constitution of

Cobalt-Iron-Vanadium Alloys," *Trans. Am. Soc. Metals*, **44**, 461 (1952).

Popcock, P. L., "Hardfacing—Applications (Stellite) to Iron and Steel Industries," *Iron and Steel*, **24**, 323 (1951).

Preston, D., "Investigation of High Temperature Sheet Materials," *Am. Soc. Testing Materials, Preprint 85*, 24 pp. (1952).

Reynolds, E. E., "The Influence of Chemical Composition on the Rupture Properties at 1200°F (648°C) of Wrought Chromium-Nickel-Cobalt-Iron-Molybdenum-Tungsten-Niobium Alloys," *University Microfilms, Publ. No. 2451*, 169 pp. (1951); *Trans. AIME, T.P. 3344E*, pp. 946.

Reynolds, E. E., Freeman, J. W., and White, A. E., "Influence of Chemical Composition on Forged Modified Low-Carbon N-155 Alloys in Solution-treated and Aged, as Related to Rupture Properties at 1200°F," *Natl. Advisory Comm. Aeronautics, Tech. Note 2449*, 111 pp. (September, 1951).

Rolls-Royce, Ltd., "Hard Wear-Resisting Ni-Cr-Co Alloys for High Temperature," British Patent **666,401** (Feb. 13, 1952).

Schmidt, Max, "Weldable and High Temperature Alloy of Cobalt and Iron," U.S. Patent **2,553,609** (May 22, 1951).

Schmucker, R. A., and Preusch, "Cast Alloy for Cutting Tools," Canadian Patent **491,130** (Mar. 10, 1953); U.S. Patent **2,551,170** (May 1, 1951).

Servi, S. I., and Grant, N. J., "Creep and Stress Rupture as Rate Processes," *J. Inst. Metals*, **80**, 33 (1951–52).

Shaw, M. C., and Smith, P. A., "Metallurgical Considerations in Machining—Physical Characteristics of Cast Alloys and Carbides," *Am. Machinist*, p. 130 (Oct. 15, 1951).

Waldron, M. B., "The Stability of the CO_2Al_9-Type Structure in the Aluminum-rich Alloys of the Al-Fe-Co-Ni-System," *J. Inst. Metals*, **79**, 103 (1951).

Yaker, C., and Hoffman, C. A., "Effect of Solution Treatment Followed by Aging Treatment on Life of Small Cast Gas-Turbine Blades of a Cobalt-Chromium-Base Alloy," *Natl. Advisory Comm. Aeronautics, Tech. Note No. 2320*, 37 pp. (March, 1951).

New References for Second Edition

Culbertson, P. P., "How to Weld Some Wrought High Alloys," *Materials & Methods*, p. 98 (February, 1955).

Demirjian, S. G., "Which Alloys for Jet Hot Spots," *Materials & Methods*, 116 (October, 1955).

"Evaluation of two High-Carbon Precision-Cast

Alloys at 1700° and 1800°F by Rupture Test," *Natl. Advisory Comm. Aeronautics, Tech. Note No. 1130*, 15 pp. (1946).

Fordham, S., Hallpike, M., and Riddihough, M. "Notes on the Technique of Temporal Bone Microtomy," (stellited knives), *Brit. Med. Bull.*, **12**, 93 (1956).

Gault, J. R., and Ironside, D. A., "The Spray Fuse Hardfacing Process for 'Stellite,' Cobalt Base Powders," *Machinery (London)*, (Jan. 2, 1959).

Hoffman, C. A. and Gyorgak, C. A., "Investigation of Effects of Grain Size Upon Engine Life of Cast A.M.S. 5385 Gas Turbine Blades," *Natl. Advisory Comm. Aeronautics, Research Mem. No. E53D06* (July 6, 1953).

Lampson, F. K., Tsareff, T. C., and Green, A. W. "Thermal-Shock Testing under Stress of Certain High-Temperature Alloys," *Am. Soc. Testing Materials, Proc.*, **57**, 965 (1957).

Morral, F. R., "Alloys for the Aircraft Industry," *Cobalt*, No. 2, 23 (1959).

"Resistance of Six Cast High-Temperature Alloys to Cracking caused by Thermal Shock," *Natl. Advisory Comm. Aeronautics, Tech. Note No. 2037*, 29 pp. (1950).

Siegfried, W., and Eisermann, F., "A Turbine Blade Alloy Castable and Low in Cobalt and Columbium," *Metal Progr.*, **67**, 141 (1955).

Urbain, M., "High Temperature Alloys," *Cobalt* No. 1, 13 (1959).

Weeton, J. W., and Signorelli, R. A., "An Investigation of Lamellar Structures and Minor Phases in Eleven Cobalt-Base Alloys Before and After Heat Treatment," *Natl. Advisory Comm. Aeronautics, Tech. Note No. 3106* (1954).

Cobalt Powder

1. Anderson, R. B., and McCartney, J. T., *Appl. Phys.*, **18**, 902 (1947).

2. Berry, B. E., "The Manufacture of Cemented Tungsten Carbide," *Murex, Ltd. Rev.*, 1 (8) (1951).

3. Blackburn, A. R., Shevlin, T. S., and Bower, H. R., *J. Am. Ceram. Soc.*, **32**, 81 (1949).

4. British Intelligence Objectives Sub-Committee "German Hard Metal Industry," Final Report No. 1385, Item No. 21, 1945, London, H. M. Stationery Office.

5. Burger, E. E., *Gen. Elec. Rev.*, **49**, 22 (1946).

6. Buswell, R. W., Pitken, W. R., and Jenkins, R. "Sintered Alloys for High-Temperature Service in Gas Turbines," Iron and Steel Institute Symposium on High Temperature Steels and Alloys for Gas Turbines, pp. 258–268 (1951).

7. Garvin, S. J., *Engineering*, **163**, 445 (May 30), 465 (June 6, 1947); *Iron Steel Inst. (London),*

Spec. Rept. No. 38, p. **67** (December, 1947).

8. Goetzel, Claus G., "Treatise on Powder Metallurgy," Vols. 1, 2, and 3, New York, Interscience Publishers, Inc., 1950.

9. Hamjiam, H. J., and Lidman, W. G., *Natl. Advisory Comm. Aeronautics, Tech. Note No. 1948,* **23** pp. (September, 1949).

10. Hood, T. A., "Manufacture of Cemented Carbides," Maribyrnong, Victoria, Australia, Inform. Circ. No. 12 (1947) Defense Research Laboratories, Dept. of Supply & Development.

11. Jackson, W. R., "Powder Metallurgy as Applied to Cemented Carbides," *Can. Mining Met. Bull.,* No. 390, 393 (October, 1944).

12. Kieffer, R., and Hotop, W., "Pulvermetallurgie und Sinterwerkstoffe," Berlin, J. Springer, 1943; *Metal Ind. (London)* (June 1, 8, 15, 1945).

13. Lihl, F., (German), *Acta Phys. Austriaca,* **4,** 360 (1951).

14. Lumley, E. J. T., Honeycombe, R. W. K., and Greenwood, J. N., *Proc. Australasian Inst. Mining & Met. No. 128,* p. 221–6 (1942).

15. Mantle, E. C., "The Sintering of Tungsten, Carbide with Cobalt Binder," *Metal Treatment,* **14,** 141 (1947).

16. Meerson, G. A., and Lipkes, Y. M., *Metal Ind. (London),* p. 290 (Nov. 7), p. 306 (Nov. 14, 1941).

17. Miroslav, P., *Hutnické listy,* **5,** 105 (1950).

18. Rostoker, W., *Trans. Am. Inst. Mining Met. Engrs.,* **180,** 672 (1949).

19. Sandford, E. J., and Trent, E. M., *Iron Steel Inst. (London), Spec. Rept. No. 38,* p. **84** (December, 1947).

20. Schumacher, E. E., and Sauden, A. C., "Powder Metallurgy," *Metals & Alloys,* **20,** 1327 (1944).

21. Steinitz, R., *Powder Met. Bull.,* **1,** 45 (1946).

22. Whitman, M. J., and Repko, A. J., *Natl. Advisory Comm. Aeronautics, Tech. Note No. 1914,* p. 49 (July, 1949).

23. Wulf, John, "Powder Metallurgy," Cleveland, American Society for Metals, 1942.

New References for Second Edition

24. Booss, J. H., *Trans. AIME,* **215,** 395 (1959).

25. Gurland, J., *J. Metals,* **6,** 285 (1954).

26. Gurland, J., and Bardzil, P., *J. Metals,* **7,** 311 (1955).

27. Warren, D., and Libsch, J. F., *Trans. AIME,* **191,** 774 (1951).

Plating of Cobalt and Cobalt Alloys

1. Brenner, A., Burkhead, Polly, and Seegmiller, Emma, *Natl. Bur. Standards (U.S.) Research Paper No. 1834,* **39,** 351 (1947).

2. Brenner, A., Chase, C., and Couch, D. E., U.S. Patent 2,643,221 (June 23, 1953).

3. Brenner, A., Chase, C., and Riddell, Grace E., *Steel,* **126,** 99 (1950); *Iron Age,* **165,** 78 (1950); *Metal Finishing,* **48,** 65 (1950).

4. Brenner, A., Chase, C., and Riddell, Grace E., U.S. Patent 2,532,284 (Dec. 5, 1950).

5. Brenner, A., Couch, D. E., and Williams, Eugenia K., *J. Research, NBS,* **44,** 109 (1950); *Natl. Bur. Standards (U.S.), Research Paper No. 2061,* 1950; *Metal Prog.,* p. 114 (1951).

6. Brenner, A., Couch, D. E., and Williams, Eugenia K., *Plating,* **37,** 36 (January, 1950); 161 (February, 1950); *J. Research NBS,* **44,** 109 (1950).

7. Brenner, A., and Riddell, Grace, *J. Research NBS,* **39,** 385 (1947); *Chem. Age (London),* **57,** 156 (1947); *Brit. Chem. Dig.,* **2,** 322 (1948); *Steel Processing,* **33,** 67 Steel, **121,** 84 (1947).

8. Clark, W. E., and Holt, M. L., *J. Electrochem. Soc.,* **94,** 245 (1948).

9. Evans, U. R., and Shome, S. C., *J. Electrodepositors' Tech. Soc.,* **26,** No. 9, 24 pp. (1950).

10. Faust, C. L., *Trans. Electrochem. Soc., Preprint 80–18,* p. 181 (1941).

11. Fedotov, N., *Trans. Electrochem. Soc.,* **87,** 547 (1945).

12. Fink, C. G., and Hutton, J. L., *Trans. Electrochem. Soc.,* **85,** 119 (1944).

13. Fink, C. G., and Lah, K. H., *Trans. Electrochem. Soc., Preprint 58–18,* p. 241 (1930).

14. Gill, A. S., *Proc. Australasian Inst. Mining & Met.,* **152–153,** 73 (1949).

15. Holt, M. L., Black, R. E., and Hoglund, P. F., *Trans. Electrochem. Soc., Preprint 84–15,* p. 139 (1943).

16. Hoglund, P. F., and Holt, M. L., *Trans. Electrochem. Soc.,* **88,** 359 (1945).

17. Kufferath, A., *Arch. Metallk.,* **2,** 135 (1948).

18. Ledford, R. F., *Plating,* **36,** 560 (1949).

19. Oldach, C. S., and Landau, R., *Metals & Alloys,* **17,** 967 (1943).

20. Rontgen, P., and Giesen, K., *Metall u. Erz,* **39,** 7 (1942).

21. Soderberg, G., Pinner, W. L., and Baker, E. M., *Trans. Electrochem. Soc., Preprint 80–32,* 401 (1941).

22. Soderberg, G., Pinner, W. L., and Baker, E. M., *Metal Ind. (London),* **67,** 200 (1945).

23. Verdieck, R., Ksycki, Mary J., and Yntema, L. F., *Trans. Electrochem. Soc., Preprint 80–11,* p. 93 (1941).

24. Young, R. S., "Cobalt," pp. 113–120, New York, Reinhold Publishing Corp., 1948.

New References for Second Edition

25. Bonn, T. H., and Wendell, D. C., U.S. Patent 2,644,787 (July 7, 1943).

26. Brown, H., U.S. Patent 2,654,703 (October 6, 1953).

27. Cuthbertson, J. W., *Chem. & Ind. (London)*. **48**, 1152 (1952).
28. Fegredo, D. M., *J. Indian Inst. Sci.*, **35(B)**, 191 (1953).
29. Hays, S., U.S. Patent 2,871,142 (Jan. 27, 1959).
30. Kufferath, A., *Arch. Metallk.*, **2**, 135 (1948).
31. Marcel de Merre, U.S. Patent 2,624,702 (Jan. 6, 1953).
32. Moline, W. E., and Clinchens, R. M., U.S. Patent 2,730,491 (Jan. 10, 1956).
33. Nokin, Jean, *Rev. universelle mines*, **13**, 220 (1957).
34. Okuno, G., *Studies in Nat. Sci.*, 46–47 (1950).
35. Salmony, Alfred, and Thews, R., "The Present Position of Cobalt Plating," *Metalloberflache*, **2**, 114 (1948).

Biological and Biochemical Aspects of Cobalt

1. Atomic Energy of Canada, Ltd., private communication.
2. Becker, D. E., Sedgwick, E., and Loosli, J. K., *Science*, **110**, 71 (1949).
3. Bonstedt, Gustave, *Vet. Med.*, **44**, 451 (1949).
4. Harding, H. E., *Brit. J. Ind. Med.*, **7**, 76 (1950).
5. Schweisheimer, W., *Iron Age*, **168**, 159 (1951).
6. Willis, L. G., "Bibliography of References to the Literature on the Minor Elements and Their Relation to Plant and Animal Nutrition," 3rd Ed., New York, Chilean Nitrate Educational Bureau, Inc., 1939; seven supplements, 1940–1947.

New References for Second Edition

7. Andrews, E. D., *New Zealand J. Sci. Technol.* **35A**, 301 (1953).
8. Beeson, K. C., *U.S. Dept. Agr., Agr. Inform Bull., No. 7*, p. 1 (1950).
9. Ekman, P., Karlsson, N., and Svanberg, O., *Acta Agr. Scand.*, **2**, 103 (1952).
10. Ferro Chemical Corporation, "Cobalt Compounds for Correcting Diet Deficiencies in Feeding Cattle and Sheep," *Tech. Bull. No 24* (Cleveland).
11. Hale, W. H., Pope, A. L., Phillips, P. H., and Bohstedt, G., *J. Animal Sci.*, **9**, 414 (1950).
12. Jordon, R. M., and Weakly, H., *S. Dakota State Coll. Agr. Expt. Sta., Tech. Bull. No. 425* p. 1 (1953).
13. Keener, H. A., Baldwin, R. R., and Percival G. P., *J. Animal Sci.*, **10**, 428 (1951).
14. Richman, D. M., and Henley, E. J., "Radioactive Cobalt," American Chemical Society Monograph, "Cobalt," Second Edition, R. S Young, Editor, New York, Reinhold Publishing Corp., 1960.
15. Smith, S. E., Koch, B. A., and Turk, K. L. *J. Nutrition*, **44**, 455 (1951).

9. COLUMBIUM

Edwin M. Sherwood*

Battelle Memorial Institute
Columbus, Ohio

WHAT'S IN A NAME?

For a long time, it appeared that almost as much attention was being given to the choice of a universal name for element 41 as to its technology. Discovered in 1801 by Charles Hatchett,[60] an English chemist, who analyzed an ore sample sent to the British Museum from Connecticut, it was at first named "columbium" after Columbia, the synonym for America. The columbium-rich ore was given the name "columbite," and this has been almost universally accepted.

Owing to its similarity to tantalum, with which it is always found in nature,† and to its difficult chemistry, it is not surprising that element 41 was rediscovered by Rose[122] in 1844 and named "niobium" after Niobe, the daughter of Tantalus. After more than 100 years of controversy, this name was adopted by the International Union of Pure and Applied Chemistry in 1950. Today, it is still endorsed by some leading chemical societies, and nearly all U. S. Atomic Energy Commission publications concerning element 41 refer to it as niobium. However, most United States metallurgists and leading United States metallurgical technical societies,[18] as well as all but one of the important United States commercial

* The author acknowledges his grateful appreciation to the Battelle Memorial Institute for its financial support in the preparation of the original manuscript for this chapter.

† It is important to note that columbium is perhaps eleven times more abundant than tantalum, however.

producers of the metal, use the name columbium. Thus, in the "Rare Metals Handbook," element 41 is called columbium.

Columbium metal is said to have been prepared first by Blomstrand in 1866,[71] who reduced columbium chloride with hydrogen. At a later date, Moissan[104] prepared columbium by reducing the oxide with carbon in an electric furnace. Still later, Goldschmidt[50] reduced the oxide with aluminum powder. In 1905 and the years following, interest arose in both columbium and tantalum as possible materials for the manufacture of filaments for incandescent lamps to replace the carbon filaments then in use. However, tantalum was finally chosen for this purpose. Also at that time, Von Bolton[149] prepared the metal in a relatively pure state by sodium reduction of the fluocolumbate and evaluated some of its more important properties. The first samples of columbium rod and sheet were prepared by Balke,[8] who used powder metallurgy techniques; this metal was first exhibited before the American Chemical Society in 1929.

SOURCES

Columbium has not been found in nature in the free state; it nearly always occurs as an oxide, together with that of tantalum, and is associated with other minerals having calcium, iron, manganese, and rare earths as bases. Tin, titanium, and zirconium may also be present. Unlike many other metals, it forms no natural sulfide compounds.

Although the mineral columbite, (Fe,Mn)

$(Cb,Ta)_2O_6$, traditionally has been considered the most important source of columbium, currently, both euxenite, a columbate-titanate of (Y, Ce, Er, U, Th, Zr), and pyrochlore, $(Na,Ca)_2(Cb,Ti_2)(OF)_7$, are gradually assuming industrial importance. The columbium oxide content of the above-mentioned minerals varies widely with locality, values from 30.8 to 62.3 per cent being common for columbite. While exact information about the columbium pentoxide content of euxenite and pyrochlore minerals is not often stated, combined columbium/tantalum pentoxide values as high as 65 per cent have been reported. In Table 9.1, the approximate analysis of a high columbium variety of pyrochlore mineral is indicated.

TABLE 9.1. ANALYSIS OF PYROCHLORE MINERAL[36]

Constituent	Wt %
Cb_2O_5	55.2
Ta_2O_5	3.4
CaO	13.6
FeO	2.3
MnO	0.1
P_2O_5	2.6
F	1.8
Na_2O	3.4

More important, however, is the relative abundance of columbium pentoxide in the various ore bodies throughout the world which permits the following estimates of reserves, in terms of contained columbium pentoxide.[63]

In Africa, columbite reserves probably exceed 70,000 tons, while pyrochlore reserves may be in excess of 1,200,000 tons. Pyrochlore reserves in Canada and Norway are said to be above 400,000 tons and 500,000 tons, respectively. United States reserves of euxenite and titanium-bearing minerals may contain 53,000 tons of columbium pentoxide. Reduction of all these reserves to metal would yield approximately 1.5 million tons of columbium, considerably in excess of the most generous estimates of possible future industrial requirements for this metal.

The current trend in the domestic columbium industry is one of expansion;[144] United States production of columbium metal in 1959 was 66 tons, twice what it was in 1958. In 1959, imported columbite mineral concentrates amounted to 1698 tons, while United States mines shipped

95 tons of concentrates. World production of concentrates declined considerably from the 7,760,000 lb value of 1957. Nigeria produced 4,307,520 lb of concentrates in 1957 and was the largest world source of the material.

The price of foreign columbite concentrates, containing 65 per cent combined oxides, with a columbium/tantalum ratio of 10 to 1, was about $1.15/lb in 1959. The United States price of columbium metal in late 1960 was about $36/lb for roundels and $45/lb for sheet.

SEPARATION OF COLUMBIUM FROM TANTALUM

The ubiquitous association of columbium with tantalum in nature, together with the great chemical similarity of these two elements, has been the major factor in preventing the rapid development of efficient processes for their commercial production. Therefore, an important step in any full-scale extractive process for columbium is the separation of columbium and tantalum compounds from each other. Ores destined for use in ferroalloy production normally are converted into columbium-rich ferrocolumbium/tantalum by carbon reduction in an electric furnace, without separation.

Fractional Crystallization. Based on Marignac's[91] fortunate discovery, in 1866, that the limited solubility of potassium fluotantalate (K_2TaF_7) could be utilized to separate it from the more soluble potassium oxyfluocolumbate $(K_2CbOF_5 \cdot H_2O)$ by fractional crystallization a relatively effective but rather tedious process was developed and used successfully for many years on a commercial basis. At present, this fractional crystallization of complex fluorides is used only to a limited extent, the current trend being toward the application of methods based on solvent-extraction or, as it is also called, liquid-liquid extraction.

In the Marignac type of process, the solutions remaining after the fractional crystallization step contain dissolved potassium oxyfluocolumbate, about 2 per cent tantalum in combined dissolved form, and other impurities, such as titanium and iron, not removed in previous operations. The tantalum can be removed by addition of potassium carbonate, or a similar basic compound, to the solution which is maintained at boiling temperature. This addition causes the tantalum to precipitate as basic tan-alum fluoride ($Ta_2O_5 \cdot 2K_2TaF_7$). Further purification then is achieved by precipitation of columbium as sodium columbate ($7Na_2O \cdot 5Cb_2O_5 \cdot 3H_2O$), which is insoluble in an excess of sodium hydroxide, and by fractional crystallization as potassium columbate ($4K_2O \cdot 3Cb_2O_5 \cdot 6H_2O$). Purified columbium oxide then is prepared by treatment of potassium columbate with hydrochloric acid.

Some variations in such aqueous separation processes are possible even though, in general, the columbates (except for the alkali salts) are insoluble. While columbic acid has only a very low aqueous solubility, chelate complexes with citric, oxalic, and tartaric acids can be formed, which thus produce a marked increase in solubility.

Solvent Extraction.[80] Although exact details of the newer columbium separation techniques, based on solvent extraction and receiving considerable industrial attention at present, have not been widely described, two processes, one developed by the Bureau of Mines[140] and the other by an industrial columbium producer,[31] can be outlined to illustrate the principles involved.

Early work at the U.S. Bureau of Mines indicated that the solvent-extraction system hydrofluoric acid/hydrochloric acid/methyl isobutyl ketone[64, 151, 152] provided an efficient method of separating columbium and tantalum. However, what was really desired was a system that not only would permit separation of columbium and tantalum but also would eliminate the other metallic impurities usually accompanying the columbium and tantalum as extracted from the ore. It was subsequently discovered that the system hydrofluoric acid/sulfuric acid/methyl isobutyl ketone had this unique and desirable characteristic.

Initial coextraction of aqueous feed solutions, prepared by dissolving hydrated oxides of columbium and tantalum in concentrated hydrofluoric acid and adding calculated amounts of sulfuric acid and water, is carried out by mixing one volume of feed solution with two volumes of methyl isobutyl ketone. Conditions for this initial operation include 100 g/1 hydrated oxides in the feed solution, with hydrofluoric and sulfuric acid concentrations $5.6N$ and $9N$, respectively. Separatory equipment then is used to draw off the organic and the aqueous phases. An equal volume of acid solution of known hydrofluoric acid and sulfuric acid concentrations is mixed with the organic phase and then separation is carried out. The columbium and tantalum present in each phase finally are precipitated with ammonium hydroxide. These hydroxides are removed by filtration, collected, and finally calcined at 800°C (1472°F). Recovery is usually greater than 90 per cent at a purity level above 99.9 per cent. Pure columbium compounds can be obtained with only one back extraction following the initial coextraction.

The only industrial solvent extraction process described to date[31] is illustrated in Figure 9.1. Columbite-tantalite ore is ball milled to 100-mesh particle size, or smaller, and fed to a leach tank, together with appropriate amounts of anhydrous hydrogen fluoride and deionized water. The resulting slurry is digested for 10 hr at 80°C (172°F) which causes dissolution of the columbium and tantalum oxides. Most of

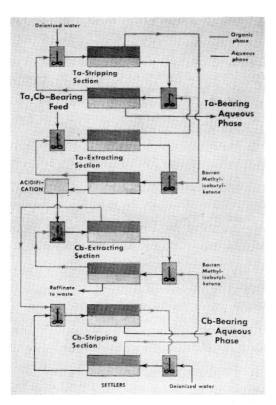

Figure 9.1. Separation of columbium from tantalum by solvent extraction. (*Reprinted, with permission, from Chemical Engineering, p. 104, November 3, 1958.*)

the impurities remain in the undissolved gangue. Dissolved impurities are removed in subsequent stages of processing. The gangue is filtered, the filter cake repulped and refiltered once, and the residue discarded. The columbium-tantalum liquor is fed to a holding tank, and the pH adjusted for proper acidity. The treated liquor then goes to the extraction cascade where mixing and settling operations are carried out in tandem. In the cascade, methyl isobutyl ketone is added in the tantalum extraction section. The columbium-bearing aqueous phase from this section is acidified, and pure methyl isobutyl ketone is then added to this product in the columbium extraction section. Finally, the columbium-bearing extract is treated with deionized water and led to a precipitation tank where ammonia is added to cause precipitation of columbium as the oxyfluoride. The precipitate is filtered, dried, and calcined to remove fluorine, yielding high-purity columbium oxide.

Other Methods. Efficient separations of columbium and tantalum on an experimental scale by ion-exchange methods have been reported.[20, 66, 82] While ion exchange appears less promising than solvent extraction, it does minimize mechanical problems and may permit more effective removal of impurities as well as provide a useful separation.

Sharp separations of columbium from tantalum can be made by chromatographic methods, provided only that the amount of tantalum present is less than the amount of columbium.[19]

Several years ago, English investigators of the Atomic Energy Research Establishment, faced with a shortage of suitable columbium concentrates, considered the use of ferrocolumbium as a feed material and developed a direct chlorination process.[43] Their goal was the production of high-purity columbium trichloride, either by hydrogen reduction of the pentachloride or by fractional distillation of the mixed chlorides, thereby avoiding many of the problems encountered in separating large amounts of tantalum from columbium feed material.

It has also been reported[26] that columbium can be separated from tantalum by treating pentoxide mixtures with aluminum halides (chloride, bromide, and iodide) under conditions of elevated temperature and reduced pressure. Fractional sublimation is used to isolate the halides formed. Aluminum iodide appears to be the most favorable agent in this application.

The possible commercial status of each of the processes described in this section cannot be evaluated at this time, but some are believed be in use on a commercial basis.

EXTRACTIVE METALLURGY OF COLUMBIUM[102, 118, 130]

Many methods have been proposed for the preparation of columbium metal. Broadly, these fall into nine general categories, as follows:

(1) reduction of oxides and halides by active metals, by nonmetals, and by electrolysis (6 categories in all)
(2) electrorefining
(3) disproportionation reactions
(4) thermal decomposition of halides

Although a great deal of effort has gone into the investigation of these various methods of preparation, those found suitable for commercial application include only carbide or carbon reduction of the oxide, and sodium reduction of the pentachloride or other halide compounds. Hydrogen reduction of the trichloride has been proposed[43] as a means of producing high-purity columbium metal powder on an expanded scale. An electrorefining process for the preparation of columbium in a fused melt of potassium fluocolumbate has also been investigated.[129]

Carbide/Oxide and Carbon/Oxide Reduction. In the commercial carbide-oxide reduction process for the production of columbium metal, a pressed bar of columbium carbide/columbium oxide mixture is resistively heated in vacuum at a temperature in the range 1600–1800°C (2912–3272°F). For a premium grade of metal reprocessing of the product yielded by this initial reduction is necessary. This is accomplished by analyzing the initial product, adding an approximately stoichiometric amount of carbide or oxide, as required, and resintering. In this way, metal of fairly high purity can be produced. However, metal lower in both carbon and oxygen is desirable for some important applications, and additional refining operations are necessary. These operations will be described in a later section of this chapter.

In the reduction of columbium oxide with carbon, the processing temperature for the mixture is reported to be 2000°C (3632°F) in a vacuum of 1 micron or less.

Sodium Reduction of the Chloride. No detailed information concerning the industrial sodium reduction processes used in preparing columbium metal has been published. By analogy with similar processes for titanium and zirconium production, however, one feasible process would cause molten columbium pentachloride to contact a pool of molten sodium floating on fused sodium chloride in an appropriate reaction vessel. The columbium pentachloride would be reduced to columbium metal powder or granules which would sink to the bottom of the reaction vessel; sodium chloride would be the by-product formed. Periodically, the accumulated metal would be removed, crushed, and leached to remove the salt, and the metal would be consolidated by appropriate means.

Alternatively, columbium pentachloride vapor could be made to contact the molten sodium, or both constituents could be vaporized and reacted.

Development of such processes for operation on a continuous basis rather than on a batchwise basis is undoubtedly a major objective, since sodium-reduction processes are considered more amenable to this type of operation than are magnesium-reduction processes. Sodium has several advantages over magnesium in such a method. With a much lower melting point and higher vapor pressure than magnesium, sodium is easier to purify. Since sodium chloride is much less hygroscopic than magnesium chloride, less contamination should be experienced from moisture with sodium-reduced sponge than with corresponding magnesium-reduced sponge.

Low-temperature reduction of columbium pentachloride in an agitated sodium amalgam is described in a U.S. patent.[49]

CONSOLIDATION AND PURIFICATION

The products of the various reduction processes for columbium may be in the form of fine powder, small granules, or roundels (small right-circular cylinders). These must be consolidated into ingot form to permit further fabrication into useful shapes. In general, additional purification is required, since the unwanted nonmetallic impurity content (principally carbon, nitrogen, and oxygen, is often quite high. For example, analysis (on a weight per cent basis) showed that a typical lot of fine columbium powder, designated in 1957 as "high-purity" material, contained 1.2 per cent oxygen, 0.29 per cent nitrogen, and 0.16 per cent carbon. Values for the nonmetallic impurity content of columbium powder obtained from another source at about the same period were 0.5 per cent oxygen, 0.1 per cent nitrogen, 0.3 per cent carbon, and 0.3 per cent hydrogen. The manufacturer's analysis for typical columbium roundels, as of mid 1958, indicated 0.10 per cent oxygen, 0.04 per cent nitrogen, and 0.05 per cent carbon. Material of still higher purity is required for many applications.

Methods useful for consolidation and purification of columbium include sintering, drip melting in a vacuum, using either high-frequency induction or electron-beam heating,* iodide refining, and consumable-electrode arc melting. Bars of consolidated columbium can be further purified by zone refining.

Sintering.[9, 35, 78, 97, 131, 155] This method of consolidation and purification has been used commercially ever since 1930. Columbium powder is pressed at 100,000 psi into bars 24 or 30 inches in length and up to one square inch in

---

* Bombardment by a focused, high-density beam of high-velocity electrons. This heating method[136] has come to be considered a practical one for melting and welding many of the reactive metals. Means of producing, accelerating and focusing electrons are well known. Much energy can be made to impinge on a small target area, 0.00015 sq in. to 0.012 sq in. in size. In the latter case, as much as 50 KW of power may be dissipated as heat on the target area. The accelerating potential can be maintained only if the region between the electrodes does not become ionized. This leads to electrical breakdown, a result of collisions between the high velocity electrons and the metal atoms evaporating from the surface. For a given geometry, the amount of ionization depends on the metal and on the size of the target area. For example, the weight of columbium vaporized/unit area/unit time from molten columbium at $2540°C$ (75 degrees above the melting point) is 1.06×10^{-5} g/cm^2/sec. This mass of metal, times the target area, forms a quantity proportional to the number of atoms per second, just above the surface, which may collide with electrons in the incident beam. When the vapor pressure of the metal being melted is high, the beam current can be interrupted periodically (the primary supply current is interrupted with a thyratron "chopper") to prevent breakdown of the discharge.

cross section. Recently, bars 1 x 4 inches in cross section have been pressed. Bars destined for conversion into rod or wire are made with a square cross section, while those used to make sheet are rectangular in cross section with a width at least twice their thickness. The pressed powder bars have sufficient green strength to permit their ends to be clamped in the water-cooled terminals of a high-vacuum sintering furnace (Figure 9.2) and to be heated by their self-resistance to the passage of an electric current.

Induction heating also can be used for this purpose. This method of heating has an inherent advantage in that a saving of material results from the absence of unsintered ends, which are unavoidable in the self-resistance

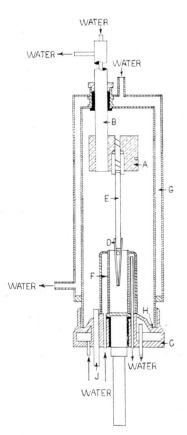

Figure 9.2. Vacuum sintering bell. (A) Upper contact; (B) water cooled copper tube; (C) cast iron base; (D) tungsten clip; (E) powder metallurgy bar; (F) reservoir; (G) water jacketed bell; (H) mercury trough; (J) vacuum connection. (*Courtesy Battelle Memorial Institute.*)

heating method. However, the equipment cost for induction heating is higher than that for direct resistance heating. In both cases, carefully designed equipment is required to minimize heat losses.

Resistance-sintered bars have a density about 90 per cent of theoretical at the end of the initial sintering period. As a rule, the highest sintering temperature lies in the range 1700–2300°C (3092–4172°F). Sintered bars are cold worked by rolling or forging to produce a 20 per cent reduction in thickness, and resintered to weld or "heal" the new contacts formed by the mechanical working. The product is a massive metal of high density that is essentially pore free.

Several major purification mechanisms are postulated to operate during sintering. In the temperature range 500–1000°C (932–1832°F), hydrogen is rapidly eliminated by outgassing. Carbon and oxygen then are removed at temperatures above 1400°C (2552°F) by combining to form carbon monoxide, which diffuses to the metal surface and is pumped away. At about 1800°C (3272°F), oxygen removal begins, presumably by vaporization of columbium monoxide. This reaction is less rapid than the carbon monoxide reaction at the highest sintering temperature. Finally, nitrogen is removed by simple outgassing at temperatures above 1900°C (3452°F). This takes place much more slowly than the other reactions. Obviously, the removal of small amounts of such impurities at very high temperatures and low pressures is controlled by the speed of outward diffusion of the gases involved. Table 9.2 illustrates the degree of purification afforded by the sintering process.

Drip Melting.[28, 29, 40, 62, 89, 139] The melting of reactive metals, such as columbium, is rendered difficult by their affinity for carbon, oxygen, and nitrogen. For example, appreciable amounts of oxygen may be acquired when the metal comes in contact with many refractory crucible materials or the atmosphere.

Several methods have been developed which avoid or minimize such contamination. One of these is the drip-melting process, in which a vertical rod of the material to be melted is gradually lowered into the field of an induction coil so that the lower end of the rod is continually melted. The molten drops then fall into a water-cooled copper crucible. As an alter-

TABLE 9.2. PURIFICATION OF COLUMBIUM BY SINTERING

| Material | Sintering Conditions | | Chemical Analysis — wt % | | | |
	Tempera-ture, °C	Time, hr	C	O₂	N₂	Reference
Commercial high-purity powder, No. 1	(Starting material)		0.16	1.2	0.29	78
Sintered bar	2150 (3902°F)	4	0.02	0.24	0.043	
Commercial high-purity powder, No. 2	(Starting material)		0.18	0.71	0.09	155
Sintered bar, converted to sheet	2300 (4172°F)	¾	0.001–0.02	0.005–0.018	0.002–0.013	

native, the induction coil can be raised, with the vertical rod held stationary. The rod may be formed by compacting or extruding sponge, powder, or other feed material in suitable form. The rod/crucible assembly for columbium melting is preferably housed in an evacuated quartz tube surrounded externally by the induction coil.

More recently, heating by electron bombardment in a vacuum of 10^{-3} mm Hg or less has been used to drip melt columbium on a fairly large scale. Figure 9.3 illustrates the system used. The impure ingot is fed into the melting equipment through a vacuum lock at the top. High-voltage electrons, supplied by a horizontal, ring-shaped, single-turn tungsten filament, are electrostatically focused on the lower end of the ingot. As the ingot melts, the drops of metal fall into a molten pool, maintained at a constant level by continually withdrawing the purified ingot downward through the exit lock. Unwanted impurities thus are largely volatilized during melting. An important technical feature of the process is the maintenance of the molten pool of metal on the upper end of the purified ingot (additional energy for this purpose is also supplied by electron bombardment), while the remainder of the ingot is supported in a water-cooled copper mold to minimize contamination. A double-melting cycle yields a high-purity ingot, while requiring about 3 to 4 KWH of useful electrical heating energy per pound of metal processed.

The rate of purification depends on the initial impurity content of the feed ingot. Using 3-inch-diameter ingots, 10 to 15 lb/hr of metal can be processed through the initial melting, while the remelt refining rate is about 80 lb/hr. This latter value corresponds to an ingot feed rate of 42 in./hr. It is claimed that the process can also be carried out using feed in the form of fine powder or flakes, as well as ingot. When unconsolidated feed is used, a spatter shield serves as the anode of the high-voltage supply. A superimposed electrostatic field deflects the electron beam 90 degrees, causing it to impinge on the feed. Molten metal, spattering on the shield, then drops directly into the crucible. Early in 1958, the largest equipment available (120 KW furnace) had a throughput capacity of 10,000 lb/month of 3-inch-diameter ingot. Figure 9.4 shows an industrial electron-beam melting installation.

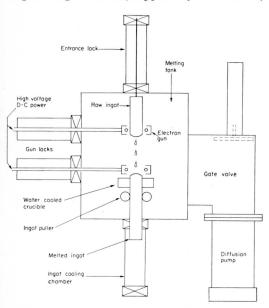

Figure 9.3. Electron beam drip melting of columbium. (*Courtesy J. Metals, February 1959.*)

Figure 9.4. Electron beam drip melting equipment. (*Courtesy Temescal.*)

Laboratory quantities of electron-beam-melted columbium, containing 0.002 wt per cent carbon, 0.0002 wt per cent hydrogen, 0.001 wt per cent oxygen, and 0.004 wt per cent nitrogen have been prepared. Commercially purified ingots up to 4 inches in diameter and 42 inches long are reported to contain less than 0.01 wt per cent oxygen, less than 0.005 wt per cent nitrogen, and less than 0.005 wt per cent carbon.

TABLE 9.3. PURIFICATION OF COLUMBIUM BY ELECTRON BEAM DRIP MELTING[139]
AND BY IODIDE REFINING[121]

Material	Analysis — ppm								Brinell Hardness No.
	O_2	N_2	C	Fe	B	H_2	Si	Ti	
Electron-Beam Drip Melting									
As rec'd, commercial powder	2500	500	300	200	<1	—	<50	<50	—
Above, as-melted	100	75	30	<100	<1	—	<50	<50	70–80
"High-purity" powder	200	100	50	<100	<1	—	<50	<50	—
Above, as-melted	55	30	<30	<100	<1	—	<50	<50	50–55
Iodide Refining									
Feed, sintered pellets	4350	180	500	—	—	21	—	—	—
Above, as-deposited*	640	10	<10	<50	—	8	90	<10	114
Feed, sheet	1950	120	60	—	—	9	—	—	<200
Above, as-deposited and double arc melted at reduced pressure	370	<10	11	—	—	14	—	—	63

* Other elements, ppm: Mo <100, W <500, Cu <10, Sn <50, Mg <10.

The estimated cost of producing high-purity columbium metal by an over-all process utilizing electron-beam melting for the consolidation and refining steps was $30/lb in mid 1958, at the 10,000 lb/month production level.

Table 9.3 illustrates the degree of purification which electron-beam drip melting affords.

Iodide Refining.[32, 121, 145, 147] Columbium has been refined experimentally using the iodide process, sometimes referred to as the Van Arkel/de Boer process. Feed metal and a small quantity of iodine, or the metal iodide, are enclosed in an evacuated vessel so constructed that both a moderate-temperature zone and a high-temperature zone can be maintained independently. This permits simultaneous synthesis and decomposition of metal iodide in the equipment. The iodine serves as a carrier, transporting metal from the feed to the deposition surface as a volatile iodide that is decomposed thermally to yield the purified metal and iodine.

Although several types of deposition surface have been employed, a resistively heated filament is most commonly used. Whenever possible, the deposition element is constructed of the same metal as that being deposited.

This process yields metal low in nonmetallic impurities and in consolidated form, usually as thin rods called "crystal bars." While the iodide process is used primarily to minimize non-metallics, good quality iodide-refined metal is low both in respect to metallic and nonmetallic impurities.

It has been reported that iodide columbium has an as-deposited Vickers hardness number in the range 64 to 80 and, further, that the as-deposited metal can be processed directly to rod and sheet by swaging (or forging) and rolling processes. The principal metallic impurity transferred from the feed to the crystal bar, in one investigation, was tantalum. Other metallic impurities in the feed—for example, aluminum, iron, manganese, molybdenum, silicon, titanium, and tungsten—were not found in the deposited metal to any appreciable extent under the deposition conditions used.

Table 9.3 indicates the analyses of iodide-refined columbium.

Consumable-Electrode Arc Melting.[11, 86, 121, 124] This method primarily offers a means of consolidating columbium into large diameter ingots, since the metal remains molten only a very short time and the degree of vacuum is not sufficient to permit rapid volatilization or extraction of impurities. However, further development of this process should not be overlooked. Table 9.3 shows that double arc melting iodide columbium at reduced pressure produces a lower level of oxygen impurity than is found in as-deposited iodide metal.

Floating Zone Refining.[21, 27, 69, 73, 74, 75, 109, 126, 134] Originally developed as a means of purifying substances used in solid-state devices, zone refining, with suitable modifications to avoid contamination by crucible materials, has proved effective in purifying consolidated columbium. Both induction and electron-beam heating have been used to cause a molten zone to traverse the length of a vertically held columbium rod ("floating" zone technique), thereby segregating at one end of the rod those impurities preferentially soluble in the liquid metal. In the floating zone refining of a small rod (diameter 0.40 inch, for example), using either of the above-mentioned methods of heating, the molten metal usually remains within the boundary of the original geometry of the rod, indicating the influence of surface tension. In contrast, if floating zone "levitation" by induction heating is used, the rod diameter can be much larger, for example, one inch or greater. In such a case, if the heating power is suddenly turned off, the molten metal in the zone immediately flows from between the solid portions of the rod. This is interpreted to mean that the hydrostatic pressure of the molten metal is restrained by the levitation force, thus permitting the refining of larger diameter rods.

Difficult adjustment of equipment to help sustain the molten zone in larger diameter bars is minimized by processing square or finned round bars of columbium. The corners or fins lose heat more rapidly than does the center of the bar, so that the molten metal is contained in a "cage" of its own material. Large-scale refining of columbium by this method has not been attempted.

PHYSICAL PROPERTIES[39, 62, 92, 120, 125, 133, 142, 154]

Columbium is described as a platinum-white, soft, ductile metal. Polished sheet, exposed to air at room temperature for long periods of time, takes on a faint bluish cast. A summary of the more important physical properties of columbium is presented in Table 9.4.

TABLE 9.4. PHYSICAL PROPERTIES OF COLUMBIUM

Property, Units	Value	Reference
Atomic number	41	
Atomic diameter, kX	2.94	(A)
Atomic volume, cc/g-atom	10.83	39
Density, g/cc	8.57	39
Atomic weight	92.91	39
Isotope, natural (atomic weight)	93	39
Isotopes, stable artificial (atomic weights)	89, 90, 91, 92, 94, 95, 96, 97, 98, 99	(B)
Lattice structure, body-centered cubic	—	39
Lattice constant, angstroms	3.294	39
Coordination number	8	39
Valence electron configuration	$4d^4\,5s^1$	(A)
Most intense spectral line, wavelength in angstroms	4058.94	(A)
Thermal-neutron-absorption cross section (for a neutron velocity of 2200 m/sec), barns/atom	1.15 ± 0.05	39
Work function, electron volts	4.0	(C)
Positive ion emission, electron volts	5.52	39
Electrochemical equivalent, mg/Coulomb	0.1926	39
Magnetic susceptibility, sec²/cm²/unit permittivity	2.28×10^{-6}	39
Melting point, °C	2468 ± 10	125
°F	4474 ± 18	
Boiling point (est), °C	4927	(D)
°F	8900	
Heat of combustion, cal/g	2379	39
Heat of melting (est), cal/g-atom*	6400	(D)
Heat of vaporization (at boiling pt), cal/g-atom*	166,500	(D)
Heat of sublimation, cal/g-atom		
at absolute zero	$171,800 \pm 490$	133
at 15°C	172,530	133
Heat capacity of the solid, cal/°C/g-atom		
at 15°C (59°F)	5.95	(D)
at 227°C (441°F)	6.14	(D)
at 727°C (1341°F)	6.62	(D)
at 1227°C (2241°F)	7.10	(D)
at 1727°C (3141°F)	7.58	(D)
at 2227°C (4041°F)	8.06	(D)
at melting point*	8.25	(D)
Heat content (at melting point*), cal/g-atom	17,050	(D)
Entropy, cal/°C/g-atom		
at 15°C	8.73	(D)
at melting point*	23.51	(D)
Enthalpy, at 15°C, cal/g-atom	1264	(D)
Free energy function, cal/°C/g-atom		
at 15°C	8.73	(D)
at melting point*	17.20	(D)
Vapor pressure, atm, [for $2304 < T < 2596$: $\log P_{atm} = -\left(\dfrac{40,169}{T}\right) + 8.872$, (T in °K)]		
at 2031°C (3688°F)	2.63×10^{-8}	133
at 2323°C (4213°F)	2.44×10^{-7}	133
Thermal conductivity, cal/cm²/°C/cm		
at 0°C	0.125	39
at 200°C (392°F)	0.135	142
at 400°C (752°F)	0.145	142
at 600°C (1112°F)	0.156	142

TABLE 9.4. PHYSICAL PROPERTIES OF COLUMBIUM (*cont.*)

Property, Units	Value	Reference
Ideal thermal resistivity, cm °K thermal conductivity		
at 15°K	0.1	[154]
at 90°K	1.7	[154]
Transition temperature, °K	9.25	[154]
Coefficient of linear thermal expansion, cm/cm/°C		
at 20°C (68°F)	7.1×10^{-6}	[39]
0–400°C (32–752°F)	7.39×10^{-6}	[142]
0–600°C (32–1112°F)	7.56×10^{-6}	[142]
0–800°C (32–1472°F)	7.72×10^{-6}	[142]
0–1000°C (32–1832°F)	7.88×10^{-6}	[142]
also, for 18°C <t <900°C		
$L_t = L_o (1 + 6.98 \times 10^{-6}t + 1.06 \times 10^{-9}t^2)$		
L_o = length at t = 0°C		[62]
Electrical resistivity, microhm-cm		
at 0°C	13.5	[154]
at 0°C	15.22	[142]
at 18°C (64°F)	14.8	[62]
at 20°C (68°F)	14.6	(E)
at −196°C (−321°F)	2.7	(E)
Coefficient of electrical resistivity, per °C		
at 18°C (64°F)	0.00395	[154]
0–600°C (32–1112°F)	0.00396	[142]

* Based on a melting point of 2427°C (4400°F).

(A) *Nat. Bur. Standards (U.S.), Circ. No. 467,* v. 1 (1949); v. 2 (1952).
(B) Strominger, D., Hollander, J. M., and Seaborg, G. T., *Rev. Mod. Phys.*, **30,** (No. 2, Pt. 2), 665–668 (April, 1958).
(C) Wright, D. A., *Proc. Inst. Elec. Engrs.*, **100,** 125–142 (1958).
(D) Stull, D. R., and Sinke, G. C., "Thermodynamic Properties of the Elements," 137–138, Washington, D.C., American Chemical Society, 1956.
(E) Begley, R. T., United States Atomic Energy Commission, *Rept. A-2388(WEC)* (1957).

MECHANICAL PROPERTIES[4,63,92,93,101,111,142,153]

As is the case with many of the less common metals of a reactive nature, the mechanical properties of columbium are very greatly dependent on the purity and previous history of the material. For example, the influences of such treatments as fabrication, thermal treatment and atmospheres, and exposure to damaging radiation are often quite marked.

Table 9.5 is a summary of data illustrating the mechanical properties of columbium metal in various forms. In every case, an attempt has been made to include the "pedigree" of the metal evaluated.

CHEMICAL PROPERTIES[39]

Columbium, as a metallic member of Group V-a in the periodic table, is characterized by the acidic properties of its most stable oxide, columbium pentoxide, and the volatility and nonpolar properties of its halides. In lower valence states, it exhibits basic properties. Figure 9.5 illustrates the electrode potential relationships among the various valence states of columbium.

As a reactive metal, columbium oxidizes readily at rather low temperatures; when processed at even moderate temperatures, it must be protected by vacuum or an inert, highly purified gaseous atmosphere.

In general, owing to the formation of protective oxide films,[146] columbium does not corrode in noncombining solutions over a wide range of pH values. However, the intrinsic active-metal nature of columbium is illustrated by its rapid dissolution in hydrofluoric acid and in aqueous alkali solutions, in which a protective oxide film does not form.

There is little doubt that the general corrosion resistance of columbium is inferior to that of tantalum.[55] Columbium is attacked slowly by most of the reagents to which tantalum is inert, and rapidly by others. In no instance is it unaffected by aqueous materials

TABLE 9.5. MECHANICAL PROPERTIES OF COLUMBIUM

Material: As-swaged rod [99]
        Analysis, wt %: C, 0.02; O_2, <0.05; N_2, 0.02; Zr, 0.05; Ta, 0.13

  Room-temperature properties:
    Yield stress (0.2% offset?), psi: 68,300
    Hardness, Rockwell "B":   71
    Elongation (in ¾ in.), %:   16
    Reduction in area, %:   90

  At 1090°C (1994°F) in argon:
    100-hr stress-rupture value, psi: 13,000
    Fatigue (at 20,000 psi) cycles: 2.6×10^6
      (measured in 5000 psi increments, starting at 5000 psi, and 10^7 cycles for each level
      of stress)

Material: Commercial sheet, 0.040 in. thick, tested in rolling direction [62]
        (History: ⅛ in. sheet, annealed, cold rolled to 0.040 in. thickness, annealed ½ hr
        at 1100°C (2012°F) in a vacuum more than 10^{-5} mm Hg)
        Test atmosphere not specified.

Temperature,		Proportional Limit, psi	Ultimate Tensile Strength, psi	Elongation in 1¼ in., %	Vickers Hardness No.
°C	°F				
20	68	41,600	49,500	19.2	94
200	392	34,700	53,500	14.2	115
300	572	29,400	44,800	13.2	94
400	752	32,000	49,000	13.3	107
500	932	28,200	44,900	9.6	96
600	1112	17,900	46,500	17.5	100
660	1220	15,900	46,600	22.4	—
800	1472	14,700	45,100	20.7	—
970	1778	11,700	27,600	37.5	—
1050	1922	9,860	18,300	42.5	—

Material: ⅛ in. dia. rod, machined [62]
        (effect of temperature on elastic modulus)
        Analysis, wt %: C, 0.02; O_2, 0.015; N_2, 0.005; Ta, 0.35
        Test atmosphere not specified, presumed to be air.

Temperature, °C	20	200	300	400	500
Young's Modulus, units of 10^6 psi	15.2	14.7	14.5	14.6	14.2

Material: 0.060 in. sheet (specimen size 0.060 in. × 0.250 in. × 7 in.)*
        (effect of temperature on elastic modulus)
        Analysis, wt. %: C, 0.02; O_2, 0.019; N_2, 0.026; Ta, 0.07; Zr, <0.03; Ti, 0.014; Fe, 0.018
        History: electron beam melted ingot, cold rolled to 0.060 in. sheet, 90% reduction;
            specimen recrystallized by a 2 hr vacuum anneal at 1100°C (2012°F).
        Test atmosphere: vacuum

* Begley, R. T. U.S. Air Force, *Rept. WADC–TR–57–344*, December, 1958.

Temperature, °C	25	93	204	310	427	600	800	900
°F	77	199	399	590	801	1112	1472	1652
Pressure, units of 10^{-3} mm Hg	0.15	0.3	0.6	1.0	2.0	3.0	4.0	4.5
Elastic Modulus, units of 10^6 psi	17.74	17.57	17.21	17.00	16.88	16.42	15.92	15.62

TABLE 9.5. MECHANICAL PROPERTIES OF COLUMBIUM (*cont.*)

Material: "Commercial" sheet   62
          (effect of cold rolling on hardness)

| Reduction in Area, % | Vickers Hardness No. | |
	Perpendicular to Rolling Direction	Parallel to Rolling Direction
0*	84	84
10	104	104
20	118.5	113.5
30	128.5	119
40	136.5	123
50	142.5	128
60	148	132.5

* Fully annealed. No edge cracking observed in any specimen.

Material: Annealed "commercial" sheet; analysis not given   155
          (effect of cold rolling on hardness)

Reduction in Thickness, %	Vickers Hardness No.
13.5	77
17.5	99
30.4	109
36.3	127
48.5	144
75	157
90.6	169
95.0	173

Material: "Commercial" (rod?)   142
          (effect of oxygen on room temperature tensile properties)
          Elongation values irregular, owing to breaking of some specimens in grips.

Oxygen Content, wt %	Mean Vickers Hardness No.	Proportional Limit, psi	Ultimate Tensile Strength, psi	Elongation, %
0.03	87	28,200	41,100	29.3
0.161	194	61,200	76,300	16.9
0.208	208	69,200	91,200	17.7
0.279	248	77,500	99,200	20.7
0.315	278	97,500	136,500	20.5
0.371	314	106,000	136,800	10.4
0.410	331	108,000	131,400	9.8

Material: "Commercial"   62
          (creep test results)

| Temperature, °C | Stress, psi | Time Required for Specified Creep Strain, hr | | | Minimum Creep Rate, microin./ in./hr | Duration of Test, hr | Total Creep Strain, % |
		0.05%	0.1%	0.2%			
400 (752°F)	8,960	160	880	—	0.44	1819	0.145
	13,440	115	445	2020	0.58	2700	0.224
	17,900	20	120	645	0.86	1600	0.286
	17,900	22	152	608	0.87	1536	0.289

TABLE 9.5. MECHANICAL PROPERTIES OF COLUMBIUM (*cont.*)

Material: "Commercial" (*cont.*)

Temperature, °C	Stress, psi	Time Required for Specified Creep Strain, hr			Minimum Creep Rate, microin./in./hr	Duration of Test, hr	Total Creep Strain, %
		0.05%	0.1%	0.2%			
500 (932°F)	8,960	—	—	—	0.52	362	0.037
	17,900	90	195	—	0.53	725	0.171
	17,900	85	140	390	0.24	1870	0.270
	22,400	22	59	123	5.3	338	0.345
600 (1112°F)	8,960	27	110	470	1.6	1325	0.340
	17,900	15	60	—	0.2	2117	0.198

Material: "Pure"   142

Temperature, °C		Stress, psi	Time Required for Specified Creep Strain, hr				Duration of Test, hr	Total Creep Strain, %	Oxygen Content, %	
			0.05%	0.1%	0.2%	0.3%			Before Test	After Test
600 (1112°F)	(a)	11,200	5	15	35	—	1359	1.08*	0.015	<0.1
600	(b)	13,440	40	130	345	1160	—	—	0.04	0.19
600	(c)	8,960	50	160	860	2130	5519	0.306	0.04	0.021
700 (1292°F)	(c)	2,240	40	290	1560	—	2314	0.22	0.04	0.22
700	(c)	4,480	80	205	550	1495	5008	0.36	0.04	<0.1
700	(c)	6,720	120	220	540	1115	3335	0.40	0.01	<0.1

* Minimum creep rate: 2.3 microin/in./hr

(a) Pressed and annealed slab
(b) As rolled
(c) Swaged bar

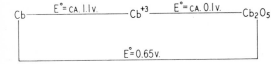

$$Cb = Cb^{+3} + 3e^-$$ $E° = CA. 1.1 v.$
$$2Cb + 5H_2O = Cb_2O_5 + 10H^+ + 10e^-$$ $E° = 0.65 v.$

Figure 9.5. Potential diagram for columbium in acid solution at 25°C. (*Reprinted with permission from Gonser, B. W., and Sherwood, E. M., "Technology of Columbium," New York, John Wiley and Sons, Inc., 1958.*)

which corrode tantalum. To cite some examples, columbium is less satisfactory than tantalum for use in aqua regia, in hydrochloric acid, or in sulfuric acid. Although it is not attacked by nitric acid at temperatures up to 100°C, a mixture of nitric and hydrofluoric acids consumes the metal rapidly. Hot concentrated hydrochloric, sulfuric, and phosphoric acids attack the metal although hot concentrated nitric does not. The metal is unaffected at room temperature by sulfuric, hydrochloric, nitric, phosphoric, tartaric, lactic, acetic, or perchloric acids, or by aqua regia, 5 per cent phenol, ammonium hydroxide, 30 per cent hydrogen peroxide, or 10 per cent ferric chloride. Acids which attack the metal slowly release sufficient hydrogen to embrittle it. For example, although the corrosion rate of a columbium sample in 10 per cent oxalic acid at 21°C (70°F) has been reported to be only 0.0006 ipy, the specimen will become brittle in 82 days. In general, precautions should be taken to prevent the metal from becoming the cathode in a galvanic couple in electrolytes, since the hydrogen discharged on it causes embrittlement.

Columbium is much less resistant than tantalum to alkaline solutions according to recent studies by Tingley.[141a] In 10 per cent sodium hydroxide at room temperature for 210 days, its corrosion rate was found to be 0.48 mils/year, and there was considerable local attack at the points of contact of the solution and the immersed rubber stoppers holding the test wire. In 1 per cent sodium hydroxide solution at 100°C (212°F), the corrosion rate was found to be 29 mils/year, and the wire became quite brittle. In 1 per cent potassium hydroxide at the same temperature, the corrosion rate was found to be 24 mils/year, and the embrittle-

ment was much less. In both 5 per cent sodium hydroxide and 5 per cent potassium hydroxide at 100°C (212°F), corrosion of columbium was severe, the average rates being about 100 mils/year with the rate increasing at the end of the test. Pitting was observed all along the wires

TABLE 9.6. CORROSION RESISTANCE OF COLUMBIUM IN VARIOUS MEDIA

Medium	Temperature,		Duration of Test, days	Corrosion Rate, ipy	Condition of Specimen after Test	Reference
	°C	°F				
HCl, dil.	20	68	—	0.00004	—	54
HCl, dil.	100	212	—	None	—	54
HCl, 18%	19–26	66–79	36	0.00000	—	138
HCl, conc.	19–26	66–79	36	0.00012	—	138
HCl, conc.	20	68	—	0.0001	—	54
HCl, conc.	100	212	67	0.004	—	143
HCl, conc.	110	230	7	0.004	Brittle	138
HNO_3, dil.	20	68	—	None	—	54
HNO_3, conc.	19–26	66–79	36	0.00000	—	138
HNO_3, conc.	100	212	—	None	—	54
$1HNO_3 \cdot 2HCl$	19–26	66–79	35	0.00002	—	138
$1HNO_3 \cdot 2HCl$	50–60	122–140	1	0.001	—	138
H_2SO_4, 20–25%	20	68	—	None	—	54
H_2SO_4, 20%	95–100	203–212	4	0.00002	—	138
H_2SO_4, 20–25%	100	212	—	None	—	54
H_2SO_4, conc.	19–26	66–79	36	0.00002	—	138
H_2SO_4, 98%	20	68	—	0.00009	Partial embrittlement	54
H_2SO_4, 98%	21	70	3650	0.0001	Partial embrittlement	143
H_2SO_4, 98%	100	212	—	0.019	—	54
H_2SO_4, conc.	145	293	30	0.18	Brittle	138
H_2SO_4, conc.	175	347	1	1.42+	Completely dissolved	143
H_3PO_4, 85%	19–26	66–79	36	0.00002	—	138
H_3PO_4, 85%	100	212	31	0.0033	Brittle	143
HF, dil.	20	68	—	Rapid	—	143
HF, dil.	100	212	—	Rapid	—	143
HF, conc.	20	68	—	Rapid	—	143
HF, conc.	100	212	—	Rapid	—	143
$(CO_2H)_2$, 10%	21	70	82	0.0006	Brittle	138
Na_2CO_3, 20%	100	212	50	0.0013	Brittle	138
NaOH, dil.	20	68	—	0.001	Brittle	138
NaOH, dil.	100	212	—	0.018	Brittle	138
NaOH, 1%	100	212	210	0.029	Brittle	141a
NaOH, 5%	100	212	5	0.047	Brittle	138
NaOH, 5%	100	212	210	0.100	Brittle	141a
NaOH, 10%	Room temp.		210	0.00048	—	141a
NaOH, conc.	20	68	—	Rapid	—	54
NaOH, conc.	100	212	—	Rapid	—	54
KOH, 1%	100	212	210	0.024	Brittle	141a
KOH, 5%	100	212	5	0.047	Brittle	138
KOH, 5%	100	212	210	0.100	Brittle	141a
H_2O_2, 30%	21	70	61	0.0002	Ductile	138
$FeCl_3$, 10%	19–26	66–79	36	0.00000	—	143
$CaCl_2$, 73%	197	350	36	nil	—	48a
	(open boiling)					
Wet Cl_2 gas contg salt brine spray	96	205	203	nil	—	48a

which became extremely brittle. The embrittlement was found to be due to the formation of hydride, which can be seen in photomicrographs as needles. Vacuum annealing at 1000°C (1832°F) for 4 hours restores the ductility of the columbium wires.

Table 9.6 presents a summary of data on the corrosion resistance of columbium in various media at room and elevated temperatures.

In the particularly inimical environments found in many types of nuclear reactors, columbium's ability to withstand attack by high-temperature water, by liquid metals (bismuth, sodium, and sodium-potassium alloy), and by other media, often at quite elevated temperatures, is well recognized. Columbium is neither corroded nor embrittled by sodium or "NaK" at temperatures well above 800°C (1472°F), provided that these liquid metals contain less than 40 ppm oxygen.[38, 94] Although only a few test results have been published, columbium has become well established as a material of construction for use in nuclear reactors.

Columbium's resistance to mass transfer in liquid lead[25] has been evaluated, on a relative basis, in small quartz thermal-convection loops. The test temperature was 800°C (1472°F), the thermal gradient 300°C (540°F) across the loops. Columbium exhibited a high degree of resistance to mass transfer and corrosion in test periods of up to 545 hours under the conditions described above, no noticeable attack being observed. Molybdenum was the only other metal which performed as well as columbium.

A useful schematic summary, indicating some of the chemistry of columbium[36] is shown in Figure 9.6, while Table 9.7 contains a summary of thermodynamic data relating to columbium and some of its compounds.

TABLE 9.7. THERMODYNAMIC PROPERTIES OF COLUMBIUM COMPOUNDS AT 25°C IN THE CONDENSED STATE*[39]

Compound	$\Delta H°$	$\Delta F°$	$S°$	$\Delta S°$
Cb_2O_4	−387.8	−362.4	(29.2)	(− 85.2)
Cb_2O_5	−455.2	−422.9	32.8	(−108.4)
CbC	− 30	− 29.6	—	− 1.4
CbN	− 59	− 55	—	(− 20)

* Values in parentheses are estimated, or uncertain.

Reaction With Gases and Carbon; Compound Formation. The impurities oxygen, nitrogen, carbon, and hydrogen have such an important influence on the physical and mechanical properties of columbium that a discussion of the reaction of columbium with these elements, as well as of the resulting compounds formed, is necessary for a thorough understanding of its technology and behavior. In addition, the halides of columbium, which are growing in industrial significance, also deserve some attention.

Table 9.8,[99] for example, indicates the depth of oxygen penetration into columbium in a 16-hour period at various temperatures. Rates of diffusion in cm²/second for nitrogen and carbon in columbium at very moderate temperatures (up to 300°C; 572°F) have been established[111] as follows:

$$\text{for nitrogen,}$$
$$D = 0.0072 \exp(-34,800/RT);$$
$$\text{for carbon,}$$
$$D = 0.0046 \exp(-33,300/RT).$$

The immediate consequence of hydrogen absorption by columbium is severe embrittlement, whether its source is a gaseous atmosphere at

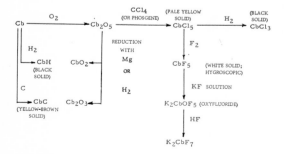

Figure 9.6. Chemical reactions of columbium. (*From Atomics and Nuclear Energy, 8, 339–342, 1957, courtesy Atomic World.*)

TABLE 9.8. EFFECTIVE DEPTH OF OXYGEN PENETRATION IN COLUMBIUM*[99]

Temperature		Oxygen Penetration, cm
°C	°F	
540	1004	0.01
650	1202	0.01
760	1400	0.03
870	1598	0.08
980	1796	0.10
1090	1994	>0.25

* Specimens 0.375 in. dia. × 0.500 in. long, tested 16 hr in air at temperature indicated.

elevated temperature or an acid solution in which the metal is made cathodic.

Oxygen. The oxidation of columbium has been studied extensively[15,22,52,54,70,77,128] since columbium's lack of oxidation resistance is, without doubt, its most serious shortcoming. This handicap must be successfully overcome before columbium can be used in the many high-temperature applications for which its otherwise excellent properties render it eminently suitable. A brief description of some of the efforts to protect columbium will be given in a later section.

The findings, to date, are somewhat as follows. At a pressure of 76 mm Hg, a parabolic oxidation-rate law obtains over the temperature range 250–375°C (482–707°F), with an activation energy of 22,800 cal/mole. A thin oxide film, assumed to be columbium monoxide, is formed under these conditions. Reaction with wet and dry air in the range 400–1200°C (752–2192°F) initially obeys a parabolic law, but after 21 hours at 400°C, it follows a linear law; a linear relationship for the formation of a nonprotective oxide layer[24] is also found between 600–1200°C (1112–2192°F). At 1000–1200°C (1832–2192°F), test specimens in rod form oxidize more rapidly than do sheet samples. Activation energies of 13,400 cal/mole at 600–900°C (1112–1652°F) and 4350 cal/mole at 900–1200°C (1652–2192°F) have been reported.

High-pressure oxidation studies indicating a linear rate law also show that oxidation rate is very sensitive to pressure.

Experiments carried out in oxygen under normal conditions of pressure at 600–1100°C (1112–2012°F) have yielded a constant heat of reaction of 5410 cal/mole. Above 1100°C, the oxidation rate is still more rapid. In the temperature range studied, the oxide formed is characterized by a thin black sublayer of oriented columbium pentoxide and columbium monoxide, and a porous outer layer of white columbium pentoxide. The heat of activation for oxidation in moist air is 10,100 cal/mole over the range 600–1200°C (1112–2192°F). It is concluded that the rate-determining reaction is the diffusion of oxygen through the black sublayer.

Of the oxides thus far reported, columbium pentoxide is the most important, since it is the form to which all others revert when heated

in air. It also can be formed by direct ignition of the metal, or of compounds (for example, the carbide), and by dehydration of columbic acid. Solid columbium pentoxide exists in one of three allotropic forms, depending on temperature.[14] The "low" form, isomorphous with tantalum pentoxide*, is stable to 900°C (1652°F). The "medium" form exists over the temperature range 1000–1100°C (1832–2012°F) and is transformed to the "high" form above 1100°C. Columbium dioxide, prepared by hydrogen reduction of the pentoxide, is described as a black powder, and has a crystal structure similar to that of rutile (for columbium dioxide, $a = 4.84$ Å, $c = 2.99$ Å; $c/a = 0.618$).

Studies of still lower oxides have been made by sintering mixtures of columbium dioxide and carbon in various ratios. The existence of columbium monoxide has been verified by x-ray diffraction, but that of columbium trioxide as a compound is questioned. Columbium monoxide is described as black, in powder form.

Nitrogen. Less attention has been paid to nitrogen than to oxygen as a contaminant in columbium. Reference is made here to the earlier discussion of purification by sintering, in which it was indicated that nitrogen can be removed, rather slowly, from columbium by simple vacuum outgassing at temperatures of 1900°C (3452°F) and above.

As might be expected from the foregoing statement, as well as from columbium's location in the periodic table, its nitrides are less stable than those of the refractory Group IV nitrides. However, the existence of columbium mononitride and a compound having the formula Cb_2N has been definitely established, while the compound Cb_3N_5 is less well characterized. Formation of the nitrides takes place by direct synthesis, or by the reaction between a columbium oxide or halide and nitrogen in the presence of hydrogen. In air, they oxidize readily, evolving nitrogen. Superconducting at 15.2°K,[34, 67, 68] the third highest transition temperature known for any substance, columbium mononitride (CbN) was, for a time, of great interest because it could be used as a material of construction for bolometers.[5, 46, 47, 88]

* The crystal structure of columbium pentoxide is pseudohexagonal orthorhombic. Cell dimensions are reported as $a_1 = 6.16 \pm 0.03$ Å, $a_2 = 3.65 \pm 0.02$ Å, and $a_3 = 3.94 \pm 0.02$ Å. The metal atoms are located at the positions (0 0 0) and (½ ½ 0).

Carbon. This element reacts directly with columbium to form the monocarbide, which is stable to 2500°C (4532°F) in nitrogen but decarburizes slightly when heated in air.[123] Columbium monocarbide can be formed by reaction of the metal with a hydrocarbon, or by reaction of the oxide with free carbon. Micro-crystals of columbium monocarbide also are prepared by the McKenna process,[95] in which the metal or its oxide is reacted with carbon in a molten metallic mass at 1800–2000°C (3272–3632°F).

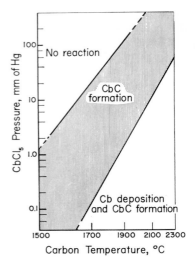

Figure 9.8. Conditions for formation of CbC coatings on graphite by vapor deposition. (*Courtesy Battelle Memorial Institute.*)

Figure 9.7. Vapor-deposited CbC coating on graphite (500X). (*Courtesy Battelle Memorial Institute.*)

Columbium monocarbide coatings for graphite, up to 0.5 mm thick and of considerable interest in nuclear engineering applications, can be formed directly on such bases by specialized vapor deposition techniques.[13] Figure 9.7 illustrates the microstructure of a vapor-deposited layer of columbium monocarbide on graphite, while Figure 9.8 indicates the conditions of temperature and pressure under which the carbide can be formed. In appearance, vapor-deposited columbium monocarbide has a bright, metallic luster with a pinkish tinge.

Hydrogen. The columbium-hydrogen system has been investigated in detail.[1, 96] Pressure-temperature-composition equilibria of this system have been determined in the range 100–900°C (212–1652°F), 10–1000 mm Hg, and for atomic ratios of hydrogen/columbium

= 0.01 to 0.85. The absorption of hydrogen results in the formation of a single-phase solid solution throughout most of the system. At about 300°C (572°F) and a pressure of 8 mm Hg, the presence of a two-phase region is indicated between hydrogen/columbium ratios of 0.21 and 0.42. At low hydrogen compositions, the equilibrium solubility follows approximately a square-root-of-pressure relationship. This indicates that hydrogen is absorbed in the atomic state. Both lattice parameter and heat of solution increase with hydrogen concentration.

Halogens.[2, 3, 26, 39, 44, 45, 81, 145] The halides of columbium are formed by direct combination with the halogens. They also can be formed by treatment of the oxide with carbon and halogens, or of the carbide with halogens. Figure 9.6 indicates some of the ways in which the fluorides and chlorides can be prepared. A means of preparing columbium trifluoride, with high chemical stability, by treatment of columbium hydride with a hydrofluoric acid/hydrogen mixture at 570°C (1058°F) has been described. The bromides are formed by methods similar to those used for the chlorides. The reaction of the metal with iodine is described as slow. More rapid formation of the iodide is reported to take place when the bromide is reacted with anhydrous hydrogen iodide.

Being nonpolar, the halides of columbium have comparatively low melting and boiling points. While beyond the scope of this chapter, further details of the chemistry of columbium halides are known which indicate that these compounds are likely to play an important role in future metal production methods. The preparation of iodide columbium, described in an earlier section, provides one of the clues for the above deduction.

Borides, Silicides, and Intermetallic Compounds. [23, 39, 76, 84, 85, 107, 148] Columbium-boron compounds, of which only the monoboride is sufficiently stable to melt without decomposing, are attacked in air at temperatures between 1100–1200°C (2102–2192°F). The high electrical resistivity, high reflectivity, and low volatility of columbium borides, however, render them useful in such applications as internal-resistance and induction heating, as well as for radiation shields. These compounds retain their hardness relatively well at elevated temperatures and hence have good high-temperature abrasion resistance.

The silicides Cb_4Si, Cb_5Si_3, and $CbSi_2$ are prepared by sintering or arc furnace melting. They are neither very hard nor oxidation resistant.

Although reports are meager concerning intermetallic compounds with columbium, $CbBe_{12}$, $CbGe_2$, $CbGe_{0.67\pm0.05}$, $CbGe_{0.54\pm0.06}$, and Cb_3Ge have been identified. The intermetallic compound Cb_3Sn has the highest superconducting transition temperature thus far observed, 18.0°K.*

ANALYSIS

Analytical methods, developed in numerous investigations of columbium, have several major functions which can be categorized as follows.

(1) Quantitative methods for the assay of ores and minerals containing columbium have been tailored to the materials investigated. Since it is now known that many of the older methods still referred to in some modern texts were inaccurate, careful selection of assay methods from published sources is necessary. Abroad, such tools as x-ray fluorescence analysis[105] have been used in analyzing ores and minerals.

(2) Numerous techniques for the detection of columbium as an impurity in other substances have been reported. Spectrochemical methods

* Scott, R. B., "Cryogenic Engineering," p. 342, New York, D. VanNostrand Company, Inc., 1959.

[72, 150] are widely used for this purpose. Wet methods[83, 90] also are in use. Analytical techniques used to evaluate separation methods for columbium and tantalum must be quite sensitive. Some of the separations can be used on a microscale as well as on a macroscale and hence, are useful in this connection.

(3) Of considerable importance is the determination of various metallic and nonmetallic impurities in columbium, particularly when metal of very high purity is to be evaluated. In one method,[7] differential spectrophotometry is used to make a total assay of high-purity metal, while in another,[6] only columbium is determined.

Specific methods for determining the following metallic impurities in columbium have been described: cadmium,[106] copper,[114] iron,[16, 117] manganese,[115] molybdenum,[113, 116] tantalum,[141] titanium,[30,117] tungsten,[116] and zirconium.[117]

Accurate determination of nonmetallic impurities, particularly gases, becomes very difficult at the ppm level, and it is in this area that real research effort has been required to develop techniques of sufficient sensitivity. Carbon is determined by combustion (200 ppm level) or by special conductimetric methods (20 ppm level). Oxygen can be determined by vacuum extraction, i.e., by fusion or distillation. Hydrogen is preferably determined by vacuum fusion, while micro-Kjeldahl, solution-distillation, and alkali-fusion methods are available for nitrogen. Detailed descriptions of the methods used for determining oxygen, nitrogen, and hydrogen in columbium are available.[51, 56, 58, 59, 100]

As columbium technology progresses and metal of still higher purity is evaluated, it is probable that special concentration techniques and neutron-activation analysis will be required to indicate properly the degree of purity of the metal.

METALLOGRAPHY[17]

Conventional metallographic techniques are used in preparing samples of columbium for examination.

Wet sectioning is done with a rubber-bonded abrasive cutoff wheel.

Initial grinding is carried out on a 180-grit wet belt at 2750 ft/min surface speed. Successively finer grades of silicon carbide grinding discs (240, 400, and 600 grit) are used for fine grinding at 1200 rpm. The discs may be dressed with wax to minimize the embedding of abrasive particles in the specimen, as well as to cool and lubricate. Water also may be used for cooling and lubrication. The 600-grit grinding step is repeated preferably before polishing is started.

Polishing is accomplished in two operations. The first, rough polishing, is carried out on a high-speed (1750 rpm) wheel covered with "Miracloth."* The cloth is charged periodically during polishing with a slurry of "Linde B"† abrasive and dilute (2-5 per cent) chromic acid. Polishing is continued under the above conditions at medium to heavy pressure until the last traces of scratches and any embedded abrasive are removed. Etch polishing may be carried out at this stage in the procedure if there are no inclusions or alloy phases which are readily attacked by the etchant.

Final polishing is carried out at 250 to 500 rpm on a wheel covered with "Microcloth."* A slurry of "Linde B" abrasive in water is used. At the outset of final polishing, additional scratches may appear as a result of the removal of smeared metal left by rough polishing. Polishing is continued until no scratches are seen, the final steps being carried out with very light pressure and very slow wheel speeds.

A composite etching procedure has been developed which appears quite satisfactory. A mixture of 50 ml lactic acid, 30 ml nitric acid, and 2 ml hydrofluoric acid, at room temperature, is swabbed on the surface for one minute or longer. Actually, this "etchant" is used to polish chemically rather than to etch the surface. Next, a mixture of 30 ml lactic acid, 10 ml nitric acid, and 10 ml hydrofluoric acid, at room temperature, is swabbed on the surface for about 5 seconds; it is then rinsed off, and the specimen is dried and inspected for degree of etch. The process is repeated one or more times if deeper etching appears necessary. The active ingredient is the hydrofluoric acid, the concentration of which may be varied in the mixture as desired.

* Miracloth and Microcloth are trade names of products sold by Buehler, Ltd., 2120 Greenwood Street, Evanston, Illinois.

† Linde B–5125, dry alumina powder; manufactured by Linde Air Products Company, 9165 S. Harbor Avenue, Chicago, Illinois.

METAL WORKING, FABRICATION, AND CUTTING

Most information heretofore available on the fabrication of columbium into the usual shapes required for materials of construction, such as plate, sheet, rod, and wire, has been developed as a result of experience gained on material produced by the methods of powder metallurgy. With the larger sizes of consolidated metal now being produced by the successful application of vacuum arc and electron bombardment melting, somewhat less complicated ingot breakdown procedures are required. However, it is still necessary to carry out all forging, forming, bending, stamping, and deep-drawing operations at, or not greatly above, room temperature, if contamination by atmospheric gases is to be minimized. Further, the tendency of columbium to seize and gall, somewhat like the stainless steels, also must be taken into account. Columbium is superior to stainless steel in its resistance to tearing, however.

Vacuum sintered, powder metallurgy columbium bars are porous and, as indicated earlier, must be cold forged with a heavy hammer until a reduction of about 20 per cent has been achieved.[9] Cold-reduced bars are then sintered again, reforged, and resintered to secure sound pore-free metal.

Columbium slugs in the as-cast condition as produced by electron-bombardment melting (Brinell hardness 100, 500 kg load) have been cold extruded into cups at room temperature.[112] Forward extruded tubes also have been produced at 425°C (797°F) without an intermediate anneal. The total reduction from slug to tube was 85 per cent. A specimen taken from the center of the tube had the following mechanical properties: ultimate tensile strength, 64,400 psi; yield strength (0.2 per cent offset), 62,200 psi; elongation in 2 inches, 9 per cent. Standard lubricants are used in extruding columbium.

The effects of cold work produced by forging, swaging, or rolling become sufficiently severe after a total reduction in area of 90 per cent as to require an annealing treatment of the metal. A one-hour anneal at 1300–1400°C (2372–2552°F) in a good vacuum (less than 10^{-3} mm Hg) is preferable.[38]

Sheet rolling is carried out on conventional 2- or 4-high mills with small diameter rolls, and requires suitable lubricants if polished sheet is to be the end product. Reductions of 5 to 10 per cent per pass, or heavier, are commonly employed. Experimental investigation[4] of the cold-worked and recrystallized texture of columbium sheet has shown that it is similar to those of other body-centered-cubic metals such as alpha iron. Columbium sheet is highly fibered, so that transverse ductility is low. This condition apparently can be improved only by a complete recrystallization heat treatment.

Rod can be produced by cold swaging or rolling, using standard equipment.

The seizing and galling tendency of columbium renders wire and tube drawing difficult, and particular attention must be paid to tool and die materials as well as to lubrication. Aluminum bronzes are the most satisfactory tool materials, although both tungsten carbide and hard-chromium plated materials have been used. Drawing waxes and sulfonated tallow are suitable lubricants.

The excellent resistance to tearing in forming operations, characteristic of columbium, is an asset in the production of tubing.[155] Discs of suitable thickness-to-diameter ratio (1:48 to 1:60), are first blanked, then cupped and drawn on a hydraulic press. Reductions of 47.5 to 51 per cent are feasible at this stage. The cups are subsequently formed into tubing according to standard tube-forming practice. Grain size in the material at the cupping stage is of vital importance if orange-peel effects are to be minimized. The tube-drawing operations normally permit 35 per cent reduction in area for a single pass, and 60-80 per cent total reduction between stress-relieving anneals. This range in total permissible reduction is occasioned by the range in thickness-to-diameter ratios of the blanks, as given above.

Columbium is form stamped by a method similar to that used for mild steel, special precautions being taken to prevent seizing. Steel dies can be used except in cases where considerable slipping of the metal takes place. Aluminum bronze and beryllium copper have been found to perform more satisfactorily in such instances. Low-melting alloys (e.g., Kirksite) can be used for short runs or experimental work. Rubber or pneumatic cushioning may also be required.

In blanking or punching, steel dies are used, with punch-die clearance close to 6 per cent of the thickness of the metal being worked. The use of light oil or carbon tetrachloride as a lubricant minimizes die scoring.

Spinning is used to form columbium into special shapes. Here, also, the practice is similar to that used for more common metals, but the shaping must be gradual. Aluminum bronze tools and yellow soap or tallow lubricants perform well. Wooden forms can be used for rough shaping, but mild steel forms are necessary in finishing operations. Columbium spinning requires light pressure and long strokes for uniform finished metal thickness. A surface speed of approximately 500 ft/min at the periphery of the work is recommended.

The machining of columbium is accomplished by conventional methods, using high-speed steel tools and high surface speeds (60 to 100 ft/min) to prevent the metal from tearing or welding to tools. The latter should be kept sharp and should be ground with as much positive rake as the strength of the steel will permit. Figure 9.9 illustrates typical rakes and angles used. Flooding the work with carbon tetrachloride provides the necessary protection, but proper precautions must be taken to avoid toxic effects from the vapor of this medium. For rough machining, feeds of 0.008 to 0.012 in./revolution of the work are suggested. The recommended feed for finishing cuts is 0.005 in. max/revolution. Actually, very shallow finishing cuts should be avoided. Fairly heavy cuts and light feeds often leave the surface in better condition than does the normal combination of roughing and finishing cuts. Filing or using emery cloth to finish the surface of lathe

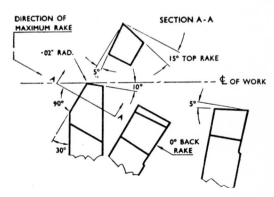

Figure 9.9. Tool design for machining columbium. (*Courtesy Welding and Metal Fabrication, p. 354, October 1956.*)

work is possible, but carbon tetrachloride is recommended as a lubricant even for these operations.

The same general procedures should be followed in milling, drilling, threading, or tapping columbium. Milling cutters should be of the staggered-tooth type and should be provided with generous back and side relief. High-speed steel drills, with points relieved to prevent rubbing, should be used and a plentiful supply of carbon tetrachloride should be provided as a lubricant. On large-diameter work, threads are preferably cut on a lathe. Taps or dies should be cleaned frequently to remove chips during use. Grinding columbium is not recommended as a finishing operation.

CLEANING

With the exception of hot caustics, conventional media and procedures may be used to clean columbium. The medium especially recommended for rendering columbium chemically clean is a saturated solution of chromium trioxide in hot concentrated sulfuric acid. Treatment in this solution is followed by a hot distilled-water rinse.

As a method of surface treatment prior to electroplating,[10] columbium may be subjected to an AC electrolytic etch in hydrofluoric acid as follows. The etching bath is concentrated (49 per cent) hydrofluoric acid, maintained at room temperature. Etching time is 1–3 minutes at current densities of 200–1000 amp/ft². A gray smut which forms on the etched surface can be removed easily in a nitric-hydrofluoric acid solution prior to plating.

Surface preparation of columbium for welding is discussed in a later section.

ELECTROPLATING[10]

Adherent electrodeposits on columbium are difficult to obtain. A satisfactory procedure has been developed in which iron is first deposited

on the parts from a rather complex bath, the composition of which is given below, and then plated specimens are heated for one hour at about 820°C (1508°F) in a vacuum of 10^{-3} mm Hg. For best results, the specimens are preheated for two hours at 200°C (392°F) in air to prevent blistering. A layer of electroplated iron 0.1 mil in thickness, so treated, provides a diffusion-bonded surface layer suitable for subsequent plating, cladding, soldering, or dip coating. The iron plating bath composition and plating conditions are as follows:

$FeSO_4 \cdot 7H_2O$	— 300 g/l
$FeCl_2 \cdot 4H_2O$	— 42 g/l
$(NH_4)_2SO_4$	— 15 g/l
$NaCOOH$	— 15 g/l
H_3BO_3	— 30 g/l
Wetting agent*	— 1 g/l
Temperature	— 60°C (140°F)
Current density	— 30 amp/ft²

* "Duponol ME," dry, supplied by E. I. du Pont de Nemours and Company, Inc., Wilmington, Delaware.

WELDING[37, 155, 158]

Columbium is welded commercially by three different methods: resistance welding, submerged-arc welding, and inert-gas-shielded arc welding. Semiautomatic electron-beam welding of columbium has been carried out experimentally.

In resistance welding,[157] excessive pressure produces too low a contact resistance between parts, so that good welds are difficult to obtain. In resistance seam welding of tubing, formed sheet is placed over a large copper mandrel which serves as one electrode. The other electrode, in the form of a disc or wheel, rolls over the overlapping edges of the metal. A succession of electrical discharges produces the seam. This type of welding is usually carried out automatically under water to prevent oxidation of the metal and to secure more uniform welds. Spot welding of columbium is feasible in air if times are kept short, say 1/2 cycle. Table 9.9

TABLE 9.9. SEAM WELDING DATA FOR COLUMBIUM[38]

Sheet Thickness, in.	Electrode Pressure (as load), lb	Width of Wheel, in.	Welding Speed, in./min	Welding Cycles		Open Circuit Voltage, volts	Closed Circuit Voltage, volts	Welding Current, amp
				On	Off			
0.020	50	⅛	36	3	2	1.6	1.25	4000
0.010	50	⅛	36	3	2	1.3	1.05	3300
0.005	25	⅛	36	3	2	0.8	0.7	1100

TABLE 9.10. ARGON-ARC MACHINE WELDING DATA FOR COLUMBIUM SHEET

Sheet Thickness, in.	Tungsten Electrode Diameter, in.	Argon Shield Nozzle Diameter, in.	Gas Flow, cu ft/hr		Welding Current, amp	Welding Speed, in./min
			Torch	Back Up		
0.012	1/16	3/8	12	5	40	20
0.020	1/16	3/8	14	5	60	20
0.030	1/16	3/8	14	5	80	20

lists some approximate data for columbium secured on seam welding equipment.

In the submerged arc welding of columbium,[157] a hand operation, the work is completely immersed in carbon tetrachloride. The edges of the pieces to be joined are placed parallel. A carbon arc is used as one electrode, the work forms the other. Welding currents of 20–40 amperes at 25–30 volts DC are employed.

Inert gas-shielded arc welding of columbium[38, 157] employs a conventional argon- or helium-shielded tungsten-tipped electric torch, and is most effective in joining sheets placed edge to edge and held tightly in place (edge and butt welds). The edges of the sheets to be welded are positioned over a slot approximately 3/8 inch wide and 1/8 inch deep. The torch is inserted in the lid of the chamber or shield which is filled with argon or helium. The inert-gas flow rate must maintain a positive pressure in the shield. Backup protection of the weld is achieved by flooding the slot with inert gas to shield the underside of the weld. The tungsten electrode is made negative to promote more ductile welds (as in welding zirconium), and the arc is initiated by a high-frequency discharge to prevent contamination of the weld by tungsten. The greater penetration of a DC arc, as compared with that of an AC arc, permits formation of a smaller pool of molten metal which is easier to protect with the shield. The minimum sheet thickness that can be welded conveniently by this method is 0.013–0.015 inch. Typical conditions for inert gas-shielded arc welding include 8 in./min rate of travel, 21 amp at 26–30 volts DC for 0.015-in. sheet, 35 amp for 0.020-in. sheet, 100 amp for 0.040-in. sheet, and 120 amp for 0.050-in. sheet. The weld metal must be protected by the shielding gas until it has cooled to the range 400–300°C (752–572°F) to prevent contamination. Machine welding data[38] for argon-shielded arc equipment are given in Table 9.10.

In welding sheet thicker than about 0.050 in., the current required to get full penetration may be great enough to cause the molten pool to spread outside the protective area of the shield. Filler rod, if required, may become oxidized and hence may contaminate the weld when it is melted. Such operations are best carried out in a dry box which is first purged and then kept under a slight pressure of purified helium or argon.

Limited application of the inert-gas-shielded arc welding technique has been reported to produce successful spot welds in columbium if the torch design is modified slightly. No backup gas is required for such welds.

Tests on welded columbium specimens have shown that, in general, the corrosion resistance of the weld metal is equal to that of the parent metal.

Argon-shielded arc welding of columbium in a chamber at reduced pressure[57] has produced more consistently ductile welds than would be possible in the same equipment at, or slightly

TABLE 9.11. ARGON-ARC WELDING OF COLUMBIUM TUBING*[57]

Tube Wall Thickness, in.	Type of Joint	Open Circuit Voltage, volts	Welding Current, amps	Current Type	Electrode Diameter, in.
0.010	Lap	60	27–28	neg d.c.	1/16
0.020	Lap	60	45–50	neg d.c.	1/32
0.020	Edge	110	45–54	a.c.	1/8
0.030	Butt	50	40–45	neg d.c.	1/8
0.030	Butt	110	45–48	a.c.	1/8

* Gas flow: 10l/min of purified (99.997%) argon.

above, room pressure. The chamber is first evacuated to 10^{-4} mm Hg for 20 minutes; then, purified argon is bled in until the pressure reaches 250 mm Hg. The flow is maintained during welding and until the specimen is cold. Degreased and wire-brushed tubular specimens with wall thicknesses in the range 0.010 to 0.030 inch are either lap, edge, or butt welded under the conditions shown in Table 9.11. In subsequent mechanical tests, the welded tubing fractures in a region well removed from the weld area.

To prepare columbium for welding,[157] the surfaces to be joined are thoroughly cleaned and degreased with carbon tetrachloride and then rubbed with fine abrasive cloth or paper to remove foreign material and oxide films. Any metal pickup on welded sheet, such as copper from resistance welding electrodes, may be removed by pickling in nitric acid.

The newest method of joining columbium sheet is that of fusion welding; the process utilizes a suitably modified version of the electron beam melting equipment described earlier.[135, 136, 137, 157] Figure 9.10 illustrates schematically a pilot-scale semiautomatic welder employing this principle. The work is kept at

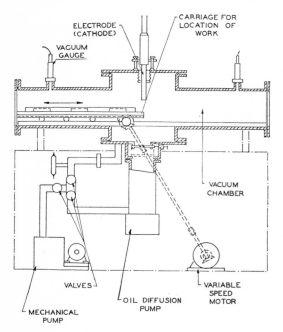

Figure 9.10. Schematic of electron beam semi-automatic welding equipment. (*Courtesy Le Vide, May-June, 1958.*)

ground potential while the cathode (electron-gun source) is at a high negative potential. The electrons, accelerated by the high potential (up to 60 KV, but normally about 10–14 KV) are focused so as to impinge on a small area of the work (0.040–0.125 in. in diameter, depending on the thickness of the material) and cause fusion when the energy density is great enough. Both straight-line and circular welds can be made with high precision.

APPLICATIONS[41, 42, 48, 61, 87, 98, 103, 119]

The voluminous body of open literature dealing with columbium that has appeared during the past few years is a measure of the interest that the technological world has developed in the metal as a potential material of construction in broad areas of application. Several applications have already been mentioned.

Columbium is of interest to nuclear engineers because of its low capture cross section for thermal neutrons, its excellent high-temperature mechanical properties, its resistance to attack by liquid metals, and its compatibility with other materials of construction both as a protective cladding or coating[110] and as an alloying agent or base.

While the problem of effectively protecting columbium against oxidation remains unsolved, many of the predicted applications for this metal are based on its now well characterized behavior at elevated temperatures and the hope that successful alloying agents or coating procedures can be developed to overcome its lack of oxidation resistance. This problem is particularly crucial in the case of jet engines and rocket- and missile-propulsion systems, and structural members for associated vehicles. In this respect, columbium is in nearly the same position as molybdenum*, although much more research has been directed toward developing a means of protecting molybdenum.

The affinity of columbium for atmospheric gases is a virtue when it is used as a getter in electron tubes where, in addition, its low work function, high thermal conductivity, resistance to sputtering, good mechanical strength, weldability, and fabricability are valuable attributes. In the electronics field, columbium also has potential value for electrolytic capacitors where

* As yet, no completely successful protective scheme has been found for molybdenum, either.

its ability to acquire an anodic film compares favorably with that of tantalum.

While less resistant than tantalum to the various corrosive media met with in the chemical process industries, columbium cannot be overlooked as a potential material of construction. Petroleum equipment manufacturers,[65] for example, are interested in columbium because of its corrosion resistance, mechanical properties, and fabricability, as well as the ease with which welding can be used for primary fabrication and for making plant repairs or modification.

Although many of the uses indicated above are potential rather than actual, there is one area of application in which columbium is well established, namely that of ferrous-base alloys. Here, however, the criteria of purity are less stringent, and the separation problem is not encountered.

Columbium is used as an alloying element in carbon and low alloy steels, in low-carbon high-alloy steels, in austenitic chromium-nickel steels, and in ferrous-base gas-turbine alloys.

Columbium is used exclusively in arc-welding rods for stabilized grades of stainless steel, since titanium cannot be successfully transferred across the arc from the rod to the work.

Only the more outstanding effects of columbium's use in ferrous alloys are summarized below.[12]

Columbium increases the strength of extra-low carbon steels at elevated temperatures. It produces marked grain refinement in carbon and low alloy steels, which is retained at temperatures as high as 1025°C (1877°F). Columbium steels show excellent resistance to graphitization after exposure at 550°C (1022°F).

In Type 304 (18–8) stainless steels, columbium is used to minimize intergranular corrosion. It combines with carbon to form carbides, thus preventing precipitation of carbon at the grain boundaries. The stress-rupture and creep strength of wrought, columbium-bearing 18–8 steel are, in general, superior to those of similar steel without columbium. In complex ferrous alloys containing columbium, improvements in hot strength and hot ductility are obtained. It also imparts resistance to thermal shock in these materials.

The use of columbium both as a base and as an alloying element in nonferrous alloys has received and continues to receive a great deal of attention. Investigation of numerous binary and ternary columbium-base alloys has been practically "across the board" throughout the periodic table, the result of efforts to improve columbium's oxidation resistance. For example, in one study,[132] the following elements were investigated as binary alloying agents with columbium: beryllium, boron, chromium, cobalt, iron, molybdenum, nickel, silicon, tantalum, titanium, tungsten, vanadium, and zirconium. Optimum oxidation resistance at 1000°C (1832°F) was obtained for the compositions containing about 9 wt per cent Cr, 5 wt per cent Mo, 15.5 wt per cent Ti, and 5.7 wt per cent V. The kinetics of oxidation has been studied for alloys with chromium, molybdenum, titanium, tungsten, vanadium, and zirconium.[79]

Binary, ternary, and quaternary columbium-base alloys containing aluminum, chromium, cobalt, iron, molybdenum, nickel, silicon, tantalum, titanium, tungsten, vanadium, and zirconium have been the subject of another extensive study.[99] The most scale-resistant alloy contained 20 wt per cent chromium, 12 wt per cent cobalt, and 68 wt per cent columbium. It was 100 times more scale resistant than columbium at 1100°C (2012°F) and had a parabolic rate constant of 7.8×10^{-5} g/cm²sec$^{1/2}$ at that temperature.

Even the very rare element scandium has been investigated as an alloying element for columbium.

In addition to the elements already mentioned, copper, iridium, germanium, rhenium, and selenium have been tried as alloying agents without notable success.[33]

Alloy studies of columbium have been made for purposes other than improving oxidation resistance. Semipure columbium (oxygen 0.38 wt per cent) has been arc melted with cerium to form an alloy having a nominal cerium content of 8 wt per cent.[127] The total oxygen content of the alloy is only 0.004 wt per cent, and the resulting ductility is good.

References

1. Albrecht, W. M., Mallett, M. W., and Goode, W. D., *J. Electrochem. Soc.*, **105**, 219–223 (1958).

2. Alexander, K. M., and Fairbrother, F., *J. Chem. Soc.*, Suppl. Issue No. 1, S223–S227 (1949).

3. Alexander, K. M., and Fairbrother, F., *J. Chem. Soc.*, **74**, 2472–2476 (1949).
4. Anders, F. J., Jr., and Pollock, W. I., "Technology of Columbium (Niobium)" (Gonser, B. W. and Sherwood, E. M., editors), pp. 60–65, New York, John Wiley and Sons, Inc., 1958.
5. Andrews, D. H. (to Research Corporation), U.S. Patent 2,522,153 (Sept. 12, 1950).
6. Backer, R. O., Goward, G. W., and Wiederkehr, V. R., U.S. Atomic Energy Comm., Rept. *WAPD-CTA(GLA)-471*, 1957.
7. Backer, R. O., Goward, G. W., and Wiederkehr, V. R., U.S. Atomic Energy Comm., Rept. *WAPD-204*, September, 1958.
8. Balke, C. W., *Ind. Eng. Chem.*, **27**, 1166–9 (1935).
9. Balke, C. W., *Trans. Electrochem. Soc.*, **85**, 25–30 (1944).
10. Beach, J. G., "Technology of Columbium (Niobium)" (Gonser, B. W. and Sherwood, E. M., editors), pp. 81–86, New York, John Wiley and Sons, Inc., 1958.
11. Benesovsky, F., Sedlatchek, K., and Wirth, W., *Berg-u. huttenmann. Monatsh.*, **100**, 219–244 (1955).
12. Binder, W. O., "Boron, Calcium, Columbium, and Zirconium in Steel," pp. 105–414, New York, John Wiley and Sons, Inc., 1957.
13. Blocher, J. M., Jr., and Campbell, I. E., "Carbide Coatings for Graphite," (paper presented at the Second Int. Conf. on the Peacetime Uses of Atomic Energy, Geneva, Sept. 1-13, 1958).
14. Brauer, G., *Z. anorg. u. Allgem. Chem.*, **248**, 1–31 (1941).
15. Bridges, D. W., and Fassell, W. M., Jr., *J. Electrochem. Soc.*, **103**, 326–330 (1956).
16. Brown, E. N., and Reed, D. V., U.S. Atomic Energy Comm., Rept. *WAPD-CTA(GLA)-511*, Jan. 16, 1958.
17. Buchheit, R., (private comm., Battelle Memorial Institute), Feb., 1959.
18. Burke, J. J., *J. Metals*, **9**, 1350–1 (1957).
19. Burstall, F. H., Swain, P., Williams, A. F., and Wood, G. A., *J. Chem. Soc.*, **77**, 1497 (1952).
20. Cabell, M. J., and Milner, I., Atomic Energy Research Estab. (G. Brit.) Rept. *AERE-C/R-1460* (1954).
21. Calverley, A., Davis, M., and Lever, R. F., *J. Sci. Instr.*, **34**, 142–147 (1957).
22. Carlson, K. M., and Pollock, W. I., "Studies of Niobium-Oxygen and Niobium-Titanium-Oxygen Systems" (paper presented at Am. Inst. Mining Metall. Engrs. High-Temperature Materials Conf., Cleveland, Ohio, April 16-17, 1957).
23. Carpenter, J. H., and Searcy, A. W., *J. Am. Chem. Soc.*, **78**, 2079–2081 (1956).
24. Cathcart, J. V., Campbell, J. J., and Smith, G. P., *J. Electrochem. Soc.*, **105**, 442–446 (1958).
25. Cathcart, J. V., and Manly, W. D., *Corrosion*, **12**, 43–47 (Feb., 1956).
26. Chaigneau, M., *Compt. Rend.*, **244**, 900–901 (1957).
27. *Chem. Eng. News*, **35**, 48–50 (Oct., 1957).
28. *Chem. Eng. News*, **36**, 51–52 (Feb. 10, 1958).
29. *Chem. Week*, **82**, 48–50 (Feb. 1, 1958), 51–52 (April 5, 1948).
30. Chernikhov, Yu. A., Melamed, Sh. G., and Dobkina, B. M., *Zavodskaya Lab.*, **24**, 677–679 (1958).
31. Chilton, C. H., *Chem. Eng.*, **65**, 104–7 (Nov. 3, 1958).
32. Chizhikov, D. M., and Grin'ko, A. M., *Doklady Akad. Nauk SSSR*, **122**, 278–279 (1958).
33. Clauss, F. J., and Barrett, C. A., "Technology of Columbium (Niobium)" (Gonser, B. W., and Sherwood, E. M., editors), pp. 92–97, New York, John Wiley and Sons, Inc., 1958.
34. Cook, D. B., Zemansky, M. W., and Boorse, H. A., *Phys. Rev.*, **79**, 1021 (1950).
35. Coolidge, W. D., British Patent 23,499 (1909) and *Trans. Am. Inst. Elec. Engrs.*, **29**, 961–965 (1910).
36. Cotter, M. J., *Atomics and Nuclear Energy*, **8**, 339–342 (1957).
37. Cox, F. G., *Steel Processing and Conversion*, **43**, 147 (Mar., 1957).
38. Cox, F. G., *Welding and Metal Fabrication*, **24**, 352–358 (1956).
39. Darnell, J. R., and Yntema, L. F., "Technology of Columbium (Niobium)" (Gonser, B. W., and Sherwood, E. M., editors), pp. 1–9, New York, John Wiley and Sons, Inc., 1958.
40. Dayton, S. H., *Mining World*, **20**, 40–43 (July, 1958).
41. Denny, J. P., and Kendall, L. F., *Machine Design*, **30**, 150 (May 29, 1958).
42. Denny, J. P., and Kendall, L. F., *Metal Progr.*, **73**, 136, 138, 140, 142, 144, 146, 148 (June, 1958).
43. Dickson, G. K., and Dukes, J. A., "Extraction and Refining of the Rarer Metals," paper No. 14, 258–271, London, The Institution of Mining and Metallurgy, 1957.
44. Ehrlich, P., Ploger, F., and Pietzka, G., *Z. anorg. u. Allgem. Chem.*, **282**, 19–23 (1955).
45. Fairbrother, F., and Frith, W. C., *J. Chem. Soc.*, **76**, 3051–3056 (1951).
46. Fuson, N., *J. Appl. Phys.*, **20**, 59–66 (1949).
47. Fuson, N., *J. Opt. Soc. Am.*, **38**, 845–853 (1948).

48. Gardner, A. R., *Prod. Eng.*, **29**, 66–70 (Mar. 17, 1958).

48a. Gegner, P. J., and Wilson, W. L. (Columbia-Southern Chemical Corp.), personal communication (1959).

49. Glasser, J., and Hampel, C. A., (to Kennecott Copper Corporation), U.S. Patent 2,703,752 (Mar. 8, 1955).

50. Goldschmidt, H., and Vautin, C., *J. Soc. Chem. Ind.*, **19**, 543 (1898).

51. Goward, G. W., and Tretow, E. F., U.S. Atomic Energy Comm., Rept. *WAPD-(GLA)-203, UC-4*, April 24, 1956.

52. Gulbransen, E. A., and Andrew, K. F., *Trans. Am. Inst. Mining and Met. Engrs.*, **188**, 586 (1950).

53. Gulbransen, E. A., and Andrew, K. F., *J. Electrochem. Soc.*, **105**, 4–9 (1958).

54. Hampel, C. A., *Corrosion*, **14**, 87t–91t (1958).

55. Hampel, C. A., "Corrosion Properties of Tantalum, Columbium, Molybdenum, and Tungsten" (paper presented at Nat. Assoc. Corrosion Engrs. meeting, San Francisco, March 17-21, 1958).

56. Hansen, W. R., and Mallett, M. W., *Anal. Chem.*, **29**, 1868–1869 (1957).

57. Harries, D. R., and Purchas, J. G., *Nuclear Power*, **3**, 219–221 (May, 1958).

58. Harris, W. F., U.S. Atomic Energy Comm., Rept. *NP-6689*, 1957.

59. Harris, W. F., "Technology of Columbium (Niobium)" (Gonser, B. W., and Sherwood, E. M., editors), pp. 57–59, New York, John Wiley and Sons, Inc., 1958.

60. Hatchett, C., *Phil. Trans. Roy. Soc. London Ser. A*, **92**, 49–66 (1802).

61. Hazelton, W. S., *J. Soc. Automotive Engrs.*, **65**, 67–69 (May, 1958).

62. Heal, T. J., "The Mechanical and Physical Properties of Magnesium and Niobium Canning Materials," Second Intern. Conf. on the Peaceful Uses of Atomic Energy (Geneva), *A/Conf. 15/P/305, UK*, June 3, 1958.

63. Higbie, K. B., "Technology of Columbium (Niobium)" (Gonser, B. W., and Sherwood, E. M., editors), pp. 10–15, New York, John Wiley and Sons, Inc., 1958.

64. Higbie, K. B., and Werning, J. R., U.S. Bur. Mines, Rept. Invest. *5239*, 1956.

65. Hooper, W. H. L., *Petroleum*, **21**, 219–224 (July, 1958).

66. Huffman, E. H., Iddings, G. M., Lilly, R. C., U.S. Atomic Energy Comm., Rept. *UCRL 1165*, Mar., 1951.

67. Hulm, J. K., and Matthias, B. T., *Phys. Rev.*, **82**, 273–274 (1951).

68. Hulm, J. K., and Matthias, B. T., *Phys. Rev.*, **87**, 799–806 (1952).

69. *Ind. Heating*, **25**, 924–926 (1958).

70. Inouye, H., U.S. Atomic Energy Comm., Rept. *ORNL-1565*, Sept. 24, 1953.

71. Jones, R. J., Can. Dep. Mines and Tech. Surveys, Mines Branch, Mem. Ser. No. **135** (1957).

72. Jordan, K., and Picard, K., *Techn. Mitt. Krupp*, **15**, 203–207 (1957).

73. Keck, P. H., and Golay, M. J. E., *Phys. Rev.*, **89**, 1297 (1953).

74. Keck, P. H., Green, M., and Polk, M. L., *J. Appl. Phys.*, **24**, 1479–81 (1953).

75. Kelly, J. C. R., Jr., "The Present Status of Electromagnetic Levitation as a High-Temperature Research Tool" (paper presented at High-Temperature Symposium, Berkeley, Calif., June 25-27, 1956).

76. Kieffer, R., Benesovsky, F., and Schmid, H., *Z. f. Metallk.*, **47**, 247–253 (1956).

77. Klopp, W. D., Sims, C. T., and Jaffee, R. I., *Trans. Am. Soc. Metals*, **50**, (Preprint No. 64) (1957).

78. Klopp, W. D., Sims, C. T., and Jaffee, R. I., "Technology of Columbium (Niobium)" (Gonser, B. W., and Sherwood, E. M., editors), pp. 106–120, New York, John Wiley and Sons, Inc., 1958.

79. Klopp, W. D., Sims, C. T., and Jaffee, R. I., "Effects of Alloying on the Kinetics of Oxidation of Niobium" (paper *P712*, presented at Second Int. Conf. on the Peacetime Uses of Atomic Energy, Geneva, Switzerland, Sept. 1-13, 1958).

80. Koerner, E. L., and Smutz, U.S. Atomic Energy Comm., Rept. *ISC-793*, August 15, 1956.

81. Korosy, F., *J. Am. Chem. Soc.*, **61**, 838–843 (1939).

82. Kraus, K. A., and Moore, G. E., *J. Am. Chem. Soc.*, **71**, 5855 (1949).

83. Kriege, D. H., U.S. Atomic Energy Comm., Rept. *LA-2049*, May, 1956.

84. Kripiakevich, P. I., and Gladyshevskii, *Doklady Akad. Nauk SSSR*, **104**, 82–84 (1955).

85. Kudielka, H., Nowotny, and Findeisen, G., *Monatsh. Chem.*, **88**, 1048–1055 (1958).

86. Kuhn, W. E., "High Temperature Technology" (Campbell, I. E., editor), pp. 288–318, New York, John Wiley and Sons, Inc., 1956.

87. Lazzerini, R., *Calore*, **39**, 7–15 (Jan., 1958).

88. Lebacqz, J. V., and Andrews, D. H., *Proc. Natl. Electronics Conf.*, **4**, 11–23 (1948).

89. Magel, T. T., Kulin, P. A., Kaufmann, A. R., *J. Metals*, **4**, 1286–1288 (1952).

90. Majumdar, A. K., and Chowdhury, J. B. Ray, *Anal. Chim. Acta*, **19**, 18–22 (1958).

91. Marignac, J., *Ann. Chim. et Phys.*, **8**, 5 (1866); **9**, 249 (1866).

92. *Materials in Design Eng.*, **46**, 85 (Sept., 1957).

93. McIntosh, A. B., *J. Inst. Metals*, **85**, 367–372 (1957).

94. McIntosh, A. B., and Bagley, K. Q., *J. Inst. Metals*, **34**, 251 (1956).

95. McKenna, P. M., U.S. Patent 2,124,509 (July 19, 1938).

96. McKinley, T. D., "The Niobium-Hydrogen System," (paper presented at Am. Inst. Mining and Metall. Engrs. Regional High-Temperature Materials Conf., Cleveland, Ohio, April 16-17, 1957).

97. Merrill, G. S., *Trans. Am. Inst. Elec. Engrs*, **29**, 1709–1729 (1910).

98. *Metal Ind.*, **92**, 527–528 (1958).

99. Michael, A. G., "The Oxidation of Columbium-Base and Tantalum-Base Alloys" (paper presented at Am. Inst. Mining Metall. Engrs. Reactive Metals Conf., Buffalo, N.Y., May 27-29, 1958).

100. Mikhailova, G. V., others, U.S. Atomic Energy Comm., Rept. *AEC-TR-3184*, 1957.

101. Miller, G. L., *Materials and Methods*, **45**, 131–135 (1957).

102. Miller, G. L., *Metal Ind.*, **92**, 507–509 (1958).

103. *Mining J.*, **250**, 325–326 (1958).

104. Moissan, H., *Compt. rend.*, **133**, 20 (1901).

105. Narbutt, K. I., and Bespalova, I. D., *Zavodskaya Lab.*, **24**, 617–619 (1958).

106. Nazarenko, V. A., and Flyantikova, G. V., *Zavodskaya Lab.*, **24**, 801–802 (1958).

107. Nowotny, H., and Wittmann, A., *Montash. Chem.* **89**, 220–224 (1958).

108. O'Driscoll, W. G., and Miller, G. L., *J. Inst. Metals*, **85**, 379–384 (1957).

109. Pfann, W. G., *Trans. Amer. Inst. Mining Met. Engrs.*, **194**, 747–753 (1952); also by the same author "Zone Melting," New York, John Wiley and Sons, Inc., 1958.

110. Powell, C. F., Rosenbaum, D. M., Palmer, R. B., and Campbell, I. E., U.S. Atomic Energy Comm., Rept. *BMI-1228*, October 2, 1957.

111. Powers, R. W., and Doyle, M., *J. Metals*, **9**, 1285–1288 (1957).

112. Quadt, R., *Western Metalworking*, **16**, 45–47 (Nov., 1958).

113. Reed, D. V., U.S. Atomic Energy Comm., Rept. *WAPD-CTA(GLA)-501*, Dec. 31, 1957.

114. Reed, D. V., U.S. Atomic Energy Comm., Rept. *WAPD-CTA(GLA)-506*, Jan. 7, 1958.

115. Reed, D. V., and Goward, G. W., U.S. Atomic Energy Comm., Rept. *WAPD-CTA(GLA)-500, UC-4*, Dec. 31, 1957.

116. Reed, D. V., Wilson, H. R., and Goward, G. W., U.S. Atomic Energy Comm., Rept. *WAPD-CTA(GLA)-620*, July 15, 1958.

117. Reed, J. F., "Technology of Columbium (Niobium)" (Gonser, B. W., and Sherwood, E. M., editors), pp. 54–56, New York, John Wiley and Sons, Inc., 1958.

118. Rendall, J. H., *Metal Treatment and Drop Forging*, **24**, 491–494 (1957).

119. Rendall, J. H., *Metal Treatment and Drop Forging*, **25**, 7–12 (1958).

120. Resnick, R., Castleman, L. S., and Seigle, L., U.S. Atomic Energy Comm., Rept. *SEP-248*, June 30, 1958.

121. Rolsten, R. F., "Iodide Columbium" (paper presented at Am. Inst. Mining Metall. Engrs. Annual Fall Meeting, Cleveland, Ohio, 1958).

122. Rose, H., *Pogg. Ann. Physik Chemie*, **63**, 317–341 (1844).

123. Runck, R. J., and Sheipline, V., "High-Temperature Technology" (Campbell, I. E., editor), pp. 114–130, New York, John Wiley and Sons, Inc., 1956.

124. Sayre, E. D., and Stoph, A. J., Proc. 1956 Nat. Symp. on Vacuum Technology, 175–181.

125. Schofield, T. H., *J. Inst. Metals*, **85**, 372–374 (1957).

126. Schumacher, E. E., *J. Metals*, **5**, 1428–1429 (1953).

127. Semmel, J. W., Jr., "Technology of Columbium (Niobium)" (Gonser, B. W., and Sherwood, E. M., editors), pp. 77–80, New York, John Wiley and Sons, Inc., 1958.

128. Seybolt, A. U., *J. Metals*, **6**, 774 (1954).

129. Sibert, M. E., U.S. Atomic Energy Comm., Rept. *AECU-3798*, June 15, 1958.

130. Sibert, M. E., Kolk, A. J., Jr., and Steinberg, M. A., "Technology of Columbium (Niobium)" (Gonser, B. W., and Sherwood, E. M., editors), pp. 20–34, New York, John Wiley and Sons, Inc., 1958.

131. Sibert, M. E., and Steinberg, M. A., "Preliminary Study of the Equilibrium of Carbon and Oxygen in Columbium with Carbon Monoxide Above 1600°C" (paper presented at Am. Inst. Mining Metall. Engrs. Reactive Metals Conf., Buffalo, N.Y., May 27-29, 1958).

132. Sims, C. T., Klopp, W. D., and Jaffee, R. I., *Trans. Am. Soc. Metals*, **5**, (Preprint No. 70). (1957).

133. Speiser, R., Blackburn, P., and Johnston, H. L., *J. Electrochem. Soc.*, **106**, 52–53 (1959).

134. *Steel*, **142**, 108–109 (Mar. 24, 1958).

135. Stohr, J. A., *Vide*, **13** (No. 75), 163–171 (May-June, 1958).

136. Stohr, J. A., *Nuclear Power*, **3**, 272–274 (1958).

137. Stohr, J. A., and Briola, J., *Soudure et Tech. Connexes*, **12**, 165–172 (May-June, 1958).

138. Taylor, D. F., *Ind. Eng. Chem.*, **42**, 639 (1950).

139. Temescal Metallurgical Corp. (private comm.) 1958.

140. Tews, Joan L., and May, S. L., "Technology of Columbium (Niobium)" (Gonser, B. W., and Sherwood, E. M., editors), pp. 36–43, New York, John Wiley and Sons, Inc., 1958.

141. Theodore, M. L., *Anal. Chem.,* **30,** 465–467 (1958).

141a. Tingley, I. I. (Dept. Mines and Tech. Surveys, Ottawa, Canada), personal communication (1959).

142. Tottle, C. R., *J. Inst. Metals,* **85,** 375–378 (1957).

143. Uhlig, H. H., "The Corrosion Handbook", New York, John Wiley and Sons, Inc., 1948.

144. *U.S. Bur. Mines, Mineral Mkt. Rept. MMS* **3188,** 1958.

145. Van Arkel, A. E., and de Boer, J. H., *Z. anorg. u. Allgem. Chem.,* **148,** 345–350 (1925).

146. Van Muylder, J., de Zoubov, N., and Pourbaix, M., CEBELCOR, *Rapp. Tech., No.* **53,** June, 1957.

147. Veigel, N. D., Sherwood, E. M., and Campbell, I. E., "The Metal Thorium" (Wilhelm, H. A., editor), pp. 104–113, Cleveland, Ohio, American Society for Metals, 1958.

148. von Batchelder, F. W., and Raeuchle, R. F., *Acta. Cryst.,* **10,** 648–649 (1957).

149. von Bolton, W., *Z. Elektrochem.,* **13,** 145–149 (1907).

150. Waterbury, G. R., and Bricker, C. E., *Anal. Chem.,* **30,** 1007–1009 (1958).

151. Werning, J. R., and Higbie, K. B., *Ind. Eng. Chem.,* **46,** 2491–8 (1954).

152. Werning, J. R., Higbie, K. B., others, *Ind. Eng. Chem.,* **46,** 644–52 (1954).

153. Wessel, E. T., and Lawthers, D. D., "Technology of Columbium (Niobium)" (Gonser, B. W., and Sherwood, E. M., editors), pp. 66–76, New York, John Wiley and Sons, Inc., 1958.

154. White, G. K., and Woods, S. B., *Can. J. Phys.,* **35,** 892–900 (1957).

155. Williams, L. R., *J. Inst. Metals,* **85,** 385–392 (1957).

156. Wyman, W. L., *Welding J.,* **37,** 49s–53s (Feb., 1958).

157. Yntema, L. F., *Metal Progr.,* **74,** 105–108 (Sept., 1958).

158. Yntema, L. F., *Western Metalworking,* **16,** 43 (April, 1958).

10. GALLIUM

A. P. Thompson*

INTRODUCTION

Gallium is historically unique in that its discovery was predicted twice before the metal was isolated. Medeleeff, in his work on correlation of the properties of the elements with their atomic weights, found evidence that led him to predict the discovery of three elements.[22] He assigned them the names eka-boron, eka-silicon, and eka-aluminum, because of their similarity to these elements, and predicted the properties of each of the three "eka" elements in 1871. De Boisbaudran, during the same period, in studying the spectral lines of elements, had proved their periodicity for similar elements. These studies led him to conclude that there was an element missing between aluminum and indium; he predicted its discovery and its major spectral lines. Intrigued by this yet undiscovered element, he undertook the search for it and, after considerable effort, in 1875 isolated a small quantity[3] from zinc blende of the Pyrenees. Later de Boisbaudran recovered some 75 g of the new metal and studied its properties. Mendeleeff, upon learning of the new element, realized that it was his predicted eka-aluminum;[23] the properties of the new element coincided almost exactly with those he had published before the discovery. Similarly, de Boisbaudran found that the spectral lines of gallium fitted into the pattern he had prophesied.

The first record of gallium produced in the United States is by F. G. McCutcheon[10] who isolated it from a metallic residue obtained in the redistillation of zinc spelter. The zinc ore

* Retired. Chapter revised by John R. Musgrave, Research Department, Chemicals and Metals Division, The Eagle-Picher Company, Joplin, Missouri.

from which this gallium was finally isolated came from the Tri-State (Missouri-Oklahoma-Kansas) field.

Gallium is in Group III, Period 4, of the periodic table and has the atomic number 31. Its atomic weight is 69.72. One of the three metals liquid at body temperature (the other two are cesium and mercury), gallium has a melting point of 29.75°C (85.5°F). This low melting point is illustrated in Figure 10.1.

Figure 10.1. Gallium, a silvery-white metal of unique properties, is liquid at body temperature. In this picture a cube of the solid metal melts as it is held in the hand. (*Courtesy Aluminum Company of America.*)

OCCURRENCE

Gallium is widely distributed in the earth's crust. It has been estimated[1, 9] that about 15 g of gallium are present in each ton of lithosphere. As might be expected from its similarity to aluminum, gallium is found in small quantities in most claylike materials. Einecke[6] presents a comprehensive survey of the occurrence in various ores, rocks, and minerals; in few cases is the amount of gallium in any type of material higher than 0.01 per cent. A survey of the periodic table suggests that gallium might be found in greater than average concentration in ores or minerals containing zinc, aluminum, and germanium.[35]

Germanite, a complex zinc-copper-arsenic-germanium sulfide, contains from 0.1 to 0.8 per cent gallium. This mineral is found in the lead-copper ores of the Tsumeb (Southwest Africa) district. Renierite, a mineral of the same general character as germanite, has been found in zinc-lead-copper ores in the Belgian Congo. It is reported to contain up to 1 per cent of gallium. These minerals apparently do not occur consistently. However, they are the richest gallium-bearing minerals which have been reported up to the present time.

Zinc ores of the Tri-State (Missouri-Oklahoma-Kansas) district were found by Waring to contain gallium, germanium, and cadmium.[38] Examination of numerous crystals of sphalerite from this field showed gallium contents from 0.001 to 0.02 per cent; the average was 0.005 per cent.[35] Other zinc sulfide ores are reported to contain gallium; however, few of them have been studied carefully.

Most aluminum-bearing minerals appear to contain some gallium, usually in the range of 0.001 to 0.01 per cent.[6] Bauxite, the major raw material for the manufacture of aluminum, falls in this class. Not all zinc ores or aluminum-bearing materials contain gallium in sufficient quantity to allow economic recovery of this metal. It is only when the concentration of the element in by-products or residues has reached a certain minimum figure that they can be used as starting point for the application of suitable recovery processes. Germanite and renierite could be used as a primary source were they available in sufficient quantities.

Like numerous other elements, gallium is found in small quantities in many coals. The percentage of gallium varies widely in different coals and is thought to be dependent on the genesis of the coal. Goldschmidt[8] has shown that the original constituents of coal absorb gallium preferentially and thereby concentrate

it to a greater extent than the average of the earth's crust. Such concentration in the coal is far too small to be important, but the burning of the coal under conditions which allow retention of the gallium, in either the ashes or solid by-products of the combustion, effectively increases such concentration. Morgan and Davies[28] have presented data on the gallium content of by-products from the burning of British coals. They report flue dust containing from 0.05 to 1.5 per cent gallium. The presence of gallium in coals or coal by-products in other parts of the world has been reported, particularly from Russia, India, and some of the Scandinavian states.

PRODUCTION AND ECONOMIC STATISTICS

Production of gallium was estimated at 200 lb for the year 1959 in the United States. Small quantities were also produced in England and Europe. Sales in the United States were estimated at 200 lb for the same year (1958). Most of the gallium was produced by two companies, the Eagle-Picher Company and the Aluminum Company of America. The present price in the United States is $3.00/g for large quantities of the high-purity gallium (99.9999%) with the usual penalty for small orders. Less pure metal is somewhat cheaper.

It has been estimated[2] that a potential production of 20 tons/year could be reached in the United States if a demand warranted such production. Large-scale production could conceivably lower the present cost.

Another potential source of gallium is coal by-products. Flue dusts from English coals[28] have been reported as promising; no studies have been reported on American coals. Some Asian coals have been reported to contain gallium.

DERIVATION

Because of the diversity of gallium-bearing materials, commercial methods of recovery are quite different.

Recovery of gallium as a by-product from the zinc ores of the Tri-State (Missouri-Oklahoma-Kansas) field depends upon the method of treating the ore. After roasted zinc sulfide ore is leached with sulfuric acid to make a crude zinc sulfate solution, subsequent purification of the solution (described below) can be used to concentrate the gallium. If the roasted zinc ore is smelted in retorts to recover zinc metal, however, the gallium usually remains in the retort residues. When the Waelz process is used for recovering zinc from such retort residues, the gallium passes into the resultant slag.[26] Such slag contains 0.01 to 0.05 per cent gallium; recovery of the gallium would involve solubilizing of the slag. As far as is known, this potential source of gallium is not presently utilized because of the high cost of such a process.

When roasted zinc ore is leached with sulfuric acid, the resultant zinc sulfate solution must be purified before use in commercial operations.[10] This purification is effected, in part, by carefully neutralizing the excess acid to precipitate what is known as "iron mud." The iron mud (from Tri-State zinc ores) contains approximately 0.07 per cent gallium and is the starting material for one process. This mud contains, in addition to the 0.07 per cent gallium, about 10 per cent aluminum and 15 per cent iron. The mud can be leached with either acid or caustic soda; the caustic process is preferred because of the corrosive action of acids on equipment. A caustic soda leach will dissolve the aluminum and gallium compounds as well as some silica and other materials. The leach liquor is carefully neutralized with acid, precipitating the compounds as hydroxides which are then filtered off. The filter cake is dehydrated to insolubilize as much of the silica as possible. The dehydrated cake is then leached with hydrochloric acid to form an impure gallium chloride solution; this solution also contains considerable aluminum. Depending on the impurities in the chloride solution, further precipitation and resolution may be necessary.

To separate the gallium from aluminum, advantage is taken of the extraction of gallium trichloride by ether from a strong hydrochloric acid; the solution is shaken with several portions of ether. The ether, while extracting the gallium trichloride, does not take up the aluminum and some of the other impurities. Since the ether and hydrochloric acid solution are immiscible, it is possible to separate the two layers. The ether is then distilled and recovered; the gallium trichloride remaining in the distillation flask still contains some impurities, notably iron. This gallium trichloride solution

is then reacted with strong caustic soda solution, precipitating the iron which is filtered off.

The clear caustic soda solution is then electrolyzed, using a platinum anode and copper cathode.[36] At 0.5 amp/sq cm for the anode and 0.33 amp/sq cm for the cathode, the voltage is 5.5. These conditions keep the cell temperature well above the melting point of gallium. The tip of the cathode is placed over a porcelain crucible which rests on the cell bottom. As the gallium is electrolyzed, the liquid metal drips off into the porcelain crucible. Cathode efficiency is about 35 per cent until the concentration of the gallium falls below 2 g/liter. Below this concentration, efficiency decreases rapidly. The electrode spacing is from 3 to 5 cm, depending on the size of the cell. Gassing is heavy during the deposition and gives adequate circulation to the electrolyte except at the bottom of the cell. This is corrected by occasional stirring.

The crude gallium so obtained is given several washes alternately with distilled water, dilute hydrochloric acid, and dilute nitric acid. The drosses formed are skimmed off and returned to the purification circuit. When no further dross is formed by nitric acid treatment and the liquid gallium forms a bright, mirrorlike pool under hydrochloric acid, chemical cleaning is considered complete.

The liquid gallium, under very dilute hydrochloric acid, is allowed to supercool and is then seeded with a small crystal of gallium. Gallium crystals, under these conditions, begin to form almost immediately and are continuously removed from the liquid until only a small amount of liquid gallium remains in the container. The crystals are washed with distilled water and then remelted and recrystallized, using the method developed by the Bureau of Standards.[11] The number of recrystallizations is dependent upon the purity desired for the finished metal.

Gallium is also recovered from sodium aluminate liquors by the Bayer process. In one process bauxite is digested with a hot caustic soda solution; the sodium aluminate so formed is filtered off from the insoluble residue and seeded with alumina trihydrate. Upon cooling, the alumina in solution begins to crystallize. At the proper stage the alumina is separated from the liquor. This waste liquor contains the major amount of the gallium as well as considerable alumina and is the starting point for recovery of the gallium.

The alkaline solution is treated[7] to reduce the aluminum content and the remaining gallium and aluminum precipitated with an acidic substance. This crude hydroxide cake is then redissolved in strong caustic soda solution, and the gallium is electrolyzed, using stainless steel anodes and cathodes. This cell is reported to be operated at a cathode current density of 0.8 amp/sq cm and 10 volts at a temperature of 80°C (176°F). The resultant metal requires further purification if high-purity metal is desired. If considerable organic matter is present in the original sodium aluminate liquor, it is necessary to include a step to eliminate these organic materials.

Another process for recovering gallium from sodium aluminate liquors from the Bayer process is based on electrolysis using a mercury cathode.[4] In this particular process, only part of the alumina is crystallized from the sodium aluminate liquor at one time. The depleted liquor is recycled; the gallium, not being precipitated with the alumina, concentrates as the aluminate liquor is recycled. When the gallium concentration has become sufficiently increased, this sodium aluminate liquor is electrolyzed, using a mercury cathode with continuous agitation. Gallium is deposited on the cathode. After electrolysis, the sodium aluminate liquor is returned to the alumina recovery system. The mercury containing the gallium is leached with hot sodium hydroxide solution. The gallium is dissolved in the caustic solution, the mercury is separated and returned to the cathode, and the gallium solution is electrolyzed to recover the metal.

In the recovery of gallium from the sodium aluminate liquor, electrolysis is carried out at 40–50°C (104–122°F) and about 4 volts with a cathode current density of approximately 0.5 amp/sq dm. Anode current density is from 20 to 60 amp/sq dm. It is reported that the electrical consumption is about 80 watt-hr/g of gallium for this initial separation.

No figures are reported for the final electrolysis of the sodium gallate but it is probable that they are in the same order as those presented in the previously described methods.

Recovery of gallium from flue dusts in England on a commercial scale has been reported.[30] Typical flue dusts used contained approximately 0.5 per cent germanium and 0.25 per cent gallium. This dust is smelted with soda, lime, copper oxide, and carbon (iron is necessary but is usually available from the flue dust). A regulus is thus formed which contains most of the germanium and gallium from the original flue dust. This regulus is treated with chlorine under a dilute solution of ferric chloride. This operation dissolves both the gallium and germanium. The germanium is then separated from the solution by distillation of the tetrachloride. After the distillation, the solution is cooled to crystallize out some of the copper salts, which are centrifuged off. The solution is then diluted and treated with aluminum to precipitate the remainder of the copper together with other precipitable metals; at the same time the iron is reduced to the ferrous state. The crude gallium chloride solution thus obtained is mixed with isopropyl ether, and the gallium chloride is extracted by the ether. (See description above on recovery from zinc ores.) After distillation of the ether, the gallium chloride is processed in a manner similar to that previously described.

A process[15] has been described for the recovery of gallium compounds from the combustion gases of coal. The combustion gases are scrubbed with a dilute caustic solution which traps the gallium and some other metals. This caustic soda solution is recirculated until the gallium content has become sufficient for economic recovery. The gallium is precipitated from the caustic soda solution with tannin. The precipitate is dried and ashed. This ash is dissolved in hydrochloric acid, and the gallium is extracted from this solution with isopropyl ether. Purification of the gallium from this stage is presumably by one of the methods previously described.

Several processes for laboratory recovery of gallium from germanite have been described. The first commercial recovery operation from this raw material is described in the article cited on recovery of gallium from flue dusts.[30] In this method germanite is ground to 100 mesh, reacted with 50 per cent caustic soda solution, and evaporated to dryness. This mass is leached with hot water to obtain a solution containing germanium and gallium as well as

Figure 10.2. Solid gallium metal, showing plastic packages for shipment of this metal (center and right). Gallium expands when it melts and might break solid containers. (*Courtesy Eagle-Picher Co.*)

some of the other materials. This alkaline solution is adjusted to pH 8 with sulfuric acid, acidified and oxidized with nitric acid, and the solution heated to boiling. The solution is then filtered and, while boiling, is neutralized with caustic soda to pH 3. This precipitates the gallium as $NaH_2Ga(AsO_4)_2 \cdot 1.5H_2O$. The gallium precipitate is filtered and dissolved in hydrochloric acid. This solution is distilled to remove germanium and arsenic as chlorides, and the final solution is extracted with isopropyl ether and treated as previously described to recover the gallium.

No process has been described for recovery of gallium from renierite, but, presumably, the same general method as used for germanite would be satisfactory.

PHYSICAL PROPERTIES

The most unique features of gallium are its long liquid range (one of the longest of any metal) and the low vapor pressures even at high temperatures. It is also noteworthy that the density of the liquid is greater than that of the solid. This characteristic must be considered in packaging, since containers must be provided which allow for expansion upon solidification. Gallium can be packed in a sealed plastic bag, the elasticity and strength of the plastic

preventing rupture, as shown in Figure 10.2. Rubber bags or bulbs can also be used for packaging.

The physical properties of gallium are given in Table 10.1.

TABLE 10.1. PHYSICAL CONSTANTS OF GALLIUM
(Superscript numbers refer to references.)

Atomic number	31[2]
Atomic weight	69.72[2]
Isotopes and abundance (%)	
Mass No. 69	61.2[2]
Mass No. 71	38.8[2]
Color	Metallic gray[6]
Crystal structure	Orthorhombic, pseudotetragonal[6]
Hardness, Mohs scale (solid)	1.5–2.5[40]
Ductility (solid)	Brittle
Density (g/cc)	
20°C (68°F) (s)	5.907[31]
29.65°C (85.37°F) (s)	5.9037[31]
29.8°C (85.6°F) (l)	6.0948[31]
1100°C (2012°F) (l)	5.445[32]
Specific volume (cc/g)	
29°C (84°F) (s)	0.1694
30°C (86°F) (l)	0.1641
Melting point	29.75°C (85.55°F)[6]
Boiling point	1983°C (3601°F)[2]
Latent heat of fusion	
(g-cal/g)	19.16[2]

TABLE 10.1. PHYSICAL CONSTANTS OF GALLIUM
(cont.)

(Superscript numbers refer to references.)

Latent heat of vaporization	
(g-cal/g)	1014[2]
Vapor pressure (mm Hg)	
1315°C (2399°F)	1[2]
1726°C (3139°F)	100
1983°C (3601°F)	760
Viscosity (dyne-sec/sq cm)	
(poise)	
97.7°C (207.9°F)	0.01612[32]
1100°C (2012°F)	0.00578[32]
Surface tension (dynes/cm)	
(Hydrogen or carbon	
dioxide) 30°C (86°F)	735[19]
(0.1–0.2 N hydrochloric	
acid) 35°C (95°F)	636[19]
Specific heat (cal/g/°C)	
29–127°C (84–261°F)	0.0977[17]
Thermal conductivity	
(cal/sec/sq cm/°C/cm)	
30°C (86°F)	0.07–0.09[2]
Linear thermal coefficient of	
expansion (cm/cm/°C)	
0–30°C (32–86°F)	1.8×10^{-5} [32]
Volume resistivity	
(microhm-cm)	
(s) 20°C (68°F)	56.8[6]
(l) 46.1°C (115°F)	28.4[6]
Electrochemical equivalent	
Ga^{+++} (mg/coulomb)	0.24083[35]
Electrode potential Ga^{+++}	
(H$_2$ = 0.0 volts)*	−0.52 volt[12]
Reflectivity (%)	
4360 Å	75.6[40]
5890 Å	71.3[40]

* National Bureau of Standards nomenclature.

CHEMICAL PROPERTIES

The chemical properties of gallium are comparable to those of aluminum; the element is amphoteric. A thin film of oxide is usually formed on the surface of gallium metal, but there is little further oxidation in air or oxygen, even at red heat. It has been thought that gallium will wet glass or other materials, but this has been traced to contamination by the oxides.[12] Oxide-free gallium may wet some surfaces; there has been insufficient work done to justify definite conclusions.

Gallium does not decompose water at 100°C.[2] It dissolves slowly in mineral acids; hot nitric acid will oxidize the metal and dissolve the oxide. Aqua regia is also a solvent for gallium. Sodium or potassium hydroxide solutions will dissolve gallium with evolution of hydrogen. Gallium will unite directly with the halogens.[21] Gallium fluoride can be prepared by treating the metal with strong hydrofluoric acid.[14] The normal valence of gallium is three. Mono- and divalent compounds have been reported but are apparently unstable.

In qualitative chemical detection, gallium chloride is separated from most other chlorides by extraction from a 6.5N hydrochloric acid solution with either ethyl or isopropyl ether.[34] Upon evaporation of the ether extract, the gallium chloride can be recovered and identified by precipitation with ferrocyanide.[29]

Gallium can be quantitatively determined by extraction (from acid solution) with a chloroform solution of 8-hydroxy-quinoline followed by spectrophotometric determination.[27]

Another quantitative determination utilizes a different principle.[24] The gallium is extracted from solution with diethyl ether and re-extracted from the diethyl ether with water. This aqueous solution is adjusted to pH 2.8 and treated with gallocyanine to form a blue lake. The blue lake is destroyed by chelation of the gallium with ethylenediamine-tetraacetic acid (EDTA). This method gives sharp end points and accurate results.

Spectrographic methods are more generally employed for quantitative analysis. One method[33] uses beryllium oxide as an internal standard and carbon powder as a dispersing agent, burning in a d-c arc and using the 2943.6Å gallium line for estimation. For determination of impurities in high-purity gallium (99.9999%) spectrographic methods, activation analysis, and resistivity measurements are employed.

A comprehensive survey of the resistance of many metals to attack by gallium is presented in the "Liquid Metals Handbook."[2] The following statement from this publication is pertinent: "Gallium is more aggressive in its attack on most solid metals at a given temperature than any other molten metal that has been tested."

Data on resistance of specific metals and nonmetals are presented below:

Tungsten—Good resistance up to 800°C (1472°F).
Tantalum—Good resistance up to 450°C (842°F); attack by gallium increases above this temperature.

Columbium—Good resistance to gallium up to 400°C (752°F); considerable attack as temperature increases above this point.

Molybdenum—Essentially the same as columbium.

Chromium—Disintegrates in gallium at 600°C (1112°F).

Titanium—Disintegrates in gallium at 450°C (842°F).

Lead—Limited resistance to gallium up to 300°C (572°F).

Other metallic elements (Cu, Pt, Zr, Ni, V, Mn, Ag, Au, Ce, Pr, Cd, Fe, Ge, Sn, and In)—All react readily with gallium to form compounds or solid solutions.

Stainless steel (18–8)—Subject to severe alloying attack by gallium at 600°C (1112°F).

"Inconel"—More severely attacked than stainless steel.

92.5% tantalum–7.5% tungsten—Excellent resistance to attack by gallium at 400°C (752°F); moderately resistant up to 600°C (1112°F).

Other alloys (FeBe, Cr-50Mn Ni-20W)—Subject to severe attack at 500°C (932°F).

Beryllia—Quite resistant to attack by gallium up to 1000°C (1832°F).

Fused silica—Unattacked by *clean* gallium up to 1160°C (2120°F). Oxide contamination from any source reduces resistance markedly.

"Alundum"—Excellent resistance to at least 1000°C (1832°F).

Graphite—Satisfactory resistance to gallium to at least 800°C (1472°F).

"Pyrex" glass—No evidence of attack by gallium at 500°C (932°F).

Zirconia—Can be used with gallium up to 500°C.

Magnesia—Poor resistance at 500°C, not recommended.

TOXICITY

The toxicity of gallium has been the subject of study at the Naval Medical Research Institute.[18] Aerosols of gallium chloride had but slight effect on rats in concentrations of 0.125 mg gallium/liter of air and exposures of ½ to 4 hr. The necessary acidity of the solution had a more adverse effect. Using gallium lactate, intravenous injections of about 40 mg gallium/kg of body weight in rats or rabbits was lethal. The symptoms resulting from lethal and near-lethal injections of gallium salts may include rapid loss in weight, hyperexcitability, and, in some cases, photophobia, blindness, and terminal flaccid paralysis.

Using gallium nitrate as test material, patches, on both man and rabbits, containing this salt resulted in no evidence of poisoning.[20]

ALLOYS

A compendium of published data on the alloys of gallium is presented in Argonne National Laboratory Report No. 4109.[40] The pertinent information is abstracted below:

Aluminum—Gallium is reported to be insoluble in aluminum metal. A eutectic containing 13 per cent gallium melts at 26.3°C (78.34°F). The addition of 2 to 4 per cent of gallium improves mechanical properties of aluminum. The aluminum-gallium alloys can be enriched with magnesium, zinc, and lithium.

Antimony—A compound GaSb (36.4 per cent by weight of gallium) is reported.

Arsenic—A compound GaAs (48.2 per cent by weight of gallium) is reported.

Bismuth—Bismuth is insoluble in gallium at the melting point (30°C) (86°F). At 225°C (437°F) about 11 per cent of gallium will dissolve in bismuth.

Cadmium—Cadmium is nearly insoluble in gallium at 30°C (86°F). Cadmium will dissolve 12 to 13 per cent of gallium to form an alloy which freezes at 258°C (496°F).

Calcium—An alloy $CaGa_2$ is reported.

Cerium—A compound $CeGa_2$ is reported.

Copper—Gallium does not dissolve appreciably in copper at 20°C (68°F). The copper-gallium phase diagram has been studied by Weibke[39] and Hume-Rothery;[13] these diagrams are reproduced in the ANL report. These alloys contain as much as 57.5 per cent of gallium. Copper-zinc-gallium and copper-gallium-germanium alloys have been investigated; copper is the major constituent of these alloys.

Gold—Solubility of gallium in gold reaches the maximum of 4.8 per cent by weight at 455°C (851°F). About 0.65 per cent of gallium can be held in solid solution by gold.

Indium—Low-melting alloys of gallium and indium, containing from 24 to 71 per cent by weight of gallium, are reported. Gallium-indium alloys are gradually attacked by water.

Iron—Alloys of gallium with iron usually contain only small percentages of gallium. An alloy of iron containing 3 per cent of gallium, 14 per cent of nickel is reported to resemble beryllium and titanium steels in hardenability.

Lanthanum—An alloy LaGa$_2$ is mentioned.

Lead—Gallium has limited solubility in liquid lead [about 5 per cent at 317°C (603°F)]. Lead is insoluble in gallium at the melting point of gallium; likewise, gallium is nearly insoluble in solid lead.

Lithium—A gallium-lithium alloy (91 per cent gallium) is reported.

Magnesium—Gallium alloys readily with magnesium. A solid solution of 4.6 per cent gallium can be prepared by quenching and aging.

Mercury—Gallium and mercury are not mutually soluble at room temperature.

Nickel—Gallium alloys easily with nickel. An alloy containing 1.3 per cent gallium has been investigated.

Platinum—Alloys of gallium and platinum form at both low and high temperatures.

Potassium—Potassium is practically insoluble in gallium at 30°C (86°F).

Silver—Alloys of gallium and silver containing up to 30 per cent gallium have been reported; 40 distinct alloys have been investigated. Alloys containing up to 14 per cent gallium resemble silver in appearance and are soft and workable. At 18 to 25 per cent gallium, the alloys are brittle; the brittleness increases above 25 per cent gallium.

Sodium—Sodium is practically insoluble in gallium at 30°C (86°F). At higher temperatures sodium-gallium alloys are formed which are quite reactive.

Tellurium—Compounds GaTe (35.3 per cent gallium) and Ga$_2$Te$_3$ (26.7 per cent gallium) are known. The existence of other compounds is doubtful.

Tin—In the liquid condition, gallium and tin are miscible in all proportions. Low-melting alloys, containing up to 69 per cent of gallium, have been investigated.

Titanium—The compound Ga$_3$Ti has been reported.

Zinc—Zinc and gallium are miscible in all proportions in the liquid state. Low-melting alloys containing up to 72 per cent gallium are reported. A eutectic of 5 per cent zinc and 94 to 95 per cent gallium melts at 25°C (77°F).

Zirconium—The compound GaZr has been studied.

FABRICATION TECHNIQUE

Gallium is available in both liquid and solid form because of its low melting point. Fabrication into various shapes has not been undertaken for any commercial purpose.

Electrodeposition of gallium has been almost entirely from sodium gallate solution. It is conceivable that potassium gallate solutions could be used to electrodeposit gallium, but there has been no work published on such a method. There is no record of any success in attempting to electrolyze acid solutions of gallium.

Because of its low melting point and resistance to oxidation, no particular difficulty is encountered in the melting of gallium.

APPLICATIONS

The most promising use for gallium is in intermetallic compounds to be used as semiconductors. The availability of high-purity gallium to be alloyed with other high-purity elements (arsenic, antimony, phosphorus) has allowed production of such semiconductors with properties approaching those which have been predicted from theory. Intermetallic compounds with gallium as one of the metals have application as high-temperature rectifiers and transistors, solar batteries and other devices where the photovoltaic effect can be utilized, and infrared optics.[41] Intensive work has been done in recent years on such materials; these compounds are beginning to be commercially produced. As they become more available for study, it is likely that many uses will be found for them because of their unique properties.

Probably the first use proposed for gallium was as a fill material for high-temperature thermometers. However, difficulties in fabrication have prevented any commercial development of such thermometers. The use of gallium as a backing material for optical mirrors has been suggested, as it reflects a high percentage of the incident light.[6] This reflectivity of gallium on glass is illustrated in Figure 10.3.

The Atomic Energy Commission has investi-

Figure 10.3. Glass surfaces that have been uniformly "wet" with liquid gallium often form excellent mirrors. In this case a common laboratory watch glass was used as a receptacle for the liquid metal. When the excess gallium was poured out of the watch glass, the convex surface was a clear, though somewhat imperfect, mirror. (*Courtesy Aluminum Company of America.*)

gated gallium as a possible heat exchange medium.[16, 26] Its long liquid range and low vapor pressure are quite desirable for such an application; the high neutron absorption cross section may not be too serious a disadvantage. The considerable reactivity of gallium with most metals at high temperature, however, poses the problem of a satisfactory container for the gallium; should a suitable material be found for the container, gallium might well be used for such an application.

Many alloys of gallium could be useful for certain applications. To date, other and cheaper alloys have proved equally satisfactory. One principal use of gallium reported by the Germans is in organic synthesis.[37] Its chloride acts as a catalyst in the Friedel-Crafts reaction. In some cases a smaller amount of catalyst is required than when other chloride salts are used; in other cases a higher yield is obtained, or the reaction time is shortened.

Although not a commercial application, it is interesting that Ga72 has shown promise in the study of bone cancer.[5] Suitable radio-active gallium compounds are absorbed by the bone cancer, allowing the detection and observation of the extent of the cancer.

References

1. Ahrens, L. H., *S. African J. Sci.*, **41**, 152–160 (1945).
2. Atomic Energy Commission, "Liquid-Metals Handbook," 2nd Ed., Washington, D.C., Government Printing Office, 1952.
3. de Boisbaudran, L., *Ann. chim. et phys. (5)* **10**, 100–41 (Jan. 1877).
4. de la Breteque, Pierre, Etudes sur Le Gallium. Doctoral Thesis, University of Aix Marseille (1955). A lengthy abstract is given in *Chemical & Engineering News*, **34**, 4300–4301 (1956).
5. Dudley, H. C., "The Biological Significance of Radiogallium (Ga72)," Project NM 011 013, Naval Medical Research Institute, National Naval Medical Center, Bethesda, Maryland, 1949.
6. Einecke, Erich, "Das Gallium," Leipzig, Verlag Von Leopold Voss, 1937. (Photolithoprinted by Edwards Bros., Ann Arbor, Mich.)
7. Frary, F. C., U.S. Patent 2,582,376 (Jan. 15, 1952); Brown, R. W., U.S. Patents 2,582,377 and 2,582,378 (Jan. 15, 1952).
8. Goldschmidt, V. M., *Ind. Eng. Chem.*, **27**, 1100–2 (1935).
9. Goldschmidt, V. M., *Nat.-naturw. Klasse*, No. 4 (1937).
10. Hildebrand, W. F., and Scherrer, J. A., *J. Ind. Eng. Chem.*, **8**, 225 (1916).
11. Hoffman, J. I., and Scribner, B. F., *J. Research Nat. Bur. Standards*, **15**, 205–9 (1935).
12. Hopkins, B. S., "Chapters in the Chemistry of the Less Familiar Elements," Chap. 8, Champaign, Ill., Stipes Publishing Co., 1939.
13. Hume-Rothery, W., Mabbott, G. W., and Evans, K. M. C., *Trans. Roy. Soc. (London)*, **233A** 1–97 (1934).
14. Isaac, E. and Tammann, G., *Z. anorg. u. allgem. Chem.*, **60**, 61 (1907).
15. Isagaki, Masaru, U.S. Patent 2,848,398 (Aug. 19, 1958).
16. Jaffee, R. I., Evans, R. M., Fromm, E. A., and Gonser, B. W., "Gallium in Nuclear Reactors: Consideration for Use as a Primary Coolant," AECD-3317, Washington, Department of Commerce, 1949.
17. Kelley, K. K., "Contributions to the Data on Theoretical Metallurgy. X. High-Temperature Heat-Content, Heat-Capacity, and Entropy Data for Inorganic Compounds," *Bur. Mines Bull. 476*, Washington, Government Printing Office, 1949.

18. Levine, M. D., and Dudley, H. C., "Studies of the Acute Toxicity of Gallium," Project NM 011 013, Rept. No. 3, Naval Medical Research Institute, National Naval Medical Center, Bethesda, Maryland, Jan. 13, 1949.

19. Mack, G. L., Davis, J. K., and Bartell, F. E., *J. Phys. Chem.*, **45**, 846 (1941).

20. Meek, S. F., Harrold, G. C. and McCord, C. P., *Ind. Med.*, **12**, 7–9 (1943).

21. Mellor, J. W., "A Comprehensive Treatise On Inorganic and Theoretical Chemistry," Vol. 5, Chap. 34, New York, Longmans, Green & Co., Ltd., 1929.

22. Mendeleeff, D. I., *Ann.*, Supplementband 8, 196–206 (Heft 2), (1871).

23. Mendeleeff, D. I., *Compt. rend.*, **81**, 969–72 (Nov. 22, 1875).

24. Milner, G. W. C., *Analyst*, **80**, 77–78 (1955).

25. "Minerals Yearbook, U.S. Bur. Mines," p. 1332, Washington, D.C., Government Printing Office, 1948.

26. *Ibid.*, pp. 1310–11, 1949.

27. Moeller, T., and Cohen, A. J., *Anal. Chem.*, **22**, 686–690, (1950).

28. Morgan, G., and Davies, G. R., *Chemistry & Industry*, **56**, 717–21, (1937).

29. Noyes, A. A., and Bray, W. C., "A System of Qualitative Analysis for the Rare Elements," New York, The Macmillan Co., 1927.

30. Powell, A. R., Lever, F. M., and Walpole, R. E., *J. Applied Chem.*, **1**, 541–51, (1951).

31. Richards, T. W., and Boyer, Sylvester, *J. Am. Chem. Soc.*, **43**, 274 (1921).

32. Spells, K. E., *Proc. Phys. Soc. (London)*, **48**, 299–311, (1936).

33. Strock, L. W., *Am. Inst. Mining Met. Engrs., Tech. Pub. No. 1866* (1945). (Published in *Metals Technol.*, April, 1945).

34. Swift, E. H., *J. Am. Chem. Soc.*, **46**, 2375–81, (1924).

35. Thompson, A. P., and Harner, H. R., *J. Metals*, **191**, 91–94, (1951).

36. Thompson, A. P., and Harner, H. R., "The Recovery, Production and Potential Uses of Gallium," paper presented before the Spring Meeting 1952 of The Electrochemical Society, printed in Enlarged Abstracts of Papers presented by the Electronics Division of The Electrochemical Society.

37. Ulich, H., and Heyne, G. *Z. Electrochem.*, **41**, 509–14, (1935) (C.A. 29:7768–9); Ulich, H., *Die Chemie*, **55**, 37–8 (1942) (C.A. 37: 2521–6); Ulich, H., Keutmann, A., and Geierhaas, A., *Z. Electrochem.*, **49**, 292–6, (1943) (C.A. 37:6650–7); Ulich, H., *Oel u. Kohle.*, **39**, 523–7, (1943) (C.A. 38:958-4).

38. Waring, W. Geo., *Trans. AIME*, **57**, 657, (1917).

39. Weibke, F., *Z. anorg. u. allgem. Chem.*, Bd. **220**, 293–311 (1934).

40. Wilkinson, W. D., "Properties of Gallium," ANL-4109, Chicago, Argonne National Laboratory, 1948.

41. Willardson, R. K., *Battelle Technical Review*, **6**, No. 8, 8–14 (August, 1957).

11. GERMANIUM

H. R. Harner

Chemicals and Metals Division
The Eagle-Picher Company
Joplin, Missouri

INTRODUCTION

In working on the relation of properties of the elements, Newlands[58] noted that, if his theories were correct, there seemed to be a missing element between silicon and tin. Seven years later Mendeleeff[51] predicted the discovery of the three "eka" elements and listed the properties to be expected for each. One of these was expected to belong to the silicon family; this was his eka-silicon. In 1886 Winkler was asked to analyze a sample of argyrodite. Repeated analyses did not account for about 7 per cent of the composition, and he finally concluded that the missing portion was a new element. Winkler[84] finally isolated the new element and named it germanium, after his native country.

Further investigation of the properties definitely fixed the position of germanium in the atomic table and confirmed the predictions of Mendeleeff. Germanium is in Group IV, Period 4, of the periodic table. The atomic number is 32; the atomic weight is 72.60.

Although germanium has been known for many years and there has been considerable study of it and its compounds, only recently has it attained importance. Commercial production in the United States began only twenty years ago.

OCCURRENCE

It has been estimated that a ton of the earth's crust contains from 4 to 7 g of germanium.[1,19] Minute amounts have been detected in many silicate minerals.

Only a very few minerals contain appreciable amounts of germanium.[63] Argyrodite (from which it was first isolated) contains from 5 to 7 per cent germanium; only small amounts of this mineral (a silver-germanium sulfide) have been located. Canfieldite, a silver-tin-germanium sulfide mineral containing about 1.8 per cent germanium, is found in Bolivia, but only in small quantities. Enargite, a copper-arsenic sulfide, is found in some quantity in western United States and is reported to contain as much as 0.03 per cent germanium.[62] None of these minerals is presently utilized for recovery of germanium, presumably because of the small quantities available.

Germanite, a complex copper-zinc-arsenic-germanium sulfide, has been mined at Tsumeb, Southwest Africa; it has been found associated with the lead-zinc-copper ores of that district. True germanite contains 10 per cent germanium,[81] but the run-of-mine ore assays only 3 to 4 per cent germanium. Some pockets of germanite have been found, but it is usually dispersed in the lead-copper ores. This is the only known mineral from which germanium is recovered as the primary metal. Renierite, a complex copper-iron-germanium-arsenic sulfide, was first discovered in the Belgian Congo.[53] Analysis of clean renierite crystals showed an average of 7 per cent germanium.[81] It is found intimately mixed with the copper-zinc ores in Katanga, Belgian Congo.[4] It has also been reported in association with germanite in the copper-lead-zinc ores in Tsumeb, Southwest Africa.[3]

Some zinc ores in the United States contain

small amounts (0.01 to 0.1 per cent) of germanium;[6] zinc ores from other parts of the world also contain traces of germanium. Silver, tin, copper, and iron ores sometimes have small amounts of germanium.

The first major recovery of germanium from ores was from the zinc ores of the Tri-State (Missouri-Oklahoma-Kansas) field;[60] subsequently, germanium was recovered from zinc ores of the Mississippi Valley.[6]

Recovery of the germanium content of the Tsumeb ores[3] and the Katanga ores[4] in recent years has added measurably to the world supply of germanium.

The presence of germanium in coals has been known for some time;[18] numerous references in recent years have reported the finding of germanium in coals from many different parts of the world.[48,65] British coals and combustion by-products have been investigated[55] and the germanium contents reported in some detail; these by-products comprise one source of raw material for recovery in England. (See under the heading "Derivation".) The United States Geological Survey has compiled data on the concentration of germanium in some American coals.[73] Data on the germanium content of coals have been reported in West Virginia,[25] Illinois,[49] and Kansas.[69] Recovery of germanium from American coals has been intensively studied, but to date there has been no commercial recovery.[16]

Recovery of germanium from zinc and other ores is economically feasible only because the germanium is concentrated in by-products during the process of recovering the primary metals; without such initial concentration of the germanium, it would not be economically possible to separate and purify it. Similarly, recovery of germanium in coal is dependent on the concentration of germanium in coal by-products (primarily flue dusts); these by-products must contain sufficient germanium to make its recovery profitable.

PRODUCTION AND ECONOMIC STATISTICS

In 1959 the consumption of germanium (metal and oxide) in the United States was estimated at 45,000 lb.[16] Actual production figures have not been released.

Production of germanium in England started in 1950;[54] no production figures are available. Belgium is a major European producer, the raw material coming from Tsumeb and the Belgian Congo.

The major producer in the United States is The Eagle-Picher Company which recovers it from zinc ore.[60] The American Zinc Company and Sylvania Electric Products, Inc., are also suppliers. American Metal Climax, Inc. is beginning production. In England, Johnson Matthey & Company is a producer; flue dusts from coals are their primary raw materials. In Belgium, germanium metal and oxide are produced at Olen by the Societe Generale Metallurgique de Hoboken and at Balen by the Societe de la Vielle Montagne S.A. The price of electronic-grade germanium metal in the United States is currently about $185/lb for large quantities. Germanium dioxide is about $110/lb.

DERIVATION

Commercial recovery of germanium has been chiefly from zinc and zinc-copper-lead ores, germanite, and flue dusts from coals.

Ores from the Tri-State district (Missouri, Oklahoma, and Kansas) are concentrated and roasted to a crude zinc oxide by conventional means. Roasted ores mixed with salt and coal are sintered at a high temperature; germanium, cadmium, and some other impurities are vaporized; and the vapors are condensed and collected in an electrostatic precipitator. This by-product fume is chemically treated to obtain crude fractions of germanium, cadmium, and the other impurities.[60]

The germanium concentrate is reacted with strong hydrochloric acid. The resultant germanium tetrachloride [b.p. 86°C (187°F)] is distilled off. The crude tetrachloride is given additional purification and finally distilled with chlorine (to hold back arsenic). The purified, redistilled tetrachloride is then hydrolyzed in water to form germanium dioxide, which is reduced to a powdered metal by heating to 650°C (1200°F) in an atmosphere of hydrogen. The powdered metal is melted at 1100°C (2012°F) in an inert atmosphere to form ingots. This method of recovery from germanium concentrates and reduction to the metal is used, with modifications, in practically all processes.

Zinc ores from the Mississippi Valley are concentrated, and the concentrate roasted and sintered in much the same fashion as the Tri-State ores; a by-product fume contains the recoverable germanium. This fume is leached with sulfuric acid under conditions which dissolve the zinc and cadmium and leave the lead, germanium, and other impurities as a sludge. The sludge is reacted with hot, strong sulfuric acid, the germanium being dissolved. The germanium in this liquor is precipitated with hydrogen sulfide, and the sulfide precipitate is roasted. The roasted material is then reacted with concentrated hydrochloric acid, and the distillation and purification are performed as described in the previous paragraph.[6]

At Balen, Belgium, lead and zinc ores are smelted in a complex circuit; germanium is concentrated in a crude zinc oxide. Leaching of this crude zinc oxide under appropriate conditions dissolves the germanium. The germanium is precipitated, and the resulting germanium concentrate reacted with hydrochloric acid and distilled from the solution as germanium tetrachloride. Further purification steps follow essentially the same procedure as described for zinc ores.[8]

The presence of germanium in zinc solutions for electrowinning of the zinc is highly detrimental. This is one of the reasons for the separation of germanium in the Balen process, since the zinc is recovered there by electrolysis. Another method for purification of the zinc solution yields a sludge which contains the germanium, copper, and arsenic. This sludge is smelted with excess sulfur to fume off the germanium for subsequent recovery.[47]

At Tsumeb, Southwest Africa, germanium occurs as germanite and renierite intimately mixed with the copper-lead-zinc ore of this district. By selective flotation a germanium concentrate is made, and the material is shipped to Olen, Belgium. Here the concentrate is processed in a vertical retort furnace under reducing conditions to obtain a germanium sulfide fume which is condensed. The fume is given an oxidizing roast; a crude germanium dioxide is obtained for the purification stages.[3]

Germanium, as renierite, is dispersed through some of the copper-zinc ores from Katanga, Belgium Congo. In the flotation process for concentration of these ores, the germanium follows the copper. During the smelting of the copper, dusts and fumes which contain appreciable amounts of germanium are collected. These dusts and fumes are baked with sulfuric acid, and the baked dust is leached with weak acid to obtain a germanium-bearing solution. After oxidation of the solution, germanium is precipitated with magnesia and copper hydrate to give a concentrate for further purification.[4]

The germanium concentrates made at Tsumeb and Katanga (described in the preceding paragraphs) are shipped to Hoboken, Belgium, for recovery and purification of the germanium.[5] Distillation of the germanium tetrachloride, hydrolysis of the tetrachloride to the dioxide, and reduction and purification of the metal are essentially as previously described.

At Tsumeb, some pockets of germanite ore have been found which have been mined separately and the germanite processed for recovery of germanium and gallium. In one process[66] the pulverized germanite ore is reacted with 50 per cent sodium hydroxide solution, and the mixture is evaporated to dryness. The dry mass is leached with hot water, and the leach solution is brought to pH 8 with sulfuric acid. Under controlled conditions, nitric acid is added to the boiling solution to give 5 per cent of free acid in the solution; after filtering, this solution is brought to pH 3 with sodium hydroxide (to precipitate the gallium), the precipitate is filtered off, and the germanium is precipitated (as dioxide) by neutralization with ammonia. The germanium dioxide is then filtered from the solution and dissolved in strong hydrochloric acid, and the resultant germanium tetrachloride is distilled and purified. Hydrolysis of the tetrachloride to germanium dioxide and subsequent reduction and melting follow the same steps as previously described.

To recover germanium (and gallium) from flue dusts,[66] the dust is smelted with soda ash, lime, copper oxide, and coal dust to form a regulus and a slag. These products can be separated; practically all of the germanium (and gallium) is concentrated in the regulus. The regulus is reacted with chlorine under a dilute solution of ferric chloride; after the reaction is complete, the solution is made strongly acid, and the crude germanium tetrachloride is distilled off. The germanium tetrachloride so formed contains appreciable quantities of arsenic chloride and is refluxed with copper turnings (for 12 hr or longer) to eliminate this impurity. Otherwise, the purification and final production of the metal follow the usual steps discussed in the processes for zinc ore and germanite.

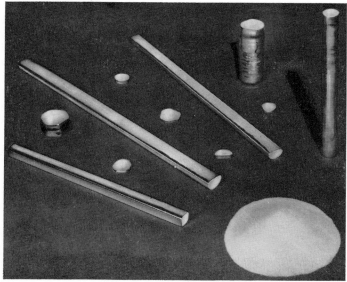

Figure 11.1. Germanium dioxide powder (lower right), germanium ingots (center and left), single crystal germanium (two bars at upper right), and assorted cross sections of these types of germanium metal. (*Courtesy Eagle-Picher Co.*)

For electronic uses the impurities allowable in the germanium metal are extremely small; the metal itself is tested for electrical resistivity rather than by chemical methods. The germanium metal obtained by reduction of the dioxide is further purified by fractional recrystallization.[5,61] The usual method is by zone refining, in which the metal (contained in a graphite boat) is slowly pulled through a horizontal tube furnace, either in an inert atmosphere or under vacuum. The tube furnace has around it a multiplicity of induction coils so that, as the germanium is moved through these coils, a narrow molten zone of metal is formed. By this method of multiple heating and cooling, the impurities are swept to the ends of the germanium ingot. The ends of the ingot are removed, and only the center section is used; the end sections are returned to the process for further purification.

Illustrated in Figure 11.1 are germanium dioxide, germanium ingots, single crystal germanium, and cross sections of the two types of bars.

PHYSICAL PROPERTIES

Germanium is usually considered as a metalloid, with properties somewhere between those of a true metal and a nonmetal. It belongs to the class of materials known as semiconductors; these materials, of which germanium is a conspicuous example, have become of major importance in electronic devices.

The physical properties of germanium are given in Table 11.1.

CHEMICAL PROPERTIES

Germanium is both divalent and tetravalent; the latter compounds are the more stable.

The metal is quite stable at 25°C (77°F); it is not affected by air, water, or oxygen. At 600–700°C (1112–1292°F), oxidation in air or oxygen proceeds rapidly.[50] Germanium combines readily with the halogens upon heating to form the corresponding tetrahalides. Chlorine reacts most vigorously, followed by bromine and iodine.

Hydrochloric and sulfuric acids have little effect on germanium at room temperature; at 100°C (212°F) sulfuric acid will dissolve germanium slowly. Both nitric acid and aqua regia will attack germanium, especially at higher temperatures. Potassium or sodium hydroxide solutions have little or no effect on germanium, but the molten alkalies quickly dissolve the metal.

Germanium forms two oxides—GeO and

TABLE 11.1. PHYSICAL CONSTANTS OF GERMANIUM

(Superscript numbers refer to references.)

Atomic number	32
Atomic weight	72.60[76]
Isotopes and abundance	
Mass No. 70	20.4%[21]
Mass No. 72	27.4%[21]
Mass No. 73	7.8%[21]
Mass No. 74	36.6%[21]
Mass No. 76	7.8%[21]
Color	Silvery
Crystal structure	Octahedral[50]
Index of refraction	4.068–4.143[9]
Hardness, Mohs scale (s)	6.25[50]
Ductility	Frangible
Density (s) at 25°C (77°F) (g/cc)	5.32[76]
Specific volume (s) at 25°C (77°F)	0.188
Melting point	936°C (1717°F)[22]
Boiling point	2700°C (approx.) (4890°F)[56]
Latent heat of fusion (g-cal/g)	111.5[22]
Latent heat of vaporization (g-cal/g)	1,200[71]
Specific heat at 25°C (77°F) (cal/g)	0.086[38]
Volume resistivity at 25°C (77°F) (microhm-cm)	60 × 10[6][44]
Electrochemical equivalent Ge++++ (mg/coulomb)	0.1881[26]
Electrode potential Ge++++ ($H_2 = 0.0$ volts)*	−0.15 (est'd)[34]

* National Bureau of Standards nomenclature.

GeO_2. The latter, germanium dioxide, is the type sold commercially.

Johnson[37] has compiled an excellent summary of the published work on the inorganic compounds of germanium; a similar digest by the same author[36] covers the extensive work on organometallic compounds of germanium.

In detection of germanium, the sample is usually fused with sodium carbonate or caustic soda. Germanium is separated from most of the other elements by dissolving the fused mass and distilling from a strong hydrochloric acid solution. The distillate is tested by the appropriate method.

Qualitative analysis for small amounts of germanium is best made by reacting with phenylfluorone. An intense rose color is formed in the presence of even traces of germanium.[13]

Precipitation as the sulfide from strong sulfuric acid solution can be used for larger quantities of germanium.

For quantitative determination, the sample is fused with caustic soda or sodium carbonate, the fused mass is reacted with hydrochloric acid, and the resultant germanium tetrachloride is distilled off in the presence of chlorine. The tetrachloride is dissolved in $6N$ sulfuric acid and precipitated as the sulfide. The sulfide is oxidized to the dioxide with hydrogen peroxide and weighed.[35]

The tetrachloride can also be reduced with sodium hypophosphite and the divalent germanium determined by titration with potassium iodate.[30]

For very small amounts of germanium, colorimetric determination with phenylfluorone[13] or oxidized hematoxylin[57] is more satisfactory than the gravimetric or titrimetric methods.

Spectrographic methods of analysis are widely used. Strock[77] has used beryllium oxide as an internal standard, carbon powder as a dispersing agent, and a crater-type electrode, burning in a d-c arc and using the 2651.1 Å line. A variation of this procedure uses lithium carbonate as an internal standard, completely vaporizing the sample at 10 amp (d-c), which requires 2 to 3 min.[80] Another method uses a pegmatite diluent without an internal standard.[20]

A critical review of analytical methods for germanium has been published by Krause and Johnson.[41]

Chemical methods for analysis of impurities in germanium for electronic use are not satisfactory. Spectrographic methods can be employed, but it is more usual to make electrical-resistivity measurements. Neutron-activation analysis has also been used.

Germanium or germanium dioxide shows no evidence of toxicity.[24] Germanium tetrachloride is irritating when inhaled; this is believed to be due to hydrolysis of the compound to GeO_2 and HCl; the released acid is probably the cause of the irritation.

Alloys. Some pertinent information on the alloys of germanium is given below.

Aluminum—The binary system germanium-aluminum forms a eutectic at 55 per cent by weight of germanium which melts at 423°C (793°F).[43,74] In the solid state, aluminum is slightly soluble in germanium; similarly, germanium is slightly soluble in aluminum.

Antimony—The system germanium-antimony forms a eutectic melting at 588°C (1090°F) and containing 28.5 per cent by weight of germanium.[68] In the solid state, germanium is slightly soluble in antimony and antimony is slightly soluble in germanium.[75]

Arsenic—The germanium-arsenic system indicates two compounds, GeAs and GeAs$_2$.[75]

Bismuth—A eutectic is formed which melts at 271°C (520°F) and is almost 100 per cent bismuth.[68,75]

Cobalt—A germanium-cobalt alloy, containing 41 per cent germanium by weight, is reported.[46]

Copper—This system has received considerable study.[28,70] Only one compound, Cu$_3$Ge, has been identified. A eutectic is formed at 650°C (1202°F) and about 39 per cent by weight germanium. Alpha copper will dissolve about 10 per cent of germanium in the solid state.[27] The ternary system Cu-Ge-Au has been investigated.[31]

Gold—The system gold-germanium forms a eutectic containing 12 per cent germanium by weight which melts at 356°C (673°F);[33] 0.8 per cent germanium is soluble in gold at 350°C (662°F); it is very slightly soluble at room temperature. Ternary systems have been investigated.[31]

Iridium—A compound IrGe is reported.[64]

Iron—Two compounds are reported.[46,68] Fe$_2$Ge melts at 1180°C (2156°F) and FeGe$_2$ at 866°C (1591°F).

Lead—Germanium and lead are mutually soluble in the liquid state, but the germanium precipitates out almost completely on cooling.[10]

Magnesium—A compound Mg$_2$Ge is known; it melts at 1115°C (2039°F) and contains 59.9 per cent germanium by weight.[40] Two eutectics are formed, one at 635°C (1175°F) (3.4 per cent germanium by weight) and another at 680°C (1256°F) (83 per cent germanium by weight).

Nickel—The binary system is complex; only one compound has been definitely identified.[46,64,68] This compound is Ni$_2$Ge,

melting at 1200°C (2192°F). Another compound is mentioned, NiGe, but there seems to be some doubt of its existence. Two eutectics are formed; one melts at 1130°C (2066°F) (33 per cent germanium by weight), the other at 775°C (1427°F) (66 per cent germanium by weight). Nickel dissolves approximately 12 per cent of germanium in the solid phase.

Palladium—A compound PdGe is reported.[64]

Platinum—A compound PtGe is reported.[64]

Selenium—Two compounds GeSe and GeSe$_2$ have been prepared.[29]

Silicon—Silicon and germanium form a continuous series of solid solutions.[75]

Silver—The silver-germanium system indicates no compounds;[11] the single eutectic contains 18 per cent germanium by weight and melts at 650°C (1202°F).

Sodium—An alloy corresponding to the formula NaGe has been prepared;[14] it slowly decomposes in moist air.

Tellurium—One compound GeTe is reported;[39] it melts incongruently at 725°C (1337°F).

Tin—Tin and germanium form a eutectic which melts at 232°C (450°F) and is almost 100 per cent tin.[75] Germanium is only slightly soluble in solid tin; likewise, tin is only slightly soluble in solid germanium.

Zinc—A eutectic is formed melting at 398°C (748°F), which contains 6 per cent germanium by weight. No compounds appear to be formed. Germanium and zinc have only slight solubility in each other in the solid state.[17]

FABRICATION TECHNIQUES

The reduction of germanium dioxide to powdered metal and subsequent melting to ingots has been described under the heading "Derivation." Further purification of the metal by recrystallization under vacuum or in an inert atmosphere is likewise covered in that section.

Germanium is supplied in ingots of 15 to 26 in. (38 to 66 cm) and of varying cross sections, as demanded by the industry. Cross-sectional areas of as much as 1 sq in. are available. Attempts have been made to fabricate the metal in ribbon form, but no such material has yet been offered for sale. Pure germanium does not lend itself to fabrication into wire, rod, or rolled shapes.

Single crystal germanium is also supplied. It is produced[61] by "seeding" a melt of germanium (held only slightly above the melting point) and slowly withdrawing the crystal from the furnace.

To obtain the desired properties for electronic applications, pure germanium must be further processed. Pressure or heating and quenching are sometimes employed. The usual one, however, is "doping" or alloying with minute amounts of appropriate metals. Many alloys have been patented for these purposes.[45,82] Alloying is usually done in an inert atmosphere or under vacuum. Several ingenious methods of incorporating these very small amounts of other metals have been devised. Diffusing of the appropriate metal into the germanium is one of these; another is electroetching.

Electrodeposition of germanium from $3N$ potassium hydroxide solution on copper cathodes produces a thin, coherent coating, but deposition stops as soon as the cathode is covered.[23] A bath of germanium tetraiodide in ethylene glycol at 150°C (302°F) is reported to deposit germanium.[15] Some success has been achieved in electrodeposition from germanium tetrachloride dissolved in propylene glycol.[78]

APPLICATIONS

The science of solid-state physics, and particularly that phase of it relating to semiconductors, has found many practical applications in the past decade. The first major strides in utilizing semiconducting properties were due primarily to the availability of high-purity germanium. While many other and diverse semiconducting materials have been or are being developed,[83] germanium is still one of the most important. It is in this field that germanium finds its major use.

The semiconducting properties of germanium first led to its use as a crystal diode rectifier[79] in World War II. In 1948 the germanium triode or transistor was developed.[7] Since that time, continuous developments and improvements have been made on germanium semiconducting devices which have opened entirely new fields for their utilization. The first germanium diode was a fine wire of appropriate

metal pressing against a thin wafer of properly prepared germanium (analogous to the old galena whisker detector). The wire and germanium wafer were soldered to separate electrical conductors, and the unit was embedded in plastic or enclosed in glass. This assembly was scarcely larger than a grain of corn.[61] Advances in technology have improved and miniaturized the original diodes; for many special applications, present-day diode assemblies are scarcely thicker than the wire in a paper clip and less than ½ cm long.

Germanium diodes, besides acting as crystal rectifiers, perform the same general functions as vacuum tube diodes. They have very small power consumption, very little heat emission, start up immediately (since there is no filament to heat), and are quite rugged. Many diverse types of germanium diodes are commercially available. One interesting property of germanium diodes[79] is their photoelectric effect, which is commercially utilized in the photodiode.

The first transistors had much the same size as the germanium diodes, except that two wires made contact with the germanium wafer instead of one; this was called a point-contact transistor. Later, another type was developed which was made up of a single tiny block of germanium suitably treated to give different properties to the end sections, in comparison with the center section; this was called a junction or area transistor. Each of these types has its advantages and limitations. These first transistors were quite small (about a ¼-in. cube); like the diodes, improvements in technology and manufacture have allowed further reduction in size and major improvements in performance. Power transistors are, of course, much larger.

The first transistors were used as amplifiers and oscillators. As new developments were made, their utility was greatly increased until, in 1959 alone, 125 million semiconducting devices were manufactured.[16] It has been only in the last 4 or 5 years that mass-production techniques have been developed which made these devices available for widespread use.

These devices have allowed miniaturization and improvements in radios, hearing aids, and communication equipment. Replacement of vacuum tubes by transistors has allowed direct long distance dialing in our telephones. Communications of all types depend heavily on such semiconducting devices. Military equipment has been vastly improved and miniaturized. These developments, which are so important to the Defense Forces, have also benefited civilian and commercial operations. The use of specialized germanium devices has allowed major advances in astronautics and missile guidance.

The theory of semiconductors and the mechanism of the behavior of germanium diodes and triodes are beyond the scope of this chapter. Shockley[72] gives an excellent theoretical treatment; O'Connor[61] gives a lucid description of the mechanism for transistors.

Germanium power rectifiers are in commercial use and have many advantages over the older types.[12] In 1956 alone, rectifiers for 50,000 KW were installed. Many types are commercially available, and their use is increasing rapidly.

Germanium is transparent to infrared light. This property is utilized in the infrared spectroscope and other optical instruments. Special germanium devices are also used in extremely sensitive infrared detectors supplementing radar for detection purposes. The high index of refraction and high dispersion of germanium glasses (in which germanium dioxide replaces silicon dioxide) has led to their use in specialized optical equipment. Magnesium germanate is used as a phosphor in fluorescent lamps.[42] A germanium resistance thermometer which will operate at temperatures near absolute zero has been developed. Germanium is being studied as a catalyst and shows considerable promise for some applications.

Gold-germanium alloys have been suggested for use in dental work or precision casting[33] because of their expansion upon solidification. The low melting gold-germanium eutectic could be used as an improved gold solder or in the reduction of the melting temperature of gold-containing alloys.

Resistors made by deposition of germanium on a thin film of silver have interesting properties.[32] Such films, formed by first depositing silver on "Pyrex" glass and subsequently depositing germanium on the silver, have resistivities from 1,000 ohms to several megohms and extremely good temperature coefficients.

The ready availability of germanium has spurred further research with it, both in the electronic field and for other applications.

References

1. Ahrens, L. H., *S. African J. Sci.*, **41**, 152–160 (1945).
2. Anon., *Eng. and Mining J.*, **157**, #5, 75 (1956).
3. Anon., *Eng. and Mining J.*, **157**, #5, 79 (1956).
4. Anon., *Eng. and Mining J.*, **157**, #5, 83 (1956).
5. Anon., *Eng. and Mining J.*, **157**, #5, 85 (1956).
6. Anon., *Eng. and Mining J.*, **157**, #5, 88 (1956).
7. Bardeen, J., and Brattain, W. H., *Phys. Rev.*, **74**, 230–1 (1948); *ibid.*, **75**, 1208 (1949).
8. Boving, Theophile and Andre, Jean, *J. of Metals*, **10**, 659 (1958).
9. Briggs, H. B., *Phys. Rev.*, **77**, 297 (1950).
10. Briggs, T. R., and Benedict, W. S., *J. Phys. Chem.*, **34**, 173–77 (1930).
11. Briggs, T. R., McDuffie, R. O., and Willisford, L. H., *J. Phys. Chem.*, **33**, 1080–96 (1929).
12. Burton, L. W. and Thurell, J. R., *Power*, **101**, #7, 73 (1957).
13. Cluley, H. J., *Analyst*, **76**, 525 (1951).
14. Dennis, L. M., and Skow, N. A., *J. Am. Chem. Soc.*, **52**, 2369–72 (1930).
15. Fink, C. G., and Dokras, V. M., *Trans. Electrochem. Soc.*, **95**, 80 (1949).
16. Fisher, Frank L., "Germanium," pp. 341–346 in "Mineral Facts and Problems," Bulletin 585, U.S. Bureau of Mines, Washington, D.C., Government Printing Office, 1960.
17. Gebhardt, Erich, *Z. Metallkunde*, **34**, 255–57 (1942).
18. Goldschmidt, V. M., *Ind. Eng. Chem.*, **27**, 1100–2 (1935).
19. Goldschmidt, V. M., and Peters, Cl., *Nachr. Ges. Wiss. Göttingen, Math. physik. Kl.*, III; IV, 141 (1933).
20. Gordon, Mackenzie, and Murata, K. J., *Econ. Geol.*, **47**, 170 (March-April 1952).
21. Graham, R. P., Macnamara, J., Crocker, I. H., and MacFarlane, R. B., *Can. J. Chem.*, **29**, 89–102 (1951).
22. Greiner, E. S., *J. of Metals*, **4**, 1044 (1952).
23. Hall, J. I., and Koenig, A. E., *Trans. Electrochem. Soc.*, **65**, 215 (1934).
24. Harrold, G. C., and Meek, S. F., *Ind. Med.*, **13**, 236–8 (1944).
25. Headlee, A. J. W., and Hunter, R. G., "Germanium in Coals of West Virginia," Geological and Economic Survey, Report of Investigations No. 8, Morgantown, West Virginia, 1951.
26. Hodgman, C. D., "Handbook of Chemistry and Physics," Cleveland, Ohio, Chemical Rubber Publishing Co., 1951–1952.
27. Hume-Rothery, Wm., Mabbott, G. W., and Channel-Evans, K. M., *Phil. Trans. Royal Soc.*, **233A**, 1–97 (1934).
28. Hume-Rothery, W., Raynor, G. V., Reynolds,

P. W., and Packer, H. K., *J. Inst. Metals*, **66**, 209–39 (1940).

29. Ivanov-Emin, B. N., *J. Gen. Chem. (USSR)*, **10**, 1813–18 (1940).

30. Ivanov-Emin, B. N., *Zavodskaya Lab.*, **13**, 161 (1947).

31. Jaffee, R. I., and Gonser, B. W., *A.I.M.E. Tech. Pub. 1998* (1946).

32. Jaffee, R. I., McMullen, E. W., and Gonser, B. W., *Trans. Electrochem. Soc.*, **89**, 277–90 (1946).

33. Jaffee, R. I., Smith, E. M., and Gonser, B. W., *Trans. A.I.M.E.*, **161**, 366 (1945).

34. Jirsa, Franz, *Z. anorg. u. allegem. Chem.*, **268**, 84–8 (1952).

35. Johnson, E. B. and Dennis, L. M., *J. Am. Chem. Soc.*, **47**, 790–3 (1925).

36. Johnson, O. H., *Chem. Revs.*, **48**, 259–297 (1951).

37. Johnson, O. H., *Chem. Revs.*, **51**, 431 (1952).

38. Kelley, K. K., "Contributions to the Data on Theoretical Metallurgy. XI. Entropies of Inorganic Substances. Revision (1948) of Data Methods of Calculation," *Bur. Mines Bull. 477*, p. 98, Washington, Government Printing Office, 1950.

39. Klemm, W., and Frischmuth, G., *Z. anorg. Chem.*, **218**, 249–51 (1934).

40. Klemm, W., and Westerlinning, H., *Z. anorg. Chem.*, **245**, 365–80 (1941).

41. Krause, H. H., and Johnson, O. H., *Anal. Chem.*, **25**, 134 (1953).

42. Kroeger, F. A., and van den Boomgaard, J., *J. Electrochem. Soc.*, **97**, 377–82 (1950).

43. Kroll, W., *Metall u. Erz*, **23**, 682–84 (1926).

44. Lark-Horovitz, K., and Whaley, R. M., "The Preparation of Pure Germanium and Its Semiconducting Alloys," Paper presented before the Ninety-Fifth Meeting of The Electrochemical Society, Philadelphia, May, 1949.

45. Lark-Horovitz, K., and Whaley, R. M., U.S. Patent 2,514,879 (July 11, 1950).

46. Laves, F., and Wallbaum, H. J., *Z. angew. Mineral.*, **4**, 17–46 (1942).

47. Lebedeff, E. Yurii, and Wetherill, Wm. H., U.S. Patent 2,889,196 (June 2, 1959).

48. McCabe, Louis C., *Ind. Eng. Chem.*, **44**, 113a (1952).

49. Machin, J. S., and Witters, Juanita, *Ill. State Geol. Survey Circular* 216, 1956—13 pages.

50. Mellor, J. W., "A Comprehensive Treatise on Inorganic and Theoretical Chemistry," Vol. 7, New York, Longmans, Green and Co., 1930.

51. Mendeleeff, D. E., *Ann.*, Supplementband, 8, 196–206, (Heft 2) (1871).

52. "Minerals Yearbook," (U.S. Bur. Mines) Washington, D.C., Government Printing Office, 1948.

53. *Ibid.*, 1949.

54. *Mining J. (London)*, **234**, 5982, 367–8 (1950).

55. Morgan, G., and Davies, G. R., *Chemistry & Industry*, **56**, 717–21 (1937).

56. National Research Council, "International Critical Tables of Numerical Data, Physics, Chemistry and Technology," Vol. 1, p. 102, New York, McGraw-Hill Book Co., Inc., 1926.

57. Newcombe, H., et al., *Anal Chem.*, **23**, 1023 (1951).

58. Newlands, *Chem. News*, **10**, 59, (July 30, 1864).

59. Noyes, A. A., and Bray, W. C., "A System of Qualitative Analysis for the Rare Elements," New York, The Macmillan Co, 1927.

60. O'Connor, Joseph A., *Chem. Eng.*, **59**, No. 4, 158–160 (1952).

61. *Ibid.*, No. 5, 154–6, 370–6 (1952).

62. Papish, Jacob, Brewer, F. M., and Holt, Donald A., *J. Am. Chem. Soc.*, **49**, 3031–2 (1927).

63. Petar, Alice V., "Gallium, Germanium, Indium and Scandium," *U.S. Bur. Mines Inform. Circ. 6401*, 5, (Nov. 1930).

64. Pfisterer, H., and Schubert, K., *Naturwissenschaften*, **37**, 112–13 (1950).

65. Pilkington, E. S., *Australian J. of Applied Science (Melbourne)*, **8**, #2, 98–111 (June, 1957).

66. Powell, A. R., Lever, F. M., and Walpole, R. E., *J. Applied Chem.*, **1**, 541–51 (1951).

67. Rossini, F. D., Wagman, D. D., Evans, W. H., Levine, S., and Jaffe, I., "Selected Values of Chemical Thermodynamic Properties," *Natl. Bur. Standards Circ. 500*, p. 151, Washington, Government Printing Office, 1952.

68. Ruttewit, K., and Masing, G., *Z. Metallkunde*, **32**, 52–61 (1940).

69. Schleicher, John A., State Geol. Survey of Kans., Bulletin 134, part 4, U. of Kans. Publications, Lawrence, Kansas (1959).

70. Schwarz, R., and Elstner, G., *Z. anorg. Chem.*, **217**, 289–97 (1934).

71. Searcy, Alan W., *J. Am. Chem. Soc.*, **74**, 4789 (1952).

72. Shockley, Wm., "Electrons and Holes in Semiconductors," New York, D. Van Nostrand Co., Inc., 1950.

73. Stadnichenko, T., Murata, K. J., Zubovic, P., and Hufschmidt, E. L., U.S. Geol. Survey, *Circ. No. 272* (1953).

74. Stohr, H., and Klemm, W., *Z. anorg. Chem.*, **241**, 305–23 (1939).

75. Stohr, H., and Klemm, W., *Z. anorg. u. allgem. Chem.*, **244**, 205–23 (1940).

76. Straumanis, M. E., and Aka, E. Z., *J. Appl. Phys.*, **23**, 330–34 (1952).

77. Strock, L. W., *Am. Inst. Mining Met. Engrs., Tech. Publ. No. 1866* (1945). (Published in *Metals Technol.*, April, 1945).

   T., Murata, K. J., Zubovic, P., and Hufschmidt, E. L., (1953).

73. U.S. Geol. Survey, *Circ. No. 272* Stadnichenko,

57. Newcombe, H., et al, *Anal. Chem.* **23**, 1023

78. Szekely, G., *J. Electrochem. Soc.*, **98**, 318–34 (1951).

79. Torrey, H. C., and Whitmer, C. A., "Crystal Rectifiers," New York, McGraw-Hill Book Co., 1948.

80. Unpublished data from the Research Laboratories of The Eagle-Picher Company, Joplin, Missouri.

81. Vaes, J. F., *Ann. soc. géol. Belg.*, T LXXII, B19–B32 (Oct. 1948).

82. Whaley, R. M., U.S. Patent 2,447,829 (Aug. 24, 1948).

83. Willardson, R. K., *Battelle Tech. Rev.*, **6**, #8, 8 (1957).

84. Winkler, C., *Ber.*, **19**, 210–1 (Feb. 8, 1886).

12. HAFNIUM

Donald R. Martin

Libbey-Owens-Ford Glass Co.
Toledo, Ohio

and

Philip J. Pizzolato

Research Division,
New York University
New York, New York

INTRODUCTION

In recent years there has been considerable interest in the use of hafnium metal as a control rod material in nuclear reactors. This use has been made possible in a large measure by the somewhat greater availability of the metal as a by-product of the increased production of reactor-grade zirconium. The high neutron absorption cross section, good corrosion resistance, and mechanical strength of hafnium make it a valuable material for use in control elements for water-cooled reactors.

Although hafnium was not discovered until 1923, claims of evidence of the concentration of this element were made many years earlier. In 1911 Urbain, working with the most soluble fractions from an ytterbium nitrate solution, isolated a small amount of material which he claimed had distinctive properties.[116] He concluded that the material contained a new member of the rare earth group, and chose the name "celtium" for the new element.

The evidence was considered inconclusive by Bohr[18] and by Coster and von Hevesy, who were convinced that element 72 was not one of the rare earths but that it was quadrivalent and a homologue of zirconium and thorium. Coster and von Hevesy reasoned that element 72 was more likely to occur with zirconium than with the rare earths, and undertook a careful x-ray study of various zirconium-containing minerals.[64] Six lines were found which coincided with the interpolated values calculated for element 72 using Moseley's law.[29] Coster and von Hevesy announced the discovery of element 72, proposing the name "hafnium" (from *Hafnia*, Latin for Copenhagen) in honor of the city in which the discovery was made.

In the heated controversy which arose regarding priority, Urbain[117] claimed that he discovered celtium (element 72) on the basis of (1) the x-ray spectral lines observed, (2) the fact that his material exhibited different properties from those of ytterbium and lutetium, and (3) the belief that the soluble end of the rare earth elements would contain zirconium and similar elements. Coster and Hevesy[30] contended that (1) the x-ray lines reported by Urbain were too faint to be valid, (2) the wave lengths of the reported lines did not coincide with the lines established for hafnium, (3) the reported properties for celtium did not agree with those displayed by hafnium, and (4) the evidence reported for celtium could be attributed to a mixture comprised primarily of lutetium and ytterbium.

OCCURRENCE

Hafnium occurs in nature in small to moderate amounts associated with zirconium in all types of zirconium-bearing minerals. The ratio of hafnium to zirconium in the earth's crust has been estimated as about 0.02. Zircons from granitic rocks are reported as having higher Hf/Zr ratios than minerals from alkalic rocks, such as nepheline syenites. Minerals from granitic pegmatites have been found to have the highest Hf/Zr ratios, particularly such peculiar varieties of zircon as alvite, cyrtolite, and naëgite, and the rare scandium silicate, thortveitite. Only one mineral, thortveitite, is reported to contain more hafnium than zirconium.[48] No large commercial concentrations of these minerals with relatively high Hf/Zr ratios are known.

Examples of secondary zirconium minerals

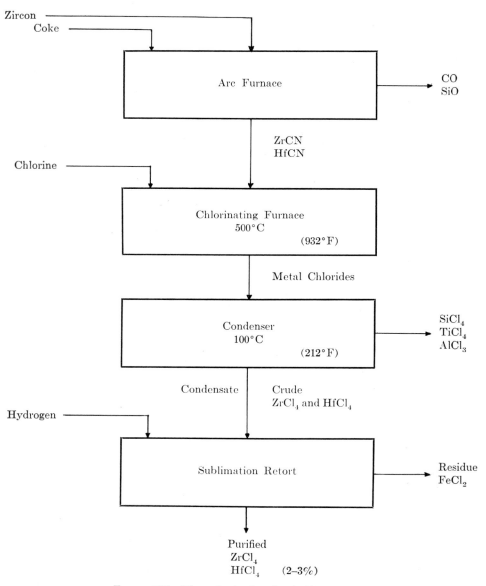

FIGURE 12.1. Flow sheet of carbonitride process.

which may contain up to 35 per cent hafnium, based on total hafnium and zirconium present, are:[62] alvite, found in Norway, Sweden, and North America; malacon, which occurs in Norway, France, and the United States; and cyrtolite, found in India, Madagascar, Sweden, Italy, Canada, and New York State.[94] Other hafnium-bearing minerals include baddeleyite, which occurs in Sweden, Italy, Ceylon, Brazil, and Montana;[94] eudialyte, found in Greenland and the Kola Peninsula of Russian Lapland;[94] zerkelite, which occurs in Brazil;[81] pegmatite, found in southern Norway;[94] and the monazite sands of Brazil and Travancore, India.[94]

It is estimated that there are 4 parts per million of hafnium in the earth's crust. This is just about the same as the content of beryllium, germanium, or uranium. It is more than the quantities of bismuth, cadmium, tantalum, silver, or mercury, but less than the amount of gadolinium, praseodymium, or samarium.[66,97]

The principal commercial sources of hafnium are the minerals zircon, $(Zr, Hf)SiO_4$, and baddeleyite, $(Zr, Hf)O_2$, which are processed primarily for their zirconium content. These minerals contain 0.5 to 2.0 per cent hafnium, referred to zirconium.

EXTRACTION

Since hafnium and zirconium are always extracted together, and since the separation of hafnium from zirconium is an important step in the production of reactor-grade zirconium, more detailed information on many of the extraction and separation processes can be found in the many excellent reviews available on zirconium,[12,83,86,105] as well as in Chapter 33 of this book.

After the zircon of the beach sands is concentrated mechanically by a combination of gravity and electrostatic methods, the zircon is broken down chemically by one of the following processes:[12]

(1) conversion of the zirconium and hafnium to carbides or carbonitrides, followed by chlorination;
(2) fusion with alkalies; or
(3) fusion with potassium fluosilicate.

The first two processes are used in this country to prepare feed stock for hafnium-zirconium

separation steps using solvent extraction. The fluosilicate fusion process has been used in Russia[103] to produce feed for the separation of hafnium from zirconium by fractional crystallization of the double fluorides (K_2MF_6).

A flow sheet for the carbonitride process[12,110] is shown in Figure 12.1.

The alkali-fusion process[13] has the advantage of not requiring the high temperatures of the electric furnace. When a caustic-zircon weight ratio of from 1.0 to 1.5 and a furnace temperature of 565°C (1050°F) are used, up to 90 per cent of the zircon can be converted to sodium zirconate and hafnate, which may then be recovered by leaching out the water-soluble sodium silicate.

SEPARATION OF HAFNIUM AND ZIRCONIUM

The main problem in the production of hafnium or reactor-grade zirconium is the separation of these metals, inasmuch as no chemical reaction is known which is exhibited by one of these elements but not by the other.[64] It is evident that any method used to open zirconium minerals will result in the removal of the two metals together. Thus any technique employed to separate the two must necessarily be fractional in character.

Of the large number of methods which have been devised for the separation of hafnium and zirconium, only three have been used on a large scale:[59]

(1) solvent extraction of the thiocyanates by hexone,[95,96]
(2) solvent extraction of the nitrates by tributyl phosphate,[31,50,72] and
(3) fractional crystallization of the double fluorides.[63]

In the first process a mixture of the thiocyanates of the metals in hydrochloric acid solution is extracted with hexone (methyl isobutyl ketone). Hafnium is preferentially extracted by the solvent, and a hafnium product containing less than 2 per cent zirconium is readily obtained. The flow sheet of a process based on this method is given in Figure 12.2.[28]

Solvent extraction of the nitrates from nitric acid solution with tri-n-butyl phosphate is a

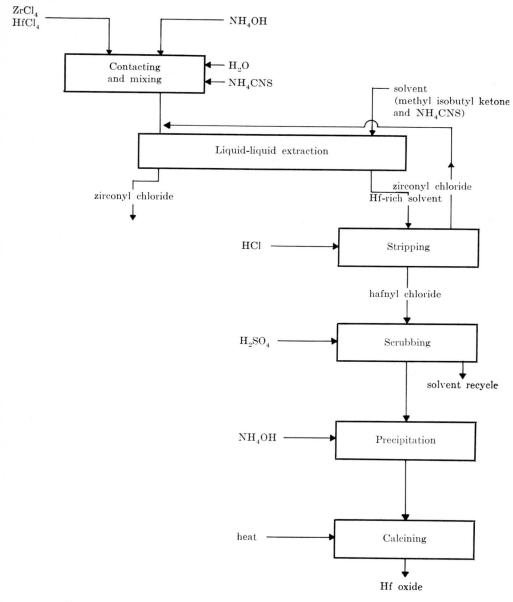

FIGURE 12.2. Schematic flow sheet for separation of hafnium and zirconium
by solvent extraction of the thiocyanates with hexone.

process of more recent origin. The tri-*n*-butyl
phosphate is usually diluted with kerosene,
dibutyl ether, or a similar solvent to lower the
density and viscosity of the organic phase.
Since zirconium rather than hafnium is preferentially extracted by the organic phase, the
production of pure hafnium is made more diffi-

cult. It has been shown, however, that this
method can be used to prepare very pure
hafnium.[50]

Although fractional crystallization of the
double fluorides was the first method used in
the laboratory to separate hafnium and zirconium, it has not been used much on a large

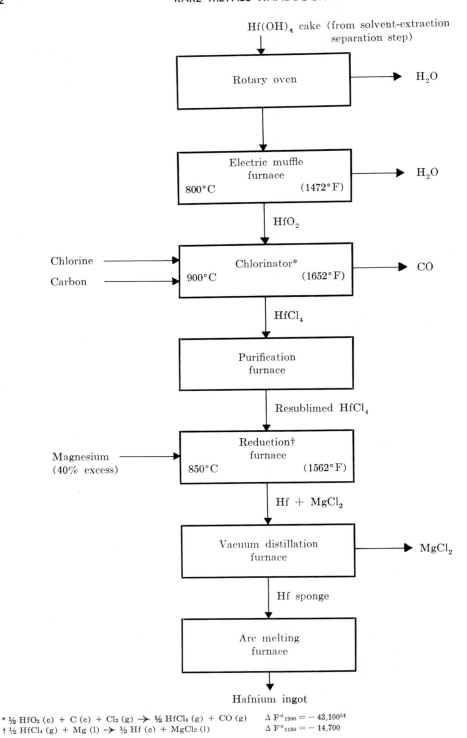

FIGURE 12.3. Kroll process for hafnium metal.

scale. This process has been used in Russia in the production of high-purity zirconium dioxide.[103]

PRODUCTION OF HAFNIUM METAL

Hafnium metal is prepared by the same methods which are used in the production of zirconium—the Kroll process, a modified Kroll process using sodium as the reducing agent, and the de Boer or hot-wire process.

Kroll Process

In the production of hafnium by the Kroll process, the techniques and equipment are essentially the same as those used in making zirconium. The modifications in the zirconium process have taken the form of alterations or changes of a partial character of equipment, procedure, and materials, occasioned by the greater sensitivity of hafnium tetrachloride to atmospheric moisture, the higher stability of hafnyl chloride, and the somewhat greater pyrophoricity of the freshly prepared sponge metal. The steps in the Kroll process for hafnium[54,105] are shown in Figure 12.3.

Sodium Process

The use of sodium to replace magnesium for the large-scale reduction of the tetrachlorides of zirconium and hafnium is a recent development. The chief advantage of the sodium-reduction method appears to be its lower cost. It is used in this country in what has been described as the industry's first semi-continuous process.[113] When sodium is used to reduce hafnium

FIGURE 12.4. Bank of cells for the production of iodide hafnium. The supervisor holds a crystal bar produced by this method. (*Courtesy Foote Mineral Co.*)

tetrachloride, the reduction step is followed by leaching of the product with water to remove salt and excess sodium from the hafnium metal sponge. Glasser and Hampel[55] have patented a process for obtaining hafnium from its chloride by use of sodium amalgam instead of sodium or magnesium metal. Several advantages for the amalgam process are claimed, among which are (1) greater mobility to the process, (2) less stringent temperature and pressure requirements, and (3) fewer impurities introduced during the reduction process.

Hot-Wire Process

The hot-wire process developed by van Arkel and de Boer[15, 17] was used to prepare the first massive specimens of hafnium. The product of the hot-wire process is a rod, or "crystal bar" of compact, ductile hafnium. For the production of hafnium by this method, the temperatures required are somewhat higher than for zirconium. The crude metal is maintained at 600°C (1112°F), and the filament at 1600°C (2912°F). The iodide process must be considered a refining method rather than a basic reduction step, since it requires hafnium metal of fairly high purity as starting material. Apparatus for the production of "iodide hafnium" is shown in Figure 12.4.

PHYSICAL, STRUCTURAL, AND MECHANICAL PROPERTIES

Metallic hafnium has a brilliant luster. It is harder and less easily worked than zirconium.[81] Like zirconium, it crystallizes in the close-packed hexagonal system,[94] and in many other physical properties it is similar to zirconium.

The disagreement in reported values of many of the properties of hafnium appears to be due to the marked dependence of these properties on the impurity content. Even for the relatively narrow range of residuals present in recent "high-purity" hafnium, this dependence is evident.[82] Since the purity of the hafnium used in the measurements is to some degree determined by the type of material, i.e., its method of preparation, metallurgical history, etc., this information is included with the measured values when it is known.

The physical, structural, and mechanical properties of hafnium are presented in Tables 12.1 to 12.16.

TABLE 12.1. PHYSICAL PROPERTIES OF HAFNIUM

Density	13.29 g/cc[25]	Arc-melted crystal bar hafnium containing less than 100 ppm Zr.
	13.09 g/cc [20°C (68°F)][1, 81] (corrected for 1.4 a/o Zr)	Arc-melted crystal bar hafnium, cold-swaged, vacuum annealed at 1040°C (1904°F), cold-swaged (11% reduction), vacuum annealed; 0.72% Zr present
	13.30 g/cc[16]	Crystal bar hafnium; Zr content unspecified
	13.36 g/cc[81]	Calculated
	13.20 g/cc[119]	Calculated

Thermal Properties

Melting point	2222 ± 30°C (4032 ± 54°F)[33]	Crystal bar hafnium (with 80 ppm Zr)
	2150°C (3902°F)[25]	Arc-melted crystal bar hafnium (<100 ppm Zr)
	1975 ± 25°C (3587 ± 45°F)[1] 2130 ± 15°C (3866 ± 27°F)[81]	As-deposited iodide crystal bar hafnium (with less than 1.0% zirconium)
Boiling Point	5400°C (9752°F)[97]	

TABLE 12.1. PHYSICAL PROPERTIES OF HAFNIUM (*cont.*)

Allotropic transition temperature
  From hexagonal close-packed to body-centered cubic.
    Values reported for the transition temperature vary from as low as 1310±10°C (2390±18°F)[41] to as high as 1950±100°C (3542±180°F),[45] which is close to the melting point of hafnium. An early estimate by Zwikker,[128] placing the transition somewhere between 1502°C (2736°F) and 1627°C (2961°F) would appear to offer some support for the value of 1660°C (3020°F) reported by Castleman and co-workers[27] on the basis of metallographic evidence.

Thermal expansion
  The linear expansion coefficient of iodide crystal bar hafnium for the range 0–1000°C (32–1832°F) has been reported as $5.9 \times 10^{-6}/°C.$[98] The linear coefficients for iodide hafnium between 20°C (68°F) and various temperatures in the range of −183°C (−297°F) and 982°C (1800°F) have been determined by Adenstedt.[1] The data are shown in Table 12.2.

Thermal conductivity	See Table 12.3
Heat capacity	See Table 12.4
Thermodynamic functions	See Table 12.5
Enthalpy	See Table 12.6
Latent heat of vaporization	72 kcal/mole[127]
Heat of formation of HfO_2	$\Delta H_{298.16} = -266,060 \ (\pm 280)$ cal/mole[71]

Electrical Properties

Electrical resistivity	See Table 12.7
Temperature coefficient of resistivity	See Table 12.7
Pressure effect on electrical resistivity	See Table 12.8
Superconducting transition temperature	See Table 12.9

Thermoelectric power
  For a hafnium-platinum couple:
    0 to 6.5±0.02 millivolts (mv) between 0 and 550°C (32 and 1022°F), with a maximum deviation of about 0.05 mv at 480°C (896°F)[1]

Hall constant
  -0.16×10^{-13} volt-cm/amp-gauss at room temperature[56]

Magnetic Properties

Magnetic susceptibility   See Table 12.10

Thermionic Properties

Electron emission[130]

T, °K*	1900	2000	2100	2200
Electron emission (ma/sq cm)	4.80	26.2	123	485

Work function   3.5 electron volts (ev)[10, 129]

* Estimated value of 0.37 for emissivity of hafnium was used to correct pyrometer readings to true temperatures.

TABLE 12.1. PHYSICAL PROPERTIES OF HAFNIUM (*cont.*)

Crystallographic Properties

Allotropic modifications	Hafnium has two allotropic forms. The alpha form is close-packed hexagonal and the beta form is body-centered cubic.

Crystal structure		Alpha Close-packed hexagonal			Beta Body-centered cubic
Lattice constants	a	3.1883 Å[81]	3.187[45]	3.197[25]	3.50Å[41] (estimated value at
	c	5.0422 Å[81]	5.041[45]	5.057[25]	room temperature)
Axial ratio	c/a	1.5814	1.582	1.582	

Atomic diameter	For coordination number 8 — 3.078 Å for alpha hafnium[90]
Free volume	20.2×10^{-27} cc[92]

Preferred orientation in hafnium

When arc-melted crystal bar hafnium containing 3 per cent zirconium is given 95 per cent reduction in thickness by cold rolling, the material shows a (0001) [1010] texture rotated 25 degree toward the transverse direction about an axis in the rolling direction. This preferred orientation is similar to the cold-rolled textures of titanium, zirconium, and beryllium.[43] The compression texture of 99.9 per cent hafnium after 78 per cent compression was found to be similar to the rolling texture.[44]

Atomic and Nuclear Properties

Atomic number	72	
Atomic weight	Chemical scale 178.6[9, 67]	In its 1955 report the International Commission on Atomic Weights recommended revision of the value for hafnium to 178.50.[124]
	Physical scale 178.543	
Atomic volume	13.37 cc/g-atom	
Covalent radius (Å)	1.442	

Isotopes

ABUNDANCE OF ISOTOPES OF HAFNIUM

Mass	Per cent abundance	Reference
170	0.004† ⎫	
171	0.004† ⎪	
172	0.005† ⎬	37
173	0.005† ⎭	
174	0.18	36, 49, 84, 85
175	0.006†	37
176	5.30 ⎫	
177	18.47 ⎪	
178	27.10 ⎬	6, 7, 49, 84, 85
179	13.84 ⎪	
180	35.11 ⎭	

Neutron absorption (thermal cross sections)	barns/atom
Absorption (for 2200 m/sec neutrons)	105 ± 5[70]
Scattering (average over Maxwellian distribution)	8 ± 2[70]

† Limit of abundance.

TABLE 12.2. LINEAR THERMAL EXPANSION BETWEEN 20°C (68°F) AND t
(mm/m or mils/inch)[1]

$t(°C)$	−183	−70	204	316	427	538	649	760	871	982
$t(°F)$	−297	−94	400	600	800	1000	1200	1400	1600	1800
Cold worked*	-1.09_0	-0.51_4	1.08_9	1.74_0	2.40_1	3.06_6	3.61_1	4.22_3	4.84_1	5.47_3‡
Annealed at 1000°C (1832°F)†	-1.14_9	-0.53_0	1.15_3	1.84_4		3.16_3		4.42_5	5.02_2	

* 3/16-in. rod cold-swaged, annealed at 1000°C (1832°F) from iodide crystal bar; cold-swaged 20%.
† 0.14-in. rod cold-swaged, annealed at 1000°C (1832°F) from iodide crystal bar; cold-swaged 20%, and then annealed at 1000°C (1832°F).
‡ Baldwin[8] states this value is about one third that of Type 347 stainless steel.

TABLE 12.3. THERMAL CONDUCTIVITY OF CRYSTAL BAR HAFNIUM CONTAINING 2 PER CENT ZIRCONIUM[31]

Temperature		Watts/(cm) (°C)	g-cal/(sec) (cm) (°C)	Btu/(sec) (in.) (°F)
°C	°F			
50*	122	0.223	0.0533	2.98×10^{-4}
100	212	0.220	0.0526	2.95×10^{-4}
200	392	0.215	0.0514	2.88×10^{-4}
300	572	0.210	0.0502	2.81×10^{-4}
400	752	0.207	0.0495	2.77×10^{-4}
500	932	0.205	0.0490	2.74×10^{-4}

* Extrapolated from 100°C (212°F).

TABLE 12.4. HEAT CAPACITY OF HAFNIUM

Temperature or temperature range			Cp [cal/(mole) (deg)]*				
°K	°C	°F	Wolcott[125] (iodide hafnium containing less than 0.1% impurities)	Friedberg[51] (crystal bar hafnium, containing about 2% zirconium)	Cristescu and Simon[32] (powdered hafnium, no analysis)	Adenstedt[1] (as-deposited crystal bar hafnium with less than 1% zirconium)	"Reactor Handbook"[98]
1.25	−271.91	−457.44	0.000813				
1.5	−271.66	−456.99	0.00100				
2.0	−271.16	−456.09	0.00147				
3.0	−270.16	−454.29	0.00255				
4.0	−269.16	−452.49	0.00400				
5.0	−268.16	−450.69	0.00600				
6.0	−267.16	−448.89	0.0102				
8.0	−265.16	−445.29	0.0223				
10.0	−263.16	−473.69	0.0480	0.0423			
12.0	−261.16	−438.09	0.0770				
14.0	−259.16	−434.49	0.130				
16.0	−257.16	−430.89	0.207				

TABLE 12.4. HEAT CAPACITY OF HAFNIUM

Temperature or temperature range			Cp [cal/(mole) (deg)]*				
°K	°C	°F	Wolcott[125] (iodide hafnium containing less than 0.1% impurities)	Friedberg[51] (crystal bar hafnium, containing about 2% zirconium)	Cristescu and Simon[32] (powdered hafnium, no analysis)	Adenstedt[1] as-deposited crystal bar hafnium with less than 1% zirconium	"Reactor Handbook"[98]
18.0	−255.16	−427.29	0.308				
20.0	−253.16	−423.69	0.434				
20.15	−253.01	−423.42	0.441				
50.0	−223.16	−369.69	—	—	3.90		
75.0	−198.16	−324.69	—	—	11.3†		
100.0	−173.16	−279.69	—	5.186	5.40		
150.0	−123.16	−189.69	—	—	5.80		
200.0	− 73.16	− 99.69	—	5.906	6.00		
250.0	− 23.16	− 9.69	—	—	6.12		
298.16	25.00	77.00	—	—	6.24		
298.16–373.16	25–100	77–212	—	—	—	6.2_7	
298–2500	25–2227	77–4041	—	—	—		$6.00 + 0.524 \times 10^{-3}T‡$

* Cal/(mole)(°C) = Btu/(lb mole)(°F).
† Burk and Darnell[23] found that hafnium containing about 2% zirconium gives a monotonically increasing Debye curve for its specific heat from 40–190°K. The anomaly at 75°K was completely absent.
‡ T in °K.

TABLE 12.5. THERMODYNAMIC FUNCTIONS FOR SOLID HAFNIUM[107]
(DERIVED FROM HEAT CAPACITY DATA OF CRISTESCU AND SIMON)*[32]

Temperature (°K)	$C_p°$ [cal/(mole) (deg)]	$H°-H_0°$ (cal/mole)	$\dfrac{H°-H_0°}{T}$	$S°$ [cal/(mole) (deg)]	$\dfrac{-F°-H_0°}{T}$
50.0	3.90	41	0.82	1.04	0.22
75.0	11.3†	238	3.17	4.14	0.97
100.0	5.40	413	4.13	6.32	2.19
150.0	5.80	694	4.63	8.59	3.96
200.0	6.00	990	4.95	10.29	5.34
250.0	6.12	1293	5.17	11.64	6.47
298.16	6.24	1590	5.33	12.74	7.41

* Wolcott[125] believes sample used by Cristescu and Simon to have been largely HfO_2.
† See footnote † in Table 12.4.

TABLE 12.6. ENTHALPY OF HAFNIUM[98]

T (°C)	127	327	527	727	1127
$H_{T°C}-H_{25°C}$ (cal/mole)	645	1895	3170	4465	7110

TABLE 12.7. ELECTRICAL RESISTIVITY AND TEMPERATURE COEFFICIENT OF RESISTIVITY OF HAFNIUM

Temperature or temperature range		Electrical resistivity ρ (microhm-cm)					
		Deem[34] (crystal bar hafnium containing 2% zirconium)	Wessel[122] (Grade 1 crystal bar hafnium consumably arc melted)	Adenstedt[1] (as-deposited crystal bar containing 0.7% zirconium)	de Boer and Fast[16]	Bridgman[21]	de Haas and Voogd[35]
°C	°F						
−269	−452	—	—	—	—	—	2.80 (4.2° K)
−196	−321	—	9.42	—	—	—	
−183	−297	—	—	—	7.86	—	
− 56	− 69	—	25.9	—			
0	32	34.1*	32.8‡	32.4	30.0	29.7	29.6
20	68	—	35.5‡	—	32.6		
50	122	40.6	39.5‡				
100	212	47.1	46.5‡				
150	302	53.6	53.6‡				
200	392	60.1	60.3‡	61.1			
250	482	66.6†	67.5‡				
300	572	—	74.8‡				
350	662	—	82.9§				
400	752	—		84.4			
600	1112	—		106.0			

°C	°F	Temperature coefficient of resistivity			
0	32	3.82×10^{-3}/°C			
0–100	32–212			4.19×10^{-3}	
0–200	32–392		4.43×10^{-3}		4.4×10^{-3}
0–800	32–1472		3.51×10^{-3}		

* Extrapolated from 29°C (84°F).
† Extrapolated from 211°C (412°F).
‡ Interpolated values.
§ Extrapolated from 348.5°C (659.3°F).

TABLE 12.8. EFFECT OF PRESSURE ON ELECTRICAL RESISTANCE OF HAFNIUM[21]

Pressure (kg/sq cm)	$-\dfrac{\Delta R}{R_0}$	
0	0.0000	Hafnium in form of annealed strip, rolled from small slivers of as-deposited crystal bar (0.7% zirconium); reduced about 80% in four passes with vacuum anneals at 1050°C (1922°F) at each pass.
10,000	0.0087	
20,000	0.0163	
30,000	0.0227	
40,000	0.0279	
50,000	0.0316	
60,000	0.0348	
70,000	0.0374	
80,000	0.0393	
90,000	0.0408	
100,000	0.0419	

TABLE 12.9. SUPERCONDUCTING TRANSITION TEMPERATURE OF HAFNIUM

Purity	State	Transition Temperature, °K		Reference
		Resistance	Magnetic	
"Very pure"	Polycrystalline bar		0.35	78
98.92% hafnium; 0.9% zirconium	(Cold-swaged and annealed polycrystalline bar)		None down to $T_s^* = 0.15$	109
	Above sample reannealed		0.37	109
98.92% hafnium; 0.9% zirconium	(Cold-swaged and annealed polycrystalline bar)	0.19–0.28	None down to $T_s^* = 0.08$	61
	Above sample reannealed	0.12–0.19	None down to $T_s^* = 0.08$	61

* Pure hafnium is probably not a superconductor down to a temperature of 0.08°K.

TABLE 12.10. MAGNETIC SUSCEPTIBILITY
OF HAFNIUM[74]

°K	$\chi \times 10^6$ emu/g
4.2	0.46
77.0	0.40
298.0	0.42
1670.0	0.57

TABLE 12.11. MECHANICAL PROPERTIES OF HAFNIUM

Modulus of elasticity
  Crystal bar hafnium (0.72% zirconium), specimen
    vacuum annealed at 1040°C (1904°F) 20.0×10^6 psi[1, 123]

Poisson's ratio   0.328 for arc-melted iodide hafnium[123]

Surface tension (at melting point)   1,460 ± 40 ergs/sq cm, Ref. 93
                                                      1,490   "   "   " , Ref. 127
                                                      1,510   "   "   " , Ref. 112

Tensile properties
  See Table 12.12 for annealed arc-melted iodide hafnium.
  See Table 12.13 for annealed and hot-rolled crystal bar hafnium.
  See Table 12.14 for extruded arc-melted iodide hafnium.

Creep properties
  See Table 12.15 for arc-melted iodide hafnium.

Compressibility   for pressures up to about 12,000 kg/sq cm[20]

At 30°C (86°F) $-\dfrac{\Delta V}{V(30°C, 1 \text{ kg/sq cm})} = 9.01 \times 10^{-7}p - 2.37 \times 10^{-12}p^2$

At 75°C (158°F) $-\dfrac{\Delta V}{V(75°C, 1 \text{ kg/sq cm})} = 8.81 \times 10^{-7}p - 2.37 \times 10^{-12}p^2$

Hardness
  See Table 12.16 for iodide hafnium and crystal bar ingot hafnium.

TABLE 12.12. TENSILE PROPERTIES OF ANNEALED ARC-MELTED IODIDE HAFNIUM*[58]
(ANNEALED AT 899°C (1650°F) FOR 20 HR IN VACUUM PRIOR TO TEST)

Temperature		Yield strength, 0.2% offset (psi)	Ultimate tensile strength (psi)	Elongation (% in 3 in.)	Reduction in area, (%)
°C	°F				
24	75	22,400	59,400	35	38
149	300	17,500	46,100	43	48
260	500	12,100	37,700	51	50
371	700	10,100	29,700	56	62
482	900	9,500	26,100	63	78
593	1100	9,700	20,500	56	65

Above data were established on specimens tested in air. This resulted in some gaseous contamination at the higher test temperatures, e.g., the 593°C (1100°F) specimen oxidized to the extent of being coated with a thin film of white powder after test.

* Hafnium contained 2.85% zirconium.

TABLE 12.13. TENSILE PROPERTIES OF ANNEALED (788°C, 1450°F)
AND OF HOT-ROLLED CRYSTAL BAR HAFNIUM STRIP[113]

	Yield strength (psi)	Tensile strength (psi)	Elongation (% in 2 in.)	Rockwell hardness
Hafnium annealed at 788°C (1450°F) for 90 min, then air-cooled	32,750	57,750	31	95B
Hot-rolled hafnium strip	63,000	79,500	15	100B

TABLE 12.14. SHORT-TIME TENSILE PROPERTIES OF EXTRUDED ARC-MELTED IODIDE HAFNIUM[8]
(⅝-IN. BARS EXTRUDED FROM 2⅜-IN. BILLET)

Temperature		Yield strength, 0.2% offset (psi)	Tensile strength (psi)	Elongation (%)	Reduction of area (%)
°C	°F				
21	70	32,600–53,000	93,000–104,200	20–27	66–68
816	1500	16,300–17,400	20,000– 21,400	43–62	88–90

At room temperature and 816°C (1500°F) short-time tensile strength is similar to that of Type 347 stainless steel; 10,000-hr stress rupture strength at 649°C (1200°F) is about one-third that of Type 347 stainless steel.

TABLE 12.15. CREEP OF ARC-MELTED IODIDE HAFNIUM AT 399°C (750°F)[58]

Stress (psi)	Plastic strain (%)	Creep rate per hour
22,000	9.2	3.0×10^{-6}
24,000	17.9	7.2×10^{-5}
25,000	18.4	3.6×10^{-4}
27,000	22.2	8.6×10^{-3}
29,000*	—	1

* Interpolated from tensile data.

TABLE 12.16. TYPICAL HARDNESS VALUES FOR IODIDE HAFNIUM TESTED IN DIFFERENT CONDITIONS

Condition	Measured hardness value	Reference
Cold-swaged, annealed at 1000°C (1832°F); cold-swaged 20%	Rockwell A 43 / Vickers 152	1, 81
Arc-melted, annealed 20 hr at 900°C (1652°F)	Vickers 180	58
	Rockwell B 78	81
Arc-melted (<100 ppm zirconium)	Rockwell A 60	25
Consumably arc-melted ingot	Bhn/3,000-kg 171 (AVG) Bhn/ 300-kg load,	58
	10-mm ball 147–165	39
Hot-rolled strip from consumably arc-melted ingot; strip annealed at 927°C (1700°F) for ½ hr and air-cooled	Rockwell B 88 (AVG)	58
Annealed strip from consumably arc-melted ingot	Rockwell A 47–51 Bhn/300-kg, 10-mm ball 139–150	39

HOT HARDNESS OF HAFNIUM[89] (CRYSTAL BAR INGOT)

Temperature (°C)	25		500
(°F)	77		932
Bhn (10/3,000/30)	194	linear decrease with increasing temperature	80

CHEMICAL PROPERTIES

In its chemical properties hafnium very closely resembles zirconium, its lighter homologue in the IVA subgroup of the periodic system, and is somewhat similar to thorium, the heavier homologue. To varying degrees, this is the result of similarities in the sizes of the respective atoms and in the distribution of their electrons. In general, the size of atoms decreases as the atomic number increases in a given series in the periodic table. In the sixth series the rare earths are responsible for the lanthanide contraction because electrons are being added to the 4f orbitals. As a consequence of this, the size of zirconium is almost identical with that of hafnium. (See Table 12.17.)

TABLE 12.17. ATOMIC RADII (Å)[91]

Periodic group	I	II	III	IV	V	VI
Series 5	Rb	Sr	Y	Zr	Cb	Mo
	2.16	1.914	1.616	1.454	1.342	1.291
Series 6	Cs	Ba	La	Hf	Ta	W
	2.35	1.981	1.690	1.442	1.343	1.299

The valence electrons of zirconium are $4d^2 5s^2$ and those of hafnium are $5d^2 6s^2$. It is expected,

therefore, that the properties of the two elements would be quite similar.

The first and second ionization potentials of hafnium are reported to be 5.5 and 14.9 electron volts (ev), respectively.[47] From the thermionic work function and the atomic surface density, the first ionization potential has been calculated to be 7.0 ev,[102] which is in agreement with an older reported value of 7.3 ev.[46]

Finely divided hafnium is pyrophoric, and metal freshly prepared *in vacuo* is so reactive that no deoxidizers for it are known.[75]

Massive hafnium, like zirconium, is extremely stable at room temperature to reactions with the common gases, and only at temperatures of a few hundred degrees centigrade does it begin to react appreciably with water, oxygen, nitrogen, and hydrogen. Rates for the oxidation of hafnium under 1 atm of oxygen pressure in the range 350–1200°C (662–2192°F) have been represented by logarithmic, parabolic, and linear rate equations.[108] The respective activation energies calculated for the rate constants were 11.4, 36.0, and 26.1 kcal/mole.

The reaction of nitrogen with hafnium in the temperature range 876–1034°C (1609–1893°F) follows a parabolic rate law with an activation energy of 57 kcal/mole of nitrogen.[42]

The activation energy is higher and reaction rates are lower than corresponding values for zirconium.

Hafnium absorbs hydrogen at a rapid rate at 700°C (1292°F) to give the composition $HfH_{1.86}$.[121] With the thermal recycling to 500°C (932°F) in hydrogen, followed by slow cooling in hydrogen at 1 atm to room temperature, the composition $HfH_{2.10}$ is obtained.[106, 115]

The resistance of hafnium to air oxidation at elevated temperatures is fairly good and somewhat greater than that of zirconium. In still air at 750°C (1382°F) its corrosion rate is 120 mg/sq dm/hr, and at 950°C (1742°F) the rate is 385 mg/sq dm/hr.[81] The corresponding rates for zirconium are 108 and 737 mg/sq dm/hr.[81] After 2 hr in still air at 950°C (1742°F), a piece of iodide hafnium plate showed a penetration of only 0.15 mm.[81, 98]

Hafnium has good resistance to high-temperature high-pressure water up to 399°C (750°F) and 3,500 psi and to steam up to 399°C (750°F).[19, 38, 39, 100, 120] It has shown good resistance also to flowing high-temperature water up to 316°C (600°F) and 30 fps.[19, 100, 120] In its resistance to corrosion by high-temperature water, hafnium is not as sensitive as zirconium to impurities such as nitrogen. It has a high tolerance limit for nitrogen of the order of 1,000 ppm.[73] In-pile corrosion tests showed that the corrosion resistance of hafnium to high-temperature water is unaffected by radiation.[52]

Although the normal valence of hafnium is four, unstable di- and trihalides have been produced by partial reduction of the tetrahalide.[79]

In aqueous solutions hafnium is always tetravalent. In a solution of its ions, hafnium is not as reactive as aluminum but is more reactive than manganese. Evidence of this is the fact that the standard potential for hafnium is 1.57 volts for the reaction:

$$Hf + 2H_2O \leftrightarrows HfO_2 + 4H^+ + 4e^-$$

For analogous reactions, zirconium has a potential of 1.43, and thorium has a potential of 1.80 volts.

Hafnium is slightly more basic than zirconium and less basic than thorium. In general, the chemistry of hafnium is more closely related to that of zirconium than to that of thorium, probably because the atomic size of hafnium is nearer to that of zirconium. For example, hafnium and zirconium have a greater isomorphic affinity than hafnium and thorium.[26]

Table 12.18 indicates the solubility and corrosion of cold-worked hafnium in stagnant reagents.[81] Similar studies on zirconium indicate that hafnium is slightly less resistant to these

TABLE 12.18. SOLUBILITY AND CORROSION OF COLD-WORKED HAFNIUM
IN STAGNANT REAGENTS AT 35±1°C (95±1.8°F)[81]

		Solubility (mg/sq dm/day)	Penetration [in./year (IPY)]
20% sodium chloride	Salt	0.80	0.00008
50% sodium hydroxide	Alkali	1.59	0.00018
10% hydrochloric acid ⎫		3.17	0.00035
10% sulfuric acid ⎬	Dilute acid	3.17	0.00035
10% nitric acid ⎭		3.19	0.00035
37% hydrochloric acid ⎫		11.9	0.00130
96.2% sulfuric acid ⎪		Soluble	
69.7% nitric acid ⎬	Concentrated acid	1.59	0.00018
Fuming nitric acid ⎭		3.97	0.00044
Hydrochloric acid: sulfuric acid 1:1 ⎫		4.39	0.00048
Hydrochloric acid: nitric acid 1:1 ⎬	Mixed acids	1143.0	0.13
Sulfuric acid: nitric acid 1:1 ⎭		1728.0	0.19

An anodic film forms uniformly over single hafnium crystals in 70 per cent nitric acid at room temperature. The thickness of the film is dependent upon the metal crystal orientation. Both high- and low-resistance films are observed. At 0.025 ma/sq cm, the cell voltage is less than 1.5 volts, whereas at 1.5 ma/sq cm the voltage rises to 185 volts and the film is broken by sparking. In each case the anodizing produces more oxide on metal crystal planes which had shown greater oxide growth on zirconium under similar conditions.[87]

Metal orientation affects the growth of the anode film formed at 0.025 ma/sq cm and 90°C (194°F), but its effect is secondary to nucleation.[87]

reagents than is zirconium.[81] The rate of dissolution of crystal bar hafnium (99.2 per cent) in hydrofluoric acid has been found to be very high, even in acid of $1N$ strength, and, among the other acids tried, only aqua regia reacts at a comparable rate.[111] With the addition of even small amounts of ammonium fluoride, however, reaction becomes rapid in other acids, except in the case of iodic acid. The acids which show little or no attack, except when ammonium fluoride is added, are nitric, sulfuric, hydrochloric, hydrobromic, hydroiodic, perchloric, phosphoric, acetic, chloroacetic, dichloroacetic, trichloroacetic, trifluoroacetic, formic, and oxalic. Hafnium is very resistant to bases, showing no attack by boiling sodium hydroxide solution even in the presence of sodium peroxide.[111]

MELTING AND FABRICATION

Since Kroll process or sodium-reduction-process hafnium sponge, when melted to ingots, produces hard, brittle material, the sponge is usually further refined into crystal bar by the iodide process before melting and fabrication. Owing to the high cost and scarcity of the metal, special melting and fabrication techniques are utilized to provide high yields of the finished material for use in reactor control elements.[57]

Crystal bar hafnium can be melted into usable, ductile ingots, using techniques similar to those used for zirconium and titanium. The most commonly used technique involves arc melting in an inert atmosphere in a water-cooled copper crucible. The highest yields of finished product meeting reactor-grade specifications have been obtained from a double arc melting technique.[39, 57] Sound ingots, which with a minimum of conditioning can be forged into rollable slab, are obtained from consumable arc melting in vacuum as a second melt. Feed for this melt is the ingot consolidated from chopped crystal bar in a nonconsumable melt (inert atmosphere) using a tungsten-tipped water-cooled copper electrode. A more direct or single-step method for ingot production involves tack welding crystal bars into a consumable electrode, which is then attached to a copper electrode.[57]

Graphite[77] and alkaline earth zirconate[118] crucibles are used to vacuum melt hafnium and

are claimed to prevent contamination and embrittlement of the hafnium thus refined.

Methods of fabricating hafnium are essentially the same as those employed for arc-melted zirconium[86] and titanium. Before forging or rolling, the ingot, of a highly reactive metal such as hafnium, produced by consumable electrode arc melting, requires surface conditioning. This is done most economically and without serious effect on the general quality of the ingot by the nondestructive technique employing an electric arc in an inert atmosphere to fuse surface metal on the side walls of the ingot.[126]

Since hafnium does not deform as readily as zirconium, higher temperatures are required for forging and rolling hafnium. Although hafnium can be more readily handled in air during heating than can zirconium, because its oxide seems to be more protective, heating of hafnium metal during processing is preferably carried out in an inert atmosphere furnace.[39] Ingots of arc-melted iodide hafnium can be readily forged at 927°C (1700°F), and a maximum forging temperature of 1093°C (2000°F) is used. Care must be taken to insure breakup of the cast structure before reductions in excess of 10 to 15 per cent are made in the forging operation.[58] The forged slab is hot rolled in the temperature range 900–927°C (1652–1700°F), with a finishing temperature not lower than 750°C (1382°F) if recrystallization is desired.

Cold rolling of hafnium should not exceed a total reduction of 30 per cent without annealing, if serious cracking is to be avoided.[57] Greater reductions are possible, using small reduction steps with short intermediate anneal operations at 800°C (1472°F). Total cold reductions of up to 50 per cent have been made, but cracking may become serious at this point. In the processing of high-quality hafnium strip for reactor applications, the hot-rolled strip is grit blasted, pickled, and cold rolled with a maximum reduction of about 5 per cent between vacuum anneals to the finished size.[39, 58]

Several different forms of hafnium are shown in Figure 12.5.

In addition to cold rolling to sheet, hafnium can be swaged, hammered, drawn into wire or rod, or extruded into rods or other simple shapes. Suitable lubricants are required for the cold drawing of iodide hafnium wire and for the extrusion of hafnium. Swaging does not re-

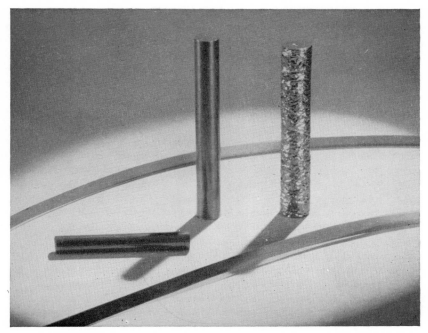

FIGURE 12.5. Hafnium crystal bar (right) is melted in an arc furnace under an argon atmosphere to obtain the crude bar (left) which can be rolled into rod or strip. (*Courtesy Foote Mineral Co.*)

quire lubrication.[8] The cold drawing of wire should be accomplished by taking individual drafts of 10 to 20 per cent with short anneals at 760°C (1400°F) after each 35 per cent total reduction.[57]

During the usual welding process, hafnium becomes brittle because of the formation of oxides, nitrides, and carbides. Welding of hafnium to hafnium and hafnium to titanium, zirconium, and zirconium alloys (Zircaloy-2) has been accomplished by an inert-gas-shielded tungsten-arc process.[53,57,65,114] However, this is not entirely satisfactory. Prolonged contact with the electrode will result in tungsten contamination.[114] It is necessary to use a special welding chamber with an inert atmosphere of helium or argon, since the standard heli-arc equipment does not produce ductile welds. Welding under a vacuum requires about 60 per cent more current, so the welding chamber is filled to atmospheric pressure with an inert gas.

The machinability of iodide hafnium is in general similar to that of iodide zirconum, and high-speed tools are satisfactory.[58]

Annealing to relieve stresses produced by cold working is usually carried out between 700–800°C (1292–1472°F), the range in which recrystallization occurs.[81] Although larger strip can be annealed in air without undue contamination, hafnium strip less than 0.05 in. thick should be annealed in vacuum or in an inert gas atmosphere.[57]

METALLOGRAPHY

Metallographic samples of iodide hafnium may be satisfactorily prepared by the use of the same procedures and etchants which have been found suitable for zirconium.

Specimens prepared by the chemical polishing technique[24] are abraded through a No. 3-0 emery or a No. 600 silicon carbide wax lap finish and subsequently dipped in, or swabbed with, the polishing solution. The recommended polishing solutions consist of concentrated nitric acid and 48 per cent hydrofluoric acid with glycerol, water, or 30 per cent hydrogen peroxide.

Hafnium specimens may be prepared also by the acetoperchloric acid electropolishing technique described for zirconium and titanium.[101] Either of the slightly different solutions recommended for the latter is suitable for hafnium. The precautions to be observed in cutting and preparing hafnium samples are similar to those outlined for zirconium and titanium.

APPLICATIONS

Hafnium has had few commercial uses because of its limited supply and high price, which have been due to the difficulty in separating it from zirconium. In recent years, however, this metal has become somewhat more readily available as a by-product of reactor-grade zirconium, and interest has developed in its potential usefulness as a control material in water-cooled nuclear reactors. In addition to having an adequate absorption cross section for thermal neutrons, hafnium has excellent mechanical properties and is extremely corrosion resistant. It is possible to use crystal bar hafnium without cladding for homogeneous control rods. One of the most important criteria for selecting control materials is resistance to radiation damage. Hafnium is regarded as a fully proved, long-life, high-burnup control material from a radiation-damage standpoint. Hafnium control rods were successfully used for a full core life in the reactor of the submarine *Nautilus*.[14, 40] Control rods of this material have also been used in the Experimental Boiling Water Reactor,[22] and in the Shippingport Reactor.

Hafnium has been used as a filament in incandescent lights, as a cathode in x-ray tubes, and as an electrode (alloyed with tungsten or molybdenum) in high-pressure discharge tubes.[3, 5, 68] Powdered hafnium has been used with barium or strontium oxide in cathodes for high-vacuum discharge tubes.[88] Hafnium-titanium alloys which are free from oxygen, nitrogen, carbon, and silicon may be used as getters in evacuated or gas-filled devices such as lamps, radio tubes, and television tubes.[76] Hafnium has been used also in rectifiers.[68]

Alloys of hafnium with manganese, chromium, iron, cobalt, nickel, copper, and silver have been prepared.[2, 11] An alloy containing 0.5 part of hafnium with about 80 parts of nickel and 20 parts of chromium is used for electrical resistance heating elements.[60] In the reduction of tungsten oxide, 0.1 to 3 per cent of hafnium nitrate may be added to control grain growth and offsetting.[5, 68]

Hafnium has been used to make special glasses.[5] A corrosion-resistant hafnium film may be produced on base metals by decomposing hafnium halides at 800–1800°C (1472–3272°F).[4] Hafnium has been electrodeposited from fused alkali fluorohafnate baths on base metals such as iron and copper.[69, 104]

Hafnium has recently become available commercially and may be more widely used in the future for control rods in nuclear reactors.

The current price of crystal bar hafnium is about $65/kg ($30/lb), or about five times that of high-grade low-hafnium zirconium sponge.[80] In sheet form it is quoted at $40/lb. About 23 tons of hafnium were produced in 1958, and in 1960 the annual production rate was about 35 tons.

The amount of hafnium produced and its cost are closely related to the demand for and the production of reactor-grade (hafnium-free) zirconium, since the most economical source of hafnium is the hafnium separated in the preparation of such zirconium. Zirconium destined for nonreactor applications, such as chemical equipment, does not have to be freed of its hafnium content. If the demand for hafnium exceeds the amount separated in the production of reactor-grade zirconium, however, additional quantities could be produced by increasing the amount of materials put through the zirconium-hafnium separation process. This would correspondingly increase the production of hafnium-free zirconium.

References

1. Adenstedt, H. K., *Trans. Am. Soc. Metals,* **44**, 949 (1952).
2. Alloys Limited, French Patent 835,468 (Dec. 22, 1938).
3. Anderson, W. T., Jr. (to Hanovia Chemical and Mfg. Co.), U.S. Patent 2,477,279 (July 26, 1949).
4. Anonymous, *Metalloberfläche,* **6A**, 109 (1952).
5. Arend, A. G., *Chem. Prod.,* 11, 30 (1948).
6. Aston, F. W., *Nature,* 133, 684 (1934).
7. Aston, F. W., *Proc. Roy. Soc. (London),* **A149**, 396 (1935).
8. Baldwin, E. E., *U.S. Atomic Energy Comm., Rept. No. KAPL-M-EEB-7* (1954).
9. Baxter, G. P., Guichard, M., and Whytlaw-Gray, R., *J. Am. Chem. Soc.,* 69, 731 (1947).
10. Becker, J. G., *Rev. Mod. Phys.,* 7, 95 (1935).
11. Belozerskii, N. A., Freidlina, B. A., and Rez-

vaya, K. I., U.S.S.R. Patent 54,976 (May 31, 1959).

12. Benedict, M., and Pigford, T. H., "Nuclear Chemical Engineering," p. 165, New York, McGraw-Hill Book Company, Inc., 1957.

13. Beyer, G. H., Spink, D. R., West, J. B., and Wilhelm, H. A., *Chem. Eng. Progr., Symposium* **Ser. No. 50**, (12), 67 (1954).

14. Blair, C., "The Atomic Submarine and Admiral Rickover," New York, Henry Holt and Company, Inc., 1954.

15. Boer, J. H. de, and van Arkel, A. E., *Z. anorg. u. allgem. Chem.,* **153**, 1 (1926).

16. Boer, J. H. de, and Fast, J. D., *Z. anorg u. allgem. Chem.,* **187**, 177 (1930).

17. Boer, J. H. de, and Fast, J. D., *ibid.,* p. 193.

18. Bohr, N., "Theory of Spectra and Atomic Constitution," 2nd Ed., p. 114, London, Cambridge University Press, 1922.

19. Breden, C. R., *Reactor Engineering Division Quarterly Report—Sec. I, Argonne National Laboratory, ANL-5571,* p. 119 (July, 1956).

20. Bridgman, P. W., *Proc. Am. Acad. Arts Sci.,* **63**, 347 (1928).

21. Bridgman, P. W., *ibid.,* **82**, 83 (1953).

22. Bullinger, C. F., *Reactor Engineering Division Quarterly Report—Sec. I, Argonne National Laboratory, ANL-5571,* p. 32 (July, 1956).

23. Burke, D., and Darnell, F., *Phys. Rev.,* **86**, 628 (1952).

24. Cain, F. M., Jr., "Zirconium and Zirconium Alloys," p. 176, a symposium, Cleveland, American Society for Metals, 1953.

25. Carlson, O. N., Schmidt, F. A., and Wilhelm, H. A., *J. Electrochem. Soc.,* **104**, 51 (1957).

26. Carobbi, G., *Atti e mem. accad sci. lettere ed arti Modena,* **7**, 3 (1947).

27. Castleman, L. S., McGeary, R. K., Shapiro, Z. M., Simcoe, C. R., and Thomas, D. E., *Westinghouse Atomic Power Division Report No. WAPD-RM-92* (October, 1951).

28. Coffer, L. W., *Chem. Eng.,* **65**, 107 (1958).

29. Coster, D., and von Hevesy, G., *Nature,* **111**, 79 (1923).

30. Coster, D., and von Hevesy, G., *ibid.,* p. 252.

31. Cox, R. P., Peterson, H. C., and Beyer, G. H., *Ind. Eng. Chem.,* **50**, 141 (1958).

32. Cristescu, S., and Simon, F., *Z. physik. Chem.,* **B25**, 273 (1934).

33. Deardoff, D. K., and Hayes, E. T., *J. Metals,* **8**; *Trans. AIME,* **206**, 509 (1956).

34. Deem, H. W., *U.S. Atomic Energy Comm., Rept. No. BMI-853* (1953).

35. de Haas, W. J., and Voogd, J., *Proc. Koninkl. Ned. Akad. Wetenschap.,* **32**, 707 (1929).

36. Dempster, A. J., *Phys. Rev.,* **55**, 794 (1939).

37. Duckworth, H. E., Woodcock, R. F., Stanford,

G. S., Coutu, A., and Stearns, R. L., *Phys. Rev.,* **85**, 929 (1952).

38. Dunning, D. N., General Electric Co., *Knolls Atomic Power Lab., Quarterly Reactor Technology Report No. 2, KAPL-1803,* p. 48 (August, 1957).

39. Dunning, D. N., *U.S. Atomic Energy Comm., Rept. No. KAPL-M-DND-2* (1957).

40. Dunning, D. N., and Ray, W. E., *Nucleonics,* **16**, 88 (1958).

41. Duwez, P., *J. Appl. Phys.,* **22**, 1174 (1951).

42. Edwards, R. K., and Malloy, G. T., *U.S. Atomic Energy Comm., File No. NP-6212* (December, 1956).

43. Eppelsheimer, D. S., and Gould, D. S., *J. Inst. Metals,* **85**, 158 (1956).

44. Eppelsheimer, D. S., and Gould, D. S., *Nature,* **177**, 241 (1956).

45. Fast, J. D., *J. Appl. Phys.,* **23**, 350 (1952).

46. Finkelnburg, W., *Z. Naturforsch.,* **2a**, 16 (1947).

47. Finkelnburg, W., and Humbach, W., *Naturwiss.,* **42**, 35 (1955).

48. Fleischer, M., *Geol. Survey Bull.* **1021-A**, Washington, D.C., Government Printing Office, 1955.

49. Flugge, S., and Mattauch, J., *Ber.,* **76A**, 1 (1943).

50. Foos, R. A., and Wilhelm, H. A., *U.S. Atomic Energy Comm., Rept. No. ISC-693* (1954).

51. Friedberg, S. A., *U.S. Atomic Energy Comm., File No. NP-5668* (1954).

52. Galonian, G. E., Callahan, E. J., and Koenig, R. F., *U.S. Atomic Energy Comm., Rept. No. KAPL-M-GEG-4* (November, 1955).

53. Gerken, J. M., and Toftegaard, S. A., *U.S. Atomic Energy Comm., Rept. No. KAPL-M-JMG-6* (1956).

54. Gilbert, H. L., and Barr, M. M., *J. Electrochem. Soc.,* **102**, 243 (1955).

55. Glasser, J., and Hampel, C. A. (to Kennecott Copper Corp.) U.S. Patent 2,703,752 (Mar. 8, 1955).

56. Goldman, J. E., *U.S. Atomic Energy Comm., Rept. No. NYO-7257* (1956).

57. Goodwin, J. G., and Hurford, W. J., *J. Metals,* **7**, 1162 (1955).

58. Goodwin, J. G., and Hurford, W. J., *U.S. Atomic Energy Comm., Rept. No. WAPD-109* (1954).

59. Googin, J. M., in "Process Chemistry," Bruce, F. R., Fletcher, J. M., and Hyman, H. H. (Eds.), Progress in Nuclear Energy, Ser. III, Vol. 2, p. 194, New York, Pergamon Press, Inc., 1958.

60. Griffiths, W. T., and Pfeil, L. B., British Patent 459,848 (Jan. 11, 1937).

61. Hein, R. A., *Phys. Rev.,* **102**, 1511 (1956).

62. Hevesy, G. von, *Chem. & Ind. (London)*, **42**, 929 (1923).
63. Hevesy, G. von, *Chem. Rev.*, **2**, (1926).
64. Hevesy, G. von, *Current Sci.*, **5**, 236 (1936).
65. Hoge, H. R., *U.S. Atomic Energy Comm., Rept. No. WAPD-MDM-5* (1954).
66. Holmes, H. P., Barr, M. M., and Gilbert, H. L., *U.S. Bur. Mines, Rept. Invest.*, **No. 5169** (1955).
67. Honigschmid, O., and Zintl, E., *Ber.*, **58**, 453 (1925).
68. Hopkins, B S., "Chapters in the Chemistry of the Less Familiar Elements," Vol. 2, Chap. 13, Champaign, Ill., Stipes Publishing Co., 1939.
69. Horizon Titanium Corp., U.S.A., British Patent 775,585 (May 29, 1957).
70. Hughes, D. J., and Schwartz, R. B., "Neutron Cross Sections," BNL-325, 2nd Ed., Washington, D.C., Government Printing Office, July 1, 1958.
71. Humphrey, G. L., *J. Am. Chem. Soc.*, **75**, 2806 (1953).
72. Hure, J., and Saint-James, R., *Proc. Intern. Conf. Peaceful Uses Atomic Energy, Geneva*, **8**, 551 (1956).
73. Kato, H., Beall, R. A., Holmes, H. P., and Ware, G. C., *U.S. Bur. Mines, Rept. No. USBM-U-210* (October, 1956).
74. Kriessman, C. J., and McGuire, T. R., *Phys. Rev.*, **98**, 936 (1955).
75. Kroll, W. J., *Mining and Met.*, **27**, 262 (1946).
76. Kroll, W. J., U.S. Patent 2,522,679 (Sept. 19, 1950).
77. Kroll, W. J., U.S. Patent 2,548,897 (Apr. 17, 1951).
78. Kurti, N., and Simon, F., *Proc. Roy. Soc. (London)*, **A151**, 610 (1935).
79. Larsen, E. M., and Leddy, J. J., *U.S. Atomic Energy Comm., File No. NP-5743* (August, 1955).
80. Link, L. E., and Zinn, W. H., in "Nuclear Engineering Handbook," H. Etherington (Ed.), Sec. 12–2, p. 107, New York, McGraw-Hill Book Company, Inc., 1958.
81. Litton, F. B., *J. Electrochem. Soc.*, **98**, 488 (1951).
82. Love, B., *Wright Field Air Force Development Center Report No. WADC-TR-57-666* (Pt. 1), 1958.
83. Lustman, B., and Kerze, F., Jr., "The Metallurgy of Zirconium," National Nuclear Energy Series, Div. VII, Vol. 4, New York, McGraw-Hill Book Company, Inc., 1955.
84. Mattauch, J., and Ewald, H., *Naturwiss.*, **31**, 487 (1943).
85. Mattauch, J., and Ewald, H., *Z. physik.*, **122**, 314 (1944).
86. Miller, G. L., "Zirconium," 2nd Ed., p. 453, New York, Academic Press, Inc., 1957.
87. Misch, R. D., and Fisher, E. S., *J. Electrochem. Soc.*, **103**, 153 (1956).
88. Netherlands Patent 69,486 (to N. V. Phillips, Gloeilampenfabriken) (Feb. 15, 1952).
89. Northwest Electrodevelopment Laboratory, *U.S. Bur. Mines, Report No. BM-11-90* (July, 1954).
90. Oliver, D. S. (Culcheth Labs.), *U.K. Atomic Energy Authority Industrial Group, No. FRDC/P-33* (May, 1953).
91. Pauling, L., *J. Am. Chem. Soc.*, **69**, 542 (1947).
92. Penner, S. S., *J. Chem. Phys.*, **16**, 745 (1948).
93. Peterson, A. W., Kedesdy, H., Keck, P. H., and Schwarz, E., *J. Appl. Phys.*, **29**, 213 (1958).
94. Radecker, W., *Chem. Tech. (Berlin)*, **2**, 131 (1950).
95. Ramsay, J. W., and Whitson, W. K., Jr., *U.S. Atomic Energy Comm., Rept. No.* **Y-817** (1951).
96. Ramsay, J. W., and Whitson, W. K., Jr., *U.S. Atomic Energy Comm., Rept. No.* **Y-824** (1951).
97. Rankama, K., Sahama, K., and Sahama, T. G., "Geochemistry," p. 39, Chicago, University of Chicago Press, 1950.
98. "Reactor Handbook," 1st Ed., Vol. 3, Washington, D.C., Office of Technical Services, U.S. Atomic Energy Commission, 1953.
99. Richardson, D., "Spectroscopy in Science and Industry. Proceedings of the Fifth Summer Conference on Spectroscopy and Its Applications," pp. 65–70, New York, John Wiley & Sons, Inc., 1938.
100. Roebuck, A. H., Breden, C. R., and Greenberg, S., *Corrosion*, **13**, 87 (1957).
101. Roth, H. P., *Metal Progr.*, **63**, 84 (1953).
102. Sachtler, W. M. H., *Z. Elektrochem.*, **59**, 119 (1955).
103. Sajin, N. P., and Pepelyaeva, E. A., *Proc. Intern. Conf. Peaceful Uses Atomic Energy, Geneva*, **8**, 559 (1956).
104. Schlechten, A. W., Straumanis, M. E., and Gill, C. B., *J. Electrochem. Soc.*, **102**, 81 (1955).
105. Shelton, S. M., Dilling, E. D., and McClain, J. H., *Proc. Intern. Conf. Peaceful Uses Atomic Energy, Geneva*, **8**, 505 (1956).
106. Sidhu, S. S., *Acta Cryst.*, **7**, 447 (1954).
107. Skinner, G. B., Beckett, C. W., and Johnson, H. L., *U.S. Armed Services Tech. Inf. Agency Document, No. ATI-81814* (1950).
108. Smeltzer, W. W., and Simnad, M. T., *Acta Met.*, **5**, 328 (1957).
109. Smith, T. S., and Daunt, J. G., *Phys. Rev.*, **88**, 1172 (1952).

110. Stephens, W. W., and Morrison, C. Q., *J. Metals,* **8,** 334 (1956).

111. Straumanis, M. E., and Ballass, J. I., *Z. anorg. u. allgem. Chem.,* **278,** 33 (1955).

112. Taylor, J. W., *Metallurgia,* **50,** 161 (1954).

113. "Technical and Application Data on Zirconium and Hafnium," Niles, Ohio, Mallory-Sharon Metals Corporation, 1958.

114. Theilacker, J. S., Baugh, E. D., Kasberg, A. H., and Stermon, R. B., *J. Metals,* **8,** 646 (1956).

115. Trzeciak, M. J., Dilthey, D. F., and Mallett, M. W., *U.S. Atomic Energy Comm., Rept. No. BMI-1112* (1956).

116. Urbain, G., *Compt. rend.,* **152,** 141 (1911).

117. Urbain, G., *Nature,* **111,** 218 (1923).

118. Urban, Stephan F. (to National Lead Co.), U.S. Patent 2,684,297 (July 20, 1954).

119. van Arkel, A. E., *Z. physik. Chem.,* **130,** 100 (1927).

120. Vaughan, L. H., and Ferguson, K. M., *Bab-cock and Wilcox Co. Rept., No. BW-5250* (1957).

121. Waldo, C. T., and Anderson, W. K., *U.S. Atomic Energy Comm., Rept. No. KAPL-M-CTW-2* (January, 1957).

122. Wessel, E. T., *U.S. Atomic Energy Comm., Rept. No. AECU-3693* (1956).

123. Westinghouse Electric Corp., *Atomic Power Division, Rept. No. WAPD-MRP-42* (1954).

124. Wichers, E., *J. Am. Chem. Soc.,* **78,** 3235 (1956).

125. Wolcott, N. M., *Phil. Mag.,* **2,** 1246 (1957).

126. Wood, F. W., Borg, J. O., and Beall, R. A., *U.S. Bur. Mines, Rept. Invest. No.* **5149** (1955).

127. Zadumkin, S. N., *Doklady Akad. Nauk S.S.S.R.,* **92,** 115 (1953).

128. Zwikker, C., *Physica,* **6,** 361 (1926).

129. Zwikker, C., *Physik. Z.,* **30,** 578 (1929).

130. Zwikker, C., *Verslag. Akad. Wetenschapen Amsterdam,* **35,** 336 (1926), *Proc. Acad. Sci. Amsterdam,* **29,** 792 (1926).

13. INDIUM

J. R. MILLS, R. A. KING, and C. E. T. WHITE

Research and Development Division
The Consolidated Mining and Smelting Company
of Canada Limited
Trail, British Columbia

INTRODUCTION

Indium was discovered in 1863 by F. Reich and T. Richter, who were examining samples of zinc blende from Freiberg for thallium. Spectrographic examination of crude zinc chloride liquor showed a prominent indigo blue line which had never been observed before. These investigators succeeded in separating a new metallic element which they called *indium,* from the characteristic indigo blue lines of its spectrum.

Indium (atomic number 49) is in Subgroup IIIB (aluminum group) of the periodic table. Other members of this group are boron, aluminum, gallium, and thallium.

Early investigations of the properties and uses of indium were handicapped because of the scarcity of the metal, only one gram constituting the world's available supply in 1924. Although consumption has increased appreciably in recent years, the present supply of indium is in excess of consumption, and production can be readily increased when additional demand develops.

Tribute is due to Dr. William S. Murray and the Indium Corporation of America for their part in promoting indium as a commercial metal. Under Dr. Murray, whose work on indium started 10 years prior to the formation of the Corporation in 1934, this organization pioneered the early investigations into properties and industrial uses of indium.

OCCURRENCE

Indium does not occur in the native state. The element is widely distributed, but in minute quantities. The earth's crust has been estimated to contain 0.1 ppm of indium,[68] about the same abundance as silver.

Indium is found in minute amounts in many minerals, most of which contain less than 0.1 per cent,[35] though pegmatite dikes of western Utah are reported to contain up to 2.8 per cent indium.[60] It has been reported in many ores including the following: sphalerite, marmatite, franklinite, smithsonite, calamine, alunite, rhodonite, phlogopite, manganotantalite, siderite, pyrrhotite, cassiterite, wolframite, hübnerite, and samarskite. In common with many of the rarer metals, indium becomes concentrated in various by-products during recovery of other metals, principally lead and zinc. Indium is most frequently associated with zinc and, as a result, is recovered commercially from zinc residues and smelter slags. At the present time these by-products constitute the only commercial sources of indium.

Indium has been reported in many countries —Russia, Finland, Sweden, Japan, Germany, Italy, Peru, Canada, and the United States.

PRODUCTION AND ECONOMIC STATISTICS

Statistical information on indium is very limited. The available information on production and shipments of indium is given in Table 13.1.

TABLE 13.1. PRODUCTION AND SHIPMENTS OF INDIUM
(a) UNITED STATES[4]
PRODUCER'S SHIPMENTS (TROY OUNCES)*

1941	7,000†	1947	13,908
1942	23,000†	1948	12,202
1943	59,568	1949	54,784
1944	82,427	1950	125,777
1945	57,434	1951	153,191
1946	9,667	1952	n.a.

* Indium content of metal and compounds.
† Estimated.
n.a. Not available after 1951.

In recent years only two United States firms have produced indium: the American Smelting and Refining Co., Perth Amboy, N.J. (indium metal and compounds) and the Anaconda Co., Great Falls, Mont. (indium metal). In addition to these primary producers, the Indium Corporation of America, Utica, N.Y., has sold indium as ingot, powder, sheet, wire, various fabricated forms, alloys, chemicals, and plating solutions; and Cerro de Pasco Corporation, New York, N.Y., has sold indium alloys.

In earlier years production was also reported by:

American Metal Company
American Steel and Wire Co. (Donora Zinc Works)
American Zinc, Lead & Smelting Company
Eagle-Picher Co.
Grasselli Chemical Company
Indium Corporation of America
National Zinc Company
Sherwin Williams Company

The United States is the largest consumer of indium, and in 1957, the peak year, almost 20 tons of domestic and imported indium were used. Data on United States production and shipments of indium have not been published since 1951, but the Anaconda Company announced production of 87,600 troy oz. of indium in 1956. The indium content of measured and indicated zinc reserves in the United States is roughly estimated to be 320 short tons.[20a]

(b) PERU,[4, 5]

Production (troy ounces)		Exports (troy ounces)
1945	1,333	1,332
1946	4,080	5,005
1947	18,056	9,804
1948	40,348	14,971
1949	—	20,751

Cerro de Pasco Corp., Oroya, was the only producer of indium in Peru. This company has not produced indium commercially since 1951, and does not plan to resume production.[7] Data for 1950 and 1951 are not available.

(c) CANADA,[22] PRODUCTION (TROY OUNCES)

1942	437	1953	6,752
1949	689	1954	477
1950	4,952	1955	104,774
1951	582	1956	363,192
1952	404	1957	384,359
1958 n.a.			

n.a.—not available after 1957.

The Consolidated Mining and Smelting Company of Canada, Limited, Trail, B.C. (Cominco), is the only Canadian producer of indium. Cominco offers indium metal and alloys in ingot and a variety of fabricated forms, and indium salts and solutions. Potential output of this company is some 35 tons of indium annually.

Production of indium has also been reported in the following countries:

Belgium (Societe Belgochimie)
Germany (Uterharzer Berg —
und Huttenwerke, Oker);
Duisberger Kupferhütte,
Duisberger
Japan (Furukowa Mining Co.);
Mitsui Mining & Smelting Co.
U.S.S.R. (Konstantinowka)

United States Price of Indium[3, 4]

In 1924 the one gram of indium metal (98 per cent indium), referred to earlier in this chapter as the only indium available, sold for $10. Indium was first quoted by Engineering and Mining Journal's *Metal and Mineral Markets*, in September, 1930, at a price of $15/g (equivalent to $466.56/troy oz) for 99 per cent indium. The quoted price was reduced gradually as the demand developed and additional supplies became available, reaching $2.25/troy oz for 99.9 per cent grade in December, 1945. The current quotation (Nov. 1960) for standard grade indium (99.97 per cent) is $1.35 to $2.25 per troy oz., depending on quantities. The principal producers are now selling large lots of standard-grade indium (99.97 per cent) on a contract basis. High purity grades of indium (99.999 and 99.9999 per cent) are available at higher prices.

DERIVATION

As mentioned previously, indium is usually recovered from metallurgical or chemical residues. Relatively little information has been published on commercial processes, but additional knowledge can be obtained from patent literature. Six processes will be outlined to illustrate various approaches to the problem of recovering indium.

Anaconda Co. Process

The Anaconda Co. has patented a process for recovering indium from zinc calcine or zinc oxide fume produced in the treatment of lead blast furnace slag.[18] Zinc calcine or oxide fume is leached with very dilute sulfuric acid, dissolving the bulk of the zinc and leaving the indium in the insoluble residue. This indium-bearing residue is leached with stronger acid (20 to 25 g/liter H_2SO_4) which dissolves the indium. Zinc oxide, sodium sulfite, or sodium bisulfite is added to the clarified solution from this second leach, and the indium is precipitated. This precipitate is purified by leaching with strong sodium hydroxide solution, washing with water and then with dilute sulfuric acid to remove zinc. The purified precipitate is dissolved in sulfuric acid, and heavy metals are removed with hydrogen sulfide. The indium is recovered as a sponge by adding zinc. The sponge may be melted and cast into bars of crude metal. Alternatively, it may be purified further by dissolving in hydrochloric acid, and purifying the resultant solution. Barium chloride is added to remove sulfate, and hydrogen sulfide to remove residual heavy metals. Following filtration, the indium is recovered electrolytically. The cathode metal is melted under a cover of caustic and cast into bars or other suitable shapes.

American Smelting and Refining Co. Processes

The American Smelting and Refining Co. has patented two processes for the recovery of indium. In the earlier patent[81] indium is recovered from residues by leaching with acid and precipitating indium as a phosphate from slightly acid solution. Indium phosphate is converted to the hydroxide with strong caustic, and the hydroxide is heated to form the oxide which is reduced with hydrogen to indium metal. This metal may be refined further by electrolysis.

Another patent assigned to American Smelting and Refining[43] describes a process for recovering indium from crude zinc-lead metal. The molten metal is treated with lead chloride and sodium chloride, forming a slag which contains the indium as chloride. This chloride slag is leached with dilute sulfuric acid, and the indium is precipitated with zinc dust. The indium-zinc sponge is melted, and the zinc is removed with chlorine. The crude indium metal is then melted, cast into anodes, and refined electrolytically.

German Process

The process in use at present in Germany for recovering indium from Rammelsberg ores has been described by R. Kleinert.[41] The Rammelsberg ore contains 0.0008 to 0.0018 per cent indium. Most of the indium follows the zinc through flotation, roasting, and reduction in vertical retorts (New Jersey process). About 75 per cent of the indium in the mill feed is found in the retort zinc. In refining this crude zinc by distillation, the indium remains with the lead, which contains about 1 per cent indium. The lead is cupeled, and indium is recovered in the litharge (about 4 per cent indium). The litharge is reached with dilute sulfuric acid, and crude indium (about 95 per cent indium) is recovered by sponging with zinc slabs. This crude indium is dissolved in sulfuric acid, and impurities are removed by sponging first with strips of indium and then with slabs of a zinc alloy containing about 1.0 per cent indium and 0.3 per cent cadmium. Refined indium with a purity exceeding 99.99 per cent is recovered from the purified solution by sponging with aluminum strips, melting under caustic soda and sodium cyanide, and casting into 1,000-g ingots.

Cerro de Pasco Corporation Process

The method used to recover indium by Cerro de Pasco Corporation has been outlined by T. R. Wright.[80] Laboratory work on the extraction of indium from complex lead-tin alloys has been described by J. Coyle,[16] and experimental work on the purification process has been discussed by T. A. A. Quarm.[59] Indium enters the lead smelter circuit with concentrates, ores, dusts, and residues which contain small amounts of zinc. It reports in the crude lead bullion and is removed in the drossing procedure. The bullion is first drossed at a low temperature to remove copper and then at a higher temperature to remove tin and indium. The tin-indium dross is reduced to metal, a mixture of zinc and lead chloride is added to the molten metal, and indium is removed as the chloride in the slag. Sulfuric and hydrochloric acids are added, and the chloride slag is leached by wet grinding. After grinding, the pulp is removed, and the filtrate is purified by cementation with strips of indium. Indium is then recovered as a sponge, using zinc rods. The sponge is washed, briquetted, melted under paraffin, and cast into bars. Indium recovered by this process has a purity of 99.8 per cent,

the chief impurity being cadmium. Quarm reports that 99.999 per cent indium can be prepared by controlled electrolysis.[59]

The Consolidated Mining and Smelting Co. Process

Cominco has operated two processes for recovering indium from metallurgical residues. In 1942 indium was produced on a laboratory scale from zinc oxide fume from lead blast furnace slag fuming operations. At the present time indium is produced commercially from slag obtained in the treatment of lead blast furnace bullion dross. The latter process, which has been described in considerable detail in papers by J. R. Mills et al.[50] and B. G. Hunt et al.[36] will be outlined briefly.

The deportment of indium in the Cominco metallurgical plants is shown diagrammatically in Figure 13.1. The width of the lines in this

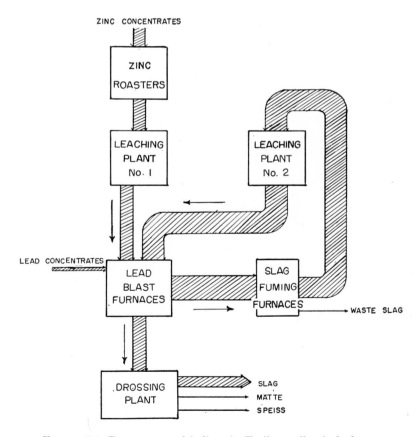

FIGURE 13.1. Deportment of indium in Trail metallurgical plants.

diagram illustrates approximately the amount of indium in the various stages of the metallurgical processes at Trail.

Indium enters the Trail plants with the zinc concentrates. In the electrolytic zinc process, indium stays in the calcine through the roasting operation, and remains in the insoluble iron residue during leaching. This residue is treated at the lead smelter for recovery of the contained lead and residual zinc values. In the lead blast furnaces the indium reports in the slag and lead bullion in roughly equal proportions. The indium content of the slag is recovered, along with the zinc and residual lead from the slag fuming furnaces. The zinc oxide from the fuming operation is treated in a separate leaching plant. The indium again remains in the residue, which is returned to the smelter along with the residue from the leaching plant treating the zinc calcine.

In Cominco's commercial process dross retreating furnace slag, which contains lead, tin, and copper as major constituents, along with 2.5 to 3.0 per cent indium, is ground, and most of the copper is removed as a flotation concentrate. The flotation tailing is dried and sintered in a rotary kiln, and the sinter is mixed with limestone and coke and reduced in an electric furnace. The electric furnace bullion is cast into anodes and electrolyzed in Betts process lead electrolyte (lead fluosilicate). Lead and tin are deposited on the cathode, and the indium remains as a slime of indium antimonide (InSb) on the anode. This slime is roasted with sulfuric acid, and the sulfated product is leached with water, dissolving the indium. The acidity of the acid leach liquor is then adjusted to pH 1.0, sodium chloride is added, and the remaining copper is removed by cementation on indium sheets. Following this, indium is recovered as a

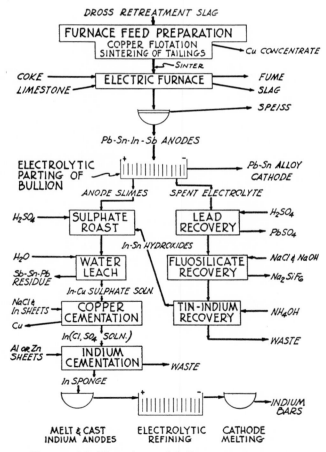

FIGURE 13.2. Flow sheet of indium recovery process.

sponge with aluminum or zinc. The sponge is washed, briquetted, melted, and cast into anodes for electrolytic refining. The purity of the anode metal is about 99.5 per cent indium, and that of the refined metal (standard grade) over 99.97 per cent indium. The accompanying flow sheet, Figure 13.2, illustrates this process.

In addition to the standard grade, Cominco produces two purer grades of indium.[40] High Purity Grade 59 (99.999 per cent indium), which is used principally in the manufacture of transistors, is made from standard-grade material by fuming and electrolyzing the fumed metal.[36] High Purity Grade 69 (99.9999 per cent indium), which is used in the production of intermetallic compounds, is made from High Purity Grade 59 indium. Typical impurity analyses of the three grades of indium produced by Cominco are shown in Table 13.2.

TABLE 13.2. "COMINCO" BRAND INDIUM TYPICAL IMPURITY ANALYSES (PARTS PER MILLION)

Grade	Cu	Pb	Tl	Cd	Sn
Standard	5	80	2	20	50
High Purity Grade 59	1	2	1	1	2
High Purity Grade 69	Each significant impurity less than 0.1 ppm				

Recovery of Indium from Plating Solutions

J. R. Dyer (Indium Corp. of America) has described a method for recovering indium from old plating solutions.[19] The solution is evaporated, and organic material is destroyed by ignition. The ignition residue is dissolved in hydrochloric acid, and silver chloride, some lead chloride, and silica are separated by filtration. The filtrate is neutralized with excess ammonium hydroxide, precipitating indium, iron, and tin as hydroxides and leaving copper, cadmium, zinc, and nickel in solution. The hydroxides are separated by filtration and dissolved in hydrochloric acid. Indium is recovered by electrolysis and purified by a second electrolysis.

PHYSICAL PROPERTIES

Indium is a silvery-white metal with a brilliant metallic luster. It is softer than lead (it can be scratched with the fingernail), malleable, ductile, and crystalline. When the pure metal is bent, it gives a high-pitched "cry" similar to tin. Indium is less volatile than zinc or cadmium, but will sublime when heated in hydrogen or in a vacuum. The molten metal will wet clean glass. General properties and constants are listed in Table 13.3.

TABLE 13.3. GENERAL PROPERTIES OF INDIUM[6, 74]

(Superscript numbers refer to references)

Atomic number	49
Atomic weight	114.82[79]
Stable isotopes	113 4.23%
	115 95.77%
Thermal neutron cross section	
Absorption (barns)	190 ± 10
Scattering (barns)	2.2 ± 0.5
Valence	Commonly 3, also 2 and 1
Crystal structure	Face-centered tetragonal
	$a_0 = 4.583$ Å, $c_0 = 4.936$ Å
Closest approach of atoms	3.24 Å
Atomic volume (cc/g-atom)	15.7
Density [g/cc at 20°C (68°F)]	7.31
Melting point (°C)	156.6[47]
(°F)	314
Boiling point (°C)	2075
(°F)	3767
Specific heat (mean) [cal/g/°C (0–100°C)]	0.058
Heat of fusion (cal/g)	6.8
Volume change during melting (%)	2.5
Heat of vaporization (cal/g at BP)	484.0

Table 13.3. General Properties of Indium[6, 74] (*cont.*)

(*Superscript numbers refer to references*)

Vapor pressure	A	12,860
Constants for the equation	B	10.71
$\log p = -\dfrac{A}{T} + B + C \log T$	C	-0.7
Applicable temperature range (°K)		430–2350
Coefficient of linear expansion $\times\,10^6$ (0–100°C)		24.8
Thermal conductivity [cal/sq cm/cm/°C/sec (0–100°C)]		0.06
Surface tension (dynes/cm)		602–0.10T
Electrical resistivity (ohm-cm)		
3.38°K		Superconducting
4.2°K		7×10^{-10} [78]
0°C (32°F)		8.4×10^{-6}
22°C (72°F)		8.8×10^{-6} [78]
156.6°C (314°F)		29.0×10^{-6}
300°C (572°F)		36.0×10^{-6} [63]
600°C (1112°F)		44.0×10^{-6} [63]
Temperature coefficient of resistivity $\times\,10^3$ (0–100°C)		4.7
Standard electrode potential (volt)		-0.34
Electrochemical equivalent (mg/coulomb)		0.39641
Magnetism		Diamagnetic

MECHANICAL PROPERTIES

The mechanical properties of indium and its binary alloys with lead, tin, cadmium, and bismuth have been investigated at Battelle Memorial Institute.[37, 38] The mechanical properties of the pure metals are listed in Table 13.4.

Indium is a highly plastic metal which can be deformed almost indefinitely under compression. Its elongation is abnormally low, because indium does not work harden. Almost all of the deformation obtained in the tensile test is localized, resulting in a high reduction in area. The figure for reduction in area given in Table 13.4 was obtained in tensile tests on sheet material, but on the standard round specimen it would be much higher. A reduction in area of 99 per cent was obtained in tests made by the United States Bureau of Standards, which reflects more truly the capacity of indium for local deformation in the tensile test.[6]

In investigating the binary alloys, it has been noted that the indium-lead alloys are the hardest and strongest over most of the range of composition, and have higher melting points than any of the others. In the indium-rich alloy region, bismuth is the most effective hardener, followed by cadmium and then lead. These effects are found in the indium solid-solution region. Tin, which has the least room-temperature solubility in indium, has the mildest strengthening and hardening effects. Indium is most effective in hardening tin. It is somewhat less effective in hardening lead, but, since the solubility of indium in lead is so much greater, the maximum hardness and strength

Table 13.4. Mechanical Properties*

	Indium	Lead	Tin	Cadmium	Bismuth
Brinell hardness	0.9	3.9	5.2	20.7	9.6
Tensile strength (psi)	380‡	2,410	1,770	10,000	
Elongation (% in 1 in.)	22	32	37	42	
Reduction in area (%)	87	74	81	76	
Compressive strength (psi)†	310	2,050	2,070	13,300	
Modulus of elasticity (psi)	1.57×10^6				

* Tests conducted on the metals as annealed 1 week at 100–130°C (212–266°F).
† True compressive stress at 10% true strain.
‡ Other values: 430 psi (99.9% indium); 388 psi (99.97+% indium).[23]

attained in the lead-indium solid solution are somewhat greater. Indium is practically insoluble in cadmium or bismuth, and it has no hardening effect on either of these metals.[37]

CHEMICAL PROPERTIES

Indium is associated with boron, aluminum, gallium, and thallium in Subgroup IIIB in the periodic table. In this subgroup the chemical properties are largely determined by the behavior of the incomplete outer electronic shell consisting of the 2 "s" electrons and 1 "p" electron. Thus principal valences of one and three may be anticipated. The increasing stability of the 2 "s" electrons in the higher atomic number atoms of this subgroup points to the characteristic valence of one for the higher atomic numbers and three for the lower atomic numbers. This is the case, as thallium occurs generally in the monovalent form whereas boron has the characteristic valence of three. Indium, being in an intermediate position, displays both valences, but the common valence is three.

The ionization potentials for the 3 valence electrons of indium are reported to be 5.76 (5 p), 18.79 (5 s), and 27.91 (5 s) volts. These values indicate that the trivalent form of indium is probably relatively nonionic or covalent in its bond forming character. This prediction is borne out by the chemical and electrochemical behavior of the element.[52]

The general level of reactivity of indium may be evaluated from the position of indium in the electromotive series of elements. The standard potential of the reaction

$$In° \rightarrow In^{+3} + 3e$$

is approximately −0.34 volt. Thus indium is slightly more noble than cadmium. However, the bonding characteristics of indium influence the apparent reactivity of the metal. The relative slowness of chemical reactions involving indium gives this element, in common with certain other metals, apparent nobility greater than would be predicted by its thermodynamic properties.

Indium dissolves slowly in cold dilute mineral acids and more readily in hot dilute or concentrated acid. Massive metal is not attacked by boiling water or alkalis. Finely divided indium (sponge or powder) forms the hydroxide on contact with water.

COMPOUNDS OF INDIUM

Like other metals, the nature of the compounds of indium is a function of valence, type of bonds formed, and the size of the atoms or ions involved in the compound. Thus indium has chemical properties similar to aluminum, iron, and tin, among the more common metals. Of these three metals, tin appears to be most closely related to indium, despite the difference in characteristic valence. Some of the more common compounds of the metal will be briefly discussed.

Indium Trisulfate

Indium trisulfate, $In_2(SO_4)_3$, may be obtained by neutralizing the hydroxide or carbonate with sulfuric acid or by dissolving the metal or oxide in warm sulfuric acid. The sulfate is a white, crystalline, deliquescent solid, readily soluble in water. In addition to the normal sulfate, either the acid or basic sulfate may be formed, depending upon the conditions of the reaction.

Indium Trichloride

Indium trichloride, $InCl_3$, is readily obtained by the direct union of the elements or by the action of hydrochloric acid on the metal. Like the trichloride of iron, aluminum, and other elements with valences above two, the molecular nature of indium trichloride is displayed by its high vapor pressure. The trichloride is a white crystalline solid, very deliquescent, and soluble in water.

Indium Trioxide

Indium trioxide, In_2O_3, may be obtained by burning the metal or, more readily, by calcining the hydroxide, nitrate, carbonate, or other salts. At comparatively low temperatures a pale-yellow amorphous oxide is formed which is converted to the crystalline form by heating at high temperatures. The amorphous form is readily soluble in acids, but the crystalline variety is relatively insoluble. The trioxide is isomorphous with hematite (Fe_2O_3) and can substitute for the latter compound in the double oxides or ferrites, such as magnetite. Indium trioxide can be readily reduced with hydrogen.

Indium Trisulfide

Indium trisulfide, In_2S_3, can be prepared by heating the metal with sulfur or by passing hydrogen sulfide into a weakly acid solution of an indium salt. Its color may vary from yellow through red to brown. The color and crystal structure of this substance appear to be related to the rate of formation which, in turn, depends on the solution from which it is precipitated by hydrogen sulfide. From a chloride solution a yellow product of small particle size or disordered structure is obtained. This is sug-gestive of rapid crystal growth. From a sulfate solution, however, the red colored salt that is formed exhibits a well-defined structure when examined by x-ray diffraction. A less rapid growth of the solid structure is suggested in this case. This behavior may be related to the eltrochemical properties of indium discussed in the following section.

Indium forms compounds with other metals such as selenium, tellurium, antimony, and arsenic, and with nonmetallic elements such as oxygen, nitrogen, hydrogen, sulfur, phosphorus, and the halogens.

Most of these interatomic compounds, including indium phosphide, arsenide, antimonide, oxide, sulfide, selenide, and telluride, are semiconductors. In recent years much research work has been done on these compounds, particularly on the phosphide, arsenide, and antimonide, and many commercial applications are under development. These applications are based on modulations in carrier density or mobility by an electrical, magnetic, or thermal field, or by photon or thermal energy.[9] The more important of these applications will be discussed on page 234.

ELECTROCHEMISTRY

An excellent review of the electrochemistry of this element has been published recently by Moeller and Hopkins.[52] The tendency of indium to form covalent bonds in its compounds ap-pears to be one of the more important properties of the element which influences its electrochemical behavior. The low conductivity of solutions of indium salts indicates their relatively nonionic character. In many electrolytes the electrode reactions of indium require moderately high activation energies. Typical of such electrolytes are the sulfate, fluoride, and perchlorate, in contrast to the chloride, bromide, and certain organic acid solutions such as the acetate and citrate in which indium exhibits reversible behavior.

The standard oxidation-reduction potential of indium is approximately -0.34 volt, and thus no great difficulty would be anticipated in the electrochemical processing of the metal. This is the case, providing an associated electrolyte is chosen which will allow reversible electrode reactions to take place. An electrolyte high in chloride-ion concentration is suitable. Electrolytic refining in such a medium, using a soluble crude indium anode and an indium cathode, is conventional practice.[36, 50]

In many respects the electrochemical properties of indium may be studied conveniently by polarography. Data obtained from this source can be very useful in interpreting process data and developing electrochemical processes for the recovery of this metal.[50, 52] The half-wave potential of a simple, noncomplexed indium ion has been determined by Schufle[66] to be -0.55 volt versus a standard calomel electrode.

CORROSION RESISTANCE

Data on the corrosion resistance of indium are not extensive. Available information has been summarized by G. B. Barton.[8]

Atmosphere

Pure indium is resistant to corrosion in air at room temperatures. A thin, tenacious oxide film, similar to the one appearing on aluminum but readily soluble in dilute hydrochloric acid, forms on indium exposed to the atmosphere. Indium retains its bright appearance to slightly above its melting point, but at higher temperatures it oxidizes rapidly to the trioxide. Sulfur and hydrogen sulfide in the atmosphere do not affect indium at ordinary temperatures. Salt spray corrosion tests [3 per cent sodium chloride at 35°C (95°F) for six weeks] showed a gain of weight corresponding to a corrosion rate of 1.93 mdd (mg/sq dm/day) for pure indium. A hard yellow film (the color of indium trioxide) was found partially covering the specimens.

Liquid Media

A series of tests has been reported showing the relative rates of attack by various acids and alkalis at room temperatures. The results are tabulated in Table 13.5.

Of the commonly used metals, indium most nearly resembles tin in behavior in aqueous acids. Neither is very resistant, particularly in the presence of dissolved oxygen. Indium, however, being very slightly amphoteric, shows excellent resistance to the action of alkaline solutions.

Lubricating oils sometimes contain organic acids formed by decomposition of the oils under operating conditions. Corrosion tests have been reported using pure indium in a Penn base SAE No. 10 oil containing 5 per cent by volume of oleic acid (considerably higher concentration of acid than would ordinarily be found in lubricating oils). Tests at room temperature showed no change in weight at the end of 12 days, and at 136°C (277°F) they showed a

loss in weight corresponding to 7.65 mdd in 14 days. A brown tarnish film was noted in the latter test.

Tests on corrosion in lubricating oil of indium-plated and lead-indium diffusion alloy bearings have also been reported. In all cases indium greatly improved the resistance of the bearings or bearing alloys to corrosion. It should be noted that indium plating rapidly diffuses into the surface of the underlying metal at operating temperatures, so that tests on plated bearings actually measure the corrosion resistance of the particular alloy rather than that of indium metal.

Relatively little specific information is available on corrosion resistance of indium alloys. Fink and co-workers[21] reported that the addition of small amounts of either tin or indium to the other metal increases markedly the corrosion resistance to 3 per cent brine or saturated oxalic acid. Derge and Markus[17] found that addition of 0.1 to 3.0 per cent indium passivates tin in carbonate solutions in the pH range 8.4 to 11.2.

Research work reported by Grymko and Jaffee[32] on alkali-resistant solders has provided some data on corrosion rates in 25 per cent potassium hydroxide. Results of tests on pure indium, pure tin, pure lead, 50–50 indium-lead, and 50–50 lead-tin are shown graphically in

TABLE 13.5. CORROSION RATE OF 99.9 PER CENT INDIUM IN ACIDS AND ALKALIS*
(ROOM TEMPERATURE)

Solution	Composition (%)	pH	Weight loss (mg/sq dm/day)	Appearance
Hydrochloric acid	1	—	123.0	Bright
Nitric acid	1	—	2,920.0	Bright with grain boundaries etched
Sulfuric acid	1	—	176.0	Bright
Acetic acid	1	2.1	130.3	Gray tarnish
Acetic acid	5	—	172.9	Gray tarnish
Citric acid	1	2.15	21.8	Bright
Citric acid	5	—	122.2	Bright
Oxalic acid	1	1.45	117.6	Very light tarnish
Oxalic acid	5	—	98.0	Bright
Lactic acid	5	—	151.5	Very light tarnish
Succinic acid	5	—	122.8	Very light tarnish
Sodium carbonate	5	—	0.7 (gain)	Very light tarnish
Sodium hydroxide	5	—	2.5 (gain)	Light-gray film

* Reprinted from "Corrosion Handbook,"[8] H. H. Uhlig (Ed.), with permission of American Smelting and Refining Company and John Wiley & Sons, Inc.

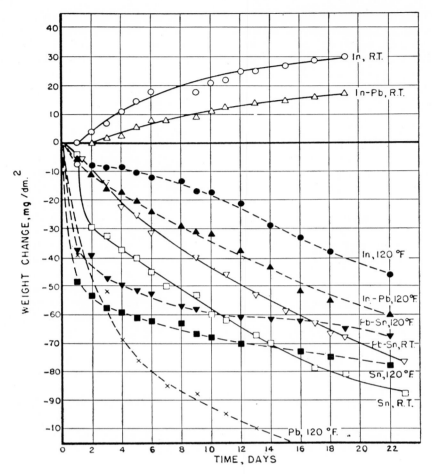

FIGURE 13.3. Total immersion corrosion tests 25 per cent potassium hydroxide.

Figure 13.3. The corrosion rate of indium in 25 per cent potassium hydroxide was determined at 1.5 mdd weight gain at room temperature and 2.1 mdd weight loss at 49°C (120°F).

Of the solders investigated, the strongest solder that resists alkaline corrosion contains 25 per cent indium, 37.5 per cent lead, and 37.5 per cent tin. Alloys containing 25 per cent or more of indium are high in resistance to attack by alkaline solutions. Joint strengths (standard "ring and plug" joint) and soldering characteristics as well as corrosion resistance were evaluated.

experiments suggest that indium is toxic, particularly on intravenous or subcutaneous injection, but less so when taken orally. It should be noted, therefore, that indium may be potentially hazardous to workers under certain conditions, but that normal hygienic precautions provide adequate protection.

Human and animal tests show that indium does not act as a skin irritant, and no cases of dermatitis have been reported by industrial workers. Indium is not suitable for use with food products as its solubility in food acids is significantly high.

TOXICITY[76]

Although no cases of accidental poisoning of industrial workers have been recorded, animal

ANALYSIS OF INDIUM

A number of methods have been developed for determining the indium content of ores and metallurgical products. Chemical, spectrographic, spectrophotometric, and electrochemical methods have all been used. Neutron-activation analysis has recently been applied to the determination of indium in rocks and minerals.[71]

Analysis of indium metal for impurities is readily performed using conventional spectrographic, spectrophotometric, or polarographic procedures. Spectrographic methods used by Cominco for the determination of trace impurities in indium and other high-purity metals have been described by C. J. Mitchell.[51]

ALLOY SYSTEMS

Many alloy systems with indium have been studied extensively. Generally, the addition of small quantities of indium has the effect of hardening, strengthening, and increasing the corrosion resistance of the metal with which it is alloyed. The following is a listing of alloy systems on which data have been published.

Binary Alloy Systems	References
Aluminum-indium	34, 57
Antimony-indium	34, 57
Arsensic-indium	34, 57
Bismuth-indium	34, 57
Cadmium-indium	34, 57
Calcium-indium	34
Cerium-indium	34, 57
Cesium-indium	34
Cobalt-indium	34
Copper-indium	34, 57
Gallium-indium	34, 57
Germanium-indium	34, 57
Gold-indium	34, 57
Indium arsenide-antimony	57
Indium arsenide-indium antimonide	57
Iodine-indium	58
Lead-indium	34, 57
Lithium-indium	34, 57
Magnesium-indium	34, 57
Manganese-indium	34, 57
Mercury-indium	34, 57
Nickel-indium	34, 57
Nitrogen-indium	34
Palladium-indium	34, 57
Phosphorus-indium	34, 57, 67
Platinum-indium	34, 57
Plutonium-indium	34
Potassium-indium	57
Praseodymium-indium	57
Rhodium-indium	34
Selenium-indium	34, 57

	References
Silicon-indium	34, 57
Silver-indium	34, 57
Sodium-indium	34, 57
Sulfur-indium	34, 57
Tellurium-indium	34, 57
Thallium-indium	34, 57
Tin-indium	34, 57
Titanium-indium	34, 57
Uranium-indium	34
Zinc-indium	34, 57

Ternary Alloy Systems	
Aluminum-antimony-indium	42
Aluminum-tin-indium	13
Antimony-arsenic-indium	69
Antimony-gallium-indium	42
Cadmium-germanium-indium	57
Cadmium-tin-indium	57
Cadmium-zinc-indium	57
Copper-nickel-indium	57
Copper-silver-indium	25, 57
Germanium-tin-indium	57
Germanium-zinc-indium	57
Lead-tin-indium	12
Tin-zinc-indium	57

Quaternary Alloy Systems	
Cadmium-germanium-tin-indium	57
Cadmium-germanium-zinc-indium	57
Cadmium-tin-zinc-indium	57
Germanium-tin-zinc-indium	57

Quinary Alloy Systems	
Cadmium-germanium-tin-zinc-indium	57

FABRICATION TECHNIQUES

Available Forms

The basic form of indium is the cast ingot. The metal is also sold in a wide range of fabricated forms, including extruded wire, ribbon and rod, rolled foil and sheet, powder, disc and spherical pellets, washers, and rings. Because of its softness, ductility, and low melting point, indium is an easy metal to fabricate, although its lack of strength is a disadvantage in preparing the smaller sizes of wire, ribbon, and thin foil. Methods used by Cominco in the production of fabricated forms have been described by B. G. Hunt *et al.*[36] Some standard forms are shown in Figure 13.4.

Indium alloys are sold in ingot form, and are also offered in fabricated shapes. Various chemicals and plating solutions are also available.

FIGURE 13.4. Some available forms of indium.

Electrodeposition

Information on indium plating processes has been summarized by Smith[73] and Ludwick.[46] Indium has been successfully plated on a number of metals, including lead, zinc, copper, cadmium, tin, gold, silver, and iron, although an undercoat is often used with iron. A number of electrolytes have been used for the electroplating of indium. The most promising commercially are cyanide, sulfate, fluoborate, and sulfamate. Operating conditions and characteristics are summarized in Tables 13.6 and 13.7.

The cyanide plating bath has been patented by Oneida Community, Ltd.[56] It was one of the first baths developed and has been quite widely used. The indium content of the electrolyte is replenished by adding concentrated indium chloride solution.

The Indium Corporation of America has developed a cyanide plating bath called "Clear Cy-an-in."[46] It is an alkaline cyanide bath, and certain advantages are claimed over the older cyanide bath. The solution is sold in concentrated form and requires only dilution with an equal amount of water.

TABLE 13.6. ELECTROPLATING OF INDIUM
PREFERRED OPERATING CONDITIONS[73]

Plating bath	Cyanide	Sulfate	Fluoborate	Sulfamate
Indium (g/liter)	30	20	60–90	30
Addition agent	Dextrose	Sodium sulfate	—	Amines
Total CN (as KCN) (g/liter)	80	—	—	—
BF_4^+ (g/liter)	—	—	125–190	—
$NH_2SO_3^+$ (g/liter)	—	—	—	225
pH	—	2.1–2.3	0.1–0.4	1.0–2.0
Temperature				
(°C)	Room	20–70	20–35	Room
(°F)	Room	68–158	68–95	Room
Anode	Inert	Indium	Indium	Indium
Current density (amp/sq ft)	20	20	10–100	20

TABLE 13.7. ELECTROPLATING OF INDIUM
OPERATING CHARACTERISTICS[46]

Plating bath	Cyanide	Sulfate	Fluoborate	Sulfamate
Throwing power	Excellent	Poor	Good	Excellent
Quality of plate	Excellent	Possible	Good	Excellent
Ease of solution analysis	Not too easy	Easy	Easy	Easy
Critical temperature	No	Controlled	21–32°C (70–90°F)	No
Color of solution	Clear	Clear	Clear	Clear
Wettability	Easy	Difficult	Difficult	Fairly easy
Use	General	Experimental	Experimental	Experimental
Anode	Insoluble	Indium	Indium	Indium
Cathode efficiency, %	40–50	30–70	40–50	90
Tendency to pit	No	Yes	No	No
Control of solution	Cyanide + metal	Metal + pH	Metal + pH	Metal + pH

Vandervell Products, Ltd., has patents describing cyanide plating baths, containing an alkali metal hydroxide and a suitable saccharide such as dextrose or sorbitol.[28,29] This type of bath can be evaporated to a solid residue for storing and shipping.[28] The solid residue is dissolved in water when plating solution is needed.

The sulfate bath is inferior to the cyanide bath in throwing power, but it is used because of its simplicity. The anode efficiency of this bath is somewhat higher than the cathode efficiency, so electrolyte must be removed periodically and replaced with water, or else an insoluble anode should be used with the indium anode to maintain the required pH and concentration. Use of the sulfate bath has been discussed by Linford.[44]

Use of the fluoborate bath has been described in a patent assigned to General Motors Corp.[48] The fluoborate bath may be made by adding indium hydroxide to fluoboric acid and diluting with water. Because the anode efficiency is higher than the cathode efficiency, this solution must also be maintained at the desired concentration by diluting with water or by using an auxiliary insoluble anode.

The sulfamate bath is described in a patent assigned to the Indium Corporation of America.[20] This process has not been used sufficiently for evaluation. Indium may be added as the sulfamate, or as the chloride or another salt. In the latter case the sulfamate radical is added as sulfamic acid.

Considerable work has also been reported on co-deposition of indium alloys. A Russian patent[45] and article[70] describe the deposition of lead-indium alloys from a fluoborate bath.

Vandervell Products, Ltd., has patents claiming the deposition of lead-indium alloys from an aqueous or "Cellosolve" (ethoxyethyl alcohol) solution of perchlorates of these metals.[27] A more recent patent assigned to Vandervell Products, Ltd., describes the deposition of lead-indium alloys from a bath containing compounds of both metals with a controlling agent such as ethylenediamine tetraacetic acid and hydrazine, using an insoluble anode.[77]

Philco Corporation has developed two processes for the electrodeposition of molten cadmium-indium alloys. One process involves the use of a fused bath of cadmium, indium, and zinc chlorides,[64,65] while the other specifies the use of a bath of cadmium, indium, and ammonium chloride in glycerol, electrolyzing at a temperature above the melting point of the alloy to deposit the eutectic alloy (75 per cent indium).[14]

Vandervell Products, Ltd., also has patents describing co-deposition of lead-tin-indium from an aqueous or "Cellosolve" solution of perchlorates of these metals,[27] co-deposition of zinc-indium or tin-indium alloys[26] and copper-indium alloys[61] from an aqueous alkali-cyanide bath containing dextrose, and co-deposition of copper-tin-indium alloys from an alkali-cyanide bath containing copper and indium as complex cyanides and tin as a stannate.[62] A patent assigned to General Motors describes coprecipitation of antimony-indium alloys from an aqueous solution containing dibasic ammonium citrate, a tetrasodium salt of ethylenediamine tetraacetic acid, indium as a soluble compound, and antimony as a complex tartrate.[72]

A patent assigned to Canadian Westinghouse

Co., Ltd., describes a novel process for plating indium and other metals and alloys that involves the application of a reversing current cycle to the base member being plated.[39] The current is first applied so that a definite thickness of metal is plated on the base member and then is reversed to deplate partially the deposit, removing the unsound and inferior top layer of the deposit. This cycling is continued until the desired thickness of metal has been built up. It is claimed that this process is faster than conventional plating techniques, and gives a smoother, more uniform deposit composed of a great number of very thin, homogeneously bonded increments of sound metal.

When indium is plated on a base metal, it can be diffused into the base metal by heating. This improves the deposit. Diffusion is effected by heating the plated part in an oven or oil bath for about 2 hr at about 175°C (347°F). The indium forms an alloy with the base metal.[46]

Vapor Deposition

Indium can be deposited on cold surfaces by evaporation in a vacuum. Mirrors for special purposes, with reflective characteristics at least as good as silver mirrors and with better resistance to atmospheric corrosion, can be made using this process.

Melting Techniques

Indium sponge is very finely divided and oxidizes readily. Consequently, indium in sponge or crystal form is usually melted under a cover to prevent oxidation. Caustic soda is commonly used to exclude air, although paraffin, purified kerosene, and a mixture of caustic soda and sodium cyanide have also been used. Massive metal can be melted in open pots without excessive oxidation.

APPLICATION

Present

Bearings. Indium's first major use was in the production of bearings, and this application continues to be a major factor in the use of standard-grade (99.97 per cent) metal. The addition of indium to bearings improves strength and hardness, increases corrosion resistance, and gives improved wettability, with a resultant increase in antiseizure properties.

The usual type of bearing treated with indium has been the steel-backed silver-lead type. In the manufacture of this bearing, a steel backing shell is first electroplated with silver, sometimes over a thin "strike" of copper or nickel. The silver layer, having high fatigue resistance, is the load-carrying component of the bearing. Above the silver layer is an electroplated lead coating, and finally an electroplated indium coating. The bearing is then heat-treated to diffuse the indium into the lead layer and produce a lead-indium alloy layer which is rich in indium at the surface.[1,54] This bearing finds application in aircraft engines, heavy-duty truck engines, and special high-performance automobile engines.

Recently, Vandervell Products, Ltd., London, England, has placed on the market a steel-backed shell bearing of lead-bronze with an indium overlay, which is mass-produced at competitive prices. This type of bearing is being used in substantial quantities by British automobile producers and also by certain German and Italian firms.

Semiconductors. Indium is an essential constituent of the germanium transistor, in which it functions both as a doping agent and as a means of attaching lead wires to the germanium crystal.[6] A variety of germanium transistors and rectifiers are now in use for various services. Among these are the point-contact, surface-barrier, and diffused alloy-junction types. Of these, the P-N-P diffused alloy-junction germanium transistor is by far the largest user of indium.

One basis for transistor action is the p-n junction. This exists when there is a transition from p-type germanium to n-type germanium in a continuous solid. N-type germanium is formed by doping highly purified germanium with specified impurities such as antimony or arsenic. These added elements having 5 electrons in their outer orbit compared to 4 for germanium, give rise to excess electrons in the germanium-crystal lattice. P-type germanium carries indium as an impurity and, since indium contains 3 electrons in its outer orbit compared to 4 for germanium, there is a deficiency of electrons in the crystal lattice. These deficiencies are known as *holes*. Under the influence of an electrical field, the extra electrons in n-type germanium move toward the positive source; in p-type germanium, electrons will jump into the holes, and the holes appear to move toward the negative terminal.

In a normal p-n-p transistor, discs or spheres of indium are alloyed into each side of a wafer of n-type germanium. On cooling, the germanium in the alloyed area recrystallizes as p-type, giving a p-n-p junction.

In addition to its electronic properties, indium has two characteristics which make it valuable for this application: (1) it wets germanium readily and can be alloyed in at a comparatively low temperature [500–550°C (932–1022°F)]. This allows easier production methods and minimizes impurity pickup. (2) It is a soft metal and does not cause strains in germanium owing to contraction after the alloying step.

Low-Melting-Point Alloys. A number of low-melting-point alloys containing indium have been developed.[6] For example, the addition of indium to Wood's metal lowers the melting point 1.45°C (2.6°F) for each 1 per cent of indium, with a minimum melting point of 47°C (117°F) at 19.1 per cent indium. The 24 per cent indium, 76 per cent gallium eutectic melts at 16°C (61°F) and is therefore liquid at room temperature.

Glass-Sealing Alloys. A very useful application of indium is for glass-to-glass or glass-to-metal seals.[6] It is particularly valuable for high-vacuum seals, readily demountable seals, and joints with glass where high temperatures cannot be used. The Cerro de Pasco Corporation offers a glass-sealing alloy, under the trade name "Cerroseal 35," containing approximately equal parts of tin and indium. The molten alloy, which is capable of wetting glass, is first applied to the preheated glass by swabbing. The joint or seal can then be completed by conventional methods.

Solder Alloys. Indium and many of its alloys adhere well to a large number of metals and nonmetals.[32] As a result, specialty solders containing indium are finding wide application. Certain low-temperature brazing alloys containing indium, including indium-copper-silver, and indium-copper-gold, have been developed. Large numbers of indium-alloy solder preforms are used in the transistor industry.

Dental Alloys. Indium has been used as an oxygen scavenger in gold dental alloys for many years.[6] The tensile strength, ductility, and resistance to discoloration of gold are improved by indium additions.

Magnetic Alloys. Several ferromagnetic Heusler alloys containing indium have been developed. Of these the copper-manganese-indium,[33] copper-magnesium-indium,[31] and manganese-carbon-indium[53] systems have received the most attention.

Intermetallic Semiconductors. Considerable research work is presently being carried out on intermetallic semiconductors formed by combining Group III and Group V elements. Among these compounds indium antimonide, indium arsenide, and indium phosphide are showing considerable promise. Indium antimonide has an extremely high electron mobility and values up to 1,000,000 sq cm/volt/sec at 77°K have been observed for high purity material. The purity required is very high, and Cominco has developed its High Purity Grade 69, containing less than 0.1 ppm of any significant impurity, for this application.

Infrared detectors and magnetoresistors using indium antimonide are already available commercially, and many other uses are expected to develop.

Electrical Contacts. Indium has been found to make excellent low-resistance contacts with oxides such as titanium dioxide and barium titanate and therefore may find uses in piezoelectric units. Interest has also developed in indium for low-noise-level contacts in specialized electrical circuits and in ultrasonic delay lines.

Nuclear Energy. Artificial radioactivity is easily induced in indium by neutrons of low energy, and for this reason it is used as an indicator in atomic reactors. Indium foil can also be used to measure thermal neutron flux in a reactor.[30] A silver-indium-cadmium alloy is used for pressurized water reactor control rods.

General. Among the minor uses of indium, its value as a resistance thermometer material[78] and as a precision temperature standard may be mentioned.[47]

Potential[6]

Resistors. Indium trioxide, either as a film or a sintered compact, has characteristics that make it potentially useful as a resistor. The

Battelle Memorial Institute, under United States Air Force contract, has developed tin-doped indium oxide films for application to aircraft windshields as an ice and fog preventative coating. The windshields are kept clear by heat from an electrical current passed through the coating. Light transmission is stated to be excellent.[2]

Thermistors. Indium trisulfide has a large negative coefficient of resistivity and is chemically and electrically stable at fairly high temperatures. These properties suggest its possible use as a thermistor.

Photoconductors. The oxide, sulfide, selenide, and telluride of indium are all photoconductors, with the selenide appearing to be the most promising.

Phosphors. A number of indium compounds exhibit fluorescence. Some development work has been undertaken on indium sulfide phosphors, but little work has been reported on other indium phosphors.

Lubricants. The addition of indium to lubricants, as solid compounds or as a fine suspension, would appear to be a promising field for development. Such desirable properties of the metal as its softness and plasticity would be of advantage in this application.[10] Certain indium soaps added to motor fuel are claimed to combat the formation of carbon deposits in an engine and to increase efficiency.[55]

Storage Batteries. Indium and certain indium alloys are currently being investigated as anode materials in small storage batteries and microcells.[11] In cells where weight and volume are at a premium, considerable advantage may be possible. The resistance of indium to attack by alkaline electrolytes during storage is also a potential advantage. Elgin National Watch Co. is using microcells with indium anodes for electronic wrist watches and other applications.[24]

References*

* Reference should be made to the comprehensive bibliography included in the book "Indium," published by The Indium Corporation of America in 1959. This annotated bibliography, compiled by Maria Thompson Ludwick, covers the period 1863 through 1958.

1. Albin, Joseph, *Materials & Methods*, **27**, #6, 88 (June, 1948).
2. Anonymous, *Chem. Eng. News*, **35**, #17, 108 (April 29, 1957).
3. Anonymous, *Eng. Mining J., Metal and Mineral Markets*, various issues.
4. Anonymous, *Mineral Inds. J.*, various issues.
5. Anonymous, *Mineral Trade Notes*, various issues.
6. Anonymous, "The Metal Indium and Its Uses," pamphlet published by The Consolidated Mining and Smelting Company of Canada Limited, 1957.
7. Barker, I. L., private communication (Dec. 9, 1958).
8. Barton, G. B., "Corrosion Handbook," H. H. Uhlig (Ed.), p. 119, New York, John Wiley & Sons, Inc., 1948.
9. Beer, A. C., *J. Electrochem. Soc.*, **105**, 743 (1958).
10. Berninger, A., British Patent **750,423** (June 13, 1956).
11. Boswell, T. L., *J. Electrochem. Soc.*, **105**, 239 (1958).
12. Campbell, A. N., *et al.*, *Can. J. Chem.*, **33**, 511 (1955).
13. Campbell, A. N., *et al.*, *J. Am. Chem. Soc.*, **74**, 1962 (1952).
14. Certa, A. J., and Manns, T. J. (to Philco Corp.), U.S. Patent 2,818,374 (Dec. 31, 1957).
15. Cohen, I., *et al.*, *Nucleonics*, **16**, #8, 122 (Aug. 1958).
16. Coyle, John, *Trans. Electrochem. Soc.*, **85**, 223 (1944).
17. Derge, Gerhard, and Markus, Harold, *Trans. AIME*, **143**, 198 (1941).
18. Doran, H. M., *et al.* (to Anaconda Co.), U.S. Patent 2,384,610 (Sept. 11, 1945).
19. Dyer, J. R., Jr., *Chem. Ind.*, **49**, 339 (1941).
20. Dyer, J. R., Jr., and Rowan, T. J. (to The Indium Corporation of America), U.S. Patent 2,458,839 (Jan. 11, 1949).
20a. Eilertson, D. E., Indium chapter in "Mineral Facts and Problems, 1960 Edition," *U.S. Bur. Mines Bull. 585*, Washington, D.C., U.S. Government Printing Office, 1960.
21. Fink, C. G., *et al.*, *Trans. Electrochem. Soc.*, **75**, 463 (1939).
22. Fraser, D. B., "Canadian Mineral Industry," Ottawa, Canada, Dept. of Mines and Technical Surveys, 1957.
23. Fullman, B., *Nature*, **182**, 862 (1958).
24. Gardner, A. R., *Prod. Eng.* **31**, #3, 66 (Mar. 17, 1958).
25. Gebhardt, Erich, and Dreher, Manfried, *Z. Metallk.*, **43**, 357 (1952).
26. Green, D. F., *et al.*, to Vanderwell Products, Ltd., British Patent 637,154 (May 17, 1950).
27. Green, D. F., *et al.* (to Vandervell Products, Ltd.), British Patent 637,159 (May 17, 1950); U.S. Patent 2,567,934 (Sept. 18, 1951).
28. Green, D. F., and Salmon, J. E., to Vanderwell Products, Ltd., British Patent 602,027 (May

19, 1948); Canadian Patent 493,416 (June 2, 1953); U.S. Patent 2,538,417 (Jan. 16, 1951).

29. Green, D. F., and Salmon, J. E. (to Vandervell Products, Ltd.), British Patent 573,848 (Dec. 10, 1945); Canadian Patent 487,850 (Nov. 4, 1952); U.S. Patent 2,497,988 (Feb. 21, 1950).

30. Greenfield, M. A., *et al., Nucleonics,* 15, #3, 57 (March, 1957).

31. Grinstead, R. R., and Yost, D. M., *J. Am. Chem. Soc.,* 75, 1803 (1953).

32. Grymko, S. M., and Jaffee, R. I., *Materials & Methods,* 31, #3, 59 (March, 1950).

33. Hames, F. A., and Eppelsheimer, D. S., *J. Metals,* 185, 495 (1949).

34. Hansen, Max, and Anderko, Kurt, "Constitution of Binary Alloys," 2nd Ed., New York, McGraw-Hill Book Company, Inc., 1958.

35. Hopkins, B. S., "Chapters in the Chemistry of the Less Familiar Elements," Chap. 8, p. 13, Champaign, Ill., Stipes Publishing Company, 1939.

36. Hunt, B. G., White, C. E. T., and King, R. A., "Commercial Production of Indium," *C.I.M. Bulletin,* 52, 359 (1959).

37. Jaffee, R. I., and Weiss, M. G., paper presented to the Electrochemical Society, Washington, D.C. (April, 1951).

38. Jaffee, R. I., and Weiss, S. M., *Materials & Methods,* 36, #3, 113 (Sept., 1952).

39. Jernstedt, G. W. (to Canadian Westinghouse Co., Ltd.), Canadian Patent 560,607 (July 22, 1958).

40. King, R. A., *Metal Progr.* 75, #1, 127 (Jan., 1959).

41. Kleinert, Reinhard, *Mining Mag. (London),* 83, 146 (Sept., 1950).

42. Koster, Werner, and Thoma, Berthold, *Z. Metallk.,* 46, 293 (1955).

43. Lebedeff, Y. E. (to American Smelting and Refining Co.) U.S. Patent 2,433,770 (Dec. 30, 1947).

44. Linford, H. D., *Trans. Electrochem. Soc.,* 79, 443 (1941).

45. Lipin, A. I., *et al.,* U.S.S.R. Patent 103,185 (July 25, 1956).

46. Ludwick, M. T., "Indium," p. 191, New York, The Indium Corporation of America, 1959.

47. McLaren, E. H., *Can. J. Phys.,* 36, 1131 (1958).

48. Martz, W. M. (to General Motors Corporation), U.S. Patent 2,409,983 (Oct. 22, 1946).

49. Melford, D. A., and Hoar, T. P., *J. Inst. Metals,* 85, 1742 (1956).

50. Mills, J. R., Hunt, B. G., and Turner, G. H., *J. Electrochem. Soc.,* 100, 136 (1953).

51. Mitchell, C. J., "The Determination of Trace Elements in High Purity Metals," paper presented at the Fifth Ottawa Symposium on Applied Spectroscopy (Sept. 15, 1958).

52. Moeller, Therald, and Hopkins, B. S., *Trans. Electrochem. Soc.,* 93, 84 (1948).

53. Morgan, E. R. (to Canadian Patents and Development, Ltd.), Canadian Patent 560,952 (July 29, 1958).

54. Mullen, U. A., *Metal Ind. (London),* 65, 394 (1944).

55. Murray, W. S., and Dyer, J. R., Jr. (to The Indium Corporation of America), U.S. Patent 2,628,895 (Feb. 17, 1953).

56. Murray, W. S., and Gray, Daniel (to Oneida Community, Ltd.), U.S. Patent 1,965,251 (July 3, 1934).

57. Peretti, E. A., "Constitution of Indium Alloy Systems," pamphlet, Utica, N.Y., The Indium Corporation of America, 1956.

58. Peretti, E. A., *J. Am. Chem. Soc.,* 78, 5745 (1956).

59. Quarm, T. A. A., *Trans. Inst. Mining and Met.,* 60, 77 (1950).

60. Romeyn, Hendrik, Jr., *J. Am. Chem. Soc.,* 55, 3899 (1933).

61. Salmon, J. E. (to Vandervell Products, Ltd.), British Patent 637,153 (May 17, 1950).

62. Salmon, J. E., and Perkins, H. R. (to Vandervell Products, Ltd.), British Patent 666,392 (Feb. 13, 1952).

63. Scala, E., and Robertson, W. D., *J. Metals,* 5, 1141 (1953).

64. Schnable, G. L. (to Philco Corp.), U.S. Patent 2,845,387 (July 29, 1958).

65. Schnable, G. L., and Javes, J. G., *J. Electrochem. Soc.,* 105, 84 (1958).

66. Schufle, J. A., private communication (1953).

67. Shafer, M., and Weiser, K., *J. Phys. Chem.,* 61, 1424 (1957).

68. Shaw, D. M., paper presented to American Chemical Society, New York (September, 1951).

69. Shih, C. H., and Peretti, E. A., *Trans. Am. Soc. Metals,* 48, 706 (1956).

70. Shluger, M. A., *et al., Zhur. Priklad. Khim.,* 31, #1, 71 (Jan., 1958).

71. Smales, A. A., *et al., Analyst,* 82, 539 (1957).

72. Smart, C. F. (to General Motors Corp.), U.S. Patent 2,750,333 (June 12, 1956).

73. Smith, A. A., Jr., in Kirk-Othmer "Encyclopedia of Chemical Technology," Vol. 7, p. 834, New York, The Interscience Encyclopedia, Inc., 1951.

74. Smithells, C. J., "Metals Reference Book," 2nd Ed. Vols. 1 and 2, London, Butterworth & Co. (Publishers) Ltd., 1955.

75. Thorpe, J. A., and Whiteley, M. A., in Thorpe's "Dictionary of Applied Chemistry," Vol. 6, p. 457, New York, Longmans, Green & Co., Inc., 1943.

76. Turner, F. M., "Some Notes on Indium with Special Reference to Its Toxic Properties," pamphlet, A.E.R.E. MED/M 18, United Kingdom Atomic Energy Authority Research Group, 1957.

77. Waterman, W. J., *et al.* (to Vandervell Products, Ltd.), British Patent 799,280 (Aug. 6, 1958); Canadian Patent 569,059 (Jan. 13, 1959).

78. White, G. K., *et al., Rev. Sci. Instr.,* **28,** 638 (1957).

79. Wichers, Edward, *J. Am. Chem. Soc.,* **80,** 4121 (1958).

80. Wright, T. R., *Mining and Met.,* **26,** 560 (1945).

81. Zischkau, Clarence, and Linford, H. B. (to American Smelting and Refining Co.), U.S. Patent 2,241,438 (May 13, 1941).

14. LITHIUM

P. E. Landolt

Consulting Engineer
New York, New York

and

Marshall Sittig

Consultant, Princeton, New Jersey

INTRODUCTION

Like a number of rare elements, lithium achieved recognition of its potential importance beginning with World War I, at which time Germany used lithium metal for two principal purposes: (1) hardened lead alloy, "B-Metal,"[121,121a,121b,121c] for railway bearings as a substitute for lead-tin-antimony alloys; and (2) light, strong aluminum alloys, "Scleron,"[18,18a,18b,18c] in which zinc was largely substituted for copper.

In World War II, interest in lithium grew rapidly for the United States defense developments. Major uses projected for lithium and its compounds in 1954 were as follows:

(1) Anhydrous lithium hydroxide for carbon dioxide absorption.

(2) Lithium chloride for dry batteries.

(3) Lithium hydride for hydrogen generation for air-sea rescue equipment.

(4) Lithium hydride as a reagent to produce borohydrides for jet-propulsion uses.

(5) Lithium metal for new alloys such as the magnesium-lithium alloys.

(6) Lithium metal, lithium aluminum hydride, and lithium amide for organic syntheses.

Now, in 1960, the major projected uses for lithium appear to be in the following areas:[26,110]

(1) Lithium hydride as a reagent to produce borohydrides for jet-propulsion uses.

(2) Lithium perchlorate as an oxidizer for solid-propellant rockets.

(3) Lithium metal for new alloys such as magnesium-lithium and aluminum-lithium alloys.

(4) Lithium alkyls as stereospecific polymerization catalysts.

(5) Lithium metal, lithium aluminum hydride, and lithium amide for organic syntheses.

(6) Lithium 6 in atomic energy.

(7) Lithium fluoride as a cell additive in the electrolytic production of aluminum.

It must be recognized that lithium compounds had been used for over a century, before the World Wars, for ceramics and medicinals, and for some years in the Edison alkaline storage battery.

The element lithium was discovered by Arfvedsen[35] in Sweden in 1807, during his examination of specimens of the mineral, petalite—a lithium aluminum silicate. This discovery was followed by the researches of many scientists, notably Sir Humphry Davy, Gmelin, Berzelius, Bunsen, and Matthiesen.[35]

Lithium is element 3 in the periodic system, only hydrogen and helium preceding it. It is the lightest metallic element. It has two isotopes, lithium 6 and lithium 7, with an atomic weight of 6.94, indicating a predominance of lithium 7.

OCCURRENCE

Lithium is found widely distributed in the earth's crust, calculated to be approximately 0.004 per cent. By way of comparison, 0.002

TABLE 14.1. WORLD PRODUCTION OF LITHIUM MINERALS

(Long Tons)

	1949	1950	1951	1952	1953	1954	1955	1956	1957	1958
United States	4,320[2]	8,309[2]	11,515[2]	13,938[2]	24,321[2]	33,777[3]	n.a.	n.a.	n.a.	n.a.
Canada	—	—	—	—	—	213[1]	57	2,395	2,570	1,960
Southern Rhodesia	—	179[1]	1,737[1]	1,321[1]	17,538[1]	48,259[1]	24,260	18,069	14,533	18,404
South West Africa	1,035[1]	8,742[1]	10,573[1]	8,751[1]	9,267[1]	6,505[4]	8,514	5,508	6,207	8,487
Uganda	200[1]	265[1]	19[1]	—	16[1]	7[1]	—	—	—	—
Union of South Africa	—	13[1]	—	—	54[1]	51[4]	—	—	—	—
Belgian Congo	590[1]	218[1]	275[1]	1,083[1]	—	365[1]	1,491	1,996	2,317	n.a.
Mozambique	18[1]	16[1]	66[1]	10[1]	5,622[1]	—	—	1,105	379	96
Portugal	—	—	—	10[1]	16[1]	9[1]	4	—	—	n.a.
Spain	—	—	—	—	31[1]	—	125	57	7	n.a.
France	—	—	—	—	—	—	—	—	—	—
Germany and Czechoslovakia	5[1]	—	—	—	—	15[1]	4	—	—	n.a.
Australia	—	—	—	—	—	—	—	—	—	—
Argentina	—	—	—	—	—	—	110	165	22	n.a.
Brazil	—	—	—	—	—	—	1,827	—	552	468

n.a. = not available.

(1) Data from Lamming, *Mining Jour.* (Lond.), Sept. 1956, p. 334.
(2) Data from U.S.B.M. *Minerals' Year Book*, 1953, Vol. 1.
(3) Lithium Preprint, Bur. of Mines *Minerals' Yearbook*, 1955.
(4) Statistical Summary of the Mineral Industry 1949–1954, *Colonial Geological Surveys*, London: Her Majesty's Stationary Office, 1956.

per cent represents the occurrence of lead, and 0.0006 the occurrence of tin. Lithium occurs as a silicate, phosphate, fluoride, and chloride. The silicate minerals provide the main commercial source of lithium raw material.

Notwithstanding the relatively high quantity of lithium in the earth's crust, actual deposits of sufficient concentration and quantity to warrant commercial mining and recovery operations are limited.

Lithium minerals are found in some quantities on all the continental land masses. From all data available the occurrences would be in the following order of commercial importance: North America, Africa, South America, Europe, Australia, Asia.

If dependent solely on the recovery of high-grade minerals, a lithium industry of any magnitude could not be developed. In earlier years the Etta mine in the Black Hills, South Dakota, yielded large quantities of spodumene of high quality, but in that period the demand for lithium products was quite limited. Desert lake brines in California yield substantial quantities of lithium as a phosphate (Li_2NaPO_4) but only as a by-product of potash and borax production.

The principal lithium minerals useful for commercial recovery are as follows:

(1) Spodumene: $Li_2O \cdot Al_2O_3 \cdot SiO_2$ containing approximately 8.0 per cent Li_2O.

(2) Lepidolite: lithium mica $R_3Al(SiO_2)_3$ (+F) containing 3 to 5 per cent Li_2O.

(3) Amblygonite: $LiAl \cdot F \cdot PO_4$ containing 8 to 10 per cent Li_2O.

(4) Petalite: a lithium aluminum silicate containing 2 to 4 per cent Li_2O.

(5) Desert lake brines containing lithium sodium phosphate (Li_2NaPO_4).

Lithium minerals are usually found in pegmatite dikes which must be of sufficient width to justify mass mining operations.[54] Depth of such mineralization increases with the length of the dikes. Depths usually vary from 200 to 500 ft; in some cases to 1,000 ft. The lithium content of these dikes useful for commercial mining operations is usually from 1 to 2 per cent lithium oxide.

Lithium minerals were usually recovered by hand picking. As the demand increased, mass mining methods were introduced, and the mineral concentrates were produced by two methods: (1) froth flotation, and (2) heavy media-sink float (magnetic reagent). Froth flotation appears to be the most satisfactory method to produce concentrates containing 4 to 6 per cent Li_2O.

PRODUCTION AND ECONOMIC STATISTICS

Table 14.1 shows world production of lithium ores and minerals for the period 1927 to 1956. The demand to date and the potential demand for lithium is approximated in Table 14.2.

To date, only a very small fraction of lithium production is devoted to lithium metal production throughout the world:

	Experimental lots for
Prior to 1914	research purposes
World, 1914–1930	< 5,000 lb/year
World, 1931–1942	< 5,000 lb/year
U.S., 1942–1946	<100,000 lb/year
U.S., 1947–1952	< 30,000 lb/year
U.S., 1952–1957	<100,000 lb/year

Increased industrial demand will be largely, if not entirely, dependent upon the cost of lithium products. Defense requirements may

TABLE 14.2. LITHIUM PRODUCTION STATISTICS[69, 70]

Period	Annual demand for lithium products, United States (as equiv.) Li_2CO_3 (lb)	Raw material as concentrates (5% Li_2O) (tons)	Raw material as mined material (tons)
Prior to World War I	400,000	2,000	10,000
	750,000	4,000	20,000
World War II	2,000,000	10,000	50,000
	3,000,000	20,000	100,000
Postwar, 1946–1950 (av.)	1,100,000	5,500	27,500
Industrial demand, 1951	2,000,000	10,000	50,000
Industrial demand, 1955	>10,000,000	50,000	250,000
Expected industrial demand, 1960	>10,000,000	50,000	250,000

@ $4.00/unit Li₂O	$ 500/1,000 lb Li	or $0.50/lb Li
6.00/ " "	750/ " " "	0.75/ " "
8.00/ " "	1,000/ " " "	1.00/ " "
10.00/ " "	1,250/ " " "	1.25/ " "
12.00/ " "	1,500/ " " "	1.50/ " "

have a marked influence on lithium products, but, ultimately, reduced costs of production will be the prime factor in creating increased interest in the use of lithium products.

Cost Considerations

As in other metallurgical products, the cost of lithium metal is largely dependent on the cost of raw material. A minimum size of mine flotation mill for economic recovery of lithium is 150 to 200 tons raw material/24 hr, producing 30 to 40 tons of 4 to 6 per cent concentrates. In 1946, such concentrates could be produced for $4/unit of lithium oxide at the mines. In 1952, these costs were of the order of $7/unit of lithium oxide, which is equivalent to 17.5 cents/lb of lithium carbonate recovered (80 per cent recovery).

To produce 1,000 lb of lithium metal, a minimum of 6,250 lb of lithium chloride is required. To produce this amount of lithium chloride, 5,700 lb of lithium carbonate are used, or 2,280 lb of lithium oxide. If extraction recovery is maintained at 90 per cent, then approximately 25 tons of raw-material concentrates containing 5 per cent lithium oxide would be required. Therefore the raw material cost per 1,000 lb of lithium metal would be as shown above.

Allowing for the cost of extraction, salt conversion, and electrolysis to produce metal, and also for capital costs, overhead, and profit, the price of lithium metal in quantities of 100,000 lb/annum or more will be approximately 10 to 15 times the raw material cost.

Capital costs including working capital will be of the order of $5 to $8/lb/annum production including all operations from extraction to metal production.

CONVERSION OF ORES TO LITHIUM CHEMICALS

Having obtained ore concentrates, the problem of extracting and recovering lithium becomes all important.[122]

Methods tried and utilized are as follows:

(1) Heating with potassium bisulfate and then leaching out lithium sulfate.[102,104,108,109]

(2) Using spodumene to furnish alumina and silica[96] to produce portland cement. Spodumene is added to limestone and calcium chloride. The entire mixture is calcined in a kiln to produce cement clinker, and the lithium is volatilized as an impure chloride.

(3) Heating spodumene concentrates at 1000°C+ (1832°F) (below fusion) to convert from alpha-phase to beta-phase spodumene.[74] The material is cooled and finely ground, incorporated with sulfuric acid, and heated to approximately 300°C (572°F), then cooled and leached to produce an impure solution of lithium sulfate.

(4) Heating spodumene ore at 1038°C (1900°F) or lepidolite ore at 871°C (1600°F) with 3 parts of ground limestone in a rotary kiln. The sinter is leached with water to give lithium hydroxide monohydrate.

The first method was utilized in Germany but did not give maximum yields or lowest costs. It was primarily a batch process.

The second method affords an interesting means of extracting lithium as a by-product, provided it is carried out on a large scale wherein portland cement can be commercially produced—at least 1,000 bbl/24 hr. Ninety-eight per cent of the lithium can be volatilized, but the subsequent purification of the condensed lithium chloride presents very difficult problems.

The third method offers a continuous process with good economy whereby at least 90 per cent of the contained lithium can be recovered. The sulfate solution is easily filtered to remove the aluminum silicate residue, purified of minor impurities, and recovered as quite pure lithium carbonate. Soda ash (Na_2CO_3) is added to the sulfate solution precipitating insoluble lithium carbonate with Glauber's salt ($Na_2SO_4 \cdot 10H_2O$) as a by-product.

The fourth method offers recovery percentages lower than the third method. When treating spodumene, the inversion step is not necessary.

TABLE 14.3. EXTRACTION PROCESSES FOR LITHIUM CHEMICALS

Producer	Foote Mineral Co.	American Potash & Chemical Corp.	American Lithium Chemicals	Lithium Corp. of America	Maywood Chemical Works
Raw material	Spodumene	Li_2NaPO_4	Lepidolite	Spodumene	Spodumene
Mines located at	Kings Mountain, North Carolina	Searles Lake, California (brine)	Rhodesia (Africa)	Quebec* and Kings Mountain, North Carolina	Black Hills, South Dakota
Chemical plants located at	Sunbright, Virginia	Trona, California	San Antonio, Texas	Bessemer City, North Carolina	Maywood, New Jersey
Initial ore treatment	Crushing and grinding	Evaporation	Crushing	Crushing and grinding	Crushing
Concentration step	Heavy-media separation, then froth flotation	Froth flotation	Hand sorting or cobbing	Froth flotation	Hand picking
Roasting step	With limestone	None	With limestone	With H_2SO_4	Undisclosed
Leaching step	Water extracts LiOH	H_2SO_4 gives $Li_2SO_4 \cdot NA_2SO_4 + H_3PO_4$	Water extracts LiOH + KOH	Water extracts Li_2SO_4	Undisclosed
Semifinal washing step	None	Sodium carbonate ppts. Li_2CO_3	Countercurrent washing and thickening	With Na_2CO_3, then lime	Undisclosed
Evaporation	Gives $LiOH \cdot H_2O$	Gives Li_2CO_3	Gives $LiOH \cdot H_2O$	Gives $LiOH \cdot H_2O$	Undisclosed

* Purchased ore imported as of 1958 (actually, Quebec Lithium Corporation supplying Lithium Corporation of America.)

Table 14.3 summarizes the processing operations of the various United States producers of lithium compounds. The third method described above is the Lithium Corp. of America process, and the fourth method is that practiced by American Lithium Chemicals and Foote Mineral Company.

With pure lithium carbonate or hydroxide as a starting chemical, all of the useful lithium compounds can be produced advantageously.

Other methods of extraction and recovery have been considered, among them the volatilization of lithium compounds from electric-furnace reductions. Lithium minerals and compounds are excellent fluxes, but as such are quite costly, necessitating very complete volatilization and recovery of the lithium, or absorption in slag with subsequent costly method of extraction and recovery.

PRODUCTION OF LITHIUM METAL BY FUSED SALT ELECTROLYSIS

In this chapter attention is focused primarily on lithium metal. Various methods have been proposed to reduce lithium compounds to metal, but results are costly as compared to the classical method. Lithium chloride admixed with potassium chloride is fused. Current is applied, depositing lithium metal on the cathode and evolving chlorine at the anode. In many respects the technology is comparable to the electrolytic reduction of magnesium chloride. Some typical operating data for commercial cells are given in Table 14.4.

To produce 1 lb of lithium metal from lithium chloride, there are required theoretically 1,750 amp-hr and a sufficient voltage to dissociate the compound to form lithium metal—approximately 2.5 volts (3,850 amp-hr/kg). Approximately 6 to 6.5 volts are required to overcome the bath resistance and line losses. Where the bath depends entirely on electrical heat, approximately 28 KWH are required to produce 1 lb of lithium metal (61.6 KWH/kg). Where the cell is heated externally by gas or oil, this may be reduced to approximately 21 KWH (46.2 KWH/kg). For each pound of lithium metal produced, approximately 5 lb of chlorine gas are produced. Where any sizable production of metal is made, the recovery of chlorine would be required. The chlorine may be absorbed to form hypochlorites or other useful chlorine compounds, or burned with hydrogen to form hydrochloric acid.

Unit cell capacity is relatively small—80 to 100 lb of lithium metal/24 hr. When demand would justify it, cell capacities may be increased advantageously to possibly 500 lb/24 hr. For large-scale production, cells may be operated in series to permit the use of standard electrical equipment, generating 125 to 250 volts d-c.

Using salts approximating a eutectic mixture, the temperature of the molten bath can be maintained at a minimum—450–500°C (842–932°F) (LiCl 60 per cent, KCl 40 per cent approximately). Deterioration of the graphite anodes is thereby minimized.

Lithium metal thus produced will contain certain impurities, principally sodium. Practically all of the sodium present in the lithium chloride is deposited with and remains in the lithium metal produced.

A typical analysis of the lithium chloride used is as follows:

TABLE 14.4. LITHIUM CELLS— OPERATING CHARACTERISTICS[112]

Current (amp)	850–900
Temperature	
°C	400–420
°F	752–788
Voltage	8–9
Anodic c.d. (amp/sq in.)	9.0
Cathodic c.d. (amp/sq in.)	13.0
Current efficiency (%)	85–90
Unit energy (KWH/lb)	18.2
Chemical consumption (LiCl/lb Li)	7.3
Chemical efficiency (%)	83.7
Cell capacity (lb)	220

LiCl	98.8%
H_2O	0.6
Alkalinity (as Li_2CO_3)	0.06
SO_4	0.01
$CaCl_2$	0.10
$BaCl_2$	0.01
Na and K as chlorides	0.40
Fe_2O_3	0.003

A typical analysis of the lithium metal produced is shown in Table 14.5.

A diagrammatic layout of an electrolytic cell to produce metallic lithium is shown in Figure 14.1.

TABLE 14.5 ANALYSES OF LITHIUM METAL

| Constituent | Electrolytic product[55] (Maywood) | | Thermal product[24] (Dominion Magnesium) |
	Regular grade (%)	Low-sodium grade (%)	Regular grade (%)
Na	0.710	0.020	0.01
Si	0.004	0.015	0.04
Al	0.002	⎫	0.03
Fe	0.001	⎬ 0.03	0.03
Ca	0.001	0.06	0.02
Cu	0.001	—	0.001
Mg	0.0003	—	0.5–0.2
K	0.020	—	0.5
N_2	—	0.03	0.1
Cl	—	0.003	
Heavy metals	—	0.09	
O_2	Not reported	Not reported	Not reported
Li	99.260	99.750	99.219–99.519

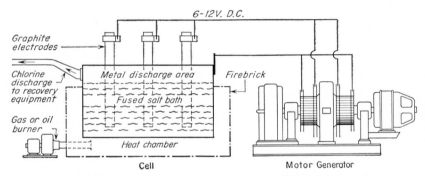

FIGURE 14.1. Diagrammatic layout of electrolytic cell for lithium production.

PHYSICAL PROPERTIES AND HANDLING OF THE METAL

The physical properties of lithium are outlined in Table 14.6. The toxicological properties of lithium are described by Schou.[101]

Lithium metal is not applicable by itself as a structural material, because of its rapid deterioration in the atmosphere and its low melting point. Thus, some fabrication is desirable to facilitate its use.

Lithium Cartridges

For practical use of lithium metal as a degasifier in nonferrous metallurgical foundry products, such as copper and copper alloys, lithium metal is placed in a metal cartridge.[71]

Lithium metal ingots are placed in a hydraulic press and extruded through a die to form a rod of suitable diameter (usually ½ in.). Given lengths of this rod are cut to give the following weights of lithium metal: 2.25, 4.5, and 9.0 g. When these are added to 100 lb of molten metal, they will make additions of 0.005, 0.01, and 0.02 per cent, respectively. Practice has shown this to be the amount usually required. The desired length of such lithium rod is encased in a copper, aluminum, or other suitable metal sheath in the form of a thin-walled tube, the ends of which are hermetically sealed to prevent atmospheric corrosion of the lithium.

Lithium Wire or Ribbon

Primarily prepared for use in organic synthesis, lithium wire (or ribbon) is extruded through a suitable die to produce a wire, of nominal ⅛-in. diameter, which is wound on a

TABLE 14.6 PHYSICAL PROPERTIES OF LITHIUM

		Reference
Atomic number	3	
Atomic weight	6.94	
Isotopes, abundance	7.39% of 6	
	92.61% of 7	
Melting point		
°C	179	10
°F	354	
Boiling point		
°C	1317	23
°F	2403	
Density (g/cc)		
20°C (68°F)	0.534	7
200°C (392°F)	0.507	74a
400°C (752°F)	0.490	74a
600°C (1112°F)	0.474	74a
800°C (1472°F)	0.457	7
1000°C (1832/F)	0.441	74a
Heat of fusion (cal/g) 179°C	103.2	25
Heat of vaporization (cal/g) 1317°C	4680	74a
Vapor pressure (mm Hg)		
745°C (1373°F)	1	74a
890°C (1634°F)	10	74a
1077°C (1970°F)	91	25
1084°C (1983°F)	100	74a
1156°C (2113°F)	200	74a
1236°C (2257°F)	400	74a
Heat capacity (cal/g/°C)		
0°C (32°F)	0.784	96a
50°C (122°F)	0.844	96a
100°C (212°F)	0.90	25
186°C (367°F)	1.01	96a
300°C (572°F)	1.02	25
800°C (1472°F)	0.99	25
Enthalpy (cal/g) 25°C (77°F)	203 ± 0.7	96a
Entropy (cal/mole/°C) 0°C (32°F)	6.70 ± 0.06	96a
Thermal conductivity (cal/sec/cm/sq cm/°C)		
0°C (32°F)	0.17	
216°C (420°F)	0.109	120
539°C (1002°F)	0.073	120
Viscosity (centipoises)		
183.4°C (362°F)	0.5918	74a
193.2°C (380°F)	0.5749	74a
200°C (392°F)	0.562	87
208.1°C (406°F)	0.5541	74a
250.8°C (483°F)	0.4917	74a
285.5°C (546°F)	0.4548	74a
400°C (752°F)	0.402	87
600°C (1112°F)	0.317	87
Electrical resistivity (microhm-cm)		
0°C (32°F)	8.55	47
100°C (212°F)	12.7	47
230°C (446°F)	45.25	74a

TABLE 14.6. PHYSICAL PROPERTIES OF LITHIUM (*cont.*)

		Reference
Surface tension (dynes/cm) 200–500°C (392–932°F)	about 400	116
Volume change on fusion (% of solid volume)	1.5	74a
Coefficient of linear thermal expansion (20°C), per °C	56×10^{-6}	96a
Thermal neutron-absorption cross section (barns/atom)	71 ± 1	
Crystallography, Å		96a
α (BBC) 20°C (68°F)	$a_0 = 3.502$	
β (FCC) −196°C (−321°F)	$a_0 = 4.41$	

reel and then placed in an airtight container. The lithium metal is protected by dry kerosene or its equivalent. One pound of such lithium wire has a length of 450 to 500 ft.

Lithium ribbon or tape is wound on a reel and sealed on the outside of the reel. Tape dimensions are $\frac{1}{4}$ and $\frac{1}{2}$ in. wide by $\frac{1}{32}$ in. thick, in reels from 1 oz to 1 lb weight of lithium metal.

Lithium Shot

Lithium metal can be formed into shot by agitation of the molten metal under a hot paraffin-oil cover. This material is also produced for organic chemical use.

Sodium-Free Lithium Metal

Lithium metal, as produced in the electrolytic cell, usually contains 0.4 to 0.7 per cent sodium. For some uses, such as the lithium-magnesium alloys, it is important to eliminate this sodium. This is accomplished by subjecting molten lithium to an elevated temperature under high vacuum (less than 100μ) whereby the sodium is vaporized, leaving the lithium metal with its much higher boiling point, nearly sodium free— 0.001 to 0.005 per cent residual sodium.

Molten Lithium

A great deal of interest has centered around the handling of molten lithium, particularly for heat transfer applications. Lithium has a very desirable combination of properties for heat transfer applications such as high specific heat, large liquid range, high thermal conductivity, low viscosity, and low density. The last item, low density, makes lithium of particular interest for coolant systems in aircraft or missiles.

To counterbalance these advantages, there are two major problems as follows:

(1) Liquid lithium can be a corrosive material, particularly if not kept scrupulously free of oxygen and nitrogen.

(2) For nuclear applications, the desirable coolant is not just lithium, but the isotope lithium 7, which has a much lower thermal neutron absorption cross section (1.0 barn) than does naturally occurring lithium (70 barns) and especially the other isotope, lithium 6, which has a cross section of 912 barns.

The first of these problems is the subject of intensive study by various contractors connected with the development of a nuclear-powered aircraft, because of the obvious attractiveness of lithium for such an application. Analytical techniques for minor impurities in lithium metal are being improved, and mechanical techniques for blanketing and filtering the molten metal are undergoing intensive research.

The second problem will require more work in order to make it economically attractive. At the present time, quite pure lithium 6 is available from the U.S. Atomic Energy Commission at 2 to 3 cents/mg ($9000 to $13,000/lb) and relatively pure lithium 7 at 15 to 30 cents/mg ($70,000 to $130,000/lb). These prices are, of course, only for small experimental quantities, but they give some idea of the challenge which is offered by large-scale production of the pure lithium 7 isotope.

Much of the information on the handling of liquid lithium has been assembled in publications such as the "Liquid Metals Handbook." An example of such information is Figure 14.2 which shows the resistance of various materials to liquid lithium.[82]

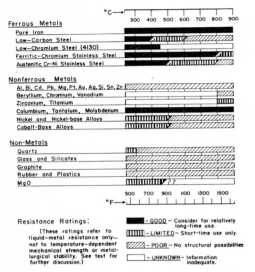

FIGURE 14.2. Resistance of materials of construction to liquid lithium. (*From "Liquid Metals Handbook."*)

COMPOUNDS DERIVED FROM THE METAL

Table 14.7 presents the stoichiometric relationship and the energy released by the reactions of lithium with oxygen and sulfur as compared with similar data for many other elements.

Lithium and Hydrogen

Lithium and hydrogen combine easily at elevated temperatures, forming the rather stable lithium hydride (LiH). This hydride has a definitely established melting point, 688°C (1270°F). It can be fused, electrolyzed, etc., just like a halogen salt. The electrical conductivity[1,2] of fused lithium hydride is relatively good.

Lithium hydride is a typical representative of the "saltlike" hydride group, which includes[4] the hydrides of lithium, calcium, strontium, barium, sodium, potassium, rubidium, and cesium. (A hydride of magnesium is not known.) The atomic arrangement of these "saltlike" hydrides resembles that of sodium chloride. Their stability decreases in the order of the elements as given above, lithium hydride being by far the most stable among them. This fact again indicates very emphatically the close relationship of lithium with the alkaline earth metals.

Lithium hydride can be prepared with a percentage of hydrogen corresponding to the formula LiH, but, because of the decreasing stability of the other "saltlike" hydrides, it is difficult to prepare these so as to contain the theoretical percentage of hydrogen. Sodium hy-

TABLE 14.7. REACTION OF OXYGEN AND SULFUR WITH LITHIUM AND OTHER ELEMENTS

Element	Grams of oxygen which combine with 1 g of element	Kcal set free when 1 g of element combines with oxygen	Grams of sulfur which combine with 1 g of element	Kcal set free when 1 g of element combines with sulfur
Li	1.152	10.33	2.309	8.75
Na	0.348	2.18	0.697	1.95
K	0.204	1.11	0.410	1.11
Rb	0.094	0.46	0.188	1.02
Cs	0.060	0.31	0.120	
Be	1.774	15.23	3.554	
Mg	0.658	6.00	1.320	3.27
Ca	0.399	3.72	0.800	2.78
Sr	0.182	1.61	0.366	1.258
Ba	0.116	0.97	0.234	0.745
Al	0.890	7.05	1.783	2.34
Zn	0.245	1.27	0.491	0.632
Mn	0.292	1.707	0.583	1.10 (approx.)
Si	1.140	6.80		
Ti	0.668	4.56		
P	1.289	5.78		
Zr	0.350	2.90	0.351	

dride (NaH), for instance, has such a high vapor pressure that its melting point cannot be determined, whereas lithium hydride is relatively stable and can be fused. Ephraim and Michel[27] state that, even at a temperature of 640°C (1184°F) (40° below the melting point), the vapor pressure of lithium hydride does not exceed 70 mm Hg.

When electrolyzing lithium hydride,[4] lithium metal is deposited on the cathode, and hydrogen is set free at the anode. This is considered of general importance because, together with the fact that the atomic arrangement of lithium hydride resembles that of sodium chloride, it demonstrates the relation of hydrogen to the halogen family.

Lithium hydride is very reactive. It readily reduces oxides, chlorides, and sulfides. For example, carbon dioxide is reduced to carbon. Moissan describes the reaction of lithium hydride with sulfur dioxide. At room temperature the following equation applies:

$$2LiH + 2SO_2 \rightarrow Li_2S_2O_4 + H_2$$

At temperatures above 50°C (122°F) lithium sulfide is formed.

Although several methods are known for the production of the "saltlike" hydrides, the interaction of metal and hydrogen at elevated temperatures has so far been considered the most suitable. One kilogram of lithium metal combines with about 1,600 liters of hydrogen, forming lithium hydride, and one kilogram of lithium hydride, if brought to reaction with water, yields nearly 2,800 liters of hydrogen.

Lithium and Nitrogen

Lithium reacts with nitrogen and forms a black nitride, Li_3N, the melting point of which is about 275°C (527°F).[100] It can be remelted in vacuum or in a nitrogen atmosphere.

Lithium nitride, when brought in contact with water, yields ammonia, just like many other "saltlike" nitrides, notably those of magnesium, calcium, strontium, and barium. The production of nitrides of sodium and potassium is very difficult, and the nitrides of rubidium and cesium are not known.[84,85]

The nitrides of the Li_3N type combine readily with nitrides of some heavy metals, e.g., iron nitride, or with heavy metals in the presence

TABLE 14.8
PHYSICAL PROPERTIES OF LITHIUM OXIDES, NITRIDE, AND HYDRIDE

Property	Lithium monoxide	Lithium peroxide	Lithium nitride	Lithium hydride
Formula	Li_2O	Li_2O_2	Li_3N	LiH
Molecular weight	29.88	45.88	34.83	7.95
Density (g/cc)	2.013[56]	2.297[28]	1.38[16]	0.775[114]
Melting point				
°C	1427[13]	425[117]	275[12]	688[80]
°F	2600	797	527	1270
Boiling point				
°C	1527[16]	—	—	—
°F	2780	—	—	—
Heat of formation (kcal/mole)	−142.4[95]	−151.7[99]	−47.5[12]	−21.34[78]
Heat capacity (kcal/mole)	0.024 at 25°C (77°F)[63] 2.497 at 100°C (212°F) 8.892 at 200°C (392°F)	—	—	8.2 at 0°C (32°F)[79] 13.5 at 527°C (980.6°F)
Heat of solution (kcal/mole)	31.3[56]			
Heat of fusion (kcal/mole)	—	—	—	7[77]
Heat of hydrolysis (kcal/mole)	—	—	—	−31.76[78]
Entropy (cal/mole deg) at 25°C (77°F)	—	—	—	5.9[65]

of nitrogen, forming well-defined double nitrides which have definite melting points. Franken-burger, Andrussow, and Dürr[30] describe the compound $Li_3N \cdot FeN$ and some of its chemical and physical properties.

Lithium and Oxygen

The oxide, Li_2O, is a stable compound of lithium and oxygen but is highly reactive with water, carbon dioxide, and many refractory compounds.

There is only one peroxide of lithium known, namely Li_2O_2. A minute amount of this per-oxide is formed through the combustion of lithium in a current of oxygen. The peroxide may also be prepared using hydrogen peroxide.[123] Magnesium and calcium display a similar reluctance toward the formation of peroxides. On the other hand, sodium, potassium, rubidium, and cesium, when burned in oxygen, form rather stable peroxides (or tetroxides) quite readily. Table 14.8 summarizes the best available data on physical properties of the hydride, nitride, and oxides of lithium.

Lithium and Silicon

Lithium is the only element of its group known to alloy, or combine, with silicon. This is another illustration of lithium's resemblance to the alkaline earth elements. These alloys are produced in an evacuated container by heating the components to temperatures well above 600°C (1112°F). The resulting product is a solid, hard, and uniform mass of metallic appearance. Heating at temperatures above 600°C (1112°F), even for many hours, does not entail the loss of any appreciable amount of lithium, and the finished lithium-silicon alloys contain lithium and silicon in practically the same proportion as in the original reacting mixture.

These lithium-silicon alloys, although very

reactive under certain conditions (much more so in this respect than the silicides of the alkali-earth metals), are relatively resistant to at-mospheric attack. Exposed to the air, they will develop a thin, grayish-white surface film. A good-sized piece of this alloy will require sev-eral months' exposure to the atmosphere before it will be decomposed. If kept in closed con-tainers, lithium-silicon alloys can be kept in-definitely.

Moissan prepared a lithium silicide, the com-position of which he believed to be Li_6Si_2. Ac-cording to Moissan, the crystals of this silicide have a bluish luster, but are deliquescent and quickly disintegrate when exposed to the at-mosphere. He estimated the specific gravity of Li_6Si_2 to be about 1.12.

The physical properties and the processes of production of the later-prepared lithium-silicon alloys are distinctly different from those of the Li_6Si_2 described by Moissan. Moissan heated his charge in vacuum and emphasized the im-portance of keeping the temperature between 400–500°C (752–932°F), at which temperature any excess of lithium present in the charge dis-tilled off. Moissan always obtained the com-pound Li_6Si_2 which decomposed into lithium and silicon, beginning at temperatures above 500°C (932°F) and complete at temperatures above 600°C (1112°F). In Table 14.9 the densities and freezing ranges of various lithium-silicon alloys are recorded and compared with Moissan's Li_6Si_2.

OTHER LITHIUM COMPOUNDS

Aside from the compounds derived from the metal generally under anhydrous conditions, there are the lithium compounds produced during aqueous processing of lithium ores. Table 14.10 summarizes the best available data on physical properties of the more important lithium salts.

TABLE 14.9. LITHIUM AND SILICON ALLOYS

Composition	Density	Freezing range	Author
60% Li–40% Si	About 1.0	500–550°C (932–1022°F)	Osborg
50% Li–50% Si	1.17	About 625°C (1157°F)	"
40% Li–60% Si	1.4	680–700°C (1256–1292°F)	"
25% Li–75% Si	1.72	700–750°C (1292–1382°F)	"
Li_6Si_2 42.3% Li–57.5% Si	1.12	Decomposes above 500°C (932°F)	Moissan

TABLE 14.10. PHYSICAL PROPERTIES OF LITHIUM SALTS

Property	LiOH	LiOH·H_2O	Li_2CO_3	LiF	LiCl	LiBr	LiI	$LiClO_4$	$LiBO_2$	Li_2SiO_3	Li_4SiO_4	$LiNO_3$	Li_2SO_4
Mole weight	23.95	41.96	73.89	25.94	42.40	86.86	133.86	106.40	49.76	89.94	119.82	68.95	109.94
Density (g/cc)	2.54[9]	1.51[91]	2.111[68]	2.64[58]	2.068[48]	3.464[6]	3.94[52]	2.428[98]	—	2.52[91]	2.33[9]	2.37[49]	2.22[56]
Melting point °C	471.1[106]	—	735[90]	840[11]	614[119]	552[11]	440[11]	236[98]	846[62]	1188[99]	1250[99]	254[50]	859[99]
Melting point °F	880	—	1355	1544	1137	1026	824	457	1555	2170	2282	489	1578
Boiling point °C	d.925[37]	—	d.1200[19]	1681[99]	1380[12]	1310[11]	1171[11]	—	d.1200[92]				
Boiling point °F	1697	—	2192	3058	2516	2390	2140	—	2192				
Heat capacity (cal/mole/°C)	19.00[5]	—	23.28[66]	2.59[14]	12.9[99]								
Heat of formation (kcal/mole)	-105.13[65]	-188.93[83]	-290.54[73]	-145.6[12]	-97.70[12]	-87.4[12]	72.5[12]	-99.9[115]	—	376.7[99]	—	115.28[99]	342.8[99]
Heat of fusion (kcal/mole)	-2.48[94]	—	—	6.2[92]	-3.2[11]	2.9[11]	1.42[11]	—	6.0[99]	7.2[99]	7.4[99]	3.1[36]	3.0[99]
Heat of vaporization (kcal/mole)	—	—	—	51.0[99]	36.0[99]	35.4	40.77[11]	—	—	—	—	—	—
Heat of solution (kcal/mole)	-4.55[8]	-0.87[118]	—	-1.04[20]	-8.49[8]	11.39[72]	14.8[21]	—	—	—	—	0.35[49]	—
Entropy (cal/mole/°C)	12.8[64]	17.07[5]	21.60[15]	—	13.9[96]	—	—	—	—	—	—	—	—
Solubility in H_2O (%)	10.9[93]	—	1.31[103]	0.133[99]	46.0[96]	60.4[51]	164[59]	35.9[97]	3.5[76]	—	—	40[17]	25[3]

Lithium Hydroxide

Lithium hydroxide is considerably less hygroscopic than either sodium or potassium hydroxide. It crystallizes from its aqueous solution as a hydrate, $LiOH \cdot H_2O$, which can be finely powdered. Compared with sodium hydroxide and potassium hydroxide, its solubility in water is about one-fifth (by weight). On the other hand, lithium hydroxide is about 100 times more soluble than calcium hydroxide and nearly 4 times more soluble than barium hydroxide. Just like sodium or potassium hydroxide, lithium hydroxide can be fused. Its tendency to decompose upon heating is not as pronounced as in the case of the alkaline earth hydroxides. It melts at 445°C (833°F), much higher than the other alkali hydroxides. However, the vapor pressure of the molten lithium hydroxide is considerably higher than that of other alkali hydroxides; it is 760 mm Hg at about 925°C (1697°F), whereas the boiling points of sodium hydroxide and potassium hydroxide lie between 1300–1400°C (2372–2552°F).

Lithium Halides

Lithium and the halogens combine readily at elevated temperatures, forming the corresponding halides. The affinity of lithium for the halogens is indicated by the heats of formation of its halides. Of all alkali fluorides, lithium fluoride has the highest heat of formation. This "anomaly" disappears with increasing size of the halogen ion. Thus the heats of formation of the alkali bromides and iodides increase with the atomic weight of the alkaline metals, i.e., they reflect the increasing electropositive nature from lithium to cesium.

The atomic arrangement of the lithium halides resembles the sodium chloride structure and not the calcium fluoride structure which is characteristic for the alkaline earth halides. In general, however, the properties of the lithium halides suggest a close relationship between lithium and the alkaline earth metals. The lithium halides—like the alkaline earth halides—combine with ammonia, methylamine, ethylamine, etc., to form well-defined compounds which are stable at moderate temperatures. Sodium chloride and potassium chloride are not hygroscopic, and lithium chloride is more del-iquescent than calcium chloride. Lithium chloride has a tendency to combine with water to form a crystalline hydrate just as magnesium or calcium chloride does.

Lithium chloride and lithium bromide have unique thermodynamic properties, greatly depressing the vapor pressure over their solutions, making them of particular interest in air conditioning.

The solubility of lithium fluoride in water is relatively low, as is the case with the alkaline earth fluorides.

The characteristics of the lithium halides in the fused condition are quite remarkable.

Various Other Lithium Compounds

Analytical chemistry takes advantage of the fact that lithium phosphate, lithium carbonate, and lithium fluoride, in contrast to the corresponding alkali salts, are comparatively insoluble in water. Furthermore, the solubility of lithium chloride in organic solvents, such as alcohols, affords a convenient means of separating lithium chloride from the other alkali chlorides. In the case of lithium fluoride, the addition of alcohol to the aqueous solution makes it still less soluble.

The sulfate of lithium displays a remarkable similarity to magnesium sulfate. It forms double salts with sodium and potassium sulfates, such as $LiKSO_4$.

ELECTROCHEMISTRY OF LITHIUM

The electrochemical behavior of lithium is remarkable in many respects, a few of which will be pointed out. In aqueous solution the single potential of Li/Li^+ is -3.02 volts $(H_2/H^+ = 0.00$ volt$)$ as compared with -2.71 for sodium, -2.92 for potassium, and -2.92 for rubidium. (The cesium potential has not been accurately determined.) Lithium thus appears to be decidedly more electronegative or less noble than the other alkali metals; however, this is not the case, as will become evident if the hydration of the alkali ions is taken into consideration. All alkali ions in aqueous solution are more or less hydrated, and the lithium ion combines with many more H_2O molecules than, for instance, cesium. This explains why the mobility of the small lithium ion is only about

TABLE 14.11. ELECTRICAL CONDUCTIVITY, K, OF SOME FUSED ALKALI AND ALKALINE EARTH HALIDES
(reciprocal ohms/cc)

Temp. (°C)	LiF (A)	LiCl (A)	LiCl (B)	NaCl (B)	KF (C)	KCl (D)	MgCl₂ (B)	CaCl₂ (D)	SrCl₂ (E)	BaCl₂ (E)	AgCl (D)
550	—	—	—	—	—	—	—	—	—	—	4.34
600	—	—	—	—	—	—	—	—	—	—	4.48
650	—	—	6.0	—	—	—	—	—	—	—	4.62
700	—	—	6.2	—	—	—	—	—	—	—	4.76
750	—	—	6.4	—	—	—	1.09				
800	—	7.90	6.6	—	—	2.19	1.18	1.90	—	—	4.98
850	—	8.45	—	3.66	—	2.30	1.26	2.12			
900	20.3	9.01	—	3.77	3.28	2.40	1.38	2.32	1.98	(1.71)	5.14
950	23.4	9.21	—	3.88	3.73	2.50	1.44	2.50	2.14	1.89	
		(930°C)									
1,000	27.2	—	—	—	(4.2)	2.61	1.54	2.66	2.29	2.05	
1,050	—	—	—	—	—	—	—	2.76	2.43	2.19	

(A) Ryschkewitsch, E., *Z. Elektrochem.*, 39, 536 (1933).
(B) Landolt-Boernstein-Roth Tables, Suppl. Vol. I, p. 583 (Investigators: Blitz and Klemm).
(C) Landolt-Boernstein-Roth Tables, Vol. II, p. 1063 (Investigators: Jaeger and Kapma).
(D) Landolt-Boernstein-Roth Tables, Vol. II, p. 1064 (Investigators: Arndt and Gessler).
(E) Landolt-Boernstein-Roth Tables, Vol. II, p. 1063 (Investigator: Arndt).

half of that of the much larger cesium ion. The pronounced tendency of the lithium ion to combine with H_2O molecules is indicated by the large number of calories set free when the lithium ion and H_2O molecules combine. It is therefore evident that the single potential of lithium in aqueous solution represents, in reality, the change in energies produced by the following two reactions:

(1) $Li \rightarrow Li^+$
(2) $Li^+ + n\ H_2O \rightarrow Li^+$ hydrated

The condition of the lithium ion is less complex in the fused state, particularly in the case of molten halides. The electrical conductivity of fused lithium halides is very good, and lithium fluoride appears to have a conductivity higher than any other halogen salt, as shown in Table 14.11.

The decomposition voltages of fused lithium halides were determined by Neumann, Richter, and Bergve. Their results reveal the interesting fact that the temperature coefficient of, e.g., lithium chloride is 1.35×10^{-3}, whereas that of the chlorides of sodium, potassium, rubidium, and cesium, likewise determined by them, is 1.5×10^{-3}. If the decomposition voltage are plotted against the temperature, the chlorides of sodium, potassium, rubidium, and cesium show a straight line relation, the curves running parallel to each other, while the curve for

lithium chloride does not run parallel to these. The decomposition voltage of lithium chloride decreases less rapidly with increasing temperature; furthermore, within the range of temperatures investigated, the lithium chloride decomposition voltage is lower than those of the other alkali metals.

The distinctive character of lithium as a transition element is further revealed upon comparing its decomposition voltage with those of the chlorides of magnesium, calcium, strontium, and barium, which were also determined by Neumann and his associates. The temperature-voltage curves of the alkaline earth chlorides likewise show a straight line relation, the curves running parallel to each other, just as in the case of the alkali chlorides. But these parallel curves approach the abscissa at an angle different from that of the curves for the chlorides of sodium, potassium, rubidium, and cesium, and that of lithium chloride, as indicated by the temperature coefficient 0.71×10^{-3} for the decomposition voltage of the alkaline earth chlorides.

Figure 14.3 reproduces some of the results obtained by Neumann and his associates. From these results we conclude that: *Lithium ion is, under the conditions indicated, the least electronegative or least basic ion of the alkali group and is less electronegative than calcium, strontium, and barium ions.*

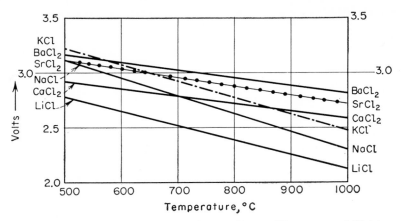

FIGURE 14.3. Decomposition potentials according to Neumann and Richter.

ALLOYS

Lithium, like many of the metallic elements of the alkali and alkaline earth groups, forms alloys with many other metallic elements. At times it plays the role of an alkali element and, at other times, the role of an alkaline earth element. Lithium alloys and forms intermetallic compounds with aluminum, zinc, and other metals. In combination with silicon, lithium shows its characteristics as an alkaline earth, but it does not form intermetallic compounds with copper, as does calcium. It may be noted, as a general rule, that lithium tends to form intermetallic compounds which are hard and brittle, with a high melting point and with slow deterioration when exposed to the atmosphere. Much work has been done on lithium systems with various metals by a number of investigators, among whom are the following: Assmann;[4] Czochralski and Rassow;[18] Fraenkel and Hahn;[29] Grube and co-workers;[38,39,40, 41,42,43,44,45] Henry and Cordiano;[53] Masing and Tammann;[75] and Pastorello.[89,89a,89b]

The state of knowledge concerning lithium in alloy systems as of 1959 is summarized in Table 14.12.

Constitutional diagrams for a number of these systems are given in the appendix to this chapter. (See Diagrams 1 to 14.)

Alloys of lithium with aluminum, zinc, lead, and magnesium appear to have engineering value.[4] These alloys contain lithium in amounts somewhat in excess of or even less than the solid solubility at ordinary temperatures. With a fraction of 1 per cent present, lithium would tend to improve the characteristics of the base metal, imparting toughness or hardness or both. The tensile strength and elastic properties of lithium-treated or lithium-containing alloy are markedly high.

Lithium-Magnesium Alloys

Observations made by Henry and others have indicated that lithium-containing alloy, with magnesium to the extent of 10 per cent lithium, does not corrode when exposed to the atmosphere. This is unique because, when the lithium content is 5 per cent or more in other metals, the product is subject to surface deterioration when in contact with the atmosphere for an appreciable period of time.

During World War II considerable work was

TABLE 14.12. STATE OF KNOWLEDGE CONCERNING LITHIUM ALLOY SYSTEMS

Phase Diagrams Established	Some Data on System	Probably Insoluble	No Data Available
Aluminium	Antimony	Chromium	Barium
Cadmium	Beryllium	Iridium	Columbium
Calcium	Boron	Iron	Germanium
Copper	Cesium	Molybdenum	Hafnium
Indium	Gallium	Osmium	Manganese
Lead	Gold	Palladium	Strontium
Magnesium	Nickel	Platinum	Tantalum
Mercury	Rhenium	Rhodium	Thorium
Potassium	Rubidium	Ruthenium	Titanium
Silver	Selenium	Tungsten	Vanadium
Sodium	Silicon	Uranium	Zirconium
Thallium	Tellurium		
Tin			
Zinc			

TABLE 14.13. INTERMETALLIC COMPOUNDS OF LITHIUM

Element	Formula	Stable up to °C	Melting point (°C)	Investigator
Mg	Li_2Mg_5	—	590	Grube, *et al.*
Al	Li_2Al_3	—	598	Czochvalski, *et al.*
Zn	$LiZn$	—	—	Fraenkel, *et al.*
	Li_2Zn_3	—	520	Grube, *et al.*
	$LiZn_2$	93	—	Grube, *et al.*
Cd	Li_3Cd	272	—	Grube, *et al.*
	$LiCd$	—	549	Grube, *et al.*
	$LiCd_3$	370	—	Grube, *et al.*
Hg	Li_3Hg	379	—	Zudowsky
	$LiHg$	—	600.5	Zudowsky
	$LiHg_2$	232	—	Zudowsky
	$LiHg_3$	−42	—	Zudowsky
Tl	Li_4Tl	381	—	Grube, *et al.*
	Li_3Tl	—	447	Grube, *et al.*
	Li_5Tl_2	—	448	Grube, *et al.*
	Li_2Tl	381	—	Grube, *et al.*
	$LiTl$	—	508	Grube, *et al.*
Pb	Li_4Pb	648	—	Grube, *et al.*
	Li_7Pb_2	—	726	Grube, *et al.*
	Li_3Pb	658	—	Grube, *et al.*
	Li_5Pb_2	642	—	Grube, *et al.*
	$LiPb$	—	482	Grube, *et al.*
Bi	Li_3Bi	—	1,145	Grube, *et al.*
	$LiBi$	415	—	Grube, *et al.*
Ag	Li_3Ag	—	450	Pastorello
	$LiAg$	—	955	Pastorello
Sn	Li_4Sn	—	765	Grube, *et al.*
	Li_7Sn_2	—	783	Grube, *et al.*
	Li_5Sn_2	720	—	Grube, *et al.*
	Li_2Sn	502	—	Grube, *et al.*
	$LiSn$	—	485	Grube, *et al.*
	$LiSn_2$	326	—	Grube, *et al.*

carried on by Battelle Memorial Institute and Dow Chemical Company for the production and use of lithium-magnesium alloys. These alloys contain as much as 8 to 12 per cent lithium and require the use of sodium-free lithium.[33]

The unique feature of these alloys is the nature of their crystal structure due to the addition of relatively large amounts of lithium. The alloy crystal is cubic body centered instead of the hexagonal structure expected in magnesium. These alloys are readily worked and develop excellent physical properties. How-ever, they are very much limited under temperature stress, as they lose strength rapidly above 150°C (302°F).

Lithium-Aluminum Alloys

According to Assmann[4] the solid solubility of lithium in aluminum is 3.5 per cent at the melting point, and 2.2 per cent at room temperature. The effect of small amounts of lithium on the physical properties of aluminum, or aluminum-rich alloys, is quite similar to that produced with magnesium, especially if silicon is present in the alloy. However, because of the lower equivalent weight of lithium, lower percentages than magnesium are required to produce the same physical effects.

Aluminum alloys containing lithium have so far found only limited industrial application. Among such lithium-aluminum alloys, scleron[18,18a,18b,18c] seems to be of special interest. A typical composition of a scleron alloy is aluminum, 83 per cent; zinc, 12 per cent; copper, 2 per cent; manganese, 0.5 to 1 per cent; iron, 0.5 per cent; silicon, 0.5 per cent; lithium, 0.1 per cent. The physical properties of scleron resemble those of mild steel or of brass. Its tensile strength, elastic properties, and hardness are reported to be superior to those of duraluminum alloys.

Lithium-Zinc Alloys

Metallgesellschaft A.-G.,[81,81a,81b,81c,81d,81e] Pack and Fox,[88] as well as Pierce and Anderson,[94,94a] have made some suggestions for the practical application of lithium-zinc alloys. Additions of lithium of the order of 0.005 per cent improve zinc alloys considerably and produce a grain refinement. The nature of the improvement apparently is similar to that produced by magnesium. Because of its low equivalent weight, a smaller quantity of lithium is required than of magnesium, and the improvement obtained through lithium is often superior.

Lithium-Lead Alloys

Czochralski and Rassow[18] investigated the lead-lithium system up to 2.15 per cent of lithium. They assumed that the solid solubility of lithium in lead is to be found between 0.04 and 0.09 per cent of lithium, at room temperature. According to Grube,[38] the solubility of lithium in lead is less than 0.1 per cent and more than 0.03 per cent. Grube also reports the following compounds of lithium and lead: $LiPb$, Li_5Pb_2, Li_3Pb, Li_7Pb_2, and Li_4Pb.

An addition of 0.05 per cent or less of lithium to lead improves the casting and physical properties of lead considerably. The lead becomes harder and tougher, maintaining a satisfactory ductility. At the same time, the tensile strength

and the modulus of elasticity are considerably increased. Furthermore, the presence of lithium in lead produces a fine grain structure and retards recrystallization. Garre and Mueller[34] compared the effect of various elements, such as copper, antimony, tin, nickel, zinc, and magnesium, with that of lithium on the grain size and hardness of lead. The results of these investigations show clearly that, of all the elements tested, lithium imparts by far the finest grain and greatest hardness in lead. Koch[67] suggested lead-lithium alloys, especially those containing small additions of cadmium or antimony, for the manufacture of cable sheaths. He states that lead containing as little as 0.005 per cent of lithium, when compared with pure lead, shows a considerable increase in tensile strength.

By far the most important application of lithium in lead has been in a lead-base, alkali-hardened bearing alloy. This alloy was developed in Germany nearly 40 years ago with the intention of replacing tin-base bearing alloys with one having superior hardness at elevated temperatures. The addition of lithium to lead was found to be essential in obtaining this end, making possible the commercial application of the new bearing alloy. The composition of this "B-Metal,"[121,121a,121b,121c] as it is known to the trade, is approximately as follows: lithium, 0.04 per cent; calcium, 0.73 per cent; sodium, 0.66 per cent; potassium, 0.03 per cent; aluminum, less than 0.2 per cent; balance, lead.

Lithium is the most effective constituent in "B-Metal." Its presence imparts great hardness, especially at elevated temperatures, high resistance to deformation, and satisfactory wearing qualities.

USES OF LITHIUM METAL

Lithium in Alloys

Although a variety of use possibilities for lithium in alloys are mentioned above, the actual volume of lithium moving into this market is small. The proved areas seem to be in aluminum and magnesium structural alloys and in copper and silver brazing alloys.

Lithium as a Degasifier and Refining Agent

Because of its chemical activity, lithium metal is able to remove gases from molten metals. Lithium combines with hydrogen, oxygen, sulfur, and nitrogen. Lithium compounds, resulting from its addition to molten metals, have relatively low densities and low melting points. This is of importance in removing solid impurities from the metal.

In many cases lithium is not soluble in or does not combine with the metal so treated; e.g., lithium is practically insoluble in molten copper and in iron.

Lithium metal is regularly used for the degasification of copper, particularly for high-conductivity castings.[71,113,113a]

It has been found that where a relatively large quantity of metal is cast, some increase in the quantity of lithium added is desirable. In general, for castings weighing 200 lb or less, the amount of lithium added for degasification would be of the order 0.01 per cent for bronzes and 0.02 per cent for high-conductivity copper. For castings weighing 200 to 2,000 lb, the addition of lithium should be increased two to three times.

Where the mass of molten metal is limited and therefore quickly cooled in the mold, the metal freezes before it can reoxidize. In the case of large masses of metal, an excess of lithium prevents reoxidation during the critical cooling period between molten metal and the solid state.

Lithium also acts as an agent for grain refinement in certain bronzes. It greatly increases the fluidity of the molten metal.

Lithium in Cast Iron

Over a period of years various efforts have been made to utilize the properties of lithium, as are those of magnesium, in the improvement of cast irons. It was found that the physical properties of cast iron are somewhat enhanced by adding minor amounts of lithium. However, within the past 5 years, in connection with the development of nodular iron, considerable evidence has been accumulated to show that additions of lithium to the iron facilitate the production of a nodular structure. The evidence further shows that smaller additions of lithium than of magnesium are required to obtain these properties. Moreover, lithium additions can be made without violent reaction, whereas magnesium additions have to be moderated by the addition of copper or nickel used in the form of copper- or nickel-magnesium alloy[22,22a,22b,97,111]—80 per cent copper or nickel, 20 per cent magnesium.

Lithium in Steels

Considerable work has been done over many years in treating molten steel with lithium and lithium alloys. By adding minor amounts of lithium to low-carbon steels some improvement in tensile strength without loss of elongation was evidenced, but to this date no method has been evolved satisfactorily to introduce lithium into steel. The difficulty arises from the fact that the molten steel temperature is appreciably above the boiling point of the lithium, which vaporizes violently.

Chrome-containing steels appear to offer an interesting possibility for lithium additions, but, again, the attendant difficulties of properly adding lithium present a problem.

It should be noted that in lithium additions to low-carbon steels, practically none of the lithium is retained in the cast material. In the chrome-containing steels, residual lithium can be determined, possibly owing to the formation of complex nitrides of lithium and chromium.

The value of lithium additions to steels lies in lithium's affinity for hydrogen, oxygen, sulfur, and nitrogen, and future investigations may justify research in this field to take advantage of the peculiar properties of lithium for the removal of certain gases from the steel by which improved physical characteristics may be realized.

Lithium in Organic Chemistry

Lithium metal is of particular interest in a wide variety of organic chemical reactions:

(1) Lithium alkyls and aryls produced from lithium metal.

(2) Lithium hydride produced from lithium metal.

(3) Lithium metal in place of magnesium in Grignard reactions.

(4) Lithium metal in condensation reactions.

(5) Lithium metal in acetylation reactions (vitamin A synthesis).

(6) Lithium amide ($LiNH_2$) produced from lithium metal in amination reactions.

(7) Lithium aluminum hydride ($LiAlH_4$) produced from lithium hydride, an ether-soluble hydride, and powerful reducing agent at low temperature.

(8) Lithium metal or lithium alkyls in stereospecific polymerization of isoprene to *cis*-polyisoprene.

Lithium in Atomic-Energy Developments

Lithium metal (lithium 7) was one of the first, if not the first, element fissioned to produce alpha particles (Rutherford *et al.*) under the impact of highly accelerated protons.

A significant nuclear reaction with lithium has been noted in the past few years for the production of tritium (H^3) through slow neutron irradiation, according to the following reaction:

$$_3Li^6 + O^{n1} \rightarrow 2He^4 + 1H^3$$

The isotope lithium 7 may also be used for control rods in fast reactors, in view of the fact that the absorption product, $_2He$, will not contaminate the pile. Because of its low melting point, lithium would have to be enclosed in a suitable thin tube, e.g. beryllium.

Nuclear power generation from light elements such as lithium may become an important possibility.

Lithium in High-Energy Fuels

Here, unfortunately, is a field heavily veiled in military secrecy. When corners of the veil are occasionally lifted, tempting glimpses of interesting possibilities for lithium are seen. The term "high-energy fuels," as used today, is usually applied to the boron hydrides, although the term is really much broader and includes any fuels whose Btu content is higher than that of conventional petroleum hydrocarbon fuels. Thus, slurries of metals in hydrocarbons, and other metalhydrides or metalorganics, all fall in the "high-energy-fuel" category.

As far as the boron hydrides are concerned, a conventional route to diborane is the reaction of lithium hydride with boron trifluoride etherate. Indications are, however, that lithium hydride in a slurry in some solvent such as ether is reacted with boron trichloride to produce diborane. The diborane is then pyrolysed to pentaborane and decaborane. These materials may then be alkylated to give the final high-energy fuels.

USES OF LITHIUM COMPOUNDS

This handbook is primarily devoted to the rare metals in metallic form, and lesser attention should therefore be given to compounds than to the metal itself. On the other hand, however, many of these metals are primarily structural materials or alloy ingredients, and their chemical derivatives have relatively little significance.

In the case of lithium, however, lithium compounds account for far more equivalent lithium than does lithium metal when the comparative markets are considered. Therefore, the pertinent physical properties of a number of important lithium compounds have been summarized in Table 14.8. Further, the fields in which lithium metal and, particularly, lithium compounds serve industry are summarized in Table 14.14.

TABLE 14.14. WHERE LITHIUM SERVES INDUSTRY

Agriculture	Air conditioning	Atomic energy	Batteries
Tobacco culture	Moisture absorption	Proton production	Primary cells
		Tritium production	(dry batteries)
		Power development	Storage batteries
Soil moisture retention	Dehumidification	Atomic hydrogen	(alkaline type)
Fungicides			
Lithium carbonate	*Lithium bromide*	*Lithium metal*	*Lithium chloride*
	Lithium chloride	*Lithium hydride*	*Lithium hydroxide*

TABLE 14.14. WHERE LITHIUM SERVES INDUSTRY (*cont.*)

Beverages	Bleaching	Ceramics	Chemicals
Flavor and tonic values	Production of solid, soluble, and stable bleaching agents	Porcelain enamels Ground coats and covercoats on steel and aluminum for acid resistance, improved bonding, lower firing temperature Pottery glazes Special glasses	Production of miscellaneous lithium compounds Catalysts
		~	
		Lithium carbonate, manganite, titanate,	*Lithium carbonate*
Lithium citrate	*Lithium hypochlorite*	*silicate zirconate, and*	
Lithium carbonate		*cobaltite*	
Lithium chloride	*Lithium peroxide*	*Lithium minerals*	

Gas purification	Heat transfer	Hydrogen	Iron and steel
Removal of trace impurities in helium, argon, etc.	Stable low melting point Salt mixtures	Hydrogen generation suitable for air transport	Nodular iron grain refinement in steels
Lithium metal			*Lithium metal and alloys*
Carbon dioxide removal			
Anhydrous lithium hydroxide			
			Desulfurization of steel
	Lithium nitrate		
		Lithium hydride	*Lithium carbonate*

Military uses	Nonferrous metals	Petroleum	Pharmaceuticals
Army Navy Air Force (information restricted)	Chrome bronzes high-conductivity copper castings	Catalysts Sulfur removal	Reagent to produce antihistamines
		Lithium metal	*Lithium amide*
	Bronze, nickel, silver, "Monel," and precious-metal	*Lithium hydride* ~	~
	castings	Lubricants	Reagent to produce
	Bearing metals	Low-temperature	synthetic vitamins
	Aluminum castings	greases	
	Lithium metal cartridges	*Lithium hydroxide* *Lithium stearate*	
	~		*Lithium metal*
	Magnesium alloys *High-purity lithium metal*		

TABLE 14.14 WHERE LITHIUM SERVES INDUSTRY (*cont.*)

Plastics	Refrigeration	Rescue and signal work	Welding
Stabilizers	Stabilization of	Balloon inflation	Flukes for aluminum
Catalysts	liquid ammonia		and magnesium
		Lithium hydride	
		~	
		Flares	*Lithium chloride*
Lithium stearate			
Lithium lactate	*Lithium nitrate*	*Lithium nitrate*	*Lithium fluoride*
Lithium carbonate			

Bibliography and References

1. Antropoff, A. von, and Germann, E., *Z. physik. Chem.*, **137**, 209–37 (1928); Chem. Zentr., II, 2429 (1928).
2. Antropoff, A. von. *Z. Elektrochem.*, **38**, 588–89 (1932); *Chem. Zentr.*, **II**, 1878 (1932); *Chem. Abst.*, **26**, 5024 (1932).
3. Appleby, M. P., Crawford, F. H., and Gordon, K., *J. Chem. Soc.*, **1934**, 1665–71.
4. Assmann, P., *Z. Metallkunde*, **18**, 256–60 (1926); *Chem. Abst.*, **20**, 1585, 3424 (1926).
5. Bauer, T. W., Johnson, H. L., and Kerr, E. C., *J. Am. Chem. Soc.*, **72**, 5174–76 (1951).
6. Baxter, G. P., *Am. Chem. J.*, **31**, 558 (1904).
7. Been, S. A., Edwards, H. S., Teeter, C. E., Jr., and Calkins, V. P., *Report NEPA-1585* (Sept. 7, 1950), Oak Ridge, Tenn., Fairchild Airplane & Engine Corp.
8. Bichowsky, F. R., and Rossini, F. D., "Thermochemistry of Chemical Substances," New York, Reinhold Publ. Corp., 1936.
9. Blitz, W. and Lemke, A., *Z. anorg. u. allgem. Chem.*, **203**, 330–44 (1932).
10. Bohm, B. and Klemm, W., *Z. anorg. u. allgem. Chem.*, **243**, 69 (1939).
11. Brewer, L., "Chemistry & Metallurgy of Misc. Materials: Thermodynamics," National Nuclear Energy Series IV-19B, New York, McGraw-Hill Book Co., 1950.
12. Brewer, L., Bromley, L. A., Gilles, P. W. and Lofgren, N. L., "The Chemistry & Metallurgy of Misc. Materials," L. L. Quill, Ed., New York, McGraw-Hill Book Co., 1950.
13. Brewer, L. and Margrave, J., *J. Phys. Chem.*, **59**, 421 (1955).
14. Bronsted, J. N., *Z. Elektrochem.*, **20**, 554 (1914).
15. Brown, O. L. and Latimer, W. M., *J. Am. Chem. Soc.*, **58**, 2228–29 (1936).
16. Burton, W. N., Coffman, S. W., and Randolph, C. L., *U.S. Office of Naval Research Report RTM-57* (1949).

17. Campbell, A. N. and Bailey, *Can. J. Chem.*, **36**, 518 (1958).
18. Czochralski, J., and Rassow, E., *Z. Metallkunde*, **19**, 111–12 (1927).
18a. Czochralski, J., and Welter, G., U.S. Patent 1,620,081, "Alloy of Lithium and Aluminum" (March, 1927).
18b. Czochralski, J., *Z. Metallkunde* (1924).
18c. Czochralski, J., U.S. Patent 1,620,082, "Aluminum Alloy Containing Lithium" (March, 1927).
19. DeForcrand, R., *Compt. rend.*, **146**, 515 (1908).
20. DeForcrand, R., *Ann. chim. phys.*, **24**, 258 (1911).
21. DeForcrand, R., *Compt. rend.*, **152**, 28, 1073 (1911).
22. De Sy, A. L., "Belgian Research Advances, Nodular Graphite Theory," *Am. Foundryman*, **15**, 838 (1949).
22a. De Sy, A. L., "Reports Latest Nodular Graphite Work," *Am. Foundryman*, **15**, 60 (1949).
22b. De Sy, A. L., "Nodular Cast Iron Produced with Li, Ca, Ba, Sr, and Na," *Metal Progress*, 357 (Sept. 1950).
23. Devaney, J. J., *Report LA-1960*, Los Alamos, New Mexico, U.S. Atomic Energy Commission.
24. Dominion Magnesium Co., Private Communication (1957).
25. Douglas, T. B., Epstein, L. F., Dever, J. L. and Howland, W. H., *J. Am. Chem. Soc.*, **77**, 2144–50 (1955).
26. Eigo, D. P., Franklin, J. W. and Cleaver, G. H., *Eng. & Mining J.* **156**, (9), 75–89 (1955).
27. Ephraim, F. and Michel, *Helv. Chim. Acta*, **4**, 900 (1921).
28. Feher, F., von Wilucki, I. and Dost, G., *Chem. Ber.*, **86**, 1429 (1953).
29. Fraenkel, W. and Hahn, R., *Metallwirtschaft*, **10**, 641–42 (1931).

30. Frankenburger, W., Andrussow, L. and Dürr, F., *Z. Elektrochem.*, **34**, 632–37 (1928).

31. Freeth, W. E. and Raynor, G. V., "Ag-Li Syst.," *J. Inst. Metals,* **82**, 569–74 (1954).

32. Freeth, W. E. and Raynor, G. V., "Mg-Li Syst.," *J. Inst. Metals,* **82**, 575–80 (1954).

33. Frost, P. D., Jackson, J. H., Loonam, A. C., and Lorig, C. H., "The Effect of Sodium Contamination on Magnesium-Lithium Base Alloys," *J. Metals,* (Sept. 1950).

34. Garre, B. and Mueller, A., *Z. Metallkunde,* **23**, 236 (1931); *Z. anorg. u. allgem. Chem.,* **190**, 120–22 (1930).

35. Gmelin-Kraut, "Handbuch der anorganischen Chemie," 8th Ed., System No. 20.

36. Goodwin, H. M. and Kalmus, H. T., *Phys. Rev.,* **28**, 1 (1909).

37. Grimes, W. R., "Reactor Handbook," *Z*, Section 6, Wash., D.C. U.S. Govt. Printing Office (May 1955).

38. Grube, G., *Z. angew. Chem.,* **45**, 550 (1932).

39. Grube, G. and Klaiber, *Z. Electrochem.,* **40**, 745–54 (1934).

40. Grube, G. and Meyer, *Z. Electrochem.,* **40**, 771–77 (1934).

41. Grube, G. and Schaufler, G., *Z. Elektrochem.,* **40**, 593–600 (1934).

42. Grube, G., von Zeppelin, H. and Bumm, H., *Z. Elektrochem.,* **40**, 160–64 (1934).

43. Grube, G. and Vosskühler, H., *Z. anorg. u. allgem. Chem.,* **215**, 211–24 (1933).

44. Grube, G., Vosskühler, H. and Schlecht, H., *Z. Electrochem.,* **40**, 270–74 (1934).

45. Grube, G., Vosskühler, H. and Vogt, H., *Z. Electrochem.,* **38**, 869–80 (1932).

46. Grube, G. and Wolf, W., "In-Li System, Hg-Li System," *Z. Elektrochem.,* **41**, 675–81 (1935).

47. Guntz, A. and Broniewski, W., *Compt. rend.,* **147**, 1474 (1908).

48. Haigh, F. L., *Am. Chem. J.,* **34**, 1142 (1912).

49. Haigh, F. L., *J. Am. Chem. Soc.,* **34**, 1138 (1912).

50. Harkins, W. D. and Clark, G. L., *J. Am. Chem. Soc.,* **37**, 1828 (1915).

51. Heiks, J. R. and Garrett, A. R., *J. Am. Chem. Soc.,* **76**, 2587–90 (1954).

52. Henglein, F. A., *Z, physik. Chem.,* **117**, 285 (1925).

53. Henry, O. and Cordiano, H. V., *Am. Inst. Mining Met. Engrs., Tech. Publ. No. 536* (1934).

54. Hess, Frank, "The Pegmatites at Tinton, S. Dakota," *U.S. Bur. Mines, R.I. 3040* (1938).

55. Heumann, F. K. and Salmon, O. N., *KAPL Report No. 1667* (Dec. 1, 1956).

56. Hodgman D. C., "Handbook of Chemistry & Physics," 38th Ed., Cleveland, Chemical Rubber Publishing Co., 1956.

57. Howland, W. H., and Epstein, L. F., "Na-Li Syst.," Advances in Chemistry Series, No. 19, "Handling & Uses of the Alkali Metals," Wash., D.C., Amer. Chem. Soc. (1957).

58. Hutchison, C. A., and Johnston, H., *J. Am. Chem. Soc.,* **62**, 1365–68 (1940).

59. Huttig, G. F. and Renscher, F., *Z. anorg. u. allgem. Chem.,* **137**, 155–80 (1924).

60. Huttner, K. and Tammann, G., *Z. anorg. Chem.,* **43**, 215–27 (1905).

61. Jaeger, F. M., *J. Washington Acad.,* **1**, 49–52 (1911).

62. Jaeger, F. M., *Z. anorg. Chem.,* **101**, 178 (1917).

63. Johnston, H. L. and Bauer, T. W., *J. Am. Chem. Soc.,* **73**, 1119–22 (1951).

64. Kelley, K. K., *U.S. Bureau of Mines Bull. 393* (1936).

65. Kelley, K. K., *U.S. Bureau of Mines Bull. 434* (1941).

66. Kelley, K. K., *U.S. Bureau of Mines Bull. 477* (1950).

67. Koch, E., U.S. Patent 1,926,545, "Lead Cable Sheaths Containing Lithium" (Sept. 1933).

68. Kremers, P., *Pogg. Ann.,* **99**, 443 (1857).

69. Landolt, P. E., *J. Electrochem. Soc.,* **102**, (12), 285–87C (1955).

70. Landolt, P. E., "Economics of Li and Metal," *Mining Eng.,* **9**, 460–64 (Apr. 1957).

71. Landolt, P. E. and Pyne, F. R., "Use of Lithium Cartridges," *Foundry* (March 1949).

72. Lange, E. and Schwartz, E., *Z. physik. Chem.,* **133**, 129–50 (1928).

73. Latimer, W. M., "The Oxidation States of the Elements and Their Potentials in Aqueous Solutions," 2nd Ed., New York, Prentice-Hall, 1953.

74. Leute, K. M. and Ellestad, R. S., U.S. Patent No. 2,516,109 (1950).

74a. Lyon, R. N., "Liquid Metals Handbook," NAVEXOS P-733 (Rev.), 2nd Ed., Atomic Energy Commission and Department of the Navy, Washington, June 1952.

75. Masing, G. and Tammann, G., *Z. anorg. u. allgem. Chem.,* **67**, 183–99 (1910).

76. Menzel, H., *Z. anorg. u. allgem. Chem.,* **166**, 63–98 (1927).

77. Messer, C. B., Damon, E. B. and Maybury, P. C., *U.S. Atomic Energy Commission Report NYO-3958* (1955).

78. Messer, C. E., Fasolino, L. G. and Thalmeyer, C. E., *J. Am. Chem. Soc.,* **77**, 4524 (1955).

79. Messer, C. E. and Gibb, T. R. P., Jr., *U.S. Atomic Energy Commission Report NYO-8022* (1957).

80. Messer, C. E., Seales, R. A. and Mellor, J.,

U. S. Atomic Energy Commission Report
NYO-8021 (1957).

81. Metallgesellschaft A.-G., German Patent
562,006 (1928-32).

81a. Metallgesellschaft A.-G., German Patent
569,147 (1928-32).

81b. Metallgesellschaft A.-G., German Patent
476,259 (1925).

81c. Metallgesellschaft A.-G., German Patent
375,244 (1920-21).

81d. Metallgesellschaft A.-G., German Patent
413,723 (1922-23).

81e. Metallgesellschaft A.-G., and Weidmann, H.,
German Patent 413,722 (1922-23).

82. Miller, E. C., "Corrosion by Liquid Lithium,"
in "Liquid Metals Handbook," NAVEXOS
P-733 (Rev.), 2nd Ed., Atomic Energy Commission and Department of the Navy, Washington, D.C., June, 1952.

84. Moers, K., Z. anorg. u. allgem. Chem., 113,
179-28 (1920).

85. Moissan, H., Compt. rend., 135, 652 (1902).

86. Moran, H. E., J. Phys. Chem., 60, 1666-67
(1956).

87. Novikov, I. I., Soloviev, A. N., Khabakh-
nashera, E. M., Gruzder, V. A., Pridantzer,
A. I. and Vasenina, M. Ya., J. Nuclear Energy
(USSR), 4, 387-408 (1957).

88. Pack, C. and Fox, J. C., U. S. Patent 1,767,011
"Alloy" (1930).

89. Pastorello, S., Gazz. chim. ital., 60, 988-92
(1930).

89a. ibid., 60, 493-501 (1930).

89b. ibid., 61, 47-51 (1931).

90. Payne, J. H., J. Am. Chem. Soc., 59, 947
(1937).

91. Pepinsky, R., Phys. Rev., 55, 1115 (1939).

92. Petit, G., and Cremieu, A., Compt. rend., 243,
360-63 (1956).

93. Pickering, S. V., J. Chem. Soc., 63, 890 (1893).

94. Pierce, Wm. R. and Anderson, E. A., U.S.
Patent 1,832,653, "Zinc Base Alloy and
Wrought Products Made Therefrom" (1931).

94a. Pierce, Wm. R. and Anderson, E. A., U.S.
Patent 1,832,733, "Zinc Base Alloy and
Wrought Products Made Therefrom" (1931).

95. Pohl, R. and Pringsheim, P., Ber. deut.
physik. Ges., 14, 49-59 (1912).

96. Ralston, O. C. and Fraas, F., "Chloride Volatilization of Lithium from Spodumene," U.S.
Bur. Mines, R.I. 3344 (1937).

96a. "Reactor Handbook", Vol. 3, Sect. 1, "General Properties of Materials," U. S. Atomic
Energy Commission, AECD-3647, March,
1955.

97. Reese, D. J., Symposium "Nodular Graphite
Cast Iron," Am. Foundryman, 16, 32 (1949).

98. Richards, T. W. and Willard, H. H., J. Am
Chem. Soc., 32, 5-49 (1910).

99. Rossini, F. D., Wagman, D. D., Evans, W. H.,
Levine, S. and Jaffe, I., Circular 500, Natl.
Bur. of Stds., Wash., D.C., U.S. Govt. Print-
ing Office (Feb. 1, 1952).

100. Sato, S., Sci. Papers Inst. Phys. Chem. Research (Tokyo), 35, 182-90 (1939).

101. Schou, M., Toxicity, Acta pharmacol. et toxicol., 15, 70-84 (1958).

102. Schumacher, E. E., Ellis, W. C. and Eckel,
J. F., Bell Telephone System, Tech. Publ.
Monograph B515, Oct. 1930.

103. Seidell, A. "Solubilities of Inorganic & Metal-
Organic Compounds," New York, D. Van
Nostrand Co., 1940.

104. Severyns, J. H., Wilkinson, E. R., and
Schumb, W. C., Ind. Eng. Chem., Anal. Ed.,
4, 371-73 (1932).

105. Shamrai, F. I. and Saldau, P. J., "Al-Li System," Bull. Acad. Sci. USSR, 1937, 631-40.

106. Shomate, C. H. and Cohen, A. J., J. Am.
Chem. Soc., 77, 285-86 (1955).

107. Simmons, J. P. and Ropp, D. C. L., J. Am.
Chem. Soc., 50, 1650-53 (1928).

108. Simon, A. and Kimmerle, H., Z. anorg. u.
allgem. Chem., 202, 382-84 (1931).

109. Sims, C. E. and Lilliequist, G. A., Am. Inst.
Mining Met. Engrs., Tech. Publ. No. 453.

110. Sittig, M., Brit. Chem. Eng., 3, (3), 130-33
(1958).

111. Smalley, O., "Nodular Cast Iron—The Patent
Situation," Iron Age, 164, 68 (1949).

112. Smatko, J., "Degussa cell oper. data," PB-
25724, FIAT Report No. 786 (April 1946).

113. Smith, W. C., U.S. Patent 1,923,955, "Alloy"
(1933).

113a. Smith, W. C., U.S. Patent 1,812,992, "Method
of Casting Metals and Alloys Therefrom"
(1931).

114. Staritsky, E. and Walker, D. J., Anal. Chem.,
28, 1055 (1956).

115. Suttle, J. F., "The Alkali Metals," Princeton,
N.J., D. Van Nostrand Co., 1957.

116. Taylor, J. W., Metallurgia, 50, 161-65 (1954).

117. Tzentnershver, M. and Blumenthal, M., Bull.
Intern. acad, polonaise, Class sci. math. nat.,
1933A, 499-522.

118. Ueda, Y., J. Chem. Soc. Japan, 52, 740 (1931).

119. Van Laar, J. J., Z. anorg. Chem., 149, 326
(1925).

120. Webber, H. A., Goldstein, D. and Fellinger,
R. C., Trans. A.S.M.E., 77, 97-102 (1955).

121. Welter, G., Z. Metallkunde, 18, 117-20 (1926).

121a. Welter, G., Z. Ver. deut. Ing., 70, 772-776
(1926).

121b. Welter, G., U.S. Patent 1,625,077, "Lithium Containing Bearing Metals" (1927).

121c. Welter, G., U.S. Patent 1,625,078, "Lead Alkali Metal Containing Bearing Metal Alloys" (1927).

122. Williamson, D. R., "Ores and Processing,"

Mineral Industries Bull., Colorado School of Mines, 1, (2), 1–8 (March 1958).

123. Winternitz, P. F., U.S. Patent 2,488,485 (1949).

124. Wolfson, M. R., "Ca-Li System," *Trans. Amer. Soc. Metals,* 49, 794–801 (1957).

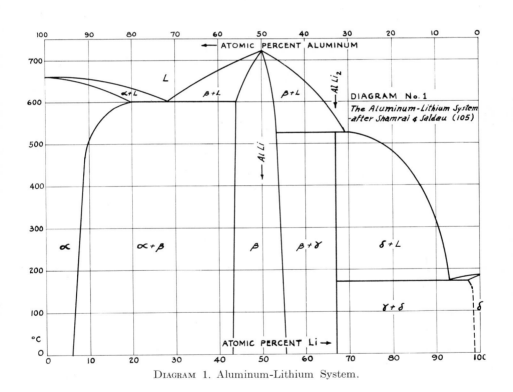

DIAGRAM 1. Aluminum-Lithium System.

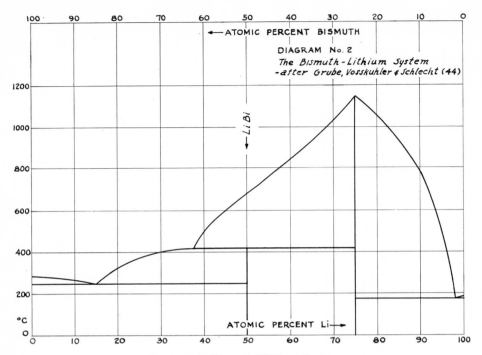

DIAGRAM 2. Bismuth-Lithium System.

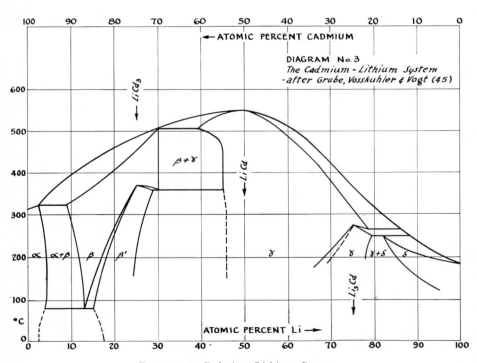

DIAGRAM 3. Cadmium-Lithium System.

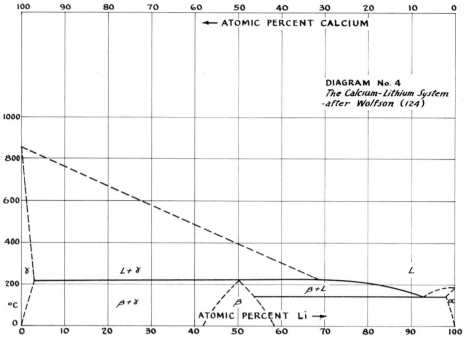

DIAGRAM 4. Calcium-Lithium System.

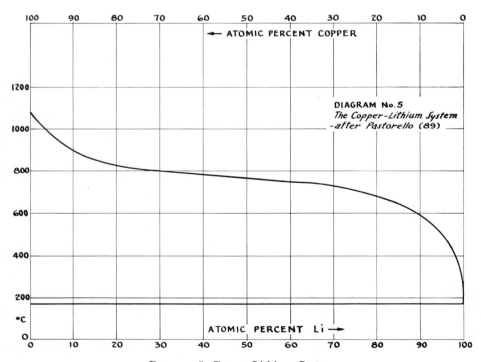

DIAGRAM 5. Copper-Lithium System.

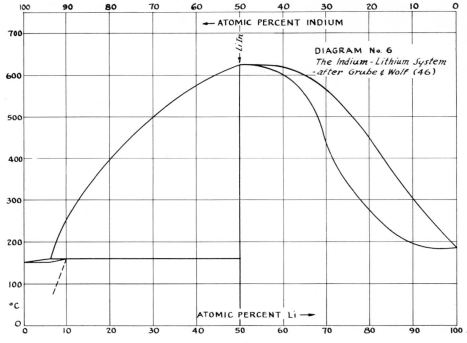

DIAGRAM 6. Indium-Lithium System.

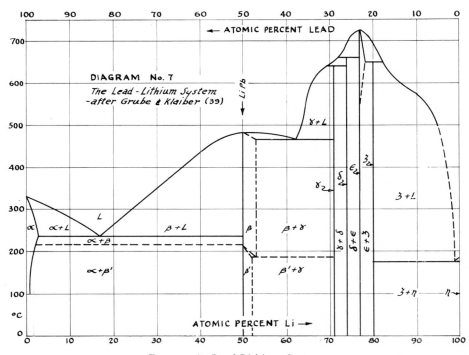

DIAGRAM 7. Lead-Lithium System.

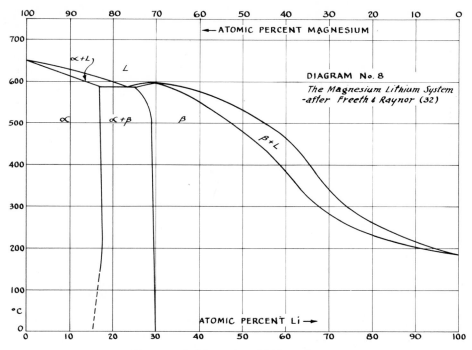

DIAGRAM 8. Magnesium-Lithium System.

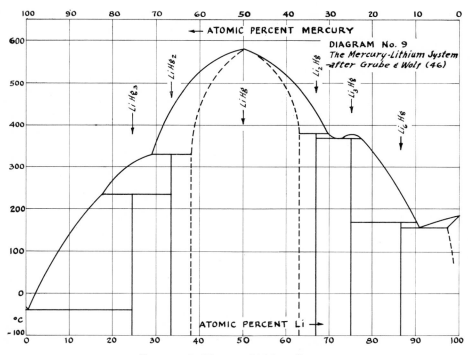

DIAGRAM 9. Mercury-Lithium System.

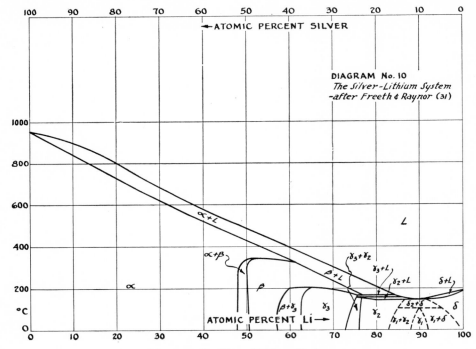

DIAGRAM 10. Silver-Lithium System.

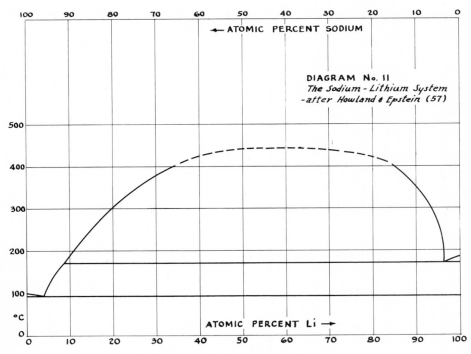

DIAGRAM 11. Sodium-Lithium System.

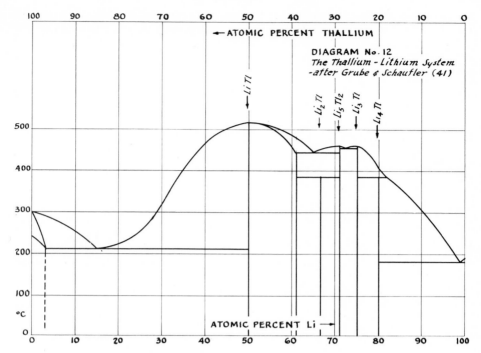

DIAGRAM 12. Thallium-Lithium System.

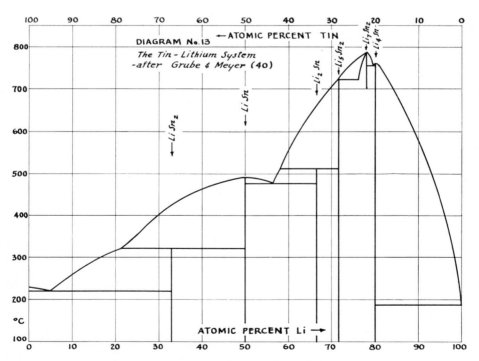

DIAGRAM 13. Tin-Lithium System.

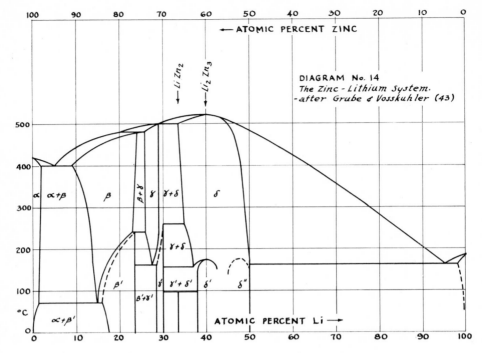

DIAGRAM 14. Zinc-Lithium System.

15. MANGANESE

CHARLES L. MANTELL

Consulting Engineer
Foote Mineral Company
Philadelphia, Pennsylvania

Manganese, a hard, brittle metal melting at 1245°C (2273°F), was first recognized as an element by the Swedish chemist Scheele, while working with the manganese dioxide ore pyrolusite, and was isolated by Gahn in 1774. Frequently found in conjunction with iron ores, the metal was named for the magnetic properties exhibited by pyrolusite from the Latin, *magnes,* or magnet; the German equivalent is *Mangan* and the French, *manganése.*

The addition of manganese as spiegeleisen, initiated in 1856 by Robert Mushet in the Bessemer steelmaking process, made that process practical. In 1888 Robert Hadfield discovered the 14 per cent manganese steels. Manganese is essential in steel manufacture for the control of sulfur content, and this application accounts for the major portion of the manganese consumed. About 14 lb of manganese, chiefly in the form of ferromanganese, is needed for each ton of steel. A major market for electrolytic manganese is in strip steel, the entire family of stainless steels, and specifically the 201 and 202 types in which manganese is employed as an austenite-former and replaces nickel.

The element, whose atomic number is 25 and atomic weight 54.93, is located in Group VIIA of the periodic table between chromium and iron horizontally. Until rhenium, atomic number 75 (1924), and technetium (or masurium or ekamanganese), atomic number 43 (1937), were discovered, manganese was the only element known in Group VIIA.

Manganese metal in pure form became an industrial metal in the late 1930's, as the result of the electrolytic process for its recovery. Relatively impure metal, made by aluminothermic or silicothermic reduction of the oxides, had been available, but only with the advent of the very pure electrolytic product has precise and extensive work on the potentialities of manganese been possible. Much of the work done on alloy systems with less pure manganese must be reviewed. The element is discussed in this book, because the pure metal is still regarded as uncommon, despite its present production of 100 tons/day of 99.97 per cent metal.

OCCURRENCE

Manganese is widely distributed in the combined state, ranking twelfth in abundance among the elements in the earth's crust. It is commonly found in association with iron ores in concentrations too low in most cases, however, to make its commercial recovery attractive. The ores of manganese are tabulated in Table 15.1.

The United States is a "have not" nation insofar as deposits of high-grade manganese ore are concerned, as pointed out in the Paley Report.[15] The manganese deposits in this country are estimated as 3,500 million long (2,240 lb) tons of ore and 75 million tons of contained manganese. More than 98 per cent is in 12 large low-grade deposits, the most important of which are at Chamberlain, South Dakota; Cuyuna Range, Minnesota; Aroostook County, Maine,

TABLE 15.1. ORES OF MANGANESE

Mineral	Color	Hardness	Manganese content when pure (%)	Chemical form	Density (g/cc)
Pyrolusite	Soft gray to black; metallic luster	6–6.5	63.2	MnO_2	4.8
Psilomelane	Black, dull, semimetallic luster	5–6	45–60	$BaMn^2Mn_8^4O_{16}(OH)_4$	3.7–4.7
Manganite	Dark gray to black	4	62.4	$Mn_2O_3H_2O$ or $MnO(OH)$	4.2–4.4
Braunite	Brown	6–6.5	62	$3Mn_2O_3 \cdot MnSiO_3$	4.8
Hausmannite	Brown to black; veins in igneous rock	5.5	72	Mn_3O_4	4.84
Rhodochrosite ⎫ Dialogite ⎬	Pink, red, gray, brown; vitreous luster	3–4	48	$MnCO_3$	3.0
Rhodonite	Red, pink, brown	6–6.5	42	$MnSiO_3$	3.63

and Artillery Peak, Arizona, as shown in Table 15.2.

Over 90 per cent of the country's consumption of manganese ore is imported, and most of the domestic ore is derived from the Butte, Montana, district as the carbonate mineral, rhodochrosite.

In 1959 the huge Amapá district mine in Brazil shipped 991,385 tons to the United States. Total United States imports were of the order of 2,400,000 short tons. Brazil, India, Ghana, and the Union of South Africa supply by far the major portion of the United States demands for manganese ore, with small amounts from Chile, Argentina, and Mexico. Ghana sup-

plied most of the battery- and chemical-grade ore. Brazil is expected to supply increasing percentages of metallurgical ore for electric furnace ferroalloys, spiegeleisen, and electrolytic metal.

Were an economic recovery procedure available, the manganese requirement for steel could be obtained on a current basis from the basic open hearth slag containing 10 to 15 per cent manganese. This concentration is equal to or better than much of the low-grade ore available, and is located at the mills.

The strategic importance of manganese has impelled the development of methods of utilizing our low-grade deposits and open-hearth slag for manganese oxides. The program has been conducted by the United States Bureau of Mines, the American Iron and Steel Institute, the General Services Administration, and private companies.

PRODUCTION AND ECONOMIC STATISTICS

The only source of pure manganese is the electrolytic process.

Production on a commercial scale began in 1939, and, by 1940, 200 tons a year were consumed, to jump to 600 tons in 1941. By 1952 the capacity of Electro Manganese Corporation at Knoxville was 3,600 tons annually, and in 1953 a second plant was brought into production. In 1956 the Electro Manganese Corporation consolidated with Foote Mineral Company, and in 1957 a third plant extension was built and brought into production.

TABLE 15.2. MANGANESE ORE DEPOSITS IN UNITED STATES (LONG TONS)

	Tonnage (millions of ore)	Tonnage (millions, manganese)	Manganese (%)
Estimated total	3,500	75	3–48
Artillery Peak, Arizona	200	8	3–4
	20	1	5
	2–3	0.3	10
	0.5	0.6	15
Chamberlain, South Dakota	2,000	50	3–15
	78	10	15
Aroostook County, Maine			6–9
Phillipsburg and Butte, Montana	0.2	0.1	48

TABLE 15.3. MANGANESE AND FERROALLOYS

	Typical analysis					Selling price in cents/lb of alloy	Selling price in cents/lb of contained Mn
	Mn (%)	Fe (%)	Si (%)	P (%)	C (%)		
Electrolytic manganese	99.98 min	0.001 max	Not found	Not found	0.004	—	34.00
Electrolytic manganese, hydrogen removed	99.98 min	0.001 max	Not found	Not found	0.004	—	34.75
Manganese metal (Thermit)	95.5 min	2.0–2.5	1.0 max	—	0.06–0.20	45.75	48.00
Low-carbon ferromanganese	Approx 90	Balance	1.0 max	0.06 max	0.07 max	—	37.15
	80–85	Balance	1.0 max	0.06 max	0.07 max	—	35.10
	80–85	Balance	1.0 max	0.20 max	0.10 max	—	34.35
	80–85	Balance	1.0 max	0.20 max	0.15 max	—	33.60
	80–85	Balance	1.0 max	0.20 max	0.30 max	—	32.10
	80–85	Balance	1.0 max	0.20 max	0.50 max	—	31.60
	80–85	Balance	5.0–7.0	0.25 max	0.75 max	—	28.60
Medium-carbon ferromanganese	80–85	Balance	1.50 max	—	1.25–1.50	—	25.50
Standard ferromanganese	74–76	Balance	1.0 max	0.35 max	7–8	12.25	16.3
Standard ferromanganese briquettes	66	Balance	1.0 max	0.35 max	7–8	14.80	22.4
Spiegeleisen	16–19	Balance	3.0 max	—	6.50 max	4.48	25.6
	19–21	Balance	3.0 max	—	6.50 max	4.57	22.8
	21–23	Balance	3.0 max	—	6.50 max	4.68	21.3

During the period 1942 to 1946, the Bureau of Mines produced some 1,500,000 lb of electrolytic manganese at its Boulder City, Nevada, plant.[9]

By 1953 the Union Carbide Metals Co., a division of Union Carbide Corporation, was operating an electrolytic manganese plant at Marietta, Ohio, using manganese slags as a raw material.

In 1960 production capacity was estimated at 100 tons/day, which is perhaps of the order of 1 per cent of the manganese consumption in the form of ferroalloys and spiegeleisen and related materials.

Electrolytic manganese is employed in strip steels, valve steels, and stainless steels; with nickel in the Type 200 series stainless steels which are chromium-manganese-nickel-iron alloys, austenitic in character; and as an alloying agent in nonferrous alloys of copper (bronzes, manganin, instrument alloys), aluminum, magnesium, nickel, and in bismuth magnetic materials. It is a raw material for pure manganese chemicals, driers, and catalysts.

Pure manganese competes with low-carbon and low-iron grades of ferromanganese for many of the uses where the latter previously have been the standard additives. Such competition exists because electrolytic manganese has negligible contents of carbon, phosphorus, sulfur, and silicon; thus it is often employed for making steels having low specifications for such elements.

Table 15.3 shows comparative materials, prices, and analyses.

An important economic consideration with respect to manganese ores is that the cost of mining and treating the low-grade domestic ores to extract a product as good as that yielded by imported ores is at least twice, and in some cases more than four times, the price of foreign ore delivered to the United States.[9,10] This factor affects the cost of pure manganese metal as well as the cost of ferromanganese.

DERIVATION

The American development based on electrolysis of manganese sulfate solutions was investigated extensively in the laboratory and pilot plant, in the 1930's, by Shelton and his co-workers at the United States Bureau of Mines. After further development and engineering studies, the process was brought to full-scale operation by the Electro Manganese Corporation at its Knoxville plant by 1939. During the period of 1942 to 1946, the Bureau of Mines set up and operated an experimental plant at Boulder City, Nevada. Although differing in many details, both operations used a diaphragm cell whose anolyte contained manganous sulfate, ammonium sulfate, and sulfuric acid at a pH of the order of 1, which anolyte became a cyclic leach liquid, and a catholyte fed to the cell at a pH of 7.2 to 7.6 in the presence of added sulfur dioxide.

As pointed out by Loonam,[12] recognition that manganese is much more electropositive than zinc makes the commercial deposition from aqueous solutions an outstanding achievement. Furthermore, manganese cannot be deposited from an acid solution, owing to the re-solution of the metal at acid pH's, and the oxide source of manganous sulfate cannot be dissolved by a

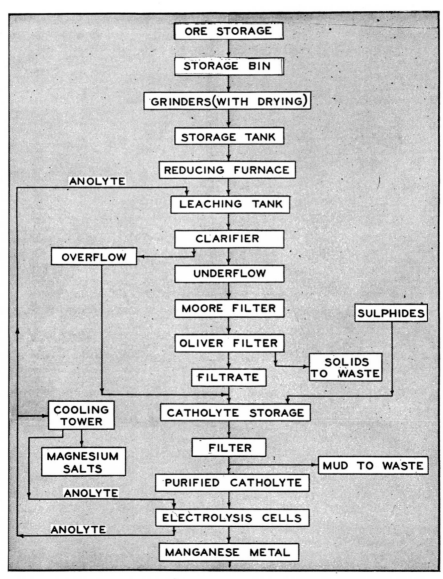

FIGURE 15.1. Process flow sheet for the electrowinning of manganese. (*Courtesy Foote Mineral Co.*)

basic solution. Two-compartment cells are required to meet these conditions.

Mantell[13] has described the Knoxville operations, including a flow sheet (Figure 15.1). Oxidized ores are reduced to make them soluble in recycled anolyte. After careful purification to remove such impurities as iron, arsenic, antimony, tin, lead, nickel, cobalt, molybdenum, silica, aluminum, calcium, and magnesium, the leach solution is returned to the cells as the catholyte.[14] Operating details are given in Table 15.4, and a view of the cell room is shown in Figure 15.2. Bennett[2] has described the technical and financial phases of the commercial development.

Jacobs et al.[9,10] have reported the work of the United States Bureau of Mines at the Boulder City, Nevada, plant (operating details are given in Table 15.4), whose output, in the main, was employed in experimental steel melting in electric furnace practice. Low-grade American ores were used. This plant benefited from the earlier Knoxville experience.

Carosella et al.[6] and Chilton[7] have described

TABLE 15.4. ELECTROLYTIC MANGANESE PROCESS, OPERATING DATA

	Foote Mineral Company	Bureau of Mines, Boulder City, Nevada	Union Carbide Metals Co.
Cells, material	Concrete, lead lined	Wood, lead lined	
Anodes			
Number	21	28	
Material	Silver-lead	Lead-silver	Silver-lead
Dimensions (in.)		$15 \times 32 \times \frac{1}{4}$ (40% void)	
Cathodes			
Number	20	27	
Material	Stainless steel	Stainless steel	"Hastelloy"
Dimensions (in.)	$36 \times 18 \times \frac{1}{8}$	$18 \times 36 \times 16$ gage	$42 \times 24 \times 16$ gage
Removed after (?) days	2	1	2–3
Diaphragms, material	Textile	Cotton canvas	Textile
Anolyte			
Feed or circulation	By gravity		By gravity
pH	1–1.4	1.5	
Composition (g/liter)			
Ammonium sulfate	120–140	135–140	120–140
Manganese as $MnSO_4$	10–18	8–10	10–12
Sulfuric acid	25–35	43–50	36–44
Catholyte			
Temperature			
°C	35–40	32–36	32–40
°F	95–104	90–97	90–104
pH	7.2–7.6	8.25	8.5
Composition (g/liter) feed			
Ammonium sulfate	125–135	155	120–140
Manganese as $MnSO_4$	25–40	25	
Sulfur dioxide	0.10	0.10	
Current, total amps	6,000	6,000	10,000
Current density (amp/sq ft)			
Anode	80	81–90	
Cathode	40	45–50	45
Current efficiency (%)	65–70	60–65	65
Voltage/tank	5–5.4	5.0–5.3	5.3
Pounds manganese/cathode		10–12	
KWH/lb product			
Direct current	4–4.5	3.5–3.8	
Alternating current	5–5.3		
Recovery to metal (%)	87	78+	74.6
Purity (%)	99.97	99.9	99.9

FIGURE 15.2. A section of the electrolytic cell room at Knoxville, Tennessee. (*Courtesy Foote Mineral Co.*)

the Union Carbide Metals Co. practice using electric furnace slags as a raw material. Operating data are given in Table 15.4, and a cell room is shown in Figure 15.3.

Manganese deposits in all three plants are removed from the cathode sheets by flexing and hammering, and are recovered in the form of chips. The product is better than 99.9 per cent pure. Chips of manganese, as removed from the cathode sheets, are shown in Figure 15.4.

From the world viewpoint, in 1951 Springer,[17] in an extensive manner, reviewed the literature

FIGURE 15.3. Cell room in Marietta, Ohio electrolytic manganese plant. (*Courtesy Union Carbide Metals Co.*)

FIGURE 15.4. Chips of manganese as removed from the cathode sheets of the electrolytic process. The smooth side was against the cathode; the rough side faced the solution. These chips are about 1½ by 2 inches in size.

on manganese electrolysis and electrowinning, and reported competitive processes to those which have found commercial success.

In 1952 Dean[8] reported the early Bureau of Mines work, but the major part of his volume is concerned with manganese alloys.

Sully[18] divided his 1955 book into sections on manganese ores, the production of ferro-alloys and pure metal, the beneficiation of low-grade ore, the properties of the metal, and constitution diagrams for the alloys.

PHYSICAL PROPERTIES

Manganese exists in four allotropic modifications, the alpha being the one stable at ordinary temperatures. Alpha and beta manganese are hard, brittle metals that will scratch glass. The pure metal is not fabricated. Gamma manganese, which changes to alpha at ordinary temperatures, is reported to be flexible and soft and can be bent and easily cut.[16]

The physical properties of manganese are summarized in Table 15.5, and its vapor pressure–temperature relationship[11] is given in Figure 15.5.

TABLE 15.5. PHYSICAL PROPERTIES OF MANGANESE

Atomic number		25		
Atomic weight		54.94		
Stable isotope		55		
Density				
Solid				
	Alpha	Beta	Gamma	
g/cc at 20°C	7.44	7.29	7.18	
lb/cu in. at 68°F	0.268	0.263	0.259	
Liquid				
g/cc		6.54		
lb/cu in.		0.236		
Atomic volume (cc/g-atom)		7.4		
Melting point		1244 ± 3°C (2271 ± 5°F)		
Boiling point (760 mm)		2097°C (3806°F)		
Specific heat (cal/g/°C at 25°C) (Btu/lb/°F at 77°F)	Alpha	Beta	Gamma	Delta
	0.114	0.154	0.148	0.191
Latent heat of fusion				
cal/g		63.7		
Btu/lb		114.7		
Latent heat of vaporization				
cal/g (at BP)		977.6		
Btu/lb		1,760		
Linear coefficient of thermal expansion				
	Alpha	Gamma		
Per °C (0–100°C)	22×10^{-6}	14×10^{-6}		
Per °F (32–212°F)	12.2×10^{-6}	7.8×10^{-6}		
Electrical resistivity at 20°C (68°F)				
Alpha (microhm-cm)		185		
Beta (microhm-cm)		44		
Gamma (microhm-cm)		60		
Magnetic susceptibility [18°C (64°F) (cgs units)]		9.9		

TABLE 15.5. PHYSICAL PROPERTIES OF MANGANESE *(cont.)*

Hardness		
Mohs scale		5.0
Rockwell C scale		
Alpha manganese		71
Gamma manganese		23

Vapor pressure (mm Hg)

°C	°F	
1244	2271	0.9
1327	2420	2.4
1527	2780	18.3
1727	3140	89
1927	3500	315
2027	3680	541
2127	3860	880
2227	4040	1,380

Heat of transformation (cal/g-atom)	
Alpha to beta, 727°C (1341°F)	535
Beta to gamma, 1100°C (2012°F)	545
Gamma to delta, 1138°C (2080°F)	430

Heat capacity equations (cal/g-atom)

Manganese (alpha), $Cp = 5.70 + 3.38 \times 10^{-3}T - 0.375 \times 10^{5}T^{-2}$ (298–1000°K)

Manganese (beta), $Cp = 8.33 + 0.66 \times 10^{-3}T$ (1000–1374°K)

Manganese (gamma), $Cp = 10.7$ (1374–1410°K)

Manganese (delta), $Cp = 11.30$ (1410–1450°K)

Manganese, liquid, $Cp = 11.0$

Standard electrode potential, $Mn = Mn^{++} + 2e$	+1.1 volts
(referred to hydrogen electrode)	

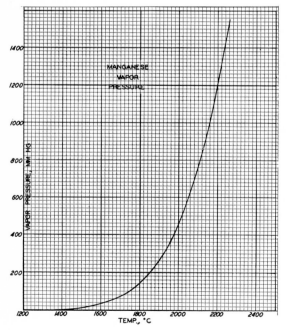

FIGURE 15.5. Vapor pressure of manganese. *(Data from Kelly, Naylor, and Shomate.)*[11]

Sully[18] has concluded, from all the factors and rates involved, that the transformation temperatures are as given in Table 15.6[3] with the related data on allotropism.

The vapor pressure of manganese at the triple point[1] is:

Vapor pressure (mm Hg)	Triple point	
	(°C)	(°F)
1.8	1280	2336
0.8	1244	2271
0.001 sublimes at	740	1364

CHEMICAL PROPERTIES

Although somewhat similar to iron in general chemical reactivity, manganese can exist in its compounds in the valence states of 1, 2, 3, 4, 6, and 7, the most stable salts being those of the divalent form and the most stable oxide the dioxide, MnO_2.

Manganese metal oxidizes superficially in air and rusts in moist air. It burns in air or oxygen at elevated temperatures, like iron; decomposes

TABLE 15.6. ALLOTROPISM OF MANGANESE

Density	Form	Stability range	Crystal structure
7.44	Alpha	Below 700°C (1292°F)	Body-centered cubic, 58 atoms to unit cell, a = 8.894Å
7.29	Beta	700–1079°C (1292–1974°F)	Body-centered cubic, 20 atoms to unit cell, a = 6.300Å
7.21	Gamma	1079–1143°C (1974–2089°F)	Face-centered tetragonal, 4 atoms to unit cell, a = 3.767Å c/a = 0.934
	Delta	1143°C–MP (2089°F)	Body centered a = 3.075
6.54	Liquid	Above 1244° ± 3°C (2271 ± 5°F)	

TRANSITION POINTS

From	To	Temperature	Condition
Alpha	Beta	700° ± 3°C (1292 ± 5°F)	Heating
Beta	Alpha	700–665°C (1292–1229°F)	Cooling
Beta	Gamma	1079° ± 3°C (1974 ± 5°F)	Heating and Cooling
Gamma	Delta	1140° ± 3°C (2084 ± 5°F)	Heating and Cooling
Delta	Liquid	1244° ± 3°C (2271 ± 5°F)	Heating and Cooling

water slowly in the cold and rapidly on heating, forming manganous hydroxide, $Mn(OH)_2$, with hydrogen evolution; and dissolves readily in dilute mineral acids with hydrogen evolution and the formation of the corresponding divalent salts.

Fluorine, chlorine, and bromine react with manganese when heated. When heated with nitrogen, various nitrides are formed, as shown in the constitution diagram (Figure 15.6) according to Zwicker;[19] when heated with ammonia, it also forms the nitride. Manganese reacts with sulfur[4] to form sulfides.

Fused manganese dissolves carbon, as does iron, ultimately forming a carbide. It reacts with carbon monoxide at temperatures above 330°C (626°F) and with carbon dioxide when strongly heated.[5]

Hydrides of manganese have not been detected, but solid and liquid manganese dissolves appreciable quantities of hydrogen; electrolytic

manganese normally contains 150 parts of hydrogen per million.[13]

A dehydrogenated, furnace-treated metal is a commercial product, as are nitrogen-bearing manganese metals employed to introduce manganese and nitrogen into special-quality corrosion resistant alloys and valve steels.

Boiling concentrated solutions of potassium or sodium hydroxide have little action on manganese.[5]

The reported chemical reactivity may be affected by impurities.

FABRICATION

The hard, brittle nature of the alpha form of electrolytic manganese, which is the stable one at ordinary temperatures, has prevented the fabrication of the pure metal alone. It can be transformed to a ductile alloy by the addition of 2 per cent copper and 1 per cent nickel.

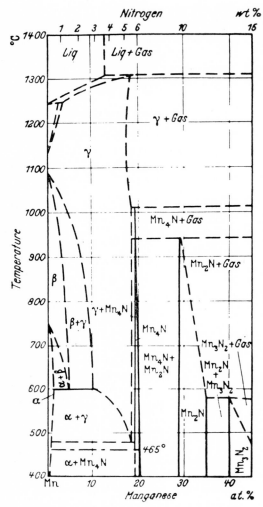

FIGURE 15.6. Equilibrium diagram of manganese-nitrogen system.[19]

ALLOYS

Sully[18] has correlated the data on the binary alloy systems of manganese with aluminum, antimony, arsenic, beryllium, bismuth, boron, cadmium (liquid immiscibility), carbon, cerium (no compounds), chromium, cobalt, copper, germanium, gold, hydrogen, indium, iron, lanthanum, magnesium, mercury, nickel, oxygen, palladium, phosphorus, platinum, silicon, silver, sulfur, tantalum, tellurium, thallium, thorium, tin, tungsten, uranium, vanadium, zinc, and zirconium; as well as the ternary systems of manganese and aluminum with chromium,

cobalt, copper, iron, silicon, and zinc; manganese and copper with gallium, indium, nickel, silver, and zinc; manganese and iron with carbon, chromium, mercury, oxygen, silicon, and sulfur; manganese and sulfur with oxygen, silicon, and ferrosilicon.

APPLICATIONS

Outside of its use as a desirable source for the preparation of high-purity manganese chemicals, chiefly salts, for pharmaceutical, food, analytical, catalytic, and scientific work, electrolytic manganese is consumed entirely as a purifying and scavenging agent and as an alloying element in ferrous and nonferrous alloys, particularly the stainless steels.

The 16 chromium–14 manganese–1 nickel steel is a low-nickel chromium-manganese alternate for 17-7 chromium–nickel steel. The corrosion resistance of this alloy is not so good as 18-8 chromium–nickel steels. It is, however, adequate for all atmospheric conditions except marine environments. It can also be used in mildly corrosive media.

The 17 chromium–14 manganese–1 nickel steel has only a moderate resistance to oxidation and cannot be used above 704°C (1300°F) in long-time application or 760°C (1400°F) in short-time application.

The high manganese in the 17 chromium–4 nickel–6 manganese and the 18 chromium–5 nickel–8 manganese alloys replaces the nickel only partially.

The corrosion resistance of these alloys approaches that of Type 302 chromium-nickel steel, except in severe oxidizing conditions or in chlorides. They can successfully replace 18-8 chromium–nickel steels in most applications, except in critical cases in the chemical industry.

The resistance to oxidation of these two grades represents an improvement over the 15 chromium–14 manganese–1 nickel grade, but it is still not quite equal to the 18-8 chromium–nickel grades.

Restricted availability of nickel brought about the development of two low-nickel high-manganese compositions commercialized sufficiently to be designated as AISI standard steels. These are Type 201, having a composition range of 16.0 to 18.0 per cent chromium, 5.5 to 7.5 manganese, 3.5 to 5.5 nickel, 0.25 maximum nitrogen, 0.15 maximum carbon; and Type 202, having a composition of 17.0 to 19.0 per cent chromium, 7.5 to 10.0 manganese, 4.0 to 6.0 nickel, 0.25 maximum nitrogen, and 0.15 maximum carbon. The composition 17 chromium–4 nickel–6 manganese discussed above might be considered an AISI Type 201 steel, and the composition 18 chromium–5 nickel–8 manganese might be considered an AISI Type 202 steel.

Types 201 and 202 are warehoused in the forms in which Types 301 and 302 are now supplied, Type 201 primarily in sheet and strip forms, and Type 202 in rod and bar stock.

The mechanical properties of AISI Type 201 are similar to Type 301 in response to cold working and rate of work hardening. It tends, however, to develop a somewhat higher yield strength at a given cold reduction than does the Type 301 steel, while retaining as much ductility. AISI Type 202 is comparable to Type 302 in mechanical properties. Like Type 302, it does not work-harden as rapidly as Types 201 and 301.

Both Types 201 and 202 have excellent toughness at ambient and low temperatures, but the higher nickel grade gives somewhat higher impact values because of greater structural stability. Izod values at −183°C (−298°F) for Type 201 are in the order of 70 ft-lb; for Type 202, they run 90 to 120 ft-lb.

More fabrication experience has been accumulated with Type 201 than with other high-manganese grades. This steel performs similarly to Type 301. Shop experience shows that brake and draw-bench forming of the two types can be performed with the same brake-die radius and width and the same draw-bench rolls. Equally good results have been obtained with both grades. There is less experience in such operations as spinning, hammer forming, and deep drawing. Possibly in some cases Type 202 should be used instead of Type 201 for such forming operations.

For all arc welding, spot, seam, and projection welding, procedures suitable for Type 301 can be used for Type 201. Weldments can be produced with equal ease and of equally high quality. Available data indicate that the soundness, shear, tension, impact, and fatigue properties of welds of Type 201 are equal to those made in Type 301.

Types 201 and 202 are annealed at 1065–1093°C (1950–2000°F) and either air-cooled or water-quenched.

Experience indicates that Type 201 can substitute for Type 301, and Type 202 can be substituted for Type 302, at least as far as strength and formability characteristics are concerned. Likewise, it seems safe to substitute the 200-series steels for their 300-series counterparts where corrosion conditions are mild (i.e., atmospheric corrosion) or mild to moderate. Under more severe corrosion conditions, suitable laboratory or field tests should precede and guide the substitution.

Manganese is vital for sulfur-content control in steelmaking and is the most commonly and widely used deoxidizer of molten steel. The greater part of it ends up in the slag of the steelmaking processes. Although ferromanganese is the standard additive agent for these purposes in the steel industry, pure manganese is used in many instances, especially where the preparation of special steels is involved and low carbon and phosphorus contents must be maintained. It can be added to basic open hearth steel, to both acid and basic electric furnace steel, and to crucible steel for purifying purposes.

Steels of 17 to 19 per cent chromium, 8 to 10 per cent manganese, 0.75 to 1 per cent copper, 0.1 per cent carbon, and 0.2 to 0.5 per cent silicon have excellent resistance to atmospheric corrosion and compare well with stainless steels. They resist all concentrations of nitric acid at temperatures up to and including the boiling point, and are relatively free from attack by many other industrial chemicals and food products.

Practically all commercial alloys of aluminum and magnesium contain manganese. Corrosion resistance and mechanical properties, such as hardness, are improved by its presence. The amounts used are seldom above 1.2 per cent for magnesium and 1.5 per cent for aluminum. In aluminum alloys, electrolytic manganese competes with manganese oxides or carbonate or low-iron ferromanganese which may be added directly to the reduction pots. In magnesium, electrolytic manganese competes with pure manganous chloride which is added to the melting pots.

The instrument alloy, manganin, comprised of

11 to 12 per cent manganese, 3 to 4 per cent nickel, and balance copper, is prepared with electrolytic manganese, as are the high-resistance nickel-chromium alloys containing about 2 per cent manganese.

High ability to damp vibrations is possessed by binary copper-manganese alloys. Manganese has been used as a substitute for nickel in the nickel silvers, and in alloys of copper, zinc, and nickel, particularly manganese-containing brasses and bronzes.

Many data on the properties and applications relating to the alloy systems copper-manganese, manganese-nickel, copper-manganese-nickel, and copper-zinc-manganese are given by Dean.[8]

References

1. Baukloh, W., and Altland, G., *Metallwirtschaft*, 18, 651 (1939).
2. Bennett, R. H., "A Decade of Electrolytic Manganese," *Mining J.,* 150, No. 10, 80–5 (1949).
3. Berak, J., and Heumann, T., *Z. Metallkunde*, 41, 19 (1950); Gayler, M. L. V., *J. Iron Steel Inst.,* 115, 393 (1927); Gruber, G., Bayer, K., and Bumm, H., *Z. Elektrochem.,* 42, 805 (1936); Isobé, M., *Science Repts. Tôhoku Univ.* A3, 78 (1951); Johannsen, G., and Nitka, H., *Physik. Z.,* 39, 440 (1938); Naylor, B. F., *J. Chem. Phys.,* 13, 329 (1945); Potter, E. V., and Lukens, H. C., *Trans. AIME,* 171, 401 (1947); Sieverts, A., and Moritz, H., *Z. physik. Chem.,* 180, 249 (1937); Wiechmann, F., *Z. anorg. Chem.,* 234, 130 (1937); Yoshisaki, H., *Science Repts. Tôhoku Univ.,* 26, 182 (1937), *Kinzoku no Kenkyu,* 14, 91 (1937).
4. Bradley, A. J., *Phil. Mag.,* 50, 1018–30 (1925).
5. Campbell, A. N., *J. Chem. Soc.,* 123, 2323 (1923).
6. Carosella, M. C., and Fowler, R. M., "A New Commercial Process for Electrowinning Manganese," *J. Electrochem. Soc.,* 104, 352–6 (1957).
7. Chilton, C. H., "High Purity Manganese via Electrolysis," *Chem. Eng.,* 65, No. 10, 136–9 (May 19, 1958).
8. Dean, R. S., "Electrolytic Manganese and its Alloys," New York, The Ronald Press, 1952.
9. Jacobs, J. H., Hunter, J. W., Yarroll, W. H., Churchward, P. E., and Knickerbocker, R. G. "First Two Years Operation of the Bureau of Mines Electrolytic Manganese Pilot Plant," *Trans. AIME,* 159, 408–28 (1944).
10. Jacobs, J. H., Hunter, J. W., Yarroll, W. H., Churchward, P. E., Knickerbocker, R. G., Lewis, R. W., Heller, H. A., and Linck, J. H., *U.S. Bur. Mines Bull., 463,* (1946).
11. Kelley, K. K., Naylor, B. F., and Shomate, C. H., *U.S. Bur. Mines Tech. Paper, 686* (1946).
12. Loonam, A. C., "Fifty Years' Progress in Electrowinning and Electrorefining," *J. Electrochem. Soc.,* 99, 295c–8c (1952).
13. Mantell, C. L., "Commercial Production of Electrolytic Manganese," *J. Electrochem. Soc.,* 94, 232–43 (1948).
14. Mantell, C. L., "Electrolytic Manganese Acceptance Grows," *The Iron Age* (Sept. 18, 1952).
15. Materials Survey—Manganese, National Security Resources Board, U.S. Department of Commerce, National Production Authority, Washington, D.C., U.S. Government Printing Office, 1952.
16. Schlain, D., and Prater, J. D., "Electrodeposition of Gamma Manganese," *J. Electrochem. Soc.,* 94, 58–73 (1948).
17. Springer, R., "Die Elektrolytische Abscheidung des Mangans," Leipzig, Akademische Verlagsgesellschaft, Geest & Portig K.-G., 1951.
18. Sully, A. H., "Manganese," New York, Academic Press, Inc., 1955.
19. Zwicker, U., *Z. Metallkunde,* 42, 274 (1951).

16. MOLYBDENUM

R. S. ARCHER

Climax Molybdenum Company
A Division of
American Metal Climax, Inc.
New York, New York

INTRODUCTION

Molybdenum is a metallic element of density 10.22, resembling steel in color, and having an unusually high melting point of about 2610°C (4730°F). It is one of the best known and most commonly used of the refractory metals, and is also one of the most important of the alloying elements used in steels, irons, and certain nonferrous alloys.

Molybdenum (symbol Mo, element number 42, atomic weight 95.95) is in Group VIB of the periodic system and is therefore related to chromium and tungsten. The neutral Mo atom contains, in addition to the completed shell of krypton with 36 electrons, another 5 electrons in the N shell and one in the O shell, in which the arrangement of electrons is $4s^2$, $4p^6$, $4d^5$, $5s^1$. Some characteristic properties of molybdenum, e.g. paramagnetism, the tendency of ions to form complex compounds, and the color of compounds, have been attributed to the fact that the N shell is incomplete. There are seven natural stable isotopes with mass numbers (in order of decreasing abundance) 98, 96, 95, 92, 100, 97, 94; several artificial radioactive isotopes (91, 93, 99, 101, 102, 105) are known.

The terms *molybdena, plumbago, graphite,* and *galena* seem to have been applied in early Greek writings to lead sulfide and minerals of similar appearance, including graphite, as well as the naturally occurring molybdenum disulfide. This confusion, especially between the minerals now called graphite and molybdenite, continued until 1778 when K. W. Scheele demonstrated that molybdenite contains sulfur and prepared molybdic acid from the mineral. About 1782 P. J. Hjelm obtained an impure metallic product by reducing the oxide with carbon and called it molybdenum.

OCCURRENCE

Molybdenum does not occur free in nature. The only important production at present is from deposits containing the mineral molybdenite (MoS_2); however, some powellite [calcium tungstomolybdate, $Ca(MoW)O_4$] is treated to recover molybdenum, and, in the past, deposits containing wulfenite, lead molybdate ($PbMoO_4$) were worked.

Free-world production of molybdenum is concentrated in the United States and Chile. Ordinarily, the largest producer is the Climax mine at Climax, Colorado. The next largest source is the copper industry, which obtains molybdenite concentrate as a by-product from several mines in the United States and Chile. The largest producer in this group has been the copper mine at Bingham, Utah. Molybdenum is also recovered as a by-product of tungsten mining at Pine Creek, California. United States reserves of commercial ore are estimated to contain more than 3 billion pounds of molybdenum.

PRODUCTION AND STATISTICS

Production of molybdenite concentrate in the United States reached a wartime peak of

61,667,000 lb of molybdenum contained in 1943, fell to a postwar low of 22,530,000 lb in 1949, and rose again to 61,781,000 lb in 1955. Production in 1959 was 50,956,000 lb. Free-world production of molybdenum in concentrates was 70,300,000 lb in 1959, of which the United States supplied 73 per cent. From 1953 through 1957, United States industrial consumption varied from 24 million to 39 million lb/year, and foreign consumption from 12 million to 25 million lb/year.

Most of the molybdenum mined is used as an alloying addition in steels, irons, and certain nonferrous alloys. A small percentage is converted to metallic molybdenum and molybdenum-base alloys, and an even smaller percentage is used as molybdenum disulfide for lubrication. Molybdenum compounds are used in catalysts, pigments, and as analytical reagents. Molybdenum has been proved an essential trace element in plant nutrition. Sodium molybdate or molybdenum trioxide may be used for this purpose.

According to the Bureau of Mines, United States production of molybdenum metal powder in 1957 was approximately 1,100,000 lb. In 1959 the consumption of molybdenum powder was 1,046,000 lb in the form of wire, rod, and sheet, and 1,160,000 lb in the form of forging billets, etc.

Prices

Prevailing prices (1958) for pure molybdenum metal are about \$4/lb for hydrogen-reduced powder and \$11 to \$16/lb for bars rolled from arc-cast ingots.

ORE PROCESSING

At Climax, where the mine is operated primarily for the recovery of molybdenite concentrate, the ore contains about 0.4 per cent MoS_2. Separation of molybdenite and some by-product minerals is accomplished by crushing, fine grinding, and flotation, employing a reagent consisting chiefly of a petroleum refinery product known as a pale neutral oil with much smaller amounts of pine oil and a synthetic wetting agent. Commercial molybdenite concentrate contains about 80 to 95 per cent MoS_2 on a dry basis.

Most of the concentrate is roasted at about 600°C (1112°F) with a large excess of air, higher temperatures being avoided to prevent sticking and volatilization. The sulfide is converted to molybdenum trioxide, MoO_3. The gangue in the original concentrate remains in the product, which is called technical molybdic oxide or roasted molybdenite concentrate.

Subsequent treatments are determined by the ultimate use. The oxide may be used as such in the steel industry. It is usually packed in steel cans or paper bags and is also mixed with pitch which functions as a binder and reducing agent to form a partially self-reducing briquette. The oxide is sometimes mixed with limestone in proportions to form calcium molybdate. Ferromolybdenum, containing about 55 to 75 per cent molybdenum, is usually made by the thermite reduction of the technical oxide. The reactants are molybdenum trioxide, ferrosilicon, aluminum, and iron ore. Limestone and fluorspar are used as fluxes.

Molybdenum trioxide of higher purity can be made by sublimation of technical oxide or by the thermal decomposition of ammonium molybdate. The product contains over 99.5 per cent MoO_3.

DERIVATION OF MOLYBDENUM METAL

Molybdenum metal is made from molybdenum powder produced by the hydrogen reduction of purified molybdenum trioxide or ammonium molybdate. The reduction is carried out in tube furnaces similar to those used in tungsten reduction. (See chapter on Tungsten, Figure 30.6.) Metal boats containing the oxide are pushed through the tubes, reaching a maximum temperature of about 1100°C (2012°F) at a rate that insures complete reduction to metal. The process is commonly carried out in two stages; the first stage produces molybdenum dioxide at about 600°C (1112°F), which is reduced to metal at 1000–1100°C (1832–2012°F) in the second stage. Conversion of powder to massive metal may be carried out by either of two methods, a powder metallurgy process developed about 1910, and an arc-casting process developed about 1944.

Powder Metallurgy Process

In the first process the molybdenum powder is compacted in dies at room temperature into ingots or bars under pressures from about 10 to 20 tons/sq in. The compacts are sintered by heating in hydrogen or vacuum. Sintering begins at 1100°C (2012°F) and takes place more rapidly as the temperature is increased. Compacts about 1 in. square, used for the production of rod and wire, have been heated by direct passage of an electric current in furnaces similar to those used for the sintering of tungsten, the maximum temperature being approximately 2200°C (3992°F). This method of heating involves the loss of the cold ends which may be sold as scrap. Some producers choose to sinter at about 1630°C (2966°F) in furnaces heated by molybdenum resistors, thus avoiding the loss of the ends of the compacts.

Compacts of substantially larger size have been made under hydrostatic pressure of 25 tons or more and heated for sintering by radiation. Sintered compacts up to 6 in. or more in diameter have been successfully forged.

Arc-Casting Process

Because of its very high melting point, it seems impracticable to melt molybdenum and cast ingots of high quality by conventional processes. In the arc-casting process a partially sintered bar serves as a consumable electrode and is melted into a water-cooled mold usually made of copper. The electrode may be prefabricated, but most of the arc-cast molybdenum made up to the present has been melted in equipment which starts with molybdenum powder, presses the electrode, and sinters it enough to hold its weight before introducing it into the arc. The operation is carried out in a high vacuum or an atmosphere of purified inert gases. By this method, ingots have been produced up to 12 in. in diameter and 2,000 lb in weight.

Figure 16.1 is an over-all view of the pressing-sintering-melting machine, built in 1950, which produces a 9-in.-diameter ingot weighing 1,000 lb at a melting rate of 10 lb/min. A newer and larger machine, which has been operating since February, 1958, produces a 12-in.-diameter ingot, weighing up to 2,000 lb, at a rate of 16 to 20 lb/min. The two machines are identical in operation, but the newer machine is built on a somewhat larger scale throughout.

Figure 16.2 shows a close-up of the top of

FIGURE 16.1. Over-all view of the pressing-sintering-melting machine used in the arc casting of molybdenum. (*Courtesy Climax Molybdenum Co. of Michigan.*)

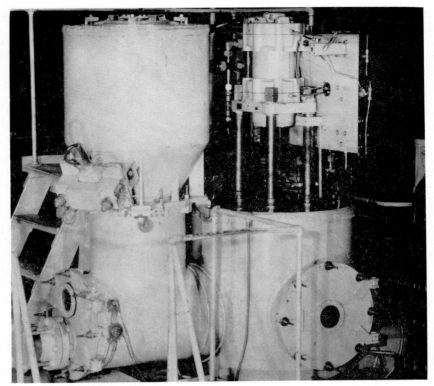

FIGURE 16.2. Hopper and housing for feed mechanism, at left. Hydraulic system for compressing electrode, at right. (*Courtesy Climax Molybdenum Co. of Michigan.*)

the machine with the powder hopper at the top left. Directly below it is the auxiliary hopper containing the vibratory feeder which discharges the powder to the consumable-electrode-forming mechanism in the chamber at the right. The hydraulic system for compressing the powder is located above this chamber.

A close-up of the main chamber is shown in Figure 16.3. Melting in this machine is a batch-type operation, but the forming of the electrode, the sintering, and the melting take place consecutively and simultaneously under a vacuum of approximately 10 to 50 μ. Figure 16.4 is a diagram showing the molybdenum powder flowing into the electrode-forming mechanism. Here the powder is compacted in a hexagonal-shaped die at a pressure of approximately 12,000 psi.

Wafers approximately $\frac{1}{2}$ in. thick are formed at the rate of 15 to 20/min, each wafer being formed on top of the previous one. As the

column of wafers proceeds downward through the apparatus, a sintering current is applied (Figure 16.5) so that the column will develop sufficient strength to support the weight of the 5-ft length of electrode extending to the bottom of the mold. Heat derived from an a-c arc causes melting of the electrode, and the molten metal drops into the water-cooled copper mold in which solidification takes place.

It is necessary that the ingot have a very low oxygen content in order to be workable. Powder of the lowest available oxygen content is used. Small amounts of carbon may be mixed with the powder before sintering and melting in order to reduce most of the oxygen contained in the powder. This may leave about 0.03 per cent carbon in the ingot.

In the arc-casting process, alloying elements are normally incorporated by mixing them with the molybdenum powder from which the electrode is made. Equipment in which the electrode

FIGURE 16.3. Close-up of main chamber. (*Courtesy Climax Molybdenum Co. of Michigan.*)

is formed and sintered under vacuum just before melting is especially advantageous when highly reactive alloying additions such as titanium and zirconium are made. The alloy which has been most widely used up to this time contains 0.5 per cent titanium. Continuing research is likely to result in the development of other commercial alloys.

WORKING OF MOLYBDENUM

Hot working is carried out by extrusion, forging, rolling, and wire drawing. Actually, these operations have usually been conducted, or at least finished, below the recrystallization temperature. Therefore, the metal is cold worked, with substantial increases in hardness and strength. As the amount of deformation increases, the recrystallization temperature is lowered; therefore, the working operations are frequently performed at lower temperatures as the reduction progresses.

Small powder metallurgy compacts to be made into rod or wire may be worked by a series of forging operations known as *swaging*, starting at about 1300°C (2372°F). The swager consists essentially of a split die which is rotated with a hammering action around the axis of the rod being worked. Swagers may be used to reduce the cross section to about 0.060-in. diameter. Carbide wire drawing dies may be employed for further reduction to about 0.020 in.; finer wire is drawn through diamond dies.

In the powder metallurgy process, molybdenum sheet is hot rolled directly from sintered compacts. Here again, rolling temperatures are progressively decreased, and, at thicknesses below about 0.040 in., the metal may be rolled cold. Molybdenum sheet is rolled as thin as 0.001 in.

When suitable equipment is available, sintered compacts up to at least 2 in. square can be hot-rolled to small-diameter rod, thus avoid-

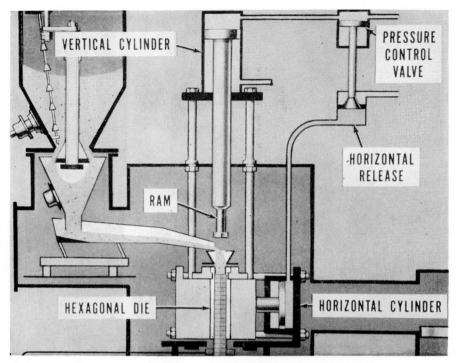

FIGURE 16.4. Diagrammatic sketch showing molybdenum powder flowing into electrode forming mechanism. (*Courtesy 1957 Gillette Memorial Lecture of ASTM by A. J. Herzig.*)

ing the slow swaging operation with its somewhat uneven working.

Current production of arc-cast products is from ingots 9 to 12 in. in diameter. These are broken down by extrusion at temperatures of 1090 to 1315°C (1994 to 2400°F). The extrusions are usually rounds 4 to 6 in. in diameter. After being cleaned, these are rolled into bar products. For the production of plates and sheets, the extrusions may be rolled or forged into sheet bars. Extrusions may also be used as forging stock for the production of hand or die forgings. For such forging operations, material is heated to about 1204°C (2200°F).

In rolling and forging operations, working temperatures and process anneals vary, depending upon the original size of the compact or ingot, the final size and shape being produced, and the properties desired. The mechanical properties of molybdenum depend, to a large degree, on the amount of working done below the recrystallization temperature. For good ductility, products should be given at least 50 per cent reduction. Most products are given a

final stress-relieving treatment by heating to a temperature about 50–100°C (90–180°F) below the recrystallization temperature. Fully recrystallized molybdenum has lower strength than stress-relieved molybdenum, so it flows more readily in working. It usually has less ductility in bending, however, than stress-relieved material, so it is ordinarily used in the fabrication of parts only if no bending or tube drawing is to be done, or if subsequent processing will involve sufficient warm work to produce the necessary properties.

Recrystallization temperatures depend upon the chemical composition of the metal, the extent of cold working, and the time at temperature. Unalloyed molybdenum, in the form of $\frac{5}{8}$-in.-diameter bars which have been reduced 50 to 90 per cent by rolling, is fully recrystallized after 1 hr at 1176°C (2150°F). Molybdenum-base alloys have been produced experimentally which require temperatures up to about 1704°C (3100°F). The Mo–0.5 Ti alloy is recrystallized after 1 hr at 1342°C (2450°F).

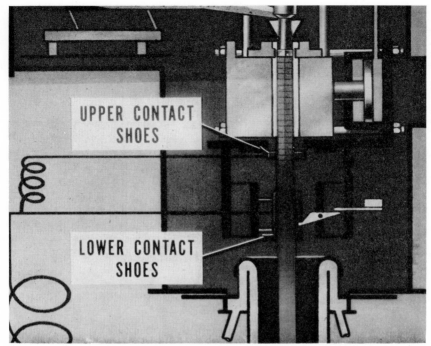

FIGURE 16.5. Sintering of wafers as they proceed downward. (*Courtesy 1957 Gillette Memorial Lecture of ASTM by A. J. Herzig.*)

Complete recrystallization results in the loss of much of the increase in hardness and strength which has been imparted by mechanical working. From the standpoint of service, therefore, it is of interest to know the highest temperatures to which molybdenum and its alloys can be heated with little or no recrystallization. On the basis of a definition of recrystallization temperature as the lowest temperature at which new grains appear which are visible under the microscope, a recrystallization temperature of 900°C (1650°F) has been reported for unalloyed molybdenum in the form of fine wire. The following tabulation applies to round bars ⅝ in. in diameter which were rolled without any intermediate annealing from recrystallized 2-in. rounds:

PHYSICAL PROPERTIES

Although molybdenum has many interesting properties, its high melting point of 2610°C (4730°F) is probably of most importance in its present commercial uses. Only tungsten and tantalum, of the more readily available metals, have higher melting points.

The high elastic modulus of molybdenum may become of increasing importance in the aircraft and missile industries. A comparison of the modulus-density ratio for several commercial alloys shows molybdenum to be outstanding over a wide temperature range (Figure 16.6). In this plot of Young's modulus divided by the density versus temperature for several alloys, the relative advantage of the molyb-

	Max temperature, (1-hr exposures)	
Nominal Composition	0% Recrystallized	2–3% Recrystallized
Mo	953°C (1750°F)	981°C (1800°F)
Mo + 0.3% Cb	1093°C (2000°F)	1104°C (2020°F)
Mo + 0.5% Ti	1215°C (2220°F)	1226°C (2240°F)
Mo + 1.0% V	1058°C (1940°F)	1072°C (1965°F)
Mo + 2.0% W	959°C (1760°F)	981°C (1800°F)
Mo + 0.5% Ti + 0.07% Zr	1286°C (2350°F)	1300°C (2375°F)

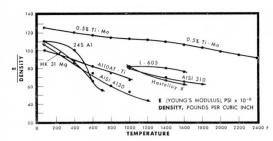

FIGURE 16.6. Young's modulus of elasticity—density ratio versus temperature, for several alloys. (*Courtesy Marquardt Aircraft Company.*)

denum–0.5 per cent titanium alloy over the entire range from room temperature to 1315°C (2400°F) is shown. Its high modulus at room temperature is responsible for the use of molybdenum for such items as boring bars and grinding quills, where the greater tool rigidity results in improved machining tolerances.

Other applications of molybdenum may take advantage of its thermal conductivity, which is several times as great as that of most high-temperature superalloys, or of the electrical conductivity, which is approximately one third that of copper.

The combination of a low coefficient of expansion with high thermal conductivity is favorable in many high-temperature applications.

The absorption cross section for thermal neutrons is relatively low, being somewhat below that of stainless steel, and has prompted the use of molybdenum in several developments in the atomic-energy field, both for thermal reactors and for the newer fast reactors.

The crystal structure of molybdenum is body-centered cubic, like that of chromium, tungsten, and alpha iron. No allotropic transformations are known.

Some physical properties of molybdenum are shown in Table 16.1.

TABLE 16.1. PHYSICAL PROPERTIES OF MOLYBDENUM*

Atomic and Thermal	
Atomic number	42
Isotopes	
Natural	92, 94, 95, 96, 97, 98, 100
Artificial	91, 93, 99, 101, 102, 105
Atomic weight	95.95
Atomic radius, coordination number 8	1.36 Å
Atomic volume	9.41 cc/g-atom
Lattice	
Type	Body-centered cubic
Constant at 25°C (77°F)	3.1405 kX
Neutron absorption cross section	
Thermal neutron	2.7 barns
Total neutron	
10/250 kev	9 barns
1,230	6
Ionization potential	7.2 ev
Apparent positive ion emission	8.6 ev
Apparent work function	4.2 ev
Melting point	About 2610°C (4730°F)
Heat of fusion (estimated)	6.7 kcal/mole
Boiling point	About 5560°C (10,040°F)
Heat of vaporization	117.4 kcal/mole
Heat of formation of MoO_3	−180.3 kcal/mole
Heat content from 298.16 to 1800°K in cal/mole	$H_T - H_{298.16} = 5.48T + 0.65 \times 10^{-3}T^2 - 1{,}692$
Heat capacity from 298.16 to 1800°K in cal/°C/mole	$C_p = 5.48 + 1.30 \times 10^{-3}T$
Entropy (crystals)	$S°_{298.16} = 6.83$ cal/°C/mole

TABLE 16.1. PHYSICAL PROPERTIES OF MOLYBDENUM* *(cont.)*

Vapor pressure

1727°C	3141°F	3.9×10^{-10} atm
2610	4730	1.7×10^{-5}
3227	5841	8.6×10^{-4}
4727	8541	1.8×10^{-1}
5560	10,040	1.0

Specific heat

		$Btu/lb/°F$
0°C	32°F	0.066
538	1000	0.057
1093	2000	0.077
1649	3000	0.088
2204	4000	0.113
2532	4590	0.128

Mean linear thermal expansion coefficients

		$Per\ °C \times 10^6$	$Per\ °F \times 10^6$
20– 149°C	68– 300°F	5.43	3.02
20– 482	68– 900	5.19	2.88
20– 649	68–1200	5.36	2.98
20– 982	68–1800	5.80	3.23
20–1316	68–2400	6.28	3.49
20–1593	68–2900	6.65	3.70

Thermal conductivity

		$Cal/sec/sq\ cm/cm/°C$	$Btu/hr/sq\ ft/ft/°F$
204°C	400°F	0.298	72
316	600	0.285	69
427	800	0.289	70
538	1000	0.275	67
649	1200	0.272	66
760	1400	0.268	65
871	1600	0.254	62
1093	2000	0.239	58
1649	3000	0.215	52
2204	4000	0.206	50

Electrical and Magnetic Properties

Electrical conductivity at 0°C (32°F)	34% IACS
Franz Wiedeman constant	2.72
Thomson coefficient from 900–2200°K	$\sigma/T = -1.05 \times 10^{-8}$ V/°K
Magnetic susceptibility	53×10^{-6} g-atom

Electrical resistivity (microhm-cm)

0°C (32°F)	5.2
27°C (81°F)	5.78
727°C (1341°F)	23.9
927°C (1701°F)	29.2
1127°C (2061°F)	35.2
1327°C (2421°F)	41.2
1527°C (2781°F)	47.2
1727°C (3141°F)	53.5
1927°C (3501°F)	59.5
2127°C (3861°F)	66.0
2227°C (4041°F)	69.2
2327°C (4221°F)	71.8
2527°C (4581°F)	78.2
2622°C (4752°F)	81.4
Temperature coefficient of electrical resistivity (per °C)	0.0047

TABLE 16.1. PHYSICAL PROPERTIES OF MOLYBDENUM* (*cont.*)

Optical and Emissivity Properties

Optical reflectivity		
5000 Å		46%
100,000		93
Total optical emissivity		
1000°C	1832°F	0.13
1500	2732	0.19
2000	3632	0.24
Thermionic emission in high vacuum		
1600°C	2912°F	About 0.5 ma/sq cm
2000	3632	About 7
Spectral emissivity		
3900 Å		About 0.43
6700		About 0.40
Radiation for 5500 Å at 20°C (68°F)		54% of black-body radiation
Total radiation		
527°C	981°F	About 0.2 watt/sq cm
1127	2061	About 3.0
1727	3141	About 19
2327	4221	About 68

Other Properties

Density at 20°C (68°F)	10.22 g/cc
	0.369 lb/cu in.
Compressibility at 30°C (86°F)	$\dfrac{\Delta V}{V_o} = -10^{-7} (3.47 - 1.2P)P$
Velocity of sound	About 16,000 ft/sec
Young's modulus of elasticity	47,000,000 psi (25°C) (77°F)
	40,000,000 psi (800°C) (1472°F)

* These data apply to unalloyed molybdenum and are based mostly on a literature survey in 1955.

MECHANICAL PROPERTIES

Molybdenum, in common with many other metals, undergoes a change from ductile to brittle behavior as the temperature of deformation is lowered. The temperature range in which this change occurs depends on purity, fabrication methods, stress patterns, strain rate, and other factors. Under certain conditions the transition from ductile to brittle failure in unalloyed molybdenum may take place at about room temperature. For example, in a series of bend tests on 0.060-in. sheet in the stress-relieved and recrystallized conditions, sharp increases in the bend angles were observed in the temperature range 16–27°C (60–80°F). In tensile tests on specimens with gage dimensions of 0.25-in. diameter by 1 in. long, at strain rates of 3 per cent/hr and 60 per cent/hr through the elastic and plastic deformation periods, respectively, transition temperatures are usually from about 18–38°C (0–100°F). In

the V-notch Charpy impact test, transition temperatures may be from about 232–510°C (450–950°F). These data show the desirability of warming molybdenum before fabricating.

Since, under some conditions, the transition from ductile to brittle behavior may occur in the range from −18 to 38°C (0–100°F), it will be seen that the "room temperature" properties of molybdenum are extremely sensitive to purity, mechanical and thermal history, stress system and strain rate, as well as the actual temperature of test. Tensile properties of arc-cast molybdenum and its alloys given in this article are based on the test specimen and strain rate described in the preceding paragraph. The 0.1 per cent offset yield strength is calculated for specimens not exhibiting a drop in load at the yield point.

Arc-cast molybdenum ingots are coarse grained, and the cast metal has little ductility at room temperature. Hardness decreases rapidly from about 180 to about 85 DPH at

TABLE 16.2. ROOM TEMPERATURE TENSILE PROPERTIES OF ARC-CAST UNALLOYED MOLYBDENUM

	Tensile strength (psi)	Yield strength (psi)	Elongation (%)	Reduction of area (%)
As cast	24,300	—	0	0
4-in. extrusion	70,900	62,700	1	0.8
2-in. rolled round	82,300	76,300	23	33.3
1-in. rolled round	92,400	72,200	30	35.5
⅝-in. rolled round	109,300	84,700	36	60.1
0.055-in. sheet	105,800	85,000	19	
0.010-in. sheet	127,200	—	11	

204°C (400°F), after which it decreases more slowly and at an almost linear rate to about 35 DPH at 1315°C (2400°F).

Some typical properties of unalloyed arc-cast molybdenum are given in Table 16.2. The wrought specimens were stress-relieved at 981–1036°C (1800–1900°F).

Although powder metallurgy products are now being made in larger sizes, much of the data which has been published on mechanical properties relate to small sizes. In very fine wire, tensile strengths up to about 300,000 psi may be obtained. Some typical mechanical properties of powder metallurgy products are given in Table 16.3.

Much of the interest today in molybdenum and its alloys is due to their outstanding strength at high temperatures. Molybdenum-base alloys have been developed with much

better high-temperature strength than unalloyed molybdenum. Their recrystallization temperatures are higher, so that strength obtained by work hardening is useful at higher service temperatures. These alloys have higher useful strengths at temperatures over approximately 926°C (1700°F) than steels or superalloys, as shown in Figure 16.7. The hardness of molybdenum in the cast condition is increased by the addition of certain alloying elements. It has not yet been found practicable to fabricate some of the harder ingots. The strength of both unalloyed molybdenum and its present commercial alloys depends largely on the amount of work performed on the materials below their recrystallization temperatures, as neither the pure metal nor any of its commercial alloys can be hardened by heat treatment. The properties obtained are dependent

TABLE 16.3. TYPICAL MECHANICAL PROPERTIES OF POWDER METALLURGY MOLYBDENUM

	Tensile strength (psi)	Elongation (% in 2 in.)	Hardness (Rockwell)
Rod 0.250 in. unannealed	75,000	5	90B
Rod 0.100 in. unannealed	100,000	5	97B
Rod 0.050 in. unannealed	120,000	5	100B
Rod 0.050 in. annealed	90,000	15	95B
Wire 0.025 in. unannealed	130,000	5	100B
Wire 0.025 in. annealed	100,000	15	95B
Wire 0.010 in. unannealed	170,000	1	24C*
Wire 0.010 in. annealed	125,000	15	100B*
Wire 0.005 in. unannealed	190,000	1	
Wire 0.005 in. annealed	140,000	15	
Sheet 0.040 in. unannealed	120,000	1	22C*
Sheet 0.040 in. annealed	85,000	4	95B*
Sheet 0.020 in. unannealed	165,000	1	26C*
Sheet 0.020 in. annealed	125,000	7	95B*
Sheet 0.010 in. unannealed	175,000	1	27C*
Sheet 0.010 in. annealed	130,000	7	95B*

* Converted.

Material described as annealed is actually stress-relieved rather than recrystallized. The above data are from "Tungsten and Molybendum," Fansteell Metallurgical Corp., 1954.

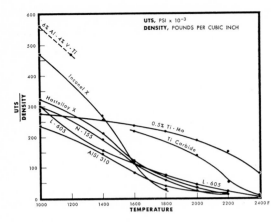

FIGURE 16.7. Tensile strength—density ratio versus temperature, for several alloys. (*Courtesy Marquardt Aircraft Company.*)

TABLE 16.4. RUPTURE STRENGTH OF WROUGHT ARC-CAST MOLYBDENUM IN THE STRESS-RELIEVED CONDITION

[Stress to Produce Rupture in 100 hr (Psi)]

Type	1600°F (871°C)	1800°F (980°C)	2000°F (1093°C)
Unalloyed	31,000	22,000	13,000
Mo–0.5 Ti	68,000	53,000	34,000
Mo–0.5 Ti–0.07 Zr	—	70,000	52,000

Recent work has indicated that the ratio of carbon to the alloying element or elements is of great importance in determining the strength of these alloys. Table 16.5 shows the effect of the carbon-titanium ratio on the tensile strength at 871°C (1600°F) and on the 100-hr rupture strength at 981°C (1800°F) for alloys containing 0.5 per cent and 1.25 per cent titanium with various carbon contents when tested in the fully recrystallized condition. Recrystallized material was used in this series of tests to eliminate any variation in strain-hardening effects which might have been present in as-rolled or stress-relieved material.

on several other factors, including temperature of working, rate of working, and chemical composition; hence, careful control of processing is necessary to obtain optimum properties.

Among the most useful alloying elements for strengthening molybdenum and raising its temperature of recrystallization are titanium, zirconium, and hafnium, especially in conjunction with carbon. Although several alloys have been produced by commercial methods from this group of additives, the most important one (1958) is the alloy containing about 0.5 per cent titanium. This composition had previously been selected, in preference to other percentages of titanium, because a definite peak in tensile strength, at both room and elevated temperatures, as well as in 100-hr rupture strength, occurred at this percentage of titanium at the carbon level of about 0.02 to 0.04 per cent characteristic of arc-cast molybdenum when this alloy was being developed.

A more recent alloy, which appears to have properties superior to the binary alloy containing 0.5 per cent titanium, but which has not been fully evaluated, contains approximately 0.5 per cent titanium and 0.07 per cent zirconium. The 100-hr stress-rupture strengths of these two alloys, compared to that of unalloyed molybdenum, are shown in Table 16.4.

At 1093°C (2000°F) this ternary alloy has almost four times the strength of unalloyed molybdenum and 50 per cent more than the binary alloy.

TABLE 16.5. EFFECT OF CARBON AND TITANIUM ON TENSILE STRENGTH

Mo–0.5% Ti (fully recrystallized)

Carbon %	1600°F (871°C) Tensile Strength (psi)	1800°F (981°C) 100-hr Rupture strength (psi)
0.004	18,000	10,500
0.024	36,400	28,000
0.14	38,200	33,000

Mo–1.25% Ti (fully recrystallized)

Carbon %	1600°F (871°C) Tensile Strength (psi)	1800°F (981°C) 100-hr Rupture strength (psi)
0.014	33,400	17,500
0.028	33,900	20,500
0.036	45,900	38,000
0.08	55,300	50,000
0.14	59,100	53,000

Extrapolation of data on some of the present alloys indicates that a 100-hr stress-rupture strength of 100,000 psi at 1093°C (2000°F) may be possible with some of the more highly alloyed systems if suitable fabrication techniques are established.

Corrosion Resistance of Metallic Molybdenum

Although resistance to corrosion is one of the potentially valuable properties of molybdenum, relatively little information based on actual service is available, probably because limitations with respect to size, shape, and fabrication methods have inhibited the development of applications in this field.

Molybdenum is resistant to several of the common chemical solutions, including hydrochloric, sulfuric, phosphoric, and hydrofluoric acids, as well as many caustic solutions under many conditions of concentration and temperature, but it is attacked by oxidizing acids, such as HNO_3 and aqua regia, molten oxidizing salts, such as KNO_3, and fused alkalis.

Results of some recent laboratory corrosion tests on unalloyed arc-cast molybdenum are given in Tables 16.6 to 16.10. The specimens,

TABLE 16.6. CORROSION OF MOLYBDENUM BY HYDROCHLORIC ACID

Acid concentration (%)	Test temperature	Corrosion rate in mils/year		
		48 hr	240 hr	670 hr
	Nonaerated			
1	71°C (160°F)	1.3	1.3	8
5	71°C (160°F)	1.1	1.1	
20	71°C (160°F)	0.5	1.1	5
5	Boiling	3.0	5.4	
20	Boiling	0.9	—	16
	Aerated—tank oxygen			
5	Room	0.3		
5	71°C (160°F)	1.4		
20	71°C (160°F)	1.4		
	Aerated—compressed air			
5	Room	0.5	—	0.5
20	Room	0.1	—	0.2
37	Room	0.2	—	0.1

TABLE 16.7. CORROSION OF MOLYBDENUM BY HYDROCHLORIC ACID + 0.5% FERRIC CHLORIDE

Acid concentration (%)	Test temperature	Corrosion rate in mils/year 48-hr periods
20	Room	29.0
37	Room	1.2
5	71°C (160°F)	150.0
20	71°C (160°F)	160.0
5	Boiling	250.0
20	Boiling	330.0

TABLE 16.8. CORROSION OF MOLYBDENUM BY SULFURIC ACID

Acid concentration (%)	Test temperature	Corrosion rate in mils/year		
		48 hr	240 hr	670 hr
	Nonaerated			
10	71°C (160°F)	0.8	3.1	24.0
20	71°C (160°F)	0.9	1.4	16.0
40	71°C (160°F)	0.7	0.6	
50	71°C (160°F)	0.5	0.4	
75	71°C (160°F)	0.7	—	0.01
95	71°C (160°F)	0.1	0.1	
10	Boiling	4.5		
40	Boiling	1.5	56.0	92.0
50	Boiling	2.5	21.0	110.0
75	Boiling	34.0	Dissolved	
95	Boiling	Dissolved		
	Aerated—tank oxygen			
10	71°C (160°F)	6.6		
20	71°C (160°F)	2.7		
40	71°C (160°F)	1.3		
	Aerated—compressed air			
10	71°C (160°F)	1.0		
20	71°C (160°F)	1.0		
10	71°C (160°F)	0.2 (N_2 bubbled)		
20	71°C (160°F)	0.2 (N_2 bubbled)		
40	71°C (160°F)	0.4	—	3.3
50	71°C (160°F)	0.3	—	0.2
75	71°C (160°F)	0.2	—	0.1
95	71°C (160°F)	Nil		

TABLE 16.9 CORROSION OF MOLYBDENUM BY PHOSPHORIC ACID

Acid concentration (%)	Test temperature	Corrosion rate in mils/year		
		48 hr	240 hr	670 hr
	Nonaerated			
10	100°C (212°F)	2.4	7.4	
50	100°C (212°F)	1.5	1.5	
85	100°C (212°F)	0.3	0.3	
10	Boiling	1.3	40.0	64.0
50	Boiling	1.5	20.0	37.0
85	Boiling	1.4	5.3	1.4
	Aerated—compressed air			
10	Room	0.27		
50	Room	0.25		
85	Room	0.20		

TABLE 16.10. CORROSION OF MOLYBDENUM
BY HYDROFLUORIC ACID

Acid concentration (%)	Test temperature	Corrosion rate in mils/year 48-hr periods
	Nonaerated	
25	Room	0.1
49	Room	0.1
25	100°C (212°F)	3.1
49	100°C (212°F)	2.3
	Aerated—compressed air	
25	Room	0.2
49	Room	0.1
25	100°C (212°F)	20.0
43	100°C (212°F)	16.0

cut from recrystalilzed sheet, were $\frac{1}{16}$ by 1 by 2 in. Volume of solution was about 200 ml/sq in.

Under some conditions, e.g. in boiling 40 per cent sulfuric acid, it will be noted that the corrosion rate is low in the 48-hr test but much higher in the 240-hr test and still higher in the 670-hr test. In each test the original acid solution was used throughout the test; hence, in the longer tests, there is more opportunity for the accumulation of reaction products in the solution. The increased rates of attack during the longer periods are thought to be due to such accumulations. Under many types of actual service, this would not occur to an important extent.

Molybdenum shows good resistance to many liquid metals being considered as heat transfer media, such as sodium, potassium, lithium, gallium, lead, bismuth, and mercury, even at elevated temperatures. It also has good resistance to molten copper. On the other hand, molybdenum is attacked more or less rapidly by some other molten metals such as tin, zinc, aluminum, and iron.

Water vapor, sulfur dioxide, nitrous and nitric oxides, and carbon dioxide have an oxidizing action on molybdenum at elevated temperatures. Molybdenum is inert in hydrogen at all temperatures and relatively inert in nitrogen up to about 1093°C (2000°F). A superficial nitride case may be formed at higher temperatures in ammonia and nitrogen. At elevated temperatures, molybdenum reacts with sulfur and hydrogen sulfide to form molybdenum sulfide. At moderate temperatures, molybde-

num reacts very slowly with iodine, while at higher temperatures, the iodide is unstable. Molybdenum reacts with chlorine and bromine above 250°C (482°F) and with fluorine at room temperature. In tests at various temperatures, molybdenum did not react with phosphorus. At high temperatures it reacts with carbon and hydrocarbons to form carbides, and with silicon to form silicides.

PROTECTION FROM OXIDATION

At temperatures above about 650°C (1202°F), unprotected molybdenum is oxidized so rapidly in air or oxidizing atmospheres at ordinary pressures that its continued use under such conditions is impractical. Since the MoO_3 formed melts at 795°C (1463°F) and begins to sublime at about 700°C (1292°F), it offers little protection to the base metal at elevated temperatures. The use of unprotected molybdenum may be practical, however, when the time of exposure at high temperatures is short. The oxidation rate is greatly reduced under low pressures such as those encountered at very high altitudes.

An ideal solution of the oxidation problem would be the development of a molybdenum-base alloy having good resistance to oxidation as well as desirable mechanical properties. Although the possibility of developing such an alloy cannot be denied, exploratory research has not yet turned up any promising leads, hence a great deal of work has been done on the development of protective coatings or surface treatments.

In appraising coatings, many properties must be considered, including resistance to oxidation, thermal shock, ballistic impact, fatigue, corrosion, and erosion. No coating now available embodies the full attainment of all of these properties. A coating should therefore be selected with a view to the specific operating conditions to be encountered.

Molybdenum sheet and simple shapes may be roll-clad with an oxidation-resistant material such as "Inconel," and molybdenum tubes have been clad with stainless steel. Both simple and more complex shapes may be coated by a variety of methods, including electrodeposition, cementation, vapor deposition, metal-bath deposition, or flame spraying. If it is important to retain the greatest possible strength, the process must be one which will not cause recrystallization of the molybdenum or molybdenum-base alloy.

Coatings consisting largely of $MoSi_2$ have excellent resistance to oxidation and thermal cycling but are apt to spall under ballistic impact. Chromium-nickel electrodeposits have shown good performance in all tests except thermal cycling.

Oxidation tests at temperatures up to 1650°C (3000°F) have established the following tentative temperature limits for some promising sprayed-metal coatings:

Al-Cr-Si	1430°C (2606°F)
Ni-Cr-B	1200°C (2192°F)
Ni-Si-B	1200°C (2192°F)

In tests at 981°C (1800°F), Al-bonded coatings have shown good resistance to oxidation and thermal shock, moderate resistance to erosion, but poor resistance to ballistic impact.

Nickel-base coatings are ductile and serve rather well until cracks occur, when oxidation results in formation of nickel molybdate which accelerates failure under thermal cycling conditions. In tests at 981°C (1800°F), the coatings exhibited good resistance to oxidation and ballistic impact and moderate resistance to erosion and thermal shock.

A great deal of laboratory testing and considerable field testing have been done on coatings of many types at temperatures from 981°C (1800°F) to well over 1650°C (3000°F). The brief statements given above represent a very small part of the published information available from these tests. In general, it may be said that several types of coatings have resisted oxidation by air at 1093°C (2000°F) for hundreds of hours and up to 1650°C (3000°F), or even higher temperatures, for shorter times. Details of coating and testing procedures and of test results are given in various references at the end of this article.

MOLYBDENUM COMPOUNDS

Molybdenum exhibits valences of +2, +3, +4, +5, and +6. It is also considered to exhibit a valence of 0 in the carbonyl, $Mo(CO)_6$. The two common valences in which it occurs in nature are +4 (molybdenite, MoS_2) and +6 (complex molybdates, $MoO_4^=$). In solution it forms not only simple anions and cations but also a large number of complex anions owing to its ability to aggregate or polymerize. These are controlled by the concentrations present and the pH of the solution. Molybdenum's usual coordination numbers are 4, 6, and 8. Transitions from one coordination number to another occur as solution conditions are changed. Oxygen and fluorine form their most stable compounds with hexavalent molybdenum, chlorine with the pentavalent, and bromine and sulfur with the tetravalent. Upon changing conditions, these compounds can disproportionate to form mixtures of compounds in which the molybdenum has different valences.

The catalytic properties of molybdenum compounds have led to their extensive use in the petroleum industry for the removal of sulfur, nitrogen, and some harmful metals. The principal compound used is molybdenum trioxide, MoO_3. Its use is often essential in processes for the production of high-octane gasolines. Residual fractions are also being treated with this catalyst to improve the quality of diesel and home heating fuels. Other chemical processes using molybdenum catalysts are the conversion of methanol to formaldehyde, benzene to maleic anhydride, and toluene to benzaldehyde.

One of the major consumers of sodium molybdate is the pigment industry, for the production of molybdate chrome orange. This is a brilliant orange pigment with great hiding power. Organic dyes and pigments are precipitated by phosphomolybdic acid, giving greater tinting strength and light fastness. As mordants, molybdenum compounds are used for dyeing with basic and acid dyes.

Ammonium molybdate, $(NH_4)_2MoO_4$, is used in chemical analysis for the determination of phosphorus. From a nitric acid solution it precipitates phosphorus in the form of ammonium phosphomolybdate having the formula $(NH_4)_3PO_4 \cdot 12MoO_3$ after drying at 110°C (230°F). Some of the phosphomolybdic acids are used as reagents for the alkaloids and in the analysis and separation of the alkali metals.

In ceramics, molybdenum trioxide acts as a wetting or fluxing agent. It promotes adhesion when used in enamels for coating metals, and it opacifies titania enamels.

In electroplating, ammonium molybdate helps produce decorative black coatings on metals.

Molybdenum disulfide, which has unusual

lubricating properties under extreme conditions, has found growing use as an additive to greases and oils. It is also used as a dry film or solid lubricant.

Molybdenum has been proved to be an essential trace element in plant nutrition, and it assists bacteria in fixing nitrogen in legumes. Both sodium molybdate and molybdenum trioxide are used.

Molybdenum forms two oxides of definite composition, MoO_2 and MoO_3. Hydrated forms of MoO and Mo_2O_3 have been reported; other oxides reported, such as Mo_3O_4 and Mo_2O_5, are thought to be mixed oxides. The trioxide is produced by roasting MoS_2 in air. It melts at 795°C (1463°F), but its vapor pressure is so high that it begins to sublime at 650–700°C (1202–1292°F).

Molybdenum disilicide, $MoSi_2$, is a highly refractory substance having good resistance to oxidation by air up to about 1700°C (3092°F). It is the principal ingredient of certain electrical-heating elements which will operate up to at least 1593°C (2900°F) in air.

FABRICATION

Although molybdenum for many years was fabricated only by swaging, drawing, rolling, and simple forming, it has been shown that it can be formed, with heating if necessary, by practically any of the processes used for fabricating the superalloys now in common use. These methods include spinning, roll forming, forging, stretch forming, deep drawing, extruding, and machining.

Figure 16.8 shows a forged ring 11⅜ in. OD by 9⅜ in. ID by 2⁹⁄₁₆ in. high, made from a 6-in.-diameter extrusion weighing about 110 lb.

Figure 16.9 illustrates an intermediate step in the stretch forming of an experimental "Inconel"-clad molybdenum-alloy guide vane for jet-engine use. The sheet is 0.050 in. thick, and forming was done at 315–426°C (600–800°F).

FIGURE 16.9. Initial stretch forming operation of "Inconel" clad molybdenum vane. (*Courtesy Westinghouse Electric Corporation.*)

An experimental honeycomb-type structure formed from 0.020-in. molybdenum sheet, spot welded and coated with the "Chromalloy W-12" coating is shown in Figure 16.10. It was heated to 1538°C (2800°F) in an oxidizing flame for 5 to 10 min and quenched in water. There is no apparent oxidation at any point.

FIGURE 16.10. Honeycomb construction. (*Courtesy T. R. Finn & Company.*)

FIGURE 16.8. Forged ring of arc-cast molybdenum. (*Courtesy Climax Molybdenum Co. of Michigan.*)

Figure 16.11 shows a section of a cup which was hot-spun from 0.040-in.-thick Mo–0.5 per cent Ti alloy sheet, using the "Floturning" process. An interesting point here is that the starting blank was formed by arc-welding two

FIGURE 16.11. Mo–0.5 per cent Ti panels, fusion-welded and then formed by spinning into the cup shape. One half the cup is shown. (*Courtesy Marquardt Aircraft Company.*)

pieces of molybdenum sheet together. The weld is visible in the center of the cup.

In one process for making tubing of unalloyed arc-cast molybdenum, slugs cut from hot-rolled and annealed bars are heated to 315–426°C (600–800°F) and cupped by backward extrusion. Tools are preheated to 260°C (500°F). The bottom of the cup is bored out before forward extrusion. Finishing operations often require intermediate anneals.

Figure 16.12 shows a rather difficult forging from the standpoint of metal flow. This is the bonnet and yoke for a special 2-in.-diameter valve for high-temperature sulfuric acid service.

FIGURE 16.12. Forged valve bonnet and yoke from arc-cast molybdenum for high temperature sulfuric acid service. (*Courtesy New England Valve Corp.*)

FIGURE 16.13. Forged valve body from arc cast molybdenum for high temperature sulfuric acid service. (*Courtesy New England Valve Corp.*)

It was forged from a rolled bar of unalloyed molybdenum in the conventional dies used for forging steel. Figure 16.13 is the machined forging of the body for the same valve.

JOINING

Mechanical means such as riveting and lock seams are the simplest methods of joining molybdenum. The initial properties of the molybdenum are completely maintained, but the joints are not necessarily fluid-tight.

For many years, small sections of sintered molybdenum have been welded by various methods, but the welds were neither very ductile at room temperature nor very strong. Certainly they would not meet the requirements for joints that would serve in critical parts of aircraft and missiles. As a result of considerable research, it has been demonstrated, within the last few years, that it is feasible to make fusion welds in arc-cast molybdenum sheet that are free from porosity and cracks and have moderate ductility at room temperature.

Atomic hydrogen or inert gas-shielded arc welding produces the most satisfactory welds in relatively heavy parts and in sheets over $\frac{1}{32}$ in. thick, and is also suitable for thinner sheet. Tungsten electrodes, with or without filler-wire additions, are used. Manual arc welding is feasible but not as reliable as automatic machine welding. Both helium and argon are used in inert-gas-shielded arc welding.

Two factors are essential to minimize embrittlement: (1) extreme cleanliness of faying surfaces and adjacent areas, and (2) careful control of the welding atmosphere with respect to oxygen and nitrogen, both of which are detrimental to ductility. Purified argon and helium are recommended, because of possible variations in commercial inert gases. Finally, a preheat at about 204°C (400°F) is favorable but not always necessary. It has been especially beneficial when welding complex assemblies.

Kulju and Kearns have given tensile and bend test results on specimens of welded Mo– 0.5 per cent Ti alloy sheet $\frac{1}{16}$ in. thick, as well as a description of the welding procedure. The welded joints had strengths comparable to those of recrystallized molybdenum but significantly lower than the wrought sheets. All specimens failed in the heat-affected zones. Nevertheless, the strengths at 871–1204°C (1600–2200°F) were far superior to any cobalt- or nickel-base alloy available. The 981°C (1800°F) weld strength was 43,500 psi, decreasing to 23,000 psi at 1204°C (2200°F). The welds had an average room-temperature bend radius of 5½T. The welded joints were said to have sufficient ductility at 149°C (300°F) to permit moderate forming.

Molybdenum can be brazed with a large variety of metals and alloys. If the parts are subsequently to be given a protective coating at high temperatures, a brazing medium must be selected which will not melt at these temperatures.

Where high service temperatures are not involved, copper or silver brazing alloys are usually chosen. For electronic parts and other non-structural applications involving temperatures above the melting points of the copper or silver brazing alloys, copper-nickel alloys with 10 to 30 per cent nickel have been used with excellent results. An alloy with 70 per cent nickel and 30 per cent molybdenum, melting at 1328°C (2425°F), has found application in special cases. Where higher operating temperatures are required, pure nickel and platinum are used. A molybdenum-boron powder with a melting point around 1900°C (3452°F) is suitable for hydrogen brazing.

Although many brazing alloys have been tried

for high-temperature structural applications and some have given encouraging results for certain parts, none has yet proved satisfactory for all applications.

APPLICATIONS

Industrial use of molybdenum metal for supports and lead wires in incandescent lamps began some time before 1915. Another major lamp application is for mandrels on which tungsten filament wire is wound so that it can be rewound for coiled-coil filament lamps. The molybdenum mandrel is removed by dissolving it in an acid mixture which does not attack tungsten. In the manufacture of lamps by this procedure, more molybdenum than tungsten is consumed. Molybdenum is widely used in electronic tubes for anodes, grids, and support members. It is strong enough to retain its shape at the high temperatures involved in the manufacture and use of such tubes. Molybdenum wire or rod is also used for seals through glass.

Molybdenum in the form of wire, rod, or strip is used for heating elements in laboratory and industrial furnaces required to operate at temperatures above the limits of the common resistance alloys. Working temperatures may be up to about 1700°C (3092°F). Oxidation of the molybdenum is avoided by the use of inert or reducing atmospheres, usually hydrogen or dissociated ammonia, or by operation in vacuum. Sometimes a molybdenum tube serves as both heating element and muffle. Heat shields of molybdenum are often used to control or localize radiation.

Molybdenum is used extensively for electrical contacts for applications not so severe as to require tungsten, but where there is a problem of arc erosion. It is used not only in the commercially pure form but also in powder metallurgy products in which it is mixed with silver or copper.

In mercury switches, molybdenum is used for electrodes which make contact with the mercury. Molybdenum does not react with mercury, but it is readily wet and makes a good electrical connection.

An important use of molybdenum wire is for producing sprayed coatings by the metallizing process. In order to obtain good adherence of sprayed coatings of some of the other metals, it is necessary to roughen the surface to be coated by operations such as grit blasting or grooving. Adherent coatings of molybdenum on steel and aluminum can usually be obtained without special surface preparation. Such coatings provide an excellent surface for subsequent sprayed coatings of other metals. The molybdenum coating itself has remarkable resistance to wear, and such coatings are finding many applications based on this property.

In radar devices, molybdenum has been used for the cathode support and accompanying structures. Its high electrical and thermal conductivities, low coefficient of expansion, and high-temperature strength are all important in this application.

Molybdenum has become increasingly important in the missile industry for several high-temperature structural parts. Although information on many of the uses is limited by security regulations, it can be stated, in general, that they include leading edges of control surfaces, rocket nozzles and nozzle inserts, support vanes, and other applications where high resistance to erosion at high temperatures is required.

Arc-cast molybdenum-base alloys have been extensively tested in jet engines for use in guide vanes and blades of the turbine section as well as for afterburner parts. For these applications, of course, protective coatings to prevent oxidation are necessary. Guide vanes formed from clad molybdenum sheet and blades forged from bar stock and then coated have been tested successfully.

In ram-jet engines, molybdenum combustion liners have been tested experimentally. A liner having a sprayed Al-Cr-Si coating has been operated at 1315°C (2400°F) for 14 min with high-velocity air on one side and high-velocity combustion gases on the other. Another potential application is for ram-jet nozzles.

In the glass industry, molybdenum is used for resistance-heating electrodes, stirring devices, pumps, and parts subject to wear. Molybdenum's resistance to the action of molten glass, its high-temperature strength, and its good electrical properties are outstanding for these applications.

The atomic energy industry is one of the most active in attempting to apply molybdenum to its requirements. Although information on many of the uses has not been released, molybdenum has been fabricated into heat exchangers, piping, and structural parts.

Molybdenum is finding some use in hot-work tools, such as points for the piercing of stainless steel billets in the production of seamless tubing, die casting cores and dies, extrusion dies, and brazing fixtures.

Molybdenum as an Alloying Element

In machine construction, alloy steel parts are generally hardened and tempered to increase their strength and resistance to wear. In steels for such parts, molybdenum may be used as the principal alloying element or in conjunction with other elements, especially chromium and nickel. The principal reason for its use is its contribution to hardenability.

Molybdenum contributes to the toughness of quenched and tempered steels by helping to prevent the development of temper brittleness. This effect, together with its contribution to hardenability, has accounted for its use in many applications where maximum toughness is required with high strength, as in armor plate and guns.

High-speed steels contain molybdenum or tungsten or both to develop the property of red hardness. Molybdenum is also used in other types of tool steel, especially those known as hot-work steels. It is added to various types of stainless steel, e.g., Type 316, to improve further their resistance to certain kinds of corrosion.

Molybdenum increases the strength of steel at elevated temperatures and has been widely used, e.g., in pipes, valves, forgings, and fittings in high-temperature steam plants, in superheater tubing, and in cracking-furnace tubes. Molybdenum increases the strength, toughness, and uniformity of gray cast iron, in which it is extensively used. It also increases the hardenability and elevated-temperature strength of gray iron.

Many of the nickel-base and cobalt-base alloys which have been developed for high-temperature use, as in gas turbine parts, contain molybdenum to increase their high-temperature strength. Molybdenum is used in certain nickel-base alloys, e.g., the "Hastelloys," developed primarily for resistance to corrosion in chemical solutions. Some titanium-base alloys also contain molybdenum.

REFERENCES

Books

American Society for Metals, "The Metal Molybdenum", 1958—(Cleveland) This book contains papers presented at a symposium held in Detroit, September 18-19, 1956. This symposium on *Technology of Molybdenum and Its Alloys* was sponsored by the Office of Naval Research. The following papers were presented:*

Herzig, Alvin, J., "The Potential and Future of Molybdenum and its Alloys", 4–9

Freeman, R. R., "Properties and Applications of Commercial Molybdenum and Molybdenum Alloys", 10–30

Toensing, C. H., "Molybdenum Metal Powder", 31–50

Scott, Howard, Taebel, W. A., and Lawthers, D. D., "Consolidation of Molybdenum by Powder Metallurgy Practice", 51–75

Gulbransen, Earl A., "Commentary on Forging", 76–79

Timmons, George A., and Yingling, Robert G., "Arc Melting Molybdenum", 80–108

Bruckart, W. L., "The Working of Molybdenum and Its Alloys", 109–126

Timmons, George A., "Commentary", 127–142

Nisbet, J. D., "Fabrication at Very High Temperature Under a Controlled Atmosphere", 143–150

Platte, W. N., "Welding of Molybdenum", 151–191

Monroe, Robert E., "Brazing of Molybdenum", 192–198

Senderoff, Seymour, "Techniques for Coating Metals with Molybdenum", 199–213

Maddin, R., "The Behavior of Molybdenum Single Crystals Under Various Stress Conditions", 214–240

Bechtold, J. H., and Wessel, E. T., "The Ductile-To-Brittle Transition in Molybdenum", 241–261

Spacil, H. S., and Wulff, J., "Effects of Oxygen, Nitrogen, and Carbon on the Ductility of Wrought Molybdenum", 262–278

Baldwin, W. M., Jr., "Commentary", 279–280

Semchyshen, M., "Development and Properties of Arc-Cast Molybdenum-Base Alloys", 281–329

Jaffee, Robert I., "Powder Metallurgy Molybdenum-Base Alloys", 330–364

* In this book a number of additional papers have been included.

Mallett, M. W., and Hansen, W. R., "Determination of Gases in Molybdenum", 365–393

Coons, W. C., "Fractographic and Metallographic Techniques for Molybdenum and Molybdenum-Base Alloys", 394–407

Begley, R. T., "Molybdenum for Aircraft Gas Turbine Applications", 408–419

Harwood, Julius J., "The Protection of Molybdenum Against High-Temperature Oxidation", 420–459

Safranek, W. H., "Commentary", 460–461

Barr, R. Q., Semchyshen, M., and Perlmutter, I. "Effects of Hot-Cold Work on the Properties of Molybdenum Alloys", 462–510

Russ, J. J., and Schrader, G. E., "Forging of Molybdenum Alloy Turbine Blades", 511–518

Northcott, L., "Molybdenum Research and Development in Great Britain", 519–527

Sims, Chester T., "Commentary", 528–529

Kieffer, R., and Pipitz, E., "Sintered and Arc-Melted Molybdenum Alloys", 530–553

American Society for Metals, Cleveland, Ohio, "Fabrication of Molybdenum", 1959. This book contains papers presented at the Molybdenum Fabrication Conference sponsored by the Southern California Chapters of the ASM, May 7-8, 1958.

Harwood, Julius J., "Molybdenum As A Structural Material", 1

Timmons, George A., "Development of Molybdenum Base Alloys", 19

Bruckart, W. L., "The Production and Quality of Molybdenum Mill Products", 39

Martin, D. C., "Welding of Molybdenum", 63

Hoppin, G. S., III, "Brazing of Molybdenum", 77

Jones, J. Byron, "Ultrasonic Welding", 88

Sohn, Jesse S., "Fusion Welding of Molybdenum Power Plant Components", 103

Jaffee, R. I., "Protective Coating Systems for Molybdenum", 119

Taebel, W. A. and Gelok, J., "Machining of Molybdenum and Its Alloys", 134

Quadt, R. A., "Press Extrusion of Molybdenum Tubing", 139

Goldberg, David C., "Forming of Clad Molybdenum", 148

Russ, J. J., "Forging of Molybdenum and Its Alloys", 169

Downey, R. C., "Testing in the Hot Rod Engine", 174

Levinstein, M. A., "Coating Development and Evaluation", 186

Yancey, R. W., "Fabrication of Electronic Tube Components", 205

Siergiej, John M., "Missile Structures and Powerplants", 214

Edwards, Eugene H., "Molybdenum Requirements in the Petrochemical Industry", 217

Woolsey, C. C., "Molybdenum Requirements in the Nuclear Energy Field", 220

Reports and Journals

Blanchard, J. R., "Oxidation-Resistant Coatings for Molybdenum," *WADC Technical Report 54–492,* Part 1 (1954); Part 2 (1955).

Coons, W. C., "Simple Electrolytic Polishing Procedures for Molybdenum Metallographic Specimens," *Trans. ASM,* 41, 1415–1424 (1949).

Couch, D. E., Shapiro, H., Taylor, J. K., and Brenner, A., "Protection of Molybdenum from Oxidation at Elevated Temperature," *J. Electrochem. Soc.,* 105, 450 (1958).

Deuble, N. L., Herzig, A. J., and Blanchard, J. R., "Arc-Cast Molybdenum," *Metal Progress,* April through October 1955 (a series).

Doane, D. V., "Oxidation-Resistant Coatings for Molybdenum," *WADC Technical Report 54–492,* Part 3 (1957).

Fieldhouse, I. B., Hedge, J. C., Lang, J. I., Takata, A. N., and Waterman, T. E., "Measurements of Thermal Properties," *WADC Technical Report 55–495,* Part 1, ASTIA Document No. AD 110404, September 1956.

Fieldhouse, I. B., Hedge, J. C., Lang, J. I., and Waterman, T. E., "Measurements of Thermal Properties," *WADC Technical Report 55–495,* Part 2, ASTIA Document No. AD 110510, November 1956.

Fieldhouse, I. B., Hedge, J. C., and Waterman, T. E., "Measurements of Thermal Properties." *WADC Technical Report 55–495,* Part 3, ASTIA Document No. AD 110526, November 1956.

Freeman, R. R., and Briggs, J. Z., "Machining Arc-Cast Molybdenum," *American Machinist,* Sept. 24, 1956.

Freeman, R. R., "The Properties and Applications of Commercial Arc-Cast Molybdenum and its Alloys," Plansee Proceedings, Metallwerk Plansee, 1958.

Harwood, J. J., "Protecting Molybdenum at High Temperatures," *Materials and Methods,* December 1956.

Jahnke, L. P., and Frank, R. G., "High Temperature Metallurgy Today," *Metal Progress,* November 1958.

Kulju, K. M., and Kearns, W. H., "Welding of Molybdenum-Alloy Sheet," *Welding Research Supplement,* October 1958.

Lucks, C. F., and Deem, H. W., "Thermal Conductivities, Heat Capacities, and Linear Thermal Expansion of Five Materials," *WADC Technical Report 55–496,* ASTIA Document No. AD 97185, August 1956.

Rasor, N. S., and McClelland, J. D., "Thermal Properties of Materials," Part 1. Properties of Graphite, Molybdenum and Tantalum to Their Destruction Temperatures, *WADC Technical Report 56–400,* Part 1, ASTIA Document No. AD 118144, March 1957.

Symposium of Molybdenum in Agriculture, *Soil Science,* 159–258 (March 1956).

Weare, N. E., and Monroe, R. E., "Welding and Brazing of Molybdenum," ASTIA AD 210486, OTS PB 151063, DMIC Report 108, Battelle Memorial Institute, March 1, 1959.

Climax Molybdenum Company Bulletins

(Editor's Note: The following bulletins represent literature studies which contain many literature references on the subjects they cover.)

Freeman, R. R., and Briggs, J. Z., "Electroplating on Molybdenum Metal," Climax Molybdenum Co. Bulletin, Sept. 1958.

Freeman, R. R., and Briggs, J. Z., "A New Look at Joining Molybdenum," Climax Molybdenum Co. Bulletin, 1957.

"Properties of Molybdic Oxide," Climax Molybdenum Co. Bulletin Cdb-1, August 1954.

"Thermodynamic Properties of Molybdenum Compounds," Climax Molybdenum Co. Bulletin Cdb-2, September 1954.

"Properties of Molybdenum Pentachloride," Climax Molybdenum Co. Bulletin Cdb-3, May 1957.

"Properties of Molybdenum Disulfide," Climax Molybdenum Co. Bulletin Cdb-5, October 1956.

"Refractory Molybdenum Silicides," Climax Molybdenum Co. Bulletin Cdb-6, January 1956.

"Refractory Molybdenum Carbides and Nitrides," Climax Molybdenum Co. Bulletin Cdb-7, February 1956.

"Refractory Molybdenum Borides," Climax Molybdenum Co. Bulletin Cdb-8, March 1956.

"Organic Complexes of Molybdenum," Climax Molybdenum Co. Bulletin Cdb-9, June 1956.

"Properties of Molybdenum Hexacarbonyl," Climax Molybdenum Co. Bulletin Cdb-13, November 1958.

"Symposium on Molybdenum (in Agriculture)," Climax Molybdenum Co. Bulletin Ag-16, reprinted from Soil Science, March 1956.

17. THE PLATINUM METALS

F. E. Beamish, W. A. E. McBryde, and R. R. Barefoot

Department of Chemistry
University of Toronto
Toronto, Canada

	Group VIII			Group I b
	Iron	Cobalt	Nickel	Copper
Atomic number	26	27	28	29
Atomic weight	55.85	58.94	58.71	63.54
	Ruthenium	Rhodium	Palladium	Silver
Atomic number	44	45	46	47
Atomic weight	101.1	102.91	106.4	107.873
	Osmium	Iridium	Platinum	Gold
Atomic number	76	77	78	79
Atomic weight	190.2	192.2	195.09	197.0

INTRODUCTION

The first known reference to platina or native platinum, a naturally occurring alloy composed of a large proportion of platinum together with palladium, rhodium, iridium, osmium, ruthenium, copper, iron, and sometimes gold, bears the date 1557.[92] The writer was Julius Caesar Scalinger (or della Scalla), an Italian poet and scholar, who noted the difficulty in melting a metal which was obtained from the Spanish possessions in South and Central America. The earliest scientific investigation of platina was instigated by William Brownrigg in 1750. Berthollet and Pelletier[9] described the work of M. de l'Isle, who obtained a malleable form of platinum in 1773–74. Pierre-Francois Chabaneau (or Chavaneau) succeeded in preparing some malleable platinum, and patented the

process in 1783.[38] However, an intensive study of the records[8] has led to the belief that pure platinum was first obtained in 1803 by W. H. Wollaston, whose brilliant researches resulted in the isolation of two of the minor constituents of platina, i.e., palladium and rhodium.[101] The aqua regia extract of platina was treated with ammonium chloride to precipitate the platinum; mercury (I) cyanide was then added to precipitate the palladium, and finally rhodium was isolated as sodium rhodium chloride.

The name "palladium" was chosen by Wollaston in honor of the asteroid Pallas, and "rhodium" because of the rose-red color of the salts of that metal. Osmium and iridium were isolated and named in 1804 by S. Tennant.[88] About the same time, H. V. Collet-Descotils, A. F. de Fourcroy, and L. M. Vauquelin also suspected the presence of iridium in platina, but their work was not conclusive.[8,60] Both

* Revised, 1959, by W. A. E. McBryde.

osmium and iridium were found in the black residue which remained after the aqua regia treatment of platina. The name "iridium" was derived from the Greek word *iris*, meaning a rainbow, and refers to the varying colors of iridium salts. The name "osmium," derived from the Greek word for smell or odor, was chosen because of the characteristic chlorine-like odor of osmium tetroxide. It was not until 40 years later that the remaining element of the platinum group was isolated. Ruthenium was discovered and named by C. Claus in 1844, although publication of the news was delayed until the following year[14] when J. J. Berzelius confirmed the results of the experiments and accepted ruthenium as a new element.[7,92] The name "ruthenium," from Ruthenia, Russia, was first used by G. Osann in 1828 to designate a substance obtained from platina; this substance was later shown to be composed of the oxides of silicon, zirconium, titanium, iron, and a small quantity of a new element.

OCCURRENCE

The platinum metals occur both in primary deposits and in placers. The primary deposits are of two main types.[64,66] The first consists of disseminations or local concentrations of the metals in olivene-rich rocks, particularly in dunite and often associated with chromite; native platinum, or iridosmine, is the principal constituent. The erosion of such deposits has been responsible for the formation of placer deposits of the platinum metals. Dunite deposits are widespread, the most important commercially being in the Ural Mountains region of the U.S.S.R., and at Overwacht in the Transvaal, Union of South Africa. The second type of primary deposit includes the magmatic nickel-copper sulfide deposits which are generally associated with norite. These deposits, in which platinum and palladium predominate, make up the greatest known reserves of platinum metals. The most extensive deposits have been found in the norite belt of the Bushveld igneous complex in the Transvaal, and in the Sudbury district of Ontario, Canada. In the Sudbury district ores, platinum and palladium occur in about the same proportions; these ores also contain small amounts of the other platinum metals as well as silver and gold. The precious metals are obtained as by-products

during the extraction of nickel and copper. The South African primary deposits contain all the platinum group metals, as well as iron, nickel, copper, cobalt, silver, and gold. In contrast to the Ontario ores, the quantity of base metals present is not sufficient to pay for the working costs. Platinum metals have also been found in quartz veins and in copper and coal deposits, although these sources are of little economic value.

Placer or alluvial deposits of great economic importance have been found in the Perm district of the Ural Mountains; in Colombia, South America; and in Abyssinia. Placers have also been found in the United States including Alaska, Australia, and Canada.

All of the metals of the platinum group are very rare. Table 17.1 contains estimates of the abundance of these metals in the earth's crust. The remaining elements of Group VIII, together with copper, silver, and gold, are included for comparison. Of the six elements, only platinum and palladium are found native.[65] Native platinum includes those alloys which contain at least 50 per cent platinum, the actual platinum content being as high as 90 per cent. Iridium, iridosmine, rhodium, and palladium are usually associated with platinum. Iron is present in considerable amounts; there is also a little copper and nickel, and occasionally gold. Representative compositions of native platinum from several sources are given in Table 17.4. When iron is present, the mineral may be magnetic. Native platinum occurs as grains or scales, and sometimes as nuggets or lumps. It is widely distributed throughout the world, the principal districts being the Ural Mountains

TABLE 17.1. ABUNDANCE OF SOME ELEMENTS[27]

Atomic number	Symbol	Earth's crust (g/ton)
78	Pt	0.01
46	Pd	0.005
77	Ir	0.001
45	Rh	0.001
76	Os	0.001[84]
44	Ru	0.001[84]
47	Ag	0.1
79	Au	0.005
26	Fe	51,000.0
27	Co	40.0
28	Ni	100.0
29	Cu	100.0

(U.S.S.R.), South Africa, Colombia, and Alaska. Native palladium resembles native platinum in appearance and in some of its properties. Small quantities of platinum and iridium are always associated with it. It is a rare mineral, being found in Colombia, Brazil, U.S.S.R., and the Transvaal. Palladian is a native platinum which contains 37 per cent palladium; allopalladium, the nature of which is uncertain, but which contains mercury, platinum, ruthenium, and copper, occurs only at Tilkerode in the Harz Mountains.

Very few compounds of the platinum metals occur as minerals. Sperrylite ($PtAs_2$, with which small amounts of rhodium are sometimes associated) occurs in the Sudbury district in Canada, in the Transvaal deposits of South Africa, and in eastern Siberia. Cooperite (PtS) and braggite [(Pt, Pd, Ni)S] are found in the Bushveld complex, and in the Potgietersrust districts of the Transvaal. Of the minerals which contain palladium principally, stibiopalladinite (Pd_3Sb) is found with sperrylite in the Transvaal, and potarite (PdHg) is found only in British Guiana. Laurite (RuS_2), which sometimes contains osmium, is very rare; it is found in Borneo and in the Transvaal.

Iridium is most often found alloyed with osmium in iridosmine (Ir > Os) and siserskite (Os > Ir). The term *osmiridium* is used more or less synonymously with the term *iridosmine*, but the latter is employed in this chapter. Iridium is also associated with platinum and gold in platiniridium and aurosmiridium, respectively. As mentioned previously, rhodium, together with other members of the platinum

TABLE 17.2. WORLD PRODUCTION OF PLATINUM METALS
(troy ounces)

Country	1949–53 Average	1954	1955	1956	1957	1958	1959
Canada							
Platinum (placer and from Cu-Ni refining)	138,340	154,356	170,494	151,357	199,565	144,565 ⎫	354,000*
Other Platinum Metals	163,861	189,350	214,252	163,451	216,582	150,720 ⎬	
South Africa							
Platinum Metals from ores		101,921	109,267	124,078 ⎫			
Concentrates	190,837			⎬	603,704	300,000*	366,000*
(P.M. content)		236,241	272,465	360,496 ⎭			
Osmiridium (from gold ores)	6,699	6,266	7,021	6,696	5,361	5,000*	—
U.S.A. (Placer and from Au-Cu refining)	32,019	24,235	23,170	21,398	18,531	14,322	14,000*
Colombia Placer	28,429	28,465	27,526	26,215	19,830	16,036	16,000*
U.S.S.R.	135,000*	200,000*	250,000*	250,000*	250,000*	250,000*	250,000*
Japan	441	1,595	849	701	587	643*	—
Congo (refineries)	21	176	—	160	325	325*	—
Ethiopia	389	230	350*	300*	300*	180	—
Sierra Leone (placer)	8	—	—	—	5	8	—
Australia							
Platinum (placer)	5	23	7	12	20	10*	—
Osmiridium (placer)	46	16	21	26	66	42	—
New Guinea	3	5	10	9	14	28	—
New Zealand	3	1	—	—	—	—	—
World Total (estimated and rounded)	700,000	940,000	1,080,000	1,100,000	1,310,000	880,000	1,000,000*

* Estimated.

group, occurs as a minor constituent of native platinum; the proportion of rhodium is usually less than 1 per cent. Small quantities of ruthenium are associated with alloys of the platinum metals, but most frequently with iridosmines which may yield 12 per cent or more of ruthenium. It must be noted, however, that some types of iridosmines are very resistant to corrosion, and as a result the analysis errors may be large.

PRODUCTION AND ECONOMIC STATISTICS

In the first edition of this handbook, the authors included estimates of world production of crude platinum up to the end of 1916, and of average annual outputs by countries from 1921 to 1952. This information is largely of historical interest, and has not been retained for this edition. Instead, Table 17.2 presents data for the period 1949 to 1959.[79,80] It is perhaps interesting to note that, in the period from 1950 to 1957, world production of the platinum metals doubled. This increase is mainly the result of a greater than fourfold expansion in the South African production; this country's output now accounts for more than half of the estimated world production. In the same period Canadian output increased by approximately 50 per cent, while that of the U.S.S.R. is estimated to have increased by 25 per cent. In 1958 a drop of about 30 per cent in world production was reported.

Notwithstanding the record production of these metals in 1957, figures for world consumption showed a decrease from the previous year, and a further decrease of about 20 per cent was estimated for 1958. This has been attributed mainly to a reduction in demand from the petroleum industry in the United States (see page 330), but undoubtedly it is related to the

period of economic recession in North America in 1957–58, which saw a decline in consumption of many base metals as well. In 1959 industrial demand increased, and in consequence there was a limited increase in production in both South Africa and Canada.

In Table 17.3 are shown prices for the platinum metals for the years 1955 to 1960. It is significant that increased production and decreased consumption brought the prices of these metals down appreciably below the figures for the previous 6 years. In fact, the price of platinum for January 1, 1959, was as low as at any time since World War II. With the resumption of demand in 1959 there has been a slight upward turn in prices, although these remain lower than the average of the previous five years.

DERIVATION

The methods by which platinum metals are obtained from their naturally occurring sources and from scrap precious metals should be discussed under various headings according to the source of the raw material. It may be advisable to point out that, by tradition, refiners of the platinum metals have long been reluctant to disclose the details of their operations; accordingly, the descriptions that follow, which are based on published material only, may depart in detail from prevailing practice.

Extraction of Platinum Metals from Canadian Nickel Ores

As has been mentioned earlier in this chapter, platinum metals occur associated with the copper-nickel sulfide ores in the Sudbury district of Ontario. The total content of platinum metals is only of the order of $\frac{1}{2}$ ppm, but, in view of the large tonnages of nickel produced,

TABLE 17.3. PRICES OF THE PLATINUM METALS, 1954 TO 1959*

	1955	1956	1957	1958	1959	1960
Platinum	79–117	97–117	77–107	51–80	75–80	82–85
Palladium	21–24	23–24	21–24	15–22	15–24	24–26
Rhodium	125	118–125	118–125	118–125	122–125	137–140
Iridium	100–135	100–110	100–110	70–100	75–80	70–75
Ruthenium	55–65	45–55	45–55	45–55	55–60	45–50
Osmium	100–140	80–100	80–100	70–110	70–90	70–90

* Prices in United States dollars per troy ounce for refined metals of at least 99.5% purity.
Source: *Eng. Mining J.*, Annual Surveys, February number.

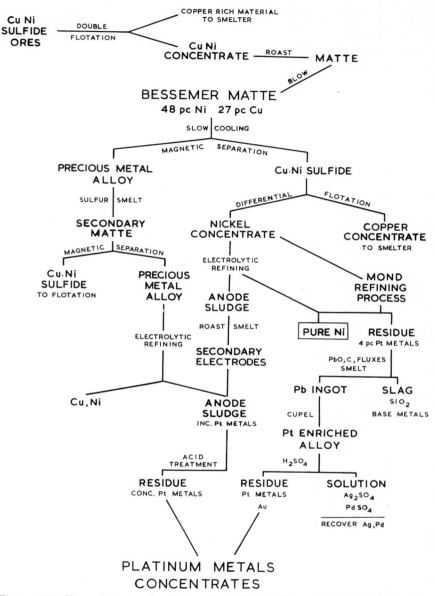

FIGURE 17.1. Flow chart for the International Nickel Co. process for the recovery and separation of platinum metals. First stage, ore to platinum concentrates.

the quantities of platinum metals made available are sufficient to make this an important source. The bulk of the nickel mining in the Sudbury basin is carried out by the International Nickel Co., a smaller proportion being mined by the Falconbridge Nickel Co. Expansion of the production of the former company includes a new project in the Mystery Lake–Moak Lake district of northern Manitoba, about 400 miles north of Winnipeg. Present indications are that this ore body will also produce platinum metals as by-products, and that this, known as the Thompson Mine, will become the second-ranking producer of platinum metals in Canada. Production is expected to begin in 1960 or 1961.

The manner of obtaining the platinum metals from these ores is obviously integrated with the processes employed for the isolation and refining of nickel and copper. These are described in recent reference works on production metallurgy (e.g., Reference 19). The essential stages in the operations of the International Nickel Co. are outlined in Figure 17.1. The bulk of the platinum metals is separated from the nickel and copper during slow cooling of the Bessemer matte. During the preparation of this, the amount of oxidation of sulfur is controlled to produce a small amount of metallic nickel and copper which acts as a collector to separate the platinum metals from the metallic sulfides. This precious metal alloy is magnetic, and may be removed by passing the ground matte through a magnetic separator. This product is melted and treated with enough sulfur to convert 80 to 90 per cent of the nickel and copper to sulfides, at the same time retaining a small proportion of these metals in the free state. On cooling this matte a still more concentrated metallic alloy containing the platinum metals separates, and is removed from the ground material magnetically. This enriched alloy can then be subjected to electrolytic refining, during which the platinum metals accumulate in the anode slimes.

A smaller amount of platinum metals is recovered during the subsequent refining of the nickel. As shown in the outline, the crude nickel oxide is treated to obtain pure nickel by either of two processes: the electrolytic refining is carried out at Port Colborne, Ontario, Canada, while the Mond carbonyl process is carried out at Clydach, near Swansea, in Wales. From the former the anode slimes are roasted and smelted to give secondary anodes which are also electrolyzed. The sludges from these contain about 2 per cent platinum metals, but, with suitable treatment by acid, they can be concentrated until their platinum metals content is about 50 per cent. In the Mond method of refining nickel, a residue from the carbon monoxide treatment is obtained which, after roasting, is leached with sulfuric acid to remove any remaining copper and nickel. A residue is obtained having a precious metals content of about 20 per cent. A representative composition for this is the following:

Platinum	1.85%	Ruthenium	0.16%
Palladium	1.91%	Silver	15.42%
Rhodium	0.20%	Gold	0.56%
Iridium	0.04%		

The material from each of these nickel refineries is sent to be processed at the Acton Refinery of the Mond Nickel Company (London, England).

Falconbridge Nickel Mines, Ltd., separate a rich concentrate by magnetic cobbing, then subject the remainder to flotation and a further wet magnetic separation. The concentrate is smelted in a blast furnace to give a matte which is further upgraded by treatment in basic lined converters to yield a high-grade shipping matte. This matte, containing about 48 per cent nickel, 28 per cent copper, and 22 per cent sulfur, is shipped to the company's subsidiary refinery at Kristiansand, in the south of Norway, for further treatment. There it is roasted, the copper removed from the calcine by acid leaching, and the nickel recovered by electrolysis. The anode slimes from this electrolysis are smelted and re-electrolyzed to give a concentrate of precious metals which is refined in the same plant in Norway. The operations of this company have been described in detail in a recent publication.[1]

Extraction of Platinum from South African Ores

The important South African deposits occur in the Merensky Reef horizon, an enormous platinum-bearing deposit forming part of the Bushveld igneous complex. The mining operations are carried out by Rustenburg Platinum Mines, Ltd. Rustenburg lies northwest of Johannesburg and west of Pretoria. The platinum occurs there mainly as sulfide mineral forms such as sperrylite, cooperite, and braggite, together with stibiopalladinite and gold. In addition, a certain amount of metallic platinum is present. The platinum metals are associated with sulfide ores such as pyrrhotite, pentlandite, and nickeliferous pyrite; in parts of the deposits these ores are extensively weathered and oxidized. The content of platinum metals is of the order of 4 to 10 ppm. There is a wide variation in the proportions of the different platinum metals, but one report,[57] based on samples from this area, gives the following ranges for the relative proportions:

Platinum	66 to 77%
Palladium	11 to 25%
Other platinum metals	1 to 7%
Gold	2 to 5%

The base metal content of these ores, as mentioned earlier in this chapter, is too low to warrant economical working on its own account. Therefore, methods of concentrating the platinum metals necessarily differ from those used for Canadian ore.

The ore is crushed, ground, and subjected to gravity concentration on tables and corduroys to give a product containing, on the average, 22 per cent platinum metals, native or as sulfides, etc. This concentrate, known as metallics, may contain as much as two-thirds of the precious metals in the ore. This concentrate is shipped to the Brimsdown Works of the Johnson Matthey Co., Ltd., London, England, for further treatment. The tailings from the gravity concentration are then subjected to flotation processes which produce a concentrate consisting of a platiniferous mixture of the sulfides of copper, nickel, and iron. This concentrate is then smelted to a matter which is further enriched and largely stripped of iron by being blown in a converter. The matte contains about 48 oz/ton of platinum metals, of which about half is platinum. It is either shipped to Johnson Matthey in England or treated near the mine by Matte Smelters (Pty.), Ltd.

The matte is smelted by fusion with coke and sodium bisulfate. On pouring and slow cooling of this melt, two layers are formed, the upper containing copper sulfide with sodium sulfide, and any gold or silver in the material; the lower layer consists of nickel sulfide together with the bulk of the platinum metals. This separation of copper and nickel, known as the *tops-and-bottoms process,* makes use of a principle utilized for many years in the treatment of Sudbury ores in Canada. The copper sulfide "tops" are melted in a reverberatory furnace, then blown to blister copper, and finally cast into anodes for refining. The nickel sulfide "bottoms" are ground and roasted in rotary furnaces to nickel oxide. This is then briquetted with coal, reduced to the metals in a reverberatory furnace, and the nickel cast into anodes for refining. The anode slimes, particularly from the crude nickel, contain the platinum metals. They are exported, like all the other platiniferous concentrates, for refining in England.

Refining of Platinum Metal Concentrates

The following account is based largely on the published description of the operations of the Acton Refinery of the Mond Nickel Co.[52] The residue from the carbonyl process, described previously, contains, as noted, about 4 per cent platinum metals and must be subjected first to a four- or fivefold concentration. It is then smelted with litharge, fluxes, and charcoal in order to remove silica and base metals. Lead sulfate, which is a major constituent of the carbonyl residue, is converted to lead and a top slag of sodium sulfate. The lead ingot so formed is cupeled to leave a precious-metals alloy considerably enriched.

This alloy is parted with boiling concentrated sulfuric acid. Such treatment dissolves the silver almost completely, and about one third of the palladium, each in the form of sulfates. The silver is recovered and purified electrolytically by the Moebius process[12] and palladium recovered from the anode slimes.

Gold, platinum, and the rest of the palladium are then extracted from the residual metal by treatment with aqua regia. The same aqua regia treatment is applied to the residues from the electrolytic nickel and copper refineries. The resulting solution of chlorides is first treated with ferrous sulfate to precipitate gold.

$$3Fe^{2+} + AuCl_4^- \rightarrow 3Fe^{3+} + 4Cl^- + Au$$

The impure gold is purified by the Wohlwill electrolytic process.[11] The platinum is next precipitated from the solution as ammonium chloroplatinate (IV) by the addition of ammonium chloride. The first precipitate, when isolated and dried, is purified by ignition to the metal which is then redissolved in aqua regia. From this solution a pure ammonium chloroplatinate is obtained which, on ignition, yields a pure platinum sponge. Palladium is next removed from solution as the diammine palladium (II) chloride. Excess ammonia is first added, followed by hydrochloric acid, and the yellow salt precipitates out.

$$PdCl_4^{2-} + 4NH_3 \rightarrow Pd(NH_3)_4^{2+} + 4Cl^-$$
$$Pd(NH_3)_4^{2+} + 2HCl \rightarrow Pd(NH_3)_2Cl_2 + 2NH_4^+$$

This salt can be purified by dissolving in excess ammonia and reprecipitating with hydrochloric acid. When the palladium compound is ignited, a sponge of the metal is obtained.

The insoluble residue from the aqua regia extraction is smelted with litharge and fluxes, and the resulting lead alloy cupeled. The precious metals alloy is then parted with nitric

PLATINUM METALS
CONCENTRATES

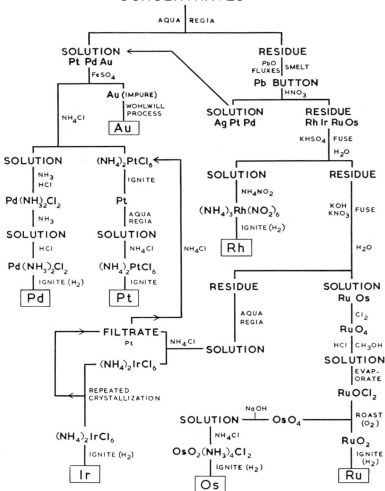

FIGURE 17.2. Flow chart for the International Nickel Co. process for the recovery and separation of platinum metals. Second stage, platinum concentrates to individual metals.

acid, which removes most of the accompanying palladium, platinum, and silver. The insoluble residue contains rhodium, iridium, and ruthenium (and a very small amount of osmium) in concentrated form. This group of metals is known sometimes as by-metals, and their subsequent treatment constitutes the difficult part of platinum metal refining. Certainly, from this point forward, the published schemes of refining show more diversity and more evidence of innovation than appear for the isolation of platinum and palladium.

In one procedure the rhodium is extracted by fusion with potassium bisulfate in the form of a soluble double sulfate.[52] The solution of this may contain traces of other platinum metals, and the rhodium must be isolated in a pure form as a precipitate of ammonium (or potassium) nitritorhodite $[(NH_4)_3Rh(NO_2)_6]$. From this, rhodium is produced by ignition, but with the added precaution that the residue must be ignited and cooled in hydrogen. In another account the dissolution of rhodium as sulfate is preceded by treatment of the by-metal residue with lead at moderate temperatures; rhodium alone of the four platinum metals will dissolve in the lead.[96] The lead alloy is subsequently leached with nitric acid and, later, hot sulfuric acid, to dissolve the rhodium, while iridium, ruthenium, and osmium remain as an insoluble residue.

The refining of rhodium to a high state of purity by these chemical operations is difficult and tedious. An account of procedures used at the United States National Bureau of Standards has been given by Wichers *et al.*[94] There are indications that some refiners are now making use of ion exchange resins to separate contaminating base metals from rhodium.[15] In most of its compounds, rhodium forms part of a complex anion, so that passage of a solution containing rhodium in one of these complexes, together with base metals in cationic form through a cation exchange resin, delivers rhodium in a purified form in the eluate.

The residue from the rhodium extraction is treated to remove the platinum, gold, and lead sulfate remaining from the nitric acid parting of the alloy. The insoluble part is treated by an oxidizing fusion with potassium hydroxide and nitrate. This converts ruthenium to the soluble potassium ruthenate (K_2RuO_4) and oxidizes iridium to a form which is insoluble in water but which can be dissolved in aqua regia. The ruthenium compound is extracted with water, and the solution is treated with chlorine. From this solution, ruthenium tetroxide is volatilized on heating, the vapors distilling and being collected in dilute hydrochloric acid containing methyl alcohol. This converts the ruthenium to an oxychloride ($RuOCl_2$) which is isolated when the absorbing solution is evaporated. Ruthenium metal is obtained from this by ignition in hydrogen.

Osmium occurs to only a small extent in Sudbury ore but does amount to something less than 1 per cent of the ruthenium content. In concentrates from other sources, osmium may occur in higher proportions. It will contaminate the ruthenium prepared by the procedure just described, but it can be removed in one of several ways. The choice of method may depend on the relative amounts of these two metals to be separated. Where ruthenium is in excess, the distillate may be caught in a warm solution of hydrochloric acid, which reduces ru-

thenium to the trichloride. Osmium tetroxide may be distilled directly from this solution, the distillate being absorbed, e.g., in alcoholic caustic. The absorbate is then digested with ammonium chloride to cause osmyltetrammine chloride [$OsO_2(NH_3)_4Cl_2$] to precipitate. Osmium metal can be obtained by ignition of this compound in hydrogen. An alternative treatment of the aqueous extract from the oxidizing fusion is the addition of alcohol to precipitate ruthenium as the hydrated dioxide. This may be removed by filtration and osmium isolated in the filtrate by precipitation as potassium osmate upon the addition of excess potassium hydroxide.

The oxidized iridium formed in the nitrate fusion is dissolved in aqua regia, and the solution partially evaporated. Ammonium chloroiridate (IV) is precipitated in a crude form by the addition of ammonium chloride. The precipitate must be purified by repeated crystallization, principally to separate platinum. When this salt has been isolated in a sufficient state of purity, it is ignited by heating. The metal so obtained contains some oxide and must be reduced by heating in hydrogen.

It should be noted that all filtrates and insoluble residues are returned to the process at appropriate stages, so that practically no material is lost. It is stated that at the Acton refinery a maximum of 0.25 per cent of the platinum metals contained in the concentrates is lost, while 1.25 per cent is retained in slags. Since the latter are returned to the nickel refinery for further treatment, most of the slag loss is recovered. The losses at the time of the nickel and copper extraction are also small, and it has been estimated that 90 per cent of the precious metals, osmium probably excepted, contained in the ore is ultimately recovered. The loss of osmium as the tetroxide probably occurs to a significant extent during such operations as smelting and cupeling; such losses invariably accompany the corresponding processes in the fire assay for precious metals.

Treatment of Native Platinum[20,23]

Prior to the development of Canadian and South African sources, platinum was almost exclusively derived from alluvial deposits of the native metal. Native platinum occurs as a mix-

TABLE 17.4. COMPOSITION OF NATIVE PLATINUM AND IRIDOSMINE

Source	Platinum	Palladium	Osmium	Ruthe-nium	Rhodium	Iridium	Gold	Irid-osmine	Iron and copper
Platinum									
Urals	73–86	0.3–1.8	0–2.3	?	0.3–3.5	2.6–4.3	0.4	0.5	8–17
South Africa	80–84	0.4			Total 0.5–1.0			—	11
Colombia	84–86	0.5–1.0	—	—	1.4	0.8	1.0	1	5–8
Iridosmine									
South Africa	12.9	—	32.7	14.3	1.0	29.6			
Tasmania	1.9	—	45.6	7.9	0.2	42.2	0.01		
Urals	10.1	—	27.2	5.9	1.5	55.2			

ture of metallic alloys in various regions of the world. The composition of these, as indicated previously, is mainly platinum with smaller amounts of the other platinum metals, together with some iron and traces of other base metals. In addition, the naturally occurring alloy iridosmine is generally found mechanically mixed with the others. Representative compositions of native platinum and of iridosmine from various sources are given in Table 17.4.

Apart from some difficulty in rendering the iridosmine soluble, the handling of these alloys to extract the various platinum metals takes the form of a wet separation comparable to that described in the previous section.

The material is first digested with aqua regia until as much as possible has been dissolved. The insoluble residue is mainly iridosmine, iridium, and possibly some nonplatiniferous minerals. This is treated separately.

From the aqua regia solution nitric acid is expelled by repeated evaporation; then crude ammonium chloroplatinate, contaminated mainly with chloroiridate, is precipitated. A purer product requires the ignition of the crude to the metal, redissolving this in aqua regia, and repeating the precipitation. Another method of separating the impurities is by fractional crystallization of sodium chloroplatinate.

The treatment of the filtrate from the platinum precipitation is based on the proportions of the various metals present. Often, zinc or iron is added at this stage to precipitate the noble metals. These can then be separated by taking advantage of the moderate solubility of finely divided gold, palladium, and platinum in diluted aqua regia. Rhodium, iridium, and ruthenium are only slightly attacked. From this solution, platinum is precipitated as be-

fore, gold is then precipitated as the metal by the addition of ferrous sulfate, and finally palladium is oxidized in solution and precipitated as ammonium chloropalladate (IV). It should be understood that the precipitates of platinum and palladium compounds are contaminated by the other metals and must be purified in order to obtain the desired metal in a pure form.

The residue of rhodium, iridium, and ruthenium is treated either by chlorination on a bed of sodium chloride, or by fusion with sodium hydroxide and peroxide, or by an alternation of these treatments. The first of these operations yields a chlororhodite soluble in water; the second produces a water-soluble ruthenate and renders iridium into a form which can be dissolved in hydrochloric acid. From the solutions prepared in this way, rhodium may be isolated in the form of a precipitate of ammonium nitritorhodite, and iridium as ammonium chloroiridate. Ruthenium is isolated by distillation of the tetroxide in a stream of chlorine into an absorbing solution of dilute hydrochloric acid. From this absorbate, ruthenium may be isolated as a precipitate by the addition of ammonium chloride. The pure metals may be obtained from these precipitates if they are ignited under reducing conditions, although it is preferable to convert rhodium to ammonium chlororhodite before the ignition.

The attack upon the residue which did not dissolve in the original aqua regia treatment, namely the iridosmine, has recently been the subject of considerable research work. The conventional treatment of this residue is to form an alloy with zinc which is later dissolved with hydrochloric acid. This produces a material which is finely divided, and which is then fused with sodium peroxide and hydroxide. Such treatment renders the osmium, most of the ruthenium, and a small part of the iridium water soluble. The aqueous solution is acidified with nitric acid, and osmium tetroxide distilled out in a stream of air. The vapors are collected in a solution of sodium hydroxide probably containing a small amount of alcohol. From this, osmyltetrammine chloride, $OsO_2(NH_3)_4Cl_2$, is isolated, and this compound can then be reduced to the metal. Ruthenium can be distilled by making the same solution alkaline, adding chlorine, and warming. The tetroxide distills and is collected as before. The part of the iridosmine that was not soluble in water after fusion is dissolved in hydrochloric acid, and iridium is isolated as ammonium chloroiridate from this solution.

The alkaline fusion treatment just described for the dissolution of iridosmine and other platiniferous material not dissolved by aqua regia introduces various contaminating elements into the resulting solution, besides being rather tedious. Recently, two procedures have been suggested to avoid this. The first[95] involves heating the sample in a sealed tube with concentrated hydrochloric acid and an oxidizing agent such as chlorine. Other mixtures, such as nitric acid and sodium chlorate, or perchloric acid, were also investigated. The temperature used in some cases was as high as 300°C (572°F), and the pressure corresponding was as high as 4,000 psi. Various platinum metal alloys and pure iridium are dissolved under the described conditions. A second procedure,[30] which has so far been attempted on only a small scale, is a dry chlorination of the alloy in the presence of an excess of sodium chloride. By this method it has been possible to render soluble various samples of iridosmine, including one from Tasmania which had completely resisted attack by alkaline fusion, and had only partially dissolved in the bomb method of wet chlorination. This procedure also has been applied to samples of native platinum which were entirely converted to soluble forms. The authors are not aware to what extent, if any, these techniques are used by commercial refiners, but it is reasonable to assume that they will be adopted as necessary.

It should be stressed that the methods described in this section are given only in briefest outline. The separations are seldom clear cut,

and each precipitate requires purification in order to eliminate other unwanted members of the platinum family. Likewise, a certain amount of each element escapes precipitation and is carried along in the mother liquor to reappear in a subsequent separation. The refining of platinum metals differs from most metallurgical operations by being really large-scale laboratory work in inorganic chemistry, and it is rarely undertaken without considerable experience in the chemistry of these elements.

Details of the methods which have been used at the National Bureau of Standards in Washington, D.C., for the production of each of the platinum metals in a pure state have been published by Gilchrist.[23]

Refining of Scrap

A significant proportion of the annual production of platinum metals is by the recovery of wastes—old dental alloys, jewelry, laboratory equipment, spent catalysts, etc., plus sweepings and spillage from refiners and electroplaters. This is brought out by the following table[80] showing the amounts of the platinum metals produced by refiners in the United States in the year 1958 (1) from native platinum plus a small amount recovered from domestic gold and copper ores; (2) from foreign sources, chiefly Colombia; and (3) by the refining of scrap metal, sweeps, and other waste products of manufacture.

	Native Sources (troy oz)	Foreign Sources (troy oz)	Secondary Sources (troy oz)
Platinum	9,025	26,384	36,426
Palladium	4,691	1,222	38,883
Iridium	1,685	1,461	1,223
Osmium	368	646	335
Rhodium	271	958	2,639
Ruthenium	22	1,462	2,008
Total	16,062	32,133	81,514

The procedures to be applied to scrap material are essentially the same as those already described for refining concentrates and native metal. Some modifications are necessary, owing to the much higher proportions of silver and gold in this sort of material. The subject has been very thoroughly discussed in a valuable reference book by Hoke[31] and in review articles by Whitely and Dietz[91] and by Dale.[18]

FABRICATION TECHNIQUES

Melting[48,93,97]

There are two principal methods in use for melting the platinum metals and their alloys. One is by direct heating of the metal in a lime crucible with an oxyhydrogen or oxygas torch. The other makes use of the principle of induction heating with high-frequency electric fields. The latter method is more commonly used in industry. In recent years the vacuum arc furnace has been introduced for research work where the quantities to be melted are small.

An interesting and recently published historical account of the melting of platinum[58] records three principal phases in the development of this technique. The first occurred following the invention, in 1801, of the oxyhydrogen blowpipe by Robert Hare in Philadelphia. The firm of J. Bishop, founded in Malvern, Pennsylvania, pioneered in the commercial fabrication of platinum apparatus in which the melting was done by the blowpipe. The second historical period began with the introduction by Deville and Debray in 1857 of a lime-block crucible or furnace in which platinum could be melted by an oxygas flame. From this time forward, melted platinum became readily available, and it assumed great importance following the introduction in 1862 of hardening of platinum by the addition of iridium. The third and contemporary period in this account began in 1921 with the application to this work of the Ajax-Northrup high-frequency electric induction furnace.

The crucibles for melting platinum by flame heating are shaped from dry burned lime at great pressures. They consist of an upper and lower member which are fastened together in an iron casing. The lower member is hollowed out in a concave shape with a groove for pouring the molten metal; the upper member is similarly hollowed out but has central holes for the insertion of the torch and for the escape of gases. The crucible must be preheated to eliminate occluded gases from the lime; if this is not done, considerable spitting will occur. Where much melting is to be done, the tip of the torch should be made of platinum-iridium alloy to prevent contamination of the melt by base metals.

The choice of crucible material for this method appears to be limited to lime and zirconia. The former is said to be preferable, because lime has a purifying effect on platinum; because it is porous, the lime acts rather like a cupel to absorb small amounts of contaminating base metals. Also, the ingot may be freed of adherent lime by treatment with hydrochloric acid. An advantage of the zirconia crucible is that it does not absorb moisture; this obviates some of the preheating and enables the crucible to be used over and over. Clay, graphite, or silica crucibles may lead to contamination by carbon or silicon, with consequent embrittlement of the metal.

There are serious drawbacks in the use of lime-block crucibles and flame heating for melting these metals, and these have been mainly responsible for the widespread adoption of induction heating for the same purpose. It has been difficult to secure lime of a quality suitable to withstand the high temperatures. Very careful regulation of the composition of the gas mixture is required throughout the melting of a batch. Any reducing character in the flame may lead to reduction of calcium or magnesium from the lime, with consequent contamination of the melted metal; on the other hand, an oxidizing flame produces gaseous inclusions in the metal which introduce difficulties in the subsequent production of foils, and may even lead to an unsound casting. Some platinum is, moreover, lost in the form of fume (see under oxidation, page 327), and the melting of alloys rich in osmium or ruthenium leads to appreciable losses of these metals as volatile oxides.

The induction furnace permits the attainment of high temperatures within the sample being melted, without requiring a large surrounding thermal mass. Consequently, one may easily remove the crucible containing the melt, if packed within a silica sheath, for pouring. Mixing of alloys, never very efficient in the lime-crucible melting, is accomplished automatically, owing to the fact that electromagnetic forces in the melt bring about energetic stirring of the metal. Crucibles are mainly made of zirconia, or of silica or alumina lined with zirconia or thoria. The nature of induction heating is such that apparatus can easily be built in which the melting of metals can be carried out *in vacuo* or in an inert gas. Ingots formed when the melting is conducted *in vacuo* appear to be freer of gas and cavities, and thus permit drawing operations with fewer breakages.

For the preparation of extremely pure platinum metals, such as may be required for research purposes or for certain electrical applications, great care must be taken to ensure freedom from contamination from the refractory materials in which melting is carried out, or from the atmosphere. Raub and his associates, who have carried out many important studies on alloy systems of the platinum metals at the Research Institute for Precious Metals and Metal Chemistry at Schwäbish Gmund in Germany, are pessimistic concerning the extent of unavoidable contamination of these metals through reactions with refractories at high temperatures. Such reactions are most likely to occur when the melting is done in reducing atmospheres. These workers use a vacuum arc furnace with a water-cooled copper crucible and a tungsten electrode. They have found no detectable contamination by either copper or tungsten. Melting is done, of necessity, in an atmosphere of argon, because their furnace will not permit work in a high vacuum; to rid the specimens of gaseous impurity, these must be annealed in vacuum.[69]

Working[48,97,98]

The operations in working the platinum metals and their alloys depend on their individual characteristics. The largest part of the commercial production is of platinum, palladium, and their alloys, which will stand considerable working without giving trouble. Usually, the ingots of these, especially those cast for drawing into wires, are heated to a white heat and are hot forged with a power hammer. This makes the metal more compact and closes up cavities or gas holes. Sivil[86] has stated: "It is probable that in the platinum industry there is more trouble with blisters than in any other metal-working industry, as, apart from the affinity of these metals for gases there are great difficulties in temperature control of the melts." For some dental alloys, particularly those containing gold, the hot forging may not be required. For flat ingots intended for plate stock, it is usual to plane off any surface imperfections, so that the first rolling may be done at temperatures above 800°C

(1472°F). The ingots are then cold-rolled, swaged, or drawn to finished size.

Rhodium and iridium are harder and more brittle, and other techniques are required for working them. Rhodium can be forged at temperatures above 800°C (1472°F)[87] and swaged into wires of 1 mm diameter. The hot swaging produces a wire of coarse-grained structure which is not ductile. It is possible to get a ductile wire by gradually decreasing the temperature while continuing to work the metal. Rhodium sheet can be prepared by successive hot rolling until the thickness is about 0.030 in., whereupon the metal becomes sufficiently ductile for cold rolling. Frequent annealing is necessary with the cold rolling. Iridium cannot be cold rolled at all, but it can be worked hot in the same fashion as rhodium, provided that it is very pure.

In drawing operations, wet lubricants do not stick very well to platinum and its alloys, and dry powdered soap is often used to lubricate the metal prior to passing it through the dies. Steel, sapphire, tungsten carbide, and diamond are all employed as die materials. Precautions must be taken to avoid any contamination of the metals and their alloys during working operations; often, plate and sheet are pickled prior to annealing to remove any iron picked up from the rolls.

All these metals harden in the working operations and should be annealed at suitable intervals. This is done, in most cases, in a muffle furnace with free access of air to provide an oxidizing atmosphere. The metal should not be allowed to come in contact with open flame during this process, for some of the alloys may pick up contamination leading to embrittlement or crystal imperfections. Some alloys require annealing in nitrogen or hydrogen, but the latter gas is sometimes absorbed, especially by palladium, causing the metal to harden. The temperature at which annealing is done is governed by the composition of the metal; the presence of rhodium or iridium necessitates a higher temperature.

Articles of platinum and palladium and their alloys can be produced by spinning, drawing, and rolling. Seamless tubing can be made easily, provided the rhodium or iridium content is not too great. The metals do not lend themselves to punch pressing or lathe work, because they do not cut cleanly. The addition of iridium to platinum and of ruthenium to palladium, how-ever, does result in some improvement. Plat-inum may be drawn down to wires 0.001 in. or smaller. Still smaller wires, suitable for cross hairs in optical instruments or for fuses, may be obtained down to 0.00004 in. by the Wollas-ton process. This consists of surrounding a platinum wire by a silver sheath and drawing the whole down to a small diameter; the silver may then be dissolved in nitric acid, leaving the very fine wire of platinum.

For soldering platinum metal articles, fine gold is recommended. The metals can also be welded together by fusion, or by hammer weld-ing below the melting point. They can also be hammer welded to iron, steel, and many non-ferrous metals. A certain amount of platinum- or palladium-clad stock is made by welding these metals to bars or sheets of nickel or silver. The whole piece may then be drawn or rolled to the desired thickness. The platinum-metal coat is generally made not less than 0.002 to 0.003 in. thick. A fairly recent develop-ment is the production of platinum-clad elec-trodes notably for application in combating corrosion. (See page 330.) For these, platinum is applied as a coating over tantalum or titanium;[16,67] in one method of fabrication, platinum sheet is rolled onto tantalum sheet or platinum tubing is drawn over tantalum rod, and then the clad material is treated in a vacuum furnace to assure a good metallurgical bond.

Ruthenium and osmium have never been successfully worked. This is said to be due to the difference in the crystal structure of these metals as compared with the other four. The same property may account for the enormous hardening power of these two when alloyed with the other metals.

Electrodeposition[5,10,82,83]

Of the six platinum metals, only platinum, palladium, and rhodium are of concern in elec-trolytic deposition, either industrially or in the laboratory. Conditions have been recorded for the complete deposition of each of these three for analytical purposes; the deposit of rhodium tends to be contaminated with oxide. Iridium is not easily reduced from solutions of its chloride or sulfate, either chemically or elec-trolytically, and methods for separating pal-

ladium or rhodium from iridium by selective deposition have been described. The separation of rhodium and iridium by electrolysis is quite difficult, because the conditions that lead to oxide contamination of the plated rhodium also induce contamination of the deposit by iridium oxide.

On a commercial scale, platinum, palladium, and rhodium are mainly applied only in thin flash deposits for decorative purposes. Rhodium plating has been successfully carried out for a longer time, and, with suitably prepared elec-trolyte solutions, it becomes a very easy matter. Rhodium deposits are characterized by their high reflectivity and hardness. With the com-mercially available rhodium plating baths, de-posits as thick as 2×10^{-5} cm are not uncom-mon. It is comparatively difficult to produce thicker impervious coatings of platinum or pal-ladium. One reason for this is that platinum has a tendency to show fine cracks in the deposit, probably owing to contraction. As a conse-quence, the coating gives little protection from acid or fumes. Similar cracking may occur with rhodium deposits thicker than 5×10^{-4} cm. Both platinum and palladium tend to plate out at less than 100 per cent current efficiency, a good deal of hydrogen being evolved simul-taneously. The hydrogen is taken up by these metals, making them hard. There would be no objection to this hardness except that to build up a plate heavier than a flash deposit requires scratch-brushing the surface intermittently, and this is difficult with a hard, brittle surface.

Rhodium has been used in flash deposits to coat silver jewelry, and it is said to preserve the distinctive luster of silver itself while elimi-nating the objectionable tarnish. In thicker deposits it is used on table silverware and on high-grade reflectors for searchlights and pro-jection lanterns. Palladium plate is used to some extent on items such as watchcases, cigarette cases, and so on. An interesting use advocated for palladium plating is as a base coat preparatory to plating gold on silver; the palladium restricts the gold from diffusing into the silver. Although it is claimed that pal-ladium can be plated on almost any metal or solder, the general practice seems to be to deposit these metals on a base coat of nickel. Where rhodium is plated on gold alloys or platinum bases this is not necessary, but, for plating on tin and lead alloys, the nickel deposit is particularly important in order to avoid a dark and streaky deposit. The nickel undercoat seems to increase the wearing qualities of rhodium plate.

Details of the composition of electroplating solutions have been recorded by most of the writers cited at the beginning of this section, and numerous patents have been registered. Platinum appears to be most successfully plated from an ammoniacal solution of diammine platinum nitrite (platinum P-salt) containing ammonium nitrate and sodium nitrite. Platinum or carbon anodes may be used, and the former are not dissolved. This bath has the advantage that it does not build up a concentration of salts as it is used over a considerable period of time. Deposition from a bath containing chloroplatinic acid and appreciable concentrations of hydrochloric acid has been recently claimed to result in a thick, adherent deposit, free from cracks.[4] Palladium may be plated from a solution entirely analogous to the above, but good results require a lower applied voltage and somewhat more careful control of pH. The use of a solution of palladous chloride with ammonium chloride as a bath is said to yield heavy deposits successfully; in this case, expendable palladium electrodes are used. The most successful plating solutions for rhodium are of rather uncertain composition but are made up from commercially available concentrated stock solutions. These apparently contain rhodium in the form of acid complex sulfates or phosphates. The prepared solution is added to one of sulfuric or phosphoric acid. For the production of thicker deposits without loss in brightness, various additives have been suggested. Selenic acid at a concentration of 0.4 to 1.0 g/liter has functioned in this way, and crack-free deposits thicker than 10^{-3} cm are said to have been achieved with sulfate baths.[71] For rhodium plating from these solutions, insoluble platinum anodes are used. It is characteristic of the plating of all these metals that the operation is carried out in warm or hot solutions and at comparatively low current densities.

A new platinum plating solution, said to be capable of producing heavy, coherent, bright deposits on a wide range of base metals, has been recently developed in the Johnson Matthey Research Laboratories. The electrolyte consists of a solution of sulfatodinitritoplatinous acid, $H_2Pt(NO_2)_2SO_4$, 5 grams per liter, maintained at a pH below 2; a bath temperature of 50°C (112°F) and a current density of 5 amp./ft² is said to be the optimum for building up heavy, bright deposits. (*Platinum Metals Review*, **4**, 56 (1960).

A method of depositing palladium by chemical reduction and without an electric current has been described. In this, the metal is deposited as thick as 6×10^{-3} cm on a variety of transition metals (catalytic surfaces) by reduction with hydrazine from an ammoniacal solution to which ethylenediaminetetraacetic acid has been added.[73]

Vapor Deposition

A general description of the technique of producing coatings of metals by high-vacuum evaporation has been given by Yarwood[102] and by Godley.[26] The method has not found wide application for the platinum metals, and it is probable that rhodium is the only one of the group that has been so handled on a commercial scale. Owing to the low vapor pressure of these metals, very high temperatures are required for their evaporation, and the apparatus must be evacuated to very low pressures. Rhodium is usually deposited electrolytically on a clean tungsten spiral, which is then inserted in the apparatus and heated by an electric current. In Germany, strips of rhodium have been directly heated by the passage of large currents, so that a much greater surface area is exposed. The metal is deposited mainly on glass for rugged and highly reflecting mirrors. Platinum cannot easily be evaporated in this way, as it tends to form into one drop on the heating wire and cause the latter to burn out. It can, however, be deposited on glass at low pressures by the technique of cathode sputtering. An account of this rather specialized method is provided in the monograph by Yarwood.

Available Forms

All of the six metals may be purchased in the form of sponges or as salts. Platinum and palladium are stocked as sheet, wire, foil, and ribbon, in various grades of purity. They are also available as semifinished jewelry, electrical contacts, standard alloys, and catalysts. The catalysts may be obtained as gauzes of various dimensions, "blacks," oxides, and dispersed forms on alumina, silica gel, charcoal, etc. Platinum, palladium, and rhodium plating solutions may be purchased. Platinum laboratory wares, such as crucibles, dishes, boats, spatulas, electrodes, etc., are available in a large number of shapes and sizes. Items such as platinum spinnerets, furnace windings, seamless tubing, thermoelements, and clad equipment can be readily supplied.

The major suppliers of platinum metals will, on request, send booklets and circulars describing their products.

PHYSICAL PROPERTIES

An essential requirement for obtaining "true," or at least reproducible, values for physical properties is that the substances be obtained, for measurement, in an extremely pure state. The failure to achieve absolute purity has undoubtedly led to some lack of satisfactory agreement about the properties of platinum metals as determined by different investigators. It is quite probable that many of the earlier measurements cannot be relied on implicitly, owing to lack of evidence concerning the degree of refinement of the specimens used. In recent years it has been frequently shown that very minute traces of impurities, including the other platinum metals, cause significant changes in such properties as hardness, electrical resistance, etc. In view of the fact that the platinum metals have a marked tendency to pick up such gases as hydrogen and oxygen, it is not difficult to see how contamination may readily be overlooked. It was remarked in the previous section that there is a likelihood of forming cavities and gas holes during the preparation of ingots of compact metal.

It is also true, as with other metals, that properties often depend on the previous history of the specimen; hardness and other mechanical properties depend on the amount of cold working or annealing that has preceded the measurement. It is not uncommon to encounter such statements as, "Heat treatment markedly affects the temperature coefficient of resistance of pure platinum."[29]

The physical properties of the pure metals will be considered first for platinum, next for palladium, and then for the pairs rhodium and iridium, and ruthenium and osmium. A short section will be devoted to some of the common alloy systems among these metals.

Platinum

While specifications are not standardized, there are three or four different grades of platinum metal available from refiners. Grade 1, designated "thermopure," "thermoelement," or "physically pure," is required for platinum resistance thermometers and thermocouples. It is known that both the temperature coefficient of resistance and the thermoelectric characteristics of platinum are extremely sensitive to the slightest trace of impurity. Grade 1 platinum has a purity in excess of 99.99 per cent. Grade 2 is designated "pure," "chemically pure," or "special pure," and contains at least 99.9 per cent of the metal. Grade 3 is the normal product for crucible and electrical use. It is ordinarily alloyed with up to 0.5 per cent of another platinum metal to increase its hardness and strength, and therefore its resistance to wear. A fourth grade of platinum, designated "commercial," contains at least 99 per cent of the metal.

The following data by Jahn[49] indicate the effect of the purity of the metal on selected physical properties.

Property	Unit	Grade 1	Grade 2	Grade 3
Density [20°C (68°F)]	g/cc	21.40	21.40	21.29
Melting point*	°C	1769	1768.5	1765.5
	°F	3216	3215	3210
Resistivity [20°C (68°F)]	microhms-cm	10.58	10 6	11.6
Temperature coefficient of resistance (0–100°C)	Per °C	0.00392	0.0039	0.0035
Tensile strength annealed	Tons/sq in.**	9	10 5	14
Hardness annealed	Vhn	42	50	65

* Adjusted from Jahn's data in accordance with the revision of the International Temperature Scale, 1948.
** 1 Ton = 2000 lb.

TABLE 17.5. PHYSICAL PROPERTIES OF PLATINUM AND PALLADIUM

Property	Platinum	Palladium
Density [20°C (68°F)] (g/cc)	21.45	12.02
Crystal lattice	Face-centered cubic	Face-centered cubic
Lattice cell, a_0 (kX units)	3.9161	3.8830
Allotropic forms	None known	None known
Melting point	1769°C	1552°C
	(3216°F)	(2826°F)
Boiling point (estimated)	4530°C	3980°C
	(8186°F)	(7196°F)
Thermal conductivity (cgs units)	0.17	0.17
Linear thermal coefficient of expansion (0°C) (per°C)	8.9×10^{-6}	11.67×10^{-6}
Relationship of thermal expansion to temperature	Refs. 21, 34, 63, 90	Refs. 34, 36, 90
Specific heat [0°C (32°F)] (cal/g/°C)	0.0314	0.0584
Relationship of specific heat to temperature	Refs. 43, 90	Refs. 36, 47
Latent heat of fusion (cal/g)	24.1	38.6
Latent heat of vaporization (cal/g)	540	
Electrical resistivity (microhms-cm)		
0°C (32°F)	9.81	10.0
20°C (68°F)	10.6	10.8
Temperature coefficient of resistance (per °C)		
(0–100°C)	0.003923	0.00377
Relationship of resistance to temperature	Ref. 90	Refs. 32, 90
Thermal neutron absorption cross section		
(barns/atom)	8.8 ± 0.4	8.0 ± 1.5
Hardness, annealed (Vhn)	40	40
Hardness, electrodeposited	600	190–400
Tensile strength, annealed (tons/sq in.)*	9	10
Proportional limit, annealed (tons/sq in.)	2	2
Young's modulus, annealed (tons/sq in.)	1.1×10^4	8×10^3

* 1 Ton = 2,000 lb.

A more complete listing of physical properties for pure platinum is given in Table 17.5. The information for this and the subsequent tables of properties has been drawn from the following list of references: 3, 22, 39, 49, 55, 70, 90, 97

The mechanical properties depend on the condition and history of the specimen as well as on its purity. Electrodeposited platinum is much harder than wrought metal. By heavy cold work, the hardness can be increased from 50 in the annealed condition to 120 or 125 Vhn. This increase is roughly comparable to that of copper. The tensile strength will increase from 10 tons/sq in. (1 ton = 2,000 lb) in the annealed state to about 15 tons/sq in. after severe cold working. The tensile strength falls to about 2 or 3 tons/sq in. when the temperature rises to 1000°C (1832°F). The limit of proportion-

ality of annealed pure platinum is very low, of the order of 1 or 2 tons/sq in. for Grade 2, but this value may rise to 13 or 14 tons/sq in. on cold working.

The hardness of platinum is deliberately raised by the addition of alloying elements. Nickel, osmium, ruthenium, copper, gold, silver, and iridium all produce considerable increase in hardness; the effect per unit weight of added element decreases approximately in the order named. Rhodium and palladium produce much less increase in hardness than do the preceding metals. The tensile strength and the limit of proportionality are also increased by the addition of various alloying elements.

Because of their importance in producing thermocouples, extensive data have been gathered for thermal emf's between platinum and other metals, and between platinum and

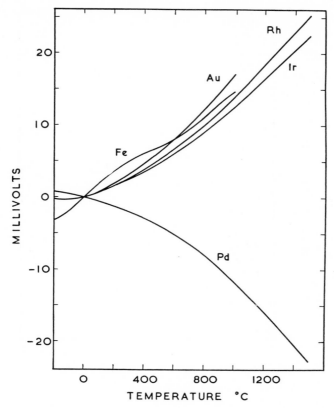

FIGURE 17.3. Thermal emf of related metals relative to platinum.
(*Data from ref. 90.*)

platinum-rich alloys. Selected data are shown in Figures 17.3 and 17.4.

The specular reflectivity of a platinum surface is moderately high, about 65 per cent on the average for visible light. This is of the same order as that of nickel, higher than that of palladium, but much lower than that of rhodium or freshly polished silver.

Palladium

Palladium is the least dense and the lowest melting of the six metals in the group. A selection of physical properties is shown in Table 17.5. Many of these, especially the mechanical properties, are altered by impurities and by the degree of cold work to which the specimen has been subjected. By cold rolling to a reduction in thickness of 50 per cent, commercial palladium has been reported to harden from 44 to 106 Vhn. Alloying elements, especially ruthenium and nickel, increase the hardness. The tensile strength and limit of proportionality are similarly increased by cold work and by the addition of certain elements, especially ruthenium and rhodium. For instance, the tensile strength of commercial palladium is about 14 tons/sq in. (1 ton = 2,000 lb) after annealing at 1100°C (2012°F), but it increases to 23.5 tons/sq in. after 50 per cent reduction by cold drawing; the tensile strength falls to about 2 tons/sq in. at 1000°C (1832°F). A representative jewelry alloy, containing 4 per cent ruthenium and 1 per cent rhodium, shows a tensile strength of about 28 tons/sq in.

Rhodium and Iridium

These two elements are characterized by being harder and tougher and higher melting

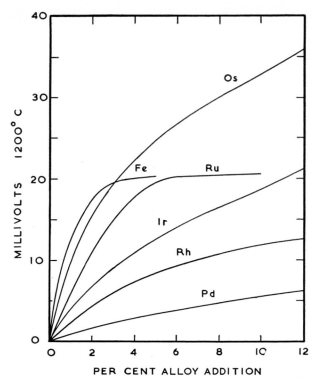

FIGURE 17.4. Thermal emf between some platinum-rich
alloys and pure platinum at 1200°C. (*Data from ref. 90.*)

than the preceding two. On this account their
working technology has not, as explained in
the preceding section, developed very far. A
selection of the properties of these elements is
given in Table 17.6.

There has been some speculation that rhodium may exist in two allotropic modifications.
The x-ray lattice parameters for finely divided
rhodium, obtained by reducing salts or by electrolysis, appear to be different from those of
massive metal obtained by melting or sintering
under pressure. The transition temperature for
the two postulated forms has been said to be
1000°C (1832°F). It is, however, observed
that there is no discontinuity in the emf-
temperature curve for platinum versus rhodium
thermocouples, as might be expected if such
polymorphic forms did exist. The structure of
a special highly refined specimen of the metal,
containing fewer than 10 ppm of impurities,
has recently been investigated[6] to secure evidence on this point. It was found that the
dimension of the unit lattice cell, a_o, changed

smoothly and continuously from room temperature to 1600°C (2912°F); and that the electrical resistivity changed continuously and
reversibly upon heating and cooling the specimen between room temperature and 1450°C
(2642°F). This evidence seems to rule out any
polymorphic transformation within the range
of temperature investigated.

The foregoing investigation also secured
values for a number of the mechanical properties of the very pure metal. It was hoped
from these to find a clue to the unusual difficulty in working this metal, as compared with
many others possessing the same kind of crystal
lattice. The hardness of the pure annealed metal
was 110 Vhn, but this increased to over 300
Vhn with about 15 per cent reduction in cross
section through rolling. The rate of work hardening is therefore unusually rapid at room temperature, and the author of the communication
cited suggests that some different mechanism
of its plastic behavior from that of other metals
with the face-centered cubic structure must be

TABLE 17.6. PHYSICAL PROPERTIES OF RHODIUM AND IRIDIUM

Property	Rhodium	Iridium
Density [20°C (68°F)] (g/cc)	12.44	22.4
Crystal lattice	Face-centered cubic	Face-centered cubic
Lattice cell, a_0 (kX units)	3.796	3.8312
Allotropic forms	Probably none	None known
Melting point	1960°C	2410°C
	(3560°F)	(4370°F)
Boiling point (estimated)	4500°C	5300°C
	(8132°F)	(9572°F)
Thermal conductivity (cgs units)	0.36	0.35
Linear thermal coefficient of expansion [0–100°C (32–212°F)]	8.5×10^{-6}	6.5×10^{-6}
Relationship of thermal expansion to temperature	Refs. 36, 90	Refs. 35, 90
Specific heat [20°C (68°F)] (cal/g/°C)	0.059	0.032
Relationship of specific heat to temperature	Refs. 36, 44, 90	Ref. 45
Latent heat of fusion (cal/g)	50.5	
Latent heat of vaporization (cal/g)	1341	
Electrical resistivity [0°C (32°F)] (microhms-cm)	4.7	5.3
Temperature coefficient of resistance (per °C) (0–100°C)	0.00457	0.003925
Relationship of resistance to temperature	Ref. 90	Refs. 33, 90
Thermal neutron absorption cross section (barns/atom)	156 ± 7	440 ± 20
Hardness, annealed (Vhn)	110	220
Hardness, electrodeposited	800	
Tensile strength, annealed (tons/sq in.)*	30.6	16
Young's modulus, annealed (tons/sq in.)	2.06×10^4	3.7×10^4

* 1 Ton = 2,000 lb.

involved. Electrodeposited rhodium shows a very much greater hardness with values up to 800 Vhn. This extraordinary hardness gives a surface free from mechanical wear.

Rhodium is of interest from an electrical standpoint, not only because of its rather lower specific resistance when compared with platinum or palladium, but because of its ability to maintain a low and stable contact resistance owing to the freedom from oxidation films on the surface. A thermocouple of platinum with a 10 per cent rhodium-platinum alloy serves to define the International Temperature Scale between 630.5–1063°C (1134.9–1945.4°F).

The reflectivity of rhodium surfaces is quite high, exceeding 80 per cent in most of the visible range of the spectrum. This is inferior to freshly polished silver, which has a reflectivity averaging about 90 per cent for visible radiation. However, since silver tends to become tarnished in normal atmospheres, its reflectivity soon falls below that of rhodium. For this reason, rhodium is widely used as a durable, highly reflecting surface material.

Iridium is very difficult to work, and for this reason few of its mechanical properties have been accurately determined; thus the value given in Table 17.6 for its hardness is only one of several appearing in the literature.

Ruthenium and Osmium

These metals are very high melting and extremely hard and brittle even at high temperatures. For these reasons, there is no record of their having been satisfactorily worked. It is to be noted that they occupy a crystal pattern different from the other four metals. The melting points of both metals have been accurately determined only recently.[19a]

The specific resistance of ruthenium is variously reported with values from 7.16 to 14.4 microhms-cm. The difficulty of fixing this value may be due to inability to obtain compact samples of known dimensions.

On the basis of measurements of specific heat and of the temperature coefficient of electrical resistance, Jaeger and Rosenbohm[45,46]

TABLE 17.7. PHYSICAL PROPERTIES OF RUTHENIUM AND OSMIUM

Property	Ruthenium	Osmium
Density [20°C (68°F)] (g/cc)	12.4	22.5
Crystal lattice	Hexagonal close-packed	Hexagonal close-packed
Lattice cell (kX units)		
a_0	2.7003	2.7298
c/a	1.5824	1.5790
Allotropic forms	See text	None known
Melting point	2250°C	3000°C
	(4082°F)	(5432°F)
Boiling point (estimated)	4900°C	5500°C
	(8852°F)	(9932°F)
Linear thermal coefficient of expansion	9.1×10^{-6}	$\|c$ axis, 5.8×10^{-6}
	[20°C (68°F)]	$\perp c$ axis, 4×10^{-6}
		mean, 4.6×10^{-6}
		[50°C (122°F)]
Specific heat [0°C (68°F)] (cal/g/°C)	0.057	0.0309
Relationship of specific heat to temperature	Refs. 36, 45, 90	Refs. 44, 90
Electrical resistivity [0°C (32°F)] (microhms-cm)	7.16–7.6	9.5
Temperature coefficient of resistance (per °C)	0.00449	0.0042
Thermal neutron absorption cross section (barns/atom)	2.56 ± 0.12	15.3 ± 0.7
Hardness, annealed (Vhn)	240	350
Young's modulus, annealed (tons/sq in.)*	3.0×10^4	4.0×10^4

* 1 Ton = 2,000 lb.

concluded that four, and possibly even five, polymorphic modifications of ruthenium exist. The values reported for the transition temperatures are $\alpha = \beta$, 1035°C (1885°F); $\beta = \gamma$, 1190°C (2174°F); and $\gamma = \delta$, 1500°C (2732°F).

Alloys of the Platinum Metals[25,49,51,69,99]

In this section it will be possible to describe only in general terms some of the alloys of these metals that have some commercial or particular scientific interest.

The principal commercial alloys involving platinum are those with copper, gold, iridium, rhodium, and ruthenium. Recent attention has been paid to alloys with cobalt on account of their strong ferromagnetic properties. Palladium forms important alloys with copper, gold, iridium, and silver, and also with ruthenium and rhodium together. There is a considerable body of published information about the properties of these and other alloys of the platinum metals; many details are given in the references cited above.

Of the alloy systems mentioned above and several others formed by platinum or palladium, solid solutions are frequently obtained throughout the entire range of composition. The alloys formed by ruthenium with these two elements have not been completely investigated, but they appear to show only restricted solubility. These findings are in accord with the principles of physical metallurgy which apply to the mutual solubility of metals.[40] The formation of solid solutions is generally favored if (1) the solvent and solute atoms are of nearly equal size, (2) the metals are of the same valency type, and (3) the two metals have the same crystal structure. If all these requirements are met, a continuous series of solid solutions is to be expected. It is apparent from Table 17.8 that the dozen elements shown have atoms of quite similar size, and, with the exception of α-iron, ruthenium, and osmium, all possess a face-centered cubic crystal lattice. The question of similar valency in these cases appears to be met in the case of the Group VIII elements and possibly copper, although Hume-Rothery points out[41] that some doubt exists concerning

TABLE 17.8. ATOMIC RADII OF TRANSITION ELEMENTS

	Iron	Cobalt	Nickel	Copper
Atomic radii (kX units)	1.27	1.25	1.245	1.275
Crystal type	BCC $= \alpha$ FCC $= \gamma$	FCC	FCC	FCC

	Ruthenium	Rhodium	Palladium	Silver
Atomic radii (kX units)	1.335	1.34	1.375	1.442
Crystal type	HCP	FCC	FCC	FCC

	Osmium	Iridium	Platinum	Gold
Atomic radii (kX units)	1.35	1.354	1.385	1.439
Crystal type	HCP	FCC	FCC	FCC

BCC = body-centered cubic; FCC = face-centered cubic; HCP = hexagonal close-packed.
The atomic radii are Goldschmidt radii for co-ordination number 12.

the number of electrons available for bond formation when dealing with the transition elements in the crystalline state.

It is, therefore, easy to see why osmium and ruthenium, with their hexagonal, close-packed crystal structure, would not be expected to show complete miscibility with platinum or palladium. Existing data, however, suggest a moderate solubility of ruthenium in these two metals, which seems reasonable on the basis of favorable size and valency factors. The complete solubility of iron with platinum or palladium is evidently associated with a raising of the temperature of the $\gamma = \delta$ transformation by small amounts of these metals. Alloys containing as little as 5 per cent platinum crystallize in a face-centered cubic lattice. The theory provides no explanation of the fact, familiar to every assayer, that rhodium and iridium scarcely dissolve at all in silver.

An interesting survey by Raub of the structure of alloys of the platinum metals with each other, with the other elements of Group VIII, and with manganese, the elements of Group VIA, and a limited number from Groups VA and IVA has appeared recently.[69] One interesting, and somewhat unexpected, observation discussed in this report is that, although the four FCC platinum metals show complete miscibility after high-temperature annealing, at lower temperatures there exist wide miscibility gaps in some of these alloys. This restriction in mutual solubility is quite certain in the case of the systems palladium-iridium [below 1500°C (2732°F)], platinum-iridium [below 980°C (1796°F)], and palladium-rhodium [below

850°C (1562°F)]. Structural changes in these alloys are slow to occur; in some cases, annealing for a year has proved insufficient to ensure attainment of equilibrium. Consequently, the limits of miscibility cannot yet be fixed with certainty. The author attempts to relate the critical temperature of the miscibility gap with the difference in the melting points of the components. In those cases where miscibility gaps were not observed, the melting points of the two metals did not differ greatly.

Another phenomenon associated with the formation of metallic solid solutions is the development of *superlattice* structures when the alloys are carefully annealed. This "order-disorder" transformation of the atoms of the participating elements results in what are sometimes considered intermetallic compounds. Several examples of this sort of lattice rearrangement are reported among the binary alloys of platinum or palladium which have received detailed study (also rhodium with copper). The principles of physical metallurgy predict that superlattice formation may occur in cases where generous mutual solubility is to be expected, but where the sizes of the participating atoms differ somewhat but not enough to discourage the formation of solutions. It is, therefore, rather interesting to note that superlattice formation seems to occur in systems of platinum or palladium with several of the base metals of the first row of Table 17.8, but no cases of this have been reported in binary systems of the platinum metals themselves. It is evident that there is some difference in atomic radii between the first-row elements in

	Platinum	Palladium
Hardness	$Ni > Ru > Cu,Au > Ir > Rh$	$Ru > Ni > Ir > Cu > Ag > Rh > Au$
Tensile strength, annealed	$Ru > Au > Ir > Rh$	$Cu > Rh\text{-}Ru > Ag > Au$
Resistivity	$Cu > Ag > Ru > Ir,Au > Rh$	$Cu > Rh > Ir$

this table and the remainder. Some of these ordered structures with the base metals, especially cobalt, exhibit interesting magnetic properties.

The addition of the elements mentioned in the second paragraph of this section to platinum or palladium brings about changes in physical properties which give the alloys certain practical advantages over the pure metals. In general, the alloying agents tend to increase the resistivity, hardness, and tensile strength of these metals. The addition of other platinum metals or gold serves also to increase their resistance to tarnish and corrosion by various chemicals.

The comparative alteration in the physical properties of platinum and palladium by various alloying agents is given above.

The choice of alloying element and the proportions of it to be used are governed by the requirements which the alloy must meet. Iridium is most commonly added to platinum to increase the hardness and corrosion resistance. The alloys remain ductile up to about 20 per cent iridium, and they can be hot worked up to about 30 per cent. Ruthenium produces a much greater increase in hardness and strength for the same percentage added, but no more than about 15 per cent can be added if the metal is to remain workable. The high cost of ruthenium has, in the past, limited its use for this purpose. Because of the loss in weight at high temperatures, attributed to the formation of volatile oxides, iridium and ruthenium are less suitable than rhodium for producing alloys to be used at high temperatures. Rhodium alloys with platinum are thus preferred for resistance wires, thermocouples, and the catalyst for the oxidation of ammonia, in spite of their inferior mechanical properties.

For increasing the hardness and mechanical strength of palladium for use in jewelry, ruthenium and rhodium are frequently used together in various proportions. Copper-palladium alloys are quite workable and fairly hard, though less resistant to corrosion than alloys with noble

metals. Silver forms ductile alloys with palladium which possess good resistance to corrosion; they are found in jewelry, denture bases, electrical contact points, and resistance wires.

CHEMICAL PROPERTIES

It is convenient to discuss the chemical properties of the platinum metals under the headings of the compact forms, sponges and powdered forms, and "blacks." Of these, the "blacks" are the most reactive and the compact forms the least.

Compact Metals

Palladium is attacked by hot concentrated nitric acid and by boiling sulfuric acid. The latter also slowly attacks platinum and rhodium. Both platinum and palladium are dissolved by aqua regia. The remaining metals—osmium, ruthenium, and iridium—are resistant to all single acids and to aqua regia.

Numerous molten oxides, hydroxides, salts, and mixtures of salts corrode the platinum group. Fused peroxides, hydroxides, and nitrates of Group IA, oxides of Group IIA, or better, mixtures of hydroxides and carbonates or nitrates of Group IA, for example, are corrosive. Fused alkali cyanides also attack the metals.

Of the nonmetals, phosphorus, arsenic, silicon, sulfur, selenium, tellurium, and carbon attack the metals at red heat. Because of this attack, great care should be taken to heat crucibles and boats used for ignitions in the laboratory in oxidizing atmospheres; the danger, otherwise, comes from reduction of compounds containing the above elements, followed by reaction with the platinum, leading to embrittlement.* Fluorine and chlorine attack all of the hot metals. Palladium is corroded by moist chlorine and bromine at room temperature;

* There is no evidence of carburization of platinum at red heat and the effect described here is presumably due to the formation of solid solutions.

platinum and palladium are tarnished by hot gases containing sulfides.

The reactions that take place when the metals are heated in air or oxygen are of great interest, but cannot be said to have been fully explained as yet. Platinum, for instance, loses weight when heated in air or oxygen to temperatures of 1000°C (1832°F) or so, but this loss in weight is not observed if the heating is done in nitrogen or argon. To account for this phenomenon, various workers have postulated the formation of a volatile oxide of the metal. Thus Schneider and Esch[81] showed that at constant temperature the rate of evaporation depends on the pressure of oxygen over the metal, and so deduced that the platinum is removed in the form of a dioxide. More recently, Lacroix[56] stated that the ratio in which platinum and oxygen volatilize in air is 2:1, whereas in oxygen this ratio is 1:2. After heating in oxygen, the surface of platinum shows considerable striation, which is said to be due, in part, to surface diffusion of the atoms at the high temperature to favor those profiles of lowest free surface energy, and partially to etching owing to removal of metallic atoms.[69] It must be pointed out, however, that the known oxides of platinum have dissociation pressures of 1 atm at temperatures far below those at which these phenomena occur, and therefore that the nature of the postulated volatile oxides remains somewhat uncertain.

Palladium is superficially oxidized if it is heated to a temperature of 700°C (1292°F). The oxide, PdO, which is formed is decomposed above 870°C (1598°F). As with platinum, palladium loses weight when heated in air or oxygen at high temperatures; there is an interesting uptake of oxygen between 900–1300°C (1652–2372°F) when the metal is first heated in oxygen, but at the higher temperatures this initial gain in weight is offset by the loss due to volatilization.

Rhodium undergoes superficial oxidation when heated in air to a red heat. The oxide formed in this way, Rh_2O_3, is decomposed to the elements above 1100°C (2012°F). Similar superficial oxidation of iridium leads to the formation of the oxide, IrO_2; this dissociates above 1140°C (2084°F). Both rhodium and iridium exhibit the same sort of loss in weight when heated in oxygen as do platinum and palladium, but the loss in the case of iridium is the greatest of the four metals. Paradoxically, none of the known oxides of iridium are volatile under the experimental conditions that accompany these losses. On heating ruthenium in air, the stable oxide, RuO_2, is readily formed. There seems to be some lack of agreement on the question of whether ruthenium loses weight when heated in air to high temperatures. If such a loss occurs at all, it is only slight, and it is extremely difficult to explain on the basis of the properties of the known oxides. Thus, although there is a familiar volatile oxide of this element, it is unstable above 106°C (223°F). Osmium, on the other hand, does lose weight rapidly when heated in air or oxygen, owing to formation of the volatile OsO_4.

Sponge and Powdered Metals

Palladium and platinum are the two metals of the group that are most easily attacked by acids. Palladium is dissolved by sulfuric acid or nitric acid, and easily by aqua regia. Palladium monoxide is formed when the metal is heated in oxygen. Fluorine with palladium at 500°C (932°F) yields PdF_3,[75] while chlorine at red heat produces $PdCl_2$.[54] The action of hydrogen on palladium is interesting. The metal will absorb as much as 800 to 900 times its own volume of hydrogen over a range of temperatures. The uptake of hydrogen corresponds roughly to the stoichiometric proportions of a compound Pd_2H, and a great many investigations have been carried out to establish whether such a compound does actually exist. From most of the data in the literature, it has been concluded that two solution phases are present rather than a pure substance;[85] some recent work does, however, support the idea of an ordered structure at low temperatures.[62] Deuterium resembles hydrogen in its action on palladium, but its solubility in the metal is less. Both gases are able to diffuse through hot palladium sheets.

Platinum resembles palladium in many of its chemical properties, but the former is much more resistant to corrosion than the latter. Fluorine acting on hot platinum yields PtF_4.[61] Chlorine and platinum form a series of chlorides —$PtCl_2$, $PtCl_3$, and $PtCl_4$—when heated together. The absorption of hydrogen by platinum is much less than by palladium. Hydrogen will also diffuse through the hot metal as it does with palladium.

Rhodium is remarkable for the fact that it is tervalent in almost all of its compounds. It is an inert metal, though less so than iridium. Hot sulfuric acid will dissolve rhodium. In addition to the fused salts mentioned previously, fused potassium hydrogen sulfate will react with rhodium to yield $Rh_2(SO_4)_3$. Rhodium sesquioxide, Rh_2O_3, is produced when the metal is heated at a temperature of 600°C (1112°F) in air or oxygen. At 500–600°C (932–1112°F), fluorine and rhodium form RhF_3, together with some RhF_4 and RhF_5.[74] The reaction with chlorine, which was mentioned previously in connection with dissolution of the metal during refining, forms $RhCl_3$.

Iridium is notably inert. Even when finely divided, it is scarcely attacked by any acid or mixture of acids. In air or oxygen at 600°C (1112°F), IrO_2 is the oxide formed. IrF_4 and IrF_6 are produced by the action of fluorine on the metal at 150°C (302°F).[76] Chlorine with iridium at 600°C (1112°F) yields $IrCl_3$. Both iridium and rhodium may be easily transformed into water-soluble double chlorides (actually chloro-complexes) by heating a mixture of the metals with sodium chloride in a current of chlorine at 600°C (1112°F). Iridium and other refractory platiniferous materials are rendered soluble by heating with a mixture of 20 volumes of hydrochloric acid and 1 volume of nitric acid or the equivalent of sodium chlorate, perchloric acid, or chlorine in a sealed tube.[95] Both rhodium and iridium, when finely divided and hot, will absorb large quantities of hydrogen.

Ruthenium is easily oxidized to RuO_2 when the metal is ignited in air or oxygen. It dissolves in aqua regia, in alkaline hypochlorite solutions, and in strong solutions of sodium peroxide or sodium hydroxide. Most fused alkalis attack ruthenium, e.g., potassium hydroxide mixed with potassium nitrate or potassium chlorate. Fluorine reacts with ruthenium at 300°C (572°F) to produce RuF_5;[78] chlorine and ruthenium at 450°C (842°F) form $RuCl_3$.[70]

Osmium is unique because of the ease of formation of the volatile oxide, OsO_4. This oxide is produced even by the action of cold air on the finely divided metal. Oxidizing agents attack osmium and form the tetroxide. Hypochlorite solutions or neutral and acidic solutions of potassium chlorate dissolve the metal. Os-

mium is attacked by many fused salts including potassium hydroxide, sodium nitrite, and potassium hydrogen sulfate. Fluorine acting on osmium at 300°C (572°F) yields OsF_4 and OsF_6. Chlorination of the metal at 650–700°C (1202–1292°F) yields $OsCl_3$ and $OsCl_4$. Both osmium and ruthenium "take up" hydrogen.

"Blacks" and Colloidal Metals

Important catalytic properties are possessed by platinum, palladium, and rhodium in very finely divided forms such as blacks, or as colloids. Platinum black is prepared by heating an alkaline solution of the chloride with ethanol. It is interesting to note that platinum black will take up oxygen when it is heated in air or oxygen, but that the oxygen is lost again at high temperatures. In general, the colloidal metals are prepared by reducing solutions of the chlorides with an agent such as hydrazine hydrate in the presence of a protective colloid. The blacks and colloids are widely used for the catalytic reduction of various types of organic compounds with hydrogen.

For a comprehensive discussion of the chemical properties of the metals and their compounds, the reader may refer to the titles listed in the bibliography.[25,59,84]

APPLICATIONS

Before considering in detail the uses of the platinum metals and some of their alloys, it may be interesting to examine the quantitative distribution of the use of these metals by the principal consuming industries in the United States. This information for the year 1958 is given in Table 17.9.[80] It is apparent that 96 per cent of the total consumption is divided roughly equally between platinum and palladium. These data show a decrease in sales from the previous year,[79] with a noticeable reduction in the amount of platinum consumed by the chemical industry.

In the following account of uses of these metals, no claim is made to completeness. Details of the applications described are frequently given in articles appearing in metallurgical journals. In 1957 Johnson, Matthey and Co., Ltd., London, England, refiners of the platinum metals mined in South Africa, began publication of a quarterly entitled *Platinum*

TABLE 17.9. SALES OF PLATINUM METALS IN THE UNITED STATES TO CONSUMING INDUSTRIES, 1958
(troy ounces)

	Platinum	Palladium	Others	Total
Chemical	148,276	93,215	14,726	257,483
Electrical	53,553	238,815	4,561	296,929
Dental and medical	14,414	36,139	519	51,003
Jewelry and decorative	42,391	25,192	8,162	75,682
Miscellaneous and undistributed	5,727	1,802	2,944	9,276
Totals	264,361	395,100	30,912	690,373

Metals Review; this is an indispensable companion to the literature of these metals, containing original articles, reports of significant publications, abstracts of the current journal and patent literature, etc. Many of the newer uses of the platinum metals are described in some detail in this quarterly. Other significant reviews and monographs include the following listed in the bibliography: 18, 50, 91, 97, 98, 100.

Platinum

The purest platinum is used for resistance thermometers and thermocouples. An interesting review of the history and uses of the platinum resistance thermometer[68] records that this device has been the basis for defining the International Temperature Scale for more than 30 years. Since 1948 the range on this scale defined by the resistance thermometer is between $-182.97°C$ ($-297.3°F$) (boiling point of oxygen) and $630.5°C$ ($1167°F$) (melting point of antimony).[28] It is required for this purpose that the platinum be of a purity such that the ratio of its resistances at 100 and 0°C (212 and 0°F) shall be not less than 1.3910; impurities in platinum lower markedly the temperature coefficient of resistance. The positive element in the thermocouple is a platinum-rhodium wire of carefully controlled composition, generally containing 10, but sometimes 13, per cent rhodium. Recently, thermocouples have been introduced in which each element is a platinum-rhodium alloy, one containing 5, the other 20, per cent of rhodium; these give improved performance at high temperatures.

The principal application of platinum in electrical work is in the form of contacts. The absence of surface film formation assures low contact resistance and reliable operation even after periods of idleness. Such contacts may be found in relays, alarm equipment, etc. When the contacts must operate at high currents, they are made from alloys with iridium (10 or 25 per cent) or ruthenium (5 or 10 per cent). Very fine platinum wires are sometimes used for small fuses. Because of the absence of corrosion, no significant change in current rating will occur if exposed or operated close to their maximum rating.

The electrodes in spark plugs designed for aircraft engines are often made with a platinum alloy. Apart from the drastic corrosive conditions under which these must operate, another problem occurs caused by the accumulation of lead from the fuel. Apparently, the lead penetrates the grain boundaries in the metal of these electrodes and causes premature disintegration. Alloys with 5 or 10 per cent ruthenium, 10 per cent palladium, plus 6 per cent ruthenium, or with 4 per cent tungsten have all been used for this purpose. Because of its low electron emission, the last-mentioned alloy has found use in making grids for radar tubes. A 5 per cent nickel alloy is used as a base for thermionic cathodes which are coated with metallic oxides.

The freedom from corrosion leads to a number of uses in chemical industry. Small pressure vessels may be lined with platinum sheet, while larger vessels may be made from platinum-clad nickel or copper. Thus, platinum-lined autoclaves are used in the manufacture of ethyl chloride. Bursting discs of platinum foil, for the protection of chemical process equipment operating under corrosive conditions at elevated pressures, have been introduced. Platinum or platinum-clad anodes are used in electrolytic work, not only because of their resistance to oxidation but often because of the large overpotential of oxygen on them. This permits the desired anodic process to take place with a minimum of oxygen evolution. The alloy containing 10 per cent iridium is principally used for this purpose. Typical applications are for the manufacture of peroxyborates, perchlorates, and peroxysulfates.

Considerable interest is being focused on platinum-clad electrodes in connection with cathodic protection against corrosion. This is being studied principally in connection with marine corrosion. A ship's hull, for instance, can be protected to a marked degree by making it the cathode of an electrolytic "cell" in which the anode is an inert or expendable metal, and impressing a potential difference between these. The anode may be fastened alongside the ship's hull or trailed behind. The first composite anodes used for this purpose were platinum-clad copper or silver. Owing to the difficulty of obtaining a pore-free coating of platinum, corrosion of the copper or silver resulted in service; this was less serious in the case of silver, since the precipitation of silver chloride, when the electrodes were used in sea water, resealed the pores or cracks. However, when platinum is applied as a coating on tantalum or titanium, anodes are produced that are virtually free of corrosion. This is due to an interesting combination of properties. These two base metals, if anodized in aqueous solution, become coated over with a protective oxide layer, and this is nonconducting to the body of the electrolyte. This is the principle of the "wet" rectifier. However, these oxide films can conduct current if placed in mechanical contact with a second metal; hence, these platinum-coated composites do not undergo appreciable deterioration of the base metal, owing to the protection given by their oxides, and yet do not require a fully pore-free coating of the noble metal. Electrodes of this type are now produced by cladding (see page 317), by electrolysis, or by vapor deposition.

In order to avoid contamination of optical glasses by metallic oxides which would impart color, the melting and pouring during their manufacture is carried out in platinum vessels. Similarly, platinum and its alloys (especially 10 per cent rhodium) are used in equipment for handling flowing molten glass such as dies and measuring orifices. Also a platinum alloy (2 per cent nickel) is used in making spinnerets and bushings for the manufacture of glass fibers. Spinnerets for the production of viscose rayon are made either from a 10 per cent rhodium alloy or from one containing 60 per cent gold with 40 per cent platinum.

Reference has already been made to cobalt-platinum alloys possessing ferromagnetic properties to an unusually high degree. Thus the alloy containing about 50 atomic per cent of cobalt is claimed to provide a more powerful permanent magnet than any other material known, and to have the advantage over many other newer permanent magnetic materials in that it is malleable and ductile before hardening, and so can be readily fabricated. One application of this alloy has appeared in the form of an electric watch in which a permanent-magnet motor is employed.

In the laboratory, platinum is used in the form of crucibles, evaporating dishes, weighing boats, and the like. Where these are to be subjected to much heating, it is desirable to use an alloy containing 3.5 per cent rhodium in order to minimize loss through volatilization. Many forms of electrodes for electrochemical analysis, conductance measurements, etc., have been described. An alloy containing 10 or 20 per cent rhodium is used to make windings for high-temperature furnaces designed to operate under oxidizing conditions.

Considerable platinum is used for jewelry; it is hardened with either iridium (5 or 10 per cent) or ruthenium (5 per cent). In Europe some platinum jewelry is made with an alloy containing from 3 to 5 per cent copper. A hard alloy with 25 or 30 per cent iridium is used in the tubing of pens, and for hypodermic needles, radium applicators, and various other small accessories.

It has long been recognized that the platinum metals possess exceptional catalytic properties. Platinum itself has been applied in a number of industrial processes, of which the following are some of the more important examples. Its use in the contact process for making sulfuric acid has now partly given way to cheaper vanadium pentoxide. For the production of nitrogen oxides in the chamber (sulfuric acid) process and for the manufacture of nitric acid from ammonia, platinum (with 10 per cent rhodium) catalyst is used in the form of a gauze. A more recent catalytic application is for the so-called re-formation of petroleum. This process was introduced a decade ago and has rapidly grown until, today, it has become probably the largest single consumer of platinum in the chemical industry. By it the octane rating of straight-run and natural gasoline is improved, and, in addition, large amounts of aromatic hydrocarbons are formed which can be separated from the product and used for purposes other than fuel. Briefly, the reactions taking place during petroleum re-formation are as follows:[17] (1) conversion of naphthenes to aromatic hydrocarbons; (2) isomerization or cracking of paraffin hydrocarbons, plus the conversion of some of these to aromatics; (3) conversion of any sulfur compounds to hydrogen sulfide and the corresponding hydrocarbon; (4) saturation of olefinic hydrocarbons, followed by the reactions of (2) and/or (3). The catalyst is usually prepared in the form of small pellets of alumina or silica-alumina impregnated with up to 1 per cent of platinum. As a hydrogenation catalyst, platinum has been used for certain specific reactions, e.g. in the synthesis of vitamins or other pharmaceutical chemicals.[53] The special advantage of platinum and palladium for this purpose is that reductions can be carried out at relatively low pressures of hydrogen. Another application of some importance is in the manufacture of hydrogen cyanide from methane, ammonia, and air by the so-called Andrussow process. For this reaction the catalyst takes the form of a gauze similar in composition and texture to that used in ammonia-oxidation catalysts.

Platinum and palladium, generally in a finely divided form and supported on a carrier such as alumina, have found numerous applications in the purification of gases by catalytic oxidation or hydrogenation. For example, small amounts of oxygen may be removed from hydrogen by passing the gas through a cartridge containing the catalyst which may be attached directly on the hydrogen cylinder. A number of similar applications have been developed, and the suggestion has been made that catalysts of this sort may come to play an increasingly important part in the control of air pollution.[37]

Palladium

This metal is often used in place of platinum, where conditions permit, because of its lower price and density. Its freedom from tarnish and resistance to corrosion make it almost as

suitable as platinum for contacts in electrical relays, e.g. in telephone equipment, where low currents are carried. For this purpose, alloys with 40 per cent copper or 40 per cent silver are frequently used. The copper alloy is very effective in circuits carrying low currents but containing sufficient capacitance that a considerable rush of current occurs as the contacts close. A review of the subject of electrical-contact materials stresses advantages of platinum metal alloys, especially for contacts involving small currents.[42] The author of this review points out that there is sometimes an advantage to be gained by having a thin film of oxide on electrical contacts used for light duty. The presence of this film may serve to discourage sticking (welding) and the formation of minute metallic bridges at the instant of separation of the contacts; both of these phenomena are regarded as origins of contact failure. Palladium alloys will form thin oxide films when heated to about 400°C (752°F), but the oxide decomposes at still higher temperatures, so that the surface does not become fouled. The article quoted also includes a valuable discussion of the selection of a proper contact material according to the application proposed for it. The 40 per cent silver alloy is also used for resistance windings because it possesses an unusually low temperature coefficient of resistance. A gold alloy containing about 50 per cent of each metal is used in temperature-limiting fuses to protect electrically heated furnaces or their contents from overheating.

Palladium is widely used as an alloying element in complex wrought and cast dental alloys. These may contain various proportions of silver and probably also copper, gold, or platinum.

An innovation in the use of palladium is as an additive to increase the passivity of stainless steel[89] or titanium.[2] Both platinum and palladium additions of between 0.1 and 1.0 per cent markedly increase the resistance of 18–9 stainless steel or of high-chromium steel toward corrosion by sulfuric acid. Recently, it has been announced by Stern[2] that as little as 0.1 per cent of palladium or platinum added to titanium renders this metal resistant to boiling solutions of hydrochloric acid or sulfuric acid. Although titanium possesses remarkable resistance to oxidizing acids, it is dissolved by reducing acids such as hydrochloric acid. The noble metal appears to act as a cathode in a galvanic cell, and, by rendering the steel or titanium anodic, encourages the formation of protective coatings of oxide on these metals.

A moderate amount of palladium is used in jewelry, and alloys containing 4.5 per cent ruthenium or 4 per cent ruthenium plus 1 per cent rhodium are most commonly recommended. In addition, so-called "white gold" is an alloy of gold decolorized by the addition of palladium.

In describing the catalytic applications of platinum, some reference has already been made to the similar behavior of palladium. It is effective for both hydrogenation and dehydrogenation reactions but is mainly used for the former. The particular advantage in the use of palladium over, e.g., nickel is that reactions may be carried out at low to moderate temperatures which, if attempted at higher temperatures, would yield undesired products because of side reactions. It has become general practice to add the catalyst for hydrogenations in the form of palladous oxide, which is more conveniently prepared than the "black" metal; the oxide is quickly reduced to metal by the hydrogen. The catalyst may also be dispersed in a finely divided condition on porous materials such as pumice or charcoal or on crystalline precipitates such as barium sulfate, calcium carbonate, or magnesia. Thus calcium carbonate may be impregnated with palladous chloride solution, becoming thinly coated thereby with palladous hydroxide; the solid is then separated and heated in hydrogen to reduce to the metal. Sometimes the catalyst may be reactivated by air or oxygen, but where this is unsuccessful the metal can be recovered for use again.

One important application of this is the gas-phase hydrogenation of acetylene to ethylene, carried out with a catalyst of palladium supported on silica gel. Another new industrial application is the production of hydrogen peroxide by the auto-oxidation of 2-ethyl anthraquinol; the quinol is converted by atmospheric oxygen to the corresponding quinone plus hydrogen peroxide, the latter is separated by countercurrent extraction into water, and the quinone is reduced back by hydrogen with a supported palladium catalyst. Reference has

already been made to the use of palladium catalysis for hydrogenations in the synthesis of various pharmaceutical chemicals.

The dissolving of hydrogen in palladium, mentioned in the preceding section, has a rather practical application.[13] The solubility of hydrogen in palladium, unlike that in other metals, falls rapidly as the temperature rises, while the rate of diffusion increases. Advantage is taken of this to admit hydrogen into vacuum apparatus in the laboratory. Palladium thimbles are sealed in the apparatus to act as hydrogen "valves." When they are heated and surrounded by an atmosphere containing hydrogen —even by the simple action of a burner flame —hydrogen, but no other gas, diffuses through the metal.

Rhodium

In addition to its use for alloying with platinum, rhodium finds application as a coating material because of the hardness and luster of its surface. It can be electrolytically deposited on many metals directly, although a base coat of silver or nickel is sometimes applied. The plated surface is ideal for the finish on high-quality scientific instruments, camera fittings, ornamental silver, and jewelry. Rhodium plate is often used to protect metal surfaces in precision apparatus for the measurement of physical constants of corrosive liquids. Mirrors and reflectors are frequently plated with this metal in order to prevent tarnishing.

Electrical contacts plated with rhodium are extremely free from contact resistance and find application in components for radio- and audio-frequency circuits. Sliding electrical contacts are also commonly rhodium-plated to take advantage of the great hardness of the electrodeposited metal.

By the recently developed technique of vacuum deposition, rhodium can be sublimed onto glass for mirrors or, in thinner layers, for interference filters for light.

Iridium

Iridium is used for hardening platinum. Because of the difficulty in working it, few applications for the pure metal have been described. Some small crucibles for high-temperature reactions have been fashioned, and the metal has been used to make extrusion dies for high-melting glasses.

Osmium

The metal is used almost entirely to produce alloys of great hardness which are used in tips of fountain-pen nibs, long-life phonograph needles, or instrument pivots. Such alloys contain about 60 per cent osmium, some ruthenium, and the remainder other platinum metals. The use of these alloys has largely superseded that of native iridosmine for the same purposes.

Ruthenium

The principal use for ruthenium is as a hardener for palladium or platinum. Some is contained in the hard alloys of osmium, used for pen tipping and so forth.

A catalyst consisting of 5 per cent metallic ruthenium supported on alumina or charcoal has been recommended for hydrogenations. It is said[24] to permit specific reduction of carbonyl groups in aliphatic aldehydes and ketones, even permitting, in some cases, the reduction of this functional group selectively in the presence of an olefinic linkage.

References

1. Anonymous, *Can. Mining J.,* **80,** 105 (1959).
2. Anonymous, *Modern Metals,* **15,** 82 (1959); *Platinum Metals Rev.,* **3,** 88 (1959); *Chem. Eng. News,* **37,** No. 15, 26 (April 13, 1959); Stern, M., and Wissenberg, H., *J. Electrochem. Soc.,* **106,** 759–764 (1959).
3. Anonymous, *Platinum Metals Rev.,* **1,** 61 (1957).
4. Atkinson, R. H., *Trans. Inst. Metal Finishing,* **36,** 7 (1958).
5. Atkinson, R. H., and Raper, A. R., *J. Electrodepositors' Tech. Soc.,* **9,** 77 (1934); *Metal Ind. (London),* **44,** 191 (1934).
6. Bale, E. S., *Platinum Metals Rev.,* **2,** 61 (1958).
7. Beamish, F. E., *Can. Mining J.,* **62,** 446 (1941).
8. Beamish, F. E., and Warren, E. W., *Can. Mining J.,* **63,** 505 (1942).
9. Berthollet, C. L., and Pelletier, B., *Ann. Chem. Liebigs,* **14,** 20 (1792).
10. Blum, W., and Hogaboom, G. B., "Principles of Electroplating and Electroforming," 3rd Ed., New York, McGraw-Hill Book Company, Inc., 1949.
11. Bray, J. L., "Non-Ferrous Production Metallurgy," 2nd Ed., p. 268, New York, John Wiley & Sons, Inc., 1947.
12. Bray, J. L., *ibid.,* p. 433.
13. Chaston, J. C., *Metallurgia,* **29,** 133 (1944).
14. Claus, C., *Pogg. Ann.,* **64,** 192, 622 (1845).
15. Clements, F. S., and Raper, A. R., (International Nickel Co.), U.S. Patent 2,552,709, May 15, 1951.
16. Cotton, J. B., *Platinum Metals Rev.,* **2,** 45 (1958).
17. Curry, S. W., *Platinum Metals Rev.,* **1,** 38 (1957).
18. Dale, H. G., "The Precious Metals," London, Institute of Chemistry of Great Britain and Ireland, 1941.
19. Dennis, W. H., "Metallurgy of the Non-Ferrous Metals," London, Sir Isaac Pitman & Sons, Ltd., 1954.
19a. Douglass, R. W., and Adkins, E. F., "Melting Points and Spectral Emissivities of Osmium and Ruthenium," to be published in Metallurgical Transactions, AIME.
20. Emeleus, H. J., and Anderson, J. S., "Modern Aspects of Inorganic Chemistry," London, Routledge and Kegan Paul, Ltd.; p. 378, Princeton, N. J., D. Van Nostrand Co., Inc., 1948.
21. Esser, H., and Eusterbrock, H., *Arch. Eisenhüttenw.,* **14,** 341 (1941).
22. Geibel, W., in "Reine Metalle," A. E. Van Arkel (Ed.), pp. 364, 374, Berlin, J. Springer, 1939.
23. Gilchrist, R., *Chem. Rev.,* **32,** 277 (1943).
24. Gilman, G., and Cohn, G., "Advances in Catalysis," Vol. 9, p. 733, New York, Academic Press, Inc., 1957.
25. Gmelin, "Handbuch der anorganischen Chemie," 8th Ed., Nos. 63–68, Berlin, Verlag Chemie, G.m.b.H.
26. Godley, P., *Iron Age,* **161,** 90 (1948).
27. Goldschmidt, V. M., *J. Chem. Soc.,* 655 (1937).
28. Hall, J. A., in "Temperature—Its Measurement and Control," Vol. 2, Chap. 8, New York, Reinhold Publishing Corp., 1955.
29. Ham, W. R., and Samans, C. H., *Science,* **104,** 38 (1946).
30. Hill, M. A., and Beamish, F. E., *Anal. Chem.,* **22,** 590 (1950).
31. Hoke, C. M., "Refining Precious Metal Wastes," New York, Metallurgical Publishing Co., 1940.
32. Holborn, L., *Ann. Physik,* **59,** 145 (1919).

33. Holborn, L., *ibid.*, p. 165.
34. Holborn, L., and Day, A. L., *Ann. Physik,* **4,** 104 (1901).
35. Holborn, L., and Valentiner, S., *Ann. Physik,* **22,** 16 (1907).
36. Holzmann, H., "Festschrift zum 50-jahrigen Bestehen der Platinschmelze," p. 147, Hanau, G. Siebert, G.m.b.H., (1931). See also *J. Inst. Metals,* **50,** 69 (1932).
37. Houdry, J. H., and Hayes, C. T., *Platinum Metals Rev.,* **2,** 110 (1958).
38. Howe, J. L., *Chem. News,* **109,** 229 (1914).
39. Hoyt, S. L., "Metals and Alloys Data Book," pp. 277, 279, 280, New York, Reinhold Publishing Corp., 1943.
40. Hume-Rothery, W., and Raynor, G. V., "The Structure of Metals and Alloys," 3rd Ed., London, Institute of Metals, 1954.
41. Hume-Rothery, W., and Raynor, G. V., *ibid.,* p. 126.
42. Hunt, L. B., *Platinum Metals Rev.,* **1,** 74 (1957).
43. Jaeger, F. M., and Rosenbohm, E., *Physica,* **6,** 1123 (1939).
44. Jaeger, F. M., and Rosenbohm, E., *Proc. Acad. Sci. Amsterdam,* **34,** 85 (1931).
45. Jaeger, F. M., and Rosenbohm, E., *ibid.,* p. 808.
46. Jaeger, F. M., and Rosenbohm, E., *Proc. Acad. Sci. Amsterdam,* **44,** 144 (1941).
47. Jaeger, F. M., and Veenstra, W. A., *Proc. Acad. Sci. Amsterdam,* **37,** 280 (1934).
48. Jahn, C. A. H., *Metal Ind. (London),* **72,** 183 (1948).
49. Jahn, C. A. H., *ibid.,* p. 206.
50. Jahn, C. A. H., *ibid.,* pp. 228, 249.
51. Jahn, C. A. H., *ibid.,* p. 267.
52. Johnson, C., and Atkinson, R. H., *Trans. Inst. Chem. Engrs. (London),* **15,** 131 (1937).
53. Jones, W. H., *Platinum Metals Rev.,* **2,** 86 (1958).
54. Keiser, E. H., and Breed, M. B., *Am. Chem. J.,* **16,** 20 (1894).
55. Kelley, K. K., *U.S. Bur. Mines, Bull. No. 383* (1935); *Bull. No. 393* (1936).
56. Lacroix, R., *Rev. mét.,* **53,** 809 (1956).
57. MacDonald, D., *Chem. & Ind. (London),* **50,** 1031 (1931).
58. MacDonald, D., *Platinum Metals Rev.,* **2,** 54 (1958).
59. Mellor, J. W., "A Comprehensive Treatise on Inorganic and Theoretical Chemistry," Vols. 15 and 16, London and New York, Longmans, Green & Co., 1942.
60. Mellor, J. W., *ibid.,* Vol. 16, p. 3.
61. Moissan, H., *Ann. chim. et phys.,* **24,** 282 (1891).
62. Nace, D. M., and Aston, J. G., *J. Am. Chem Soc.,* **79,** 3619, (1957).
63. Nix, F. C., and MacNair, D., *Phys. Rev.,* **61,** 74 (1942).
64. O'Neill, J. J., and Gunning, H. C., "Platinum and Allied Metal Deposits of Canada," Ottawa, Canada, Department of Mines, 1934.
65. Palache, C., Berman, H., and Frondel, C., "Dana's System of Mineralogy," Vol. 1, New York, John Wiley & Sons, Inc., 1944.
66. "Platinum and Allied Metals," 2nd Ed., London, Imperial Institute, Mineral Resources Dept., 1936.
67. Preiser, H. S., *Platinum Metals Rev.,* **3,** 38 (1959).
68. Price, R., *Platinum Metals Rev.,* **3,** 78 (1959).
69. Raub, E., *J. Less Common Metals,* **1,** 3 (1959).
70. "Reactor Handbook," Vol. 3, Sec. 1, U.S. Atomic Energy Commission, AECD-3647 (1955).
71. Reid, F. H., *Trans. Inst. Metal Finishing,* **36,** 74 (1959); Mond Nickel Co., British Patent 808,958, Feb. 11, 1959.
72. Remy, H., and Wagner, T., *Z. anorg. u. allgem. Chem.,* **157,** 344 (1926).
73. Rhoda, R. N., *Trans. Inst. Metal Finishing.* **36,** 82 (1959).
74. Ruff, O., and Ascher, E., *Z. anorg. u. allgem. Chem.,* **180,** 42 (1929).
75. Ruff, O., and Fischer, J., *Z. anorg. u. allgem. Chem.,* **183,** 206 (1929).
76. Ruff, O., and Fischer, J., *Z. anorg. u. allgem. Chem.,* **179,** 161 (1929).
77. Ruff, O., and Tschirch, F. W., *Ber.,* **46,** 929 (1913).
78. Ruff, O., and Vidic, E., *Z. anorg. u. allgem. Chem.,* **143,** 171 (1925).
79. Ryan, J. P., *Eng. Mining J.,* **160,** 95 (1959).
80. Ryan, J. P., and McBreen, K. M., "Minerals Yearbook (U.S. Bur. Mines)," Washington, D.C., Government Printing Office, 1957.
81. Schneider, A., and Esch, U., *Z. Elektrochem.,* **49,** 55 (1943).
82. Schumpelt, K., in "Plating and Finishing Guide Book," N. Hull and G. B. Hogaboom (Eds.), New York, Metal Industry Publishing Co., 1945.
83. Schumpelt, K., *Trans. Electrochem. Soc.,* **80,** 489 (1941).
84. Sidgwick, N. V., "The Chemical Elements and Their Compounds," Vol. 2, p. 1454, London and New York, Oxford University Press, 1950.
85. Sidgwick, N. V., *ibid.,* p. 1554.
86. Sivil, C., *Trans. Am. Inst. Mining Met. Engrs. Metals Div.,* **5,** 246 (1931).

87. Swanger, W. H., *J. Research NBS*, **3**, 1029 (1929).

88. Tennant, S., *Phil. Trans.*, **94**, 411 (1804).

89. Tomashov, N. D., *Akad. Nauk. S.S.S.R.*, 17 (1956). See also *Platinum Metals Rev.*, **2**, 117 (1958).

90. Vines, R. F., and Wise, E. M., "The Platinum Metals and Their Alloys," New York, International Nickel Co., 1941.

91. Warwick, B. A., *Chem. Age (London)*, **78**, 501 (1957).

92. Weeks, M. E., "The Discovery of the Elements," 4th Ed., p. 236, Easton, Pa., Journal of Chemical Education.

93. Whitely, J. O., and Dietz, C., *Am. Inst. Mining Met. Engrs. Tech. Publ. No. 84* (1928).

94. Wichers, E., Gilchrist, R., and Swanger, W. H., *Am. Inst. Mining Met. Engrs. Tech. Publ. No. 87* (1928).

95. Wichers, E., Schlect, W. G., and Gordon, C. L., *J. Research NBS*, **33**, 363 (1944).

96. Wise, E. M., in "Encyclopedia of Chemical Technology," New York, Interscience Publishers, Inc., 1953.

97. Wise, E. M., in "Metals Handbook," T. Lyman (Ed.), Cleveland, American Society for Metals, 1948.

98. Wise, E. M., in "Modern Uses of Non-Ferrous Metals," C. H. Mathewson (Ed.) New York, American Institute of Mining and Metallurgical Engineering, 1935.

99. Wise, E. M., and Eash, J. T., *Am. Inst. Mining Met. Engrs. Tech. Publ. No. 584*, published in *Metals Technol.* (1934).

100. Wolf, H., *Metall*, **12**, 585 (1958).

101. Wollaston, W. H., *Phil. Trans.*, **94**, 419 (1804).

102. Yarwood, J., "High Vacuum Technique," 2nd Ed., New York, John Wiley & Sons, Inc., 1945.

18. PLUTONIUM

W. N. Miner, A. S. Coffinberry, F. W. Schonfeld, J. T. Waber,
R. N. R. Mulford, and R. E. Tate

University of California
Los Alamos Scientific Laboratory
Los Alamos, New Mexico

INTRODUCTION

The discovery of plutonium was heralded by the terrifying explosion of the atomic bomb over Nagasaki in 1945. No other element has been so forcefully and dramatically introduced to the people of the world. Nor does any other element possess the number of exceptional characteristics that make plutonium unique as a metal.

Plutonium has the distinction of being the first synthetically produced element to be seen by man.[177] It has the remarkable number of six allotropic modifications in the relatively small temperature range between room temperature and its melting point at 640°C (1184°F). The metal also possesses the unique property of contracting at an appreciable rate with increasing temperature throughout a relatively large temperature range.[46] As if this were not enough, it is one of the most toxic substances known, the permissible contamination levels for plutonium being the lowest for any of the radioactive elements.[171] Furthermore, the peaceful application of plutonium as a source of energy in power reactors of the future[184] is estimated to be capable of multiplying the energy contained in the world's uranium reserves by a factor of more than 100.[109] It is small wonder, then, that considerable scientific effort has been directed toward a better understanding of this unusual metal.

The particular plutonium isotope that was first identified, as a result of the investigations of Wahl, Seaborg, and Kennedy[178] in studying the tracer chemical properties of neptunium, had a mass number of 238. These investigations, made during 1941 and 1942 at the University of California, led to the acquisition of considerable knowledge of the chemical properties of plutonium, and in 1942 the first pure compound of plutonium was prepared.[180] In 1943, scientists of the "Metallurgical Project" at the University of Chicago made the first reductions of plutonium. Minute beads of metal were produced, first by Baumbach, and shortly thereafter by Fried. Although these tiny beads of plutonium weighed less than 50 micrograms (mcg), it was possible to determine their density, melting point, and microstructure.[46,79]

When gram quantities of plutonium became available, the major research on the metallurgy of the element was transferred to the site at Los Alamos.[192] Since then, several laboratories in the United States, Canada, United Kingdom, U.S.S.R., and France have contributed greatly to the metallurgical knowledge of plutonium.

In practice, the most important isotope of plutonium is plutonium 239. Because it undergoes fission with both high- and low-energy neutrons, and can be produced in appreciable amounts, it is of prime importance in the release of nuclear energy.

SOURCES

Plutonium is formed as the result of radioactive capture of neutrons by uranium 238 and

TABLE 18.1. PLUTONIUM CONTENT OF URANIUM AND THORIUM ORES
(after Levine and Seaborg)

Ore	Uranium content (%)	Ratio Pu²³⁹/ore (weight)	Ratio Pu²³⁹/U × 10¹²
Canadian pitchblende	13.5	9.1×10^{-13}	7.1
Belgian Congo pitchblende	38	4.8×10^{-12}	12
Colorado pitchblende	50	3.8×10^{-12}	7.7
Belgian Congo pitchblende concentrate	45.3	7×10^{-12}	15
Brazilian monazite	0.24	2.1×10^{-14}	8.3
North Carolina monazite	1.64	5.9×10^{-14}	3.6
Fergusonite	0.25	1×10^{-14}	4
Carnotite	10	4×10^{-14}	0.4

the subsequent two-stage beta decay of the intermediate products. In nuclear reactors fueled with natural uranium (containing 0.7 per cent uranium 235), neutrons produced by the fission of uranium 235 are captured in uranium 238 to yield plutonium 239 by the so-called "pile reactions"[105]

$$U235 + n \rightarrow \text{Fission Products} + 2.5\,n + 200\ \text{Mev}$$

$$U238 + n \rightarrow U239 \xrightarrow[23.5\,\text{min}]{\beta^-} Np239 \xrightarrow[2.33\,\text{d}]{\beta^-} Pu239$$

Isotopes from plutonium 232 to plutonium 246 have been synthesized, but at present plutonium 239, with its half life of 24,360 years, is the most important in the production of nuclear fuels and weapons.[105]

Although plutonium does occur naturally in minute quantities, for all practical considerations it is a synthetic element. In 1942 Seaborg and Perlman[188] and Garner, Bonner, and Seaborg[83] established the presence of plutonium 239 in pitchblende and other uranium minerals in concentrations of about 1 part in 10¹⁴. Since then, Peppard and co-workers[153] and Levine and Seaborg[122,176] have demonstrated the existence of plutonium in nature in somewhat greater amount. A summary of their results is presented in Table 18.1.[122]

No isotopes of plutonium other than plutonium 239 have been found to occur naturally. The plutonium 239 in nature probably results from neutron capture by uranium 238 followed by decay of uranium 239 and neptunium 239, and represents a steady-state concentration.[105] Since Peppard and co-workers were able to isolate only a microgram of plutonium 239 from each 100 tons of ore concentrate, it is obvious that even the richest uranium deposits are not likely to supersede synthetic methods as a source of plutonium.

Plutonium is now being produced in a variety of nuclear reactors in many parts of the world. The reactor fuel is uranium having the normal content of uranium 235 or slightly enriched in that isotope. The form in which the uranium fuel is used varies, but it is most frequently introduced as the metal (densest form) in order to minimize the size of the reactor.[105] In general, only a relatively small proportion of the uranium 235 is consumed before the fuel is removed from the reactor for chemical processing in which the plutonium is separated from the uranium and fission products.

PRODUCTION

Plutonium production figures, except for France, are not available. In the United States the main plutonium-production facilities are at the General Electric Company's Hanford Atomic Products Operation near Richland, Washington, and at the E. I. duPont de Nemours and Company's Savannah River project in South Carolina. In the United Kingdom plutonium production has, until recently, been centered at the Windscale Works[99] in Cumberland. As a consequence of an accident[7,126] that occurred there in 1957, however, operation of the two reactors at Windscale has been discontinued, and it is expected that future British production of plutonium will be obtained from power-converter reactors, such as those at Calder Hall and Chapel Cross.[160] In Canada plutonium has been produced in the reactors at Chalk River, Ontario, since October, 1947.[85]

The French production of plutonium, at

present, amounts to about 44 lb/year, but, with the addition of two more reactors being put into operation at Marcoule, production is expected to reach 220 lb/year.[130] A $12 million plutonium separation plant will be built at Mol, Belgium, by 12 OEEC (Organization for European Economic Cooperation) members of the Eurochemie Company. This plant is scheduled to be completed in 1961.[127]

No information is available, at present, concerning plutonium production facilities in the U.S.S.R. The publication of papers on plutonium physical metallurgy, presented in Moscow in 1955 and at the Second Geneva Conference in 1958, indicates, however, that the Russians have for several years possessed adequate quantities of plutonium for metallurgical research purposes.[9,79,113] Other reports from the U.S.S.R. establish that they have also possessed the appreciably larger amounts of material required for complete plutonium fuelings of several experimental reactors.[120,121] Presumably, however, a very major portion of the Russian plutonium production has gone into the stockpiling of nuclear weapons.

Judkins[103] reports that the present price of plutonium in ingot form lies between $12 and $45/g. The present AEC estimate[128] is that plutonium will be worth about $12/g as a fuel for nuclear reactors when this use becomes technically and economically feasible.

The cost for conversion of the nitrate solutions to plutonium metal has been estimated to be as high as $2.40/g, although the present AEC recommendation is $1.50/g. Conceivably, these processing costs might be reduced to $1.00 or even 50 cents/g in large-volume plants of the future.[129]

DERIVATION

This discussion of the derivation of plutonium will be limited to outlining a few of the various separation and reduction processes that have been developed. Although fuel-element fabrication and reactor operation are closely related subjects and should, perhaps, be included in a complete description of the extractive metallurgy of plutonium, the manufacture of plutonium in reactors is too broad a subject to be reviewed here.[85,176]

The major problem in recovering plutonium is its separation from the associated uranium and fission products. This problem is enor-mously complicated by the presence of the highly radioactive fission products, which, because of health considerations, make it mandatory for many of the operations to be performed remotely. In order for the final plutonium product to be handled without shielding, it is necessary to reduce the concentration of fission products associated with the plutonium and irradiated uranium by a factor of 10^6 to 10^7.[105]

The amounts of plutonium that are present in irradiated uranium are usually of the order of only a few grams of plutonium to several tons of uranium. In addition, the several types of uranium-fueled reactors in existence, as well as the multiplicity of reactors in various stages of design and development, affect the details of separation processes because of the different nuclear conditions and metallurgical environments under which plutonium formation occurs.

In spite of the obvious difficulties, a number of satisfactory procedures have been developed for the separation and recovery of plutonium. A rough classification of these methods includes (1) precipitation, (2) organic solvent extraction, (3) ion exchange, and (4) pyrometallurgy. The choice of a method, or combination of methods, depends largely on the economics of the particular situation. Although an ion-exchange method might be advantageous for a relatively small batch operation, organic solvent extraction might be required for economical production of plutonium in a routine, large-scale application. It is likely that the highly irradiated fuels which will be associated with the high-power-density reactors of the future will require pyrometallurgical methods.[117]

In general, chemical procedures depend on the fact that plutonium can exist in a number of oxidation states and that its chemical properties are different in different states.[105] For example, plutonium (VI) is much less stable than uranium (VI), but plutonium (III) is more stable than uranium (III). Thus it is possible to prepare solutions in which uranium (VI) is present while plutonium is present in the lower (III) or (IV) oxidation states. Separation is then relatively easy to achieve. Fission-product separation is also based on the difference in properties of the fission products as compared with plutonium in one or more of its oxidation states. Rydberg and Sillén[169] have summarized a large amount of data relative to the isolation of plutonium on the basis of oxidation-reduction procedures and have described a number of unit separation processes.

The initial step in the recovery of plutonium from irradiated fuel elements is a cooling period, involving storage under water for from 2 to 4 months, to allow decay of radioactivity from fission products (mainly xenon 133 and iodine 131), to allow time for the isotope uranium 237 to decay to neptunium 237, and to insure adequate time for the transformation of neptunium 239 to plutonium 239.

Precipitation Processes

Bismuth Phosphate Method. Precipitation is the oldest of the separation methods used to recover plutonium from irradiated natural uranium. The most important example is the bismuth phosphate process which uses $BiPO_4$ and LaF_3 as carrier precipitation agents. Although this method is not in current use, its historical significance and the fact that the experience gained in its operation has been advantageously applied to other precipitation methods make it desirable to discuss the process briefly. Seaborg[179] and Thompson and Seaborg[201] have written detailed accounts of the conception and development of this process.

Neutron-irradiated uranium is dissolved in nitric acid, and sulfuric acid is added to form a complex with uranium which prevents its subsequent precipitation. Plutonium (IV) is then coprecipitated with $BiPO_4$. The precipitate is dissolved in nitric acid, plutonium (IV) is oxidized to (VI), and the by-product precipitate of bismuth phosphate is formed and removed. The plutonium (VI) remaining in solution is reduced to (IV) and is again precipitated with $BiPO_4$ to repeat the decontamination cycle. Following this second cycle, the carrier is changed to LaF_3, and a similar oxidation-reduction step allows further decontamination and concentration of the plutonium. At this point the plutonium is concentrated sufficiently to allow final purification without the use of carriers, and plutonium peroxide is precipitated from the acid solution. The principal disadvantage of the bismuth phosphate process lies in the difficulty of eventually recovering the uranium.

Acetate Process. Another precipitation method is the acetate process.[181] Plutonium is coprecipitated with sodium uranyl acetate which is redissolved and, after reduction of the plutonium to the (IV) state, is reprecipitated, leaving the plutonium in solution. Fission products are removed by repeating the cycle with less uranium carrier. This method was used in 1943 for the isolation of several milligrams of plutonium from about $\frac{1}{2}$ ton of cyclotron-neutron-irradiated uranium, and was considered for use at Hanford. However, it has the great disadvantage that the entire bulk of uranium has to be handled as a precipitate.

Organic Solvent Extraction Processes

Of the several separation methods available, the ones that have been used routinely in large-scale plutonium-production operations involve organic solvent extraction.[62,105,183,205] Two of these methods, Purex and Redox, or variations thereof, have been used extensively. The uranium fuel is dissolved in nitric acid to form a solution containing uranium, plutonium, and fission products. The extraction techniques are based on the solubility differences of the components in an organic liquid which is essentially immiscible with water.

In the following descriptions of solvent extraction processes, references are made primarily to American practice. Procedures in foreign countries, although basically similar, differ in certain details, such as compositions of the organic extractants employed. British applications of solvent extraction methods are discussed by Pratt,[157] Howells et al.,[93] and Buck et al.;[13] French practices by Goldschmidt, Regnaut, and Prevot,[87] Regnaut et al.,[161] and Prevot, Corpel, and Regnaut;[158] and Russian procedures by Shevchenko, Povitsky, and Solovkin[190] and by Vdovenko and Kovalskaia.[206]

Purex Process. In the Purex process[75,98,105] the feed solution of nitrates [uranium (IV), plutonium (IV), and fission products] is extracted to separate uranium and plutonium from the bulk of the fission products. Salting strength is adjusted by the addition of excess nitric acid. The organic solvent is tributyl phosphate (TBP) in a kerosene carrier, and the extraction is made in various kinds of contacting streams. The TBP solvent containing the uranium and plutonium is contacted with dilute nitric acid in a "partitioner" which reduces the plutonium to the (III) state and results in the complete transfer of plutonium from the organic to the aqueous phase. Further purification of the plutonium is accomplished by reoxidizing it to the (IV) state and re-extracting with TBP. Flanary[75] and Irish and Reas[98] have given detailed descriptions of the purex process.

Redox Process. The Redox process[105,118,182] is another continuous extraction process which has been used successfully for a number of years. It is similar to the Purex process in that it performs the same functions and has the same products, but it differs in the use of organic solvent and salting agent. Hexone (methyl iso-butyl ketone) is the solvent, and aluminum nitrate is the common ion salting agent. Reduction and oxidation of plutonium are accomplished with $Fe(SO_3NH_2)_2$ and $Na_2Cr_2O_7$, respectively. A detailed description of the Redox process has been given by Lawroski and Levenson.[118]

TTA Process. In a third solvent extraction process, plutonium is extracted from aqueous feed with a benzene-thenoyltrifluoracetone (TTA) solution which effects the separation from uranium and essentially all of the fission products except zirconium.[62,105,182] TTA is a chelating agent. Traces of fission products are scrubbed from the organic phase with dilute nitric acid. The plutonium is then stripped from the organic phase by scrubbing with a reducing agent. Since plutonium (III) is not extracted by TTA to a significant extent, it is transferred to the aqueous phase. Zirconium is not stripped with the plutonium but is removed from the solvent by an oxalic–nitric acid scrub.

This process has an advantage in not using metal salting agents, thus reducing waste-disposal problems. A significant disadvantage, however, is that the chelation rate is slow, which makes the process somewhat inconvenient for continuous operation.

Ion Exchange Processes

Complete ion exchange methods[105,117,183] for the isolation of plutonium have been studied in the laboratory and in small-scale pilot plants, but they have not yet progressed beyond that stage. A more important present application makes use of ion exchange as an auxiliary step with other basic types of separation processes,

where it has proved to be effective in concentrating plutonium solutions. Excellent fission product removal has been obtained. This application of ion exchange methods has been discussed in detail by Bruce[12] and by Tober.[202]

In pilot plant operations at Fontenay-aux-Roses,[158,161] the French metallurgists employ a three-stage resin treatment for final purification of the plutonium solution before its conversion to a dry salt and reduction to metal. The first treatment is with a cation resin, but the last two stages use an anion resin, which, compared to cation resins, appears to be inherently capable of more efficient separation of plutonium from uranium, fission products, and other impurities, and makes possible a simpler flow sheet.[53] Anion exchange methods for the concentration and purification of plutonium are discussed by Aiken[2,202] and by Ryan and Wheelwright.[168]

Although chemical attack on the ion exchange resins is not a problem, their degradation by radiation, or a combination of radiation and chemical attack, is more severe.[67] For relatively small-scale operations of a nonroutine nature, the loss of resin and the method of replacement do not present difficult operating or cost problems (1 lb of resin at from $2 to $3/lb is sufficient to recover over 20 g of plutonium at a single loading),[67] but for prolonged, routine, large-scale applications, the ion exchange processes do not yet appear to be economical.

Pyrometallurgical Processes

Pyrometallurgical processes have not yet been developed sufficiently to have immediate application for recovering plutonium. Considerable research and development is, however, being undertaken to find suitable methods that may be used with the highly irradiated fuels of the future.[73,116,117,136,183,204] These processes, as opposed to the chemical separation methods discussed above, offer several advantages. Processing the fuel materials as molten metals would allow bypassing the stages of bulk chemical conversion during purification and the subsequent step of converting the plutonium salts to metal. Variations in fuel-alloy composition, which may cause difficulty in chemical-processing systems, will probably be of less concern in pyrometallurgical processes. Also, fission products could be isolated in a compact form that would be more suitable for utilization or disposal.[117]

The three types of pyrometallurgical operations that have received the most attention for processing and concentrating plutonium are distillation, salt extraction, and molten metal extraction.

Distillation. Plutonium can be concentrated by vacuum distillation from molten uranium in the temperature range between 1500–1800°C (2732–3272°F).[3,73,144] At 1540°C (2804°F) the vapor pressure of plutonium is 300 times that of uranium.[132] Greater than 99 per cent recovery of plutonium has been achieved, and the experimental results have been found to agree with the theoretical calculations. At present, the major problems appear to be the choice of construction materials and the design of plutonium collectors.[117]

A more promising distillation method involves the conversion of uranium to the hexafluoride. Direct formation of uranium hexafluoride can be accomplished by dissolving the irradiated fuel in the trifluoride of either chlorine or bromine.[89,95,207] The uranium hexafluoride is decontaminated and separated from the fluorinating agents and reaction products by distillation. The plutonium remains behind in the dissolver vessel as an insoluble plutonium tetrafluoride residue. This residue may either be dissolved in aqueous aluminum nitrate, for plutonium recovery by solvent extraction, or it may be possible to fluorinate the plutonium to its hexafluoride and recover it by distillation techniques.

The principal disadvantages of the fluoride volatility processes are the comparatively high cost of fluorine and the fact that fluorine technology is relatively new. These factors tend to be offset, however, by the small volumes of process and waste streams and the over-all simplicity of the fluoride processes.[96,117,159,193,194,207]

Salt Extraction. The salt extraction of plutonium from molten uranium has been accomplished successfully by using halides such as UF_4 or $MgCl_2$. In a molten mixture of UF_4 and uranium metal (equal weight ratios of salt to metal), 90 per cent of the plutonium goes into the salt phase. Repeated extractions should make it possible to recover practically all of the plutonium from the uranium. In this pro-

cedure the plutonium is recovered as the fluoride or chloride and later must be reduced to the metal.[117,144]

Molten Metal Extraction. Both silver and magnesium are immiscible with molten uranium, and both have favorable capacities for extracting plutonium.[3,73,133,144,208] When magnesium is used, account must be taken of its high vapor pressure at the melting temperature of uranium. Volatilization of the magnesium allows it to be separated from plutonium. When silver is used, its subsequent separation from plutonium is difficult. At present, distillation of the silver is the preferred method.[15,117]

Cerium and lanthanum have also been investigated as possible extractants.[73,208] These elements display liquid immiscibility with uranium, and the extraction of fission products, especially those of the rare-earth elements, has been found to be high. However, the removal of plutonium appears to be marginal.

Although these molten metal solvent extraction methods do not appear to be highly selective in separating uranium and plutonium from fission products, they do appear to be adaptable to remote control, and they seem promising if rather high levels of radioactive contamination of the recovered metal can be tolerated.

METAL PREPARATION

The product from the organic solvent extraction processes is a dilute solution of plutonium nitrate in nitric acid. The methods that have been developed for conversion of these plutonium salts to plutonium metal have been discussed by Harmon and Reas.[91]

In order to avoid significant precipitation losses and to minimize the size of the processing equipment, the starting solution (product from the extraction process) is concentrated to contain from 10 to 100 g of plutonium/liter. This may be accomplished by evaporation, solvent-extraction, or ion-exchange methods. Plutonium metal may then be obtained from the concentrate by precipitating a compound, e.g., plutonium (III) fluoride, which is then directly reduced to metal, or by precipitating a compound such as plutonium (III) oxalate, plutonium (IV) oxalate, or plutonium (IV) peroxide, which is converted anhydrously to PuF_4 prior to reduction. The choice of a process

Reaction	Δ H at 291°K, kcal/mole Pu	Melting Point of Slag	
		°C	°F
$PuF_4 + 4Li \rightarrow Pu + 4LiF$	−159	870	1598
$PuF_4 + 2Ca \rightarrow Pu + 2CaF_2$	−149.5	1330	2426
$PuF_3 + 3/2Ca \rightarrow Pu + 3/2CaF_2$	− 54.8	1330	2426
$PuCl_3 + 3/2Ca \rightarrow Pu + 3/2CaCl_2$	− 56.0	772	1422
$PuBr_3 + 3/2Ca \rightarrow Pu + 3/2CaBr_2$	− 55.5	765	1409
$PuI_3 + 3/2Ca \rightarrow Pu + 3/2CaI_2$	− 59.9	575	1067

depends on the purity of the starting solution, the ease with which the plutonium can be recovered from the starting solution, the decontamination factors desired, and the process equipment required.

Plutonium metal may be prepared by reducing any of the several plutonium halides with an appropriate alkali or alkaline-earth metal.[27,35,79,91] Above are some of the possible reduction reactions.

Calcium reduction of PuF_4 is the preferred reaction, mainly because PuF_4 is nonhygroscopic, and calcium is easier to handle than lithium. Plutonium chloride, bromide, and iodide are very hygroscopic, and great care must be taken to insure the absence of moisture prior to the bomb reduction operation. Generally, the reduction of PuF_4 is performed in an induction or resistance-heated refractory-lined vessel capable of withstanding 400 psig at temperatures to 1600°C (2912°F). About 25 per cent excess calcium, relative to the stoichiometric requirements, is added to the PuF_4, and the reaction is initiated at about 600°C (1112°F). The addition of a booster charge containing equivalent amounts of calcium and iodine provides additional heat and improved slag characteristics. The optimum ratio of iodine to PuF_4 is a function of the amount of charge to be reduced. Yields greater than 99 per cent are possible by means of the bomb reduction process.[91]

The purity of normal production plutonium is about 99.87 weight per cent. The metal may contain impurities to the extent of 500 ppm iron, 400 ppm carbon, 200 ppm chromium, 200 ppm nickel, 100 ppm antimony, and 100 ppm silicon. When sufficient care is exercised, however, the bomb reduction technique is capable of producing plutonium having a purity of 99.97 weight per cent. Johnson[102] has described a method which results in the production of

high-purity plutonium through (1) purification of the feed by means of two successive peroxide precipitations, (2) purification of all reagents, (3) use of redistilled calcium for reduction, and (4) use of high-purity calcium oxide crucibles. Tate and Anderson,[198] and North,[212] have investigated the purification of plutonium metal by zone refining. They have succeeded in significantly reducing the content of specific impurity elements, but the over-all improvement in purity has been far from spectacular.

ISOTOPES

A number of isotopes of plutonium are known, all of which are radioactive. Seaborg[176,186,187] has summarized the data concerning the isotopes of the transuranium elements, and that portion of his data that concerns plutonium is listed in Table 18.2. The absolute masses of the nuclides are reported as calculated from their energies relative to the absolute mass of lead 208. The value used for the compilation is 208.04140 (physical scale).

PHYSICAL PROPERTIES

Plutonium is unique among the elements in that it has six solid-state modifications. Furthermore, the alpha phase (room-temperature allotrope) has an unusually large positive coefficient of expansion and a negative coefficient of resistivity, whereas the delta phase [stable on heating between 319–451°C (606–844°F)] has a negative coefficient of expansion and a positive coefficient of resistivity. In all phases the electrical resistivity is high and of a character more suggestive of a semiconductor than a metal.

Apparently, the presence of impurities in plutonium has a strong influence on a few of its

TABLE 18.2. ISOTOPIC MASSES (PHYSICAL SCALE) AND RADIOACTIVE DECAY PROPERTIES OF
PLUTONIUM ISOTOPES (after Seaborg)

Isotope	Mass	Half life	Mode of disintegration*	Formation
232	232.11343	36 min	EC† ($\leq$98%) α ($\geq$2%) : 6.58	U^{235} (α, 7n)
233	233.11549	20 min	EC (>99%) α (0.1%) : 6.30	U^{233} (α, 4n)
234	234.11631	9 hr	EC (94%) α (6%) : 6.19	U^{235} (α, 5n) Cm^{238} α decay
235	235.11862	26 min	EC α (3×10^{-3}%) : 5.85	U^{235} (α, 4n)
236	236.11969	2.85 yr	α (5.763, 5.716, 5.610, 5.448) β stable	U^{235} (α, n) Cm^{240} α decay
237m		0.18 sec	IT‡	Cm^{241} α recoils
237	237.12228	45.6 days	EC (>99%) α (3.3×10^{-3}%) : 5.65, 5.36	U^{238} (α, 5n) U^{235} (α, 2n)
238	238.12374	86.4 yr	α (5.495, 5.452 plus others ranging from 5.35 to 4.61) β stable	Cm^{242} α decay Np^{237} (n, γ) Np^{238} $\xrightarrow{\beta^-}$
239m$_2$	—	1.93×10^{-7} sec	IT	Cm^{243} α decay
239m$_1$	—	1.1×10^{-9} sec	IT	Cm^{243} α decay
239	239.12672	24,360 yr	α (5.147, 5.134, plus others ranging from 5.10 to 4.66) β stable	Np^{239} β^- decay
240	240.12878	6,580 yr	α (5.159, 5.115 plus others ranging from 5.01 to 4.85) β stable	Pu^{239} (n, γ)
241	241.13197	13.0 yr	β^- (>99%) 0.0205 α (3×10^{-3}%) : 4.893, 4.848	Pu^{240} (n, γ)
242	242.13423	3.73×10^5 yr	α (4.898, 4.854) β stable	Pu^{241} (n, γ)
243	243.13781	4.98 hr	β^- (0.58, 0.49, 0.37)	Pu^{242} (n, γ)
244	244.14024	7.6×10^7 yr	α β stable	Pu^{243} (n, γ)
245	245.14413§	10.1 hr	β^-	Pu^{244} (n, γ)
246	246.14698	10.85 days	β^- (0.33, 0.15)	Pu^{245} (n, γ)

* Energy of radiation in million electron volts.
† EC = electron capture.
‡ IT = isomeric transition.
§ Uncertain value.

physical properties. For several years the delta-prime phase escaped detection principally because of its elimination or suppression by very minor amounts of impurity elements, and there has been a tendency on the part of some who have worked with plutonium to attribute to impurities many of its more unusual properties, as well as the variability of experimental results obtained in earlier studies of its behavior. The results of more recent work with relatively high-purity metal suggest, however, that impurities may have less effect on the properties of plutonium than had previously been suspected.

In Table 18.3 are listed some of the physical constants of plutonium. The atomic weight of plutonium, like that of any other element, depends on its isotopic composition, which, for reactor-produced metal, is a function of the characteristics and operation of the reactor.[5,176] Once plutonium 239 atoms are formed by the "pile reactions" discussed above, and as long as they remain in the reactor, they are subject to further neutron bombardment, which will convert some of them to plutonium 240, and some of the latter to plutonium 241 or higher isotopes. In fact, all of the isotopes plutonium 236, plutonium 238, plutonium 239, plutonium 240, plutonium 241, plutonium 242, and plutonium 243 may be found in detectable amounts in neutron-irradiated uranium,[176] but reactor-produced plutonium normally contains only plutonium 239, plutonium 240, and plutonium 241 in sufficient quantities to have a practically significant influence on atomic weight. For ex-

ample, among the results of early experiments on the in-reactor irradiation of plutonium,[5] it was found that a specimen irradiated to a total exposure of 8×10^{19} nvt analyzed 95.37 (atomic) per cent plutonium 239, 4.43 per cent plutonium 240, and 0.20 per cent plutonium 241. Reference to the isotopic masses listed in Table 18.2 indicates that this specimen had an atomic weight of 239.18 in the physical scale, or 239.11 according to the chemical scale of atomic weights.

More recent irradiations of plutonium in the MTR have provided better data on the dependence of isotopic composition on irradiation history,[74,100,185] and Triplett[203] has computed the isotopic composition of reactor-produced plutonium for irradiations from zero to 13,000 megawatt days/standard ton. Reactor-produced

TABLE 18.3. SOME PHYSICAL CONSTANTS OF PLUTONIUM

Atomic number	94
Isotopic mass, plutonium 239 (physical scale)	239.13
Isotopic mass, plutonium 239 (chemical scale)	239.06
Computed atomic weight of reactor-irradiated plutonium (8×10^{19} nvt, chemical scale)	239.11
Melting point[23]	$639.5° \pm 2°C$ ($1183° \pm 4°F$)
Boiling point[155]	$3235° \pm 19°C$ ($5855° \pm 34°F$)
Vapor pressure [1120–1520°C (2048–2768°F)][155]	$\mathrm{Log}_{10}P_{mm} = -(17{,}587 \pm 73)/(t + 273.18) + 7.895 \pm 0.047$
Average heat of vaporization [1120–1520°C (2048–2768°F)][155]	80.46 ± 0.34 kcal/g-atom
Surface tension of liquid metal at 640°C (1184°F)	437–475 dynes/cm[151] 490–580 dynes/cm[200]

Heats of transformation[65]	$\alpha \rightarrow \beta$	$\Delta H = 958 \pm 10$ cal/g-atom
	$\beta \rightarrow \gamma$	$\Delta H = 140 \pm 15$
	$\gamma \rightarrow \delta$	$\Delta H = 156 \pm 5$
	$\delta \rightarrow \delta'$	$\Delta H = 17 \pm 10$
	$\delta' \rightarrow \epsilon$	$\Delta H = 470 \pm 10$
Heat of fusion	$\epsilon \rightarrow$ liq.	$\Delta H = 480$–530 cal/g-atom[152] $\Delta H = 760 \pm 115$ cal/g-atom[113] $\Delta H = 940 \pm 150$ cal/g-atom[29]
Heat capacities[29, 65]	α $C_p = 8.1$ cal/g-atom/°C	at 25°C (77°F)
	β $C_p = 9.9$	at 160°C (320°F)
	γ $C_p = 11.0$	at 280°C (536°F)
	δ $C_p = 10.9$	at 350°C (662°F)
	δ' $C_p = 13.2$	at 455°C (851°F)
	ϵ $C_p = 10.4$	at 500°C (932°F)

plutonium also undergoes a small change in isotopic composition as a function of time alone (i.e., in the absence of neutron irradiation), but this change is significant with respect to atomic weight only if an appreciable amount of plutonium 241 (13-yr half life) is present.

The range of values, 437 to 475 dynes/cm, listed in Table 18.3 for the surface tension of liquid plutonium at the melting temperature is computed from the results of Olsen, Sandenaw, and Herrick,[151] who, by the hydrostatic weighing of a tungsten sinker in liquid plutonium, measured the density of the latter as a function of temperature. The sinker was suspended by a tantalum wire, and, because liquid plutonium wets tantalum, it was necessary to apply a correction for the surface tension of the liquid metal. The product, $\gamma \cos \theta$, where γ is the surface tension and θ the angle of contact between the plutonium and the tantalum, was evaluated as a function of temperature, but the value of θ could be determined only for the temperature at which the liquid plutonium solidified on cooling. The range of values, 437 to 475, results from uncertainty in the measurement of θ.

It is known that tantalum is very slightly soluble in liquid plutonium, so that the value used for the radius of the tantalum wire in computing $\gamma \cos \theta$ may have been somewhat too large. If so, the true value of the surface tension is correspondingly larger than the range reported in Table 18.3. Theoretical predictions

of the surface tension, derived by Taylor[200] from known physical constants of plutonium, indicate a range of 490 to 580 dynes/cm. It now seems apparent that an earlier experimental value, 100 dynes/cm, reported by Comstock and Gibney,[51] was greatly in error because of the presence of an appreciable thickness of oxide film on the surface of their liquid metal.

The heat of fusion of plutonium has been determined by British,[29] French,[152] and Russian[113] investigators. Although there appears to be some discrepancy between the results of the different researches, a precision of only about 20 per cent is claimed for the French work, and similarly wide limits of uncertainty are indicated for the British and Russian results. All three investigations have established, however, that the heat of fusion of plutonium is much smaller than the known values of this property for most other metals.

Allotropic Modifications

Crystal structure data for the plutonium allotropes are given in Table 18.4. The temperature ranges of stability listed in column 2 of Table 18.4 are based on transformation temperatures determined by Cramer *et al.*[23,46,48] during the heating portion of dilatometer runs with heating rates of the order of 0.75°C/min (Figure 18.1). Thus these transformation temperatures do not represent equilibrium conditions, except approx-

TABLE 18.4. CRYSTAL STRUCTURES OF THE PLUTONIUM ALLOTROPES

Allotrope	Range of stability on heating	Space lattice and space group	Unit cell dimensions (Å)	Atoms per unit cell	X-ray density (g/cc)
Alpha [43,224]	Below 122°C (252°F)	Simple monoclinic, $P2_1/m$	at 25°C (77°F): $a = 6.182 \pm 0.001$ $b = 4.826 \pm 0.001$ $c = 10.956 \pm 0.001$ $\beta = 101.74 \pm 0.01°C$	16	19.84
Beta[43,223]	122–206°C (252–403°F)	Body-centered monoclinic, probably I2/m	at 190°C (374°F): $a = 9.284 \pm 0.003$ $b = 10.463 \pm 0.004$ $c = 7.859 \pm 0.003$ $\beta = 92.13 \pm 0.03°C$	34	17.70
Gamma[222]	206–319°C (403–606°F)	Face-centered orthorhombic, Fddd	at 235°C (455°F): $a = 3.1587 \pm 0.0004$ $b = 5.7682 \pm 0.0004$ $c = 10.162 \pm 0.002$	8	17.14
Delta[68]	319–451°C (606–844°F)	Face-centered cubic, Fm3m	at 320°C (608°F): $a = 4.6371 \pm 0.0004$	4	15.92

TABLE 18.4. CRYSTAL STRUCTURES OF THE PLUTONIUM ALLOTROPES

Allotrope	Range of stability on heating	Space lattice and space group	Unit cell dimensions (Å)	Atoms per unit cell	X-ray density (g/cc)
Delta-prime[25]	451–476°C (844–889°F)	Body-centered tetragonal, I4/mmm	at 450°C (842°F) :* a = 3.3261 ± 0.0008 c = 4.4630 ± 0.0014	2	16.07
Epsilon[68]	476–640°C (889–1184°F)	Body-centered cubic, Im3m	at 490°C (914°F) : a = 3.6361 ± 0.0004	2	16.51
Liquid[151]	Above 640°C (1184°F)	—	—	—	at 655°C (1211°F) : 16.62†

* Dimensions reported for 450°C (842°F) are extrapolated from measurements at higher temperatures.
† Density measured by hydrostatic weighing of a tungsten sinker.

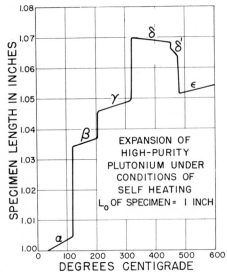

FIGURE 18.1. The dilatometric expansion of high-purity plutonium on heating.

and 199°C (390°F) for the lower and upper limits of the beta/gamma transformation, and they bracketed the equilibrium temperature of the gamma/delta transformation to between 308–311°C (586–592°F). In their dilatometer runs they found only negligible hysteresis effects for the delta/delta-prime and delta-prime/epsilon transitions,[23,33,212] so that temperatures observed for these transformations on heating may be regarded as being approximately representative of equilibrium. As the result of a

imately for the delta/delta-prime and delta-prime/epsilon transitions. The three lower transitions, alpha to beta, beta to gamma, and gamma to delta, occur at higher temperatures with faster heating rates,[33,212] and (in reversed direction) at appreciably lower temperatures on cooling.[21,33,48,147,152,212] The character of the hysteresis between the heating and cooling curves obtained in dilatometer runs of plutonium is illustrated in Figure 18.2.

By means of isothermal transformation experiments, Cramer et al.[23] attempted to narrow the spread between transition temperatures on heating and cooling. Although they were substantially unsuccessful in the case of the alpha/beta transition, they obtained 174°C (345°F)

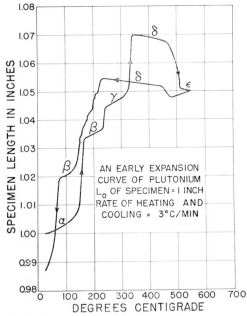

FIGURE 18.2. An early dilatometric expansion curve of plutonium for a complete cycle of heating and cooling (*after Seaborg and by permission of the Yale University Press, Inc. from "The Transuranium Elements," 1958.*)

detailed investigation of the delta-prime/epsilon transformation with a high-temperature x-ray diffractometer, Elliott and Larson[25] concluded, however, that in plutonium of very high purity the delta-prime/epsilon transition occurs on heating at $480° \pm 2°C$ ($896° \pm 4°F$).

Isothermal transformation studies of the alpha/beta transition have shown that, probably because of the complexity and low temperature of this transformation, the incubation time becomes very long as the equilibrium transition temperature is approached. For this reason, most investigators have reported about a $40°C$ ($72°F$) spread [from 120–$80°C$ (248–$176°F$)] between the transformation temperatures observed on heating and on cooling. Only Lee and Mardon[33,212] have been successful in estimating an equilibrium transformation temperature, which they reported to be $117° \pm 2°C$ ($243° \pm 4°F$). This value seems somewhat high, however, in relation to trends observed in the more detailed work of Nelson and Thomas,[147,149] who also studied the kinetics of the alpha-to-beta and beta-to-alpha transformations (Figures 18.3 and 18.4) but employed shorter isothermal treatments.

In early experiments (1945) on the pressure dependence of the temperature of the alpha/beta transformation, Bridgman[10] undertook to determine the equilibrium transformation pressure at higher temperatures. He found that at $163°C$ ($325°F$) the equilibrium pressure for the alpha/beta transformation is $3,100$ kg/sq cm, and at $205°C$ ($401°F$) it is $7,060$ kg/sq cm. A linear extrapolation of these values gives $129°C$ ($264°F$) as the equilibrium transformation temperature at atmospheric pressure. Because this result is obviously too high, Bridgman concluded that the linear extrapolation is erroneous and that the curve of the pressure dependence is concave toward the pressure axis, which is normal for most solid substances.

In an investigation of isothermal reaction behavior that involved the beta/gamma transition, Nelson[148] obtained results (Figures 18.5 and 18.6) in good agreement with those of Cramer et al.[23] for the temperature spread of this transition. Details of the work of Nelson, and of Nelson and Thomas, on the transformation kinetics of plutonium are discussed below.

In Table 18.5 are listed estimates of the equilibrium transformation temperatures of plutonium that take into account all of the experimental results discussed above. Wide limits of uncertainty are indicated where appropriate. Table 18.5 also lists the volume changes that accompany each of the phase transformations of plutonium, including melting. For the solid state transformations, except the delta/delta-prime transition, these volume changes have been computed from the unit-cell dimensions and thermal expansion coefficients (x-ray data) listed in Tables 18.4 and 18.6. The volume changes computed from x-ray data will not, in general, agree with the length changes observed in dilatometer runs because the latter, in addition to depending on changes in crystal structure and interatomic distance, are influenced by such extraneous factors operative during the transitions as (1) the formation of microvoids,[45,48,149] (2) the closing of microvoids by a sintering type of process,[48] (3) plastic deformations giving rise to changes in the dimensions and shape of the specimen,[21,33,48] (4) effects caused by preferred orientation, (5) temperature gradients within the specimen caused by the radioactive self-heating of plutonium[23,46,170] (of the order of 0.010 cal/sec/

TABLE 18.5. ESTIMATED EQUILIBRIUM TRANSFORMATION TEMPERATURES OF PLUTONIUM AND TRANSFORMATION VOLUME CHANGES COMPUTED FROM X-RAY DATA

Phase transformation	Transformation temperature		Volume change in per cent $\dfrac{v_1 - v_2}{v_1} \times 100$
	°C	°F	
Alpha $\rightarrow$ beta	110 ± 10	230 ± 18	9.62
Beta $\rightarrow$ gamma	190 ± 10	374 ± 18	2.67
Gamma $\rightarrow$ delta	310 ± 5	590 ± 9	6.90
Delta $\rightarrow$ delta-prime	452 ± 2	846 ± 4	−0.36*
Delta-prime $\rightarrow$ epsilon	480 ± 4	896 ± 7	−2.16
Epsilon $\rightarrow$ liquid	639.5 ± 2	1183 ± 4	−0.82†

* Value determined by linear dilatometry.[23]
† Value determined by volume dilatometry.[111]

cc,[170,196] the exact value depending on isotopic composition), and (6) retained beta phase (in alpha), which influences the magnitude of the alpha/beta volume change.[48,147,149] Because, however, the delta/delta-prime volume change and the volume change on melting are both quite small, in these two cases the volume changes observed by direct dilatometric methods are believed to be better values than those computed from x-ray data (i.e., relatively small errors in the x-ray expansion coefficients will cause much larger percentage errors in the computed values of small transformation volume changes). Thus the data of Table 18.5 are not entirely consistent with those of Tables 18.4 and 18.6. The volume decrease listed in Table 18.5 for the delta-to-delta-prime transition is computed from the value obtained by Cramer et al.[23] by linear dilatometry; the decrease in volume that occurs when plutonium melts has been measured by Knight[111] using a liquid NaK volume dilatometer.

Because of the large volume change involved, the temperature of the alpha/beta transformation is rather strongly influenced by changes in pressure. For pressures up to 7,000 bars, Bridgman[10,49] obtained a linear slope of 0.0109°C/bar for the increase of transformation temperature with increasing pressure. Schonfeld and Spindler[49] later obtained the values 0.0073°C/bar at 1,000 bars and 0.0102°C/bar at 5,000 bars. From the latter data the value 985 cal/g-atom was calculated for the latent heat of the alpha/beta transformation, a result in good agreement with the calorimetric determination, 958 cal/g-atom (Table 18.3), of Dean, Kay, and Loasby.[65] From this standpoint, therefore, the results of Schonfeld and Spindler appear to be better values.

Transformation Kinetics

The kinetics of the beta-to-alpha and alpha-to-beta, and the gamma-to-beta-to-alpha and alpha-to-beta-to-gamma transformations in plutonium have been studied by Nelson[147,148] and by Nelson and Thomas.[149] These investigators used a fluid-displacement method to obtain heating and cooling curves and isothermal reaction curves showing the fraction of a phase transformed as a function of time. Time-temperature transformation (TTT) curves were derived from these data and are presented in Figures 18.3, 18.4, 18.5, 18.6, and 18.7 for the

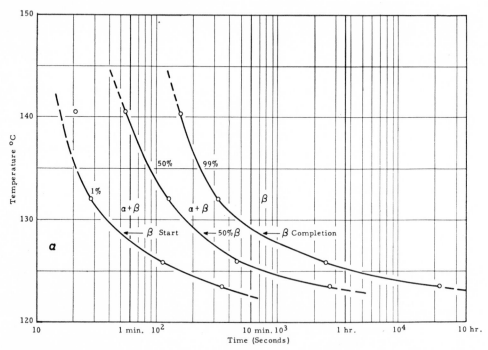

FIGURE 18.3. The time-temperature-transformation curve of the alpha-to-beta transformation of plutonium. (*Courtesy Nelson and Thomas.*)[147, 149]

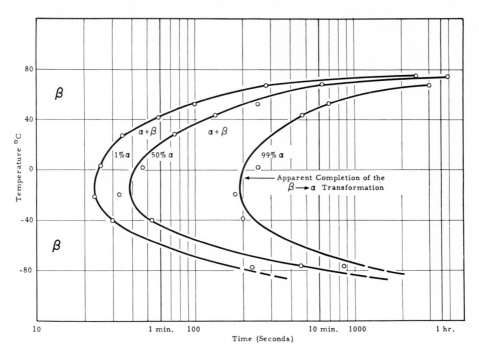

FIGURE 18.4. The time-temperature-transformation curve of the beta-to-alpha transformation of plutonium. (*Courtesy Nelson and Thomas.*)[147,149]

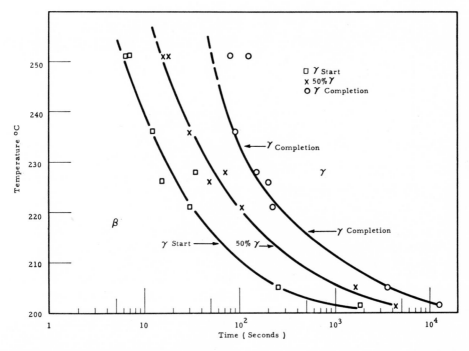

FIGURE 18.5. The time-temperature-transformation curve of the beta-to-gamma transformation of plutonium. (*Courtesy Nelson.*)[148]

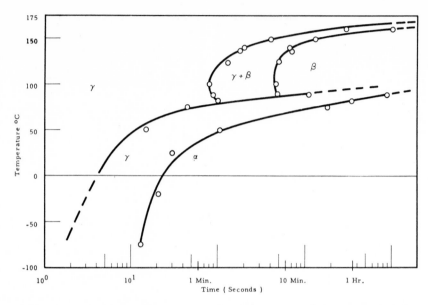

FIGURE 18.6. The time-temperature-transformation curve of the gamma-to-beta-to-alpha transformations of plutonium. (*Courtesy Nelson and Thomas.*)[148, 149]

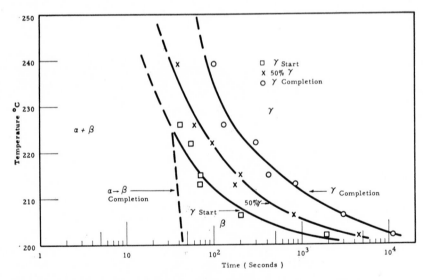

FIGURE 18.7. The time-temperature-transformation curve of the alpha-to-beta-to-gamma transformations of plutonium. (*Courtesy Nelson.*)[148]

$a{\rightarrow}\beta$, $\beta{\rightarrow}a$, $\beta{\rightarrow}\gamma$, $\gamma{\rightarrow}\beta{\rightarrow}a$, and $a{\rightarrow}\beta{\rightarrow}\gamma$ transformations, respectively.

Evidence obtained suggests that the alpha-to-beta reaction does not go to completion at temperatures above about 0°C (32°F) and that the amount of beta phase retained at a given temperature is increased by a higher impurity content. The rate of formation of alpha from beta was also found to be quite sensitive to impurities, being slower for a higher impurity content. The time for 50 per cent transformation of beta to alpha at −21°C (−6°F), the temperature of the maximum rate of transformation, was 20 sec for a sample having 200 ppm and 70 sec for a sample having 1,500 ppm of impurities.

Thermal Properties

The heats of transformation, fusion, and vaporization of plutonium, together with the heat capacities at constant pressure of the solid allotropes, are listed in Table 18.3. The heat capacity of the liquid phase has not been determined. The heat capacity of alpha plutonium[65] reported in Table 18.3 is a room-temperature value. Sandenaw[36] has found that, at temperatures below room temperature, the heat capacity of the alpha phase behaves normally in that it decreases with decreasing temperature and presumably approaches zero as 0°K is approached. At very low temperatures Sandenaw found that the heat capacity decreased uniformly if the cooling rate was rapid (as in quenching), but, after holding his specimens at about 50°K for an extended period (of the order of 24 hr), he obtained anomalous peaks in his specific heat curves in the range below 160°K.[36]

For the alpha and beta phases, the heat capacities at constant volume, C_v, can be calculated from the values of C_p given in Table 18.3 together with data presented below for the compressibilities and thermal expansion coefficients of these phases. From these data the following values have been computed:

$C_v = 7.3$ cal/g-atom/°C at 25°C (77°F) (α).

$C_v = 9.4$ cal/g-atom/°C at 160°C (320°F) (β).

Sandenaw[36] has derived values for C_v from his experimental results for C_p at very low temperatures. These values indicate that the Debye characteristic temperature of alpha plutonium is 127°K. From sound velocity data obtained at room temperature, however, Laquer[32] has calculated the Debye characteristic temperature to be 178°C (352°F). In principle, the latter calculation should be based on sound velocities at the absolute zero, but the difference would yield a higher value of the characteristic temperature and thus result in an even greater disparity with Sandenaw's value. Support for Sandenaw's value is provided by the computations of Kay,[29] who, by applying compressibility and melting-point data to the formulas of Einstein and Lindemann,[143] respectively, has estimated that the Debye characteristic tem-

perature of plutonium should lie in the range of 92–130°K.

In Table 18.6 are given the coefficients of linear thermal expansion for all of the solid allotropes of plutonium and the coefficient of volume thermal expansion for liquid plutonium. The temperature ranges, t_0 to t_1, indicated in the second column of Table 18.6 are those throughout which the experimental measurements were made and are the ranges for which the mean coefficients in the third column have been computed from the relation: $\bar{a} = (l_1 - l_0)/l_0 (t_1 - t_0)$; so that t_0 is the reference temperature for the mean coefficient (i.e., $1 = l_0$ when $t = t_0$; and for the liquid phase, $v = v_0$ when $t = t_0$). Coefficients determined by x-ray diffraction are listed wherever available, because the same extraneous factors, referred to above as sources of error in the dilatometric measurement of transformation volume changes, usually also lead to erroneous results when the dilatometric method is employed to measure thermal expansion in the temperature ranges between transformations. The magnitude of the errors caused by the sum of these extraneous influences is greatest, however, for the solid allotropes stable at higher temperatures and may be quite small in dilatometric measurements of the thermal expansion of the alpha, beta, and gamma phases. Coefficients determined dilatometrically for these phases have, in fact, in many instances been found to agree closely with x-ray values. Because x-ray measurements have not been made at temperatures below room temperature, the mean coefficient determined dilatometrically by Cramer et al.[23] for alpha plutonium from −186 to 100°C (−303 to 212°F) is listed in Table 18.6 in addition to the x-ray coefficients for alpha plutonium in the range of 21–104°C (70–219°F).

This mean coefficient for the range −186 to 100°C (−303 to 212°F) is computed from the following more exact relation found by Cramer et al. (t in °C): $1 = l_0 [1 + (46.8 \pm 0.05) 10^{-6} t + (55.9 \pm 0.4) 10^{-9} t^2]$, which shows that the value of the instantaneous true coefficient, $a = dl/ldt$, increases appreciably with increasing temperature. Among all of the plutonium allotropes, only the alpha phase manifests such a marked deviation from linear behavior, and, because of this deviation, the equation obtained dilatometrically is obviously a better description of

TABLE 18.6. THE THERMAL EXPANSION OF PLUTONIUM (PER °C)

Allotrope and principal coefficient	Temperature range, (t_0 to t_1)	Mean coefficient of linear expansion [($\times 10^6$) $1 = l_0$ at $t = t_0$]	Experimental method and references
Alpha, $\bar{\alpha}_p$	−186–100°C (−303–212°F)	42.3	Linear dilatometry[23, 48]
Alpha, $\bar{\alpha}_1$	21–104°C (70–219°F)	64 ± 5	X-ray diffraction[43, 45]
$\bar{\alpha}_2 = \bar{\alpha}_b$	—	72 ± 5	
$\bar{\alpha}_3$	—	28 ± 5	
$\bar{\alpha}_p$	—	55 ± 5	

At 21°C (69.8°F) the direction of a_1 is 10° from the monoclinic a-axis and 91.7° from the c-axis.

Beta,* $\bar{\alpha}_1$	83–252°C (181–466°F)	85 ± 9	X-ray diffraction[43, 45, 223]
$\bar{\alpha}_2 = \bar{\alpha}_b$	—	15 ± 5	
$\bar{\alpha}_3$	—	13 ± 6	
$\bar{\alpha}_p$	—	38 ± 6	

At 83°C (181.4°F) the direction of a_1 is 37° from the monoclinic a-axis and 55.1° from the c-axis.

Gamma, $\bar{\alpha}_a$	210–310°C (410–590°F)	−19.7 ± 1.0	X-ray diffraction[222]
$\bar{\alpha}_b$	—	39.5 ± 0.6	
$\bar{\alpha}_c$	—	84.3 ± 1.6	
$\bar{\alpha}_p$	—	34.6 ± 0.7	
Delta, $\bar{\alpha}$	320–440°C (608–824°F)	− 8.6 ± 0.3	X-ray diffraction[68]
Delta-prime, $\bar{\alpha}_a$	452–480°C (846–896°F)	444.8 ± 12.1	X-ray diffraction[25]
$\bar{\alpha}_c$	—	−1063.5 ± 18.2	
$\bar{\alpha}_p$	—	− 65.6 ± 10.1	
Epsilon, $\bar{\alpha}$	490–550°C (914–1022°F)	36.5 ± 1.1	X-ray diffraction[68]
Liquid, $\bar{\alpha}_v$	655–960°C (1211–1760°F)	89.7†	Hydrostatic weighing[151]

* The beta phase contained 2 per cent uranium.
† Mean coefficient of volume expansion.

the thermal expansion of polycrystalline alpha plutonium free from preferred orientation than is the directionally averaged mean coefficient $\bar{\alpha}_p = 55 \times 10^{-6}$, derived from the x-ray measurements. That the dilatometric expression is in good agreement with the x-ray coefficients is shown by the fact that it yields a mean coefficient $\bar{\alpha} = 53.8 \times 10^{-6}$ for the temperature range 21–104°C (70–219°F).

The alpha, beta, gamma, and delta-prime phases of plutonium, being crystallographically anisotropic, also manifest anisotropic expansion behavior. For the gamma and delta-prime allotropes, the directions of the principal coefficients of thermal expansion are the same as the directions of the crystallographic axes, so that

the principal coefficients are accordingly designated $\bar{\alpha}_a$, $\bar{\alpha}_b$, *and* $\bar{\alpha}_c$ in Table 18.6. In the monoclinic alpha and beta phases, however, only the direction of the principal coefficient $\bar{\alpha}_2$ is the same as that of the crystallographic b-axis, so that $\bar{\alpha}_2 = \bar{\alpha}_b$. In the tensor ellipsoids of thermal expansion for the two monoclinic structures, the directions of the principal coefficients $\bar{\alpha}_1$ and $\bar{\alpha}_3$ are, of course, perpendicular to each other and to the direction of $\bar{\alpha}_2$, and hence they lie in the plane of the crystallographic axes a and c. In alpha plutonium the principal direction lying within the obtuse angle ($\beta = 101.74$ deg) between a and c and making an angle of 10 deg with a is designated $\bar{\alpha}_1$. In the beta phase the direction of $\bar{\alpha}_1$ similarly lies in the obtuse angle ($\beta = 92.13$ deg) between the a- and c-axes and makes an angle of 37 deg with the a-axis.

For the gamma and delta-prime phases the value of the directionally averaged coefficient $\bar{\alpha}_p$ (i.e., the coefficient for the macroscopically isotropic expansion of polycrystalline metal having randomly oriented grains) is derived from the exact relationship:

$$(l + \bar{\alpha}_p \Delta t)^3 = (l + \bar{\alpha}_1 \Delta t)\,(l + \bar{\alpha}_2 \Delta t)\,(l + \bar{\alpha}_3 \Delta t),$$

rather than from the approximation formula:

$$3\bar{\alpha}_p = \bar{\alpha}_1 + \bar{\alpha}_2 + \bar{\alpha}_3.$$

For the alpha and beta phases application of the two different formulas results in no significant difference in the value of $\bar{\alpha}_p$.

The volume coefficient listed in Table 18.6 for liquid plutonium is a mean value computed for the range of 655–960°C (1211–1760°F) from the following expression of Olsen, Sandenaw, and Herrick[151] for the density of liquid plutonium as a function of temperature (t in °C):

$$\rho = (17.567 - 0.001451\ t)\mathrm{g/cc}.$$

Because this relationship between density and temperature is linear, the dependence of volume on temperature is nonlinear. Hence the variation with temperature of the volume of liquid plutonium is most conveniently computed from the density variation by using the above equation to obtain the latter.

The thermal conductivities of alpha and beta plutonium have been measured by Sandenaw and Gibney[36,170] for the temperature range −158 to 140°C (−252 to 284°F). Their results, shown by the curve of Figure 18.8, indicate

values of approximately 0.020 cal/cm/sec/°C for the alpha phase at 25°C (77°F) and 0.037 cal/cm/sec/°C for beta plutonium at 140°C (284°F). The lowest value they measured was 0.0035 cal/cm/sec/°C at −158°C (−252°F).

Measurements of the thermal conductivity of alpha plutonium have also been made by investigators at Harwell.[212] Their results [0.008 and 0.006 cal/cm/sec/°C at 40–105°C (104–221°F), respectively] indicate a much lower thermal conductivity than that found by Sandenaw and Gibney and a temperature dependence opposite in sign from that which Sandenaw and Gibney observed. The Los Alamos workers regard the avoidance of heat conduction losses along their thermocouple wires as being of great importance in obtaining valid results. The account of the British work does not indicate whether or not the Harwell investigators gave equally great attention to this problem.

Electrical and Magnetic Properties

The best values for the electrical resistivity of plutonium as a function of temperature appear to be those of Sandenaw and Gibney,[36,170] whose results for two specimens of high-purity metal (99.95 and 99.96 weight per cent plutonium) are shown in Figure 18.9. In this figure the values plotted are relative to the absolute resistivity (146.45 × 10⁻⁶ ohm-cm) of alpha plutonium at 0°C (32°F). In Table 18.7 are listed the averages of the absolute resistivities found for these two specimens at various temperatures. Also listed in Table 18.7 are the mean temperature coefficients of resistivity

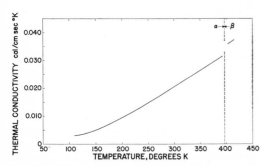

FIGURE 18.8. The thermal conductivities of alpha and beta plutonium. (*Courtesy Sandenaw and Gibney.*)[36,170]

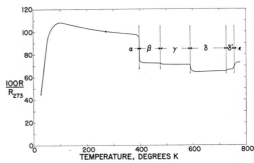

FIGURE 18.9. The electrical resistivity of plutonium as a function of temperature and relative to its absolute resistivity (146.45 microhm-cm) at 273.15°K. (*Courtesy Sandenaw and Gibney.*)[36,170]

TABLE 18.7. ELECTRICAL RESISTIVITIES AND TEMPERATURE COEFFICIENTS OF
RESISTIVITY OF PLUTONIUM (after Sandenaw and Gibney)

Allotrope	Temperature		Absolute resistivity (ohm-cm × 10^6)	Temperature range [t_1–t_2 (°C and °F)]	Mean coefficient of resistivity ×10^4
	°C	°F			
Alpha	−247	−413	64.8		
	−223	−369	128.0	−247– −223 (−413– −369°F)	+184.05
	−173	−279	156.9		
	−123	−189	153.5	−147–+20 (−233–68°F)	−4.18
	0	32	146.45		
	107	225	141.4	29–107 (84–225°F)	−2.08
Beta	147	297	108.5	147–197 (297–387°F)	−0.62
Gamma	232	450	107.8	232–317 (450–603°F)	−0.50
Delta	352	666	100.4	352–452 (666–846°F)	+0.72
Delta-prime	462	864	102.1	462–474 (864–885°F)	+4.43
Epsilon	501	934	110.6	488–501 (910–934°F)	0.00

computed according to the relation: $\bar{a}_R = (R_2 - R_1)/R_0 \ (t_2 - t_1)$; so that 0°C (32°F) is the reference temperature for the mean coefficients computed for the temperature ranges t_1 to t_2, R_0 being the absolute resistivity of alpha plutonium at 0°C (32°F).

Sandenaw[36] has reported results obtained by Olsen and Matthias in a search for superconductivity in plutonium at low temperatures. No superconductivity was found on cooling a specimen of the alpha phase to approximately

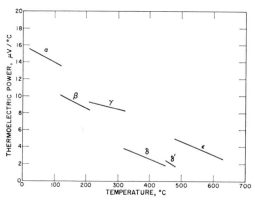

FIGURE 18.10. The thermoelectric power of plutonium as a function of temperature. (*Courtesy Lee and Hall.*)[119, 212]

1.3°K; the material remained strongly paramagnetic at this temperature.

The thermoelectric power of plutonium has been determined by Lee and Hall[119] and reported by Waldron et al.[212] The thermal emf of a plutonium-platinum thermocouple was measured between 20–630°C (68–1166°F) and, from the data obtained, the absolute thermoelectric power, dE/dt, was calculated for each of the six allotropes of plutonium. The results are shown in Figure 18.10, and selected values for each allotrope are listed in Table 18.8. The values of dE/dt were derived by subtracting the absolute thermoelectric power of platinum[137] from the relative thermoelectric power of plutonium referred to platinum, as calculated from the slope of the emf/temperature curve.[119]

The first measurements of the magnetic susceptibility of plutonium as a function of temperature were made by Comstock in 1952. The results of his work were reported briefly, but only in part, by Jette[100] in 1955. They were later presented in greater detail by Sandenaw.[36]

Subsequent measurements of the magnetic susceptibility of plutonium have been reported by Dawson,[64] by Konobeevsky,[112] and by Seguin et al.[189] In all of the latter investigations the values obtained were somewhat higher than

TABLE 18.8. ABSOLUTE THERMOELECTRIC POWER OF PLUTONIUM

(after Lee and Hall)

Allotrope	Temperature		Thermoelectric power $[dE/dt$ (volts/°C $\times 10^6$)]
	°C	°F	
Alpha	27	81	15.51
Beta	127	261	10.00
Gamma	227	441	9.20
Delta	327	621	3.72
Delta-prime	452	846	2.32
Epsilon	527	981	4.24

those of Comstock. Because, however, Comstock employed the Gouy method, whereas it appears that the other investigators used the less precise Faraday method, his results are probably still the best values available.

Since the Gouy method takes changes of specimen length into account, and because, during heating and cooling, hydraulically pressed plutonium expands and contracts differently from as-cast plutonium, Comstock obtained slightly different results for cast and pressed metal. (Changes in specimen length must be estimated, since they cannot be measured directly while the susceptibility measurements are being made.) An average curve drawn through his experimental points for the two materials is shown in Figure 18.11, and in Table 18.9 are listed selected values of the magnetic susceptibility, together with temperature coefficients for each of the plutonium allotropes. The values listed in Table 18.9 have been obtained by means of computations based on Comstock's original data rather than by measurement of Figure 18.11. The temperature ranges t_0 to t_1 listed in column 5 of Table 18.9 are the ranges for which the mean temperature coefficients of magnetic susceptibility have been

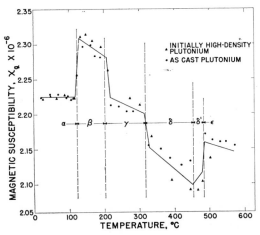

FIGURE 18.11. The magnetic susceptibility of plutonium as a function of temperature. (*Courtesy Comstock.*)[36]

TABLE 18.9. THE MAGNETIC SUSCEPTIBILITY OF PLUTONIUM

(after Comstock)

Allotrope	Temperature		Magnetic susceptibility per gram, χ_g, emu/g	Temperature range $[t_0-t_1$ (°C)]	Temperature coefficient of χ_g ($\times 10^5$) ($\chi = \chi_0$ at $t = t_0$)
	°C	°F			
Alpha	20	68	2.23	20–118 (68–244°F)	− 1.8
Beta	132	270	2.31	132–198 (270–388°F)	−16.4
Gamma	224	435	2.23	224–302 (435–576°F)	−11.5
Delta	358	676	2.13	358–446 (676–835°F)	−12.3
Delta-prime	464	867	2.12	464–477 (867–891°F)	+36.3
Epsilon	488	910	2.15	488–570 (910–1058°F)	−12.5

calculated, with t_0 being the reference temperature [i.e., $\chi = \chi_0$ at $t = t_0$ in the expression $(\chi_1 - \chi_0)/\chi_0(t_1 - t_0)$].

Although Comstock did not investigate temperatures below 20°C (68°F), both Dawson and Seguin et al. made measurements down to the liquid-nitrogen region. Seguin et al. found the magnetic susceptibility of alpha plutonium to be very nearly constant all the way down to −200°C (−328°F) increasing only slightly with decreasing temperature according to the slope $d\chi/dt = -0.4 \times 10^{-6}$ for the range −200 to 100°C (−328 to 212°F).[189] Dawson, on the other hand, observed almost a doubling of the susceptibility of his specimen on cooling from room temperature to −183°C (−297°F).[64] Seguin et al. have suggested that Dawson's sample must have contained a significant concentration of a paramagnetic impurity.[189]

Elastic Properties

The elastic properties of alpha plutonium have been studied both by static and dynamic methods. Because of internal stresses and defects inherent in alpha plutonium (discussed below in relation to strength properties), it seems probable that dynamic rather than static methods have provided the best values of such properties as the elastic moduli, Poisson's ratio, and compressibility. The most extensive investigations of these values have been made by Laquer,[32,49] who employed two different sound velocity techniques in studying the elastic behavior of a large number of alpha-plutonium specimens. His results for the highest-purity metal (99.97 weight per cent plutonium) that he measured are given in Tables 18.10, 18.11, and 18.12. Laquer found that his as-measured values varied with the experimental bulk density of his specimens. Hence his final best values, given in Table 18.10, are computed for alpha plutonium having theoretical (x-ray) density. The temperature coefficients that appear in Table 18.11 were determined as close approximations to the values of the instantaneous coefficients at 30°C (86°F). The pressure coefficients of Table 18.12 are mean values calculated for the range 0 to 2,000 bars by using atmospheric pressure as the reference pressure.

Dynamic methods have also been employed by British and Russian investigators in making measurements of the elastic properties of alpha plutonium. Their results, together with values obtained by British and American workers who used static methods, are listed in Table 18.13. For most of the values in Table 18.13 the density of the metal was not reported, and presumably no corrections were made for deviations of bulk density from the theoretical density.

The compressibilities listed in Table 18.13 are for pressures below 2,000 bars, but measurements by Bridgman[10] were extended to much higher pressures. He has reported his data in

TABLE 18.10. ELASTIC PROPERTIES AT 30°C (86°F) OF ALPHA PLUTONIUM HAVING THEORETICAL X-RAY DENSITY [19.79 G/CC AT 30°C (86°F)]

(after Laquer)

Property	Symbol	Range of observed values	Extrapolation to x-ray density	Units
Young's modulus	E	8.9–10.1	10.0 ± 0.1	$\times 10^{11}$ dynes/sq cm
		12.9–14.6	14.5 ± 0.2	$\times 10^6$ psi
Shear modulus	G	3.8–4.3	4.38 ± 0.04	$\times 10^{11}$ dynes/sq cm
		5.5–6.2	6.35 ± 0.06	$\times 10^6$ psi
Poisson's ratio	σ	0.14–0.20	0.15 ± 0.01	
Adiabatic compressibility	x_S	1.8–2.2	2.1 ± 0.1	$\times 10^{-12}$ sq cm/dyne
		1.8–2.2	2.1 ± 0.1	$\times 10^{-6}$/atm
Isothermal compressibility	x_T	2.1–2.5	2.4 ± 0.2	$\times 10^{-12}$ sq cm/dyne
Sound velocities				
Rod velocity	v_0	2.17–2.26	2.25 ± 0.01	$\times 10^5$ cm/sec
Infinite medium velocity	v_L	2.27–2.30	2.31 ± 0.01	$\times 10^5$ cm/sec
Shear velocity	v_T	1.40–1.49	1.49 ± 0.01	$\times 10^5$ cm/sec
Density	ρ	19.00–19.72	19.79	g/cc

TABLE 18.11. TEMPERATURE COEFFICIENTS AT 30°C (86°F) OF THE ELASTIC PROPERTIES OF ALPHA PLUTONIUM (after Laquer)

Property	Temperature coefficient	Value ($\times 10^5$/°C)
Young's modulus	$\dfrac{dE}{E\,dt}$	-201 ± 14
Shear modulus	$\dfrac{dG}{G\,dt}$	-213 ± 10
Poisson's ratio	$\dfrac{d\sigma}{\sigma\,dt}$	$+90 \pm 130$
Compressibility	$\dfrac{d\chi}{\chi\,dt}$	$+166 \pm 70$
Thin-rod sound velocity	$\dfrac{dv_0}{v_0\,dt}$	-93 ± 7
Infinite medium velocity	$\dfrac{dv_L}{v_L\,dt}$	-88 ± 11
Shear velocity	$\dfrac{dv_T}{v_T\,dt}$	-99 ± 5

TABLE 18.12. MEAN PRESSURE COEFFICIENTS TO 2,000 BARS OF THE ELASTIC PROPERTIES OF ALPHA PLUTONIUM [AT 30°C (86°F)] (after Laquer)

Property	Pressure coefficient	Value ($\times 10^6$/bar)
Young's modulus	$\dfrac{\Delta E}{E_0 \Delta p}$	$+17.7 \pm 1.1$
Shear modulus	$\dfrac{\Delta G}{G_0 \Delta p}$	$+14.4 \pm 1.3$
Poisson's ratio	$\dfrac{\Delta \sigma}{\sigma_0 \Delta p}$	$+26.6 \pm 6.6$
Compressibility	$\dfrac{\Delta \chi}{\chi_0 \Delta p}$	-28.4 ± 2.9
Thin-rod sound velocity	$\dfrac{\Delta v_0}{v_0 \Delta p}$	$+7.77 \pm 0.55$
Infinite medium velocity	$\dfrac{\Delta v_L}{v_L \Delta p}$	$+9.21 \pm 0.42$
Shear velocity	$\dfrac{\Delta v_T}{v_T \Delta p}$	$+6.12 \pm 0.65$

the form $\Delta v/v_0$ for successively higher steps in pressure up to 100,000 kg/sq cm (1.42 $\times$ 10^6 psi). Laquer[32] has recomputed Bridgman's data into the form of approximately instantaneous compressibilities $\Delta v/v \Delta p$ for which the pressure increments (Δp) vary from 1,000 to 10,000 kg/sq cm. A plot of these instantaneous compressibilities as a function of pressure gives a curve[32] which, for the lower pressures investigated by Laquer, agrees well with his values of both compressibility and pressure coefficient of compressibility. An extrapolation of Bridgman's data gives a value of about 2.0 $\times$ 10^{-6}/bar at atmospheric pressure (Table 18.13). The instantaneous compressibility drops to 1.5 $\times$ 10^{-6}/bar

at about 12,000 bars, to about 1.0 $\times$ 10^{-6}/bar at 50,000 bars, and to approximately 0.5 $\times$ 10^{-6}/bar at 100,000 bars. Thus the volume of alpha plutonium at 100,000 kg/sq cm is 89.8 per cent of its volume at atmospheric pressure.[10]

The isothermal compressibility of beta plutonium at 200°C (392°F) for the range 0 to 2,000 bars was reported by Schonfeld and Spindler[49] to be (2.3 $\pm$ 1.0) $\times$ 10^{-6}/bar. Bridgman[10] has concluded, however, that the compressibility of the beta phase is about 25 per cent greater than that of alpha plutonium. A difference in this direction is to be expected because of the lower density of beta plutonium.

TABLE 18.13. ELASTIC PROPERTIES OF ALPHA PLUTONIUM AS DETERMINED BY VARIOUS INVESTIGATORS

Investigator	Method	Young's modulus (psi $\times 10^6$)	Shear modulus (psi $\times 10^6$)	Poisson's ratio	Isothermal compressibility ($\times 10^{-6}$/bar)
Laquer[32, 49]	Dynamic	14.5	6.3	0.15	2.4 $\pm$ 0.2
Lee and Hancock[49]	Dynamic	12.5			
Konobeevsky et al.[113]	Dynamic	12.9	5.4	0.21	
Lord[29, 49]	Static	11.9			
Kay and Lowthian[29]	Static	14.4	—	0.13	
Bridgman[10, 49]	Static	—	—	—	~2.0
Schonfeld and Spindler[49]	Static	14.0–15.5	—	—	2.5 $\pm$ 0.5*
Nelson[150]	Static	11.5–15.5			
Gardner and Jefferes[82]	Static	11.4–14.9, average 13.8			

* Measured at 150°C (302°F).

Mechanical Properties

For obvious reasons, plutonium is not expected ever to become important as a structural material, and, accordingly, very few data relating to its strength properties have been ascertained. It is apparent that the existence of six solid allotropes, and the large volume changes associated with their transformations, prohibit the use of solid unalloyed plutonium metal as a fuel element in a reactor.[30,76,106,197]

It seems obvious, moreover, that these large transformation volume changes, in conjunction with the anisotropy of most of the plutonium phases, must necessarily generate internal stresses and defects that significantly affect both elastic and plastic properties. Because, however, all of the solid phases except alpha are relatively soft and easily deformable, such stresses and defects are of major importance with respect to strength properties only at temperatures below about 90°C (194°F). Thus the alpha phase is quite hard and brittle almost to the limit of its stability range, its thermal expansion is anisotropic, and its monoclinic crystal structure suggests that it possesses very few (if any) well-defined slip planes. Hence one expects very high thermal stresses to be present at room temperature, and it is known that, depending on thermal history, the alpha phase contains a variable number of microvoids.[45,149]

One of the reasons for believing that the mechanical properties of alpha plutonium are influenced by internal stresses and defects is the great difference that has been observed between measured values of the ultimate tensile strength and the ultimate compressive strength. At room temperature, the values obtained in tension are less than half those found in compression. Typical stress-strain curves obtained by Schonfeld[172] are shown in Figure 18.12. Thus, for cast and machined specimens, compressive strengths at 25°C (77°F) have been found to be of the order of 125,000 to 155,000 psi, but ultimate tensile strengths observed at Los Alamos have not been greater than 44,400 to 54,600 psi.[172]

Other tensile test data for alpha plutonium have been published only by metallurgists at Hanford. For cast unmachined specimens Nelson[150] has reported ultimate tensile strengths from 50,000 to 51,800 psi and a yield strength of 45,000 psi (presumably at 0.02 per cent

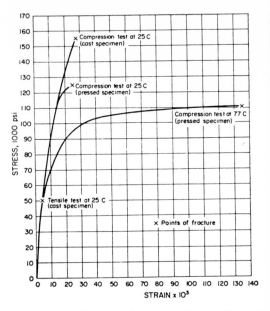

FIGURE 18.12. Stress-strain curves for tensile and compression tests of alpha plutonium. (*Courtesy Schonfeld and by permission of Interscience Publishers, Inc. from the Materials Volume of the "Reactor Handbook," 1960.*)

offset). In an investigation of tensile properties at room temperature, Gardner, Bloomster, and Jefferes[81,82] obtained ultimate strengths from 43,700 to 77,200 psi for cast and machined specimens. Some of their specimens had been annealed for 30 to 90 min at 360–400°C (680–752°F), and prior to testing all of them were cold treated at −23°C (−9°F) to transform any retained beta phase to alpha. Although the annealing treatment was found to have no effect on strength properties, the most obvious explanation for the generally higher ultimate strengths observed (relative to those found by Schonfeld and Nelson) is the elimination of retained beta by the cold treatment at −23°C (−9°F).

Yield strengths at 0.02 per cent offset were found to vary from 30,600 to 45,800 psi and moduli of resilience from 9.1 to 45.0 in.-lb/cu in. The reason for the large variation in the latter values is that the modulus of resilience depends on the square of the proportional limit (in itself quite variable) according to the expression $s^2/2E$, where s is the stress at the proportional limit (point A in Figure 18.13) and s/E is the strain. Average tensile properties for cast plutonium of 99.50 per cent purity, 19.50 g/cc

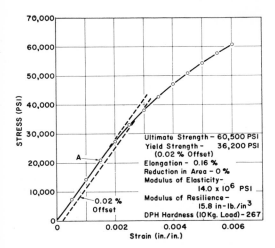

FIGURE 18.13. The stress-strain curve for a tensile test of alpha plutonium at 32°C. (*Courtesy Gardner, Bloomster, and Jefferes.*)[81, 82]

density, and diamond pyramid hardness (DPH) of 270 have been reported to be:[82] ultimate strength, 62,000 psi; yield strength, 37,000 psi; modulus of elasticity, 13.8 × 10⁶ psi; and modulus of resilience, 12.7 to 26.1 in.-lb/cu in. The tensile behavior of a typical specimen is shown in Figure 18.13. In this figure the proportional limit appears to be about 21,000 psi.

Schonfeld[172] found the proportional limit to be 25,000 psi. His determinations of yield strength were based on a 0.2 per cent offset and hence were of the same magnitude as his ultimate tensile strengths, from 45,000 to 55,000 psi. In some tests, in fact, failure occurred at less than 0.2 per cent extension. His results for yield strengths in compression were somewhat higher, ranging from 50,000 to 75,000 psi. He undertook to perform tensile tests at temperatures down to that of liquid nitrogen, but the results were inconclusive because of the extreme notch sensitivity of plutonium, which becomes very important at about −40°C (−40°F) and leads to failures outside the gage length of the test specimens.

Reduction of area and elongation values obtained by Schonfeld at room temperature were always less than 1.0 per cent and usually less than 0.5 per cent. At temperatures below 20°C (68°F) the values he obtained for both properties were substantially zero. For their tensile tests at room temperature, Gardner, Bloomster, and Jefferes[81, 82] have reported elongations at failure to be about 0.15 per cent.

The shear strength of alpha plutonium at room temperature, as calculated from results obtained in compression tests, is of the order of 80,000 psi. Tensile tests of threaded joints, however, gave values for the shear strength varying between 35,000 and 45,000 psi.[172]

In notched-bar tests of alpha plutonium at 22°C (72°F), Schonfeld, Tate, and Anderson[172] obtained impact strengths of 1.5 to 2.0 ft-lb (15-lb hammer at velocities of 11.3 to 16 fps). The test bars were Charpy type (keyhole notch), 10 by 10 by 50 mm, ASTM type B. The general mechanical behavior of plutonium suggests that its impact strength approaches zero at lower temperatures, but that there is some slight increase in the impact strength of the alpha phase at temperatures above 75°C (167°F).

Cramer and Schonfeld[56] have determined the hardness of unalloyed plutonium between −160 and +220°C (−256 and +428°F). Their data are presented in Figure 18.14. Points at and below room temperature were obtained with a Tukon microhardness tester using a 10-kg load, and elevated-temperature hardnesses were measured with a modified Rockwell tester using a ⅛-in. steel ball and a 30-kg load. All results have been converted to DPH numbers, which may be expressed as kg/sq mm[131] Gardner, Bloomster, and Jefferes[81, 82] found the hardnesses at room temperature of their alpha plutonium tensile specimens to vary from DPH

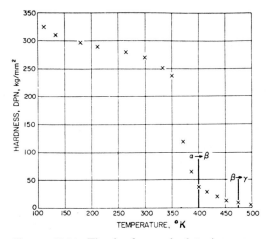

FIGURE 18.14. The hardness of plutonium as a function of temperature. (*Courtesy Cramer and Schonfeld and by permission of Interscience Publishers, Inc. from the Materials Volume of the "Reactor Handbook," 1960.*)

TABLE 18.14. ROOM-TEMPERATURE MICROHARDNESSES
OF STABILIZED ALLOTROPES OF PLUTONIUM*
(after Cramer)

Allotrope	Hardness [DPH number, kg/sq mm (25-g load)]
Alpha	295
Beta	100*
Gamma	110*
Delta	40–70*

* The hardnesses of the high-temperature phases depend, in part, on the presence of the alloying elements that stabilize them at room temperature.

250 to 283 (10-kg load), with the average value being about DPH 265.

By means of relatively small additions of appropriate alloying elements, three of the high-temperature modifications of plutonium can be stabilized at room temperature. Cramer[54] has measured the microhardnesses at room temperature of such stabilized phases, and his average results are given in Table 18.14, together with a typical microhardness value for the unalloyed alpha phase. It should be borne in mind that the hardnesses of the stabilized phases are influenced to some degree by the presence of the alloying elements.

CHEMICAL PROPERTIES

General

Plutonium exhibits four valence states: (III), (IV), (V), (VI). A few solid compounds exist, such as PuS, in which the plutonium oxidation state appears to be (II), but the bonding in these compounds is thought to be largely metallic. The multiplicity of valences arises from the closeness of some of the electron energy levels. Electrons are easily exchanged between the inner 5f shell and the valence shell. Because of the complexity of the electronic structures of plutonium and its neighbors, the position of plutonium in the periodic table is currently a matter of controversy. It is generally accepted, however, that plutonium is a member of a 5f series somewhat analogous to the 4f rare earth series, but the element with which to start the 5f series is in question.

The (III) and (IV) valence states of plutonium are the ones most commonly observed, both in solution and in solid compounds. For work with aqueous solutions, however, precautions must be taken to insure that only one valence state is present, as all four can coexist in equilibrium. The (V) valence state is relatively unstable, tending to disproportionate to (IV) and (VI). The (VI) state exists in strongly oxidizing aqueous solutions as plutonyl ion, PuO_2^{++}, and only a few solid compounds, such as PuF_6, have been prepared. Solid PuO_3, for example, has not been prepared, despite several attempts, and it is believed not to exist.

Metallic plutonium is readily dissolved in concentrated hydrochloric acid, hydriodic acid, or perchloric acid with the evolution of hydrogen and the formation of Pu^{+3} ion. Strong sulfuric or nitric acids do not react readily with the metal, and aqueous bases such as sodium hydroxide solutions do not react. Dilute acids will attack the metal, but an insoluble residue is left which is thought to consist of polymeric plutonium hydroxides or hydrous oxides. At elevated temperatures all of the common gases react with metallic plutonium: carbon monoxide forms carbides; carbon dioxide, carbides and oxides; ammonia and nitrogen, nitrides; the halogens and halogen acids, halides; and hydrogen forms hydrides. Water vapor in excess forms PuO_2, and in limited amounts forms a mixture of PuO_2 and plutonium hydride.

Plutonium forms stable compounds with all of the nonmetallic elements except the rare gases. Most of the simple inorganic compounds of plutonium are quite stable as compared with the analogous compounds of other metals. Thus, oxides of only a few other metals are suitable for use as refractories with molten plutonium, and the reduction of plutonium compounds to metal is achieved by only a limited number of strong reducing agents. Nearly all of the solid plutonium compounds can be converted to PuO_2 by ignition in air at 1000°C (1832°F).

A few selected compounds are described in Table 18.15. A more complete description of plutonium compounds is given by Cunningham[63] and by Katz and Seaborg,[105] and the intermetallic compounds have been reviewed by Ellinger.[24] (See Table 18.16 in the subsequent section on *Intermetallic Compounds*, page 366). Crystallographic and hardness data for a number of binary compounds of plutonium with nonmetallic and metalloid elements (as well as intermetallic phases) are given in Table 18.16. The thermodynamics and phase diagram of the pluto-

TABLE 18.15. CHARACTERISTICS OF SOME PLUTONIUM COMPOUNDS

Compound	Appearance	Crystal structure	Density (g/cc)	Melting point °C	Melting point °F
PuC	Silvery metallic, pyrophoric as powder	Cubic, NaCl type	13.99		
Pu_2C_3	Silvery metallic, pyrophoric	Cubic	12.70		
$PuCl_3$	Green	Hexagonal	5.70	760	1400
PuOCl	Green	Tetragonal	8.81		
PuF_3	—	Hexagonal	9.32	1425	2597
PuOF	Metallic	Tetragonal	9.76	>1635	>2975
PuH_2	Gray metallic flakes, pyrophoric	Cubic, CaF_2 type	—	Decomposition pressure = 1 atm at 870	1598
PuN	Brown, pyrophoric	Cubic, NaCl type	14.25		
Pu_2O_3	Black metallic, oxidizes in air	Hexagonal, La_2O_3 type	—	2250	4082
PuO_2	Green, powdery, stable to high temperature in air (well crystallized, is quite inert chemically)	Cubic, CaF_2 type	—	Estimated >2500 in air, decomposes in vacuum at 2250	4082
Pu_2S_3	Black	Two varieties exist, one is cubic, Ce_2S_3 type, the other has not been determined	—		
PuS	Golden-bronze	Cubic, NaCl type	10.60		

nium oxides have been discussed by Holley et al.[92]

Comprehensive discussions of the analytical chemistry of plutonium have been written by Metz[138] and by Metz and Waterbury.[140]

Electrochemistry

The formal oxidation potentials of the various plutonium species in $1M$ $HClO_4$ solution at 25°C (77°F) are:[52]

Plutonium ions are almost entirely uncomplexed in perchlorate solutions. The above differences in potentials therefore indicate the tendency of the different valence states of plutonium to form complexes. For example, with nitrate ions Pu^{+4} is more strongly coordinated than the other states. In the presence of sulfate ions, the tetravalent state is further stabilized owing to the even stronger complexing of Pu^{+4} with SO_4^{-2}.[14]

$$Pu^0 \xrightarrow{\ 2.02\ } Pu^{+3} \xrightarrow{\ -0.9819\ } Pu^{+4} \xrightarrow{\ -1.161\ } PuO_2^+ \xrightarrow{\ -0.925\ } PuO_2^{++}$$

$$-1.043$$

$$-1.022$$

and in $1M$ HNO_3 at 25–30°C (77–86°F) are:

$$Pu^0 \xrightarrow{\ 2.02\ } Pu^{+3} \xrightarrow{\ -0.92\ } Pu^{+4} \xrightarrow{\ -1.10\ } PuO_2^{++}$$

$$-1.04$$

Electrodeposition

Metallic plutonium cannot be deposited from aqueous solutions because the metal will reduce water to give a deposit of PuO_2 and evolve hydrogen at the cathode. Electrodeposition of plutonium from solutions of $PuCl_3$ in fused mixtures of barium chloride, potassium chloride, and sodium chloride at about 800°C (1472°F) has been successfully accomplished. This method was investigated as a possible preparation method for plutonium metal when plutonium first became available,[192] but it has not been used as a production method. Recently, Blumenthal[8] has been restudying this technique.

CORROSION

Although plutonium is a reactive metal, it is relatively inert in dry air and may be stored under this condition. Traces of moisture strongly accelerate the corrosion attack, however. In the presence of plutonium, commercial desiccants are effective only at relatively low temperatures (near room temperature and below) for removing and holding the moisture content of gases. As the temperature is increased to about 75°C (167°F), desiccants such as silica gel or alumina actually contribute water to plutonium and thus hasten its attack. In this connection, it is important to remember that the self-heating in plutonium which results from its natural radioactivity will raise the temperature of solid pieces weighing a few hundred grams from 28–56°C (50–100°F) above the ambient temperature.

The available information on the corrosion behavior of plutonium and several of its alloys at temperatures below 100°C (212°F) has been recently reviewed by Waber.[210] Drying the air with magnesium perchlorate reduces the corrosion rate about sixty-fivefold in the temperature range 55–75°C (131–167°F). The temperature dependence of attack is equivalent to an activation energy of approximately 17 kcal.

Alloying additions of zirconium have been found to lower the rate of attack by moist air but have little influence on the oxidation by dry air. An aluminum alloy containing 10 weight per cent plutonium withstood attack by pure oxygen during exposure for a week at 400°C (752°F). The Al_2O_3 formed was barely detectable, and the average depth of penetration was estimated to be not greater than 8 μ.[40]

The behavior of plutonium at temperatures in the vicinity of 400°C (752°F) has been investigated briefly by Dempsey and Kay,[66] and by Waber and Wright.[40] Specimens 0.020 in. thick were completely oxidized in a little more than 1 hr at 320°C (608°F), in 20 min at 343°C (649°F), and in about 6 min at 400°C (752°F).

TOXICITY AND HANDLING

The highly toxic nature of plutonium is a consequence of its radioactivity, and the permissible levels for intake of plutonium by the human body are the lowest of those for any of the radioactive elements. The extreme health hazard is occasioned by the tendency for plutonium, inhaled or ingested, to concentrate directly in the blood-forming sections of the bones where it may produce bone diseases even after many years. Plutonium may enter the body through cuts or abrasions of the skin, through inhalation, or through ingestion. Absorption from the lungs appears, however, to be the most important route of entry into the body.[114] From 1 to 10 per cent of the amount inhaled, depending on such factors as particle size and solubility, may be deposited in the bones. Once in the body, elimination is slow, the excretion rate being such that an individual may be expected to retain 80 per cent of his body burden 50 years after his original exposure.[114]

The maximum permissible body burden is that amount which can be maintained indefinitely in an adult without eventually producing significant body injury. This body burden for plutonium 239 is now set at 0.047 microcuries,[114] which is equivalent to 0.75 micrograms. The physiological effects of significant body burdens of plutonium 239 have been reviewed by Langham.[114]

Because of this potential hazard, the handling and processing of plutonium must be subjected to rigorous control. Usually, this is achieved by confining the plutonium to glove boxes or well-ventilated chemical fume hoods.[134,214] Experience has shown that the general contamination hazard can be minimized by paying prompt and careful attention to decontamination.

Schulte and Meyer[174] have discussed methods for controlling contamination that have been developed at the Los Alamos Scientific Laboratory. Jette and Coffinberry[101] have stated rules for handling plutonium in research and production operations that are prescribed by the Health Division at Los Alamos.

Among the various laboratories throughout the world where plutonium metallurgical research is done, somewhat different philosophies of dealing with its health hazard have been adopted. In contrast to the Los Alamos approach, in which full account is taken of the knowledge gained through wide experience with plutonium, at the Argonne National Laboratory and at the Hanford Atomic Products Operation in the United States, and at the Atomic Energy Research Establishment (Harwell) and the Atomic Weapons Research Establishment (Aldermaston) in Great Britain, a larger allowance is made for the factor of ignorance. This allowance consists of the complete containment at all times of all forms of plutonium in hermetically tight enclosures (glove boxes, etc.), in contrast to the Los Alamos philosophy of attaining maximum cleanliness with respect to contamination by means of maximum accessibility to the plutonium materials and equipment under conditions known to be completely safe. In other words, a cardinal principle of the Los Alamos practice is to minimize any and all accumulations of plutonium, whether inside or outside enclosures, and constantly to maintain all surfaces as free from contamination as possible through establishing the easiest possible accessibility to them. This practice permits, at times, the handling of massive pieces of clean metal or alloy in an open hood, or even entirely unenclosed in a well-ventilated room.

This difference in viewpoint has been discussed by Coffinberry and Waldron,[47] and experience with the Los Alamos procedures has been reported by Cramer and Schonfeld.[57] Details of the Argonne and Hanford practices are presented, respectively, by Kelman et al.[107] and by Wick and Thomas.[218] British procedures and facilities are described by Lord and Waldron.[125]

At Los Alamos the chemical operations involved in plutonium production, being amenable to a much greater degree of automation than are the metallurgical research activities, are performed in tight enclosures and are controlled remotely.[142] The Los Alamos facilities for the analytical chemistry of plutonium have been described by Metz.[139]

Since its significant radioactivity is normally limited to alpha emission (having a very short mean free path), radiation protection is ordinarily not required in handling plutonium. If, however, plutonium is exposed to larger amounts of radiation than are required for its production in a reactor, it may contain isotopic species that are strongly gamma active. Highly irradiated plutonium cannot, in general, be worked with in hot cells that are designed for handling irradiated uranium, because such cells are not sufficiently tight to prevent the escape of air-borne alpha contamination. Hence, for work with such materials as irradiated plutonium-containing fuel elements, special $\alpha\beta\gamma$ hot cells are required. The design and use of $\alpha\beta\gamma$ hot cells have been described by Lilienthal;[123] Peterson, Thomas, and Green;[154] and Goertz[86] in the United States; and by Brown and Hyam[11] and other authorities[215] in the United Kingdom. Roesch[162] has discussed protection against the moderate intensities of x rays and gamma rays emitted by plutonium that has been subjected to intermediate amounts of neutron irradiation, sufficient to increase appreciably its content of higher plutonium isotopes but not enough to produce significant quantities of fission products. Alloys, compounds, or solutions containing both plutonium and a light element, such as beryllium,[199] may by (α,n) reaction produce neutron emission of sufficient intensity to constitute a health hazard to personnel handling them.

A final but by no means unimportant consideration in the safe handling of plutonium is its nuclear criticality hazard. This hazard is a consequence of the increase in rate of neutron multiplication that occurs when the mass of a plutonium assembly is increased, or when neutron-moderating or neutron-reflecting materials are brought into close proximity to it. The avoidance of this hazard is necessarily a responsibility of nuclear physicists, who are required to prescribe rules for the proper spatial distribution of plutonium-containing materials in storage and handling. Schwennesen[175] and Ketzlach[108] have discussed the design basis for achieving nuclear safety in processing plants for the extraction of plutonium from irradiated uranium, and Ford and Walford[77] have described critical assembly experiments performed at Dounreay for the purpose of defining safe design and operating conditions within a fissile material processing plant. It is apparent that the critical mass consideration limits the size and may determine the shape of any one piece of plutonium that can be handled in alloying and fabrication operations.

ALLOYS

Phase Diagrams

Much of the work that has been done in delineating the phase diagrams of plutonium alloys is adequate for tentative conclusions only, and all diagrams should be considered to be subject to change and refinement as additional experimental data are determined. The following is a listing of some of the binary plutonium alloy systems for which data have been published and for which phase diagrams, or portions thereof, have been constructed.

Aluminum	Mercury
Beryllium	Molybdenum
Bismuth	Nickel
Calcium	Columbium
Cerium	Osmium
Chromium	Oxygen
Cobalt	Ruthenium
Copper	Tantalum
Hydrogen	Thorium
Iron	Tungsten
Lead	Uranium
Lithium	Vanadium
Magnesium	Zinc
Manganese	Zirconium

Representative diagrams for some of these binary systems are shown in an appendix to this chapter.

Information concerning alloys of plutonium with arsenic, barium, carbon, germanium, gold, hafnium, indium, neodymium, neptunium, potassium, praseodymium, rhenium, silicon, sodium, strontium, thallium, tin, and titanium has been reported by Schonfeld et al.,[37,173] Waldron et al.,[41,212] and Bochvar et al.,[9] but the data are too meager to allow construction of even partial phase diagrams.

The diagrams listed above have been reported by these same authors and also in part by Konobeevsky;[112] Wensch and Whyte (plu-

tonium-nickel);[216] Mulford and Sturdy (plutonium-hydrogen);[145] Mardon et al., (plutonium-iron);[135] Poole, Williamson, and Marples (plutonium-thorium);[156] Ellinger, Elliott, and Cramer (plutonium-uranium);[69] Ellinger, Land, and Cramer[70] (plutonium-cerium); Cramer, Ellinger and Land[55] (plutonium-zinc); and Rhinehammer, Etter and Jones[161a] (plutonium-copper). Phase-equilibrium relationships in the delta-prime region of a number of binary alloy systems have been determined by Elliott and Larson.[25]

Alloying Behavior

Although the alloying behavior of plutonium bears some resemblance to the alloying characteristics of both uranium and the rare earth elements, in many respects it is markedly different from both. It might be said to occupy a position intermediate between these two, but if so, the further observation should be made that the similarity of plutonium alloys to those of the rare earth metals appears to be greater than their resemblance to the alloys of uranium. Waber[209] has discussed the theoretical implications of the alloying behavior of plutonium. This behavior may be conveniently summarized by means of a few general statements regarding the reactions of plutonium with the various families of other metals in the periodic table.[9]

The alloying behavior of plutonium with respect to the A subgroups of the periodic table will be considered first. Although only its reactions with lithium, sodium and potassium have been investigated experimentally, plutonium appears to be completely immiscible with all of the alkali metals in both the liquid and the solid states. The same statement can be made with regard to calcium, strontium and barium among the alkaline earths, but plutonium is soluble to the extent of about 15 atomic per cent in liquid magnesium, and if (like uranium) it forms a liquid miscibility gap with beryllium, this gap is a very narrow one lying on the high beryllium side of the compound $PuBe_{13}$. Plutonium forms two compounds with magnesium by solid-state reaction[37,173] (See Table 18.16).

Among the group IIIA earth metals, plutonium has been found to have a large liquid miscibility gap with lanthanum, and by analogy with uranium is suspected of reacting in a similar manner with scandium and yttrium. It has, however, been found to be completely miscible in the liquid state with all of the rare earth (f-transition) metals that have been studied (cerium, praseodymium, neodymium), and it appears also to have complete liquid miscibility with all of the actinide metals that have been investigated (thorium, uranium, neptunium). In fact, as far as is now known, plutonium is completely miscible in the liquid state with all metals other than the exceptions noted above and one more, silver, discussed below.

Plutonium has been found to form rather extensive solid solutions (especially delta-phase plutonium) with the rare earth metals, but it appears to form no compounds with them. Among the actinides, however, it is known to form one compound with thorium and two intermediate solid solutions of wide homogeneity range with uranium.[69] (See Table 18.16.) Epsilon plutonium has complete solid solubility with gamma uranium and with gamma neptunium.[212] Except for neptunium, additions of either lanthanide or actinide metals have not been found to lower the melting temperature of plutonium more than about 30°C (54°F).

The d-transition metals of groups IVA, VA, and VIA form only two known compounds with plutonium and cause very little or no eutectic lowering of its melting temperature. Both of the compounds are products of solid-state reaction in the plutonium-zirconium system (Table 18.16). In common with the rare earths and metals of groups IIB and IIIB, the group IVA metals (titanium, zirconium, and hafnium) are extensively soluble in delta plutonium, and the solubilities of titanium and hafnium in the epsilon phase are of the order of 30 atomic per cent.[212] Beta zirconium forms a continuous series of solid solutions with epsilon plutonium.

In the binary systems of plutonium with d-transition elements of groups VA, VIA, VIIA, and VIIIA, all solid solubilities are quite restricted. As has been noted by Konobeevsky,[9,112] there exists among these systems a trend toward an increasing number of compounds with increasing number of d electrons in the d-transition metal. Thus vanadium, columbium, tantalum, chromium, molybdenum, and tungsten form no compounds with plutonium;

manganese and rhenium each form one compound; iron, ruthenium, and osmium form two, five, and four compounds, respectively; and cobalt and nickel each form six compounds. Another fairly systematic trend that seems to prevail among these binary systems is that a decreasingly lower eutectic temperature near the plutonium end of the phase diagram accompanies an increase in the number of d electrons, except that the lowest of all the known eutectic temperatures occurs in the plutonium-cobalt instead of the plutonium-nickel system. Thus, as mentioned above, the groups VA and VIA metals cause little or no eutectic lowering of the melting temperature of plutonium; manganese, ruthenium, and osmium form eutectics at temperatures from 115–145°C (207–261°F) lower than the 640°C (1184°F) melting temperature of plutonium; and iron, cobalt, and nickel form eutectics at temperatures from 175–232°C (315–418°F) lower than 640°C (1184°F).

In the plutonium-iron and plutonium-cobalt systems there is a striking occurrence of the phenomenon of retrograde melting.[25,135] Thus, a 2 atomic per cent iron alloy that is entirely solid epsilon phase at 440°C (824°F) becomes about one-fifth liquid (i.e., liquid plus approximately 80 volume per cent delta phase) on cooling to 420°C (788°F); at 400°C (752°F) it is again entirely solid (delta plus Pu_6Fe). A similar situation exists in the plutonium-cobalt system, except that temperatures are slightly lower and the phases formed on resolidification are delta and Pu_3Co (instead of delta and Pu_6Co).[25]

The tendency toward a eutectiferous form of phase diagram persists, but in much reduced degree, in the binary systems of plutonium with the group IB metals. Thus, a plutonium-rich eutectic with copper melts at 625°C (1157°F),[9] and a plutonium-gold eutectic has a composition and melting temperature close to those of pure plutonium. As mentioned above, however, silver forms immiscible liquids with plutonium. A preliminary investigation of the plutonium-silver system has indicated that the solubility of silver in liquid plutonium is negligible, but that the maximum solubility of plutonium in liquid silver is of the order of 35 atomic per cent. Silver appears to form one or more compounds with plutonium, as do copper and gold (Table 18.16).

TABLE 18.16. CRYSTAL STRUCTURE AND MICROHARDNESS DATA FOR SOME BINARY COMPOUNDS OF PLUTONIUM (after Ellinger[24] and Cramer)[54]

Compound	Structure type	Crystal lattice	Unit-cell dimensions Å	Formula units in unit cell	Space group	Calculated density (g/cc)	Hardness [DPH number (kg/sq mm)]
$PuAg_3$	—	Hexagonal	a = 12.730, c = 9.402 (Runnalls)[163]	16	P6	11.33	180
Pu_3Al	Partially ordered $SrPb_3$	Tetragonal	a = 4.499, c = 4.538	1	P4/mmm	13.45	125
$PuAl$	—	Cubic	a = 10.76 (Bochvar et al.)[9]	—	—	—	340
$PuAl_2$	Cu_2Mg	Face-centered cubic	7.838	8	Fd3m	8.06	550
$PuAl_3$	$PuAl_3$	Hexagonal	a = 6.10, c = 14.47 (Larson et al.)[115]	6	$P6_3/mmc$	6.67	495
$PuAl_4$	UAl_4	Body-centered orthorhombic	a = 4.42, b = 6.26, c = 13.66 (Runnalls)[163]	4	Imma	6.02	400
$PuAs$	NaCl	Face-centered cubic	5.855 (Gorum)[88]	4	Fm3m	10.39	155
$PuAu$	—	—	—	—	—	—	190
$PuBe_{13}$	$NaZn_{13}$	Face-centered cubic	10.28	8	Fm3c	4.35	565
$PuBi$	NaCl	Face-centered cubic	6.35	4	Fm3m	11.62	120
$PuBi_2$	—	—	—	—	—	—	
PuC	NaCl	Face-centered cubic	4.97	4	Fm3m	13.6	600
Pu_2C_3	Pu_2C_3	Body-centered cubic	8.129 (Zachariasen)[219]	8	Ī43d	12.70	805
Pu_6Co	U_6Mn	Body-centered tetragonal	a = 10.46, b = 5.33	4	I4/mcm	17.00	165

Compound	Structure type	Crystal system	Lattice parameters	No.	Space group	Density	Temp.
Pu_3Co	—	Orthorhombic	a = 3.470 b = 10.939 c = 9.196 (Elliott and Larson)[72]	4	Cmcm	14.76	170
Pu_2Co	Fe_2P	Hexagonal	Pu-rich: a = 7.902 c = 3.549 Co-rich: a = 7.763 c = 3.648	3	P321	14.0	245
$PuCo_2$	Cu_2Mg	Face-centered cubic	7.081	8	Fd3m	13.35	625
$PuCo_3$	$PuNi_3$	Rhombohedral	—	3	R3m	—	420
Pu_2Co_{17}	Th_2Ni_{17}	Hexagonal	a = 8.325 c = 8.104	2	$P6_3/mmc$	10.10	620
$PuCu_2$	—	—	—	—	—	—	250
Pu_6Fe	U_6Mn	Body-centered tetragonal	a = 10.404 c = 5.355	4	I4/mcm	17.07	200
$PuFe_2$	Cu_2Mg	Face-centered cubic	7.191	8	Fd3m	12.53	560
$\alpha - Pu_3Ga$ (low temperature)	Partially ordered $SrPb_3$	Tetragonal	a = 4.471 c = 4.530	1	P4/mmm	14.42	150
$\beta - Pu_3Ga$ (high temperature)	Partially ordered $AuCu_3$	Simple cubic	4.505	1	Pm3m	14.29	
Pu_5Ga_3	—	—	—	—	—	—	325
$PuGa$	—	—	—	—	—	—	265
$PuGa_2$	AlB_2	Hexagonal	a = 4.246 c = 4.119	1	P6/mmm	9.77	370
$PuGa_3$	Ni_3Sn	Hexagonal	a = 6.30 c = 4.54	2	$P6_3/mmc$	9.48	
Pu_3Ge	—	—	—	—	—	—	360

TABLE 18.16. CRYSTAL STRUCTURE AND MICROHARDNESS DATA FOR SOME BINARY COMPOUNDS OF PLUTONIUM
(after Ellinger[24] and Cramer)[54] (cont.)

Compound	Structure type	Crystal lattice	Unit-cell dimensions Å	Formula units in unit cell	Space group	Calculated density (g/cc)	Hardness [DPH number (kg/sq mm)]
Pu_2Ge_3	Pseudo AlB_2	Hexagonal	Pseudo unit: a = 3.975, c = 4.198	½	P6/mmm	10.06	405
$PuGe_2$	$ThSi_2$	Body-centered tetragonal	a = 4.102, c = 13.81	4	I4/amd	10.98	450
$PuGe_3$	$AuCu_3$	Simple cubic	4.223	1	Pm3m	10.07	335
$PuH_{2.0}$ to $PuH_{2.7}$	CaF_2	Face-centered cubic	$PuH_{2.0}$: 5.359, $PuH_{2.5}$: 5.34	4	Fm3m	10.40	145
PuH_3	PuH_3	Hexagonal	a = 3.78, c = 6.76	2	$P6_3$/mmc	9.61	
$PuHg_3$	UHg_3 (?)	Hexagonal					
$PuHg_4$	UHg_4	Pseudo body-centered cubic	3.61	2	in pseudo unit		
Pu_3In	$AuCu_3$	Simple cubic	4.703	1	Pm3m	13.3	185
$PuIn_3$	Partially ordered $AuCu_3$	Simple cubic	4.607 (Bochvar et al.)[9]	1	Pm3m	9.9	
$PuMg_2$	CaF_2	Face-centered cubic	7.34	4	Fm3m	4.83	
$PuMg_x$ where x is approximately 2	—	Hexagonal	a = 13.8, c = 9.7				
$PuMn_2$	Cu_2Mg	Face-centered cubic	7.29	8	Fd3m	11.95	470
PuN	NaCl	Face-centered cubic	4.908	4	Fm3m	14.22	580
$PuNi$	TlI	Orthorhombic	a = 3.59, b = 10.21, c = 4.22 (Cromer and Roof)[61]	4	Cmcm	12.9	250

Compound	Structure type	Crystal system	Lattice constants (Å)	Atoms/cell	Space group	Density	
$PuNi_2$	Cu_2Mg	Face-centered cubic	Pu-rich: 7.141 Ni-rich: 7.115	8	Fd3m	13.1	580
$PuNi_3$	$PuNi_3$	Rhombohedral	a = 6.22 $\alpha = 47.4°$ (Cromer and Olsen)[60]	3	R3̄m	11.8	485
$PuNi_4$	$PuNi_4$	Monoclinic	a = 4.87 b = 8.46 c = 10.27 $\beta = 100.0°$ (Cromer and Larson)[59]	—	C2/m	11.3	225
$PuNi_5$	$CaZn_5$	Hexagonal	Pu-rich: a = 4.872 b = 3.980 Ni-rich: a = 4.861 c = 3.982	1	P6/mmm	10.8	525
Pu_2Ni_{17}	Th_2Ni_{17}	Hexagonal	a = 8.29 c = 8.01	2	$P6_3/mmc$	10.3	500
PuO	NaCl	Face-centered cubic	4.96	4	Fm3m	13.9	
Pu_2O_3	La_2O_3	Hexagonal	a = 3.841 c = 5.958	1	P3̄m1	11.47	235
Pu_2O_3 to Pu_4O_7	Mn_2O_3	Body-centered cubic	Pu_2O_3: 11.04	16	Ia3	10.2	1020
PuO_2	CaF_2	Face-centered cubic	5.396	4	Fm3m	11.46	105
$PuOs_2$	$MgZn_2$	Hexagonal	a = 5.34 c = 8.68 (Konobeevsky)[112]	4	$P6_3/mmc$	19.2	
PuP	NaCl	Face-centered cubic	5.664 (Gorum)[88]	4	Fm3m	9.87	235
$PuPb_3$	Probably ordered $AuCu_3$	Simple cubic	4.808	1	Pm3m	12.86	235

TABLE 18.16. CRYSTAL STRUCTURE AND MICROHARDNESS DATA FOR SOME BINARY COMPOUNDS OF PLUTONIUM (after Ellinger[24] and Cramer[54] (cont.)

Compound	Structure type	Crystal lattice	Unit-cell dimensions Å	Formula units in unit cell	Space group	Calculated density (g/cc)	Hardness [DPH number (kg/sq mm)]
$PuRe_2$	$MgZn_2$	Hexagonal	a = 5.396, c = 8.729	4	$P6_3/mmc$	18.45	
$Pu_{19}Ru$	—	—	—	—	—	—	160
Pu_3Ru	—	—	—	—	—	—	200
Pu_5Ru_3	—	—	—	—	—	—	250
$PuRu$	CsCl	Simple cubic	3.363	1	$Pm3m$	14.87	210
$PuRu_2$	Cu_2Mg	Face-centered cubic	7.476	8	$Fd3m$	14.06	390
PuS	NaCl	Face-centered cubic	5.536 (Zachariasen)[220]	4	$Fm3m$	10.60	
Pu_2S_3 to Pu_3S_4	Th_3P_4	Body-centered cubic	8.454 (Zachariasen)[221]	10⅔ Pu atoms, 16 S atoms	$I\bar{4}3d$	8.41	
$PuSi$	FeB	Orthorhombic	a = 5.727, b = 7.933, c = 3.847	4	$Pbmm$	10.15	500
Pu_2Si_3	Pseudo AlB_2	Hexagonal	Pseudo unit: a = 3.876, c = 4.090	½	$P6/mmm$	8.77	
$PuSi_2$	$ThSi_2$	Body-centered tetragonal	a = 3.967, c = 13.72	4	$I4_1/amd$	9.08	
$PuSn_3$	$AuCu_3$	Simple cubic	4.630	1	$Pm3m$	9.96	
$PuTe$	NaCl	Face-centered cubic	6.183 (Gorum)[88]	4	$Fm3m$	10.33	
Pu_2Th	—	Orthorhombic (?)	a = 9.820, b = 8.164, c = 6.681 (Poole et al.)[156]	6 (?)	—	—	180

Pu$_3$Tl	AuCu$_3$	Simple cubic	4.723 (Bochvar et al.)[9]	1	Pm3m	14.5	
PuTl$_3$	Disordered Mg	Hexagonal	a = 3.458 c = 5.519 (Bochvar et al.)[9]	½	P6$_3$/mmc	12.4	
Eta Pu-U 2–70% uranium	—	Simple tetragonal	Pu$_3$U: a = 10.57 c = 10.76	52 atoms	—	17.2	
Zeta Pu-U 25–75% uranium	—	Simple cubic (may be simple tetragonal)	PuU: 10.664	58 atoms	—	18.95	25% U: 200 65% U: 450
PuZn$_2$	Cu$_2$Mg	Face-centered cubic	Pu-rich: 7.760 Zn-rich: 7.747	8	Fd3m	10.54	390
Pu$_2$Zn$_9$	—	—	—	—	—	—	410
PuZn$_8$	—	—	—	—	—	—	385
Pu$_2$Zn$_{17}$	U$_2$Zn$_{17}$	Hexagonal	—	—	—	—	350
Pu$_6$Zr	—	Orthorhombic	a = 10.39 b = 10.44 c = 11.18 (Bochvar et al.)[9]	8	—	16.7	
PuZr$_2$	UZr$_2$	Hexagonal	a = 5.055 c = 3.123 (Waldron et al.)[212]	1	P$\bar{6}$m2	10.13	

As far as is now known, plutonium forms compounds with all of the B-subgroup metals and metalloids. Another generalization that can be made is that most of these compounds have melting temperatures appreciably higher than the melting temperatures of the components in their respective binary systems. Hence, liquidus curves tend to rise sharply near the extremities of the phase diagrams, with little or no eutectic lowering of the melting temperatures of the end members. These characteristics appear to be common to the alloying behaviors of all the lanthanide and actinide metals.

Except for the solid solutions in delta and epsilon plutonium of groups IIB and IIIB metals (including aluminum), solid solubilities are quite restricted among the phases occurring in the binary alloys of plutonium with B-subgroup elements. Solid solubilities to the extent of several atomic per cent in both the epsilon and delta phases have, however, been experimentally established for zinc, aluminum, and most of the elements of the IIIB group.[9] Most of the delta solid solutions (including those of the rare earth and group IVA metals) are either stable at room temperature or can be retained to room temperature by rapid cooling from their high-temperature stability ranges. It has not been found possible, however, to retain any of the epsilon solid solutions to room temperature. The stability relations of a number of delta solid solutions (and their transformation behaviors) under high pressure have been investigated by Elliott and Gschneidner.[71]

The occurrence of significant solid solubility in the alpha, beta, gamma, and delta-prime phases of plutonium is much rarer than its incidence in the delta and epsilon allotropes. Only neptunium has been reported to have detectable solubility in alpha plutonium,[212] and the experimental evidence relating to possible solid solubility in the beta and gamma phases has been difficult to interpret. In many cases of the retention of the beta or gamma phases to room temperature, it has not been clear whether the retained phase represented equilibrium conditions at a higher temperature or a supersaturated solid solution resulting from a martensitic transformation of the delta solid solution. Such retained phases have been observed in alloys of plutonium with aluminum, magnesium, thorium, uranium, titanium, and zirconium. Only titanium is known to be soluble in delta-prime plutonium to an extent greater than about 1.5 atomic per cent.[25]

Intermetallic Compounds

In common with the lanthanide and other actinide metals, plutonium forms no intermetallic compounds of the Hume-Rothery types. Also like the other f-transition metals, it does form a considerable number of Friauf-Laves (MX_2) phases, especially of the cubic $MgCu_2$ type. In many of the binary phase diagrams of plutonium a PuX_2 compound is the most stable of a series of intermediate phases in the sense that it has the highest melting temperature and therefore melts congruently with an open maximum, whereas the other intermediate phases undergo peritectic decomposition on heating.

Plutonium also forms a number of $CaZn_5$-type structures with other metals. Cromer and associates,[59,60,61,115] who have performed almost the only structure investigations of plutonium compounds by x-ray single-crystal methods, have found that many of the structures of phases having compositions intermediate between PuX_2 and PuX_5 (e.g., $PuNi_4$) are composed of units of both of these structures stacked in an alternating sequence. They have also found the structures of analogous cerium compounds to have essentially the same character.[58,60]

By far the greatest number of structure determinations of the intermetallic compounds of plutonium has been made by Ellinger, who has employed the powder method of x-ray diffraction in this work. Crystal structure data for these and other binary compounds of plutonium have been reported by Ellinger,[24] Coffinberry and Ellinger,[20] Coffinberry and Waldron,[50] Runnalls and Boucher,[163,165] and Bochvar et al.[9] In Table 18.16 are tabulated selected crystal structure data for these compounds, together with microhardness values measured by Cramer.[54] Except where indicated otherwise, the unit-cell dimensions given in Table 18.16 are values determined by Ellinger.[24]

Reactor Applications

Interest in the alloys of plutonium stems primarily from their potentialities for use as fuels in nuclear reactors. Such fuels may be either of two types, liquid or solid. The concept of a liquid plutonium alloy fuel was suggested as early as 1946, and the first alloy studies of plutonium included attempts to find moderately dilute liquid alloys of plutonium having low melting temperatures, i.e., solutions of plutonium in low-melting metals that were not so dilute as to require too large a mass of the alloy to be used in order to attain supercritical neutron multiplication in a reactor.[22] Because, however (as indicated above), plutonium forms high-melting compounds with most other metals, and especially with the low-melting B-subgroup metals (such as mercury, gallium, tin, lead, etc.), its solubility in most of these metals at low temperatures is very limited, and it has been found that only magnesium and bismuth offer promise of dissolving adequate amounts of plutonium at reasonably low temperatures.[22,80] Liquid magnesium will dissolve 15 atomic per cent plutonium at a eutectic temperature of 552°C (1026°F), and the maximum solubility of plutonium in liquid bismuth at 700°C (1292°F) is almost 8 atomic per cent—more than twice that of uranium at the same temperature. The fuel possibilities of the plutonium-magnesium alloys have received little attention, but interest in plutonium dissolved in liquid bismuth has been indicated by Gurinsky,[28] Miles et al.,[141] and Frost et al.[80]

The existence of the low-melting eutectics of plutonium with iron, cobalt, and nickel has led to consideration of these compositions as liquid fuels for the LAMPRE reactor concept at Los Alamos.[31,45,84,90,109] Because these binary eutectic alloys contain more plutonium than is desired for most reactor applications, however, a third component, to act as a diluent without appreciably increasing melting temperatures, has been sought and found in cerium. Hence phase diagram studies of the ternary alloys of plutonium and cerium with cobalt, nickel, or copper[18,19] are being undertaken at Los Alamos and at the Mound Laboratory (of the Monsanto Chemical Company) at Miamisburg, Ohio. Also, a limited investigation of the plutonium-cerium-cobalt system has been made at Harwell.[213]

It was found, in preliminary research on the ternary systems of a fluxing metal (iron, cobalt, nickel, or copper) with plutonium and cerium, that the plutonium-cerium-copper alloys may be adequately low melting if their plutonium content is not too high,[18,45] but that the plutonium-cerium-iron alloys are sufficiently low melting only if their plutonium content is higher than that desired for most reactor uses. For these reasons the plutonium-cerium-copper alloys are being studied, but the plutonium-cerium-iron system has been dropped from consideration.

For reasons discussed below, some reactor designers have been interested in ternary liquid fuel alloys containing uranium (instead of cerium) as the diluent, together with plutonium and a fluxing metal. A number of ternary alloys of plutonium, uranium, and a third metal that have been investigated have been found, however, to be too high melting to be satisfactorily held in the liquid state in any suitable container material,[44] and for this reason the ternary alloys with uranium are not being investigated further.

It has been quite generally assumed that, compared to solid fuels, liquid fuels should be much less subject to radiation damage and should make possible easier methods of fission product removal. It has not yet been demonstrated experimentally, however, that liquid fuel alloys are entirely free from all types of deleterious effects that might be caused by radiation.

With respect to plutonium content, alloys that have been used, or considered for use, as solid reactor fuels are primarily of two general types—(1) very dilute and (2) moderately concentrated. Except for several critical assemblies and experimental reactors of low power,[4,85,104,121,197] the only plutonium alloys that have actually been employed as solid fuel in operative nuclear reactors are aluminum-plutonium alloys.[1,39,42,78,124,164,167,197,217] Alloys of this type, which usually contain of the order of 2 to 20 weight per cent (0.2 to 2.8 atomic per cent) plutonium, belong to the class of very dilute fuel alloys. They are suitable for use in thermal reactors, but are unsatisfactory for fast reactors because of the requirement of a very large critical mass that is imposed by their low plutonium content. In these alloys the plutonium is present as the compound $PuAl_4$ dispersed throughout a matrix of substantially pure aluminum, which affords them the important property of good thermal conductivity.[84,90] Such alloys have demonstrated excellent performance with respect to withstanding the effects of irradiation, as much as 60 per cent burn-up of the plutonium atoms having been attained with only minor increases in hardness and volume (swelling).[164]

Other very dilute alloys that may be expected to have properties similar to those of aluminum-plutonium are copper-plutonium (Pu_2Cu_{11} in a copper matrix) and iron-plutonium ($PuFe_2$ in an iron matrix). The potentialities of these alloys have been discussed by Tate.[197] Still other dilute alloys that have been considered for use as fuel consist of solid solutions of plutonium in such phases as alpha uranium, alpha thorium, alpha zirconium and gamma (cubic, room temperature) cerium.[17] Since these phases are, however, capable of dissolving 10 or more atomic per cent of plutonium, they are more properly discussed below, in the category of moderately concentrated solid fuel alloys.

By "moderately concentrated" is meant alloys containing of the order of 5 to 50 atomic per cent plutonium. Compositions near the lower end of this range can be obtained as single-phase alloys by virtue of the solid solubilities mentioned in the preceding paragraph. Two of these solid-solution types have been tested for irradiation stability, with the following results: (1) an alloy containing 15 weight per cent plutonium in alpha thorium (cubic) has manifested rather good performance in an irradiation test,[34,211] but (2) solid-solution alloys of plutonium in alpha uranium (orthorhombic) have uniformly shown poor resistance to irradiation damage.[34,110,211] In general, concentrations of plutonium higher than about 10 to 12 atomic per cent introduce undesirable intermediate phases into the binary alloys of plutonium, but an alloy containing 40 atomic per cent plutonium in zirconium has been found to be single-phase retained delta plutonium (cubic) at room temperature.[211] A test of this alloy showed it to have remarkably good irradiation stability.[34,211]

Because neutron irradiation of uranium 238 results in the formation of plutonium 239 (see "pile reactions," page 337), "breeding" of new plutonium 239 can be accomplished by introducing uranium 238 into the neutron flux of a plutonium-fueled reactor. If the uranium is added to the fuel alloy containing the plutonium, the rate of reactivity loss by this alloy is decreased by virtue of the breeding of new

plutonium to replace a part of that which is burned. For this reason, the concept of a uranium-plutonium fuel alloy has been attractive to many designers of power reactors, and the composition range of greatest interest is from 20 to 40 atomic per cent plutonium. Such alloys, however, consist either entirely or in major part of the zeta phase of the plutonium-uranium system, which has been shown to possess such undesirable metallurgical properties as high brittleness, low strength, pyrophoricity, poor corrosion resistance, and poor irradiation stability.[16,30,69,106] Although means of avoiding these adverse features other than further alloying appear to exist,[16,30] the development of ternary alloys containing uranium, plutonium, and a third element has been extensively undertaken with the objective of suppressing the formation of the zeta phase.[30,106,212] This objective has been attained most successfully by additions of molybdenum to the uranium and plutonium, although other elements (e.g., ruthenium)[30,106] are believed to be effective in aiding molybdenum to suppress the zeta phase by increasing the thermodynamic stability of the gamma-uranium/epsilon-plutonium (body-centered cubic) solid solutions.[197] A partial account of phase equilibrium relationships in the uranium-plutonium-molybdenum system has been given by Waldron *et al.*[212]

The uranium-plutonium-molybdenum alloys have manifested fairly good irradiation stability in tests carried to moderately high burn-up.[34,110,211] It is believed that the isotropic crystal structure of the body-centered cubic phase (as distinguished from anisotropic alpha uranium, e.g.) is an important factor contributing to the superior resistance to radiation damage demonstrated by this and other cubic phases. Because molybdenum is a major product of the fissioning of plutonium 239, metallurgists at the Argonne National Laboratory have conceived the idea of stabilizing the gamma-uranium/epsilon-plutonium phase by means of a so-called uranium-plutonium-fissium alloy, the "fissium" being a mixture of fission products among which molybdenum, ruthenium, and other stabilizing elements are prominently represented. Such an alloy possesses certain advantages with respect to reactor operation and fuel reprocessing.[26,38,76] Moreover, alloys of this type appear to have somewhat better irradiation stability than do the uranium-pluto-

TABLE 18.17. COMPOSITION OF A TYPICAL
URANIUM-PLUTONIUM-FISSIUM ALLOY
(after Kelman and Dunworth)

Element	Weight per cent	Atomic per cent
Ruthenium	4.3	8.79
Molybdenum	2.8	6.07
Palladium	2.5	4.86
Rhodium	0.7	1.41
Zirconium	0.5	1.14
Fissium	10.8	22.27
Plutonium	20.0	17.37
Uranium	69.2	60.36

nium-molybdenum compositions.[30,106,110] The composition of a typical uranium-plutonium-fissium alloy is given in Table 18.17.

METALLOGRAPHY

Specimen Preparation

Cramer and Schonfeld[57] have given a detailed description of the methods used in plutonium metallography. Basically, the metallography of plutonium and its alloys is similar to that of the more common metals. The high toxicity of plutonium makes it necessary, however, to adopt elaborate procedures to prevent physical contact between the operator and specimen. Hence, considerable attention must be given to the problems of ventilating, enclosing, and storing. In some laboratories, all metallographic preparations and examinations of plutonium and its alloys are performed with the metal enclosed in hermetically sealed glove boxes containing a highly purified, inert atmosphere; in others, relatively simple glove boxes enclose only those operations that are likely to produce finely divided material, and well-ventilated hoods are used for the cleaner operations of mounting, electropolishing, and electroetching.

During preparation for metallographic examination, specimens are carried through the steps of rough grinding, fine grinding, and mechanical polishing. Electropolishing and electroetching are ordinarily used to prepare plutonium or plutonium-rich samples for microscopic examination, and excellent results for some phases or alloys that are not particularly amenable to electroetching have been obtained recently through the use of cathodic etching.[97]

For many plutonium-lean alloys, ordinary chemical etching is adequate.

One procedure that yields satisfactory results for pure plutonium and most plutonium-rich alloys is the following: The specimen is rough-ground through four metallographic papers, 320- and 600-grit silicon carbide papers, and 3/0 and 4/0 emery papers; it is then rough-polished on billiard cloth charged with 600-grit alumina, or on "Microcloth" charged with 15-μ diamond powder. Fine polishing is done with "Microcloth" charged with either gamma-alumina or 1-μ diamond. Polishers are operated at 125 or 250 rpm, and carbon tetrachloride is used as a lubricant and to rinse abrasive from the specimen. The specimen is then electroetched. If alpha, beta, or mixed allotropes are to be examined, the electrolyte may contain 7 parts of tetraphosphoric acid, 36 parts of water, and 57 parts of 2-ethoxyethanol. This electrolyte is used at room temperature with a potential of 5 to 12 volts. A similar electrolyte, but in the proportions of 12:33:55, works well for the delta allotrope, and, in the proportions of 2:3:5 at 12 volts, it is suitable for prolonged etching of the softer allotropes in order to remove the effect of cold work. If the potential is increased to 16 volts for 3 min, an anodized surface is produced that is optically active in polarized light. In general, etching times are quite short—10 to 45 sec except when special effects, such as anodizing or removal of cold work, are desired. Plutonium is relatively passive to water after electroetching, and may be rinsed in distilled water and blown dry with warm air.

Mounting

Because alpha plutonium transforms to the beta phase at 122°C (252°F), the ordinary mounting media that require curing in the temperature range 120–150°C (248–302°F) are not satisfactory for use with pure plutonium or many plutonium-rich alloys. Instead, mounting resins which polymerize at room temperature or slightly higher are used.

Autoradiography

Autoradiomicrographs have been found useful in determining the distribution of plutonium-rich phases in alloys and in distinguishing

intermediate phases according to their plutonium contents. A suitable emulsion has been
found on "Kodak" spectrographic plates, Type
VO. During exposure it is necessary that the
specimen be in contact with the emulsion, which
unavoidably becomes contaminated. Hence the
plates must be developed with regard for a
considerable quantity of alpha-active material
that may be adhering to their surfaces. After
a plate is processed, the image may readily
be projected at a known magnification to produce a positive image on orthochromatic film,
and the contaminated plate may be destroyed.
Contact prints made from the positive film
yield true reproduction of the radiomicrograph
at reasonable magnifications.

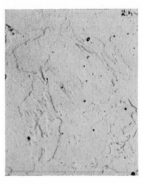

FIGURE 18.15c. Zone-refined alpha plutonium, etched
by cathodic bombardment, bright-field illumination, 250X. (*Photomicrograph by K. Imlah.*)[97]

FIGURE 18.15a. Zone-melted alpha-plutonium, electrolytic etch, bright-field illumination, 100X. (*Photomicrograph by E. M. Cramer.*)

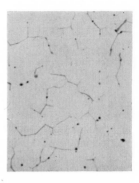

FIGURE 18.15d. Beta plutonium in an alloy containing 2.5 atomic per cent aluminum and sufficient impurity to delineate grain boundaries partially, electrolytic etch, bright-field illumination,
250X. (*Photomicrograph by E. M. Cramer.*)

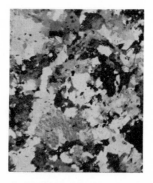

FIGURE 18.15b. High-purity alpha plutonium, electrolytic etch, polarized light, 125X. (*Photomicrograph by C. O. Matthews.*)

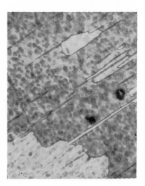

FIGURE 18.15e. Beta plutonium in an alloy containing 10 atomic per cent uranium, electrolytic
etch, polarized light, 250X. (*Photomicrograph by
E. M. Cramer.*)

FIGURE 18.15f. Beta plutonium in an alloy containing 5 atomic per cent titanium, etched by cathodic bombardment, bright-field illumination, 500X. (*Photomicrograph by K. Imlah.*)[97]

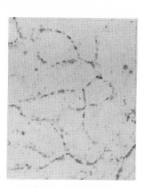

FIGURE 18.15i. A delta plutonium alloy with grain boundaries delineated by surface oxide, electrolytic etch, bright-field illumination, 500X. (*Photomicrograph by J. C. Clark.*)

FIGURE 18.15g. A four-component plutonium alloy containing a mixture of alpha and gamma phases plus unidentified inclusions, electrolytic etch, bright-field illumination, 100X. (*Photomicrograph by E. M. Cramer.*)

FIGURE 18.15j. A delta plutonium alloy, electrolytic etch, polarized light, 200X. (*Photomicrograph by C. O. Matthews.*)

FIGURE 18.15h. The alloy of Figure 18.15g under polarized light, 250X. (*Photomicrograph by E. M. Cramer.*)

FIGURE 18.15k. An autoradiomicrograph of an aluminum alloy containing 1 atomic per cent plutonium, 25X. The white areas are $PuAl_4$; the black matrix is substantially pure aluminum. (*Autoradiomicrograph by C. R. Tipton.*)

Examples of Results

Figures 18.15a through 18.15j are photomicrographs of pure plutonium and plutonium-rich alloys showing microstructures of the alpha, beta, gamma, and delta phases. The results of electrolytic and cathodic etching are compared, as well as the effects of bright-field and polarized illumination. It is apparent that grain boundaries in the various allotropes are not revealed by bright-field illumination following an electrolytic etch unless a significant amount of an intermediate (or impurity) phase is present, or strong oxidation effects exist on the electroetched surface. Etching by cathodic bombardment[97] does, however, give some indication of grain boundaries, and they are clearly revealed under polarized light if the critical electroetching condition (see above) required to yield the polarized-light reaction has been realized.

Figure 18.15k is an autoradiomicrograph of an aluminum-plutonium alloy showing dendrites of $PuAl_4$ in a matrix of essentially pure aluminum.

FABRICATION

Foundry

The melting and casting of plutonium are complicated by the reactivity of the metal. Commonly, plutonium and high-plutonium alloys are melted and cast in high-vacuum furnaces in order to avoid reaction between the plutonium and air. For dilute plutonium alloys the characteristics of the major alloying component may be the controlling factor in melting and casting. Aluminum alloys containing less than 20 weight per cent plutonium have been prepared in a pot furnace operated in an argon-filled glove box. First the aluminum is melted, and then the required amount of plutonium is added in small pieces while the melt is vigorously stirred.[124] Recently, it has been found feasible to conduct this type of melting operation in a glove box containing an air atmosphere.[217]

In a number of laboratories the arc melting technique has proved to be satisfactory. Usually, an atmosphere of mixed argon and helium, purified by a getter such as zirconium, is used in the arc furnace. The arc melting technique eliminates the problem of selecting a suitable crucible material. Because of the strong reducing property of plutonium, only the more stable oxide, carbide, nitride, boride, and silicide compounds have been found to be suitable container materials for the molten metal. High-fired magnesia and calcia crucibles are generally used to contain molten plutonium, provided that the maximum temperature to be encountered is limited to about 1200°C (2192°F) in order to avoid excessive reaction between the crucible and the melt. Graphite crucibles can be used if the length of time at temperature is short and if appreciable carbon pickup can be tolerated. Coating the graphite with magnesium fluoride or calcium fluoride extends the usefulness of such crucibles. For higher temperatures, in the vicinity of 1500°C (2732°F) thoria crucibles have been used with some success.

Some of the refractory metals have also been employed as crucible materials. Tungsten is probably the least reactive toward plutonium, but it has been difficult to obtain in suitable shapes having low enough porosity to contain molten plutonium. Tantalum crucibles have been investigated extensively and show promise for containing molten plutonium if the temperature is limited to a maximum of about 1000°C (1832°F).

The relatively low melting point, high fluidity, and high density of plutonium, together with its very small volume increase on solidification,[111] are highly favorable casting characteristics. The large positive and negative volume changes in the solid state, however, resulting from the allotropic transformations, make the casting of intricate shapes impractical. The casting of simple shapes, such as cylinders and spheres, usually presents no problem. For some applications involving the casting of more complicated shapes, it has been possible to design molds that can be disassembled at temperatures sufficiently high to permit the gamma-to-beta and the beta-to-alpha transformations to proceed without being restrained by the mold.

Magnesia is a commonly used mold material. Graphite, protected by a coating of magnesium fluoride or calcium fluoride, is also used and permits molds to be constructed to close tolerances. Metal molds are coming into more extensive use, and a wide variety of metals have been successfully used for this purpose. Copper, either water cooled or massive enough to provide an adequate heat-sink, has proved to be a satisfactory material for mold construction. For casting dilute plutonium alloys, the characteristics of the major alloying component dictate the selection of mold materials. A uranium alloy containing 20 weight per cent plutonium has been cast successfully into thoria-coated glass tubes by means of gas-pressure injection casting to form prototype fuel rods for the EBR-II reactor.[191]

Mechanical Working

At present, details of the technology of the mechanical working of plutonium and high-plutonium alloys are not declassifiable, but developments with the more dilute plutonium alloys, which have been centered almost exclusively in the plutonium-aluminum system, may be reported here.

A number of useful shapes have been produced from alloys containing 20 weight per cent or less plutonium.[39,124,217] In this series of alloys there is negligible solid solubility of plutonium in the aluminum, the compound $PuAl_4$ being distributed in a matrix of aluminum. The technology of fabricating these alloys generally parallels that of the commercially available high-aluminum alloys. Hot and cold rolling, extruding, forging, and wire drawing are performed in the normal manner, provided that the machinery is suitably enclosed to prevent the spread of plutonium contamination. These plutonium-aluminum alloys are noteworthy in that they strongly resist oxidation and may be decontaminated by chemical and ultrasonic cleaning techniques[39,217] to provide a surface free of loose contamination. This greatly facilitates subsequent cladding of the alloy.

APPLICATIONS

At present, plutonium is used in nuclear weapons, nuclear fuel, neutron sources, threshold detectors for determining neutron spectra, and in the production of higher plutonium isotopes and transplutonic elements.

By far the greatest proportion of plutonium production throughout the world has been intended for use as components of nuclear weapons. Recently, however, there has been a growing awareness that a nuclear power economy based on uranium will produce substantial quantities of plutonium as a by-product. Furthermore, the efficient utilization of the world's uranium reserves makes it necessary to convert the abundant, fertile, but nonfissionable uranium 238 into fissionable plutonium 239. It has been estimated that the conversion of uranium 238 to plutonium 239 will result in increasing the world's energy reserves, as represented by the known and economically recoverable uranium reserves, by a factor of more than 100.[109] Thus, it may be expected that the development of plutonium-fueled power reactors will become increasingly important in the future.

Because, as explained above, plutonium cannot be employed for nuclear fuel in the form of the pure metal, it must be combined with other elements for reactor use. The fuel applications of plutonium alloys are discussed above under "Reactor Applications" in the section on "Alloys." The use of plutonium alloys and compounds as nuclear fuels has been reviewed by Tate.[197]

The intense alpha activity of plutonium makes it important as a component of plutonium-beryllium neutron sources. Unlike mechanical mixtures of beryllium and alpha-emitting materials, the compound $PuBe_{13}$ has a predictable neutron yield for a given weight of compound.[20,50,112] The characteristics of $PuBe_{13}$ as a neutron source have been described by Stewart,[195] Runnalls and Boucher,[166] and Tate and Coffinberry.[199] If plutonium having a maximum concentration of plutonium 239 and a minimum amount of the higher isotopes is used, the long half life of plutonium 239 allows the production of neutron sources that are relatively stable with respect to time. Such sources are useful for the calibration of neutron-detecting instruments. A different type of neutron source may be made from highly irradiated plutonium alone, where the source of neutrons is the spontaneous fission of plutonium 240.

Another use of plutonium dependent on its fission cross section is as a threshold detector for the determination of neutron spectra. In this technique a plutonium foil is surrounded by B^{10} to eliminate fission by thermal neutrons. Determination of the activity of fission fragments after exposure to the neutron flux provides a measure of the intensity of neutrons having energies above the threshold value of

4 kv. Detectors having higher thresholds, such as neptunium and uranium, are required for the determination of the complete spectrum.[94]

The neutron-capture cross section of plutonium is utilized to make higher isotopes of plutonium and transplutonic elements. Since large numbers of neutrons are required in order to effect the transmutations in appreciable quantity, irradiation of plutonium in a reactor is the most practical method for producing these interesting species. Modest quantities of elements having atomic numbers as high as 100 have been produced in this manner.[6,74,146,185]

References*

1. Abramson, R., Boucher, R., Fabre, R., and Monti, H., *Proc. 2nd UNICPUAE,* **6,** 174–183.
2. Aiken, A. M., *Chem. Eng. Progr.,* **53,** 82 (1957).
3. Aiken, A. M., and McKenzie, D. E., "The High Temperature Processing of Neutron-Irradiated Uranium," Chap. 7-4 of *Progress in Nuclear Energy,* Vol. 1, Ser. III, pp. 316–321, London, Pergamon Press, Ltd., 1956.
4. Ball, J. G., and Lord, W. B. H., *J. Inst. Metals,* **86,** 369 (1957–58).
5. Bartlett, A. A., and Swinehart, D. F., *U.S. Atomic Energy Comm., Rept. No. LA-561* (1946).
6. Bentley, W. C., Diamond, H., Fields, P. R., Friedman, A. M., Gindler, J. E., Hess, D. C., Huizenga, J. R., Inghram, M. G., Jaffey, A. M., Magnusson, L. B., Manning, W. M., Mech, J. F., Pyle, G. L., Sjoblom, R., Stevens, C. M., and Studier, M. H., *Proc. ICPUAE,* **7,** 261–270.
7. Bishop, T., *Metal Progr.,* **76,** 105 (1959).
8. Blumenthal, B., *U.S. Atomic Energy Comm., Rept. No. ANL-5975,* pp. 63–67 (March, 1959).
9. Bochvar, A. A., Konobeevsky, S. T., Kutaitsov, V. I., Menshikova, I. S., and Chebotarev, N. T., *Proc. 2nd UNICPUAE,* **6,** 184–193.
10. Bridgman, P. W., *J. Appl. Phys.,* **30,** 214 (1959).
11. Brown, J. E., and Hyam, E. D., *Proc. 2nd UNICPUAE,* **17,** 597–651.

*In this reference list, the abbreviation *Proc. ICPUAE* means *Proceedings of the International Conference on the Peaceful Uses of Atomic Energy, New York,* United Nations, 1956. The abbreviation *Proc. 2nd UNICPUAE* means *Proceedings of the Second United Nations International Conference on the Peaceful Uses of Atomic Energy, Geneva,* United Nations, 1958.

12. Bruce, F. R., *U.S. Atomic Energy Comm., Rept. No. TID-7534,* Book 1, pp. 303–331, Symposium on the Reprocessing of Irradiated Fuels, Brussels, Belgium, 1957.
13. Buck, C., Howells, G. R., Parry, T. A., Warner, B. F., and Williams, J. A., *Proc. 2nd UNICPUAE,* **17,** 25–45.
14. Carlson, G., *Proc. 2nd UNICPUAE,* **17,** 111–117.
15. Chiotti, P., and Voight, A. F., *Proc. 2nd UNICPUAE,* **17,** 368–375.
16. Chiswik, H. M., Dwight, A. E., Lloyd, L. T., Nevitt, M. V., and Zegler, S. T., *Proc. 2nd UNICPUAE,* **6,** 394–412.
17. Coffinberry, A. S., U.S. Patent 2,867,530 (Jan. 6, 1959).
18. Coffinberry, A. S., U.S. Patent 2,886,504 (May 12, 1959).
19. Coffinberry, A. S., U.S. Patent 2,901,345 (Aug. 25, 1959).
20. Coffinberry, A. S., and Ellinger, F. H., *Proc. ICPUAE,* **9,** 138–146.
21. Coffinberry, A. S., and Miner, W. N. (Eds.), "The Metal Plutonium," to be published; Chap. by Abramson, R., "A Dilatometric Study of Plutonium."
22. Coffinberry, A. S., and Miner, W. N., *ibid.,* Chap. by Coffinberry, A. S., "Later Plutonium Metallurgical Research at Los Alamos."
23. Coffinberry, A. S., and Miner, W. N., *ibid.,* Chap. by Cramer, E. M., Hawes, L. L., Miner, W. N., and Schonfeld, F. W., "Dilatometry and Thermal Analysis of Plutonium Metal."
24. Coffinberry, A. S., and Miner, W. N., *ibid.,* Chap. by Ellinger, F. H., "Review of the Intermetallic Compounds of Plutonium."
25. Coffinberry, A. S., and Miner, W. N., *ibid.,* Chap. by Elliott, R. O., and Larson, A. C., "Deltaprime Plutonium."
26. Coffinberry, A. S., and Miner, W. N., *ibid.,* Chap. by Foote, F. G., "Plutonium Metallurgy at the Argonne National Laboratory."
27. Coffinberry, A. S., and Miner, W. N., *ibid.,* Chap. by Grison, E., "Plutonium Metallurgy in France."
28. Coffinberry, A. S., and Miner, W. N., *ibid.,* Chap. by Gurinsky, D. M., "A Plutonium Liquid-Metal-Fuel Reactor."
29. Coffinberry, A. S., and Miner, W. N., *ibid.,* Chap. by Kay, A. E., "Some Physical and Physico-Chemical Properties of Plutonium Metal."
30. Coffinberry, A. S., and Miner, W. N., *ibid.,* Chap. by Kelman, L. R., and Dunworth, R. J., "The Development of Plutonium-Containing Fuels at Argonne National Laboratory."

31. Coffinberry, A. S., and Miner, W. N., *ibid.*, Chap. by Kiehn, R. M., "The Role of Plutonium in Nuclear Power."

32. Coffinberry, A. S., and Miner, W. N., *ibid.*, Chap. by Laquer, H. L., "Sound Velocity Measurements on Alpha-Phase Plutonium."

33. Coffinberry, A. S., and Miner, W. N., *ibid.*, Chap. by Lee, J., and Mardon, P. G., "Some Physical Properties of Plutonium Metal Studied at Harwell."

34. Coffinberry, A. S., and Miner, W. N., *ibid.*, Chap. by Pugh, S. F., "Plutonium Fuels for Power Reactors."

35. Coffinberry, A. S., and Miner, W. N., *ibid.*, Chap. by Runnalls, O. J. C., "The Preparation of Plutonium-Aluminum and Other Plutonium Alloys."

36. Coffinberry, A. S., and Miner, W. N., *ibid.*, Chap. by Sandenaw, T. A., "Results of Measurements of Physical Properties of Plutonium Metal."

37. Coffinberry, A. S., and Miner, W. N., *ibid.*, Chap. by Schonfeld, F. W., "Plutonium Phase Diagrams Studied at Los Alamos."

38. Coffinberry, A. S., and Miner, W. N., *ibid.*, Chap. by Shuck, A. B., "Some Concepts of Solid Fuels for Heterogeneous Fast Reactors."

39. Coffinberry, A. S., and Miner, W. N., *ibid.*, Chap. by Tate, R. E., "Fabrication of Billets Containing Plutonium for the MTR Fuel Elements."

40. Coffinberry, A. S., and Miner, W. N., *ibid.*, Chap. by Waber, J. T., and Wright, E. S., "The Corrosion of Plutonium."

41. Coffinberry, A. S., and Miner, W. N., *ibid.*, Chap. by Waldron, M. B., "Phase Diagrams of Plutonium Alloys Studied at Harwell."

42. Coffinberry, A. S., and Miner, W. N., *ibid.*, Chap. by Wauchope, K. L., "The Preparation of Plutonium-Aluminum Alloy Fuel Elements for the N.R.X. Reactor."

43. Coffinberry, A. S., and Miner, W. N., *ibid.*, Chap. by Zachariasen, W. H., "Crystal Structure Studies of Plutonium Metal."

44. Coffinberry, A. S., and Miner, W. N., Los Alamos Scientific Laboratory, unpublished data, 1957.

45. Coffinberry, A. S., Schonfeld, F. W., Cramer, E. M., Miner, W. N., Ellinger, F. H., Elliott, R. O., and Struebing, V. O., *Proc. 2nd UNICPUAE*, **6**, 681–685.

46. Coffinberry, A. S., and Waldron, M. B., "The Physical Metallurgy of Plutonium," Chap. 4 of *Progress in Nuclear Energy*, Vol. 1, Ser. V, pp. 355–357, London, Pergamon Press, Ltd., 1956.

47. Coffinberry, A. S., and Waldron, M. B., *ibid.*, pp. 360–369.

48. Coffinberry, A. S., and Waldron, M. B., *ibid.*, pp. 372–382.

49. Coffinberry, A. S., and Waldron, M. B., *ibid.*, pp. 382–384.

50. Coffinberry, A. S., and Waldron, M. B., *ibid.*, pp. 388–403.

51. Comstock, A. A., and Gibney, R. B., *U.S. Atomic Energy Comm., Rept. No. LA-1348* (1952).

52. Connick, R. E., "Oxidation States, Potentials, Equilibria and Oxidation-Reduction Reactions of Plutonium," Chap. 8, pp. 221–300, in "The Actinide Elements," G. T. Seaborg, and J. J. Katz, (Eds.), New York, McGraw-Hill Book Company, Inc., 1954.

53. Cooper, V. R., and Walling, M. T., *Proc. 2nd UNICPUAE*, **17**, 291–323.

54. Cramer, E. M., Los Alamos Scientific Laboratory, unpublished data, 1958.

55. Cramer, E. M., Ellinger, F. H., and Land, C. C., "The Plutonium-Zinc Phase Diagram," pp. 169–170, in "Extractive and Physical Metallurgy of Plutonium and Its Alloys," W. D. Wilkinson, (Ed.), New York, Interscience Publishers, Inc., 1960.

56. Cramer, E. M., and Schonfeld, F. W., Los Alamos Scientific Laboratory, unpublished data, 1956.

57. Cramer, E. M., and Schonfeld, F. W., *Proc. 2nd UNICPUAE*, **17**, 668–675.

58. Cromer, D. T., and Larson, A. C., *Acta Cryst.*, **12**, 855 (1959).

59. Cromer, D. T., and Larson, A. C., "The Crystal Structure of $PuNi_4$," to be published in *Acta Cryst.*

60. Cromer, D. T., and Olsen, C. E., *Acta Cryst.*, **12**, 689 (1959).

61. Cromer, D. T., and Roof, R. B., *Acta Cryst.*, **12**, 942 (1959).

62. Culler, F. L., *Proc. ICPUAE*, **9**, 464–483; also, Chap. 5-2 of *Progress in Nuclear Energy*, Vol. 1, Ser. III, pp. 172–194, London, Pergamon Press, Ltd., 1956.

63. Cunningham, B. B., "Preparation and Properties of the Compounds of Plutonium," Chap. 10, pp. 371–434, in "The Actinide Elements," G. T. Seaborg, and J. J. Katz, (Eds.), New York, McGraw-Hill Book Company, Inc., 1954.

64. Dawson, J. K., *J. Chem. Soc.*, Part III, 3393 (1954).

65. Dean, D. J., Kay, A. E., and Loasby, R. G., *J. Inst. Metals*, **86**, 379 (1957–58); 464 (1957–58).

66. Dempsey, E., and Kay, A. E., *J. Inst. Metals*, **86**, 379 (1957–58).

67. Dietrich, J. R., and Zinn, W. H., "Solid Fueled Reactors," pp. 811–812, Reading, Mass., Addison-Wesley Publishing Company, 1958.

68. Ellinger, F. H., *Trans. Am. Inst. Mining Met. Petrol. Engrs.*, **206**, 1256 (1956).

69. Ellinger, F. H., Elliott, R. O., and Cramer, E. M., *J. Nuclear Materials*, **1**, 233 (1959).

70. Ellinger, F. H., Land, C. C., and Cramer, E. M., "The Plutonium-Cerium Phase Diagram," pp. 149–166, in "Extractive and Physical Metallurgy of Plutonium and Its Alloys," W. D. Wilkinson, (Ed.), New York, Interscience Publishers, Inc., 1960.

71. Elliott, R. O., and Gschneidner, K. A., "The Behavior of Some Delta-Stabilized Plutonium Alloys at High Pressures," pp. 243–262, in "Extractive and Physical Metallurgy of Plutonium and Its Alloys," W. D. Wilkinson, (Ed.), New York, Interscience Publishers, Inc., 1960.

72. Elliott, R. O., and Larson, A. C., Los Alamos Scientific Laboratory, unpublished data, 1957.

73. Feder, H. M., *U.S. Atomic Energy Comm., Rept. No. TID-7534*, Book 2, pp. 667–718, Symposium on the Reprocessing of Irradiated Fuels, Brussels, Belgium, 1957.

74. Fields, P. R., Pyle, G. L., Inghram, M. G., Diamond, H., Studier, M. H., and Manning, W. M., *Nuclear Sci. and Eng.*, **1**, 62 (1956).

75. Flanery, J. R., *Proc. ICPUAE*, **9**, 528–531.

76. Foote, F. G., "Production and Use of Plutonium," Part III, Chap. IV, pp. 123–132, in "The Industrial Challenge of Nuclear Energy, II" (Second Information Conference, Amsterdam, June 24–28, 1957); Paris, Organization for European Economic Cooperation, 1958.

77. Ford, G. W. K., and Walford, J. G., *Proc. 2nd UNICPUAE*, **17**, 545–554.

78. Freshley, M. D., *U.S. Atomic Energy Comm., Rept. No. TID-7546*, Book 2, pp. 789–811, Fuel Elements Conference, Paris, 1957.

79. Fried, S., Westrum, E. F., Jr., Baumbach, H. L., and Kirk, P. L., *J. Inorg. & Nuclear Chem.*, **5**, 182 (1958).

80. Frost, B. R. T., Addison, C. C., Chitty, A., Geach, G. A., Gross, P., James, J. A., Metcalfe, G. J., Raine, T., and Sloman, H. A., *Proc. 2nd UNICPUAE*, **7**, 139–165.

81. Gardner, H. R., Bloomster, C. H., and Jefferes, J. M., *Proc. 2nd UNICPUAE*, **6**, 686–689.

82. Gardner, H. R., and Jefferes, J. M., *U.S. Atomic Energy Comm., Rept. No. HW-57130* (1958).

83. Garner, C. S., Bonner, N. A., and Seaborg, G. T., *J. Am. Chem. Soc.*, **70**, 3453 (1948).

84. Gibney, R. B., *U.S. Atomic Energy Comm., Rept. No. LAMS-1080* (1950).

85. Glasstone, S., "Descriptions of Nuclear Reactors," Chap. 13, pp. 788–838, in "Principles of Reactor Engineering," Princeton, N.J., D. Van Nostrand Company, Inc., 1955.

86. Goertz, R. C., *Proc. 2nd UNICPUAE*, **17**, 585–596 and 659–663.

87. Goldschmidt, B., Regnaut, P., and Prevot, I., *Proc. ICPUAE*, **9**, 492–497.

88. Gorum, A. E., *Acta Cryst.*, **10**, 144 (1957).

89. Gustison, R. A., Barber, E. J., Benton, S. T., Bernhardt, H. A., and McMillan, T. S., "The Chlorine Trifluoride Process," Chap. 6-3 of *Progress in Nuclear Energy*, Vol. 1, Ser. III, pp. 281–285, London, Pergamon Press, Ltd., 1956.

90. Hall, D. B., *Proc. 2nd UNICPUAE*, **13**, 300–306.

91. Harmon, K. M., and Reas, W. H., *U.S. Atomic Energy Comm., Rept. No. TID-7534*, Book 1, pp. 332–348, Symposium on the Reprocessing of Irradiated Fuels, Brussels, Belgium, 1957.

92. Holley, C. E., Mulford, R. N. R., Huber, E. J., Head, E. L., Ellinger, F. H., and Bjorklund, C. W., *Proc. 2nd UNICPUAE*, **6**, 215–220.

93. Howells, G. R., Hughes, J. G., Mackay, D. R., and Saddington, K., *Proc. 2nd UNICPUAE*, **17**, 3–24.

94. Hurst, G. S., Harter, J. A., Hensley, P. N., Mills, W. A., Slater, M., and Reinhardt, P. W., *Rev. Sci. Instr.*, **27**, 153 (1956).

95. Hyman, H. H., and Katz, J. J., "The Bromine Trifluoride Process for Metallic Uranium Fuel Elements," Chap. 6-2 of *Progress in Nuclear Energy*, Vol. 1, Ser. III, pp. 274–280, London, Pergamon Press, Ltd., 1956.

96. Hyman, H. H., Vogel, R. C., and Katz, J. J., *Proc. ICPUAE*, **9**, 613–626.

97. Imlah, K., *U.S. Atomic Energy Comm., Rept. No. LA-2287* (1959).

98. Irish, E. R., and Reas, W. H., *U.S. Atomic Energy Comm., Rept. No. TID-7534*, Book 1, pp. 83–106, Symposium on the Reprocessing of Irradiated Fuels, Brussels, Belgium, 1957.

99. Jay, K. E. B., "Atomic Energy Research at Harwell," pp. 3–5, London, Butterworth & Co. (Publishers), Ltd., 1955.

100. Jette, E. R., *J. Chem. Phys.*, **23**, 365 (1955).

101. Jette, E. R., and Coffinberry, A. S., "Plutonium and Its Alloys," Chap. 1.15, pp. 235–242, in "The Reactor Handbook," Vol. 3, Sec. 1, "General Properties of Materials," *U.S. Atomic Energy Comm., Rept. No. AECD-3647* (1955); also "Reactor Hand-

book: Materials," New York, McGraw-Hill Book Company, Inc., 1955.

102. Johnson, K. W. R., *U.S. Atomic Energy Comm., Rept. No. LA-1680* (1954).

103. Judkins, M. F., *Nucleonics,* **16,** p. 97 (1958).

104. Jurney, E. T., Hall, J. H., Hall, D. B., Gage, A. M., Godbold, N. H., Sayer, A. R., and Swickard, E. O., *U.S. Atomic Energy Comm., Rept. No. LA-1679* (1954).

105. Katz, J. J., and Seaborg, G. T., "The Chemistry of the Actinide Elements," Chap. 7, pp. 239–330, New York, John Wiley & Sons, Inc. 1957.

106. Kelman, L. R., *U.S. Atomic Energy Comm., Rept. No. TID-7546,* Book 2, pp. 751–777, Fuel Element Conference, Paris, 1957.

107. Kelman, L. R., Wilkinson, W. D., Shuck, A. B., and Goertz, R. C., *U.S. Atomic Energy Comm., Rept. No. ANL-5509* (1955); also *Nucleonics,* **14,** No. 3, 61 (March, 1956); No. 4, 65 (April, 1956); No. 5, 77 (May, 1956).

108. Ketzlach, N., *Chem. Eng. Progr.,* **53,** 357 (1957).

109. Kiehn, R. M., *U.S. Atomic Energy Comm., Rept. No. LA-2112* (1957).

110. Kittel, J. H., and Paine, S. H., *Proc. 2nd UNICPUAE,* **5,** 500–509.

111. Knight, F. W., Los Alamos Scientific Laboratory, unpublished data, 1958.

112. Konobeevsky, S. T., "Phase Diagrams of Some Plutonium Systems," pp. 362–375 in Session of the Division of Chemical Science, Conference on the Peaceful Uses of Atomic Energy, Moscow, Russia, 1955; also pp. 207–214 in English Translation by Consultants Bureau (for sale by the Superintendent of Documents, Washington, D.C.).

113. Konobeevsky, S. T., Zaimovsky, A. S., Levitsky, B. M., Sokursky, Y. N., Chebotarev, N. T., Bobkov, Y. V., Egorov, P. P., Nikolaev, G. N., and Ivanov, A. A., *Proc. 2nd UNICPUAE,* **6,** 194–203.

114. Langham, W. H., "Physiology and Toxicology of Plutonium[239]," in Proceedings of the Seventh Hot Laboratories and Equipment Conference, 1959 Nuclear Congress, Cleveland, Ohio; also in *Health Phys.,* **2,** 172–185 (1959).

115. Larson, A. C., Cromer, D. T., and Stambaugh, C. K., *Acta Cryst.,* **10,** 443 (1957).

116. Lawroski, S., *U.S. Atomic Energy Comm., Rept. No. TID-7534,* Book 2, pp. 479–497, Symposium on the Reprocessing of Irradiated Fuels, Brussels, Belgium, 1957.

117. Lawroski, S., *Proc. ICPUAE,* **9,** 575–582.

118. Lawroski, S., and Levenson, M., *U.S. Atomic Energy Comm., Rept. No. TID-7534,* Book 1, pp. 45–68, Symposium on Reprocessing of Irradiated Fuels, Brussels, Belgium, 1957.

119. Lee, J. A., and Hall, R. O. A., *UKAEA Rept. No. AERE-M/R-2800* (1959).

120. Leipunsky, A. I., Blokhintsev, D. I., Aristarkhov, I. N., Bondarenko, I. I., Kazachovsky, O. D., Pinkhasik, M. S., Stavissky, U. Ja., Stumbur, E. A., Ukraintsev, F. A., and Usachev, L. N., *Atomnaya Energ.,* **2,** 497 (1957); also English translation, *Soviet J. Atomic Energy,* **2,** 607 (1958).

121. Leipunsky, A. I., Grabin, V. G., Aristarkhov, N. N., Bondarenko, I. I., Kazachkovsky, O. D., Lubimtsev, O. L., Pashkov, S. A., Pinkhasik, M. S., Renne, K. K., Stavissky, U. Ja., Ukraintsev, F. A., and Usachev, L. N., *Proc. 2nd UNICPUAE,* **9,** 348–357.

122. Levine, C. A., and Seaborg, G. T., *J. Am. Chem. Soc.,* **73,** 3278 (1951).

123. Lilienthal, J. R., "Los Alamos Alpha-Gamma Cells," in Proceedings of the Seventh Hot Laboratories and Equipment Conference, 1959 Nuclear Congress, Cleveland, Ohio.

124. Lord, W. B. H., and Wakelin, R. J., *Rev. mét.,* **55,** 620 (1958).

125. Lord, W. B. H., and Waldron, M. B., *J. Inst. Metals,* **86,** 385 (1957–58).

126. Luntz, J. D. (Ed.), *Nucleonics,* **15,** No. 11, p. 130 (1957).

127. Luntz, J. D. (Ed.), *Nucleonics,* **16,** No. 1, p. 22 (1958).

128. Luntz, J. D., *ibid.,* p. 49.

129. Luntz, J. D., *ibid.,* p. 53.

130. Luntz, J. D., (Ed.), *Nucleonics,* **16,** No. 8, p. 19 (1958).

131. Lyman, T. (Ed.), "Metals Handbook," p. 95, Cleveland, American Society for Metals, 1948.

132. McKenzie, D. E., *Can. J. Chem.,* **34,** 515 (1956).

133. McKenzie, D. E., *ibid.,* p. 749.

134. Maraman, W. J., *Proc. 2nd UNICPUAE,* **17,** 676–680.

135. Mardon, P. G., Haines, H. R., Pearce, J. H., and Waldron, M. B., *J. Inst. Metals,* **86,** 166 (1957–58).

136. Martin, F. S., and Miles, G. L., "The Principles of High Temperature Fuel Processing," Chap. 7-1 of *Progress in Nuclear Energy,* Vol. 1, Ser. III, pp. 291–300, London, Pergamon Press, Ltd., 1956.

137. Masing, G., "Handbuch der Metallphysik," Vol. 1, Part 1, p. 398, Leipzig, Akademische Verlagsgesellschaft, M. B. H., 1935. (Published in the United States by Edwards Bros., Inc., Ann Arbor, Mich., 1944.)

138. Metz, C. F., *Anal. Chem.,* **29,** 1748 (1957).

139. Metz, C. F., *Proc. 2nd UNICPUAE,* **17,** 681–690.

140. Metz, C. F., and Waterbury, G. R., "The Transuranium Actinide Elements," Chap. 52 in "A Treatise on Analytical Chemistry," I. M. Kolthoff and P. J. Elving (Eds.), New York, Interscience Publishers, Inc. (in press).

141. Miles, F. T., Sheehan, T. V., Gurinsky, D. H., and Kouts, H. J. C., *Proc. 2nd UNICPUAE,* **9,** 180–187.

142. Morgan, A. N., Baker, R. D., Hazen, W. C., Henrickson, A. V., McNeese, W. D., and Thomas, R. L., *Proc. 2nd UNICPUAE,* **17,** 537–544.

143. Mott, N. F., and Jones, H., "The Theory of the Properties of Metals and Alloys," p. 13, London, Oxford University Press, 1936.

144. Motta, E. E., *Proc. ICPUAE,* **9,** 596–603; also Chap. 7-3 of *Progress in Nuclear Energy,* Vol. 1, Ser. III, pp. 309–315, London, Pergamon Press, Ltd., 1956.

145. Mulford, R. N. R., and Sturdy, G. E., *J. Am. Chem. Soc.,* **77,** 3449 (1995); **78,** 3897 (1956).

146. Murphy, W. J. (Ed.), *Chem. Eng. News,* **33,** 1956 (1955).

147. Nelson, R. D., *U.S. Atomic Energy Comm., Rept. No. HW-55778* (1958).

148. Nelson, R. D., *U.S. Atomic Energy Comm., Rept. No. HW-56843* (1958).

149. Nelson, R. D., and Thomas, I. D., *Proc. 2nd UNICPUAE,* **6,** 170–173.

150. Nelson, T. C., *U.S. Atomic Energy Comm., Rept. No. HW-32276* (1954).

151. Olsen, C. E., Sandenaw, T. A., and Herrick, C. C., "The Density of Liquid Plutonium Metal," *U.S. Atomic Energy Comm., Rept. No. LA-2358* (1959).

152. Pascard, R., *Acta Met.,* **7,** 305 (1959).

153. Peppard, D. F., Studier, M. H., Gergel, M. V., Mason, G. W., Sullivan, J. C., and Mech, J. F., *J. Am. Chem. Soc.,* **73,** 2529 (1951).

154. Peterson, P. J., Thomas, R. L., and Green, J. L., *Proc. 2nd UNICPUAE,* **17,** 664–667.

155. Phipps, T. E., Sears, G. W., Seifert, R. L., and Simpson, O. C., *Proc. ICPUAE,* **7,** 382–385.

156. Poole, D. M., Williamson, G. K., and Marples, J. A. C., *J. Inst. Metals,* **86,** 172 (1957–58).

157. Pratt, H. R. C., *Proc. ICPUAE,* **9,** 520–527; also Chap. 5-7, *Progress in Nuclear Energy,* Vol. 1, Ser. III, pp. 242–248, London, Pergamon Press, Ltd., 1956.

158. Prevot, I., Corpel, J., and Regnaut, P., *Proc. 2nd UNICPUAE,* **17,** 96–106.

159. Prusakov, V. N., Simonov, N. F., and Trotsenko, N. M., *Proc. 2nd UNICPUAE,* **17,** 468–472.

160. Reece, M. C. (Ed.), *Atomic World,* **9,** 367 (1958).

161. Regnaut, P., Faugeras, P., Brut, A., Helou, R., and Redon, A., *Proc. 2nd UNICPUAE,* **17,** 73–95.

161a. Rhinehammer, T. B., Etter, D. E., and Jones, L. V., "The Plutonium-Copper Phase Diagram," to be published in the proceedings of the International Conference on Plutonium Metallurgy, Grenoble (France), April 1960.

162. Roesch, W. C., *Proc. 2nd UNICPUAE,* **23,** 339–345.

163. Runnalls, O. J. C., *Can. J. Chem.,* **34,** 133 (1956).

164. Runnalls, O. J. C., *Proc. 2nd UNICPUAE,* **6,** 710–717.

165. Runnalls, O. J. C., and Boucher, R. R., *Acta Cryst.,* **8,** 592 (1955).

166. Runnalls, O. J. C., and Boucher, R. R., *Can. J. Phys.,* **34,** 949 (1956).

167. Runnalls, O. J. C., and Wauchope, K. L., *U.S. Atomic Energy Comm., Rept. No. TID-7546,* Book 2, pp. 778–788, Fuel Elements Conference, Paris, 1957.

168. Ryan, J. L., and Wheelwright, E. J., *Proc. 2nd UNICPUAE,* **17,** 137–144.

169. Rydberg, J., and Sillén, L. G., *Acta Chem. Scand.,* **9,** 1241 (1955).

170. Sandenaw, T. A., and Gibney, R. B., *J. Phys. Chem. Solids,* **6,** 81 (1958).

171. Sax, N. I., "Dangerous Properties of Industrial Materials," New York, Reinhold Publishing Corp., 1957.

172. Schonfeld, F. W., Tate, R. E., and Anderson, R. W., Los Alamos Scientific Laboratory, unpublished data, 1957.

173. Schonfeld, F. W., Cramer, E. M., Miner, W. N., Ellinger, F. H., and Coffinberry, A. S., "Plutonium Constitutional Diagrams," Chap. 10-10 in *Progress in Nuclear Energy,* Vol. 2, Ser. V, pp. 579–599, London, Pergamon Press, Ltd., 1959.

174. Schulte, H. F., and Meyer, D. D., *Proc. 2nd UNICPUAE,* **23,** 206, 210.

175. Schwennesen, J. L., *Proc. 2nd UNICPUAE,* **17,** 514–530.

176. Seaborg, G. T., "Nuclear Properties of the Plutonium Isotopes," Chap. 7, pp. 189–220, in "The Actinide Elements," G. T. Seaborg, and J. J. Katz (Eds.), New York, McGraw-Hill Book Company, Inc., 1954.

177. Seaborg, G. T., "The Transuranium Elements," p. 1, New Haven, Conn., Yale University Press, 1958.

178. Seaborg, G. T., *ibid.*, pp. 4–10.
179. Seaborg, G. T., *ibid.*, pp. 19–29.
180. Seaborg, G. T., *ibid.*, pp. 38–42.
181. Seaborg, G. T., *ibid.*, p. 69.
182. Seaborg, G. T., *ibid.*, pp. 70–72.
183. Seaborg, G. T., *ibid.*, pp. 95–101.
184. Seaborg, G. T., *ibid.*, pp. 107–108.
185. Seaborg, G. T., *ibid.*, pp. 164–168.
186. Seaborg, G. T., *ibid.*, p. 183.
187. Seaborg, G. T., *ibid.*, pp. 295–296.
188. Seaborg, G. T., and Perlman, M. L., *J. Am. Chem. Soc.*, 70, 1571 (1948).
189. Seguin, M., Folmer, M. M., Friedel, J., and Grison, E., *Compt. rend.*, 246, 3243 (1958).
190. Shevchenko, V. B., Povitsky, N. S., and Solovkin, A. S., *Proc. 2nd UNICPUAE*, 17, 46–48.
191. Shuck, A. B., Argonne National Laboratory, private communication (1958).
192. Smith, C. S., *Metal Progr.*, 65, 81 (1954).
193. Steunenberg, R. K., Fischer, J., Vogler, S., Steindler, M. J., Adams, M., Goring, G., Vogel, R. C., Rodger, W. A., Mecham, W. J., and Seefeldt, W. B., *Proc. 2nd UNICPUAE*, 17, 452–467.
194. Steunenberg, R. K., and Vogel, R. C., *Proc. 2nd UNICPUAE*, 17, 438–451.
195. Stewart, L., *Phys. Rev.*, 98, 740 (1955).
196. Stout, J. W., and Jones, W. M., *Phys. Rev.*, 71, 582 (1947).
197. Tate, R. E., "Plutonium Fuel Elements," Chap. 8, pp. 110–143, in "Nuclear Fuel Elements," H. H. Hausner, and J. F., Schumar (Eds.), New York, Reinhold Publishing Corp., 1959.
198. Tate, R. E., and Anderson, R. W., "Some Experiments in Zone Refining Plutonium," pp. 231–241, in "Extractive and Physical Metallurgy of Plutonium and Its Alloys," W. D. Wilkinson (Ed.), New York, Interscience Publishers, Inc., 1960.
199. Tate, R. E., and Coffinberry, A. S., *Proc. 2nd UNICPUAE*, 14, 427–431.
200. Taylor, J. W., Atomic Energy Research Establishment, Harwell, private communication (1956).
201. Thompson, S. G., and Seaborg, G. T., "The First Use of Bismuth Phosphate for Separating Plutonium from Uranium and Fission Products," Chap. 5-1 of *Progress in Nuclear Energy*, Vol. 1, Ser. III, pp. 163–171, London, Pergamon Press, Ltd., 1956.
202. Tober, F. W., *Proc. 2nd UNICPUAE*, 17, 574–584.
203. Triplett, J. R., *U.S. Atomic Energy Comm., Rept. No. HW-33912* (1955).
204. United Nations, *Proc. 2nd UNICPUAE.* A series of papers on recent developments in pyrometallurgical processing appears in Vol. 17, pp. 352–494.
205. United Nations, *Proc. 2nd UNICPUAE.* A series of papers on recent developments in solvent extraction processes appears in Vol. 17, pp. 111–199 and 291–351.
206. Vdovenko, V. M., and Kovalskaia, M. P., *Proc. 2nd UNICPUAE*, 17, 329–332.
207. Vogel, R. C., and Steunenberg, R. K., *U.S. Atomic Energy Comm., Rept. No. TID-7534,* Book 2, pp. 498–559, Symposium on the Reprocessing of Irradiated Fuels, Brussels, Belgium, 1957.
208. Voigt, A. F., *Proc. ICPUAE*, 9, 591–595; also Chap. 7-5 of *Progress in Nuclear Energy*, Vol. 1, Ser. III, pp. 322–328, London, Pergamon Press, Ltd., 1956.
209. Waber, J. T., "Some Principles of the Alloying Behavior of Plutonium," pp. 111–147, in "Extractive and Physical Metallurgy of Plutonium and Its Alloys," W. D. Wilkinson (Ed.), New York, Interscience Publishers Inc., 1960.
210. Waber, J. T., *Proc. 2nd UNICPUAE*, 6, 204–214.
211. Waldron, M. B., Adwick, A. G., Lloyd, H., Notley, M. J., Poole, D. M., Russell, L. E., and Sayers, J. B., *Proc. 2nd UNICPUAE*, 6, 690–696.
212. Waldron, M. B., Garstone, J., Lee, J. A., Mardon, P. G., Marples, J. A. C., Poole, D. M., and Williamson, G. K., *Proc. 2nd UNICPUAE*, 6, 162–169.
213. Waldron, M. B., and Poole, D. M., Atomic Energy Research Establishment, Harwell, unpublished data, 1959.
214. Walton, G. N. (Ed.), "Glove Boxes and Shielded Cells," Part I, New York, Academic Press, Inc., 1958.
215. Walton, G. N., *ibid.*, Part II.
216. Wensch, G. W., and Whyte, D. D., *U.S. Atomic Energy Comm., Rept. No. LA-1304* (1951).
217. Wick, O. J., Nelson, T. C., and Freshley, M. D., *Proc. 2nd UNICPUAE*, 6, 700–709.
218. Wick, O. J., and Thomas, I. D., *Proc. 2nd UNICPUAE*, 17, 531–536.
219. Zachariasen, W. H., *Acta Cryst.*, 5, 17 (1952).
220. Zachariasen, W. H., *Structure Repts.*, 12, 139 (1949).
221. Zachariasen, W. H., *Structure Repts.*, 12, 179 (1949).
222. Zachariasen, W. H., and Ellinger, F. H., *Acta Cryst.*, 8, 431 (1955).
223. Zachariasen, W. H., and Ellinger, F. H., *Acta Cryst*, 12, 175 (1959).
224. Zachariasen, W. H., and Ellinger, F. H., *J. Chem. Phys.*, 27, 811 (1957).

Phase Diagrams

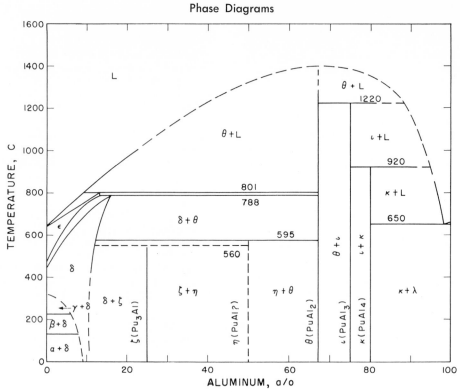

FIGURE 18.16. The plutonium-aluminum system. (*Courtesy Schonfeld et al.*)[37,173]

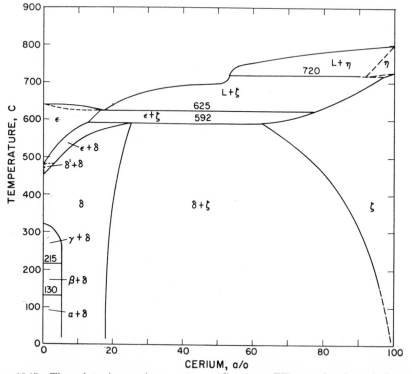

FIGURE 18.17. The plutonium-cerium system. (*Courtesy Ellinger, Land, and Cramer.*)[70]

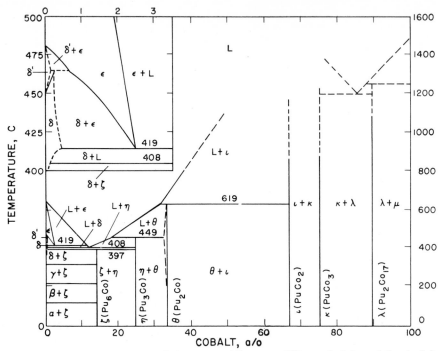

FIGURE 18.18. The plutonium-cobalt system. (*Courtesy Ellinger, Imlah, and Land; Schonfeld et al.;*[37,173] *and Elliott and Larson.*)[25]

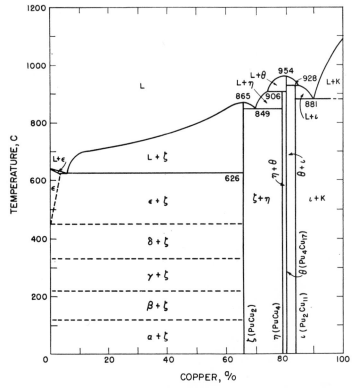

FIGURE 18.19. The plutonium-copper system. (*Courtesy Rhinehammer, Etter and Jones.*)[161a]

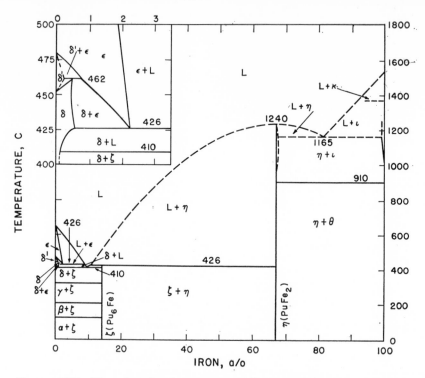

FIGURE 18.20. The plutonium-iron system. (*Courtesy Schonfeld et al.,*[37, 173] *Elliott and Larson,*[25] *Mardon et al,*[135] *and Konobeevsky.*)[112]

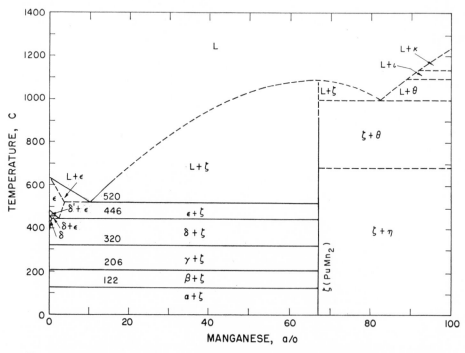

FIGURE 18.21. The plutonium-manganese system. (*Courtesy Schonfeld et al.*)[37, 173]

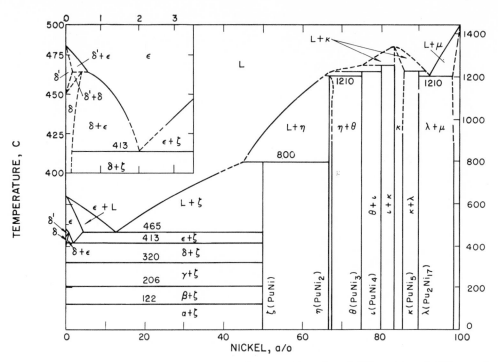

FIGURE 18.22. The plutonium-nickel system. (*Courtesy Wensch and Whyte*,[216] *and Elliott and Larson.*)[25]

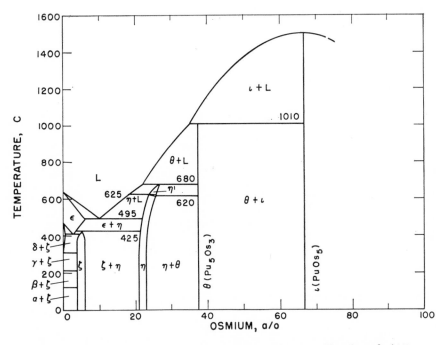

FIGURE 18.23. The plutonium-osmium system. (*Courtesy Konobeevsky.*)[112]

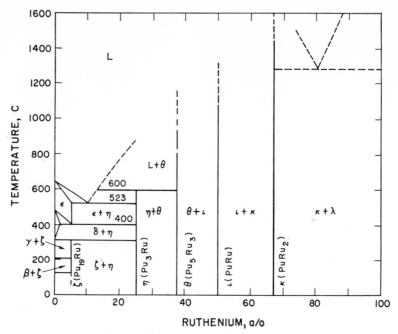

FIGURE 18.24. The plutonium-ruthenium system. (*Courtesy Ellinger, Imlah, and Land; and Schonfeld et al.*)[37,173]

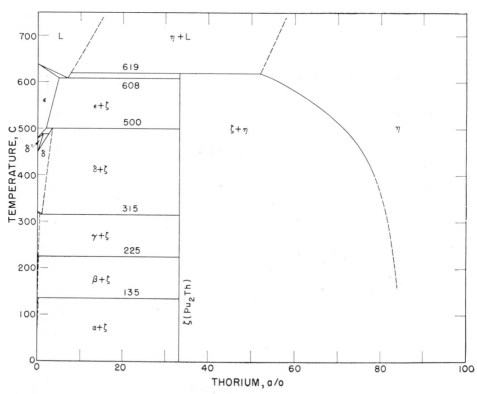

FIGURE 18.25. The plutonium-thorium system. (*Courtesy Schonfeld et al.,*[37,173] *Elliott and Larson,*[25] *and Poole, Williamson and Marples.*)[156]

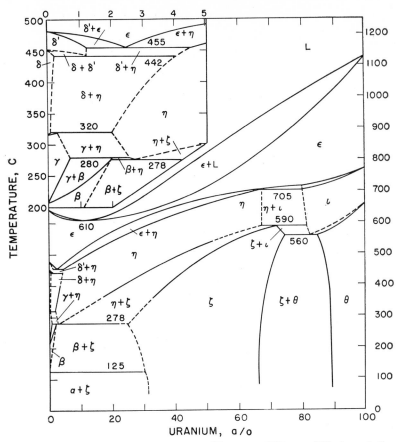

FIGURE 18.26. The plutonium-uranium system. (*Courtesy Ellinger, Elliott, and Cramer.*)[69]

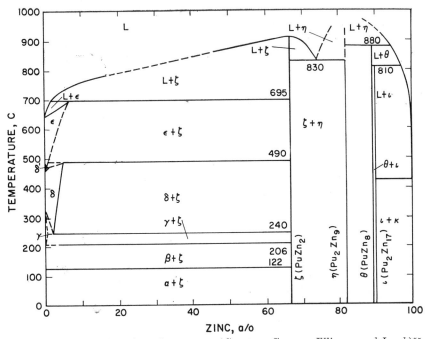

FIGURE 18.27. The plutonium-zinc system. (*Courtesy Cramer, Ellinger, and Land.*)[55]

391

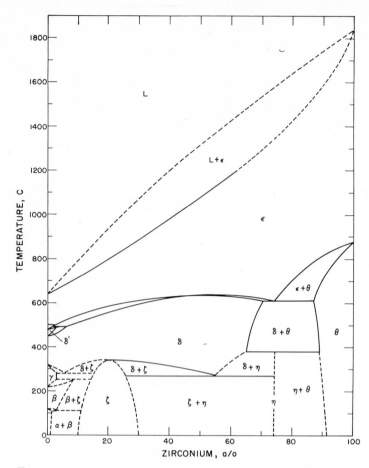

FIGURE 18.28. The plutonium-zirconium system. (*Courtesy Marples, Poole, Waldron, Williamson and Angwin.*[212] There are significant differences between this diagram and the plutonium-zirconium phase diagram of Bochvar *et al.*)[9]

19. RARE EARTH METALS

Howard E. Kremers

American Potash & Chemical Corporation
New York, New York

INTRODUCTION

The rare earths are the group of 15 elements in Group III of the periodic table having numbers from 57 to 71, inclusive. Their properties are related in many ways to those of yttrium, scandium, and actinium, in the same group, but most closely resemble those of yttrium. They are sometimes known as the *lanthanides* or the *lanthanons*.

Structurally, the rare earths are inner transition elements characterized by progressive filling up of the $4f$ electrons from 2 to 14 (in three cases 1 $5d$ electron), while maintaining a complete octet of 2 $5s$ and 6 $5p$ electrons. Since the electrons progressively added are distant from the valence electrons, all of the rare earth elements are remarkably similar in chemical properties, especially in aqueous solutions and hydrated crystals. These differences are small, and, consequently, the rare earths easily form solid solutions and mixed crystals.

In nonsolvated systems the masking effects of solvation do not hide the differences in the rare earths so greatly, and these differences become more apparent. This is true especially with the metals and anhydrous salts, and is quite noticeable in properties related to the

TABLE 19.1. THE RARE EARTHS AND YTTRIUM

Element	Atomic number	Atomic weight	Valences	Oxide (ignited in air)	
Lanthanum	57	138.92	3	La_2O_3	
Cerium	58	140.13	3, 4	CeO_2	
Praseodymium	59	140.92	3, 4	Pr_6O_{11}	Cerium group
Neodymium	60	144.27	3	Nd_2O_3	
Promethium	61	145.	3	Pm_2O_3	
Samarium	62	150.35	2, 3	Sm_2O_3	
Europium	63	152.0	2, 3	Eu_2O_3	
Gadolinium	64	157.26	3	Gd_2O_3	Terbium group
Terbium	65	158.93	3, 4	Tb_4O_7	
Dysprosium	66	162.51	3	Dy_2O_3	
Holmium	67	164.94	3	Ho_2O_3	
Erbium	68	167.21	3	Er_2O_3	
Thulium	69	168.94	3	Tm_2O_3	Yttrium group
Ytterbium	70	173.04	2, 3	Yb_2O_3	
Lutetium	71	174.99	3	Lu_2O_3	
Yttrium	39	88.92	3	Y_2O_3	

Table 19.1 lists the rare earth elements and yttrium with their typical valences and oxides and their classical distribution into "cerium," "terbium," and "yttrium" groups. Yttrium, in its properties, generally occupies a position between dysprosium and holmium.

inner electron shells, viz. the absorption spectra, magnetic properties, etc.

Progressive filling of the rare earth $4f$ electrons results in a decrease in atomic radii with increasing atomic numbers. This reduction in radii is known as the *lanthanide contraction*.

Although not a rare earth, the element yttrium is often classed with the rare earths because of its general occurrence with and similarity to them.

OCCURRENCE

Although the rare earths are found in a great many minerals, the only significant ores are massive monazite and monazite sand, bastnasite and related fluocarbonate minerals, and minerals of the yttrium group such as xenotime, gadolinite, and euxenite.

Massive monazite crystals are found in many pegmatites, but generally the amount is too small for commercial production. Small crystals of monazite are found in many acid granites and pegmatized gneisses, and, where the concentration is sufficiently high, weathering of these rocks results in placer deposits from which monazite can be extracted as monazite sand.

The most important sources of monazite sand are the beach placers at Travancore, India; the states of Espirito Santo, Rio de Janeiro, and Bahia, in Brazil; Jacksonville, Florida; and Australia. Stream placer deposits of significance are located in many parts of the world; most production has come from those in Idaho, North and South Carolina, and deposits in the Malay States and Korea. Many other localities are potentially significant producers.

Massive monazite from vein deposits in the Van Rhynsdorp district of the Union of South Africa has been a significant source of both rare earths and thorium.

The bastnasite deposits in San Bernardino County, California, are capable of supplying the industry for many years.

Production of yttrium-group ores is considerably smaller than that of monazite or bastnasite. Some xenotime is recovered from monazite placer deposits where it occurs with monazite. Euxenite is recovered from a placer deposit at Bear Valley, Idaho.

The relative abundances of the rare earths

TABLE 19.2. TYPICAL ANALYSES OF COMMERCIAL RARE EARTH ORES

	Monazite (Idaho) (%)	Bastnasite concentrate (California) (%)
La_2O_3	17	24.6
Ce_2O_3	29.9	47.1
Pr_2O_3	3.9	4.4
Nd_2O_3	11	12.6
Sm_2O_3	1.3	0.7
Eu_2O_3	0.001	
Gd_2O_3	0.5	
Other terbium-group oxides	0.2	0.5
Yttrium-group oxides	0.1	
Y_2O_3	0.9	
Total rare-earth oxides $+ Y_2O_3$	64.8	89.9
ThO_2	3.5	0.1
MgO	0.1	
CaO	0.3	
BaO		
$Al_2O_3 + Fe_2O_3$	0.6	
TiO_2	0.2	
ZrO_2	0.1	10.0
F		
P_2O_5	28	
SiO_2	1	
SO_3		
Loss on ignition		

are reflected in the compositions of monazite and bastnasite. Table 19.2 lists typical analyses of commercial ores of these minerals.

The rare earths, together with other elements, are formed in the fission of uranium and plutonium. In fact, the fission products from atomic reactors are the only sources of promethium.

PRODUCTION AND ECONOMIC STATISTICS

Sale of rare earth chemicals in the United States in the last few decades has been fairly constant at about the equivalent of 3 to 4 million pounds of rare earth oxide per year. Most of this is produced in the form of commercial rare earth oxide, rare earth fluoride, rare earth chloride, cerium oxide, cerium hydrate, and smaller amounts of other rare earth chemicals in various degrees of purity. Most of the rare earth chloride produced is used for rare earth metal (misch metal) production, and this consumption of rare earths is about one quarter of the total production of rare earth materials.

In 1960, commercial cerium metal containing 90 to 98 per cent Ce sold for about $12.00/lb, and misch metal sold for about $3.15/lb in quantity lots. These are representative of the lowest-cost rare earth metals. High-purity rare earth and yttrium metals became commercially available in small lots in the late 1950's at prices ranging from about $150 to $300/lb for the more abundant rare earths, to as high as $1,500 to $3,000/lb for europium, terbium, thulium, and lutetium metals, which are the rarest of the rare earths and in some cases are the most difficult to prepare in metal form. When first offered, these high-purity metals commanded quite high prices. Eventually, as production increases, the more abundant individual rare earth metals should compare roughly in cost to zirconium and titanium.

American producers of misch metal and related commercial-purity rare earth metals are American Metallurgical Products Co., Inc., Pittsburgh, Pennsylvania; Ronson Metals Corporation, Newark, New Jersey; and Mallinckrodt Chemical Works, St. Louis, Missouri.

Basic United States processors of rare earth ores are Davison Chemical Company division of W. R. Grace & Co., Pompton Plains, New Jersey; Vitro Chemical Company, Chattanooga, Tennessee; American Potash & Chemical Corporation, West Chicago, Illinois; and Michigan Chemical Corporation, St. Louis, Michigan.

American companies offering high-purity individual rare earth metals are American Potash & Chemical Corporation; Lunex Company, Pleasant Valley, Iowa; Michigan Chemical Corporation; and Research Chemicals, Inc., Burbank, California.

EXTRACTION AND SEPARATION OF THE RARE EARTHS

Monazite and bastnasite ores are generally opened by heating with sulfuric acid. This treatment converts the ores into rare earth sulfates which are dissolved from the reaction product with water. Thorium is removed from the rare earths, if they are obtained from monazite, by several methods, the most common being the precipitation of thorium pyrophosphate from the thorium–rare earth sulfate

solution. The rare earths are recovered from the solution by precipitation as rare earth oxalates or sodium rare earth double sulfates, and these compounds are converted to the desired commercial rare earth salt.

Most commercial rare earth salts contain the rare earths in much the same ratio as they occur in the ore. Substantial quantities of cerium salts and other more or less separated rare earth salts of the cerium group, however, are made commercially.

Cerium is separated from the rare earths by oxidation to the tetravalent ceric state. The properties of tetravalent cerium are quite different from those of the trivalent rare earths, and separation of cerium from the other rare earths is done relatively easily by methods such as the precipitation of basic ceric salts, the crystallization of ammonium hexanitratocerate, etc.

The separation of the remaining rare earths is difficult because their properties are very similar. For large-scale separations of the cerium group of rare earths, fractional crystallization of salts such as the double ammonium or magnesium rare earth nitrates was formerly used extensively. By this method, very pure lanthanum salts are made commercially. The ion-exchange method is used for the separation and purification of the remaining rare earths and yttrium. The method consists of absorbing the mixed rare earths on the top of a cation ion-exchange resin column in the copper cycle, and then eluting the rare earths selectively from the resin column with ammonium ethylenediaminetetraacetate solution.

DERIVATION

Methods used for preparing the rare earth metals are summarized in Table 19.3.

Commercial Preparation

Although rare earth metals can be prepared by reduction of the chlorides with calcium, or by thermal decompositions of the amalgams, large-scale commercial production is limited to the electrolysis of the fused anhydrous chlorides.

All of the practical methods for making the rare earth metals usually start with the anhy-

TABLE 19.3. METHODS OF PREPARING RARE EARTH METALS

Method	Application	References
Electrolysis		
Of fused chlorides in NaCl, KCl, etc.	Commercial preparation of misch metal, Ce, La, Nd, and "didymium." Laboratory preparation of Ce, Pr, Nd, Sm	6, 29, 31, 32, 43, 51, 59, 90, 91, 92, 93, 94, 103
Of fused chlorides with molten Mg-Cd cathode	Gives alloys from which Mg and Cd can be distilled in A atmosphere at 900–1200°C (1652–2192°F) to give rare earth metal containing 5% Mg. Except with Sm, fusion in vacuum gives purer rare earth metals	97
Of CeO_2 dissolved in fused CeF_3	Small-scale preparation of high-purity Ce	24, 56, 58
Of anhydrous chlorides in alcohol with Hg cathode	Rare earth amalgams are obtained from which Hg cannot be completely removed	38, 53
Of fused $SmCl_3$ and $GdCl_3$ with molten Cd cathode	Cd alloys are obtained from which Cd can be distilled, giving fairly pure Sm or Gd	92, 93
Hydrogen reduction		
Of anhydrous chlorides	Poor conversion. Sm, Eu, and Yb are reduced only to the dichloride	36
Metal reduction*		
Using Mg, Ca, Na, K, Al with anhydrous rare earth chlorides, bromides, or fluorides	Alloys formed with the reducing metal, or powdered metals of doubtful purity (with fluorides and Na) obtained. Under proper conditions, very pure Ce can be obtained by reducing CeF_3 with Li. Distillation of Ca metal alloy gives pure metals	1, 6, 7, 18, 19, 20, 22, 24, 39, 41, 42, 55, 75, 84, 86, 95, 111
Using Ba with anhydrous samarium bromide	Gives Sm-Ba alloy from which Ba can be distilled, giving pure Sm metal	57
By adding anhydrous Ce, Nd, or Gd chlorides to molten Mg	Mg-rare earth alloys obtained from which Mg can be removed by distillation to give 99% rare earth metal	96
Using Ca, Mg, Al, C, Si with CeO_2	Pyrophoric powders or CeC_2 and $CeSi_2$ obtained. In H_2 and N_2 atmospheres, hydrides and nitrides are formed	31, 106
By Thermite process with Al, Zr, etc., and rare earth oxide, nitride, etc., with chlorate booster	No definite evidence that rare earth metals are formed	39, 44, 45, 55, 58, 68
With sodium amalgam using aqueous chloride and acetate solutions	Amalgams of Eu, Sm, and Yb containing Na	50
Using rare earth oxides and molten Mg at 1000°C (1832°F)	Alloys containing small amounts of rare earth metal are formed	49

TABLE 19.3. METHODS OF PREPARING RARE EARTH METALS (*cont.*)

Method	Application	References
Using rare earth fluorides and molten Mg at 800°C (1472°F)	Alloys with high contents of rare earth metal are formed when NaCl-CaCl₂-CaF₂ flux is used; the amount of rare earth metal in the alloy increases as the rare earth atomic number increases except for Ce and Sm. Practical for small-scale preparation of Pr, Nd, Gd	49
Using La metal and Sm_2O_3 or Yb_2O_3	Gives La_2O_3 and Sm or Yb metal	18

* Generally gives higher-purity metals than electrolytic methods.

drous rare earth chlorides. The commercial preparation of misch metal, "didymium"* metal, and cerium metal begins with hydrated rare earth chlorides containing about one third by weight of water of crystallization. This is the form of rare earth chloride supplied by the ore processor to the metal manufacturer. These chlorides are made by evaporating neutral rare earth chloride solutions to the point where the evaporated solution contains 44 to 46 per cent rare earth oxide. The boiling point of such solutions is about 135°C (275°F). Before evaporation the solutions are carefully treated to remove small amounts of the phosphate and sulfate carried over from prior treatments in the ore processing, as these are detrimental in the production of rare earth metals. The evaporated rare earth chloride solutions are allowed to solidify by cooling, and then are packed for shipment. A typical commercial rare earth chloride, before dehydration, will contain impurities approximately as follows: SO_3, 0.05 per cent; P_2O_5, 0.1 per cent; CaO + MgO, 2 per cent; Fe_2O_3 + Al_2O_3, 0.4 per cent; SiO_2, 0.5 per cent; and Na_2O, 0.5 per cent. Higher-purity grades are also made for preparing higher-purity metals.

* Didymium, as here used, refers to the cerium-free mixture of rare earths obtained commercially from monazite or bastnasite. The classical meaning of didymium denotes a mixture of neodymium and praseodymium such as is obtained in the fractional separation of the mixed cerium-free rare earths; since such neodymium-praseodymium mixtures are of variable composition and should be more definitely defined in terms of their compositions, the industry generally prefers the usage of didymium as given above. Some misch metal producers denote didymium as "cerium-free misch metal."

Commercial metal producers must dehydrate the rare earth chloride prior to electrolysis of the fused chloride. This dehydration is usually accomplished by melting the hydrated chloride in cast iron pots or steel pans, or in ceramic vessels where access to air is restricted. On heating, the chloride evolves water until the water content is diminished to a point where the mass begins to solidify. Heating is continued until most of the water is expelled, together with some hydrochloric acid resulting from the hydrolysis of the rare earth chloride, until a porous, solid, nearly anhydrous rare earth chloride is obtained. Such anhydrous rare earth chlorides will contain up to about 10 per cent water insoluble basic chlorides resulting from hydrolysis of the chloride during dehydration. Drying the hydrated salts in a partial vacuum at 370°C (698°F) gives anhydrous chlorides containing much less oxychloride.

Commercially produced rare earth metals can be classified into the following groups: misch metal, didymium metal, cerium metal, lanthanum metal, neodymium-praseodymium metal, and lanthanum-enriched misch metals. These are produced from the corresponding commercial rare earth chlorides. Typical analyses of such chlorides, in terms of their rare earth compositions, are given in Table 19.4. The metals produced from these chlorides (Table 19.5) will differ in composition somewhat from them, since there is a tendency for the rare earths of higher atomic number to be more resistant to electrolysis than the rare earths of lower atomic number.

Most commercial rare earth metals will contain 98 to 99 per cent rare earth metal, with traces to less than 1 per cent of calcium, magnesium, carbon, aluminum, manganese, phos-

TABLE 19.4. COMPOSITION OF RARE EARTH METAL CONTAINED IN
COMMERCIAL RARE EARTH CHLORIDES (FROM MONAZITE)

	Rare earth chloride (%)	Didymium chloride (%)	Cerium chloride (%)	Lanthanum chloride (%)	Nd-Pr chloride (%)
Ce	46.9	Trace to 1	97 to 99	0.001	1
La	24.5	44.7		99.9+	10
Pr	6.0	10.5		0.01	15
Nd	19.5	37.6	1 to 3		65
Sm	2.1	4.2		Nil	
Gd	0.5	1.0			9
Y and other rare earths	0.5	1.0			

phorus, and silicon and up to 1 per cent iron. The compositions given in Table 19.5 are those of the contained rare earth metal.

The anhydrous chlorides may be prepared *in situ* in the electrolysis pot by heating the hydrated chlorides, or they may be prepared separately (preferred) and then fused for electrolysis in the electrolysis pot. The anhydrous chlorides are fused with sodium, potassium, or calcium chlorides in an iron pot or refractory-lined pot which serves as the anode.[46,70] The pot is externally heated by gas until fusion occurs, and electrolysis with graphite anodes suspended vertically in the pot usually generates enough heat to keep the chlorides molten after electrolysis starts.

The temperature of the fusion during electrolysis is kept above the melting point of the metal [about 750°C (1382°F) for misch metal] so that the metal collects in a pool at the bottom of the pot, from which it may be withdrawn and cast into ingots. Electrolysis is generally done at temperatures of about 800–900°C (1472–1652°F). As metal is withdrawn, additional amounts of rare earth chloride may be added to the pot, and electrolysis continued until the melt accumulates sufficient impurities to result in poor-quality metal or low yields.

The relatively small amount of basic chloride formed during dehydration of the rare earth chloride aids in keeping the melt fluid, but large amounts of basic chloride interfere with coalescing of the metal particles during electrolysis.

Traces of phosphate and sulfate in the raw materials are undesirable since they markedly increase the rate of atmospheric corrosion of the finished metal.

Cathode current densities are about 3 to 4 amp/sq dm; too high or too low current density gives finely dispersed metal which interferes with electrolysis.

High-Purity Metals[1,2,14,17,48,56,77,79,86]

Electrolytic methods are not generally suitable for the preparation of extremely pure metals because there is a significant introduction of impurities from the anode, cathode, and melt.

Exclusion of atmospheric gases, however, and electrolysis with graphite anodes in specially constructed cells designed to contain the melt in a frozen layer of the melt salts can produce extremely pure cerium. This cerium is electrolyzed from a CeF_3-LiF-BaF_2 melt at tem-

TABLE 19.5. COMPOSITIONS OF COMMERCIAL RARE EARTH METALS
(Per cent composition of rare earth metal)

Metal	Ce	Nd	Pr	Sm	La and other rare earths
Lanthanum	<0.1	<0.1	<0.1	<0.1	99.9
Neodymium-praseodymium	1	78	15	2	4
Cerium	97	0.9	0.5	0.1	1.5
Misch metal*	52	18	5	1	24
La-enriched misch metal*	47	19	6	1	27

* Obtained from monazite, and often sold or referred to as "cerium metal."

peratures near the melting point of cerium, and ceric oxide is continuously added to replenish the cerium metal removed from the melt. The metal produced is extremely pure, containing less than a few hundred parts per million impurities. The method has also been used to make pure yttrium from a $KCl-YCl_3$ melt.[56]

Work by Spedding and his co-workers[1,75,84,86] has developed techniques for the preparation of very pure rare earth metals by reduction of the pure rare earth salts with calcium followed by volatilization of the calcium from the resulting rare earth–calcium alloy. By this method, lanthanum, cerium, neodymium, praseodymium, gadolinium, and didymium metals are prepared in very pure form in good yields; samarium cannot be prepared in this way.[1,16,75,86] This method can be applied to all of the rare earths, with the exception of samarium, europium, and ytterbium, which have stable divalent states. The technique consists of placing an intimate mixture of anhydrous rare earth chloride and purified ground calcium metal (about 10 per cent excess calcium over that required for the reaction $2RECl_3 + 3Ca = 3CaCl_2 + 2RE$) in a degassed tantalum crucible contained in a graphite jacket.

The pure anhydrous rare earth chlorides are made either by the dehydration of hydrated rare earth chlorides with hydrogen chloride gas,[40] or by the reaction of rare earth oxide or hydrated rare earth chloride with ammonium chloride followed by vacuum sublimation of the excess ammonium chloride.[67]

If oxide contamination in the metal is not important, magnesia crucibles may be used, but where oxygen-free metals are required, tantalum crucibles are satisfactory. The graphite-jacketed crucible and its contents are heated in a purified argon atmosphere in an induction furnace to the reaction temperature [575°C (1077°F) for lanthanum], and, after the reaction is complete, the metal is consolidated by heating at a temperature about 100–200°C (212–392°F) above the melting point of the rare earth metal. The calcium chloride slag is then leached away from the metals with water. In order to remove the 1 to 5 per cent calcium and 0.1 to 1 per cent magnesium contained in the rare earth metal, the latter is heated in an induction furnace at 1400°C (2552°F) in vacuum to volatilize these impurities. The resulting rare earth metals contain less than 150 ppm calcium. The volatilization of calcium and magnesium is done in magnesia, lime, beryllia, or tantalum crucibles.

When less-pure metals are required, the calcium reduction is done in calcium oxide-lined steel bombs, or in dolomite crucibles in steel bombs capable of producing 900 g/run. In this technique the powdered calcium and anhydrous rare earth chloride mixed with iodine, which serves as a booster, is sealed in the bomb, and the bomb is externally heated in a gas furnace at 650–750°C (1202–1382°F). When the bomb temperature reaches about 400°C (752°F), the mixture reacts as a result of the oxidation by the booster, and the heat of the reaction raises the temperature, causing the reduction of the rare earth chloride and producing a temperature of about 1400°C (2552°F) in the bomb. The high final temperature allows the rare earth metal to agglomerate and become slag free. To remove calcium from the metal, it is heated in an induction furnace in high vacuum, preferably in tantalum crucibles. This method is successful for cerium, lanthanum, praseodymium, and neodymium in good yields, but it fails for samarium and fairly pure yttrium, although it can be used for impure yttrium containing about 30 per cent rare earths.[86] Failure for yttrium is due to the relatively high melting point of the metal, which prevents satisfactory agglomeration.[1]

Samarium metal is difficult to prepare; those rare earths having a stable divalent state (samarium, europium, and ytterbium) are difficult to reduce to the metal. Calcium reductions of samarium trifluoride, samarium triiodide, samarium trichloride, and samarium dichloride are unsuccessful. Barium reduction of samarium tribromide gives low yields of pure samarium metal.[60] Samarium and ytterbium metals are prepared by heating samarium or ytterbium oxide with lanthanum metal in a vacuum, and distilling out the samarium or ytterbium metal formed; this method is based on the fact that lanthanum has a lower vapor pressure than have the other rare earths, and the heat of formation of lanthanum oxide is high enough to favor reduction of samarium or ytterbium oxide with the formation of lanthanum oxide.[18]

A more universal method for making quite pure rare earth and yttrium metals (except samarium, europium, and ytterbium) is calcium reduction of the anhydrous fluorides. The anhydrous fluorides are prepared by (1) hydrofluorination of the oxide with anhydrous HF at a temperature of 575°C (1066°F), (2) drying fluorides precipitated from aqueous solutions with hydrofluoric acid [the precipitate corresponds to $REF_3 \cdot \frac{1}{2}H_2O$, and is dehydrated by washing with absolute alcohol followed by heating in a stream of helium at 400°C (752°F) and 10 cm Hg pressure], and (3) by fusing the rare earth oxide with ammonium bifluoride.

From the anhydrous fluorides, the metal is prepared by mixing the fluoride with 10 to 15 per cent excess calcium metal powder in a tantalum crucible. The charge is heated in an argon atmosphere to initiate the reaction, so that both the metal produced and the calcium fluoride slag are molten at the completion of the reaction. This final temperature is over 1418°C (2575°F), the melting point of calcium fluoride.

For yttrium and some of the other rare earths, magnesium is sometimes added to lower the melting point of the metal phase, and calcium chloride may be added to reduce the slag melting point.

Metalothermic reduction of anhydrous halides, by allowing the reductive metal in vapor form to contact the molten halide at temperatures below the rare earth metal melting point, results in production of the metal in crystal sponge form. Owing to the relatively low temperatures used in reduction, contamination by crucible materials and nonvolatile reagents is considerably reduced. This method is successfully used for yttrium, gadolinium, and dysprosium. The sponge can be vacuum melted and cast into ingots, or it can be compressed into electrode compacts at 1,000 psi for consumable arc melting.

PURIFICATION OF RARE EARTH METALS[34,48]

Metals prepared by electrolysis of the fused chlorides often contain inclusions of soluble halides. These can be removed to some extent by a water wash followed by remelting under fused sodium chloride or a fused eutectic flux.

The individual rare earth metals are usually handled in carbon, molybdenum, tantalum, or tungsten crucibles, or are arc melted in water-cooled copper molds. There is always some pickup of crucible material, which varies in amount with the rare earth. Molten yttrium, e.g., wets tantalum and molybdenum, and recovery of ingots from crucibles of these materials requires destruction of the crucible.

Metals prepared by metalothermic reduction methods will contain variable amounts of the reducing metal, and as much as 1 per cent of the latter may remain in the metal sponge. If calcium or magnesium is used as the reducing agent, these can be reduced to less than a few hundred parts per million by heating the metal in high vacuum (10^{-3} mm Hg).

Crucible materials are often contaminants in rare earth metals. Oxides having high heats of formation, such as beryllia, magnesia, lime, thoria, zirconia, etc., might be expected to be good container materials, but 1 or 2 per cent of the crucible metal may be picked up by the rare earth metal. This is due to an equilibrium reaction between the rare earth metal and the oxide.

The rare earth metals form amalgams, but compounds such as the oxides, carbides, etc., do not. Therefore, such compound inclusion could be removed by amalgam formation followed by distillation of mercury. The product is a pyrophoric rare earth powder which may be melted in an inert atmosphere. Ultimate purification may be difficult, however, owing to retention of mercury in the form of stable mercury–rare earth metal compounds.

Vacuum remelting is an effective way of removing relatively volatile calcium and magnesium. Consumable arc melting in vacuum removes volatile metals only.

Those rare earth metals having relatively high vapor pressures (samarium, europium, and ytterbium) can be purified by distillation in a vacuum. This effectively removes molybdenum, tantalum, and oxides, but the high temperatures required tend to introduce crucible contaminants.

The Van Arkel process for purifying metals does not work with rare earth metals. Zone refining has been reported only for gadolinium and yttrium, and is not particularly effective in removing oxygen and nitrogen impurities.

Solid state electrolysis of yttrium ingots results in some migration of oxygen and nitrogen to the anode. The method consists of applying a high-amperage d-c current to the heated metal rod suspended by water-cooled electrodes in a static argon atmosphere.

Electrolytic refining of crude metals using salt baths has been attempted.[56]

TABLE 19.6. INDIVIDUAL RARE EARTH METALS

Metal	Approximate composition or impurity level*
Cerium (electrolytic) Lanthanum (electrolytic)	Fe—less than 0.1%, C and Si—less than 0.05%
Lanthanum Cerium Praseodymium Samarium Europium Gadolinium Terbium Dysprosium Holmium Erbium Thulium Ytterbium Lutetium Yttrium	Ca—less than 0.1% Mg—less than 0.1% Fe—less than 0.1% Ta†—less than 1% except for Lu where it may reach 3% Mo†—up to several per cent O—up to 1% N—less than 0.025% C—less than 0.02%
Yttrium 80%	20% rare earths, several per cent oxygen
Yttrium-Mg alloy	15–20% Mg, 60–70% Y, 10–15% other rare earths, about 5% nonrare earth impurities

* Rare earth impurities depend largely on purity of starting material. Usual rare earth purities are 99 and 99.9 per cent.
† Amount present depends on whether or not Ta or Mo was used for crucible material, and on the melting point of the rare earth metal; more crucible-material pickup is encountered with metals having higher melting points.

Typical compositions and impurity levels in various high-purity rare earth and yttrium metals are given in Table 19.6.

PHYSICAL PROPERTIES

Unoxidized surfaces of the metals have a metallic to bright silver luster. The more reactive metals quickly tarnish in air, to give dark-colored oxide coatings. Tarnishing is more rapid in moist air, and with the most reactive or less pure metals, a loosely adhering oxide film is formed which spalls off, exposing more metal surface for oxidation.

Physical, thermal, elastic, and magnetic and electric properties and vapor pressures are given in Tables 19.7 to 19.11. Typical properties of misch metal and ferrocerium are given in Table 19.12.

Crystal structures[25,52] of the rare earth metals and yttrium are given in Table 19.7. The most common form at room temperature is hexagonal close packed. Lanthanum, praseodymium, and neodymium have the hexagonal, lanthanum (A3′) type structure; and scandium, yttrium, and all of the rare earths from gadolinium to lutetium, except ytterbium, have the hexagonal close-packed, magnesium (A3) type structure. Cerium and ytterbium, at room temperature, have the face-centered cubic, copper (A1) type structure. Samarium, at room temperature, crystallizes in a hexagonal structure having a c-axis four and one half times that of a normal hexagonal structure. These structures are illustrated in Figure 19.1. Europium shows the body-centered cubic, tungsten (A2) type structure, and, in this respect, europium differs from all of the other rare earths. The structure of promethium is unknown.

Temperature-dependent allotropes of cerium have been extensively studied. Cooling the face-centered cubic room temperature γCe gives βCe starting at about −10°C (14°F) and continuing to about −178°C (−288°F). Below this temperature, αCe begins to form from γCe. The amount of βCe formed depends on the cooling rate, impurities, and previous history of the material. Cold working of cerium at room temperature represses or eliminates the γCe to βCe change, and room-temperature working of cooled cerium results in change of βCe to γCe. Cold working at −196°C (−321°F) increases the amount of transforma-

TABLE 19.7. PHYSICAL PROPERTIES OF RARE EARTH AND YTTRIUM METALS

Metal	Atomic number	Atomic weight	Structure Type	Å a	Å c	Radius (Å) Atomic	Radius (Å) Ionic	Melting point	Boiling point (approx) Temperature (°C)	Transformation	Density (g/cc)	Thermal neutron absorption cross section (barns/atom)
α La	57	138.92	H	3.770	12.131	1.877	1.22	920 (1688°F)	3470 (6278°F)	260 (500°F)	6.174	9.3 ± 0.3
β La			C	5.304		1.875				868 (1594°F)	6.186	
γ La			Cb	4.26		1.90					5.97	
α Ce	58	140.13	C	4.85		1.71	1.18	795 (1463°F)	3468 (6274°F)	−196 (−321°F)	8.23	0.73 ± 0.08
β Ce			H	3.68	11.92	1.82				−73 (−99°F)	6.66	
γ Ce			C	5.1604		1.825				725 (1337°F)	6.771	
δ Ce			Cb	4.11		1.83					6.67	
α Pr	59	140.92	H	3.6702	11.828	1.828	1.16	935 (1715°F)	3127 (5660°F)	800 (1472°F)	6.782	11.6 ± 0.6
β Pr			Cb	4.13		1.84					6.64	
α Nd	60	144.27	H	3.6582	11.202	1.821	1.15	1024 (1875°F)	3027 (5481°F)	862 (1584°F)	7.004	46 ± 2
β Nd			Cb	4.13		1.84					6.80	
α Sm	62	150.35	R	8.996	26.25	1.802	1.13	1072 (1962°F)	1900 (3452°F)	917 (1683°F)	7.536	5600 ± 200
β Sm				4.07		1.81					7.40	
Eu	63	152.0	Cb	4.578		2.042	1.13	826 (1519°F)	1439 (2622°F)		5.259	4300 ± 100
α Gd	64	157.26	H	3.6315	5.777	1.802	1.11	1312 (2394°F)	3000 (5432°F)	1262 (2304°F)	7.895	46,000 ± 1,000
β Gd			Cb	4.06		1.81					7.80	
α Tb	65	158.93	H	3.599	5.696	1.782	1.09	1356 (2473°F)	2800 (5072°F)	1317	8.272	46 ± 4
β Tb												
Dy	66	162.51	H	3.5923	5.6545	1.773	1.07	1407 (2565°F)	2600 (4712°F)		8.536	950 ± 50
Ho	67	164.94	H	3.5761	5.6174	1.766	1.05	1461 (2662°F)	2600 (4712°F)		8.803	65 ± 3
Er	68	167.21	H	3.5590	5.592	1.757	1.04	1497 (2732°F)	2900 (5252°F)		9.051	173 ± 17
Tm	69	168.94	H	3.5372	5.5619	1.746	1.04	1545 (2813°F)	1727 (3141°F)		9.332	127 ± 4
α Yb	70	173.04	C	5.481		1.940	1.00	824 (1515°F)	1427 (2600°F)	798 (1468°F)	6.977	37 ± 4
β Yb			Cb	4.44		1.98					6.54	
Lu	71	174.99	H	3.5050	5.5486	1.737	0.99	1652 (3006°F)	3327 (6020°F)		9.842	112 ± 5
α Y	39	88.92	H	3.6451	5.7306	1.801	1.06	1509 (2748°F)	2927 (5300°F)	1459 (2658°F)	4.478	1.31 ± 0.08
β Y			Cb	4.11		1.83					4.25	
Misch	57–71	140.0						600–650 (1112–1202°F)			6.67	

H, hexagonal close packed; C, face-centered cubic; R, rhombohedral; Cb, body-centered cubic.
References: 16a, 25.

TABLE 19.8. THERMAL PROPERTIES OF RARE EARTH AND YTTRIUM METALS

Metal	Specific heat (cal/mole—°C at 0°C)	ΔH_f	ΔH_v	ΔH_s at 25°C	Linear thermal expansion Coefficient ×10⁶/°C	Temperature °C	Temperature °F	Thermal conductivity at 28°C [cal/(sec) (sq cm) (°C/cm)]	Heat of combustion (kcal/g)
			(kcal/mole)						
La	6.65	2.4	96	87.6	4.9	25	77	0.033	
					7.9	400	752		
Ce	6.89	2.2	95		8.5	25	77	0.026	1.851
					6.7	400	752		
Pr	6.45	2.4	79	85.3	4.8	25	77	0.028	
					6.8	400	752		
Nd	7.20	2.6	69	76.7	6.7	25	77	0.031	1.493
Sm	6.49	2.6	46‡	49.9	—	—	—		1.438
Eu	6.00	2.3	42‡	41.1	32	50	122		
Gd	11.20	3.7	72‡	77.7	6.4	25	77	0.021	1.379
Tb	6.54	3.9	70‡		7.0	25	77		
Dy	6.72	4.1	67‡	71.4	8.6	25	77	0.024	
Ho	6.45	4.1	67‡		9.5	400	752		
Er	6.65	4.1	67‡	72.6	9.2	25	77	0.023	1.352
Tm	6.45	4.4	59‡	57.5	11.6	400	752		
Yb	6.00	2.2	38‡	40.0	25.0	25	77		
Lu	6.45	4.6	90‡	70.6	12.5	400	752		
Y	6.57 (50°C)	4.1	93‡		10.8	400	752	0.0244	
Misch					†				

† See Table 19.12.
‡ Approximate.
References: 5, 16a, 33, 61, 73, 74, 80, 81, 87.

TABLE 19.9. ELASTIC PROPERTIES OF RARE EARTH AND YTTRIUM METALS

Metal	Sonic velocity, ×10⁻⁵ cm/sec, for wave type: Longitudinal	Shear	Modulus (dyne/cm² × 10⁻¹¹)* Young's (calc'd)	Shear	Poisson's ratio (calc'd)	Compressibility, adiabatic (cm²/kg × 10⁶ at 27°C)
La	2.8	1.5	3.84	1.49	0.288	3.24
Ce	2.3	1.3	3.00	1.20	0.248	4.95
Pr	2.7	1.4	3.52	1.35	0.305	3.28
Nd	2.7	1.4	3.79	1.45	0.306	3.02
Sm	2.7	1.3	3.41	1.26	0.352	2.56
Eu						6.99
Gd	3.0	1.7	5.62	2.23	0.259	2.52
Tb	2.9	1.7	5.75	2.28	0.261	2.45
Dy	3.0	1.7	6.31	2.54	0.243	2.39
Ho	3.0	1.7	6.71	2.67	0.255	2.14
Er	3.1	1.8	7.33	2.96	0.238	2.11
Tm						
Yb	1.8	1.0	1.78	0.70	0.284	7.12
Lu						
Y	4.3	2.4	6.63	2.62	0.265	2.09
Misch			†			

* Dyne/sq cm = 1.4504 × 10⁻⁵ psi.
† See Table 19.12.
References: 10, 72.

TABLE 19.10. MAGNETIC AND ELECTRICAL PROPERTIES OF RARE EARTH AND YTTRIUM METALS

Metal	Magnetic properties			Electrical resistivity	
	Susceptibility ×10⁶ emu (25°C)	Moment, (Bohr magnetons)	Curie temperature (°K)	ohm-cm ×10⁶ at 25°C	Temp. coef. of resistance ×10³/°C at 0°C
La	115	0*		57	2.18
Ce	700	2.4		75	0.87
Pr	5,470	3.6		68	1.71
Nd	3,460	3.6		64	1.64
Sm	1,320	1.5		92	1.48
Eu	224	—	15a	81	4.80–25°C
Gd	ferromag.	7.95	289f	134	0.9 –1.76
Tb	172,000	9.0	230f	116	
Dy	590	10.2	85,175b	91	1.19
Ho	437	10.9	20,132b	94	1.71
Er	300	10.0	20f	86	2.01
Tm	152	7.6	51a	90	1.95
Yb	81	—		28	1.30
Lu	17.9	0		68	2.40
Y	slightly +	0*		53	2.71

* Approximate.

f = ferromagnetic below this temperature.

a = paramagnetic above and antiferromagnetic below this temperature.

b = paramagnetic above higher temperature, antiferromagnetic between temperatures, ferromagnetic below lower temperature.

References: 11, 12, 16a, 25, 61, 73, 74. For magnetic properties of Gd-La and Gd-Y alloys, see Reference 88.

TABLE 19.11. VAPOR PRESSURES OF RARE EARTH AND YTTRIUM METALS

Metal	$\text{Log P}_{(mm\ Hg)} = \dfrac{(a \pm b)\ (e)}{T\ (°K)} + (c \pm d)$					Vapor pressure, °C for pressure of	
	a	b	c	d	e	1 mm Hg	10⁻³ mm Hg
La	−17,185	372	6.605	0.201	1	2331	1535
Ce	−23,400	440	11.58	0.29	1	1748	1331
Pr	−17,188	243	8.092	0.156	1	1850	1275
Nd						1767	1193
Sm							
Eu							
Gd							
Tb							
Dy						1463	1005
Ho							
Er							
Tm	1.2552	0.0045	−9.1761	0.0457	10⁴		
Yb							
Lu							

References: 61, 82, 108, 109.

TABLE 19.12. PROPERTIES OF MISCH METAL AND FERROCERIUM*

	Misch	Ferrocerium
Specific gravity	6.67	6.65
Melting point (°F)	1100–1200	1600–1800
(°C)	593–649	871–982
Hardness (Rockwell 15T)	35	85
Brinell equivalent	None	120
Modulus of elasticity (psi)	3.2×10^6	7.1×10^6
Ultimate tensile strength (psi)	11,500	14,900
Yield strength (elastic or proportional limit) (psi)	5,500	10,900
Elongation in 2 in. (%)	1.3	0.27
Shear strength (double shear test) (psi)	12,100	13,400
Coefficient linear thermal expansion		
24°C (75°F) (ref. temp.)	0	0
100°C (212°F)	0.0001	0.0007
288°C (550°F)	0.0015	0.0029
399°C (750°F)	0.0025	0.0043
593°C (1100°F)	0.0032	0.0098
649°C (1200°F)	—	0.0130

* Courtesy Ronson Metals Corporation, 45–65 Manufacturers Place, Newark, New Jersey.

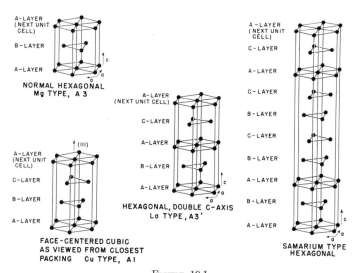

FIGURE 19.1.

tion to αCe. The low-temperature phase changes of cerium show wide hysteresis loops.

Cerium has a face-centered cubic structure with $a = 4.85$Å at liquid-nitrogen temperature, and this is the same form found for the metal under 15,000 atm pressure. At room temperature the face-centered cubic and hexagonal close-packed forms are stable; the former is formed by rapid cooling, and the latter by heat-treating the pure metal. Commercial cer-

ium contains sufficient calcium and magnesium to inhibit the formation of the face-centered cubic structure.

Some elements stabilize the allotropic forms of the rare earth metals. Magnesium and copper stabilize the high-temperature body-centered cubic form of lanthanum and cerium, whereas thorium, uranium, plutonium, and carbon stabilize the face-centered cubic phase. It has been suggested that, in general, those elements having a valence less than three stabilize the body-centered form, and those with valences more than three stabilize the face-centered cubic modification. Various other stabilizing effects have been reported.

Several of the rare earth metals show anomalous behavior in volume and electrical resistance at high pressures. Yttrium, neodymium, samarium, europium, thulium, and lutetium do not show these anomalies.

In cerium, iron contents over about 5 ppm change the magnetic moment. Several per cent iron in cerium change the shape of the magnetic susceptibility-temperature relationship, but do not change the position of the magnetic abnormalities. The presence of magnesium with iron changes the magnetic properties considerably. Magnesium and calcium impurities in cerium and in gadolinium lower the Curie points and modify the low-temperature expansion abnormalities.

MECHANICAL PROPERTIES

The rare earth metals are generally soft and malleable, but malleability and hardness depend, to a large extent, on the impurities present. Large amounts of cationic impurities, such as oxygen, sulfur, nitrogen, and carbon, greatly change the mechanical properties, leading to greater hardness and lowered ductility. For example, oxide-free cerium is very malleable and can be rolled, but oxide inclusion obtained on recasting or remelting reduces the malleability greatly. Unless they are very pure, metals prepared electrolytically are harder than those prepared by other methods. Hardness also depends, to some extent, on the method of casting the metal and the age of the metal. Electrolytic cerium metal often becomes harder on aging at room temperature.

Cast rare earth metals show both inter- and intragranular inclusions. The grain size is usually large, and increases with decrease in inclusions.

Except for europium and ytterbium, hardness generally increases with rare earth atomic number. Specific hardness values depend on the prior history of the specimen. As a general rule, high-purity polycrystalline metals have DPH (10-kg load) values varying from approximately

TABLE 19.13. ROOM-TEMPERATURE MECHANICAL PROPERTIES OF YTTRIUM, SCANDIUM, AND THE RARE EARTH METALS*

	Approximate hardness (DPH kg/sq mm)	Ultimate tensile strength (psi × 10⁻³)	Tensile yield strength (psi × 10⁻³)	Per cent tensile elongation	Ultimate compressive strength (psi × 10⁻³)	Per cent compressive deformation	Young's modulus of elasticity (psi × 10⁻⁶)	Shear modulus (psi × 10⁻⁶)	Poisson's ratio	Compressibility (sq cm/kg)
Sc	85	—	—	—	57					
Y	60	15–20	10–15	5–10	114	17	9–10	3.8	0.27	2.1
La	40	19	18	8	31	—	5.6	2.2	0.29	3.2
Ce	25	15	13	24	43	33	4.4	1.7	0.25	5.0
Pr	40	16	15	10	47	18	5.1	2.0	0.31	3.3
Nd	35	25	24	11	36	36	5.5	2.1	0.31	3.0
Sm	45	18	16	3	—	—	5.0	1.8	0.35	2.6
Eu	20	—	—	—	—	—	—	—	—	—
Gd	55	28	26	8	—	—	8.2	3.2	0.26	2.5
Tb	60	—	—	—	—	—	8.3	3.3	0.26	2.5
Dy	55	36	33	6	—	—	9.2	3.7	0.24	2.4
Ho	60	38	32	7	—	—	9.7	3.9	0.26	2.1
Er	70	42.4	42.3	4	111	22	10.6	4.3	0.24	2.1
Tm	65	—	—	—	—	—	—	—	—	2.6
Yb	25	10	9.5	6	—	—	2.6	1.0	0.28	7.1
Lu	85	—	—	—	—	—	—	—	—	2.3

* Mechanical property values are best estimates from data reported in the literature and experience at GE-ANPD.[69]

25 to 50 for lanthanum and cerium to 50 to 90 for the heavier rare earths. Most of the metals work-harden appreciably.[69]

The mechanical properties of the individual metals are summarized in Table 19.13.

Ultimate and yield tensile strengths of the rare earths generally correlate with melting points, and increase in the heavier metals, except for ytterbium, which is more like the alkaline earths. Working increases strength, particularly with the heavier members. The heavier rare earths, from gadolinium on, may have high enough strengths to be considered as high-strength alloying materials. Yttrium compares with aluminum and magnesium in elastic properties, and in strength with titanium.[69]

The effect of small amounts of impurities and metal additions on the mechanical properties of rare earth metals has not been extensively studied. For yttrium, these effects have been well defined.[13] The common interstitial impurities (carbon, nitrogen, oxygen, and hydrogen) have little effect on the ductility and strength of yttrium when present in small amounts. This is in contrast to the action of these on most metals. The hardness, ductility, and yield strength of yttrium are affected in greatest degree by the thermal history, grain orientation, and amount of cold working. Titanium, vanadium, and chromium form similar alloy systems with yttrium, giving eutectics displaced toward the yttrium-rich end of the diagram; they have no deleterious effects on ductility up to concentrations of 5 per cent. Silicon, aluminum, iron, and nickel have very little solubility in yttrium and have little effect on yield and tensile strengths in concentrations up to 0.5 per cent. At higher concentrations up to 5 per cent, ductility is lowered.

CHEMICAL PROPERTIES

The rare earth metals are active reducing agents, although they are moderately stable in dry air. The reactivity of the metals with moisture in air depends, to a large extent, on their purity; traces of sulfate and phosphate, e.g., in the rare earth chloride used for making misch metal for lighter flints cause premature oxidation of the metal or flints in air. By atmospheric oxidation, hydrated oxides are formed with a large volume increase; this results in destruction of a protective oxide film, so that the metal surface is continually exposed.

The corrosive attack of air and water on the metals varies considerably. Europium is attacked most easily, followed by lanthanum, cerium, praseodymium, and neodymium. These metals quickly develop oxide coatings in air. The other metals and yttrium are reasonably stable in air. With water, europium first forms a yellow, water soluble compound, $Eu(OH)_2 \cdot H_2O$, which then oxidizes to white material which is probably hydrous europic oxide.[83] Moisture and water slowly attack the metals, hot water reacting faster. The metals are readily soluble

TABLE 19.14. THE CORROSION RATES OF RARE EARTH METALS IN AIR* (MILLIGRAMS/SQ DM/DAY)

Temperature (°C)	35		95		200	400	600
(°F)	95		203		392	752	1112
Relative Humidity	<1%	75%	<1%	75%			
Lanthanum	80	950	510	21,000	30	3,200	13,000
Cerium	—	—	—	—	—	200,000	
Praseodymium	8	76	900	5,000	80	38,000	130,000
Neodymium	2	7	60	2,000	70	380	4,800
Samarium	0	0	0	100	15	17	35
Gadolinium	1	2	0	35	0	210	16,000
Terbium	0	0	0		0	1,600	40,000
Dysprosium	0	0	0	43		350	6,600
Holmium	1	1	1	—	11	110	5,400
Erbium	1	1	0	—	10	90	720
Ytterbium	—	—	—	—	—	170	
Yttrium	1	1	2	9	4	40	1,900

* Reference: 48.

in dilute acids but are rather resistant to concentrated sulfuric acid. Some values for the corrosion rates of rare earth metals in air are given in Table 19.14.

The metals reduce carbon monoxide and carbon dioxide and decompose carbon tetrachloride. The latter is therefore not suitable for extinguishing rare earth metal fires. The metals reduce the oxides of iron, cobalt, nickel, manganese, chromium, molybdenum, vanadium, columbium, tantalum, silicon, boron, tin, lead, titanium, and zirconium. Electrode potentials are given in Table 19.15.

TABLE 19.15. ELECTRODE POTENTIALS OF THE RARE EARTHS*

	$E°$
La (s) = La^{+3} + 3e$^-$	+2.4
Ce (s) = Ce^{+3} + 3e$^-$	2.335
Pr (s) = Pr^{+3} + 3e$^-$	2.2
Nd (s) = Nd^{+3} + 3e$^-$	2.246
Sm (s) = Sm^{+3} + 3e$^-$	2.2
Eu (s) = Eu^{+3} + 3e$^-$	2.2
Gd (s) = Gd^{+3} + 3e$^-$	2.2
Tb (s) = Tb^{+3} + 3e$^-$	2.2
Dy (s) = Dy^{+3} + 3e$^-$	2.2
Ho (s) = Ho^{+3} + 3e$^-$	2.1
Er (s) = Er^{+3} + 3e$^-$	2.1
Tm (s) = Tm^{+3} + 3e$^-$	2.1
Yb (s) = Yb^{+3} + 3e$^-$	2.1
Lu (s) = Lu^{+3} + 3e$^-$	2.1

* Except for Ce and Nd (data from Spedding and Miller[85]) the values are approximate (Yost, Russell, and Garner[107]). The potential is given in volts with reference to the hydrogen electrode.

The metals ignite in air at about 150–180°C (302–356°F) [lanthanum ignites in air at 440–460°C (824–860°F)], and most impure preparations and high cerium content alloys are pyrophoric. The pyrophoric nature of the metals on filing probably depends, to a large extent, on the amount and type of impurities; cerium metal containing no oxide inclusions is not pyrophoric on cutting or filing, but oxide inclusions cause heating which ignites the metal fragments.

The metals burn vigorously in halogen vapors above 200°C (392°F). Nitrides are formed when they are heated in nitrogen at temperatures over 1000°C (1832°F). They react with sulfur at its boiling point to form the sesquisulfides. Carbides, silicides, phosphides, arse-

nides, antimonides, and bismuthides are also formed by direct union. With hydrogen, interstitial hydrides are formed. Hydrogen is slowly absorbed exothermically by the metals at room temperature, and more rapidly at 300°C (572°F) to give brittle, amorphous solids of indefinite composition approximating RE H$_{2.8}$. These are stable in dry air but ignite in moist air. Heating the hydrides in a vacuum at temperatures above 1000°C (1832°F) liberates hydrogen. The hydrides are soluble in acids and are decomposed by alkalis.

Europium and ytterbium metals are soluble in liquid ammonia, giving blue solutions.[102] Europium is the most reactive of the rare earth metals; it corrodes rapidly in air and resembles calcium in its reaction with water. In fact, both europium and ytterbium more closely resemble the alkaline earth metals than do the other rare earth metals. This is true with respect to chemical activity and to many physical properties such as crystal structure, volatility, melting points, coefficients of expansion, and compressibility.

Table 19.16 summarizes the attack on refractory materials by the molten rare earths.

WORKING RARE EARTH METALS[2a,8,105]

The working of yttrium is better known than that of the rare earths. The techniques applicable to yttrium generally work for the other rare earths, with the exception of ytterbium and europium which are quite soft.

Cast billets must be worked to improve the structure and reduce the rather large characteristic grain size. This primary working increases elongation and toughness, and this is done both hot and cold by extrusion, forging, rolling, and swaging. Annealing of ingots by heating to 510°C (950°F), followed by slow cooling, tends to soften the heavier rare earths but has little effect on the lighter elements. Annealing and working at elevated temperatures requires protective cladding or inert atmospheres to prevent corrosion. At high temperatures, all of the rare earth metals have great affinity for oxygen, hydrogen, and other reactive gases.

Successful fabrication is dependent to a large extent on the metal purity; oxygen contamination above several tenths of a per cent usually makes working more difficult.

At least some of the rare earth metals can

TABLE 19.16. ATTACK ON REFRACTORIES BY MOLTEN RARE EARTH METALS[1, 24]

Refractory	Application and limitations
Oxides	Cerium metal shows less attack on refractory oxides than do Nd, Pr, and didymium. All oxides are slightly attacked, giving an oxide skin on the metal which inhibits pouring
Magnesia	Best refractory oxide; usable up to 1200°C (2192°F)
Lime	Good; unattacked up to 1000°C (1832°F)
Beryllia	Fair; usable up to 1250°C (2282°F) in some applications
Alumina Zirconia Thoria Silica	Attacked by molten metals
Rare earth oxides	Slightly attacked, but usable up to 1200–1400°C (2192–2552°F). The oxides are wetted by the molten metals
Metals	
Tantalum Molybdenum	Good. Ta usable up to 1700°C (3092°F), Mo up to 1400°C (2552°F) in vacuum, attacked if exposed to air over 500°C (932°F). Although wetted by rare earth metals, they are insoluble in the metal. Ta is superior to magnesia. Not attacked by fused rare earth halides
Tungsten	Slowly attacked by metal, resistant to fused rare earth chlorides
Copper Iron Nickel	Attacked by rare earth metal to various degrees, depending on temperatures used. Cast iron may be used for commercial-sized electrolysis pots
Others	
Fluorite	Good resistance at low temperatures; rapidly attacked at high temperatures, giving Ca-RE alloy
Graphite Carbon	Attacked slowly by molten metals, but resistant to fused RE halides
Glass, porcelain, etc.	Unsatisfactory

Note: Degree of attack on refractories depends on the scale of operation and the temperatures used. The information given in this table is therefore only a general summary.

be extruded hot at 482–900°C (900–1652°F) with protective coatings of aluminum oxide or copper. Although there is a tendency for some of the rare earth metals to react with copper cladding, this reaction is minimized by extrusion at the following temperatures: Sm, 500°C (932°F); Gd, 650°C (1202°F); and Dy, 650°C (1202°F).[2a] Europium, because of its softness, can be extruded through small dies.

Forging refines grain size but must be done carefully to prevent cracking on initial deformation. A typical hot forging operation with arc-melted yttrium metal starts with 6-in.-diameter ingots which are heated to 871°C (1600°F) in an inert atmosphere. Press forging is done at ⅛-in. reductions per pass quadriaxially to 4-in. diameter with intermediate annealing at

871°C (1600°F). After forging, the metal can be hot rolled or swaged at temperatures above its recrystallization point [538–650°C (1000–1202°F) for yttrium]. Optimum hot rolling and swaging temperature for yttrium is 760–871°C (1400–1600°F) with 10 to 25 per cent reductions per pass; no protective coating is required by yttrium in these mechanical operations, since the small amount of surface oxide formed is easily removed. If higher recoveries are necessary, canning before hot forging is necessary. With yttrium, the ingot is coated with alumina, is canned in Type 446 stainless steel, and is worked at 871°C (1600°F). Good-quality yttrium metal can be hot rolled to thin sheets if a sufficient number of passes and anneals are made. Small amounts of chromium, aluminum, or vanadium increase the cold workability of yttrium.

Cold rolling can be done on most of the rare earth metals if oxygen, calcium, and magnesium are kept low and the metal is hot worked first and annealed during cold working.

The rare earth metals machine much like mild steel, except for the softer metals cerium, europium, and ytterbium, which behave like soft metals. Fine particles and chips tend to ignite, and the work should be oil cooled. Chips and fines should not be allowed to accumulate but should be stored under oil in metal containers until they can be disposed of by burning or remelting. Machining should be done to give chips as large as practical to reduce the fire hazard. Oil used for machining or milling coolant should have a high flash point. Many of the metals, particularly yttrium, can be machined dry. Grinding presents no problems if a free cutting wheel and a water-soluble or high flash point oil is used.

Casting of useful shapes is not successful, and this operation is restricted to vacuum melting for ingot casting. Due to the tendency of rare earth metals to reduce oxide refractories, the latter cannot be used as crucible materials if purity is to be maintained. Skull melting must be resorted to if induction melting is used.

Welding, at least with yttrium, is generally unsuccessful, even if done in an inert gas atmosphere. Cracks often develop through the weld center on cooling, especially with metal containing more than a few tenths of a per cent oxygen.

Misch metal, the primary commercial form of mixed rare earth metal, is usually supplied in wafflelike plates weighing 40 to 60 lb, and in the form of ingots, rods, pellets, wire, turnings, or powder. Casting is done in a vacuum, in an inert gas atmosphere, or under a molten salt flux such as barium chloride.

APPLICATIONS

The largest uses for rare earths require compounds rather than the metals. Most of these applications are for the mixture of rare earths in the ratios occurring in their ores, and for cerium materials.

Misch metal has been made commercially since the early 1900's, and electrolytic cerium, lanthanum, and didymium metals have been marketed since the 1940's. The high-purity individual rare earth and yttrium metals became generally available from commercial sources in acceptable purities in the late 1950's.

About one quarter of the rare earth chemicals produced are used in carbon arc lighting applications. Rare earth cored carbons are indispensable to the motion picture industry, both in studio lighting and in theater projection. Army, Navy, and Coast Guard searchlights also use these rare earth cored carbons. Another quarter of the production of rare earths used in the form of mixed rare earth metal (misch metal) and cerium metal. These metals are used in lighter flints, magnesium alloys, and in some of the ferrous alloys. In rare earth alloy production, some applications use rare earth salts instead of metals.

The third quarter of rare earth production is used in the glass industry. Didymium and cerium salts, and some separated rare earths, have important uses in both the coloring and the decolorizing of glass. Cerium oxide and some forms of specially prepared rare earth oxides are widely used in the polishing of spectacle and optical instrument lenses and in the surface preparation of mirror glass and other glass specialties.

The remaining quarter of the rare earth usage is divided among many miscellaneous applications.

Alloys of the Rare Earth Metals

Misch metal is the most important rare earth alloy. It is often sold as "cerium metal," and under the trade names "CerAlloy" and "Lanceramp." Its normal composition is approximately 45 to 50 per cent Ce, 18 per cent Nd, 5 per cent Pr, 1 per cent Sm, and 22 to 25 per cent La, and small amounts of other rare earth metals. The rare earth metal content of commercial misch metal is about 94 to 99 per cent, the main nonrare earth impurities being Al, Ca, Cu, Mn, Mg, Si, Ni, Pb, Fe, and carbon. Magnesium is sometimes intentionally added as a stabilizer to retard atmospheric corrosion.

For specialized metallurgical uses, misch metal containing a lower cerium content (30 per cent Ce) and a higher "didymium" content is also made. Ferrocerium is an alloy of misch metal and iron containing, usually, about 25 per cent

TABLE 19.17. PHASE DIAGRAMS FOR RARE EARTH SYSTEMS

System	Compounds	Reference
Lanthanum		
Al	$LaAl$, $LaAl_2$, $LaAl_4$	27
Sb	La_2Sb, $LaSb$, $LaSb_2$, La_3Sb_2	101
Ce	None, solid solution	101
Cu	$LaCu$, $LaCu_2$, $LaCu_3$, $LaCu_4$	27
Au	La_2Au, $LaAu$, $LaAu_2$, $LaAu_3$	27
Pb	La_2Pb, $LaPb$, $LaPb_2$	27
Mg	$LaMg$, $LaMg_2$, $LaMg_3$, $LaMg_9$	100
Mn		63
Ni	La_3Ni, $LaNi$, $LaNi_2$, $LaNi_3$, $LaNi_4$, $LaNi_5$	99
Ag	$LaAg$, $LaAg_2$, $LaAg_3$	27, 101
Tl	La_2Tl	64
Sn	La_2Sn, $LaSn_3$, La_2Sn_3	89
Ti	No compounds, solubility in Ti small	65
Zn	$LaZn_9$, $LaZn_{11}$	67
Ce-La-Ag		101
Fe	No compounds, miscible in liquid state, immiscible in solid state	28
U	Solubility of La small	26
As, Bi, C, Cd, Cr, Ga, H, Fe, Hg, N, O, Si, Na, S, O-S data available, but no diagrams		28
Cerium		
Al	Ce_3Al_2, $CeAl$, $CeAl_2$, $CeAl_4$	64
Bi	Ce_3Bi, $CeBi$, $CeBi_2$, Ce_4Bi_3	27
Co	Ce_3Co, $CeCo_2$, $CeCo_3$, $CeCo_5$	99
Cu	$CeCu$, $CeCu_2$, $CeCu_4$, $CeCu_6$	27
Au	$CeAu_3$, $CeAu_2$, $CeAu$	64
In	Ce_3In, Ce_2In, $CeIn$, Ce_2In_3	101
Fe	$CeFe_2$, $CeFe_5$	37
Pb	Ce_2Pb, $CePb$, $CePb_3$	64
Mg	$CeMg$, $CeMg_2$, $CeMg_3$	100
Ni	Ce_3Ni, $CeNi$, $CeNi_2$, $CeNi_3$, $CeNi_4$, $CeNi_5$	27
Si	$CeSi$	27
Ag	$CeAg$, $CeAg_2$, $CeAg_3$	64
Tl	Ce_2Tl, $CeTl$, $CeTl_3$	64
S	CeS, Ce_2S_3, Ce_2S_2	21
Th	None, solid solution	104
Sn	Ce_2Sn, Ce_2Sn_3, $CeSn_3$	89
Ti	No compounds to 50% Ce	65
Zn	$CeZn_9$, $CeZn_{11}$	67
U	Solubility of Ce small	26
As, B, Be, C, Cd, Cr, Ga, H, Hg, N, O, Pu, Te data available, but no diagrams		11
Praseodymium		
Al	$PrAl$, $PrAl_2$, $PrAl_4$	27
Cu	$PrCu$, $PrCu_2$, $PrCu_4$, $PrCu_6$	27
Ga	$PrGa_2$, $PrGa$, Pr_3Ga_2, Pr_3Ga	35
Au	Pr_2Au, $PrAu$, $PrAu_2$, $PrAu_4$	27
Pb	Pr_2Pb, $PrPb$, $PrPb_3$	64
Mg	$MgPr$, Mg_5Pr, Mg_9Pr	64
Ni	Pr_3Ni, $PrNi$, $PrNi_2$, $PrNi_5$	99
Ag	$PrAg$, $PrAg_2$, $PrAg_3$	27
Tl	Pr_2Tl, $PrTl$, $PrTl_3$	64
Sn	Pr_2Sn, Pr_2Sn_3, $PrSn_3$	89
U	Solubility of Pr small	26
As, Bi, C, Cd, Ge, Hg, N, O, Si, Zn data available, but no diagrams		28

TABLE 19.17. PHASE DIAGRAMS FOR RARE EARTH SYSTEMS (*cont.*)

System	Compounds	Reference
Neodymium		
Al, C, O, Si data available, but no diagrams		28
Solubility in U small		26
Samarium		
O, Si, and Sr-S data available, but no diagrams		28
Solubility in U small		26
Europium		
O, S, Se, Te data available, but no diagrams		28
Solubility in U small		26
Gadolinium		
O, Ni, N, Mn, Mg, H data available, but no diagrams		28
Solubility in U small		26
Terbium		
Solubility in U small		26
Dysprosium, Holmium, Thulium, Lutetium		
O binary data available, but no diagrams		28
Solubility in U small		26
Zn-Dy		2a
Erbium		
O and N data available, but no diagrams		28
Solubility in U small		26
Ytterbium		
O, Si, Te data available, but no diagrams		28
Solubility in U small		26
Yttrium		
Binary systems formed, but diagrams not available		28
Solubility in U small		26
Mg	$Mg_{17}Y_3$, Mg_5Y_2, MgY	15, 23

Fe. It consists essentially of Ce + $CeFe_2$. Commercial cerium metal is about 95 to 99.5 per cent Ce; the content of the other rare earths is on the order of a few tenths to several per cent.

Phase diagrams for many binary and some tertiary alloy systems have been determined. The more important data available on these is summarized in Table 19.17, and the literature cited should be consulted for details.

Ferrous Alloys. The most common ferrous alloy of the rare earths is the common lighter flint which contains about 30 per cent iron, the balance being misch metal with traces of other impurities. The flints are painted to prevent atmospheric corrosion.

Many claims have been made for beneficial effects produced in many types of ferrous alloys by addition of misch metal. Some are well defined, and others are ill defined and in many cases nonreproducible.

In ferrous alloys, misch metal probably acts largely as a desulfurizer, particularly when silicon, magnesium, or aluminum are also added as deoxidizers. Desulfurization apparently involves the formation of rare earth sulfides which rise to the slag. If the slag is basic and reducing in nature, the sulfides are retained in the slag; if the slag is acid or neutral, the sulfur returns to the metal as iron or manganese sulfides. When misch metal is used as a desulfurizer, the sulfide inclusions present are as randomly dispersed small globules.

Rare earth compounds, when added to steel, do not appear to remove sulfur but are reported, in some cases, to promote grain refinement, leading to better workability. Rare earth compounds will not improve the workability of inherently hot short alloys. There is some evidence that rare earth compounds can improve the transverse properties of steels, particularly in nickel-chromium-molybdenum steels.

Nodular cast iron can be made with misch metal, but magnesium also works, and it is cheaper. Misch metal, as a ladle graphitizer alone, gives irons intermediate between gray iron and malleable iron. Misch metal is useful, however, in conjunction with magnesium and other materials which tend to cause graphite nodulation because cerium overcomes the tendency of traces of titanium, bismuth, lead, antimony, tin, aluminum, and arsenic to inhibit graphitization. About 0.05 per cent misch metal is required for this inhibition correction, and is often used with about 1 per cent ferrosilicon.

Additions of misch metal up to about 1 per cent increase the fluidity of steels, but additional amounts decrease fluidity. Misch metal has also been added to steel to increase hardness and impact strengths, to improve ductility and weldability, and to give cast steels having properties better than those of forged steels.[66]

Low-alloy austenitic stainless steels, such as Type 308, 310, 316, etc., benefit from small additions of misch metal in some steel plants. Increased hot workability, resulting in better yields, is the main benefit. High-alloy stainless steels, such as "Carpenter 20," are inherently hot short, and about 0.02 per cent misch metal transforms these steels into ductile alloys. Some producers report improvement in resistance of stainless steels to oxidation with misch metal additions, and reductions in nickel content are sometimes possible.

Misch metal additions to ferrous alloys are usually small, on the order of a few pounds per ton at most. Retention of rare earths in the steel is usually very small or insignificant. The rare earths may be added in the form of ferrocerium which is a commercially available misch metal–iron alloy.

For nuclear reactor control rod applications, gadolinium-type 347 stainless-steel alloys have been prepared.[2a] Up to 30 per cent gadolinium can be incorporated without segregation. Titanium alloys containing up to 20 per cent gadolinium are homogeneous, and zirconium and zircoloy alloys with dysprosium, erbium, and

samarium can be prepared and fabricated by more or less conventional hot and cold working techniques. Attempts to introduce europium in these alloys are not too successful, because of the volatility of europium.

Cerium additions (0.25 to 0.5 per cent) to iron-aluminum alloys reduce the grain size. Ferrocerium in cast iron (0.2 per cent) enables complex castings to be made having good mechanical properties. Small amounts of cerium or lanthanum enable technical columbium to be shaped by plastic deformation.[66]

Rare earth and yttrium metals are only slightly soluble in iron-base alloys. In iron-chromium alloys, even this small solubility can profoundly affect workability, grain refinement, and high-temperature resistance to recrystallization. High-temperature oxidation resistance of iron-chromium alloys, such as AISI Type 446 alloy, is increased by adding 1 per cent yttrium; the limit of oxidation resistance can be increased from 1100°C (2012°F) to 1372°C (2500°F). Although the addition of 5 per cent aluminum to Type 446 alloy improves oxidation resistance, the alloy becomes coarse grained on heating and is brittle when welded; yttrium additions do not cause these bad effects. Reduction in aluminum content to 3 per cent with use of 1 per cent yttrium raises the operating limit to 1427–1482°C (2600–2700°F) owing to the formation of a smooth retentive oxide layer. In austenitic stainless steels and nickel-based alloys, yttrium additions do not improve oxidation resistance.[15]

Nonferrous Alloys. Magnesium alloys containing about 3 per cent misch metal and about 1 per cent zirconium show improved creep resistance at higher temperatures than is practical for conventional magnesium alloys. The rare earths increase high-temperature strength owing to local precipitation hardening at the grain boundries. Zirconium provides a grain refining effect. The alloys are useful at temperatures up to about 300–315°C (400–600°F) and find application primarily in jet engine castings.

Aluminum alloys containing misch metal have better high-temperature strengths, and nickel alloys containing rare earths have better high-temperature oxidation resistance. Misch metal is used as a hardening agent in copper alloys. Cerium is soluble in titanium to the extent of about 0.5 per cent, and reduces its strength and ductility; gadolinium in concentrations up to about 5 per cent, however, imparts higher ultimate and tensile strengths.

In molten aluminum baths for hot dip coating of steels, the addition of 1.5 to 2 per cent misch metal gives better-looking surfaces and dissolves aluminum oxide coatings on the dipped parts. It also aids dispersion of Fe-Al solids in the bath.

Titanium, treated with 0.2 to 0.7 per cent Ce followed by internal oxidation of cerium to cerium dioxide dispersed in the titanium, gives material showing better stress rupture properties than untreated titanium,[30] although additions of cerium up to about 0.4 per cent give a cerium-rich phase at grain boundaries which does not benefit mechanical properties.[3]

Less than 0.01 per cent cerium increases the life of nickel-chromium resistance heating element alloys in the temperature range of 1150–1200°C (2102–2192°F) by causing the formation of a strongly adherent protective oxide layer. Similar effects have been noted with cobalt alloys.[9,47]

Rare earth metals have limited solubility in chromium, but small additions of yttrium improve the nitrogen barrier properties of chromium oxide, increasing the useful operating temperature appreciably. Although many of the other individual rare earths also control scaling and nitrogen absorption in chromium, they are not as effective as yttrium. The effect of yttrium is to act as a scavenger and a grain refiner.[15]

In vanadium 0.5 to 2 per cent yttrium has a pronounced oxygen scavenging effect, allowing vanadium to be cold worked. The effect is due to the scavenging action of liquid yttrium on oxygen in the two-liquid immiscibility region of vanadium; the resulting yttrium oxide floats to the surface, leaving the vanadium phase free of oxygen.

Misch metal compares with barium in getter action in electronic tubes. An alloy of misch metal, aluminum, and thorium is reported to be the best getter. It is marketed in this country as "CerAlloy 400" and in Europe as "Ceto."

The rare earth metals are active reducing agents and combine with most nonmetals and metalloids. They therefore are useful intermediates in the direct union preparation of a wide variety of compounds. Representative compounds are the monosulfides, arsenides, antimonides, bismuthides, tellurides, selenides, borides, carbides, etc. With some exceptions, these materials are best prepared from the metals.

The high affinity of the rare earth metals for oxygen and nitrogen undoubtedly is and will be the basis for many of their present and future applications.

References

1. Anon., *Report of U.S. Atomic Energy Commission AECU-3800* (1958).
2. Ahmann, D. H., *Report of U.S. Atomic Energy Commission AECD-3205* (1950).
2a. Anderson, W. K., and Theilacker, J. S., "Neutron Absorber Materials for Reactor Control," Ch. 9, to be published.
3. Antes, H. W., and Edelman, R. E., *Foundry*, **85**, No. 1 (Jan. 1957).
4. Asprey, L. B., Eyring, L., and Heppler, W., *Report of U.S. Atomic Energy Commission UCRL-71* (1948).
5. Barson, et al, *Phys. Rev.*, **105** (2), 418–24 (1957).
6. Billy, M., and Trombe, F., *Compt. rend.*, **193**, 421 (1931).
7. Bommer, H., and Hohmann, E., *Z. anorg. u. allgem Chem.*, **241**, 268–72 (1939).
8. Bohlander, K. M., "Mechanical Fabrication of Rare Earth Metals," paper presented at ASM-AEC symposium, Chicago, Ill., Nov., 1959.
9. Breen, J. E., and Lane, J. R., "Effect of Rare Earth Additions on High Temperature Properties of a Cobalt-Base Alloy," *U.S. Naval Res. Lab. Rept. R-4523*, April, 1955.
10. Bridgman, P. W., "The Physics of High Pressure", pp. 160–1, London, G. T. Bell & Sons, Ltd., 1949.
11. Bridgman, P. W., *Proc. Am. Acad. Arts & Sci.*, **83** (1), 1–22 (1954).
12. Bridgman, P. W., *Proc. Am. Acad. Arts & Sci.*, **84**, 111–29 (1955).
13. Carlson, O. N., Bare, D. W., Gibson, E. R., and Schmidt, F. A., "Survey of the Mechanical Properties of Yttrium and Yttrium Alloys," paper presented at 3rd Pacific Area Nat. Meeting of ASTM, San Francisco, Oct. 11-16, 1959, paper No. 116.
14. Carlson, O. N., Schmidt, F. A., and Spedding, F. H., *Report of U.S. Atomic Energy Commission ISC-744* (1956).
15. Collins, J. F., Calkins, V. P., and McGurty, J. A., "Application of Rare Earths to Ferrous

and Non-Ferrous Alloys," paper presented at ASM-AEC symposium, Chicago, Ill., Nov. 1959.

16. Daane, A. H., *Report of U.S. Atomic Energy Commission AECD-3209* (1950).

16a. Daane, A. H., "Physical Properties of the Rare Earth Metals," paper presented at ASM-AEC symposium, Chicago, Ill. Nov 1959.

17. Daane, A. H., and Spedding, F. H., *Report of U.S. Atomic Energy Commission TID-5061* (Del.) 215–22 (1951).

18. Daane, A. H., and Spedding, F. H., *J. Am. Chem. Soc.*, **75**, 2272 (1953).

19. Denge, G., and Martin, A. E., *Report of U.S. Atomic Energy Commission CT-2276* (1944).

20. Docroly, C., Van Impe, J., and Tydgat, D., *Rev. mét.*, **49**, 458–62 (1952).

21. Eastman, E. D., *et al.*, *J. Am. Chem. Soc.*, **72**, 2248 (1950).

22. Eyring, L., and Cunningham, B. B., *Report of U.S. Atomic Energy Commission UCRL-264* (1948).

23. Gibson, E. D., and Carlson, O. N., *Trans. Am. Soc. Metals,* **52** (1959 preprint No. 146) (1960).

24. Gray, P. M. J., *Trans. Inst. Mining Met.*, **61**, 141–70 (1952).

25. Gschneidner, K. A., "Crystallography of the Rare Earth Metals," paper presented at ASM-AEC symposium, Chicago, Ill., Nov. 1959.

26. Haefling, J. F., and Daane, A. H., to be published.

27. Hansen, M., "Constitution of Binary Alloys," New York, 2nd Ed., McGraw-Hill Book Co., Inc., 1958.

28. Haughton, W., ed., "Constitution of Alloys Bibliography," London, Inst. Metals, 1956.

29. Hillebrand, W. F., and Norton, T. H., *Pogg. Ann.*, **155**, 633–9 (1875).

30. Hiltz, R. H., and Grant, N. J., *AIME Trans.*, **212**, 383–7 (1958).

31. Hirsch, A., *J. Ind. Eng. Chem.*, **3**, 880–896 (1911); **4**, 65–66 (1912); *Trans. Am. Electrochem. Soc.*, **20**, 57 (1911).

32. Hopkins, B. S., *Trans. Electrochem. Soc.*, **89**, 295–300 (1946).

33. Huber, E. J., and Holley, C. E., *J. Am. Chem. Soc.*, **75**, 5645–7 (1953).

34. Huffine, C. W., and Williams, J. M., "Refining and Purification of Rare Earth Metals," paper presented at ASM-AEC symposium, Chicago, Ill., Nov. 1959.

35. Iandelli, A., *Gazz. Chim. Ital.*, **79**, 70 (1949).

36. Jantsch, G., Skalla, N., and Grubitsch, H., *Z. anorg. u. allgem. Chem.*, **216**, 75–9 (1933).

37. Jepson, J. O., and Duwez, P., *ASM Preprint No. 2* (1954).

38. Jukkola, E. E., Audrieth, L. F., and Hopkins, B. S., *J. Am. Chem. Soc.*, **53**, 1805 (1931); **56**, 303 (1934).

39. Karl, A., *Bull. soc. chim. France,* **1**, 871 (1934).

40. Kleinheksel, J. H., and Kremers, H. C., *J. Am. Chem. Soc.*, **50**, 959-67 (1928).

41. Klem, W., and Bommer, H., *Z. anorg. u. allgem. Chem.*, **231**, 138–71 (1937).

42. Kremers, H. C., *Trans. Am. Electrochem. Soc.*, **47**, 365–71 (1925).

43. Kremers, H. C., and Beuker, H., *Trans. Am. Electrochem. Soc.*, **47**, 353–64 (1925).

44. Kuhne, K. A., German Patent 179,403 (1904).

45. Kuzel, H., British Patent 23,215 (1909).

46. Livingston, J., and Kent, H., "The Cerium Metal and Lighter Flint Industry in Germany and Austria," Office of Military Govt. for Germany (US), Field Information Agency, Final report No. 909, Sept. 30, 1946.

47. Lohr, J. M., U.S. Pats. 2,687,954 and 2,687,956, Aug. 1954 (to Driver Harris Co.).

48. Love, B., "Selection and Evaluation of Rare or Unusual Metals for Application to Advanced Weapons Systems, Part I—A Literature Survey," *WADC Technical Report* **57-666**, *ASTIA Doc. No. 155685,* Wright Dev Center, U.S. Air Force, *PB-151311* (June, 1958).

49. Mahn, F., *J. recherches centre natl. recherche sci. Labs. Bellevue (Paris),* **1950**, No. 10, 28–31.

50. Marsh, J. K., *J. Chem. Soc.*, **1942**, 398, 523; **1943**, 8.

51. Mazza, L., *Atti X° congr. intern. chim.*, **3**, 604–9 (1939).

52. McHargue, C. J., Yakel, H. L., Jr. and Jetter, L. K., *Acta Cryst.*, **10**, 832 (1957).

53. Meintz, R. E., Audrieth, L. F., and Hopkins, B. S., *Z. anorg. Chem.*, **211**, 237 (1933).

54. "Metals Handbook," Am. Soc. for Metals, Cleveland, Ohio, 21–22 (1948).

55. Moldenhauer, M., *Chem. Ztg.*, **38**, 147 (1914).

56. Morrice, E., and Knickerbocker, R. G., "Rare Earth Electrolytic Metals," paper presented at ASM-AEC symposium, Chicago, Ill., Nov., 1959.

57. Morrogh, H., *Am. Foundryman*, **13**, (4), 91–106 (1948).

58. Muthmann, W., *Ann.*, **320**, 116 (1902); **331**, 60–3 (1904).

59. Muthmann, W., Hofer, W., and Weiss, L., *Ann.*, **320**, 231–69 (1902).

60. Onstatt, E. I., *J. Am. Chem. Soc.*, **75**, 5128 (1953).

61. "The Reactor Handbook," AECD-3647, Vol. 3, Sect. 1 (1955).
62. Reed, J. B., Hopkins, B. S., and Audrieth, L. F., "Inorganic Synthesis," Vol. 1, 28–33, New York, McGraw-Hill Book Co., (1939).
63. Rolla, L., and Iandelli, A., *Ber. deut. Chem. Ges.*, **75B**, 2091 (1942).
64. Rolla, L., *et al.*, *Z. Metallk.*, **35**, 29 (1943).
65. Savitski, Ye. M., and Bouchanov, G. S., *Z. Neorg. Khim.*, **2**, 11 (Nov. 1957).
66. Savitski, Ye. M., "Rare Metals and Alloys," Moscow, Technology House (Dom Tekhniki), 1959.
67. Schramm, J., *Z. Metallk.*, **33**, 357 (1941).
68. Von Siemens, E. W., and Halske, J. G., British Patent 10,867 (1900).
69. Simmons, C. R., "The Mechanical Properties of Yttrium, Scandium and the Rare Earth Metals," paper presented at ASM-AEC symposium, Chicago, Ill. Nov., 1959.
70. Singer, R., Airey, H., Grimmett, L., Leach, H., and Bennett, R., "The Cerium Industry in German Territory, Including Reports on Radium and Mesothorium," *British Intelligence Sub. Committee, Final Report No. 400*, Item No. 21, Sept. 1945.
71. Smirnov-Verin, S., *Novosti Tekhniki*, **1940**, No. 23, 20–1.
72. Smith, J. A., Carlson, C. E., and Spedding, F. H., *J. Metals AIME Trans.*, 1212–3 (Oct. 1957).
73. Spedding, F. H., *et al.*, "Progress in Low Temperature Physics," Ch. XII, ed. by Gorter, North Holland Pub. Co., Amsterdam (1957).
74. Spedding, F. H., "Progress in Nuclear Energy, Series V, Metallurgy and Fuels," ed. by Finneston, Pergammon Press, London (1956).
75. Spedding, F. H., and Daane, A. H., *J. Am. Chem. Soc.*, **74**, 2783–85 (1952).
76. Spedding, F. H., Daane, A. H., and Hermann, K. W., *Acta Crystallographica*, **9**, (7), 559–63 (1956).
77. Spedding, F. H., and Daane, A. H., *J. Metals*, **6**, 504 (1954).
78. Spedding, F. H., and Daane, A. H., *AIME Trans.*, **200**, 504–10 (1954).
79. Spedding, F. H., and Daane, A. H., "Progress in Nuclear Energy," Vol. I, Series V, Ch. 5, Pergammon Press, London and New York (1956).
80. Spedding, F. H., and Daane, A. H., *Report of U.S. Atomic Energy Commission ISC-834* (1957).
81. Spedding, F. H., and Daane, A. H., *Report of U.S. Atomic Energy Commission ISC-902* (1957).
82. Spedding, F. H., and Daane, A. H., *Am. Chem. Soc. Abstracts of Papers of 132nd Meeting* (1957).
83. Spedding, F. H., Hanak, J. J., and Daane, A. H., *AIME Trans.*, **212**, 379–83 (1958).
84. Spedding, F. H., and McGuinis, W. J., *Report of U.S. Atomic Energy Commission ISC-149* (1951).
85. Spedding, F. H., and Miller, C. F., *J. Am. Chem. Soc.*, **74**, 4195–8 (1952).
86. Spedding, F. H., Wilhelm, H. A., Keller, W. H., Ahmann, W. H., Daane, A. H., Hach, C. C., and Ericson, R. P., *Report of U.S. Atomic Energy Commission AECD-3208* (1950); *ISC-75* (1951); *Ind. Eng. Chem.*, **44**, 553–6 (1952).
87. Stull, D. R., and Sinke, G. C., "Thermodynamic Properties of the Elements," *Advances in Chemistry*, Series No. 18, Am. Chem. Soc., Washington, D.C. (1956).
88. Thoburn, W. C., Legvold, S., and Spedding, F. H., *Phys. Rev.*, **110**, 1298–1301 (1958).
89. Tin Research Institute, "Equilibrium Data for Sn Alloys," Battelle Memorial Institute (1949).
90. Trombe, F., *Trans. Electrochem. Soc.*, **66**, 57 (1934).
91. Trombe, F., *Compt. rend.*, **200**, 459 (1935); **201**, 656 (1935).
92. Trombe, F., *Ann. chim.*, [11], **6**, 349–458 (1936).
93. Trombe, F., *Tech. mod.*, **30**, 855–61 (1938).
94. Trombe, F., *Compt. rend.*, **206**, 1380 (1938).
95. Trombe, F., and Mahn, F., *Compt. rend.*, **217**, 603 (1943).
96. Trombe, F., and Mahn, F., *Ann. chim.*, [11], **19**, 345–61 (1944).
97. Trombe, F., and Mahn, F., *Compt. rend.*, **220**, 778–9 (1945).
98. Trombe, F., *Revue de Metallurgie*, **52**, 2–33 (1956).
99. Vogel, R., *Z. Metallk.*, **37**, 98 (1946).
100. Vogel, R., and Heumann, T., *Z. Metallk.*, **37**, 1 (1946).
101. Vogel, R., and Klose, H., *Z. Metallk.*, **45**, 633 (1954).
102. Warf, J. C., and Korst, W., *Acta Crystallographica*, **9**, (5), 452–454 (1956); *J. Phys. Chem.*, **60**, (11), 1590 (1956).
103. Weibke, F., *Z. Electrochem.*, **45**, 518–20 (1939).
104. Weiner, L. C., *et al.*, *J. Inst. Metals*, **86**, 185 (1957).
105. Williams, J. M., and Huffine, C. L., "Forming and Fabrication of Yttrium Metal," paper presented at ASM-AEC symposium, Chicago, Ill., Nov., 1959.

106. Winkler, C. A., *Ber.*, **23**, 772 (1890); **24**, 873 (1890).

107. Yost, D. M., Russell, H., and Garner, C. S., "The Rare Earth Elements and their Compounds," New York, John Wiley & Sons, 1947.

108. Young, R. A., and Ziegler, W. T., *J. Am. Chem. Soc.*, **74**, 5251 (1952).

109. Zachariasen, *Acta Crystallographica*, **2**, 57 (1949).

110. Ziegler, W. T., Proj. No. 116–18, Navy Dept. Office Naval Research Contract No. NR-ori-192, Task Order I, Annual Rept. Oct. 1, 1947 to Sept. 30, 1948 (1949).

111. Zintl, E., and Neumayr, S., *Z. Electrochem.*, **39**, 84–6 (1933).

20. RHENIUM

A. D. Melaven

Department of Chemistry
University of Tennessee
Knoxville, Tennessee

INTRODUCTION

Many claims and counterclaims regarding the discovery of element number 75, a homologue of manganese, appear in the chemical literature.[21] Credit for the actual discovery of the element is now generally attributed to Walter Noddack and Ida Tacke,[65] who announced in 1925 that they had detected the presence of the element in platinum ores and columbite. Simultaneously, O. Berg and I. Tacke[9] published confirming evidence for the existence of element 75 in the above-mentioned ores. This latter evidence was based on x-ray examination of concentrates obtained from the platinum and columbite ores.

Although the claims of Noddack, Tacke, and Berg did not go unchallenged, their suggested name of rhenium, after the German province of Rhineland, is still retained. Rhenium together with manganese, element number 25, and technetium, element number 43, constitute Group VIIB of the periodic table.

OCCURRENCE

Rhenium does not occur in nature in the elementary or compound form as a distinct mineral species. It is, however, widely distributed in nature in very minor amounts. Its average concentration in the earth's crust, as reported by Noddack and Noddack[63] and by Goldschmidt,[33] is of the order of 1×10^{-9}, or 0.001 ppm. A Finnish gadolinite (a beryllium–iron–rare earth silicate) was reported by Aartovaara[1] to contain rhenium in higher concentration than in any mineral previously reported. In addition to gadolinite, rhenium is reported to occur in a wide variety of minerals, notably molybdenites, rare earth minerals, columbite, tantalite, platinum ores, copper sulfides, and oxides of manganese.[21,63]

By virtue of its position in the periodic table, one might expect rhenium to occur most abundantly associated with manganese in minerals of the latter element. Contrary to these expectations, however, rhenium has been found to occur only in very minor amounts in certain manganese minerals, and none serves as a source for the extraction of rhenium. Of the minerals investigated to date, molybdenite (MoS_2) is the most promising commercial source of the element. Excluding the sample of Finnish gadolinite mentioned above, which apparently is in short supply, certain deposits of molybdenite contain the highest natural concentrations of rhenium.[21,41] Indeed, it is from this latter source that virtually all of the rhenium of commerce has been prepared. Although no confirming evidence is at hand, it seems quite probable that the rhenium in molybdenite occurs as the sulfide, either ReS_2 or Re_2S_7. It is of interest to note also that, whereas the two known commercial sources of rhenium are molybdenites, the molybdenite was, in each case, originally associated with sulfide ores of copper.[24,25,56]

PRODUCTION AND ECONOMIC STATISTICS

In 1929 Ida and Walter Noddack[64] described the preparation of 1 g of rhenium metal from

660 kg of a Norwegian molybdenite. This constituted the largest single preparation of the metal in the 4 years following the announced discovery of the element by the same authors in 1925.

Prior to World War II, all of the rhenium of commerce was extracted from the molybdenite residues recovered from the Mansfeld copper schists of Germany.[24,25] Annual production capacity was reported to be 120 kg/year at a cost of approximately $2.40/g. Recovery of rhenium from this East German source apparently was abandoned during World War II and for several years thereafter. Indications are now that the Mansfeld deposit, under domination of the Russians, is again serving as a source of rhenium.

At present there are two sources of rhenium in the United States, each having their origin in the roasting of molybdenite flotation concentrate from copper sulfide ores. Rhenium-bearing molybdenite from the copper sulfide ores mined in the vicinity of Miami, Arizona, by the Miami Copper Company* has served as a source of rhenium for the past 15 years. More recently, the rhenium-bearing molybdenite concentrates from the Utah and New Mexico copper sulfide ores of the Kennecott Copper Corporation of Salt Lake City have developed into the most important domestic source of the metal.

Molybdenite-roaster flue dust from the Miami Copper Company is processed at the University of Tennessee. In the course of the intermittent operations over the past 15 years, approximately 300 lb of rhenium metal, in the form of potassium perrhenate, have been recovered from approximately 25 tons of the flue dust. This source was found to be of variable composition, with the rhenium content varying from 16,000 ppm in the middle 1940's to from 1,700 to 3,000 ppm at present.

The Kennecott Copper Corporation, through its fabricating subsidiary, The Chase Brass and Copper Company of Waterbury, Connecticut, recently announced a scheduled production of rhenium metal in powder and fabricated forms of the order of 100 lb/year, with a potential future production well in excess of this amount.[60]

* As of June 10, 1960 the Miami Copper Company was dissolved and its assets taken over by Tennessee Corporation.

The total United States production potential of rhenium has been estimated at 20,000 to 30,000 lb/year.[77] One recent estimate cites a value of 50 tons for the world reserve of rhenium.[19] This appears to be a very conservative estimate.

Shortly after the start of World War II, the remaining supplies of foreign rhenium in this country were quoted at prices ranging from $8/g for potassium perrhenate to $15/g for the metal powder. The domestic product, when first introduced in this country, was quoted at $6/g for potassium perrhenate and $10/g for the metal. Substantial reductions in the price of the metal and its compounds have since been made. Prices currently in effect range from $250/lb (60 cents/g) for potassium perrhenate to around $600/lb for high-purity rhenium powder. Fabricated forms of the metal, as quoted by Chase Brass and Copper Company, vary from $780/lb for ¼-in.-square bar to $1,060/lb for strip 0.080 in. thick and $2,125/lb for rhenium foil 0.001 in. thick by 1 to 2 in. wide.[89] Rhenium VII oxide (Re_2O_7) ammonium perrhenate, and sodium perrhenate are also currently available in this country at prices intermediate between those quoted for potassium perrhenate and rhenium metal.

DERIVATION

The process for the technical preparation of rhenium having its origin in the Mansfeld copper schists of Germany has been described by Feit.[24] A summary of the process used prior to 1940 follows.

Treatment of the Mansfeld copper ore, by an unstated metallurgical process, gave rise to a complex sulfide slime containing salts of copper, molybdenum, nickel, iron, vanadium, and rhenium, together with minor amounts of other elements. After weathering in air for several months to more than a year, the sludge was leached with water. The leachings were next concentrated by spontaneous evaporation in the open, with the consequent precipitation of calcium, copper, and nickel as sulfates.

After separation of the solid sulfates, the leach was further concentrated by heating, and then was cooled to remove more of the heavy metal sulfates. This process was continued until the leach had a specific gravity of 2. At this point the solution was treated with a solution of ammonium sulfate to precipitate the insoluble nickel-ammonium salt. Further evaporation of the mother liquor, followed by addition of solid ammonium sulfate, gave, on cooling, additional nickel-ammonium sulfate together with complex ammonium salts of the heteropoly acids of phosphorus, vanadium, and molybdenum. The ammonium sulfate treatment was continued until only ammonium sulfate separated. The pale-yellow liquor remaining from the above series of concentrations and precipitations gave, on treatment with potassium chloride, an impure potassium perrhenate. Solution of the latter in hot water, followed by filtration to remove a flocculent precipitate, gave a colorless filtrate from which nearly pure potassium perrhenate separated on cooling.

An alternative method applied with more success consisted of subjecting the sludge to "a special oxidation process" at a temperature not exceeding 100°C (212°F) for a period of several months. This oxidized product was then leached with water, and the filtrate was concentrated by evaporation to separate the major part of the heavy metal sulfates. The solution containing the rhenium as perrhenate ion (ReO_4^-) was then diluted with water from previous extractions and treated with a saturated solution of potassium chloride. The crude potassium perrhenate separating at this point contained small amounts of molybdenum, iron, nickel, and copper. It was then dissolved in boiling water and treated with caustic alkali to precipitate the hydroxides of iron, copper, and nickel. The filtrate from this operation consisted of a solution of potassium perrhenate and soluble potassium molybdate. The potassium perrhenate that separated on cooling the solution was then recrystallized three or four times from water.

The Kennecott Copper Corporation patented process, developed by S. R. Zimmerley and E. E. Malouf[96] and assigned to Kennecott Copper Corporation, describes a different approach to the recovery of rhenium. Immediate source material of the rhenium is a molybdenite concentrate obtained from copper sulfide ores of the Kennecott Corporation and its subsidiaries.

As set forth in the Kennecott patent, the molybdenite is subjected to a multiple-hearth roast at a temperature of the order of 550–650°C (1022–1202°F). In this range of roast-

ing temperatures, the MoS_2 is converted to MoO_3. The MoO_3 is not appreciably volatile over this temperature range. In the course of the roasting operation, the rhenium is converted to volatile oxides of the metal. The roaster gases, in addition to containing oxides of rhenium (principally Re_2O_7), also contain minor amounts of volatile compounds of molybdenum and suspended solids. The bulk of the suspended solids are removed in a cyclone precipitator and recycled through the roaster. The roaster gases are next subjected to a countercurrent water scrubbing treatment to dissolve the volatile compounds of rhenium and molybdenum and to trap suspended solids not removed by the cyclone precipitator.

The countercurrent scrubbing serves to concentrate the rhenium values. The recycling system also includes a thickener for removing from the rhenium-bearing solution solids carried over with the gases from the cyclone precipitator. After the solution becomes sufficiently concentrated in rhenium, it is split in about a 1:20 ratio, and the minor volume is then subjected to filtration. The major portion of the solution is treated with make-up water prior to repassage through the scrubber.

The clarified impure rhenium-bearing solution is next passed through a bed of anionic exchanger resin, such as a strongly basic alkyl amine type of resin. Anions of the resin are thus exchanged for anions of rhenium and anions of molybdenum (i.e., ReO_4^- and MoO_4^-). At the breakthrough of rhenium into the effluent, passage through the column is stopped. The column is next eluted with a solution of sodium hydroxide to remove the molybdenum as sodium molybdate. The resin is next treated with a 0.5 molar solution of perchloric acid. In this eluting stage the perchlorate ions replace the perrhenate ions on the resin, resulting in a rhenium-bearing effluent solution of high purity.

The rhenium-bearing effluent (water solution of perrhenic acid, $HReO_4$) may then be treated with ammonia to convert the rhenium to ammonium perrhenate, NH_4ReO_4, a compound that lends itself readily to hydrogen reduction to form a high-purity powder form of the metal.

The process in use at the University of Tennessee[55] for the extraction of rhenium is, in some respects, similar to that described by Feit. The over-all process, however, is much

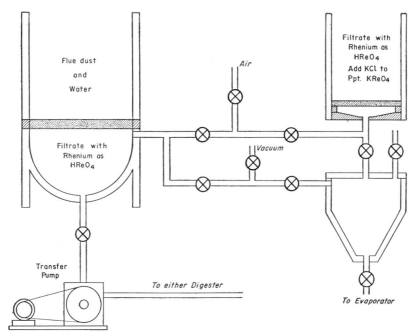

FIGURE 20.1. Extraction of rhenium.

simpler and less time consuming than the German method.

The flue dust from which the rhenium is extracted is obtained from the Miami Copper Company of Miami, Arizona. The original ore, mined primarily for its copper content, contains copper as the sulfide, together with a small amount of molybdenite. Associated with the latter is rhenium, presumably as the sulfide. After crushing and grinding the ore, the sulfides are concentrated by flotation. A second flotation operation serves to separate the copper and molybdenum sulfides, the rhenium following along with the molybdenum.

Roasting of the molybdenite converts the molybdenum to molybdenum (VI) oxide, MoO_3, and the rhenium to rhenium (VII) oxide, Re_2O_7. The conversion, however, is not 100 per cent complete, and as a result there is collected at one stage of the operation a product described as "molybdenite roaster flue dust." This product contains unaltered molybdenite, water soluble complex molybdenum compounds of an undetermined composition, and rhenium (VII) oxide or soluble perrhenates, together with minor amounts of other constituents. On exposure to moist air the flue dust frequently absorbs water. The moist product or its water solution, as might be expected, is acidic.

Extraction of Rhenium

Extraction of the rhenium from the flue dust is carried out in a large "Ceratherm-500"* vacuum filter equipped with a "Filterstone"* porous plate. The upper bowl of 100-gal capacity is separated from the 50-gal lower bowl by the 2-in.-thick porous filter plate. With air passing up through the porous plate, 200 lb of water, or washings from a previous extract, are placed in the upper bowl of the digester and 200 lb of flue dust are added. The digestion is carried out for 1 hr or until all solids are uniformly dispersed. With the air stream cut off, a vacuum is applied to the lower bowl to separate the soluble fraction containing the rhenium from the insoluble fraction which consists largely of molybdenite. The filtrate is then transferred to a storage tank where it is allowed to remain for several hours in order to allow any fine particles of molybdenite to settle. In the meantime the molybdenite cake remaining on the porous plate is digested with two separate 100-lb batches of fresh water. The washings are combined for use in digesting fresh flue dust.

The supernatant liquid from the initial extraction is transferred to a second digester,

* The U.S. Stoneware Company, Akron, Ohio.

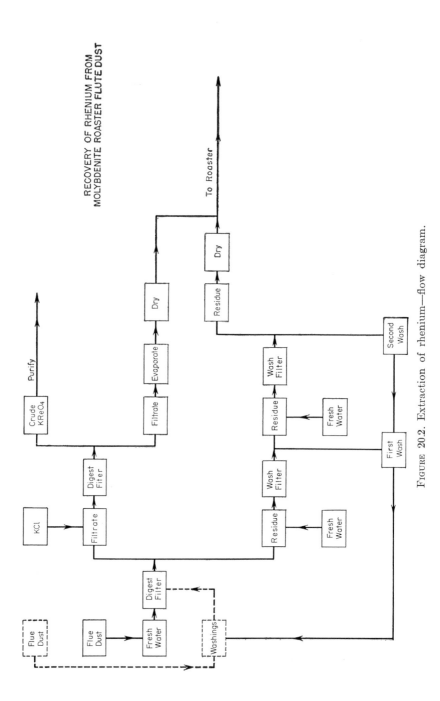

RECOVERY OF RHENIUM FROM
MOLYBDENITE ROASTER FLUTE DUST

FIGURE 20.2. Extraction of rhenium—flow diagram.

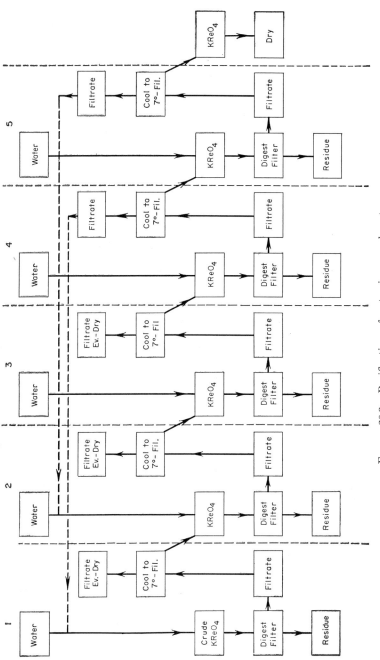

FIGURE 20.3. Purification of potassium perrhenate.

similar to the flue dust digester, but on a smaller scale. With air passing through the solution, 1 lb of finely ground potassium chloride is added per 1.5 gal of extract. The air stirring is continued for 30 min to 1 hr to insure complete solution of the potassium chloride and precipitation of the potassium perrhenate. The reaction taking place in this operation is

$$KCl + ReO_4^- \rightarrow KReO_4 + Cl^-.$$

On completion of the digestion, a vacuum is applied to the lower receiver to separate the insoluble potassium perrhenate from the soluble portion.

Two beneficial effects result from the above processing operations. In the initial digestion there is a noticeable rise in temperature on solution of the flue dust in water. Second, on treating the extract with solid potassium chloride, the digestion mixture is cooled, thereby rendering the potassium perrhenate less soluble.

The processing equipment used in the extraction and precipitation operations is represented in Figure 20.1. Figure 20.2 is a flow diagram of the process.

Purification of the Potassium Perrhenate

The crude potassium perrhenate, as prepared above, is generally light brown in color and, on a dry basis, runs from 85 to 95 per cent potassium perrhenate. The impurities for the most part are insoluble in water at 100°C (212°F), but there is also present a small amount of water-soluble molybdenum compounds. The crude potassium perrhenate, soluble to the extent of approximately 14 g/100 g of water at 100°C (212°F), is dissolved in a slight excess of boiling distilled water and filtered. The residue is discarded, and the filtrate cooled to 7°C (45°F) where the solubility of the perrhenate is roughly 0.55 g/100 g of water. The supernatant liquid from this first recrystallization is separated from the recrystallized perrhenate by filtration. The crystals are washed with a small amount of cold distilled water and redissolved at 100°C (212°F), the solution filtered, and the filtrate again cooled to 7°C (45°F) to reprecipitate the potassium perrhenate. In all, the potassium perrhenate is dissolved and recrystallized five times from distilled water. The final product is dried

at 110°C (230°F). The filtrates from the first three stages of purification are evaporated to dryness, and the residues are added to and processed with a new batch of crude perrhenate. The filtrates from the last two stages of purification are used instead of distilled water in the first two stages of purification of additional crude material. The purification process is represented in block outline form in Figure 20.3.

Preparation of Rhenium Metal

The preparation of rhenium metal from potassium and ammonium perrhenate using hydrogen, at 1 atm pressure and elevated temperatures, as the reducing agent has been described by Hurd and Brimm.[42] The processes described below are modifications of the above method, designed to handle larger quantities of the perrhenate and to shorten the reduction time.

Preparation from Potassium Perrhenate. A silver tube containing the pure potassium perrhenate is placed in a high-pressure reaction vessel, and hydrogen gas is admitted at a pressure of 1,000 to 1,500 psi. As the temperature is raised, there is a steady rise in pressure until 235°C (455°F) is reached, at which temperature there is a sudden drop in pressure, indicating that reduction has started. At this point, additional hydrogen is added to provide an excess of the reducing agent. The temperature is gradually raised to 350°C (662°F) and allowed to remain there for 30 min. The reaction taking place in the bomb is

$$2KReO_4 + 7H_2 \rightarrow 2Re + 2KOH + 6H_2O.$$

After cooling the bomb to room temperature, the pressure is released and the silver tube and contents are removed. The metal is thoroughly washed with hot distilled water to remove the bulk of the alkali. The product is then washed with a hot, dilute solution of hydrochloric acid to destroy excess alkali, and finally with hot distilled water until the washings show a negative test for chloride ion. The rhenium metal powder is then washed with 95 per cent ethanol and vacuum dried at room temperature. The metal powder from one run, or the combined powder from two runs, is replaced in the bomb and the reduction, washing, and drying are carried out as before. The amount of material that can be processed at any one time is limited only by the capacity of the apparatus at hand.

Preparation from Ammonium Perrhenate. In the method described by Hurd and Brimm[42] for the preparation of rhenium metal from ammonium perrhenate, the starting material is potassium perrhenate. The potassium perrhenate, in a solution of hydrochloric acid, is treated with hydrogen sulfide to precipitate rhenium sulfide. The sulfide is then suspended in an ammoniacal solution and oxidized with 30 per cent hydrogen peroxide. The products of the reaction are ammonium perrhenate and ammonium sulfate. The combined mixture of solid salts is then reduced in a stream of hydrogen. Final reduction is carried out at 1000°C (1832°F) for 2 hr. All reaction products are volatile except rhenium, and the rhenium produced by this method is generally in a higher state of purity than that produced by reduction of potassium perrhenate.

Owing to an increasing demand for pure rhenium (VII) oxide and pure ammonium perrhenate as well as for the high-purity metal that can be prepared from ammonium perrhenate, the following method is used at the University of Tennessee.

Rhenium metal prepared by hydrogen reduction of potassium perrhenate is converted to the oxide (Re_2O_7) by passing oxygen gas over the metal powder at a temperature ranging from 350–500°C (662–932°F). The oxide, being quite volatile, passes to the exit end of the "Pyrex" combustion tube and condenses in the form of yellow flakes.

If the desired end product is ammonium perrhenate, the oxide is dissolved in a small amount of water to form perrhenic acid ($HReO_4$). Ammonia gas is then slowly forced through an inverted funnel, the bell part of which is immersed to a depth of $\frac{1}{8}$ to $\frac{1}{4}$ in. in the solution of perrhenic acid. The gas is allowed to pass until the solution is faintly ammoniacal. The ammonium perrhenate crystals are separated from the solution by decantation. The salt is dissolved and recrystallized twice from distilled water and dried at 100°C (230°F).

Several hundred grams of the dry ammonium perrhenate are transferred to a quartz boat, and boat and contents are placed in a quartz tube 3 in. in diameter by 4 ft long, the central

18 in. of which is wound with "Nichrome" resistance wire. The tube is flushed out with nitrogen, and hydrogen at a slow, steady rate is passed through the tube. The temperature is gradually raised to 380°C (716°F) and held there until decomposition of the ammonium perrhenate is complete. For a charge of perrhenate equivalent to 200 g of metal, this generally takes about 1 hr. Finally, the temperature is raised to 700–800°C (1292–1472°F) and held for 1 hr to complete the reduction. The furnace is then gradually cooled in a stream of hydrogen to 100–150°C (212–302°F), at which time the hydrogen is replaced with nitrogen and the system is allowed to cool to room temperature. The product prepared in this manner from high-purity ammonium perrhenate needs no washing, as all products except the metal are volatile.

Preparation from Rhenium (V) Chloride. Preparation of high-purity rhenium by this halide method is described by Sims et al.,[78f,78g,79] and by Rosenbaum, Runck, and Campbell.[73] Rhenium metal prepared from potassium or ammonium perrhenate or massive rhenium scrap is first treated with hydrogen at 1000°C (1832°F) in a "Vycor" tube to insure complete reduction of any oxides present. The system is then purged with helium while cooling to 750°C (1382°F), and purging is continued at this temperature for 1 hr to insure complete removal of hydrogen. Chlorine gas is next substituted for the helium, and maintaining a slight positive exit pressure of chlorine, the rhenium is converted to $ReCl_5$ which volatilizes away from the reaction zone and is condensed in an air-cooled trap. Under the conditions specified the $ReCl_5$ is formed at the rate of approximately 150 g/hr.

The rhenium (V) chloride thus formed is next added cautiously to cold water surrounded by an ice bath. This treatment with water results in the formation of several hydrolysis products, the chief of which is hydrated rhenium (IV) oxide, ReO_2. Filtration of the gelatinous product is facilitated by prior treatment of the suspension with a stream of carbon dioxide for 30 min prior to filtration. The filtered product is next washed with distilled water and dried in a vacuum desiccator.

The dried ReO_2 is next placed in a molybdenum boat inserted in a tube furnace and reduced with hydrogen for 1 hr at 400°C (752°F), followed by another hour of treatment at 600°C (1112°F). After cooling to room temperature, the loosely sintered mass is ground in an agate mortar and subjected to a 2-hr treatment in a stream of hydrogen at 800°C (1472°F). The system is then purged free of hydrogen with an inert atmosphere while cooling to room temperature.

Products of hydrolysis of the $ReCl_5$ other than ReO_2 are oxidized to perrhenic acid with 30 per cent hydrogen peroxide, the acid thus formed is neutralized with ammonium hydroxide, and the resulting ammonium perrhenate is purified and reduced to the metal with hydrogen. Metal powder thus prepared is then ready for chlorination. Over-all efficiency of the process on the basis of recovered rhenium is 95 per cent, with total impurities amounting to only 0.049 per cent in the metallic rhenium.

PHYSICAL AND MECHANICAL PROPERTIES

The high temperatures encountered in certain areas of nuclear and rocket engineering as well as rapid advances in the fields of electronics and high-temperature measuring devices have given considerable impetus in recent years to an exhaustive evaluation of the physical and mechanical properties of the refractory metals and their alloys. In this connection rhenium, because of several unique properties, has received increasing attention of late. An excellent and detailed summary of the work of Sims, *et al.*, on the physical, mechanical, and electrical properties of rhenium, rhenium alloys, tungsten, and other refractory metals is given in their series of *Quarterly Progress Reports*, "Investigations of Rhenium," published by the Battelle Memorial Institute.[78] Some of the significant general properties of rhenium discussed in the Battelle Reports are outlined briefly below, and specific atomic and physical properties are listed in Table 20.1.

Among the elements, rhenium has a melting point exceeded only by tungsten and carbon,[20] a density exceeded only by osmium, iridium, and platinum,[20] and a modulus of elasticity exceeded only by osmium and iridium.[78a] In addition, rhenium has other desirable and out-

TABLE 20.1. ATOMIC, PHYSICAL, AND MECHANICAL PROPERTIES OF RHENIUM
(Superscript numbers refer to references)

Atomic number	75[8]
Atomic weight	186.31[40]
Isotopes	185, 187[5, 6]
Atomic radius	1.3777 Å[2, 32, 34, 77]
Crystal structure	Hexagonal close packed[20, 34, 78a]
Lattice constants	a = 2.758 ± 0.001 Å[78a, 85]
	c = 4.454 ± 0.001 Å[78a, 85]
	c/a = 1.615[78a]
Color	Typically metallic in massive form—black to metallic in powder or electrodeposited form
Allotropic transition	None[20]
Recrystallization temperature	1400°C (2550°F) (will vary with degree of cold work)[20]
Density	21.02 g/cc, 0.76 lb/cu in.[20, 70, 78c]
Melting point	3180°C (5756°F)[20, 70, 78c]
Boiling point (estimated)	5900°K (10,160°F)[77, 78c]
Modulus of elasticity	67×10^6 psi[20, 70]
Tensile strength	
Pure, annealed (room temperature)	1.64×10^5 psi, 28 per cent elongation
Pure, worked (room temperature)	3.22×10^5 psi, 2 per cent elongation
Pure, worked [1850°F (1010°C)]	1.24×10^5 psi, 1 per cent elongation
Pure, worked [2700°F (1482°C)]	0.40×10^5 psi, 1 per cent elongation[20, 70, 78c, 78e]

TABLE 20.1. ATOMIC, PHYSICAL, AND MECHANICAL PROPERTIES OF RHENIUM (*cont.*)

(Superscript numbers refer to references)

Coefficient of linear thermal expansion	6.6×10^{-6} to $6.8 \times 10^{-6}/°C$, between 20–1000°C (68–1832°F). 3.6 micro in./in. °F at 68°F[20, 70, 78C]
Specific heat	$C_p = 0.03256 + 0.6625 \times 10^{-5}t$ cal/g/°C Between 0–1200°C (32–2192°F). Mean value between 0–20°C (32–68°F) = 0.03262 cal/g/°C 0.033 Btu/lb/°F[20, 44, 77, 79]
Thermal conductivity	0.17 cal/sq cm/°C/sec/cm 493 Btu/sq ft/hr/in./°F at 68°F[20, 70]
Electrical resistivity	19.14×10^{-6} ohm-cm[2, 20, 78a]
Temperature coefficient of electrical resistance	$3.11 \times 10^{-3}/°C$ between 0–100°C (32–212°F) $1.98 \times 10^{-3}/°C$ between 0–2700°C (32–4892°F)[2, 78a]
Superconductivity	Becomes superconducting at 0–95°K[4]
Hardness	250 (Brinell) 135 (Vickers) for pure cast 286 to 325 (Vickers) depending upon degree of swaging and annealing[26, 78d, 78g]
Vapor pressure	4.65×10^{-5} mm Hg or 6.11×10^{-8} atm at 2500°C (4532°F), 1.24×10^{-9} atm at 2221°C (4030°F), to 7.37×10^{-7} atm at 2726°C (4939°F)[71, 78b, 78c]
Molal entropy	8.887 ± 0.023 cal/mole/deg at 298.16°K[83]
Heat of sublimation (calc.)	152 to 187 kcal/mole[71, 78c]
Latent heat of fusion	7.9 kcal/mole[71, 78c]
Latent heat of vaporization	152 kcal/mole[71]
Spectral data	Persistent spectral lines at 3000, 3425, 3452, 3462, and triplet at 3640 Å[3, 52, 53, 61, 75]
K series	[43]
L series	[10, 91]
M series	[47, 48]
Photoelectric threshold (Long wave limit)	
Not in vacuum	2671–2677 Å[23]
Partial vacuum	2810–2830 Å[23]
Completely outgassed	2480 Å and 2662 ± 4 Å[23, 79]
Photoelectric work function	4.74 volts[47] 4.97 volts[23] 5.10 volts[2] 4.66 ± 0.01 volts[79]
Magnetic moment in nuclear magnetons	3.1433 for Re 185 3.1755 for Re 187[54, 74, 77, 84]
Specific magnetic susceptibility	$0.369 \times 10^{-6} \pm 0.006$[66]
Atomic paramagnetism	68.7×10^{-6} [66]
Parachor	
From ReO_2Cl_3	78.9
From Re_2O_7	68.9
From ReO_3Cl	76.4[11]

standing properties which command consideration in the field of metal refractories. For instance, although the vapor pressure of rhenium is higher than that of tungsten by a factor of 10 at 2500°C (4532°F),[78b] its water-cycle characteristics at 10^{-4} mm Hg pressure and temperatures ranging from 1400–1800°C (2552–3272°F) is superior to that of tungsten, the latter metal eroding approximately 176 times as fast as rhenium.[78a] However, using a higher vacuum and employing techniques to remove as much water vapor as possible, it was found that at 1600°C (2912°F) the loss in weight of a rhenium filament was approximately 1.6 times as great as the loss in weight from a tungsten filament over a period of time in excess of 200 hr.[79] This result, disregarding any water-cycle effect, is in keeping with the higher vapor pressure of rhenium.

Rhenium appears to be unique among refractory metals in that it does not form carbides.[80] At elevated temperatures, however, the metal dissolves carbon and a eutectic reaction occurs at 2840°C (5144°F) and 1.3 weight per cent carbon. Diffusion of carbon into rhenium occurs rapidly at high temperatures, resulting in increased hardness, but specimens so treated still show considerable ductility, suggesting that the metal in filament form might have useful applications in carbonaceous atmospheres.

In the presence of molten copper, silver, tin, and zinc, rhenium is essentially unattacked, but it dissolves readily in molten iron and nickel. The metal reacts slightly with molten aluminum.[78f,79] The metal is stable in contact with alumina at reduced pressure and elevated temperatures, suggesting the possible use of rhenium wire on aluminum oxide furnace cores if used in an inert atmosphere.[20,79]

The hardening effect of rhenium on platinum is quite striking. For instance, whereas the Vickers hardness number (VHN) for pure cast platinum is about 40 and that for pure rhenium is 135, the VHN for Re-Pt alloys varies from 104 for 1 Re-99 Pt to 229 for 10 Re-90 Pt. This hardening effect of rhenium on platinum is greater than the hardening effect of the metals nickel, osmium, iridium, and rhodium on platinum.[78g]

Thermocouples of Re-Mo and Re-W produce high emf's and show good sensitivity to temperature.[79] Other thermocouple systems involving rhenium or rhenium alloys with platinum or platinum group metal alloys show considerable promise in the field of high-temperature thermometry.

The stress-rupture strength of rhenium is very high at elevated temperatures.[20,70,78d] At 1000°C (1832°F), for instance, the rupture time for a 50-ml wire varied from 30 sec at 80,000 psi stress to 16.5 hr at 40,000 psi stress. During the test there was a total elongation of approximately 2 per cent on 3-in. specimens. At 2000°C (3632°F) the elongation increases to over 4 per cent.

The ultimate tensile strength of annealed rhenium sheet is listed as 168,000 psi; this value increases as the rhenium is reduced by cold rolling and reaches a value of 322,000 psi after a reduction of 30.7 per cent.[20,70,78c,78e]

Even at elevated temperatures [up to at least 1371°C (2500°F)], the ultimate tensile strength of rhenium is very much higher than that of other refractory metals such as tungsten, molybdenum, tantalum, columbium, and chromium. At 538°C (1000°F) it is about 111,000 psi, at 1093°C (2000°F) about 81,000, at 1371°C (2500°F) about 49,000, at 1649°C (3000°F) about 32,000, at 1927°C (3500°F) about 22,000, and at 2205°C (4000°F) about 12,500.

To take advantage of the unique physical and mechanical properties of rhenium at elevated temperatures it should be borne in mind that the metal undergoes serious and rapid degradation in oxygen, air and other oxidizing environments, being much less resistant in this respect than columbium, molybdenum, tantalum, or tungsten.[70] The metal, being slightly noble in character, stands up well in hydrogen and other inert atmospheres at elevated temperatures, is resistant to attack by hydrochloric acid, and shows good resistance to salt-water corrosion and the mechanical effects of electrical erosion.[20]

CHEMICAL PROPERTIES

For anyone interested in a detailed summary of the chemical properties of rhenium and its compounds, several excellent reference works are available.[21,37,41,50,62,76] Much of the information recorded below is taken from these sources.

The chemical activity of rhenium depends to a large extent on the manner in which it is prepared. If prepared in a fine state of subdivision by hydrogen reduction of one of its powdered salts, it may actually be pyrophoric if steps are not taken to remove excess hydrogen. The finely divided metal apparently acts catalytically to oxidize the hydrogen, sufficient heat being liberated to ignite the metal. On the other hand, a polished surface of the compact metal is not readily tarnished, even on long exposure to air.

Rhenium metal, plated on strips of platinum, silver, tantalum, copper, and brass, retains a high luster as long as the specimens are preserved in a perfectly dry atmosphere. On exposure to moist air, however, the metal is gradually oxidized, the end product being perrhenic acid ($HReO_4$). Contrary to the behavior of rhenium plate on a metallic base, a bright plate of rhenium on a spectrographic graphite electrode has retained its initial appearance for several years, during which time no attempt was made to preserve it in a dry environment.[82] Levi and Espersen[46] have found that rhenium plate on a tungsten filament, if heated to 1000°C (1832°F) in an atmosphere of hydrogen immediately after the plating operation, is stable in moist air at room temperature for indefinite periods.

By virtue of its position in the periodic table, rhenium would be expected to exhibit a characteristic valence of 7. Actually, this has proved to be its most stable valence state. In addition to this most stable state, it also exhibits valence of -1, 2, 3, 4, 5, and 6. Although the valence states of 4, 6, and 7 are the most common, there is a tendency for rhenium in valence states from 1 to 6 to disproportionate to give products in which the rhenium is partially converted to a lower state and partially to a higher state, usually 7. This tendency is exhibited in the following reaction:

$$3ReO_3 + heat \rightarrow ReO_2 + Re_2O_7.$$

The metal heated in air or oxygen is readily converted to Re_2O_7 at temperatures of 350°C (662°F) or above:

$$4Re + 7O_2 \rightarrow 2Re_2O_7.$$

The reaction may proceed stepwise, as it has been observed that the red oxide (ReO_3) frequently makes its appearance during the initial heating.

The halogen elements, with the exception of iodine, react with rhenium with decreasing vigor in passing from fluorine to bromine. In no case, however, is the maximum valence state of rhenium realized. This is probably due to the fact that even in the case of fluorine the rhenium atom is not capable of accommodating 7 atoms of the halogen. Characteristic reactions of the metal with the halogens are given below.

$$Re + 3F_2 \rightarrow ReF_6$$

$$ReF_6 + H_2 \xrightarrow{200°C} ReF_4 + H_2F_2$$

$$2Re + 5Cl_2 \rightarrow 2ReCl_5$$

$$ReCl_5 + heat \rightarrow ReCl_3 + Cl_2$$

$$2Re + 3Br_2 \rightarrow 2ReBr_3$$

All of the halides of rhenium on contact with water or moist air undergo hydrolysis, and frequently disproportionation. The actual products formed will depend on the nature of the halide in question but generally include two or more of the following: complex halogen and oxyhalogen acids of the metal; rhenium (IV) oxide, ReO_2; perrhenic acid, $HReO_4$; rhenium metal; hydrohalogen acids; and free halogen.

Sulfides of the metal may be prepared by the action of sulfur vapor on the finely divided powder at elevated temperatures or by the action of hydrogen sulfide on acid solutions of the perrhenate.[12] The best known sulfides of rhenium are ReS_2 and Re_2S_7.

Rhenium carbonyl, $[Re(CO)_5]_2$, has been prepared by Hieber and Fuchs[36] by treating Re_2O_7 with carbon monoxide at 250°C (482°F) and 200 atm pressure.

Phosphides[35] and arsenides[90] of the metal have been prepared by direct union of the elements, but nitrogen is without effect on the metal even at elevated temperatures.

There appears to be some controversy in regard to the existence of rhenium carbide. Trzebiatowski[86] reports that the metal, heated in an atmosphere of carbon monoxide or methane, will decompose the latter two compounds, with consequent incorporation into the lattice of rhenium of a small amount of carbon.

Rhenium is not acted upon by hydrochloric acid. With strong oxidizing acids such as nitric and hot sulfuric, the metal is vigorously attacked and converted to perrhenic acid. Hydrogen peroxide in ammoniacal solution converts the metal, its oxides, and its sulfides to ammonium perrhenate.

DETECTION AND ANALYTICAL ESTIMATION OF RHENIUM

The detection of rhenium in native ores is not easy, even by spectroscopic means, owing to the low concentration of rhenium and the interference of elements with which it is generally associated. As the rhenium-bearing ores are processed, certain fractions become enriched in rhenium, and detection of the element by spectroscopic and chemical means is frequently readily accomplished.

The potassium thiocyanate–stannous chloride color test, introduced by Geilmann, Wrigge, and Weibke,[27] is one of the most useful chemical tests for rhenium. If to a solution containing rhenium in the form of perrhenate ion, in the presence of hydrochloric acid and potassium thiocyanate, some stannous chloride is added, a yellow to orange-red color is produced. The color produced, by matching with appropriate standards, serves as a means of quantitatively estimating the amount of rhenium present. Molybdenum interferes with this color test but may be removed by methods suggested by Hoffman and Lundell,[39] Hiskey and Meloche,[38] Malouf and White,[49] and Melaven and Whetsel.[57]

A very satisfactory method for the determination of larger quantities of rhenium is the gravimetric method of Willard and Smith,[92] using tetraphenylarsonium chloride as the precipitating agent, or the modified method suggested by Smith and Long,[81] using the same reagent.

FABRICATION TECHNIQUES

The preparation of rhenium metal powder, the usual commercial form of the element, has been given in some detail in the section on derivation of the metal.

Consolidation of rhenium powder into the form of bar, wire, and sheet has been accomplished, in spite of certain properties of the metal that make it difficult to work. As described by Kates,[45] the powder is first consolidated by pressing and then is resistance-sintered by passing an electric current through the bar housed in a vacuum chamber or in an atmosphere of hydrogen. Such procedure is capable of producing a compact bar with a density in excess of 90 per cent of theoretical. Bars so produced are described by Kates as having excellent room-temperature and elevated-temperature ductility in the early stages of deformation. During later stages of deformation and size reduction, however, the metal exhibits the property of work hardening or deformation hardening to a considerable degree, the hardness of an annealed bar, e.g., being essentially doubled for a 10 per cent reduction in area. This necessitates relatively light reductions in cross section between anneals, and, to complicate matters, the annealing temperature for light reductions is of the order of 1482–1982°C (2700–3600°F).

In spite of the difficulties encountered in the working of rhenium, it is very ductile in the annealed state and can be swaged, bent, coiled, and rolled, as long as it is shaped with a minimum of cold work.

The electrodeposition of rhenium on a variety of metal surfaces and graphite has been accomplished with success. Fink and Deren[26] report that bright, coherent deposits of the metal may be obtained from a variety of baths containing potassium perrhenate. Young[93] describes methods for the plating of rhenium and rhenium-nickel alloys. Netherton and Holt[59] give semi-quantitative information on cathode current efficiencies from a sulfuric acid bath. Smith, Melaven, and Kline[82] have obtained bright deposits of rhenium on a variety of metals and graphite. Good deposits were obtained using a bath similar to one described by Fink and Deren[26] but containing a higher concentration of sulfuric acid. The electrolyte consists of 11 g of potassium perrhenate and 12 g of concentrated sulfuric acid/liter. Electrolysis is carried out at 28–50°C (82–122°F) with a current density of 100 to 200 amp/sq ft.

The vapor phase deposition of rhenium on filaments of high-melting-point metals, notably tungsten, is the subject of several patents.[14,15,28,29,88] In general, the technique consists of heating the filament to be plated to a high temperature in the presence of a volatile rhenium halide, or in the presence of a volatile rhenium halide and an indifferent gas such as nitrogen. Thermal decomposition of the halide results in the deposition of rhenium on the metal filament. Properties of the rhenium-plated filaments are described.

APPLICATIONS

A number of possible applications of rhenium have been suggested, but, because of the high cost and present rarity of the element, none has received any widespread commercial use. Perhaps the most promising use is in the fields of electronics and of high-temperature measurement, the rhenium-tungsten thermocouple element, e.g., being serviceable to temperatures above 2000°C (3632°F). Other possible applications, based on the high melting point of the metal, are suggested in a patent issued to P. R. Mallory and Company.[87] The alloy is described as one containing tungsten, molybdenum, and rhenium for use in electrical make-and-break contact points. Alloys consisting of platinum and rhenium or platinum and rhenium together with iron, rhodium, and iridium for use as thermocouple elements are the subject of a British patent.[16,17] Similar alloys are described by Goedecke.[31]

Becker and Moers[7] describe the tungsten-rhenium alloy system and point out that inter-metallic compounds of the two exist. The binary system of iron and rhenium is described in some detail by Eggers.[22] A refractory alloy consisting of more than 90 per cent tungsten, less than 10 per cent rhenium, and not more than 1 per cent vanadium is described by Laise.[18] The addition of iridium, iron, nickel, and cobalt to platinum-rhenium alloys improves the mechanical properties of the alloy and prevents grain growth.[17]

The catalytic properties of rhenium, some of its compounds, and a few of its alloys have been investigated. Platonov and co-workers[69] describe the preparation of an active rhenium catalyst from ammonium perrhenate and describe in detail the dehydrogenation of a number of alcohols to aldehydes and ketones.[67] It was found to be less suitable as a hydrogenation catalyst.[68] The preparation of colloidal rhenium and its use as a catalyst are described by Zenghelis and Stathis,[95] who also have reported the use of rhenium as a catalyst in the synthesis of ammonia.[94] The kinetics of the decomposition of ammonia on rhenium catalysts is the subject of an investigation by McGeer and Taylor.[51] Colloidal rhenium or its compounds, absorbed from suspension on activated charcoal, have been used in the hydrogenation of coal,

coal tar, and mineral oil.[30] The use of rhenium or rhenium alloyed with platinum metals, or silver for the oxidation of ammonia is described by Siebert.[17] The oxidation of SO_2 to SO_3, using rhenium or a 90 per cent tungsten, 10 per cent rhenium mixture as the catalyst, is the subject of a patent assigned by Noddack and Noddack to Siemens and Halske A.-G.[13]

References

1. Aartovaara, G. A., *Tek. Fören. i Finland Förh.*, **52**, 157 (1932); cf., *C. A.*, **26**, 5460 (1932).
2. Agte, C., Alterthum, H., Becker, K., Heyne, G., and Moers, K., *Naturwissenschaften*, **19**, 108 (1931).
3. Agte, C., Alterthum, H., Becker, K., Heyne, G., and Moers, K., *Z. anorg. u. allgem. Chem.*, **196**, 129 (1931).
4. Aschermann, G., and Justi, E., *Physik. Z.*, **43**, 207 (1942).
5. Aston, F. W., *Nature*, **127**, 591 (1931).
6. Aston, F. W., *Proc. Roy. Soc. (London) A.*, **132**, 487 (1931).
7. Becker, K., and Moers, K., *Metallwirtschaft*, **9**, 1063 (1930); cf., *C. A.*, **25**, 2043 (1931).
8. Berg, O., *Physik. Z.*, **28**, 864 (1927).
9. Berg, O., and Tacke, I., *Naturwissenschaften*, **13**, 571 (1925).
10. Beuthe, H., *Z. Physik*, **50**, 762 (1928).
11. Briscoe, H. V. A., Robinson, P. L., and Rudge, A. J., *J. Chem. Soc.*, 2673 (1932).
12. Briscoe, H. V. A., Robinson, P. L., and Stoddart, E. M., *J. Chem. Soc.*, 1439 (1931).
13. British Patent 346,652 (Oct. 8, 1929).
14. British Patent 351,216 (June 4, 1930).
15. British Patent 364,502 (June 4,1931).
16. British Patent 381,137 (June 20, 1931).
17. British Patent 385,859 (June 8, 1931).
18. British Patent 520,025 (April 12, 1940).
19. *Chemical and Engineering News*, p. 60, July 7, 1959.
20. Denny, J. P., and Kendall, L. F., Jr., *Mechanical Eng.*, **80**, No. 8, 67, August 1958.
21. Druce, J. G. F., "Rhenium," Cambridge, England, University Press, 1948.
22. Eggers, H., *Mitt. Kaiser-Wilhelm-Inst. Eisenforsch., Düsseldorf*, **20**, 147 (1938); cf., *C. A.*, **32**, 7879 (1938).
23. Engelmann, A., *Ann. Physik*, **17**, 185 (1933).
24. Feit, W., *Z. angew. Chem.*, **43**, 459 (1930).
25. *Ibid.*, **46**, 216 (1933).
26. Fink, C. G., and Deren, P., *Trans. Electrochem. Soc.*, **66**, 381 (1934).

27. Geilmann, W., Wrigge, F. W., and Weibke, F., *Z. anorg. u. allgem. Chem.,* **208,** 217 (1932).

28. German Patent 527,105 (June 5, 1929).

29. German Patent 537,936 (July 9, 1930).

30. German Patent 693,707 (June 20, 1940).

31. Goedecke, W., *Siebert Festscher.,* **72** (1931); cf., *C. A.,* **26,** 4216 (1932).

32. Goldschmidt, V. M., *Naturwissenschaften,* **17,** 134 (1929).

33. *Ibid.,* **18,** 999 (1930).

34. Goldschmidt, V. M., *Z. physik. Chem. B.,* **2,** 244 (1929).

35. Haraldsen, H., *Z. anorg. u. allgem. Chem.,* **221,** 397 (1935).

36. Hieber, W., and Fuchs, H., *Z. anorg. Chem.,* **248,** 256 (1941).

37. Hiskey, C. F., and Bacon, J. A., *J. Tenn. Acad. Sci.,* **15,** 381 (1940).

38. Hiskey, C. F., and Meloche, V. W., *Ind. Eng. Chem., Anal. Ed.,* **12,** 503 (1940).

39. Hoffman, J. I., and Lundell, G. E. F., *J. Research Natl. Bur. Standards,* **23,** 497 (1939).

40. Honigschmidt, O., and Sachtleben, R., *Z. anorg. u. allgem. Chem.,* **191,** 309 (1930).

41. Hopkins, B. S., "Chapters in the Chemistry of the Less Familiar Elements," Vol. 2, Ch. 20, Champaign, Ill., Stipes Publishing Co., 1939.

42. Hurd, L. C., and Brimm, E., "Inorganic Syntheses," Vol. 1 (Booth, H. S., Editor-in-Chief), p. 164, New York, McGraw-Hill Book Company, Inc., 1939.

43. Ingelstam, E., *Nova Acta Regiae Soc. Sci. Upsaliensis,* **10,** 7 (1937); cf., *Chem. Zentr.,* **1,** 4735 (1937).

44. Jaeger, F. M., and Rosenbohm, E., *Proc. Acad. Sci. Amsterdam,* **36,** 786 (1933); cf., *C. A.,* **28,** 1257 (1934).

45. Kates, L. W., *Materials and Methods,* **39,** No. 3, 88, March, 1954.

46. Levi, R., and Espersen, G. A., *Phys. Rev.,* **78,** 231 (1950).

47. Lindberg, E., *Z. Physik.,* **50,** 82 (1928).

48. *Ibid.,* **56,** 402 (1929).

49. Malouf, E. E., and White, M. G., *Anal. Chem.,* **23,** 497 (1951).

50. Maxted, E. B., "Modern Advances in Inorganic Chemistry," Ch. 5, Oxford, England, Clarendon Press, 1947.

51. McGeer, J. P., and Taylor, H. S., *J. Am. Chem. Soc.,* **73,** 2743 (1951).

52. Meggers, W. F., *Bur. Standards J. Research,* **6,** 1027 (1931).

53. Meggers, W. F., *Phys. Rev.,* **37,** 219 (1931).

54. Meggers, W. F., King, A. S., and Bacher, R. F., *Phys. Rev.,* **38,** 1258 (1931).

55. Melaven, A. D., and Bacon, J. A. (to University of Tenn. Research Corp.) U.S. Patent 2,414,965 (Jan. 1947).

56. Melaven, A. D., and Bacon, J. A., unpublished work, University of Tenn.

57. Melaven, A. D., and Whetsel, K. B., *Anal. Chem.,* **20,** 1209 (1948).

58. Moeller, K., *Naturwissenschaften,* **19,** 575 (1931).

59. Netherton, L. E., and Holt, M. L., *J. Electrochem. Soc.,* **95,** 324 (1949).

60. *New York Times,* Feb. 10, 1959.

61. Noddack, I., *Z. Electrochem.,* **34,** 629 (1928).

62. Noddack, I., and Noddack, W., "Das Rhenium," Leipzig, Germany, Leopold Voss, 1933.

63. Noddack, I., and Noddack, W., *Z. Physik. Chem.,* **154 A,** 207 (1931).

64. Noddack, W., and Noddack, I., *Z anorg. u. allgem. Chem.,* **183,** 353 (1929).

65. Noddack, W., and Tacke, I., *Naturwissenschaften,* **13,** 567 (1925).

66. Perakis, N., and Capatos, L., *Compt. rend.,* **196,** 611 (1933).

67. Platonov, M. S., *J. Gen. Chem. (U.S.S.R.),* **11,** 683 (1941); cf., *C. A.,* **36,** 397 (1942).

68. Platonov, M. S., Anisimov, S. B., and Krasheninnikova, V. M., *Ber.,* **68 B,** 761 (1935).

69. Platonov, M. S., and Tomilov, V. I., *J. Gen. Chem. (U.S.S.R.),* **7,** 776 (1937).

70. Pugh, J. W., *Journal of Metals,* **10,** No. 5, 335, May, 1958.

71. Quill, L. L., Editor, "The Chemistry and Metallurgy of Miscellaneous Materials," New York, McGraw-Hill Book Co., 1950.

72. Richardson, D., "Spectroscopy in Science and Industry. Proceedings of the Fifth Summer Conference (Mass. Inst. Tech.) on Spectroscopy and Applications." Boiling Point Determinations by Spectroscopic Methods, New York, John Wiley and Sons, Inc., 1938; cf., *C. A.,* **32,** 4080 (1938).

73. Rosenbaum, D. M., Runck, R. J. and Campbell, I. E., *J. Electrochem. Soc.,* **103,** 518–21 (1956).

74. Schmidt, T., *Z. Physik.,* **108,** 408 (1938).

75. Schober, H., *Sitzber. Akad. Wiss. Wien. Math. naturw. kl. Abt. IIa.,* **140,** 79 (1931)., cf., *C. A.,* **26,** 374 (1932).

76. Sidgwick, N. V., "The Chemical Elements and Their Compounds," Vol. 2, p. 1291, Oxford, England, Clarendon Press, 1950.

77. Sims, C. T., Wyler, E. N., Gaines, G. B., and Rosenbaum, D. M., "A Survey of the Literature on Rhenium." *WADC Technical Report 56-319,* ASTIA Document No. AD 110596, June 1956, Office of Technical Services, U.S. Department of Commerce, Washington 25, D.C.

78. Sims, C. T., *et al.,* "Investigations of Rhenium," Progress Reports to Aeronautical Research

Laboratory, Wright Air Development Center, Contract No. AF-33(616)-232. Battelle Memorial Institute, Columbus, Ohio.

78a. Fifth Quarterly Progress Report, September 1953.

78b. Sixth Quarterly Progress Report, December 1953.

78c. Seventh Quarterly Progress Report, March 1954.

78d. Ninth Quarterly Progress Report, September 1954.

78e. Tenth Quarterly Progress Report, December 1954.

78f. Eleventh Quarterly Progress Report, March 1955.

78g. Twelfth Quarterly Progress Report, June 1955.

79. Sims, C. T., *et al.*, "Investigations of Rhenium," *WADC Technical Report 54-371, Supplement 1*, ASTIA Document No. AD 97301, pg. 57, September, 1956, Office of Technical Services, U.S. Department of Commerce, Washington 25, D.C.

80. Sims, C. T., *et al.*, "Investigations of Rhenium for Electron-Tube Applications," ASTIA Document No. AD 152419, Fifth Scientific Report, June 1958, Battelle Memorial Institute, Columbus, Ohio.

81. Smith, W. T., Jr., and Long, S. H., *J. Am. Chem., Soc.*, **70**, 354 (1948).

82. Smith, W. T., Jr., Melaven, A. D., and Kline, J. W., unpublished work, University of Tennessee.

83. Smith, W. T., Jr., Oliver, G. D., and Cobble, J. W., *J. Am. Chem. Soc.*, **75**, 5785 (1953).

84. Sommer, L. A., and Karlson, P., *Naturwissenschaften*, **19**, 1021 (1931).

85. Stenzel, W., and Weerts, J., *Z. Krist.*, **84**, 20 (1933).

86. Trzebiatowski, W., *Z. anorg. u allgem. Chem.*, **233**, 376 (1937).

87. U.S. Patent 2,234,969 (March 18, 1941).

88. van Arkel, A. E., *Metallwirtschaft*, **13**, 405 (1934); cf., *C. A.*, **28**, 5011 (1934).

89. *Wall Street Journal*, Feb. 12, 1959.

90. Weichmann, F., Heimburg, M., and Biltz, W., *Z. anorg. u. allgem. Chem.*, **240**, 129 (1939).

91. Wennerlof, I., *Z. Physik.*, **47**, 422 (1928).

92. Willard, H. H., and Smith, G. W., *Ind. Eng. Chem., Anal. Ed.*, **11**, 305 (1939).

93. Young, C. B. F., *Metal Ind. (N.Y.)*, **34**, 176 (1936).

94. Zenghelis, C., and Stathis, El., *Österr. Chem. Ztg.*, **40**, 80 (1937); cf., *C. A.*, **31**, 4777 (1937).

95. Zenghelis, C., and Stathis, K., *Atti X° congr. intern. chim.*, **2**, 821 (1938); cf., *C. A.*, **33**, 8081 (1939).

96. Zimmerley, S. R. and Malouf, E. E. (to Kennecott Copper Corporation) U.S. Patent 2,809,092 (Oct. 1957).

21. RUBIDIUM and CESIUM

Clifford A. Hampel

Consulting Chemical Engineer
Skokie, Illinois

INTRODUCTION

Rubidium, atomic number 37 and atomic weight 85.48, and cesium, atomic number 55 and atomic weight 132.91, are the fourth and fifth members of the alkali metal group, Group I of the periodic table, of which lithium, sodium, and potassium are the first three. These elements were discovered by Bunsen and Kirchhoff in 1861 and 1860, respectively, by the use of the spectroscope. Rubidium was named for the prominent red lines in its spectrum, and cesium for its prominent blue lines.

Both elements are soft, ductile, low-density, silvery-white metals of low melting points. Cesium melts at 28.5°C (83°F), and is one of the three metals (with mercury and gallium) which are liquid at room temperature. Rubidium melts at 39°C (102°F).

In both physical and chemical properties, rubidium and cesium resemble the other alkali metals. They are monovalent in their compounds, which are very stable to oxidation and reduction. In the vapor phase these metals consist almost exclusively of monoatomic molecules. Rubidium and cesium are the second and first most electropositive elements and the second and first most alkaline elements.

OCCURRENCE

Rubidium is the sixteenth most prevalent element in the earth's crust (about as abundant as chlorine) but is not found in any mineral as a principal constituent. Rather, it occurs widely dispersed in potassium minerals in very low concentrations. This lack of concentration in any mineral deposits undoubtedly accounts for the scarcity of production and application of this rather prevalent element. However, it is also found in lepidolite ores of South Africa imported into this country for extraction of their lithium content, and some of the lepidolites contain as much as 1 to 1.5 per cent rubidium and much smaller amounts of cesium. The extensive processing of these lithium ores in recent years has resulted in an increasing availability of rubidium and cesium by-product concentrates that are being used as sources of rubidium and cesium compounds.

One operation based upon African lepidolite produces a 70 per cent potassium by-product which contains 23 per cent rubidium carbonate and 2 per cent cesium carbonate. This material, marketed under the trade name "Alkarb" by American Potash & Chemical Corp., is used in the glass industry as an equivalent of potassium carbonate in the production of glass for television tubes and vacuum tubes for electronic applications. It is also the raw material for the rubidium and cesium products made by that company.

Cesium is the fortieth most prevalent element in the earth's crust (about as abundant as germanium) and is found in minerals such as pollucite ($2Cs_2O \cdot 2Al_2O_3 \cdot 9SiO_2 \cdot H_2O$), a hydrated silicate of aluminum and cesium. A large deposit of pollucite containing 25 to 30 per cent cesium has recently been discovered in the Bernic Lake region of Manitoba, and Chemalloy Minerals, Ltd., has announced plans to extract cesium from this ore.[7] Other deposits are found in the island of Elba, in Maine, and in the Black Hills of South Dakota.

PRODUCTION AND PRICE STATISTICS

The production of rubidium and cesium metals amounts to less than 100 lb/year, but currently developing interest in new applications, especially for cesium, as ion propellents for missiles may alter drastically this situation.

Prices for the two metals have varied between $1 and $5/g, depending upon the supplier, purity, quantity, and packaging. This price picture should turn downward when and as greater production is required and achieved.

The present outlook is that the pricing of rubidium and cesium metals in quantities of about 10,000 pounds would be in the range of something less than $100 per pound. At the 200,000-pound contract level, pricing would probably be on the order of $25 per pound.

As of January, 1960, rubidium compounds of a 95 per cent minimum assay technical grade were listed at $15/lb for the carbonate, $14.50 for the chloride, $17 for the fluoride, and $13 for the sulfate. Cesium compounds of a 96 per cent minimum assay technical grade were listed at $27.50/lb for the carbonate, $34.50 for the chloride, $36 for the fluoride, and $32.50 for the sulfate.

DERIVATION

Cesium compounds can be derived from pollucite by treating the finely powdered mineral with hydrochloric acid, dehydrating the silica, and filtering off the insoluble residue. Cesium is separated from the filtrate by precipitation of a double chloride of lead ($2CsCl \cdot PbCl_4$) or antimony ($3CsCl \cdot 2SbCl_3$) by lead nitrate or antimony trichloride, respectively.[9,10,12,13] Cesium chloride can be recovered from these compounds by hydrolysis, which leaves cesium chloride in solution. Several other complex chlorides can also be used to effect the separation of cesium chloride quite free of other alkali metals, one of the best being the cesium chlorostannate intermediate, Cs_2SnCl_6.[8]

A more recent development is the use of sodium zinc ferrocyanide which, when added to a mixed alkali carbonate solution, causes the precipitation first of cesium and, in subsequent steps, of rubidium zinc ferrocyanide.[1,11] These insoluble products can be decomposed to form carbonates by heating in air, and the soluble rubidium and cesium carbonates can be dissolved by leaching the decomposition mixture with water.

The currently used techniques are discussed by Lam and Foster,[11] who describe the problems involved in obtaining relatively pure cesium and rubidium compounds from raw materials, chiefly the previously mentioned K_2CO_3–Rb_2CO_3–Cs_2CO_3 source, that contain two or more alkali metals.

Elemental rubidium and cesium can be prepared by several methods:

(1) electrolysis of fused salts, such as the chloride or cyanide, under an inert atmosphere;

(2) thermal decomposition of such compounds as the hydride and azide under vacuum or an inert gas; and

(3) chemical reduction of such compounds as the oxides, hydroxides, carbonates, halides, sulfates, or chromates with metals like calcium, magnesium, barium, aluminum, and silicon at elevated temperatures.

Of these methods, the ones most frequently practiced are the heating of rubidium or cesium carbonate with magnesium at about 675°C (1247°F) under hydrogen, or the heating of rubidium or cesium chloride with calcium at the same temperature under vacuum. In both cases the metals are condensed from the vapor state in the absence of air, frequently under an inert oil to protect them from reaction with the atmosphere.

PHYSICAL PROPERTIES

The physical properties of rubidium and cesium are presented in Table 21.1.

About 27.2 per cent of ordinary rubidium is beta-emitting rubidium 87 with a half life of 6.3×10^{10} years. It decomposes to strontium, and can be used to determine the age of rubidium-containing rocks.

The only natural isotope of cesium is cesium 133, but cesium 137 is one of the products of the atomic fission of uranium. It is also a beta emitter and has a half life of 33 years. Along with strontium 90, it is one of the most troublesome radioactive wastes to handle in the commercial applications of atomic fission.

Among the most interesting physical properties of rubidium and cesium are their large ionic radii, their low ionization potentials, their low densities and melting points, their high position in the electromotive series, and their low electron work functions. Both metals are

TABLE 21.1. PHYSICAL PROPERTIES OF RUBIDIUM AND CESIUM

	Rubidium	Cesium
Atomic number	37	55
Atomic weight	85.48	132.91
Crystal form	Body-centered cubic	Body-centered cubic
Latice constants (Å) [−173°C (−279°F)]	a = 5.62	a = 6.05
Atomic radius (Å)	2.43	2.62
Ionic radius (Å)	1.48	1.69
Density (g/cc) solid	1.532 (20°)	1.90 (20°)
liquid	1.475 (39°)	1.84 (28.5°)
Atomic volume (cc/g-atom) (20°)	55.9	69.95
Melting point		
°C	39	28.5
°F	102	83
Boiling point		
°C	688	705
°F	1270	1301
Volume change on melting (% of solid volume)	2.5	2.6
Latent heat of fusion (cal/g)	6.1	3.766
Latent heat of vaporization (cal/g)	212	146
Specific heat (cal/g/°C)	0.0913 [39–126°C (102–259°F)]	0.060 [28.5°C (78°F)]
	0.0907 [50°C (122°F)]	0.058 [50°C (122°F)]
	0.080 [0°C (32°F)]	0.052 [20°C (68°F)]

Vapor pressure, temperature for	°C	°F	°C	°F
1 mm Hg	294	561	278	532
10 " "	387	729	387	729
100 " "	519	966	515	959
200 " "	569	1056	570	1058
400 " "	628	1162	635	1175

	Rubidium	Cesium
Thermal conductivity (cal/sec/°C/cm)	0.075 [50°C (122°F)]	0.044 [28.5°C (83°F)]
	0.07 [39°C (102°F)]	
Coefficient of linear thermal expansion (per °C × 10⁻⁶)	90 [20°C (68°F)]	97 [0–26°C (32–79°F)]
	340 [40–100°C (104–212°F)]	
Viscosity (centipoises)	0.6734 [38°C (95°F)]	0.6299 [43.4°C (110°F)]
	0.6258 [50°C (122°F)]	0.4753 [99.6°C (211°F)]
	0.4844 [99.7°C (211.5°F)]	0.4065 [140.5°C (286°F)]
	0.4133 [140.5°C (286°F)]	0.3750 [168°C (334°F)]
	0.3234 [220.1°C (428°F)]	0.3430 [211°C (412°F)]
Electrical resistivity (microhm-cm)	11.6 [0°C (32°F)]	20 [20°C (68°F)]
	13.4 [35°C (95°F)]	22.2 [27°C (81°F)]
	19.6 [40°C (104°F)]	36.6 [30°C (86°F)]
	23.15 [50°C (122°F)]	37.0 [37°C (99°F)]
	25.32 [75°C (167°F)]	
	27.47 [100°C (212°F)]	
Temperature coefficient of electrical resistivity (per °C)	0.006 [0°C (32°F)]	
Ionization potential of gaseous atoms (volts)	4.16	3.87
Electron work function (ev)	2.09	1.81
Electrode potential (volts)		
Rb → Rb⁺ + e	2.9259	
Cs → Cs⁺ + e		3.02

TABLE 21.1. PHYSICAL PROPERTIES OF RUBIDIUM AND CESIUM (*cont.*)

	Rubidium		Cesium	
Thermoelectric power (microvolts per °C difference when cold junction is 0°C) Constants for equations: $Q = A + Bt, t = °C$ (values with respect to lead)	A −8.26 for −183 to 0°C (−297 to 32°F)	B −3.02	A 0.66 for −183 to 0°C (−297 to 32°F)	B −0.10
	−0.28 for 38–100°C (100–212°F)	−6.00	7.735 for 28–100°C (82–212°F)	−3.34
Thermal neutron absorption cross section (barns)	0.73		29	
Important spectral line (Å)	7800.2		8521.1	
Magnetic susceptibility (cgs units)	0.09×10^{-6} [18°C (64.4°F)]		-0.10×10^{-6} [18°C (64.4°F)]	
Hardness (Mohs' scale)	0.3		0.2	
Heat of formation (kcal/mole)				
Rb_2O	82.92			
Rb_2O_2	107.05			
Rb_2O_4	135.0			
Cs_2O			82.20	
Cs_2O_4			137.64	

A great deal of the above data was taken from the "Liquid Metals Handbook," R. N. Lyon (Ed.), Washington, *NAVEXOS P–733*, Atomic Energy Commission and Department of the Navy, June, 1952, which gives extensive references to the original literature sources. Other data are from "Handbook of Chemistry and Physics," C. D. Hodgman (Ed.), Cleveland, Chemical Rubber Publishing Co., and "Handbuch des Chemikers," B. P. Nikolski, (Ed.), Vols. I, II, and III, Berlin, Veb Verlag Technik, 1956–1959.

TABLE 21.2. COMPARISON OF PHYSICAL PROPERTIES OF THE ALKALI METALS

	Atomic weight	Radius (Å)		Melting point (°C)	Boiling point (°C)	Ionization potential (volts)
		Atom	Ion			
Lithium	6.940	1.56	0.60	179.0	1317	5.363
Sodium	22.997	1.86	0.95	97.9	883	5.12
Potassium	39.10	2.23	1.33	63.7	760	4.318
Rubidium	85.48	2.43	1.48	38.5	688	4.16
Cesium	132.91	2.62	1.69	28.5	705	3.87

	Density (g/cc) [20°C (68°F)]	Latent heat of fusion (cal/g)	Latent heat of vaporization (cal/g)
Lithium	0.534	158	4680
Sodium	0.97	27.05	1005
Potassium	0.87	14.6	496
Rubidium	1.532	6.1	212
Cesium	1.90	3.766	146

	Electron work function (ev)
Lithium	2.49
Sodium	2.28
Potassium	2.24
Rubidium	2.09
Cesium	1.81

photosensitive and are ionized readily and efficiently by visible light and by infrared and ultraviolet radiations.

The interesting gradation of physical properties among the alkali metals is demonstrated in Table 21.2.

CHEMICAL PROPERTIES

In their chemical reactions, rubidium and cesium are very similar to potassium, differing from it in no important aspect. Both metals react vigorously with air and water and must be protected from exposure to them.

Rubidium forms four oxides: the yellow monoxide, Rb_2O; the dark-brown dioxide or peroxide, Rb_2O_2; the black trioxide, Rb_2O_3; and the dark-orange tetroxide, Rb_2O_4. Upon exposure to air, it becomes covered rapidly with a gray-blue film that is a mixture of Rb_2O, Rb_2O_2, and Rb_2O_4. Cesium forms the same series of oxides.

The vigor of the reaction of cesium with water is demonstrated by the fact that this metal reacts with ice at all temperatures above $-116°C$ $(-177°F)$, liberating hydrogen. The reaction with cold water is explosive.

Cesium hydroxide is the strongest base known and must be stored in silver or platinum out of contact with air because of its reactivity with glass and CO_2. Rubidium hydroxide is also a powerful base.

Both rubidium and cesium halides form double halide complexes with other metals such as antimony, bismuth, cadmium, cobalt, copper, iron, lead, manganese, mercury, nickel, thorium, and zinc. Many of these are quite insoluble and have been used as intermediates in the separation and recovery of rubidium and cesium from mixtures with other alkali metals. In addition to double halide salts, both elements form a series of polyhalides, such as $RbIBrCl$, $RbBrCl_2$, CsI_3, $CsBr_2I$, etc., wherein two of the halide atoms must be of valence -1 and the third of valence $+1$.

Although all the alkali metals tend to form complex salts, the tendency is greatest with cesium, grading down to lithium in order of atomic weights.

The soluble rubidium and cesium compounds include the carbonates, chlorides, bromides, iodides, hydroxides, chlorates, nitrates, sulfates, sulfides, and chromates. The relatively insoluble compounds include the perchlorates, permanganates, chloroplatinates, chlorostannates, fluosilicates, and periodates.

Cesium, like lithium, forms alkyl and aryl compounds of a wide variety.

Rubidium and cesium form alloys with the alkali metals, the alkaline earth metals, mercury, antimony, bismuth, and gold. Alloys with the last three metals have the property of releasing electrons under the influence of light, and can be employed in photoelectric tubes. The alloy corresponding to the bimetallic compound, $SbCs_3$, shows the highest photoelectric quantum yield.

APPLICATIONS

The present industrial applications of rubidium and cesium are limited and include use as getters in vacuum tubes and as photoelectric cell components. For these purposes they may be introduced into the tubes as metals, or more commonly as a salt mixed with a reducing agent, for example, CsCl and Ca, in a capsule. When the capsule is heated with a high frequency source, the reduction reaction occurs, and the metal is deposited as a thin layer on the inside glass wall of the tube.

Cesium is used in scintillation counters and in infrared detection devices, such as the "sniperscope" on rifles for night firing.

Under intensive current investigation in a large number of research and development laboratories are two applications for rubidium and cesium which will drastically affect the use and consumption of these two metals: ion propulsion engines for space missiles and the conversion of heat to electricity.

Ion propulsion engines are based upon the acceleration of ions and their discharge into space to provide the push for rockets. Since rubidium and cesium are easily ionized at rather low temperatures and have respectable atomic weights, they offer great potential for this purpose. One such engine, developed at the National Aeronautics and Space Administration Lewis Research Center, operates as follows: Cesium is fed to a boiler where it is vaporized; the vaporized atoms, heated to about $1650°C$ $(3000°F)$, are ionized as they pass over hot tungsten strips mounted in a passage; and the plasma (ionized gas) is accelerated to a high velocity as it passes through a series of rings upon which is imposed a high voltage to produce a powerful electrical field. The high-velocity ion stream leaving the rear of the engine provides the thrust.[2,5,6]

Figures 21.1 and 21.2 are two views of an experimental ion propulsion engine made by Wright Air Development Division, United States Air Force.

The mass of cesium ions being greater than that of ions of lighter elements gives cesium an advantage for this purpose, since the thrust attained is directly proportional to the atomic weight of the ions. One of the several problems arising in an ion engine is that the ejection of positive ions builds up negative ions in the engine or vehicle, a phenomenon known as *space charge*. In outer space where there are no negative ions present, as there are in the atmosphere, this results in the rocket being followed by a wake of positive ions attracted by the negative charge on the vehicle. One way to overcome this is to use a "gun" which fires into space the electrons stripped from the fuel atoms when they are converted to positive ions, thus neutralizing the latter.

It is anticipated that the ion engine would be used to move vehicles through space once they are in orbit and that a nuclear power plant would provide the energy to run the engine.[2] The calculation has been made that an ion engine consuming only 11.6 lb of cesium/hr would give a 1,000-ton space ship a rated thrust of 200 lb, an amount ample to provide an acceleration of 4,500 miles/day/day.[6]

One form which a thermolectric generator using rubidium or cesium can take utilizes the magnetohydrodynamic (MHD) principle. Cesium ions formed by heat are passed at very high temperature through a magnetic field, and since they form an electrical conductor, they act like an armature of a conventional generator and cause electricity to be generated.

Another method of converting heat to electricity with the aid of cesium or rubidium uses the thermionic mechanism. When the hot electrode or plate of a diode tube containing cesium or rubidium vapor is heated, electrons leave the hot plate and pass to a cold electrode so that a current is generated. The effectiveness is greater than in the case of a vacuum

FIGURE 21.1. Experimental ion propulsion engine built by Wright Air Development Division, United States Air Force. Ion beam leaves the center of the round plate and strikes the target (extreme right foreground) at which the assembly, being checked, is directed. Engine is mounted in a chamber which is evacuated to a high vacuum. (*Courtesy Wright Air Development Division.*)

FIGURE 21.2. Close-up view of experimental ion propulsion engine to which
last-minute connections are being made. The circular disk on the front is
one of the high voltage acceleration rings through which the ion beam
passes. (*Courtesy Wright Air Development Division.*)

diode tube, because the ionized cesium or rubidium boosts the rate at which ions boil off
the hot plate, creates a plasma that neutralizes
the space charge in the tube, and reduces
energy losses at the cold plate. An alternating
current with a frequency of about 100 kc/sec is
produced.[3,4]

Cesium and rubidium are of importance in
the above three applications because cesium,
followed by rubidium, is the most easily ionized element. Other physical properties that are
factors in these uses are the low melting points,
low boiling points, and high vapor pressures
of these metals.

When and as these major developments
mature, the demands for these hitherto little-
used alkali metals will increase, and production
will rise to meet the demands at an anticipated
lower cost for rubidium and cesium.

References

1. Barton, G. B., Hepworth, J. L., McClanahan,
   E. D., Jr., Moore, R. L., and Van Tuyl, H. H.,
   "Fission Product Recovery from Chemical
   Processing Plant Waste Solution," General
   Electric Co., Richland, Wash.

2. *Chem. Eng. News,* **38,** No. 5, 94 (Feb. 1,
   1960).

3. *Ibid.,* **38,** No. 3, 17 (Jan. 18, 1960).

4. *Chem. Week,* **86,** No. 4, 65 (Jan. 23, 1960).

5. *Ibid.,* **86,** No. 5, 44 (Jan. 30, 1960).

6. *Ibid.,* "Ultra Energy Propellents," **83,** No. 41,
   155 (Oct. 12, 1957).

7. *Chicago Daily News,* Feb. 11, 1960 (a UPI
   national story).

8. Druce, J. H. E., "Preparation of Inorganic
   Chlorostannates," *Chem. News,* **117,** 193–6
   (1918).

9. Hackspill, L., and Georges, T., "Direct Preparation of Metallic Cesium from Swedish
   Pollucite," *Compt. rend.,* **230,** 1119 (1950).

10. Kennedy, J. J., "The Alkali Metal Cesium and
    Some of its Salts," *Chem. Rev.,* **23,** 157–63
    (1938).

11. Lam, Hung-Kei H., and Foster, H. R., Jr.,
    "Preparation of Cesium and Rubidium
    Metals," paper presented at Div. Ind. Eng.
    Chem., American Chemical Society, San Fran-
    cisco, April 27, 1958.

12. Lehner, Kemmerer and Whitford, "Extraction
    of Cesium from Pollucite," *Ind. Eng. Chem.,*
    16, 1280 (1924).

13. Wells, H. W., "On the Purification of Cesium
    Material," *Am. Chem. J.,* **26,** 265–8 (1901).

22. SCANDIUM

A. H. DAANE

Ames Laboratory, AEC, Iowa State University
Ames, Iowa

INTRODUCTION

Mendeleeff, in 1871, predicted a new element in his periodic table and, along with some properties of the element, gave its position in the periodic table as under boron (eka-boron) in Group III. Lars Nilson, an agricultural chemist in Sweden, discovered this new element in 1876, while carefully analyzing the ore euxenite, and named it scandium after his homeland. Little scandium has been available for study, so, for lack of detailed information about the properties of this element, it has been grouped with the rare earths in many treatments because of their common Group-III position. This has generally been satisfactory, although, as the chemical and physical properties of scandium are becoming known, it is apparent that this element deserves a treatment separate from the rare earths. Scandium is the first element of the first transition group with one 3d electron, and exhibits the enhanced binding in the metallic state characteristic of "d" electron metals.

CHEMICAL PROPERTIES

Since scandium is a very electropositive metal, its oxide is basic and is soluble in acids to give colorless solutions of the trivalent ion; no other valence state has been observed for this metal. Scandium hydroxide may be precipitated from solutions on addition of bases, and oxalate ion precipitates the oxalate, although this substance is not as insoluble as the rare earth oxalates. Fluoride ion precipitates the hydrated $ScF_3 \cdot \frac{1}{2}H_2O$. Pokras and Bernays[9] have described gravimetric methods that may be used to determine scandium, but these generally require preliminary separations to be effective. Recently, Fritz and Pietrzyk[3] have reported an ethylenediaminetetraacetic acid (EDTA) titrimetric procedure for scandium that has been shown to be effective in the presence of a number of ions commonly encountered with scandium.

OCCURRENCE

Scandium is present in the earth's crust in a concentration of about 5 ppm and is, accordingly, about as abundant as beryllium and some of the rare earth elements. It is very widely dispersed, occurring in low concentrations in the minerals wolframite, wiikite, and cassiterite, and may be detected in most soils. Although scandium is chemically similar to the rare earths, its ion size places it with aluminum, magnesium, hafnium, and zirconium in geochemical equilibria, so that it is not found to a great extent in rare earth ores. Goldschmidt[4] has described the geochemistry of scandium in detail.

In 1911 Schetelig, in Norway, discovered a new mineral, thortveitite, which contained the startling amount of 30 to 40 per cent Sc_2O_3, and this mineral was subsequently found in Madagascar also. Thortveitite occurs in very small amounts as protruding or residual prismatic crystals from the weathering of pegmatite dykes such as the black Norwegian uranite, and, because of its light tan color and prismatic needle form, the thortveitite can be recognized and recovered. Perhaps partially because of lack of need for it, but primarily because of its scarcity, less than 50 lb of this mineral had been removed from quarries in Norway from the time of its discovery in 1911 to 1952.

Although scandium occurs in only very small amounts in some uranium ores, the processing of large quantities of these ores recently in the United States Atomic Energy Commission's program of acquiring uranium has made a quantity of scandium available from this source.

ORE TREATMENT

A detailed analysis of thortveitite has been given by Marble and Glass,[7] showing this mineral to contain 46 per cent SiO_2, 34 per cent Sc_2O_3, 9.5 per cent heavy rare earths, 5 per cent Al_2O_3, 3 per cent Fe_2O_3, 1.5 per cent light rare earths, 0.5 per cent MnO, and smaller amounts of CaO, MgO, ThO_2, and little hafnium or zirconium, although Goldschmidt suggests distinct amounts of these latter two elements to be in some samples of thortveitite. Marble and Glass accomplished the degradation of thortveitite by a series of sodium carbonate fusions or by hydrofluoric acid treatment. In either case, the resulting solution is subjected to a series of oxalate or hydroxide precipitations under carefully controlled conditions, resulting in a relatively low yield of scandium oxide.

Recently, Spedding et al.[12] have described a treatment of thortveitite that recovers the scandium in much higher yields. The powdered thortveitite is mixed with three times its weight of ammonium hydrogen fluoride and heated at 375–400°C (708–752°F) for 12 hr in a platinum boat while passing a stream of dry air over the charge. This removes all of the SiO_2 as the volatile SiF_4, which results in a salt containing 65 to 70 per cent ScF_3, plus the fluorides of the other elements in the ore that do not volatilize under these conditions. Although this mixed fluoride may be dissolved in concentrated H_2SO_4, the process is quite tedious, and the solution is effected by first mixing the salt with 62 per cent of its weight of calcium metal and heating this charge in a tantalum crucible to 1400°C (2552°F) in an inert atmosphere, producing a scandium-rich alloy phase (70 per cent Sc) and calcium fluoride slag. This metallic phase is readily soluble in hydrochloric acid to give a solution from which pure Sc_2O_3 is obtained by a combination thiocyanate-ether extraction, ion exchange process.

In obtaining Sc_2O_3 from the processing of uranium ore, isotopes of thorium superimpose radioactivity as an added problem in obtaining high purity. Ion exchange and solvent extraction techniques have been employed in this work also to obtain pure Sc_2O_3.

PREPARATION

Scandium metal was first prepared by Fischer and co-workers,[2] in 1937, by the electrolysis of scandium chloride in a molten salt bath, but the product contained about 5 per cent impurities, mostly iron and silicon, so that the physical properties of the element could not be given from this work. Subsequent preparations of scandium have also been either impure, or of unstated purity,[8] so that the data on the physical properties of the metal have been somewhat inconsistent as well as scarce.

As part of a program of study of the rare earth elements in the Ames Laboratory at Iowa State University, Wakefield, Spedding, and Daane[13] have devised methods of preparing scandium metal and have also examined some of its properties. These preparative methods, given below, all utilize scandium fluoride as a reactant, which may be prepared by either of the following methods:

Preparation of Scandium Fluoride

Ammonium Hydrogen Fluoride Process. Ammonium hydrogen fluoride and scandium oxide are mixed together in stoichiometric amounts (2.5:1 weight ratio of ammonium hydrogen fluoride to Sc_2O_3) corresponding to Equation 22.1:

$$Sc_2O_3 + 6NH_4HF_2 \rightarrow$$
$$2ScF_3 + 6NH_4F + 3H_2O. \qquad (22.1)$$

It is to be noted that only half of the fluoride in the ammonium hydrogen fluoride is assumed to enter into the reaction; undoubtedly, some of the ammonium fluoride dissociates

$$NH_4F \rightarrow NH_3 + HF. \qquad (22.2)$$

to present additional HF in the reaction, but, since the amount is uncertain, it is neglected.

The mixture is placed in a platinum or "Monel" boat and heated for 8 to 12 hr in a "Monel" tube to 300°C (572°F) in a stream of dry air. This treatment provides a 95 per cent conversion of Sc_2O_3 to ScF_3, with the last 5 per cent being difficult to convert because of a crust of ScF_3 formed around the unreacted Sc_2O_3. If this product is ground and mixed with another quantity of ammonium hydrogen fluoride in the same weight ratio of 2.5:1 and heated as before, a good grade of ScF_3 is obtained that reduces well to give metal as described below.

Hydrogen Fluoride Process. Scandium oxide may be converted to ScF_3 by heating it to 700°C (1292°F) in a stream of HF gas in a "Monel" tray and tube:

$$Sc_2O_3 + 6HF \rightarrow 2ScF_3 + 3H_2O. \quad (22.3)$$

As the efficiency of the HF gas decreases as it has to diffuse through a layer of ScF_3 to reach the unreacted Sc_2O_3 (as in the ammonium hydrogen fluoride process above), approximately a 200 per cent excess quantity of HF is passed through the furnace to achieve a good quality ScF_3.

The ammonium hydrogen fluoride process is generally preferred for small-scale work and is preferable for laboratories not equipped to handle tank HF.

Preparation of Scandium Metal

Direct Reduction of ScF_3. Following the general method used for preparing rare earth metals as described by Spedding and Daane,[10,11] scandium metal has been prepared by the direct reduction of scandium fluoride with calcium.[13] Pulverized ScF_3 is mixed with 10 per cent more granular calcium (redistilled) than required by the stoichiometry of the reaction:

$$2ScF_3 + 3Ca \rightarrow 3CaF_2 + 2Sc. \quad (22.4)$$

The charge is placed in a tantalum or tungsten crucible in a silica tube induction furnace which is evacuated and filled with purified argon gas to 1 atm pressure. The charge is heated to 1600°C (2912°F) to melt the slag and the metal, which separate cleanly into two layers, with the metal layer on the bottom. This clean separation of slag appears somewhat surprising at first, in view of the fact that the room-temperature densities of scandium metal and calcium fluoride are such that a reverse layering would be expected (Sc 3.0 g/cc, CaF_2 3.2 g/cc). The expansion of salts on melting, however, is very much larger than that of metals, and is undoubtedly the prime factor in relegating the slag to the upper layer at the freezing point of scandium. The excess calcium from the reaction is largely concentrated in the slag layer, and this too lowers the density of the slag to promote the separation.

After breaking away the slag, the scandium ingot is remelted in the tantalum crucible in a vacuum to remove the 0.5 to 2 per cent calcium remaining after the reduction. The resulting scandium contains from 3 to 5 per cent tantalum as the one big impurity, with carbon, nitrogen, silicon, iron, calcium, and other rare earths present to the extent of less than 300 ppm each. This large tantalum content is highly undesirable in a process designed to prepare a pure metal, but as this impurity is present as primary tantalum dendrites uncombined with any scandium, it does not interfere with the use of this material in some studies.

Zinc-Alloy Process. To carry out the reduction of ScF_3 at a lower temperature than that required in the above process, and thus eliminate much of the tantalum content of the final product, a zinc-alloy reduction process may be used. This is similar to the Ames Laboratory process for preparing thorium, devised by Wilhelm et al., described in the chapter on thorium in this book. As used to prepare scandium, pulverized ScF_3, redistilled calcium, zinc, and lithium fluoride are mixed in the quantities corresponding to the reaction:

$$2ScF_3 + 3Ca \text{ (10 per cent excess)} + \\ 8Zn + 12LiF \rightarrow \\ 3(CaF_2 \cdot 4LiF) + 2(Sc \cdot 4Zn) \text{ alloy.} \quad (22.5)$$

The charge is placed in a tantalum crucible and is welded shut under a partial atmosphere of helium (150 mm Hg). This bomb is then heated to 1100°C (2012°F) in an inert atmosphere, and, at this temperature, both the scandium-zinc eutectic alloy and the calcium fluoride–lithium fluoride eutectic are liquids, allowing clean separation of the two phases. Since the liquid alloy is in contact with tantalum at a much lower temperature than is the scandium metal in the direct reduction process described above, much less tantalum is dissolved into the scandium alloy.

After cooling, the brittle alloy is crushed to

pea-size chunks and is then heated in a vacuum to 1200°C (2192°F) to distill away the zinc, leaving behind a porous sponge of pure scandium metal. This sponge may then be consolidated into solid metal by conventional inert atmosphere arc melting processes, although the vapor pressure of scandium is sufficiently high that about 10 per cent of the charge is dispersed around on the inside of the furnace as "fog" in this operation.

The product of this method contains only a trace of tantalum and less than 500 ppm zinc, with other impurities essentially the same as the metal prepared by the direct reduction process. It is believed that, in most cases, these figures given for impurities are conservatively higher than the actual amounts. With only small amounts of metal available, it has not been possible to divert samples to permit development of analytical methods to the desired accuracy.

One disadvantage of this process is that the zinc and the lithium fluoride added to achieve the convenience of working at a lower temperature require a crucible volume three times that needed to produce the same quantity of scandium by the direct reduction process. In addition, these additives undoubtedly contribute some of their own impurities to the final product.

PURIFICATION OF SCANDIUM METAL

From Wakefield's vapor-pressure data,[13] it is apparent that distillation is an obvious technique to use in combination with either of the above preparative methods to obtain high-purity metal. The preferred combination is first to utilize the direct reduction process to obtain metallic scandium in good yields, with tantalum the only impurity present in large quantities. Distillation of this material effectively eliminates this impurity as well as the major portion of the other impurities present in smaller amounts.

The distillation of scandium is accomplished by heating the metal to 1650–1700°C (3002–3092°F) in a vacuum of 10^{-5} mm Hg or better in the apparatus shown in Figure 22.1. The tantalum crucible extends to within 2 in. of the top of the heated zone of the furnace, and the condenser, consisting of a sheet of 0.005-in. tantalum wrapped around the crucible and

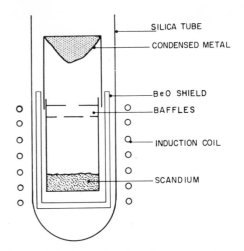

FIGURE 22.1. Apparatus for distilling scandium.

held in place with a band of tantalum wire, extends out of the heated zone. The condenser is capped with a press-fitted tantalum lid with a ⅛-in. hole in its center to allow rapid pumping out of the system at the start. When the distillation is taking place, the bottom of the crucible from which the vapor moves is at a temperature of 1650–1700°C (3002–3092°F), and the top of the condenser is at 800–1000°C (1472–1832°F). The two collimators are an inch apart, with the lowest one about 2 to 3 in. above the surface of the liquid scandium. These baffles serve to direct the vapor to the upper portion of the condenser section, so that the major portion of the condensate is on the underside of the lid. The condensate is a conically shaped fibrous deposit of bright metal with the tip essentially fused metal. The condenser may be disassembled, peeled away from the condensate, and reused. This compact, partially fused mass of metal may be consolidated by arc with recoverable losses by vaporization of up to 10 per cent, as previously mentioned.

Analysis of the distilled metal shows it to contain no detectable tantalum, with other impurities as follows: Fe, < 0.05 per cent; Ca, < 0.02 per cent; Mg, < 0.03 per cent; Cr, < 0.06 per cent; and C and N, about 100 ppm each.

PROPERTIES

Scandium metal has a silver metallic luster with a slight yellowish cast after exposure to air. The metal is soft and is easily fabricated

TABLE 22.1. PHYSICAL PROPERTIES OF SCANDIUM

Atomic number	21
Atomic weight	44.96 (100% isotope 45)
Melting point	1539°C (2802°F)
Boiling point	2727°C (4941°F)
Transformation temperature	1335°C (2435°F)
Density	2.99 g/cc
Crystal structure, to 1335°C (2435°F)	Hexagonal close packed, a = 3.308 ± 0.001 Å
	c = 5.267 ± 0.003 Å
	c/a = 1.59
above 1335°C	Probably body-centered cubic
Atomic volume	15.0 cc/mole
Metallic radius	1.64 Å
Heat capacity [25°C (77°F)]	6.01 cal/mole/°C
Heat of fusion	3.85 kcal/mole
Heat of vaporization at 1630°C (2966°F)	78.6 ± 0.7 kcal/mole
Linear coefficient of expansion [0–900°C (32–1652°F)]	12×10^{-6}/deg
Electrical resistivity (room temperature)	66×10^{-6} ohm-cm
Temperature coefficient of resistivity [room temperature to 100°C (212°F)]	5.4×10^{-8} ohm-cm/deg
Ultimate compressive strength (psi)	57,000
Hardness	Rockwell F 98 (severely cold rolled and unannealed)
Thermal neutron absorption cross section	24.0 ± 1.0 barns/atom

if pure. It reacts rapidly with acids, but it does not tarnish rapidly in air and is not attacked rapidly by water. At higher temperatures [500–800°C (932–1472°F)] scandium may be oxidized in air. Scandium shows a remarkable property in common with some of the heavy rare earth metals and yttrium: it is not attacked by a 1:1 mixture of concentrated nitric acid and 48 per cent hydrofluoric acid, and as a consequence, this mixture may be used to dissolve tantalum away from scandium.

Table 22.1 lists the physical properties of scandium.

FABRICATION

Scandium containing oxygen and other non-metallic elements as impurities is quite difficult to fabricate, and, like yttrium, appears to have greatly improved fabricability when pure. Although it has not as yet been available in quantities that would permit studies of fabrication by extrusion, scandium has been rolled and swaged successfully. It may be welded by inert atmosphere arc welding, and may be spot welded.

ALLOYS

As little scandium metal has been available, scarcely any work has been done on alloy sys-

tems of this element. The similarity of scandium to yttrium and the rare earth metals appears to extend to alloying behavior in the few cases where data exist to permit comparison. Consequently, in the absence of experimental evidence, a corresponding rare earth alloy system may be used as a first approximation for the case with scandium. This assumption is not likely to be universally valid, for cases are known where there are distinct differences between the behavior of two rare earth metals with another element. In addition, the metallic radii of the rare earths are quite large (1.73 to 1.87 Å) compared to that of scandium (1.64 Å), so that scandium would be much more likely than the rare earths to form solid solution alloys with some of the metals having radii nearer this smaller value, such as hafnium (1.59 Å), magnesium (1.60 Å), plutonium (1.64 Å), uranium (1.56 Å), and zirconium (1.60 Å).

The following outline of the behavior of scandium toward other metals includes a few cases of actual experimental observations, but, mostly, it represents predictions based on a degree of similarity of scandium to yttrium and the rare earths.

Group IA (Alkali Metals). There is little or no alloying tendency. Possibly there is liquid immiscibility, as evidenced by behavior in reduction processes.

Group IIA (Alkaline Earth Metals). Scandium is soluble enough in magnesium to harden it. There appear to be no intermetallic compounds between magnesium and scandium and between calcium and scandium.

Group IIIB (Yttrium and the Rare Earths). Considerable solid solubility is likely, with no intermetallic compounds.

Group IVB (Ti, Zr, Hf). Complete solid solubility between the high temperature forms of titanium and scandium has been observed by Beaudry;[1] this is the best evidence available that scandium is body-centered cubic above 1335°C. Attempts to confirm this by high temperature x-ray studies and by quenching have not been successful. The hexagonal forms of titanium and scandium are soluble in each other to the extent of about 10 per cent; some solid solubility has been observed by other workers.[5,6]

Group VB (V, Cb, Ta). There is essentially no solid solubility, but there is increasing liquid solubility of Ta, Cb, V in Sc. There are no intermetallic compounds.

Group VIB (Cr, Mo, W). No intermetallic compounds or solid solubility are likely. (This is known to be the case for W). Liquid solubility of these metals in liquid scandium is less than in the V, Cb, Ta group.

Groups VIIB, VIIIB, IB, IIB, IIIA, IVA. Compounds of these elements with scandium are likely or known (Sc-Au, ScC, ScN, Sc_2O_3, ScH_3, Sc-Cd, Sc-Zn). Some compounds are easily decomposed in vacuum on heating (Sc-Zn, Sc-Cd).

Th, U, Pu. Some solid solubility is possible. Intermetallic compounds are unlikely.

TOXICITY

No toxicity data are available on scandium at the present time. Based on analogy with yttrium and the rare earths, it would not be expected that scandium would present a serious health hazard, but it should be treated with respect until its toxic character is established.

References

1. Beaudry, B. J., and Daane, A. H., to be published, Ames, Iowa.
2. Fischer, W., Brunger, K., and Grieneisen, H., *Z. anorg. Chem.*, **231**, 54 (1937).
3. Fritz, J. S., Pietrzyk, D. J. (paper submitted to *Anal. Chem.* for publication).
4. Goldschmidt, V. M., "Geochemistry," Oxford, Clarendon Press, 1954.
5. Kornilov, I. I., *Izvest. Akad. nauk SSSR, Otdel. Khim. nauk*, **1954**, 392 (1954).
6. Love, B., *WADC Report RC 106* (1958).
7. Marble, J. P., and Glass, J. J., *Am. Mineralogist*, **27**, 696 (1942).
8. Petru, F., Prochazka, V., and Hajck, B., *Czechoslov. Chem. Commun.*, **22**, 1534 (1957).
9. Pokras, L., and Bernays, P. M., *Anal. Chem.*, **23**, 757 (1951).
10. Spedding, F. H., and Daane, A. H., *J. Metals*, **6**, 504 (1954).
11. Spedding, F. H., and Daane, A. H., Chapter 5 in "Progress in Nuclear Energy," Vol. 1, edited by H. M. Finniston and J. P. Howe, New York, McGraw-Hill Book Co., 1956.
12. Spedding, F. H., Powell, J. E., Daane, A. H., Hiller, M. A., and Adams, W. H., *J. Electrochem. Soc.*, **105**, 683 (1958).
13. Wakefield, G. F., Spedding, F. H., and Daane, A. H., *Trans. AIME*, **218**, 608 (1960).

23. SELENIUM

JOHN R. STONE and PETER E. CARON*

American Smelting and Refining Company
New York, New York

INTRODUCTION

In 1817 John Jacob Berzelius, a professor of chemistry in Stockholm and secretary of the Swedish Academy of Science, was studying, along with J. G. Gahn, a method formerly in use at Gripsholm, Sweden, for the production of sulfuric acid. As a part of this study, an examination of the acid itself revealed a sediment which gave forth an offensive odor previously identified by Kloproth as an indicator of the presence of tellurium. J. G. Gahn, it appears, recalled detecting a similar odor in those plants where the Fahlun copper concentrates were smelted and the resulting sulfur used to produce sulfuric acid. In the hopes of finding a new source of the then rare element, tellurium, in this acid, Berzelius obtained larger quantities of this residue, but his work proved to no avail for he could find no trace whatsoever of tellurium. He did notice, though, as a result of his tests, that there remained unaccounted for an unknown substance whose chemical properties closely resembled those of tellurium. So closely akin were these two elements that Berzelius decided to call the former selenium, from the Greek word *selene*, meaning the moon, tellurium having been derived from the Latin word *tellus*, meaning the earth.

Although discovered in 1817, selenium remained a laboratory curiosity for some 50 years. Finally, in 1873, Willoughby Smith, while testing various materials for electrical conduc-

* Revised by M. F. Perkins and Peter E. Caron. American Smelting and Refining Company, New York, N.Y.

tivity, discovered quite by accident that the current resistance of this element decreased as the intensity of illumination increased, and furthermore, that resistance increased slightly as the temperature likewise increased above 170°C (338°F). This led, among other things, to the development of the photoelectric cell, of which more will be said later on, but the important fact is that for the first time it brought selenium into the public eye. Once there, a multitude of applications developed, until it now plays a very definite part in our everyday life.

OCCURRENCE

Selenium, the fortieth element in plentifulness, falling between bismuth and gold, rarely occurs in its native state. Although occasionally found in conjunction with native sulfur, and in the form of selenides of other metals in such minerals as clausthalite, $PbSe$; eucairite, $CuAgSe$; crookesite, $(CuTlAg)_2Se$; naumannite, Ag_2Se; and zorgite, $PbCuSe(?)$, it is most frequently found as an accessory mineral in base-metal ores of lead, copper, and nickel. Whenever any of the above are treated, selenium is recoverable as a by-product.

The main sources of selenium in this country originate in the copper-mining states of Utah, Arizona, and New Mexico, the Montana ores running low in this element. Selenium from these sources and from Mexican copper mined in the states of Durango and Zacatecas is recovered by the American Smelting and Refining Company, Anaconda Copper Mining Company, the American Metal Climax Company, and, re-

447

cently, Kennecott Copper Corporation in this country. In Canada the International Nickel Company of Canada, Ltd., recovers selenium from the Sudbury copper-nickel ores, and the Canadian Copper Refiners, Ltd., of Montreal from the copper anodes derived from the copper-zinc ores of Flin Flon, Manitoba. In Australia selenium is produced by the Electrolytic Refining and Smelting Company, Pty. Ltd., in Sweden by the Boliden Mining Company, in Belgium by the Société Général of Hoboken, in Japan by the Taihi, Besshi, and Nippon mining companies; and in the Western Zone of Germany by the Norddeutsche Affinerie of Hamburg. Prior to World War II, selenium was produced in what is known as the East Zone of Germany, but that source, along with all other production in the U.S.S.R. and other Soviet-dominated countries behind the Iron Curtain, has become an unknown factor today.

DERIVATION

Many years ago the sole source of selenium was thought to be from the flue dusts of metallurgical processes utilizing sulfide ores; however, recovery from this source is virtually nonexistent today, and the anode muds or slimes from electrolytic copper refineries provide the source of most of the world's selenium. Basically, there would appear to be three main methods of recovering selenium—by roasting with soda, by roasting with sulfuric acid, and by smelting with soda and niter; variations of these are found to accommodate the variances in basic raw materials being handled.

In the first method, that of roasting with soda, the decopperized slimes are mixed with soda and raised to temperatures well below the sintering point with sufficient air to oxidize the selenium. The selenium is recovered as sodium selenate from the water-leached calcine by evaporation. The sodium selenate is reduced to the selenide by coke, then redissolved, and blown with air, and the selenium is precipitated with sulfur dioxide, the sodium hydroxide being carbonated and recirculated.

In the sulfuric acid roasting the raw slimes are treated with sulfuric acid prior to roasting. During the course of roasting, the selenium dioxide is driven off and collected in a wet-scrubber Cottrell system. The remainder of the selenium is largely recovered by the conventional soda smelting process.

The soda smelting process is a pyrometallurgical one in which the decopperized slimes are mixed with soda and silica. After the first slags are drawn off, the molten charge is rabbled with air, and some of the selenium is volatilized and caught in a scrubber Cottrell system. To the charge is now added caustic and niter. The slag which results, high in both selenium and tellurium, is crushed and leached with water, to which is added fresh sulfuric acid to precipitate the tellurium. The solution is then treated with sulfur dioxide to precipitate the selenium.

There are at present in the United States and Canada seven producers of this element, with a total output of between 1 and 1.4 million pounds annually. Stimulated by the Korean conflict, increased demand for selenium, especially for rectifier manufacture, starting in 1951, led to an acute shortage for this element. Material improvements in recoveries by selenium producers resulted in increased production, ending the shortage by the fall of 1956. At present and for the foreseeable future, the supply of selenium should be adequate to take care of any reasonable demand, based both on production potential and stocks in the hands of producers.

Pricewise, selenium can hardly be termed an inexpensive commodity at $7.00/lb retail in its commercial form, as quoted by domestic producers. This price for domestic material has ranged from a low in the early 1930's of $1.50/lb to a high of $15.50/lb in 1956.

PHYSICAL PROPERTIES

Selenium, atomic number 34, is the third member of Group VI of the periodic arrangement of elements. Selenium is more metallic than sulfur but less metallic than tellurium, the two next of kin in the group.

Selenium can be caused to exist as a solid, as a liquid, or as a vapor at temperatures easily handled in any metallurgical laboratory.

The Solid State

The forms of selenium are not so well defined as are those of sulfur. As many as six allo-

TABLE 23.1. PROPERTIES OF THE OXYGEN-SULFUR FAMILY[15]

	Oxygen	Sulfur	Selenium	Tellurium
Atomic weight (1956)	16.000	32.066	78.96	127.61
Specific gravity (solid)	1.426	Monoclinic	Vitreous	
		1.96	4.28	6.25
		Yellow		
		amorphous	Hexagonal	
		1.92	4.79	
Temperature				
°C	−252.5	20	20	20
°F	−422	68	68	68
Color	Blue	Yellow	Dark red, gray, metallic	Silver
Melting point			Hexagonal	
°C	−218.4	119.25	217	449.5 ± 0.3
°F	−318	246.4	423	841 ± 0.5
Boiling point				
°C	−182.96	444.6	684.9 ± 1.0	989.0 ± 3.8
°F	−297.4	831.7	1265 ± 1.8	1812 ± 6.8

tropic forms are sometimes claimed, but a more simple classification recognizes only three allotropic forms of solid selenium, some of which are known in more than one condition. Table 23.2 gives a summary of the more common properties of the allotropes.

Amorphous Selenium. Amorphous selenium occurs as red powder, vitreous, and collodial selenium.

RED POWDER. The amorphous red powder results when solutions of selenous acid of pH 7 to pH 3, and even more acidic, with such acids as hydrochloric or sulfuric, are treated with strong reducing agents such as sulfur dioxide, hydrazine, or hydroxylamine hydrochloride. The red powder turns black on standing, and, on heating, yields the hexagonal form.

VITREOUS. Vitreous selenium, a black mass prepared by quench cooling liquid selenium, is glassy and brittle, showing conchoidal fractures, and is described as a supercooled liquid. It is a dielectric, being electrified by friction.

Newly produced vitreous selenium will start to soften at 40–50° (104–122°F) when heated.

TABLE 23.2. PROPERTIES OF THE ALLOTROPIC FORMS OF SELENIUM[8, 15, 21, 25]

	Amorphous		Crystalline	
Form	Powder	Vitreous	Monoclinic	Hexagonal
Color	Red	Black, red in thick layers	Deep red	Gray to dark gray
Specific gravity	4.25	4.28	4.46	4.79
Melting point	Softens at 40–50°C (104–122°F); changes state	Softens at 40–50°C (104–122°F)	170–180°C (338–356°F)	217°C (423°F)
Boiling point				
°C	684.9 ± 1.0	684.9 ± 1.0	684.9 ± 1.0	684.9 ± 1.0
°F	1265 ± 1.8	1265 ± 1.8	1265 ± 1.8	1265 ± 1.8
Solubility				
Water	Insoluble	Insoluble	Insoluble	Insoluble
H_2SO_4 (conc)	Soluble	Soluble	Soluble	Soluble
HNO_3 (conc)	Soluble	Soluble	Soluble	Soluble
CS_2	Slightly soluble	Slightly soluble	Slightly soluble	Insoluble
C_2H_5OH	Insoluble	Insoluble	Insoluble	Insoluble

As little as 0.0003 per cent by weight of tellurium in the selenium will increase the plasticity. Vitreous selenium containing 1 per cent of chlorine is quite plastic when first quench cast, but within 24 hr, even at room temperature, it will show substantial conversion to the hexagonal state.

By reflected light, glassy (vitreous) selenium is mirror black. Thin layers by transmitted light (daylight) appear blood red. Vitreous selenium is about as hard as glass, is perhaps more brittle, and shows a pronounced conchoidal fracture. Vitreous selenium is a very poor conductor of heat but, if stored in a warm place, gradually crystallizes to the hexagonal state which is a better conductor of both heat and electricity. Except for semiconductor use, especially xerographic plates, vitreous selenium, as such, may be considered an electrical insulator.

COLLOIDAL. Colloidal selenium is prepared by the reduction of dilute aqueous solutions of soluble selenium with such reducing agents as sulfur dioxide, hydrazine hydrate, dextrose, or titanium trichloride. It can also be prepared by pouring a solution of selenium in carbon disulfide into a large volume of ether, and by passing an electric current through a solution of selenous acid between a platinum anode and a selenium-coated cathode.

The colors obtained vary from violet to red, depending on the conditions during precipitation.

Crystalline Selenium. Crystalline selenium occurs as either monoclinic or hexagonal forms.

MONOCLINIC. Monoclinic selenium is obtained by the low-temperature evaporation of carbon disulfide containing dissolved selenium. Heat and several other conditions convert the monoclinic selenium to the hexagonal state.[7]

HEXAGONAL. Hexagonal selenium is considered the most stable state of selenium under ordinary conditions. It has a gray metallic appearance, is a fair conductor of heat and electricity, is fairly inert to atmospheric conditions, has fair mechanical strength, and is easy to produce by heating any form of selenium until crystallization is complete.[16,33,34]

The Liquid State

The melting point of hexagonal selenium is 217°C (423°F) and represents a definite transition from solid to liquid. Amorphous selenium begins to soften at about 100°C (212°F), and its behavior at increasing temperatures depends on the rate of heating. It liquefies at 217°C (423°F).

Molten pure selenium, no matter from what allotrope it is obtained, is not very fluid until heated several dozen degrees above the melting point of 217°C (423°F).

Unlike sulfur, selenium becomes more fluid with increasing temperature. Liquid selenium can be boiled at atmospheric pressure [684.9°C (1265°F)][2] in a porcelain dish or in a quartz dish without bumping. Liquid selenium probably contains several molecular species.

The Vapor State

Selenium vapor at the boiling point is a mixture of Se_8 and Se_2. The vapor pressure is represented by[2]

$$\log_{10} \text{pressure} = -\frac{4989.5 \pm 4.5}{T} + 8.0886 \pm 0.0048$$

where pressure is in millimeters of mercury and T is in degrees Kelvin.

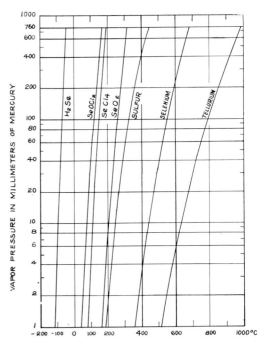

FIGURE 23.1. Vapor-pressure-temperature curves for selenium, sulfur, tellurium, hydrogen selenide, selenium oxychloride, selenium tetrachloride, and selenium dioxide.

In Figure 23.1 are curves showing the vapor pressure–temperature relationship for selenium, selenium dioxide, selenium tetrachloride, hydrogen selenide, selenium oxychloride, sulfur, and tellurium.

Electrical Conductivity

Solid State. Hexagonal selenium is a p-type extrinsic semiconductor below the melting point. Halogens increase the p-type conductivity. The energy gap, as determined by a photovoltaic method, is placed at 1.79 ± 0.01 ev (Hannay,[9] page 430).

An extensive study of the electrical properties of crystalline selenium has been reported by Henkels.[13,14]

Selenium as the single crystal is not a commercial item, but the study of the single crystal in conjunction with the study of the microcrystalline states gives information on the properties of selenium as a semiconductor. The values for the electrical properties of selenium in the solid state are so dependent on the methods of preparation that the original publications should be consulted.

Liquid State. A study of the electrical conductivity of liquid selenium from 200–500°C (392–932°F) has been reported by Henkels.[12]

The resistivity in ohm-centimeters of the pure liquid selenium is expressed by the following equation:

$$\log_{10}\rho = A + \frac{B}{T}$$

where A is −3.81
    B is 5850
    T is in degrees Kelvin
    ρ is specific resistivity in ohm-centimeters

Separate additions of chlorine, of iodine, or of phosphorus in each case lower the resistivity.

Effect of Light on Electrical Properties of Selenium

The effects of light radiating upon selenium should be considered under two headings: (1) photoconductivity and (2) photovoltaic action.

Photoconductivity. Photoconductive action was discovered in 1871 by Willoughby Smith, who reported a decrease in the electrical resistance of selenium during illumination.[29] The increase in conductivity during illumination is the result of an increase in the number of

carriers; i.e., holes and electrons caused by the action of the photons of light. When the illumination is cut off, the conductivity decays to the value in effect prior to the illumination.[20]

The photoconductive selenium cell, like the photoconductive tube, requires an external source of electrical energy for operation. Unfortunately, the photoconductive selenium cell, unlike the phototube, passes appreciable current even when in the dark. In some cells the current during illumination may be twenty-five-fold the dark current, but an eight- to tenfold increase is the more usual value.

Photovoltaic Action. Photovoltaic action refers to the conversion of the energy of light directly into electrical energy. The exposure meter for the measurement of light in photography is an example. The mechanical features of the exposure meter will be described on page 456.

The photons of light passing through the zone of the p-n junction enter the zone of the p-type semiconducting layer of selenium. The n-type of semiconductor is often cadmium oxide.[28] The conditions at the barrier layer, i.e., the p-n junction, become such that an electron moves in the direction from the selenium through the cadmium to the collecting grid and around through the external electrical circuit and back to the selenium.

The energy of the photon must exceed the photoelectric threshold value of the photovoltaic cell to cause voltaic action. The wave frequency of the light must exceed a minimum value to trigger the cell, no matter how many photons are impinging upon the surface in unit time.

CHEMICAL PROPERTIES[8,15,21,25]

The chemical properties of selenium are as would be expected of a Group VI element intermediate in atomic weight to sulfur and tellurium. Selenium and tellurium are more metallic in character than sulfur.

In all of its compounds selenium displays the properties of a nonmetal, its acid-forming tendency being marked, especially in its higher valence.

Oxygen

Many references state that selenium burns in air with a blue flame. The flame is blue,

TABLE 23.3. SOME PHYSICAL PROPERTIES OF METALLIC SELENIUM[8, 21, 25]

Atomic weight (1956)	78.96
Atomic number	34
Isotopes: 14 are listed in 1956 tables, the weights ranging from	70 through 84
Density at 25°C (77°F)	
Vitreous	4.28 g/cc
Hexagonal	4.79 g/cc
Atomic volume	16.4 cc/g-atom
Melting point	
Vitreous	Indefinite
Hexagonal	217°C (423°F)
Boiling point (760 mm Hg)	684.9 ± 1.0 (1265 ± 1.8°F)
Specific heat [0–217°C (32–423°F)]	0.081 cal/g/°C
Latent heat of fusion	16.5 cal/g
Latent heat of vaporization (760 mm)	79.6 cal/g
Linear coefficient of thermal expansion at 20°C (68°F)	37 μ in./°C
Thermal conductivity: depends on crystal structure	
Electrical conductivity: depends on crystal structure and impurities present	

but selenium is not an easily ignitible or rapidly combustible substance.

The oxidation state of selenium is −2 in the selenides, +4 in the selenites, and +6 in the selenates.[27] Potential values for the oxidation states are given by Latimer.[22]

The chemical valences of importance in analytical procedures are 2, 4, and 6, as given by Lundell.[23]

Selenium dioxide is a white crystalline solid in the form of four-sided needles, melts at 340°C (644°F) in a sealed tube, and sublimes at 315°C (599°F). It is hygroscopic and extremely soluble in water, forming selenous acid, H_2SeO_3.

Selenous acid resembles sulfurous acid, H_2SO_3, in the method of formation, in the nature and kinds of salts formed, and its general behavior with oxidizing and reducing agents. Reducing agents, including sulfur dioxide, SO_2, precipitate elementary selenium. Selenites are formed by neutralizing selenous acid with hydroxides and carbonates. The selenites are distinctly poisonous.

Selenous acid is a weak acid. According to unpublished work in the Research Laboratories of the American Smelting and Refining Company, selenous acid can be determined quantitatively by titrating with standard sodium hydroxide in the presence of mannitol.

Selenium trioxide, SeO_3, is a pale-yellow, amorphous, relatively unstable solid, breaking down into selenium dioxide and oxygen. At-

tempts to prepare the trioxide by methods analogous with those used for sulfur trioxide, SO_3, have been unsuccessful. It has been prepared by exposing a solution of selenium in selenyl dichloride, $SeOCl_2$, to dry ozone.

Selenic acid, H_2SeO_4, is formed by the oxidation of selenous acid by such reagents as potassium permanganate, chlorine, or bromine. This acid is quite similar to sulfuric acid with respect to acid strength, salt formation, and its power, when concentrated, to char many organic compounds. It is partially reduced at room temperature by such mild reducing agents as hydrogen sulfide, sulfur dioxide, sulfur, and selenium. Stronger reducing agents, including concentrated hydrochloric acid, must be employed to reduce selenic acid completely.

Hydrogen

Hydrogen starts to combine directly with selenium at temperatures below 250°C (482°F), reaching a maximum yield at about 575°C (1067°F). Above that temperature the reaction tends to reverse.

The hydrogen selenide, H_2Se, formed is a colorless gas, combustible but relatively stable in dry oxygen, possesses a disagreeable odor, and is extremely poisonous.[5]

Hydrogen selenide is also prepared by the action of dilute acids on metallic selenides, such as Na_2Se, FeSe, or Al_2Se_3.

Detailed directions for the preparation of

hydrogen selenide via aluminum selenide are given on page 183 of "Inorganic Syntheses."[17] Aluminum selenide or any selenide should be made with caution.

Some of the more reactive selenides liberate hydrogen selenide when treated with water.[17,19] Thus, selenides must be handled with caution and, when placed in storage, must be protected from contact with water and acids. Hydrogen selenide is estimated by Elkins[5] to be about three-hundredfold more toxic than hydrogen sulfide. Water at 10°C (50°F) has some solvent action on hydrogen selenide, and can move and release serious quantities of the gas at locations remote from the original selenide, thus enlarging the danger zone.

Halogens

Most of the various halides of selenium can be prepared by direct combination of the correct weight of the desired halogen with the corresponding weight of selenium. The problem is not of obtaining reaction between selenium and the halogen but of obtaining the stoichiometric ratio desired.

Fluorine. Selenium combines directly with fluorine at ordinary temperatures, forming selenium tetrafluoride, SeF_4. This compound is a colorless, intensely irritating liquid which boils at slightly above 100°C (212°F) and freezes to a white solid at —90°C (—130°F). It is hydrolyzed by water.

Selenium hexafluoride, SeF_6, a colorless gas, is formed by the interaction of the two elements at —76°C (—105°F).

Chlorine. Chlorine is the halogen most frequently used with selenium, especially by the manufacturers of selenium dry-plate electrical rectifiers.

Selenium monochloride, Se_2Cl_2, is a heavy liquid of deep-red color made by the direct combination of the elements (Mellor,[25] page 894).

Selenium tetrachloride, $SeCl_4$, is prepared by the action of an excess of chlorine upon selenium or upon selenium monochloride. The crystals, white to pale yellow, sublime when heated (Mellor,[25] page 898).

Selenium oxychloride, $SeOCl_2$, is a heavy, corrosive liquid. It fumes in air. Water decomposes it into hydrochloric acid and selenous acid. The oxychloride, as usually prepared, is a yellow, heavy liquid (sp gr 2.44) which boils at 179.5°C (355°F) and decomposes in contact with moisture. Details for preparation are given in "Inorganic Syntheses."[18] It mixes in all proportions with benzene, chloroform, carbon tetrachloride, and carbon disulfide. A powerful solvent, selenium oxychloride dissolves sulfur, selenium, and tellurium, as well as rubber, "Bakelite," gums, resins, celluloid, gelatin, glue, and asphalt.

Bromine and Iodine. Selenium monobromide, Se_2Br_2, and selenium monoiodide, Se_2I_2, are prepared by the direct union of the elements. The corresponding tetrahalides, $SeBr_4$ and SeI_4, have also been prepared.

Selenium oxybromide, $SeOBr_2$, is prepared by the interaction of selenium dioxide and selenium tetrabromide. It is a reddish-yellow crystal melting at 41.6°C (107°F) It is soluble in several of the common organic solvents. The oxybromide is a strong oxidizing and brominating agent, and combines with some metals explosively.

Sulfur. Selenium and sulfur are miscible in all proportions in the liquid state but form several series of mixed crystals. A phase diagram is given by Hansen,[10] page 1162.

Nitrogen. Selenium and nitrogen have been combined indirectly to form selenium nitride, SeN.

Acids. Much of the information in the literature on the dissolving action of various solvents for selenium needs revising. The effects of trace impurities upon the dissolving rates of selenium have been overlooked.

Hydrochloric acid does not attack elemental selenium.

Dilute nitric acid is a poor solvent for crude selenium and is substantially without action on high-purity selenium.

Concentrated nitric in the cold is a rapid solvent for crude selenium but has very slow solvent action on high-purity selenium.

Hot concentrated nitric acid reacts violently with crude selenium, but the reaction with selenium of 99.99 per cent purity is discouragingly slow, requiring 1 hr to dissolve 10 to 20 g.

Sulfuric acid, $6N$, cold or hot, acting on crude or high-purity selenium, does not dissolve enough selenium in 1 hr to give a green color to the acid.

Hot sulfuric acid, $36N$, acting on crude or on high-purity selenium, in 5 min dissolves

TABLE 23.4.[10, 26]

| System | Eutectic | | | Compounds formed |
| | Composition* | Temperature | | |
		(°C)	(°F)	
Silver-selenium	26±% Se	840	1544	Ag_2Se
Copper-selenium	2.2% Se	1063	1945	Cu_2Se
Iron-selenium	No eutectic	—	—	FeS and $FeSe_2$
Mercury-selenium	Lies very close to 100% Se	—	—	HgSe
Lead-selenium	55% Se	681	1258	PbSe
Antimony-selenium	40% Se	530	986	Sb_2Se_3
Sulfur-selenium	62 to 63% Se	105	221	
Tellurium-selenium	Complete liquid and solid solution			
Thallium-selenium	23% Se†	284	543	Tl_2Se_3
Zinc-selenium	—	—	—	ZnSe

* Weight per cent.
† Two other eutectics are sometimes reported.

enough selenium to give an intense green color to the acid.

Alkalis. Some forms of selenium are soluble in dilute aqueous caustic solutions, in aqueous cyanides, and aqueous sulfites.[24]

Cyanide solutions and also sulfite solutions have been used extensively to extract selenium from selenium-bearing flue dusts.[24]

Fusion of selenium-bearing flue dusts with potassium hydroxide, followed by extraction with water, yields solutions containing potassium selenite, K_2SeO_3, and potassium selenide, K_2Se.

Selenium or selenium dioxide fused with potassium nitrate yields potassium selenate, K_2SeO_4. Fusion of selenium compounds with alkali peroxides yield selenates. Such fusions should be made in small quantities and behind safety shields.

Metals. Molten selenium is either partially or completely miscible with most of the metals. In most cases the fused mass consists of the metal selenide or a mixture of the metal selenide and selenium. Table 23.4 gives the eutectic points of some of the binary systems of selenium.

With most of the metals, including those not mentioned in Table 23.4, selenium forms definite chemical compounds.

TOXICITY[31]

Selenium and its compounds are highly toxic, the maximum allowable concentration in air being about 0.10 ppm.

Contact with metallic or amorphous selenium has not been reported as a source of skin injury, although selenium salts have given rise to a contact dermatitis.

USES OF SELENIUM

The principal users of selenium are the electronics industry, the ceramics and pigment industries, and the steel industry.

Electronics Industry

Selenium is used in the electronics industry to produce dry-plate electrical rectifiers, xerographic plates, photocells, solar batteries, and television cameras. Each use requires a suitable grade of selenium in the range of 99.99 to 99.999 per cent selenium and with a halogen content compatible with the item to be manufactured.

Selenium Rectifiers. A selenium dry-plate rectifier consists of a base plate of iron or aluminum sandblasted or etched, then either nickel plated or flash coated with a thin layer of bismuth, and a layer of selenium of 0.002 to 0.003 in. thick applied by vaporization in a vacuum chamber or applied by sifting a layer of pulverized selenium onto the base plate and then compressing for several minutes in a hydraulic press provided with heated platens. The resulting sandwich is heat treated for about 30 min at slightly above 210°C (410°F). Next, the artificial barrier is applied to increase the resistance of the unit to the flow of current in the reverse direction. Finally, a counterelectrode of Wood's metal or the like is applied, and the unit is placed in an electrical circuit to condition and improve the blocking resistance. The discs are then assembled into commercial units, dipped into insulating lacquer, and packaged for shipment.

Some details of the manufacture of selenium rectifiers are given by Escoffery,[6] Henisch,[11] and Crow.[3]

Many scientific facts have been learned by the electronics industry about semiconductors since the publication of the first edition of the "Rare Metals Handbook," as shown in the textbook by Spenke.[32]

Two types of miniature selenium rectifiers are shown in Figures 23.2 and 23.3.

The rectifying action of a dry-plate selenium rectifier is known to take place at the interface between the p-type selenium and the n-type barrier layer of cadmium sulfide (U.S. Patent 2,488,369).

Selenium is a p-type, extrinsic semiconductor below its melting point. Lattice defects at the ends of the chains (crystal structure) are believed to be the principal source of carriers. Halogens have the effect of increasing the p-type conductivity, whereas mercury increases the resistivity without converting selenium to n-type (Hannay,[9] page 430).

Cadmium sulfide is an n-type semiconductor that remains n-type despite considerable contamination, accidental or intentional. The p-type conductivity was never observed. The crystals remained n-type or become insulators (Hannay,[9] page 585).

FIGURE 23.3. Miniature standard bridge-type selenium rectifiers. (*Courtesy International Rectifier Corp., El Segundo, Calif.*)

The direction of easy flow of positive electrical current in the selenium rectifier is through the base plate, then through the layer of selenium, through the rectifying junction, and, finally, through the counterelectrode alloy. The movement of electrons in the easy-flow direction is the opposite of the direction outlined for the positive current.

Xerography. Xerography is a method for the reproduction of images by light. The method is especially useful for the rapid copying and duplicating of letters, drawings, and prints and is of interest to the Signal Corps for the production of maps.

A plate containing a thin layer of selenium is given a strong positive electrical charge. The design to be copied is projected by light upon the charged surface of the selenium layer. The light discharges the electrically charged selenium in proportion to the light reaching the plate, thus producing a latent image. The image is developed by dusting the plate with a powder of negatively charged particles which adhere to the portions of the plate where the charged selenium was not struck by the projected light.

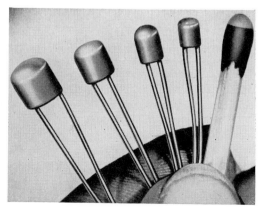

FIGURE 23.2. Miniature encapsulated-type selenium rectifiers. (*Courtesy International Rectifier Corp., El Segundo, Calif.*)

Additional simple steps allow the image to be used as a master copy for additional prints. The process is shown, step by step, on page 409 of the reference to Ridenour.[30]

Vidicon Television Camera. The vidicon television pickup tube, developed by the Radio Corporation of America, also makes use of the photoconducting property of amorphous selenium. The illuminated portions of the pattern projected upon the selenium layer transmit a light signal when scanned by the electron beam. A sketch plus a photograph of the vidicon is given on page 408 of the reference to Ridenour.[30]

The Photocell (Photovoltaic Type). The photocell here considered is more properly known as a photovoltaic cell, as described on page 557 of the reference to Reich.[29] The cell is also classed as a "barrier-layer cell" because it contains a rectifying interface. The use of the name "rectifier-type, sandwich photocell" is obvious when it is realized that the structure mechanically and electronically is almost identical with the dry-plate selenium rectifier. On page 416 of the reference to Dow[4] is given a sketch showing the construction of the cell and showing how the photons of light penetrate through the transparent counterelectrode to the photoelectric boundary, causing ejected electrons to flow in a direction opposite to the entrance of light.

Solar Batteries. Solar batteries may be considered as photovoltaic cells which have been designed for the maximum conversion of solar radiations into electrical energy, without regard to the type of selective response needed in a photocell designed for use in photography.

Glass and Ceramics Industry

Of all the uses of selenium, the requirements of the glass and ceramics industry are perhaps the oldest and certainly one of the largest. As a decolorizer, selenium is added to glass to counteract the greenish-tint effect caused by the iron present therein. Selenium combined with cadmium forms cadmium-selenide reds which are widely used in the glass industry to produce the familiar ruby-colored glass. These same cadmium-selenide reds also find wide application in the field of ceramics and enamels. These so-called glass colors have proved a boon to the bottling industry, where they are widely used in attractive permanent labeling to replace paper labels or uncolored raised lettering on milk bottles, beer bottles, and the like.

Pigment Industry

The cadmium-seleno lithopones, as used in the paint industry, have given that industry a permanent, nonfading, red-colored paint.

Steel Industry

In the mid-1930's one of the large steel companies found that the addition of selenium to stainless steel not only acted as an excellent degasifier but also increased machinability, both desirable properties in certain types of stainless steel, such as 18-8. Although sulfur can be used as a substitute, it does not impart the desirable properties to stainless steel that selenium does, and the use of selenium in the industry continues at a steady pace.

Miscellaneous Uses

Selenium has been used as a vulcanizing agent in the rubber industry and in concentrations of 0.1 to 2 per cent to promote resistance to heat, oxidation, and abrasion, and to increase resilience. In its acid form it is used to etch steel. As selenium dioxide it is used as an oxidizing agent in the preparation of the wonder drug, cortisone. Although selenium dioxide has long been known as an oxidizing agent, it has been found to act also as an antioxidant additive to lubricating oils and might therefore be classified as a valuable lubricant addition agent.

The photographic industry looks to selenium not only for the manufacture of photocells but also for its toning baths for sepia prints.

Not only does selenium increase the machinability of stainless steel but, as an addition to copper, transmits the same benefits. It has also found use as an addition agent in brighteners for copper plating. Another interesting use for this metal has been suggested in the guise of a flameproofing agent for electric switchboard cables. In addition to its many and varied uses, in its oxychloride form it is one of the most powerful solvents known and finds use as a solvent of synthetic phenic resins, at one time considered insoluble.

Although initial work on cadmium selenide

phosphors for colored television tubes has been unrewarding owing to an aging factor, efforts to overcome this drawback are continuing. In the field of thermoelectrics, bismuth selenide is being considered as a substitute for bismuth and lead tellurides. Such thermoelectric devices which would provide a compact means having no moving parts of either current generation by application of heat to the device (Seeback effect), or refrigeration or heating, are of considerable interest at present. The latter effects, refrigeration and heating, are accomplished by passing a current through a junction of these two dissimilar metals, bismuth and telluride, resulting in the pumping of heat from one junction to another in a two-junction system, called a *couple* (Peltier effect).

The idea of introducing a toxic substance into the tissues of living plants as a means of protecting them against insect attack, though perhaps somewhat revolutionary, is an accepted practice in the case of sodium selenate in the control of red spider on certain greenhouse plants.

Selenium oxychloride also finds use as a reagent for the separation and purification of various hydrocarbons. Charcoal may be activated for gas absorption with it. It may also be used as a paint and varnish remover and as a solvent for rubber resins, glue, and other organic substances.

References

1. Booth, H. S., "Inorganic Syntheses," Vol. 1, New York, McGraw-Hill Book Company, Inc., 1939.
2. Brooks, L. S., "The Vapor Pressure of Tellurium and Selenium," U.S. Atomic Energy Commission AECD-2546, Technical Information Branch, AEC, Oak Ridge, Tenn.
3. Crow, L. R., "Metallic Rectifiers," Indianapolis, Howard W. Sames & Co., Inc., 1957.
4. Dow, W. G., "Fundamentals of Engineering Electronics," New York, John Wiley & Sons, Inc., 1937.
5. Elkins, H. B., "The Chemistry of Industrial Toxicology," New York, John Wiley & Sons, Inc., 1950.
6. Escoffery, C. A., *Trans. Electrochem. Soc.*, **90**, 129 (1946); Escoffery, C. A., and Halperin, S., *ibid.*, p. 163.
7. "Gmelins Handbuch der anorganischen Chemie," 8. Auflage, System Nummer 10, Teil A, 1950; Teil B, 1949, Weinheim, Germany, Verlag Chemie GMBH.
8. "Handbook of Chemistry and Physics," 40th Ed., Cleveland, Chemical Rubber Publishing Co., 1959.
9. Hannay, B., "Semiconductors," New York, Reinhold Publishing Corp., 1959.
10. Hansen, M., "Constitution of Binary Alloys," New York, McGraw-Hill Book Company, Inc., 1958.
11. Henisch, H. K., "Metal Rectifiers," Oxford, England, Clarendon Press, 1949.
12. Henkels, H. W., *J. Appl. Phys.*, **21**, 725 (1950); Henkels, H. W., and Maczuk, J., *J. Appl. Phys.*, **24**, 1056 (1953).
13. Henkels, H. W., *J. Appl. Phys.*, **22**, 916 (1951).
14. Henkels, H. W., and Maczuk, J., *J. Appl. Phys.*, **25**, 1 (1954).
15. Hopkins, B. S., "Chemistry of the Less Familiar Elements," Champaign, Ill., Stipes Publishing Co., 1939.
16. Hume-Rothery, W., and Raynor, G. V., "The Structure of Metals and Alloys," 3rd Ed., London, Institute of Metals, 1954.
17. "Inorganic Syntheses," Vol. 2, New York, McGraw-Hill Book Company, Inc., 1946.
18. *Ibid.*, Vol. 3, p. 130, New York, McGraw-Hill Book Company, Inc., 1950.
19. King, A., "Inorganic Preparations," Princeton, N.J., D. Van Nostrand Company, Inc., 1936.
20. Kittel, C., "Solid State Physics," New York, John Wiley & Sons, Inc., 1956.
21. Lange, N. A., "Handbook of Chemistry," 9th Ed., Sandusky, Ohio, Handbook Publishers, Inc., 1956.
22. Latimer, W. M., "The Oxidation States of the Elements and Their Potentials in Aqueous Solutions," Englewood Cliffs, N.J., Prentice-Hall, Inc., 1938.
23. Lundell, G. E. F., and Hoffman, J. I., "Outlines of Methods of Chemical Analysis," New York, John Wiley & Sons, Inc., 1938.
24. Lunge, G., "The Manufacturer of Sulfuric Acid and Alkali," Vol. 1, Part 3, p. 1468, Princeton, N.J., D. Van Nostrand Company, Inc., 1913.
25. Mellor, J. W., "A Comprehensive Treatise on Inorganic and Theoretical Chemistry," Vol. 10, chapters on sulfur and selenium, London, Longmans, Green & Co., Ltd., 1930.
26. "Metals Handbook," Cleveland, American Society for Metals, 1948.
27. Pauling, L., "College Chemistry," San Francisco, W. H. Freeman & Co., 1957.
28. Preston, J. S., *Proc. Roy. Soc. (London)*, **A202**, 449 (1950).
29. Reich, H. J., "Theory and Applications of

Electron Tubes," New York, McGraw-Hill Book Company, Inc., 1944.

30. Ridenour, L. N., "Modern Physics for the Engineer," New York, McGraw-Hill Book Company, Inc., 1954.

31. Sax, N. I., "Handbook of Dangerous Materials," New York, Reinhold Publishing Corp., 1951.

32. Spenke, E., "Electronic Semiconductors,"

translated by D. Jenny *et al.*, New York, McGraw-Hill Book Company, Inc., 1958.

33. von Hippel, A. R., *J. Chem. Phys.*, **16**, 372 (1948).

34. von Hippel, A. R., and Bloom, M. C., *J. Chem. Phys.*, **18**, 1243 (1950).

35. Yost, D. M., and Russell, H., Jr., "Systematic Inorganic Chemistry," Englewood Cliffs, N.J., Prentice-Hall, Inc., 1944.

24. SILICON

DONALD W. LYON and JACK E. FIELD

E. I. du Pont de Nemours & Company
Pigments Department
Edge Moor, Delaware

INTRODUCTION

The history of silicon began shortly after 1800 when Davy concluded that silica was a compound, not an element. In 1771 Scheele[88] had prepared silicon fluoride and hydrolyzed it to form silicic acid, but it was 1811 before Gay-Lussac and Thenard[31] first prepared what was probably very impure amorphous silicon by passing the tetrachloride over heated potassium. Berzelius[8] finally succeeded in preparing silicon by the same general method in 1824: he purified the product by prolonged leaching of the by-product fluosilicate. In addition, he obtained silicon from the reaction of potassium fluosilicate with potassium. The resulting silicide was decomposed with water.

Crystalline silicon was prepared first by Deville,[20] in 1854, by electrolysis of impure sodium aluminum chloride. Shiny platelets of silicon were obtained by dissolving the aluminum from the granular melt which had contained about 10 per cent silicon.

The forerunner of the present large-scale commercial process was developed by Potter,[76] who studied the interaction of silica and carbon with the production of silicon carbide as an intermediate which reacted further to form the element. Becket[7] and Tucker[98] devised acid purifications for preparing silicon of a fair degree of purity (over 99 per cent). "Hyperpure" silicon (99.97 per cent) was derived by a du Pont team,[61] who reduced the tetrachloride with zinc.

The element is located in Group IV of the periodic table. It exhibits a marked similarity to carbon in many of its compounds, particularly where it is the more electropositive element in a compound. Silicon is also closely related to germanium, tin, and lead. Its resemblance to the IVB elements, titanium, zirconium, hafnium, and thorium, is less marked, and decreases with increasing atomic weight of the element in question.

OCCURRENCE

Only oxygen is more abundant in the earth's crust than silicon, which is present to the extent of about 28 per cent. It occurs always combined with oxygen, as silica or metallic silicates. Silica in some form makes up about 78 per cent of the sandstones, 60 per cent of the igneous rocks, 58 per cent of the shales, and 5 per cent of the limestones: the average for the earth's outer shell is nearly 60 per cent silica.

Silicon occurs as silica in quartz, which is found in many large deposits, in mountains, and in sands. Most of the semiprecious gem stones are comprised of quartz with traces of impurities.

Silica is assimilated by certain plants and by animal organisms from aqueous solution. Its presence has also been detected in numerous stars and meteorites.

PRODUCTION AND ECONOMIC STATISTICS

Approximately 14,000 tons of silicon "metal" (97 per cent Si) were produced in 1959. Silicon

TABLE 24.1. FERROSILICON—IMPORTS AND
PRODUCTION 1947 TO 1958

Year	Imports (short tons silicon content)	Production (short tons ferrosilicon)
1947	2,141	769,653
1948	734	814,297
1949	931	647,981
1950	3,785	742,407
1951	10,997	861,889
1952	2,235	781,888
1953	2,206	808,605
1954	3,980	286,350
1955	5,963	382,699
1956	5,005	460,193
1957	3,813	417,025
1958	2,398	286,396

Reference source: "Minerals Yearbook," United States
Department of Interior, Bureau of Mines.

is available primarily in the form of ferrosilicon, an alloy containing about 50 per cent
of each constituent, at an average unit price
of $292/ton in 1959. Imports of ferrosilicon,
together with United States production, are
shown in Table 24.1.

Regular-grade silicon (97 per cent Si, 1 per
cent Fe maximum) sells for 19 cents/lb. Ferrosilicon is also available as 2½- or 5-lb briquettes
(40 per cent Si) at about 8 to 10 cents/lb.

The 97 per cent material can be purified by
repeated leaching to yield a 99.7+ per cent
product, which has a price of $7/lb. This grade,
however, is still too impure for semiconductor
use.

TABLE 24.2. PURE SILICON PRODUCERS—
UNITED STATES

Company	Location
Allegheny Electronic Chemicals	Erie, Pa.
Dow-Corning	Hemlock, Mich.
Du Pont	Brevard, N.C.
Grace	Puerto Rico
Mallinckrodt	St. Louis, Mo.
Merck	Danville, Pa.
Monsanto	St. Louis, Mo.
Sylvania	Towanda, Pa.
Texas Instruments	Dallas, Texas
Trancoa	Westfield, Mass.
Union Carbide (Kemet Division)	Cleveland, Ohio

Very pure silicon (semiconductor grade) is
being sold at $90 to $600/lb. Commercial offer-
ings of single crystal silicon are available at
premium prices.

A list of pure-silicon producers is given in
Table 24.2. Total capacity at the end of 1958
was estimated at 165,000 lb/year, and the production of high-purity silicon in 1958 amounted
to 50,000 to 60,000 lb, according to the "1958
Minerals Yearbook."

DERIVATION

Silicon has been prepared by a number of
methods. The tetrachloride can be reduced with
hydrogen, using a hot carbon filament,[78] or a
hot wire,[100] or with aluminum,[84,106] magnesium,[4]
or zinc.[61] Other processes include the reduction
of trichlorosilane or silane. The thermal decomposition of SiI_4 is also being used. The fluoride
or alkali fluosilicates have been reduced with
alkali metals[9,20,31,39,103] or with aluminum.[111]

Silica can be converted to silicon by treatment with carbon or silicon carbide in the
electric furnace,[64,76,89,98] and by reduction
with aluminum[51,57] or magnesium.[103]

Electrolysis of silica rendered molten in alkali
metal oxides,[3] sodium chloride–aluminum chloride,[20] or aluminum chloride[105] has yielded the
element.

The principal commercial derivation of the
element on a large scale involves an electric
furnace technique, in which silicon dioxide and
carbon are the principal raw materials. Carbon
electrodes are used; these extend well into the
charge of coke and sand. The silicon is tapped
from the bottom of the furnace, and cast into
pigs of 600 to 800 lb.

PHYSICAL PROPERTIES

The physical properties of silicon are given
in Table 24.3. Arc-spectrum data are reported
by McLennan and Edwards.[62] Spark spectra
are also given by these authors, and by Salet.[85]
Silicon has a continuous flame spectrum, according to Huggins.[43]

Silicon has been prepared in the amorphous
form as a brown powder[13,108,109] which can
easily be melted or vaporized.[104] Crystalline
silicon is grayish and metallic in color. Commercial forms of high-purity silicon are shown
in Figure 24.1.

TABLE 24.3. PHYSICAL PROPERTIES OF SILICON

(Numbers in parenthesis refer to references)

Atomic number	14	
Atomic radius	11.17 Å	
Atomic weight	28.09	(6)
Atoms/cc	4.96×10^{22}	(73)
Boiling point	2480°C (4496°F)	(41)
Cathodoluminescence (minimum voltage for		
excitation)		(27)
Of amorphous silicon (whitish-yellow)	1,600	
Of crystalline silicon (red)	2,400	
Coefficient of thermal expansion—mean value		
between 15–1000°C (59–1832°F)	4.68×10^{-6}	(5)
At 25°C	$4.2 \ \times 10^{-6}$	(73)
At −157°C (−250.6°F)	Zero	(99)
At liquid air temperatures	Negative	(99)
Color		
Amorphous	Dark brown	
Graphitoidal	Black, six-sided plates	
Crystalline	Dark, steel gray; small crystals reported as transparent and light orange	
Critical pressure (atm)	1,450	(102)
Critical temperature (calculated)	4920°C (8888°F)	(102)
Crystal structure	Cubic (identical with diamond); forms octahedral crystals; 8 atoms to unit cube, side of cube 5.42 to 5.43 Å	(58, 68, 101)
	Amorphous and crystalline silicon give identical x-ray patterns	(19)
Dielectric constant	12	(15)
Electrical conductivity (ohm-cm)		(72)
−190°C (−310°F)	2×10^3	
300°C (572°F)	15	
500°C (932°F)	0.4	
Energy gap	1.12 ev	(15)
Entropy (cal/mol/°K)		(79)
Solid silicon		
298°K	4.50	
500°K	7.58	
1000°K	11.85	
1500°K	15.48	
Liquid silicon		
2000°K	23.75	
Gaseous silicon		
298°K	40.13	
500°K	42.76	
1000°K	46.14	
1500°K	48.20	
2000°K	49.66	
Free energy (cal/mol/°K) $\left[\dfrac{-(F - H_{298})}{T} \right]$		(81)
Solid silicon		
298°K	4.50	
500°K	5.46	
1000°K	7.70	
1500°K	10.56	

TABLE 24.3. PHYSICAL PROPERTIES OF SILICON *(cont.)*
(Numbers in parenthesis refer to references)

Liquid silicon		
2000°K	12.29	
Gaseous silicon		
298°K	40.13	
500°K	40.63	
1000°K	42.55	
1500°K	44.12	
2000°K	45.31	
Hardness		
Mohs scale	7	
Brinell	240	(25)
Heat of combustion, Si to SiO_2 (cal)	191,000	(63)
Heat content		(80)
Solid silicon $(H_T - H_{298})$		
500°K	1.06	
1000°K	4.15	
1500°K	7.37	
Liquid silicon		
2000°K	22.92	
Gaseous silicon		
500°K	1.065	
1000°K	3.60	
1500°K	6.12	
2000°K	8.70	
Heat of fusion (kcal/mol)	11.1	(41)
Heat of vaporization (cal/mol)	71,000	(82)
Lattice constant [25°C (77°F)]	5.429×10^{-8} cm	(73)
Magnetic susceptibility (Si with 0.085% Fe)	0.13×10^{-6}	(42)
Melting point	1420°C (2590°F)	(73)
Mobility (300°K)		
Electron	1300 sq cm/volt sec	(73)
Hole	500 sq cm/volt sec	(73)
Modulus of elasticity (psi)	15,490,000	(53)
Modulus of rupture (psi)	9,046	(53)
Molecular rotary power (calculated from that of quartz)	0.27	(34, 91)
Plasticity number (Pt = 116)	89.3	(26)
Reflectance (polished commercial Si in the visible)	26–35%; highest in the blue, falls away rapidly toward the infrared	(14)
Refractive index		(104)
μ	3.87	
μk (absolute coefficient)	0.47	
Infrared	3.5 (at 1.2 μ)	(12)
	3.4 (at 2.6 μ)	(12)
Resistivity, intrinsic (300°K)	230,000 ohm-cm	(73)
Specific gravity	2.33	(73)
Specific heat (c) of 99.2% Si		
0°C	0.1597 cal/g/°C	(90)
0–100°C	0.181 cal/g/°C	(73)
Equation:		

$$c = 0.165428(\Theta - 17) + 0.0001584310(\Theta - 17)^2 - 0.0000003742(\Theta - 17)^3$$

Thermal conductivity (cal/cm/sec/°C)	0.20	(56)

TABLE 24.3. PHYSICAL PROPERTIES OF SILICON *(cont.)*

(Numbers in parenthesis refer to references)

Vapor pressure (mm Hg)		(22)
1920°K	1	
2120°K	10	
2360°K	100	
Vibration frequency		
Red ray	13.57×10^{12}	(35)
Violet ray	3.69×10^{15}	(35)
Gamma ray	9.6×10^{12}	(105)
Volume compressibility	0.98×10^{-12} sq cm/dyne	(73)

A discussion of silicon whiskers is given by Brenner[10]

Figure 24.1. Commercial forms of high purity polycrystalline silicon. (*Courtesy E. I. Du Pont de Nemours & Company.*)

CHEMICAL PROPERTIES

Silicon behaves similarly to carbon in many reactions. The most important of these have led to the development of the silicones and related compounds. Silicon is, almost without exception, quadrivalent. It is less electropositive than the metals; usually it forms compounds in which the silicon is part of the anion.

Silicon combines readily with all the halogens to form compounds of the type SiX_4. It burns with difficulty in air, but reacts with oxygen at a red heat, sulfur at 600°C (1112°F), and nitrogen at 1000°C (1832°F). Silicon combines with boron, carbon, titanium, and zirconium in the electric furnace.

Silicon readily dissolves in molten magnesium, copper, iron, and nickel to form silicides. It dissolves also in aluminum and silver, and separates as crystals on cooling. Gaseous and liquid hydrogen fluoride dissolve silicon, but it is inert to the aqueous acid. The element can be dissolved in mixtures of nitric and hydrofluoric acids. It reacts slowly with steam at red heat, with the liberation of hydrogen.

Most oxides are reduced by silicon at high temperatures. Thus, in the well-known Pidgeon process,[75] silicon is used to reduce magnesium from its oxide. Silicon reacts with fused caustic, sodium carbonate, potassium dichromate, chlorate, and nitrate.

APPLICATIONS

The present uses of elemental silicon are not numerous; however, it is extremely important in certain applications.

The best known and widest application of the element is in rectifiers and transistors. Silicon rectifiers are described by Torrey and Whitmer;[97] Scaff, Theurer, and Schumacher;[87] and others.[48,49,55,69,83,93,112] A good treatment of this subject is given by Hunter.[45]

In semiconductor devices (diodes, power rectifiers, transistors, solar cells), single crystals of silicon must be used. Controlled amounts of

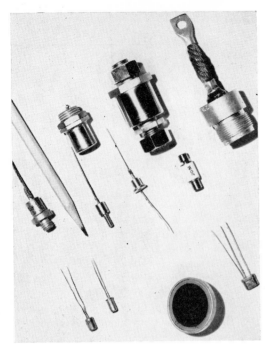

Figure 24.2. Silicon semiconductor devices. The upper seven items are rectifiers. In the lower row from left to right are two diodes, a solar cell, and transistor. (*Courtesy E. I. Du Pont de Nemours & Company.*)

impurities are added during a "doping" step, which can occur during the production of the single crystals, or in a subsequent operation. Space does not permit a complete treatment of this subject, which is discussed more fully in many references.[37,45,92]

Figure 24.2 illustrates several semiconductor devices.

The use of silicon in transistors is increasing, principally because its maximum operating temperature in transistors is about 250°C (482°F), as compared to 75°C (167°F) for germanium. Silicon has high resistivity, even at comparatively high temperatures. The availability of silicon is also a factor, although the less common germanium is much more readily purified.

Silicon is transparent to infrared radiation in the 2- to 8-μ range[60] and has found some use as lenses for infrared.[28] Infrared absorption spectra above 8 μ are discussed by Lax and Burstein.[60]

Silicon can be fired with ceramic materials to form heat resistant articles,[36] or, in combination

with carbon, it can produce a refractory composition in which some of the silicon remains in the elemental form.[1] Cast articles consisting mainly of silicon have been patented for use in chemical ware, pipes, and crucibles.[2]

Silicon, like beryllium and rhodium, can be evaporated in a vessel constructed of tungsten wire and sintered thoria. It can be deposited from the vapor from sodium chloride or alumina supports. Metals can be coated with silicon by reducing silicon tetrachloride with hydrogen; steel and molybdenum, e.g., can be siliconized in this way.

Silicon can function as an autoxidation catalyst.[67] High-purity silicon serves as the element in photocells.[70] As an electrode material, this element can be used for electrometric titration of acids and bases.[9] Mirrors for dentists' use or for other purposes are formed with a reflecting surface of silicon formed by electrodeposition.[96]

The use of silicon in the preparation of various silicides has been well developed. More recently, it has found important commercial use as a starting material for the synthesis of silicones.[4]

Alloys of silicon with antimony, bismuth, cobalt, gold, lead, silver, tin, and zinc have been described.[46] No compounds are found in these binary phase systems. Alloys with aluminum also have been prepared.[47,71] Ferrous metals can be coated or alloyed with silicon.[59] High-silicon (15 per cent)–iron castings are corrosion resistant; however, they are impossible to machine. These and other alloys of silicon and iron, and silicon, carbon, and iron are comprehensively treated by Greiner et al.[33] The same authors also discuss silicon and silicon-manganese steels, including those which also contain nickel, molybdenum, chromium, and vanadium.

Since silicon is the most abundant and one of the cheapest elements (97 per cent form), is light, and is corrosion and heat resistant, it may seem surprising that it has not come into much wider use. The primary reason for its limited use is that it is not ductile from room temperature to at least 600°C (1112°F).

In the immediate future it would appear that the greatest demand for high-purity silicon will be for uses where advantage can be taken of (1) its electrical properties, (2) its optical properties, and (3) siliconizing metal products to form corrosion and heat resistant materials. Continuing research will undoubtedly lead to new applications after purity is improved and the price of the pure element is reduced.

SINGLE CRYSTALS

Several methods have been used for the preparation of single crystals of silicon,[11,16,50] the Czochralski method[16] and modifications[94] being commonly employed. In this procedure a single crystal "seed" is dipped into molten silicon held at the melting point, then slowly withdrawn. Pure quartz crucibles are generally used, but a recent technique[17] for growing small, perfect crystals utilizes a silicon pedestal on which a molten puddle of silicon is maintained as the feed stock. Typical Czochralski single crystals are shown in Figure 24.3.

Figure 24.3. Typical silicon single crystals grown by the Czochralski technique. (*Courtesy E. I. Du Pont de Nemours & Company.*)

The floating zone technique, developed by Keck[52] and described by Pfann,[74] is used for crucibleless melting, refining, and crystal grow-

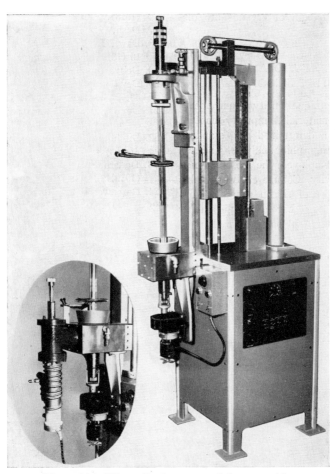

Figure 24.4. Silicon floating zone refining assembly. (*Courtesy Lepel High-Frequency Laboratories, Inc.*)

ing. The silicon, in rod form, is heated by a high-frequency induction field until it has melted completely through. If the rod is supported at both ends, the molten zone can be maintained by the surface tension of the liquid and a combination of magnetic and electrical levitation effects. Since pure silicon is a poor conductor at room temperature, it must be preheated to about 600°C (1112°F) before it can couple with the field. If a single crystal "seed" is used, the rod can be converted to a single crystal by sweeping the zone through the bar, usually from bottom to top, in an inert atmosphere. The float zone method has two major advantages; the silicon does not come in contact with the container, such as the quartz crucible in the Czochralski system, and a crystal of more uniform quality can be produced. A photograph of a silicon floating zone assembly is given in Figure 24.4.

Growth and perfection of crystals are discussed by Doremus.[24]

CHARACTERIZATION AND ANALYSIS OF VERY PURE SILICON

Because of the unique purity requirements of semiconductor materials, impurity content cannot usually be determined by standard chemical or spectrographic analyses. Indirect measurements are employed, the most common of which is resistivity. Commercially available semiconductor grades of silicon normally contain minute quantities of boron and phosphorus (in the range of 0.1 to 10 parts per billion, as a rule). The latter can be removed by zone refining, because of its greater solubility in liquid silicon. Boron, however, cannot be eliminated by this technique, because of its unfavorable segregation coefficient.

Boron and other Group-III elements (Al, Ga, etc.) behave as electron donors, and cause silicon to become positively charged (p-type). Phosphorus and Group-V elements (As, Sb, etc.), when present in excess, produce n-type (negative) silicon.

References

1. Acheson, E. G., U.S. Patent 1,014,199.
2. Allen, T. B., U.S. Patents 1,037,713; 1,073,560 (1912).
3. Andrieux, L., and Dodero, M., *Compt. rend.,* **198**, 753–5 (1934).
4. Anonymous, *Chem. Week,* **68** (24), 8 (June 30, 1951).
5. Baraduc-Muller, L., *Rev. mét.,* **7**, 828 (1910).
6. Batuecas, T., *Nature,* **159**, 705 (1947).
7. Becket, F. M., U.S. Patent 1,386,227 (1921).
8. Berzelius, J. J., *Pogg. Ann.,* **1**, 121, 169, 204 (1824); **2**, 210 (1824); **61**, 10 (1844).
9. Boltunov, Y. A., and Isakova, K. J., *J. Gen. Chem.* (U.S.S.R.) **7**, 2838–41, 2899–2902 (1951).
10. Brenner, S. S., *Science,* **128**, 569 (1958).
11. Bridgman, P. W., *Proc. Amer. Acad. Arts Sci.,* **60**, 305 (1925).
12. Briggs, H. B., *Phys. Rev.,* **77**, 287 (1950).
13. Cambi, L., *Atti accad. nazl. Lincei, Sez. I,* **20**, 440–2 (1911).
14. Coblentz, W. W., *J. Franklin Inst.,* **170**, 187 (1910).
15. Conwell, E. M., *Proc. Inst. Radio Eng.,* **40**, 1327–37 (1952).
16. Czochralski, J., *Z. physik. Chem.,* **92**, 219 (1918).
17. Dash, W. C., *J. Applied Phys.,* **29**, 736 (1958).
18. Davy, H., *Phil. Trans.,* **98**, 333 (1808); **100**, 16 (1810).
19. Debye P., *Physik. Z.,* **17**, 277–283 (1916).
20. Deville, H. St.-C., *Ann. chim. et phys.,* [*3*], **43**, 27–36 (1854); **49**, 62–78 (1857).
21. Deville, H. St.-C. and Caron, H., *Ann. chim. et phys.,* [*3*], **63**, 26 (1861); **67**, 435 (1863).
22. Ditchburn, R. W., and Gilmour, J. C., *Rev. Modern Phys.,* **13**, 310–27 (1941).
23. Dodero, M., *Bull. soc. chim.,* **6**, 209–18 (1939).
24. Doremus, R. H., Roberts, B. W., and Turnbull, D., "Growth and Perfection of Crystals," New York, John Wiley and Sons, 1958.
25. Edwards, C. A., *J. Inst. Metals,* **20**, 61 (1918).
26. Edwards, C. A. and Herbert, A. M., *J. Inst. Metals,* **25**, 175 (1921).
27. Ewles, J., *Phil. Mag.,* [*6*], **45**, 957 (1923).
28. Fan, H. Y. and Becker, M., "Symposium Volume of the Reading Conference," London, Butterworth Publ. Co., 1951.
29. Fortunatov, N. S., *Mem. Inst. Chem. Acad. Sci. Ukr. S.S.R.,* **2**, 257–9 (1935).
30. Fox, M., and Pearsall, C. S., U.S. Patent Application 604,013.
31. Gay-Lussac, J. L., and Thenard, L. J., *Ann. chim. et phys.,* [*1*], **69**, 204 (1809).
32. Gonser, B. W., *Sci. Monthly,* **74**, 52–7 (1952).
33. Greiner, E. S., Marsh, J. S., and Stoughton, B., "Alloys of Iron and Silicon," New York, McGraw-Hill Book Co., 1933.
34. Haagen, A., *Pogg. Ann.,* **131**, 117 (1867).

35. Haber, F., *Ber. Phys. Ges.*, **13**, 1122 (1911).
36. Haeuber, H., U.S. Patent 1,916,836 (1933).
37. Hannay, N. B., "Semiconductors," New York, Reinhold Publ. Corp., 1959.
38. Hass, G., *Z. anorg. Chem.*, **257**, 166–72 (1948).
39. Hempel, W., and von Haasy, H., *Z. anorg. Chem.*, **23**, 32–42 (1900).
40. Hino, J., and Stauss, H. E., *J. Metals*, **4**, 656 (1952).
41. Hoffman, F., and Schulze, A., *Physik. Z.*, **38**, 901–5 (1937); *Metallwirtschaft*, **17**, 3 (1938).
42. Honda, K., "The Magnetic Properties of Matter," New York, The Macmillan Co., 1928.
43. Huggins, W., *Proc. Roy. Soc.*, **18**, 546 (1870).
44. Hull, A. W., *Phys. Rev.*, [*2*], **10**, 684 (1917).
45. Hunter, L. P., "Handbook of Semiconductor Electronics," New York, McGraw-Hill Book Co., 1956.
46. Jette, E. R., and Foote, F., *J. Chem. Phys.*, **3**, 605–16 (1935).
47. Jetter, L. K., and Mehl, R. F., *Am. Inst. Mining Met. Engrs., Inst. Metals Div., Tech. Publ. No. 1508* (1942).
48. Johnson, V. A., Smith, R. N., and Yearien, H. J., *J. Applied Phys.*, **21**, 283–9 (1950).
49. Jones, D. E., Ramsley, C. E., Ryde, J. W., and Williams, S. V., Canadian Patent 474,212 (1946).
50. Kapitza, P., *Proc. Roy. Soc.*, **119**, 358 (1928).
51. Karges, R. A., *J. Chem. Educ.*, **13**, 593 (1936).
52. Keck, P. H., and Golay, M. J. E., *Phys. Rev.*, **89**, 1297 (1953).
53. Kinzel, A. N., and Cunningham, T. R., *Metals Technol.*, **6**, Tech. Publ. No. **1138** (1939).
54. Kleinknecht, H., *Naturwissenschaften*, **39**, 400 (1952).
55. Kobayaski, A., *J. Phys. Soc. Japan*, **3**, 41–7 (1948).
56. Konigsberger, J., and Weiss, J., *Ann. Physik*, [*4*], **35**, 16 (1911).
57. Kuhne, K. A., German Patent 147,871 (1902).
58. Kustner, H., and Remy, H., *Physik. Z.*, **24**, 25–29 (1923).
59. Lauenstein, C. F., and Ulmer, P. F., U.S. Patent 2,105,888 (1938).
60. Lax, M., and Burstein, E., *Phys. Rev.*, **97**, 39–52 (1955).
61. Lyon, D. W., Olson, C. M., and Lewis, E. D., *J. Electrochem. Soc.*, **96**, 359–63 (1949).
62. McLennan, J. C., and Edwards, E., *Phil. Mag.*, [*6*], **30**, 482 (1915).
63. Mixter, W. G., *Am. J. Sci.*, [*4*], **24**, 130–140 (1907).
64. Moissan, H., *Ann. chim. et phys.*, [*7*], **9**, 300–1 (1895); *Bull. soc. chim.*, [*3*], **13**, 972 (1895).
65. Moissan, H. and Siemens, F., *Ber.*, **37**, 2540 (1904).
66. Moriya, Y., *Electrotech. J. (Japan)*, **2**, 219 (1938).
67. Moureu, C., Dufraisse, C., and Laplagne, P., *Compt. rend.*, **187**, 1266–9 (1928).
68. Neuberger, *Z. Krist.*, **92**, 313–4 (1935).
69. Ohl, R. S., U.S. Patents 2,402,663 (1946); 2,415,841 (1947).
70. Ohl, R. S., U.S. Patent 2,443,542 (1948).
71. Pacz, A., German Patent 632,953 (1936).
72. Pearson, G. L., and Bardeen, J., *Phys. Rev.*, **75**, 869 (1949).
73. Pearson, G. L. and Brattain, W. H., *Proc. IRE*, **43**, 1804 (1955).
74. Pfann, W. G., "Zone Melting," p. 89, New York, John Wiley and Sons, 1958.
75. Pidgeon, L. M., *Trans. Can. Inst. Mining Met.*, **49**, 621–635 (1946).
76. Potter, H. N., U.S. Patents 875,285 (1907); 875,672 (1907); 908,130 (1908).
77. Potter, J. G., U.S. Patent 1,917,271 (1933).
78. Pring, J. N., and Fielding, W., *J. Chem. Soc.*, **95**, 1497–1506 (1909).
79. Quill, L. L., "The Chemistry and Metallurgy of Miscellaneous Materials," pp. 16, 24, New York, McGraw-Hill Book Co., 1950.
80. *Ibid.*, pp. 18, 22.
81. *Ibid.*, pp. 18, 26.
82. *Ibid.*, p. 28.
83. Ransley, C. E., Ryde, J. W., and Williams, S. V., U.S. Patent 2,419,966 (1947).
84. Rauter, G., *Liebig's Ann.*, **270**, 235–266 (1892).
85. Salet, G., *Compt. rend.*, **73**, 1056 (1870).
86. Scaff, J. H., U.S. Patent 2,402,582 (1946).
87. Scaff, J. H., Theurer, H. C., and Schumacher, E. E., *J. Metals*, **1**, 383–8 (1949).
88. Scheele, C. W., *Handl. Svenska Akad.*, **33**, 120 (1771).
89. Scheid, R., British Patent 18,659 (1907).
90. Schrauf, A., *Pogg. Ann.*, **127**, 344 (1866).
91. Schimpff, H., *Z. physik. Chem.*, **71**, 257 (1910).
92. Shockley, W., "Electrons and Holes in Semiconductors," Princeton, N.J., Van Nostrand Co., 1950.
93. Stephens, W. E., *Electronics*, **19**, (7), 112–9 (1946).
94. Teal, G. K., "Some Recent Developments in Silicon and Germanium Materials and Devices," presented at National Conference on Airborne Electronics, May 10, 1954.
95. Theurer, H. C., Canadian Patent 452,409 (1948); U.S. Patent 2,475,810 (1949).
96. Tillyer, E. D., U.S. Patent 1,278,521 (1918).

97. Torrey, H. C., and Whitmer, C. A., "Crystal Rectifiers," pp. 301–330, New York, McGraw-Hill Book Co., 1948.

98. Tucker, N. P., *J. Iron Steel Inst.*, **15**, 412–416 (1927).

99. Valentiner, S., and Wallot, J., *Ann. Physik*, [*4*], **46**, 837 (1915).

100. Van Arkel, A. E., *Metallwirtschaft*, **13**, 405–8, 511–4 (1934).

101. Van Arkel, A. E., *Z. Krist*, **67**, 235–8 (1928).

102. Van Laar, J. J., *Proc. Acad. Sci. Amsterdam*, **18**, 1220 (1916).

103. Vigoroux, E., *Ann., chim. et phys.*, [*7*], **12**, 5–74, 153–196 (1897); *Compt. rend.*, **120**, 94–6, 554–7 (1905); *Bull. soc. chim.*, [*4*], **1**, 16 (1907).

104. Von Wartenberg, H., *Ber. Physik. Ges.*, **12**,
105–20 (1910); *Z. Elektrochem.*, **18**, 658 (1912).

105. Wagstaff, J. E. P., *Phil. Mag.*, [*6*], **47**, 66 (1924).

106. Weaver, V. M., U.S. Patents 1,238,604 (1917); 1,241,796 (1917); 1,296,575 (1919).

107. Western Electric Co., Inc., British Patent 590,458 (1947).

108. Wigand, A., *Ann. Phys.*, **21**, 95 (1907).

109. Wilke-Dorfurt, E., *Chem. Zentr.*, **1909**, II, 1965.

110. Winkler, C., *Ber.*, **23**, 2652 (1890); *J. Prakt. Chem.*, [*1*], **91**, 198 (1864).

111. Wohler, F., *Ann.*, **97**, 266 (1856); **102**, 382 (1857).

112. Yearien, H. J., *J. Applied Phys.*, **21**, 214–21 (1950).

25. TANTALUM

CLIFFORD A. HAMPEL

Consulting Chemical Engineer
Skokie, Illinois

Tantalum, atomic number 73, atomic weight 180.95, is located in Group VB of the periodic table below its sister element, columbium, and adjoined by hafnium on the left and tungsten on the right.

It is a strong ductile metal characterized by: (1) its high density, 16.6 g/cc; (2) its high melting point, 2996°C (5425°F), the third highest among the metals, exceeded only by rhenium, 3180°C (5756°F) and tungsten, 3410°C (6170°F); (3) the tenacious thin oxide layer on its surface which gives it superior rectifying and capacitance properties; and (4) its extreme inertness to attack by all acids, except hydrofluoric and fuming sulfuric, at ordinary temperatures.

History

Tantalum was discovered in 1802 by Ekeberg of Sweden; he named it after Tantalus in Greek mythology because of the difficulty of dissolving the oxide. In 1801 Hatchett of England had announced the discovery of columbium;[37] because of the similarity of the properties of the compounds of these two elements, for over forty years the two were regarded as identical, although Wollaston suspected their dissimilarity. In 1844 H. Rose, a German chemist, made exhaustive studies of the columbite of Bodenmais and showed that this mineral contained two metallic acids, one of tantalum and the other of what he supposed to be a new metal which he named niobium (for Niobe, the daughter of Tantalus).[82]

According to the distinguished American chemist J. Lawrence Smith,* in a note published in 1877,[87] Rose believed in 1844 that the tantalum of this mineral was the same as what was equally well-known as columbium. Thus it appears that he regarded the other metal in the mineral as a new element and did not simply apply another name to Hatchett's columbium. "Subsequent examination, however, convinced Rose that the two metallic acids obtained from the Bodenmais columbite were really the original columbic acid of Hatchett, discovered in 1801, and the tantalic acid discovered by Ekeberg in 1802."[87] In the face of this it is not understood why Rose's new name, niobium, was accepted then, as well as in more recent years, in place of Hatchett's original and valid name, columbium.

In 1866 Marignac[56] developed his classical method of separating the two sister elements utilizing the difference in the solubilities of their complex potassium fluorides. This permitted studies of the compounds of each element.

None of the early investigators actually isolated anything more than an impure form of either metal. The first ductile tantalum was produced by W. von Bolton in 1903 in the

* Professor of Chemistry at the University of Louisville (1854–1866), Smith was president of the AAAS in 1874 and in 1877 became the second president of the American Chemical Society. He was a contemporary of Rose (1798–1873), and since he had studied chemistry under Liebig in the early 1840's, undoubtedly was very familiar with Rose's work as well as with the European chemical literature.

Siemens-Halske plant in Berlin. It was the first metallic filament for incandescent lamps, and approximately 11 million tantalum lamps were made before tungsten began to replace tantalum for this application in 1909.

Tantalum was first produced in the United States in 1922 by C. W. Balke and commercial production has continued since that time. It is interesting to note that one of Balke's motives in making tantalum was to take advantage of its chemical inertness and use it as an anode in the corrosive chlorine cell electrolyte. He soon discovered that an oxide film of Ta_2O_5 prevented the flow of current when tantalum was connected as an anode in solutions. This film, however, makes tantalum an excellent electrolytic valve for use in the rectification of alternating current, and the first large commercial application of the metal was in the Balkite battery charger, used extensively in the radio receiving sets of the 1920's.

Occurrence and Sources

Tantalum ranks fifty-fourth in order of concentration of elements in the earth's crust, and is definitely an uncommon metal. It is always found associated with columbium, which is about eleven times as prevalent. The most important mineral source is a ferrous manganese tantalate-columbate, $(Fe,Mn)(Ta,Cb)_2O_6$. If the Ta_2O_5 content exceeds the Cb_2O_5 content the mineral is called tantalite; if the reverse is true it is called columbite. These minerals are usually found in pegmatite dikes in quantities which seldom exceed a few pounds per ton.

Tantalum is also present in other minerals such as pyrochlore, fergusonite, samarskite, euxenite, and polycrase. In most of these the columbium content exceeds that of tantalum. As the demand for columbium grows, the processing of high-columbium low-tantalum ores should make available increasing amounts of tantalum concentrates from these sources. In fact, a good deal of the tantalum has been and continues to be derived from concentrates higher in columbium than tantalum because of the relative scarcity of tantalite concentrates.

Tantalite has been produced chiefly in western Australia where it was mined from alluvial deposits in the Pilbarra District (now a minor source); in eastern Brazil; Nigeria; and the Belgian Congo (now the major source).

Tantalum concentrates are being produced as by-products of tin (cassiterite) placer mining operations in the Belgian Congo and to a minor extent in Malaya. Currently, concentrates of this type from the Belgian Congo account for one-third of the United States imports of tantalite concentrates.

The United States has only minor and scattered deposits of tantalite; tantalum ore mining is almost entirely a foreign industry. More than 99 per cent of the United States tantalite supply is imported. In 1958 some 84 per cent of the imports came from the Eastern Hemisphere. This dependence on water-borne ore imports is one factor opposing the greater use of tantalum.

The ores are concentrated by hand separation, washing, tabling, and electrostatic and electromagnetic means. The concentrates as received ordinarily contain 60 per cent or more of combined oxides (Ta_2O_5 and Cb_2O_5), and associated impurities are iron, tin, titanium, zirconium, silica, and manganese. In the concentrates imported into this country the ratio of Ta_2O_5 to Cb_2O_5 varies from 12:1 to 3:4, with the average probably about 1:1 for the bulk of the material.

Data are listed in Table 25.1 for imports of tantalum mineral concentrates for the years 1956-1958. The breakdown for 1959 is not available, but total imports in 1959 declined to an estimated 652,000 pounds from the 1958 total of 1,036,000 pounds.

Production and Price Statistics

Data on the domestic shipments of columbium-tantalum concentrates, imports of concentrates, ore consumption, and metal production are summarized in Table 25.2. It will be noted that the quantities of metal produced are much less than the quantities contained in the ores consumed. This is because the greater portion of both columbium and tantalum concentrates is fed directly to electric furnaces to produce ferrocolumbium and ferrotantalum-columbium. These alloys are used in some austenitic stainless steels where about one per cent columbium and tantalum acts to prevent carbide precipitation.

While prices for imported tantalite are not quoted publicly, material containing approximately 60 per cent Ta_2O_5 sold in 1959 for

TABLE 25.1. TANTALUM-MINERAL CONCENTRATES IMPORTED FOR CONSUMPTION IN THE UNITED STATES (POUNDS) (BUREAU OF THE CENSUS)

Country	1956	1957	1958	1959
South America				
Argentina	4,409	—	11,635	
Brazil	140,039	199,205	159,015	
French Guiana	14,532	3,075	—	
Europe				
Belgium-Luxembourg[1]	—	6,391	10,681	
Germany, West	—	—	135,431	
Portugal	7,054	5,966	32,513	
Sweden	—	—	992	
Asia				
Singapore	—	—	6,000	
Africa				
Belgian Congo	953,092	491,124	370,120	
Madagascar	20,165	6,835	7,716	
Mozambique	4,409	24,046	149,777	
Nigeria	31,174	16,815	34,537	
Rhodesia and Nyasaland	22,166	38,975	77,667	
Uganda	—	—	2,034	
Union of South Africa	6,511	6,910	27,368	
Australia	109,314	28,923	10,102	
Grand total	1,312,865	828,265	1,035,588	652,000
Value	$1,180,118	$948,638	$1,838,338	—

[1] Presumably country of transshipment rather than original source.

TABLE 25.2. TANTALUM-COLUMBIUM SALIENT STATISTICS (SHORT TONS)

	1950–54 (average)	1955	1956	1957	1958	1959
United States						
Mine shipments:						
Cb-Ta concentrates[1]	6	6	182	185	214	95
Imports:						
Cb mineral concentrates	1613	4806	2350	1674	1278	1698
Ta mineral concentrates	264	954	656	414	518	326
Ore consumption:[2]						
Contained Cb	218*	390	540	612	393	576
Contained Ta	109*	190	270	312	200	259
Metal production:						
Columbium	f.w.**	f.w.	f.w.	f.w.	33	66
Tantalum	f.w.	f.w.	f.w.	f.w.	96	122

[1] Oxide content of euxenite plus total weight of columbite-tantalite.
[2] Metal content of all raw materials, including tin slag, consumed for all industrial purposes, including production of ferroalloys.
* Average of 1952–54 only.
** Figure withheld to avoid disclosure of individual company confidential data.
Above data from U.S. Bureau of Mines.

$3.50-4.25 per pound of contained tantalum pentoxide. This represented a decline from the prices in the neighborhood of $6.25/lb at the beginning of 1958.

Prices for tantalum metal have been decreasing in recent years as the number of producers and the total plant production capacity have increased. As of late 1960 tantalum powder was generally available at about $40 per pound, melting stock at $35 per pound, and sheet at $55-60 per pound.

Extraction

In addition to the usual problems encountered in separating a desired metal from the other components of a given raw material, the extraction of tantalum from ores or concentrates is even more difficult because of the presence of its chemically similar sister metal columbium. In this respect tantalum and columbium are quite like zirconium and hafnium insofar as the problem of complete separation of the two is concerned.

Fractional Crystallization. The classical separation method of Marignac, in use since the early 1920's, has been almost completely superseded by solvent extraction methods in recent years. The fractional crystallization process as practiced industrially[77] consists of these steps:

1. Pulverized (about 200 mesh) tantalum concentrates are fused with sodium hydroxide in a continuous furnace to form crude sodium tantalites and columbates.

2. Cooled flakes of the fusion mass are leached with hot water and then with hydrochloric acid to remove most of the iron, manganese, silica, tin, and titanium impurities. Insoluble tantalic and columbic acids (hydrated oxides) are formed by this treatment.

3. The mixed tantalic and columbic acids are dissolved in hydrofluoric acid, and sufficient potassium hydroxide or fluoride or carbonate is added to form a solution of potassium fluotantalate, K_2TaF_7, and potassium columbium oxyfluoride, K_2CbOF_5.

4. After the hot solution has been filtered to remove insoluble matter the filtrate is allowed to cool in a crystallizer. Potassium fluotantalate, which has a solubility of 7.5 gpl in water at room temperature, precipitates from the solution, while the $K_2CbOF_5 \cdot H_2O$, which has a solubility of 91.5 gpl in water, remains in solution.

5. The K_2TaF_7 crystals are separated from the slurry by filtration and dried in a steam heated tray dryer.

6. Tantalum powder is obtained by electrolysis of fused K_2TaF_7 or by sodium reduction of this salt.

The above steps are primarily batch operations, and the fractional crystallization process is better suited to production of pure tantalum than of pure columbium. It is for these and other reasons that this process has been largely abandoned as a commercial process in recent years in favor of the liquid-liquid extraction method of extracting and separating tantalum and columbium from ores.

Liquid-Liquid Extraction. The present widely used method of separating tantalum and columbium by liquid-liquid extraction grew out of work conducted in the early 1950's by several investigators, chiefly those of the U.S. Bureau of Mines, Albany, Oregon,[39,98,99] and the Ames Laboratory of the U.S. Atomic Energy Commission.[24,102] The basic principles relate to the effect of acid concentration on the relative solubilities of tantalum, columbium, and other metal fluorides in aqueous and methyl isobutyl ketone systems.

When an acidic aqueous solution of the fluorides of tantalum, columbium, and the other metals present in the mineral concentrates is placed in contact with methyl isobutyl ketone, the tantalum fluoride is extracted by the organic phase at a low acidity and the columbium fluoride at a high acidity. By contrast, the other fluorides tend to remain in the aqueous phase. The solubilities are so different that clean extractions of very pure tantalum and very pure columbium can be obtained in a relatively few extraction stages.

In industrial practice,[14,104] the fine-ground ore (−200 mesh) is digested with concentrated hydrofluoric acid, prepared from anhydrous HF and deionized water, in tanks lined with polyethylene or Haveg. The tantalum and columbium oxides dissolve while the bulk of the impurities remains in the gangue. The tantalum-columbium liquor is separated from the undissolved solids by filtration and/or decantation and pumped to a holding tank. From here on the processes differ somewhat.

Figure 25.1. Liquid-liquid extraction cascade for separation of tantalum and columbium; mixers and settlers (center) are constructed of polyethylene. (*Union Carbide Metals Co.*)

In one plant[14] a stepwise extraction is used. The tantalum-columbium feed solution is adjusted to a low acidity and fed to the polyethylene extraction cascade where it is treated with methyl isobutyl ketone in mixers and settlers operating in tandem (Figure 25.1). The tantalum is first extracted into the organic phase at the low acidity and then stripped from that phase by deionized water to yield an aqueous solution of extremely pure tantalum fluoride. The tantalum-free feed solution is acidified to a high acidity with sulfuric or hydrochloric acid and treated with pure methyl isobutyl ketone in the columbium extraction section of the cascade. Here the columbium content is extracted into the organic phase, leaving essentially all the remaining dissolved impurities in the aqueous phase. The organic phase is then treated with deionized water to remove columbium fluoride from the ketone as a very pure material in aqueous solution.

In another plant[104] simultaneous extraction is practiced. The tantalum-columbium feed solution is diluted to the equivalent of 20 per cent hydrofluoric acid and pumped to the polyethylene extraction cascade. Here it passes countercurrent to methyl isobutyl ketone in columns where both tantalum and columbium are extracted into the organic phase. The

strong acid solution containing virtually all of the dissolved impurities is discarded. Deionized water is used to strip the organic phase of its columbium component. Further stripping of the organic phase with deionized water reduces the acid normality of the ketone to the point where tantalum (H_2TaF_7) is stripped from the organic phase.

The mechanisms involved in the fluoride-ketone extraction process have been discussed by Taylor;[91] Koerner, Smutz, and Wilhelm;[50] Foos and Wilhelm;[24] Werning, Higbie, *et al.*;[99] and others. One suggestion is that tantalum and columbium fluorides are extracted by ketones through hydrogen bonding.

The pure aqueous solution containing tantalum, most likely in the form of H_2TaF_7, is heated and treated with ammonium hydroxide in a precipitation tank to form insoluble tantalum hydroxide (or hydrated oxide):

$$H_2TaF_7 + 7NH_4OH \rightarrow$$
$$Ta(OH)_5 + 7NH_4F + 2H_2O.$$

After being filtered and washed, the wet cake is dried and calcined to yield tantalum pentoxide of high purity. As an alternative, potassium fluoride can be added to the aqueous solution to produce potassium fluotantalate, K_2TaF_7:

$$H_2TaF_7 + 2KF \rightarrow K_2TaF_7 + 2HF.$$

The precipitated K_2TaF_7 is then recovered by filtration and dried.

The columbium aqueous extract solution is also treated with ammonium hydroxide to form pure columbium hydroxide which is separated by filtration, washed, dried, and calcined to the oxide (as described in the "Columbium" chapter, p. 152).

The advantages of the liquid-liquid extraction process for the separation and production of pure tantalum and columbium compounds are many. The tantalum-columbium ore, slag, or concentrates can be treated directly for the extraction of both tantalum and columbium free of each other and all metallic impurities regardless of the Ta:Cb ratio in the raw material. The process is rapid, gives very high recovery efficiencies, and is easier to operate and control than are other processes. Continuous operation of at least the liquid-liquid extraction portion of the over-all process is more feasible than the fractional crystallization process.

Other Methods. A host of other methods of extracting and separating tantalum and columbium have been investigated. These include acid and alkaline treatments, use of chelating agents, chlorination, ion exchange, and chromatographic adsorption, to mention a few. Miller[61] gives an extensive review of the proposed techniques as of 1958.

Production of Tantalum Metal

Reduction of tantalum compounds to metal is feasible by any of several methods. The ones reported to be in use industrially are electrolysis, sodium reduction, and interaction of tantalum oxide and tantalum carbide.

Electrolysis. The electrolysis of molten potassium fluotantalate, to which is added tantalum oxide (Ta_2O_5) or some other oxide as a depolarizer to prevent the anode effect,[91] has been the reduction process used for producing most of the pure tantalum metal made to date. Operated at approximately 900°C (1652°F), the electrolysis is conducted batchwise in open cast-iron pots which act as cathodes. The anodes are graphite rods suspended in the pot. Tantalum is deposited in the form of crystalline aggregates of small particles, and K_2TaF_7 and oxide are fed to the pot at intervals during the run. When the deposit has filled the pot the electrolysis is stopped. About 50 per cent of the tantalum compounds fed to the cell is reduced[91] so that the tantalum particles are surrounded by K_2TaF_7 at all times. This protects them from attack by the air at the cell temperature.

Several studies made of this electrolysis process have established that electrolysis of potassium fluotantalate alone is not feasible, and that tantalum oxide or some other oxide must be present for satisfactory performance.[16,17,25,71] (See also Miller.[62])

After the pot and its contents have cooled to room temperature the cake containing the tantalum powder is removed, pulverized, and washed with water to remove the soluble salts. The powder is recovered on a concentrating table, washed with strong acids, such as aqua regia, to remove harmful impurities, dried, screened, graded, and blended. Tantalum powder made by the above process typically contains (in per cent) Ta 99.85, Cb less than 0.05, C 0.12, Fe 0.015, and Ti less than 0.01.

The mesh analysis averages 30 per cent +200, 40 per cent −200 +400, and 30 per cent −400.[91]

Another electrolytic process now being used operates with fused K_2TaF_7 held in a graphite pot which acts as the anode while the tantalum is deposited on a removable metal cathode rod.[14] The tantalum forms as dendrites (Figure 25.2) which are subsequently washed with water and acids for removal of salts and impurities. The closed cell is operated at 800–950°C (1472–1742°F) under vacuum or purified argon, and the electrolyte is K_2TaF_7 admixed with alkali metal chlorides, although the details of the operation have not been published. The average impurity level is about 500 ppm in the tantalum produced.

Figure 25.2. Tantalum dendrites deposited on cathode of electrolytic cell operating with fused potassium fluotantalate. Cell shown opened for tantalum removal. (*Union Carbide Metals Co.*)

The dendrites are compressed cold into electrodes for use in arc melting or electron beam melting furnaces where they are converted into massive ingots.

Sodium Reduction. Sodium is used to reduce

potassium fluotantalate to metallic tantalum by the reaction:

$$K_2TaF_7 + 5Na \rightarrow Ta + 2KF + 5NaF.$$

The reaction is conducted in a steel bomb loaded with the two reactants. When the bomb is heated externally, the exothermic reaction proceeds vigorously, thus the use of a special chamber for the operation is indicated for safety reasons. After the bomb has been cooled its contents are removed and treated with water and other reagents, such as methanol, to react with the excess sodium and to dissolve soluble salts. The tantalum powder is then washed with acids and finally dried. Metal made by this process is a very pure fine powder of smaller particle size than that made by electrolytic reduction.

Tantalum-Carbide Tantalum-Oxide Reaction. This process uses the method developed by Balke[8] for the preparation of tantalum and columbium, and is based on the reaction of stoichiometric quantities of pure tantalum carbide and oxide according to the equation:

$$5TaC + Ta_2O_5 \rightarrow 7Ta + 5CO.$$

As now practiced industrially,[104] tantalum carbide is first made by charging a graphite crucible with an intimate mixture of carbon

Figure 25.3. View of tantalum carbide furnace where tantalum oxide and carbon are heated to produce tantalum carbide. The mix is held in a graphite crucible in the furnace. (*Wah Chang Corp.*)

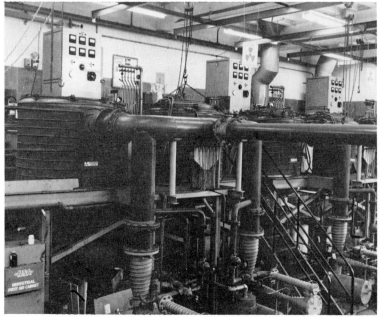

Figure 25.4. View of tantalum reduction furnace floor where pellets of a mixture of tantalum oxide and tantalum carbide are reacted in vacuum induction furnaces to produce tantalum pellets or roundels. (*Wah Chang Corp.*)

(lampblack) and Ta_2O_5 and heating it in a high frequency furnace to produce the carbide, TaC (Figure 25.3). Ground carbide and the requisite amount of tantalum oxide are mixed, pelletized, and fed to a vacuum induction furnace where the reduction occurs (Figure 25.4). Both the formation of the TaC and the reduction reaction occur at about 2000°C (3632°F). As they leave the second furnace, the pellets or roundels (small cylinders) of porous metal are usually sintered together.

The metal pellets are then converted to the hydride by exposure to hydrogen at about 500°C (932°F). The brittle hydride is crushed to a powder and dehydrided by heating it to over 1000°C (1832°F) in a vacuum in which it is allowed to cool.

A typical analysis of the tantalum metal made by the above process is given in Table 25.3. The purity of the metal depends on the purity of the carbide and oxide used in the process, and on the degree of contamination that occurs during the several operations.

TABLE 25.3. TYPICAL ANALYSIS OF TANTALUM PRODUCED BY OXIDE-CARBIDE PROCESS[104]
(Impurities in parts per million, maximum)

Al	20	Mg	20	Sn	20
B	1	Mn	20	Ti	150
Cb	500	Mo	20	V	20
Cr	30	Ni	20	W	100
Cu	40	Pb	20	Zr	100
Fe	100	Si	50	Zn	20

Total C, O, N and H   100

Consolidation and Purification

While the tantalum powder produced by the several reduction processes can be used directly in some applications, such as capacitors of the porous type, for most purposes it must first be converted to massive form. An additional purpose of such consolidation is to achieve greater purity in the metal by eliminating at least a portion of the undesired elements present in the as-reduced tantalum. Very small amounts of impurities greatly affect the properties of tantalum.

Because of the extremely high melting point of tantalum and the great chemical reactivity it exhibits when heated, special techniques must be used to convert it to massive form. In general they are similar to those applied to other refractory and reactive metals, such as columbium, hafnium, molybdenum, titanium, tungsten and zirconium. The methods used industrially are sintering, vacuum or inert atmosphere arc melting, and electron beam melting.

Figure 25.5. View of 2000 ton Bliss press where tantalum powder is compacted into bars prior to sintering operation. (*Wah Chang Corp.*)

Sintering. The classical method of consolidating and purifying tantalum powder is by a lengthy vacuum sintering at temperatures on the order of 2600°C (4712°F) maximum. As now practiced, tantalum powder, usually without a binder, is compressed at room temperature into bars in sizes ranging up to 10 kilograms. Pressures in the range of 30 to 50 tons per square inch are used, requiring very large presses (Figure 25.5). The green bars are strong enough to handle carefully, and in size are a few feet long with cross sections ranging from ¾ x ¾ inch to ½ x 2 inches or more.

The green compacts are sintered in a vertical position in vacuum sintering furnaces by passing a high amperage current through them for

Figure 25.6. High vacuum sintering vessels used to sinter green bars of tantalum powder made in press shown in Figure 25.5 to produce ingots. The bars are sintered by passage of high amperage current through them for several hours. (*Wah Chang Corp.*)

several hours (Figure 25.6). The temperature of the bars is raised gradually and held at various stages to permit various purifying reactions to occur. As determined by Klopp, Maykuth, Ogden, and Jaffee,[47] at 1900–2200°C (3452–3992°F) carbon and oxygen combine to form carbon monoxide, a reaction which will remove most of the carbon if a stoichiometric excess of oxygen is present; at 2000–2400°C (3632–4352°F) excess oxygen volatilizes as tantalum oxide; and at about 2600°C (4712°F) nitrogen evolves as N_2. Metallic elements and compounds, the vapor pressures of which are appreciable over the sintering temperature range, boil out of the tantalum. Additives may be deliberately used to react with impurities to form compounds that are more easily volatilized at the sintering temperature. For example, Balke[7] has described the addition of magnesium oxide to tantalum powder to remove carbon by the reaction which forms carbon monoxide and magnesium at a temperature of 1800–2000°C (3272–3632°F).

Power consumption in sintering tantalum is a few hundred kilowatt hours per pound, varying with the length and number of sintering cycles involved.

Sintering yields a tantalum bar the density of which is about 90 per cent of the true value. Cold working eliminates the small pore volume and a second sintering forms a ductile non-porous bar of essentially true density which can be forged and rolled into sheet or drawn into wire at room temperature.

The size of the ingot produced by sintering is limited by the capacity of the press needed to compact the powder into bars and by the size of the electrical power system required to provide current for the resistance sintering. Also, the production rate for a given sintering installation is low because the furnace must be maintained for a long time at a very high temperature and a very low pressure for the sintering of only a few pounds of metal per run.

Arc Melting. The arc melting technique, applied so widely in the production of large ingots of titanium, zirconium, and other similar metals, is used to form ingots of tantalum weighing a hundred pounds or more. Further scale-up of furnace equipment can make feasible the forming of 500 pound ingots.

A variety of types of equipment and modes of operation are applied to the arc melting of tantalum. Most operations use a consumable electrode, made of hydrostatically pressed powder or dendrites or roundels, which is melted in a vacuum by striking a short arc between the electrode and tantalum held in a cold mold (a water-cooled copper crucible). A small pool of molten metal is maintained in the center of the upper surface of the tantalum ingot. The electrode is advanced downward as its lower

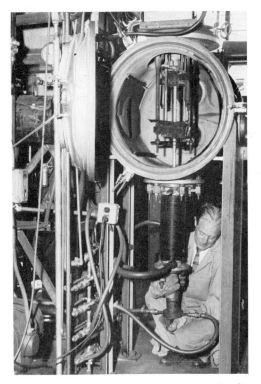

Figure 25.7. Consumable electrode arc melting furnace for forming massive ingots of tantalum. Feed mechanism shown in top (opened) chamber advances electrode downward. Cold mold shown at bottom with tantalum ingot being withdrawn. (*National Research Corp.*)

The furnace operates under 2 to 5 microns of mercury pressure maintained by a 1,000 CFM mechanical-booster high vacuum pump backed up with a mechanical pump. A 4-inch diameter cold mold lined with a double extra heavy copper pipe to give an inner mold diameter of 3.5 inches is used.

Melting is conducted at 30 volts and 4,500 to 5,000 amperes at a melting rate of 0.5 pounds per minute. The power consumption is approximately 4.5 kilowatt hours per pound to produce ingots weighing 70 to 90 pounds.

In another variation of this operation by the same producer,[74] tantalum powder is pressed into pellets ¾ inch diameter and ¾ inch long which are placed in a column in the electrode feeder. While under a vacuum of about one micron of mercury pressure they are welded together to form a rod by passing an electrical current through them. The electrode so formed is melted at a rate of 2 to 2.5 pounds per minute to form ingots weighing 110 pounds.

Ingots of tantalum as large as 8 to 12 inches

end melts and drops into this pool. When the mold is filled it is allowed to cool under vacuum to about 150°C (302°F) before the furnace is opened and the ingot removed.

One type of furnace is shown in Figure 25.7, and the tantalum ingot as it appears when withdrawn from the mold is seen in Figure 25.8. Ingots are machined to remove surface defects; the final ingots ready for forging, rolling, etc. into mill forms are shown in Figure 25.9.

Details of one mode of arc melting tantalum are given by Torti.[96] Electrodes are made by compressing high purity tantalum powder, −12 +325 mesh, into short bars 1¾ to 2 inches in diameter. The bars are given a quick premelting treatment by direct resistance heating under vacuum to 1500°C (2732°F) for about one minute to stabilize them and improve their strength; then they are welded under argon with a tungsten electrode into the electrode to be fed to the arc furnace.

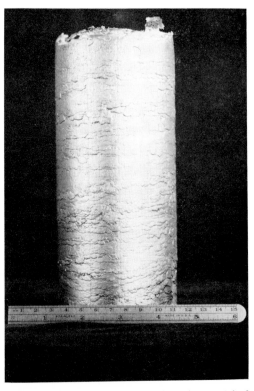

Figure 25.8. Arc melted tantalum ingot, 8-inch diameter, as it appears when withdrawn from furnace. (*National Research Corp.*)

Figure 25.9. Arc melted tantalum ingots. Those with rough surfaces are machined to yield the smooth ingots on the right. The ingots on the scale weigh about 70 pounds each. (*Wah Chang Corp.*)

in diameter can be made by the arc melting process.

Despite the relatively short time the tantalum remains at or near the melting point, arc melting results in considerable purification of the electrode feed material. A recent study by Torti[96] discloses that hydrogen is reduced by one order of magnitude to 1 to 5 ppm, while nitrogen remains the same, about 27 ppm. Oxygen is removed both as tantalum oxides and as carbon monoxide. The best oxygen removal is obtained when the carbon in the electrode (present as an impurity or deliberately added when the electrode is formed) is 50 per cent of the stoichiometric carbon-oxygen ratio for carbon monoxide formation. Under this condition the oxygen content is reduced by about one order of magnitude to approximately 34 ppm. Iron, chromium, nickel, columbium, and silicon are reduced in content by factors of 3, 6, 4, 3, and 7, respectively, the final contents being in the range of 14–40 ppm for each. These results were obtained with high purity tantalum made by sodium reduction of a tantalum salt.

Electron Beam Melting. Heating by electron bombardment is one of the newer techniques of consolidating tantalum into massive form while at the same time purifying the metal. The electron beam melting can operate only under a high vacuum so contamination by gases during melting is automatically avoided. Also, the use of a cold mold (water-cooled) to receive the molten metal prevents reaction with the crucible.

As practiced on a production basis, 10 to 20 kv electrons from a cathode (e.g., tungsten filament) are focused by an electrostatic field on the feed material which is the anode. Electrons are also focused on the upper end of the ingot being formed to maintain a molten pool of metal from which impurities can escape. A vacuum of 10^{-4} mm Hg or better is maintained by high capacity vacuum pumps which must handle gaseous impurities which boil out of the molten metal. As the ingot forms it is withdrawn into the lower part of the furnace.

While the feed is usually in the form of an electrode made by pressing and sintering tantalum powder, other forms of feed metal can be used. These include arc melted ingots which require purification, powder, dendrites, roundels, flake, and scrap metal. Materials other than bars or rods which can be fed as a consumable electrode require a variation in the furnace design and operation.

More details of the electron beam melting device and techniques are given in the chapter on "Columbium," pages 153–157.

Power consumption is in the range of 6 to 8 kilowatt hours per pound of tantalum. Ingots up to 4 inches in diameter and 42 inches long are being made at production rates of 100

TABLE 25.4. ANALYSES OF TANTALUM INGOTS MADE BY ELECTRON BEAM MELTING

	Lot 1[13]		Lot 2[1, 41]
	Before melting	After melting	After melting
Al	<250 ppm	<50 ppm	—
C	36	20	30 ppm
Cb	<100	<25	100–300
Cu	< 50	<50	30
Cr	—	—	3
Fe	<100	<10	8
H	100	< 1	1.4
Mo	<100	<25	—
N	30	10	10
Ni	<100	<10	3
O	82	< 6	16
Si	<250	28	—
Ti	50	<10	—

Each lot was made by a different melting apparatus and presumably from tantalum obtained by different extraction processes.

pounds or more per day. The output for a given melting assembly depends on the amount of impurities to be removed, a factor that controls the length of time the tantalum must be held in the molten state.

With respect to impurity removal, impurities having a vapor pressure of at least 10^{-5} atmospheres at the surface of the molten metal can volatilize easily. In the case of tantalum this results in the drastic reduction of the contents of metals like iron, nickel, chromium, titanium, and columbium, as well as a decrease in the interstitial elements. Table 25.4 contains analyses of electron beam melted tantalum.

Physical Properties

The physical properties of tantalum are summarized in Table 25.5. While most of the physical properties are well established, many determinations have been made on powder metallurgy metal containing several hundred ppm of impurities that affect physical properties. The availability of electron beam melted metal of much greater purity may well result in changes in the values of some physical properties as studies are made on this purer metal.

TABLE 25.5. PHYSICAL PROPERTIES OF TANTALUM

		Reference
Atomic number	73	
Atomic weight	180.95	
Atomic diameter, Å	2.854	
Atomic volume, cc/g-atom	10.90	
Density, g/cc	16.6	
lb/cu in.	0.600	
Isotopes, natural (atomic weight)	181 (100%)	
Isotopes, artificial (atomic weight)	176, 177, 178, 179, 180, 182, 183, 184, 185, 186	
Thermal neutron cross section, barns/atom (for a neutron velocity of 2200 m/sec)		
absorption	21.3 ± 1.0	
scattering	5 ± 1	
Lattice structure	body-centered cubic	
Lattice constant, Å	3.296	
Coordination number	8	
Melting point, °C	2996	(47, 55)
°F	5425	
Boiling point, °C	6100	(81)
°F	11,012	
Latent heat of fusion, cal/g	41.5	(89)

TABLE 25.5. PHYSICAL PROPERTIES OF TANTALUM (*cont.*)

		Reference
Latent heat of vaporization, cal/g	995	(89)
Heat of combustion, at 30°C, cal/g	1346	(42)

Heat capacity, cal/g-atom/°C   (89)

at	25°C (77°F)	6.08	at 1527°C (2781°F)	7.02
"	127°C (261°F)	6.27	" 1827°C (3321°F)	7.15
"	227°C (441°F)	6.38	" 2127°C (3861°F)	7.28
"	327°C (621°F)	6.46	" 2427°C (4401°F)	7.40
"	527°C (981°F)	6.57	" 2727°C (4941°F)	7.53
"	927°C (1701°F)	6.76		
"	1227°C (2241°F)	6.90		

Entropy, cal/g-atom/°C   (89)

at	25°C (77°F)	9.90	at 1227°C (2241°F)	20.40
"	127°C (261°F)	11.71	" 1527°C (2781°F)	21.66
"	227°C (441°F)	13.13	" 1827°C (3321°F)	22.76
"	327°C (621°F)	14.30	" 2127°C (3861°F)	23.72
"	527°C (981°F)	16.17	" 2427°C (4401°F)	24.58
"	927°C (1701°F)	18.87	" 2727°C (4841°F)	25.37

Specific heat, cal/g/°C   (80a)

0°C (32°F)	0.0340	1727°C (3141°F)	0.041
227°C (441°F)	0.0350	2227°C (4041°F)	0.0465
727°C (1341°F)	0.0365	2727°C (4941°F)	0.056
1227°C (2241°F)	0.0385		

Vapor pressure, atm × 10⁻⁹   (18a)

Vapor pressure, atm $\times$ 10^{-9}

2351°C (4264°F)	6.216	2615°C (4739°F)	169.8
2365°C (4289°F)	7.390	2652°C (4806°F)	240.8
2487°C (4509°F)	39.66	2675°C (4847°F)	365.5
2566°C (4651°F)	96.92		

Thermal conductivity, cal/sec/cm/cm²/°C

20°C (68°F)	0.130	(19)
568°C (1055°F)	0.1625	(20a)
828°C (1523°F)	0.1715	(20a)
1106°C (2022°F)	0.1795	(20a)
1416°C (2580°F)	0.1885	(20a)
1547°C (2816°F)	0.188	(20a)
1830°C (3326°F)	0.198	(19)

Linear thermal expansion, % increase of length at 24°C (75°F)   (31a)

°C	°F	Δ L/L
−148	−235	−0.1
24	75	0.0
310	590	0.2
593	1100	0.4
866	1590	0.6
1116	2040	0.8
1360	2480	1.0
1593	2900	1.2
1810	3290	1.4
2016	3660	1.6
2204	4000	1.8
2382	4320	2.0
2549	4620	2.2
2713	4915	2.4
2866	5190	2.6

L = length at 24°C (75°F), Δ L = increase at temperature given

TABLE 25.5. PHYSICAL PROPERTIES OF TANTALUM (*cont.*)

			Reference
Coefficient of linear thermal expansion, cm/cm/°C			
over range of 20–500°C (68–932°F) and at all intervals in this range		6.6×10^{-6}	(38)
over range of 20–1500°C (68–2732°F)		8.0×10^{-6}	(18)

Electrical resistivity, microhm-cm

°C	°F		Reference
−183	−297	3.5	(83)
20	68	12.5	(44)
25	77	13.5	(55)
25	77	13.6	(29, 85)
100	212	18.5	(21)
400	752	31.6	(21)
700	1292	43.6	(21)
1000	1832	54.8	(21)
1500	2732	72.0	(44)
2000	3632	87.0	(44)

For tantalum containing 0.00% oxygen: (29)

°C	°F	
0	32	13.6
250	482	22.8
500	932	32.0
750	1382	41.2
1000	1832	50.4

		Reference
Transition temperature, °K	4.38	(88)

Temperature coefficient of electrical resistivity

		Reference
0–100°C (32–212°F)	3.17×10^{-3}	(21)
0–1000°C (32–1832°F)	$3.0 \ \times 10^{-3}$	(19)

Work function, electron volts

		Reference
for (211) crystal	4.352 ± 0.01	(86)
for random crystals	4.12	(88)

Electron emission, ma/cm²   (19)

at 1000°C (1832°F)	$1 \ \times 10^{-5}$
at 1230°C (2246°F)	4.7×10^{-3}
at 1730°C (3146°F)	19.5

Electronic emission constant, amp/cm²(°K)²

		Reference
for (211) crystal	120	(86)
for random crystals	60	(80)

		Reference
Secondary emission, δ max = 1.35 (primary energy at δ max 600 volts)		(88)
Positive ion emission, electron volts	10.0	

Spectral emissivity

Wave length, microns	Temperature, °C	°F		Reference
9.0	25	77	0.06	(55, 88)
5.0	25	77	0.07	(55, 88)
3.0	25	77	0.08	(55, 88)
1.0	25	77	0.22	(55, 88)
0.6	25	77	0.55	(55, 88)
0.5	25	77	0.62	(55, 88)
0.66	900	1652	0.459	(55, 88)
0.66	1100	2012	0.442	(55, 88)
0.66	1800	3272	0.416	(55, 88)
0.66	2500	4532	0.392	(55, 88)
0.65	2127	3861	0.361	(31)

TABLE 25.5. PHYSICAL PROPERTIES OF TANTALUM (*cont.*)

				Reference

Spectral emissivity (*cont.*)

Wave length, microns	Temperature, °C	°F		Reference
0.65	2327	4221	0.358	(31)
0.65	2527	4581	0.356	(31)
0.65	2727	4941	0.353	(31)
0.65	2996	5425	0.350	(31)
0.467	1100	2012	0.505	(55, 88)
0.467	1800	3272	0.460	(55, 88)

Total emissivity

°C	°F		Reference
1400	2552	0.20	(88)
1500	2732	0.21	(88)
2000	3632	0.25	(88)
2127	3861	0.292	(31)
2327	4221	0.300	(31)
2527	4581	0.308	(31)

Total radiation, watt/cm² (19)

°C	°F	
1330	2426	7.3
1530	2786	12.8
1730	3146	21.2

Radiation capacity, % (19)

°C	°F	
20	68	49.3
930	1706	45.0
1730	3146	41.8

Refractive index 2.05

Magnetic susceptibility, cgs units (53)

°C	°F	
25	77	0.849×10^{-6}
1870	3398	0.685×10^{-6}

Electrochemical equivalent, mg/coulomb 0.3749

Standard electrode potential for Ta/Ta^{+5}, E° in volts 1.12 (35)

Thermoelectric power

Tantalum-platinum couple (cold junction at 0°C) (3)

Temperature at hot junction, °C	°F	emf, mv	Temperature at hot junction, °C	°F	emf, mv
−200	−328	+0.21	400	752	2.91
−100	−148	−0.10	600	1112	5.95
0	32	0.0	800	1472	10.05
100	212	+0.33	1000	1832	15.20
200	392	0.93	1200	2192	21.41

Tantalum-tungsten couple (in vacuum) (70)

°C	°F	emf	°C	°F	emf
800	1472	10.65	1800	3272	22.25
1000	1832	13.72	2000	3632	22.90*
1200	2192	16.65	2625	4757	20.90
1400	2552	19.05	3000	5432	18.50
1600	2912	20.90			

* results reproducible to 2000°C, inconsistent at higher temperatures

TABLE 25.5. PHYSICAL PROPERTIES OF TANTALUM (*cont.*)

						Reference

Thermoelectric power (*cont.*)

Tantalum-molybdenum couple (in vacuum) (70)

Temperature at hot junction, °C	°F	emf, mv	Temperature at hot junction, °C	°F	emf, mv
800	1472	12.20	1800	3272	19.45
1000	1832	14.80	2000	3632	18.85
1200	2192	16.90	2200	3992	17.70
1400	2552	18.35	2400	4352	15.90
1600	2912	19.25	2500	4532	14.90
1700	3092	19.45			

Tantalum-mercury couple (49)

emf $= AT^b$ for 100–1500°C (212–2732°F)

where emf $=$ mv; T $=$ °C; A $= 1.629 \times 10^{-4}$; and b $= 1.682$.

Mechanical Properties

Tantalum is a strong, ductile, hard metal somewhat comparable to mild steel. Although working improves its hardness and tensile strength, tantalum becomes work hardened much more slowly than most metals; thus very high reductions may be practiced between anneals.

The presence of interstitial impurities C, O, N, and H, greatly affect the mechanical properties of the metal. Since their presence is influenced largely by the mode of preparation of the massive metal, and the past handling and exposure history of the sample used for testing, considerable variation in the reported mechanical properties of tantalum can be expected and, in fact, are found in the literature.

Three types of tantalum have been used for test purposes: powder metallurgy or sintered, arc melted, and electron beam melted. Generally, the powder metallurgy metal contains the highest content of interstitial impurities as well as metallic impurities. This was the only metal available until about 1955-1956, at which time arc melted material began to be produced and evaluated. Electron beam melted metal became available still more recently. Therefore, much of the data on mechanical properties reported in the literature prior to about 1956 is based upon the relatively impure powder metallurgy product whose important contents of impurities (even though low as impurities are usually regarded) have major effects upon the mechanical properties. It must be noted that the effects are not altogether deleterious for some applications of tantalum. For example, tantalum containing a few hundred ppm of N and O is very much stronger than metal containing a total of 50 or less ppm of N and O. This is shown in Table 25.6 which is

TABLE 25.6. RUPTURE STRENGTH OF HIGH PURITY TANTALUM CONTAINING OXYGEN[a] AND NITROGEN[b] (from Holden, Schwartzberg, and Jaffee)[41]

Temperature, °C	Time, hr	Rupture Strength, 1000 psi			Strength Increased([c]), %	
		High purity Ta	Ta-N	Ta-O	Ta-N	Ta-O
750 (1382°F)	0.1	17.0	25.0	22.5	47	32
	1.0	16.0	22.5	17.5	41	9
	10	15.0	19.5	15.0	30	0
	100	14.0	17.0	14.0	21	0
1000 (1832°F)	0.1	8.4	10.0	—	19	—
	1.0	6.1	7.2	8.6	18	24
	10	4.5	5.2	4.3	16	−4
	100	3.2	3.6	3.2	13	0

a 560 ppm addition
b 225 ppm addition
c In comparison with high purity tantalum of analysis given in Table 25.4, Lot 2, for electron beam melted tantalum

TABLE 25.7. MECHANICAL PROPERTIES OF TANTALUM

		Reference
Modulus of elasticity, psi		
at −180°C (−292°F)	27.4×10^6	(51)
at − 73°C (−100°F)	28.3×10^6	(10)
at − 50°C (− 58°F)	27.0×10^6	(51)
at 25°C (77°F)	27.0×10^6	
at 200°C (392°F)	26.0×10^6	(51)
at 350°C (662°F)	25.5×10^6	(51)
at 500°C (932°F)	24.8×10^6	(51)
Shear modulus of elasticity (estimated), psi	10×10^6	
Poisson's ratio	0.35	(52)
Compressibility, $\Delta V / \Delta V_0$		(11)
(99.95% powder metallurgy metal; almost		
identical results with 99.9% metal)		
at 5,000 kg/cm² pressure	0.00243	
" 10,000 " "	0.00485	
" 15,000 " "	0.00726	
" 20,000 " "	0.00967	
" 25,000 " "	0.01208	
" 30,000 " "	0.01448	
Brittle to ductile transition temperature:		
none detected down to −196°C (−321°F)		(10, 100)
Tensile properties	See Table 25.8	
Hardness	See Table 25.9	
Fatigue characteristics	See Table 25.10	
Impact properties	See Table 25.11	
Creep and rupture properties	See Tables 25.6 and 25.12	
Recrystallization temperature	See Table 25.13	
Effects of nitrogen and oxygen	See Tables 25.6, 25.14 and 25.15	

based on rupture strength studies by Holden, Schwartzberg, and Jaffee[41] in their excellent paper on the high temperature properties of tantalum.

In general, the trend with tantalum, as with most other similar metals, is to produce and use the purest possible element. It is easier to add known amounts of modifying components to a high purity metal to attain desired properties than it is to alter the characteristics of a metal containing impurities whose composite effect on properties is uncertain and variable. In the case of tantalum the higher purity arc melted and electron beam melted products have several practical advantages over the powder metallurgy metal: (1) larger ingots can be obtained which result in larger structural forms, such as sheets that require less welding when fabricating equipment, etc.; (2) better welds can be made with these metals than with metal containing interstitial impurities which vaporize and/or segregate during welding; (3) more uniform properties of a large variety

can be expected in the fabricated tantalum products, especially for electronic applications; (4) alloys of predictable improved properties can be prepared with more certainty of consistent results.

Mechanical properties of tantalum are listed in Tables 25.6-25.15; variations in mechanical properties caused by mode of metal preparation, temperature, annealing, etc. are given in Tables 25.8-25.15. Where possible, analysis and history of the metal tested are indicated.

Table 25.8 covers many of the studies made on the tensile properties of tantalum. Included are data showing the effects of type of metal preparation (including impurity levels), temperature, annealing, and cold working. The somewhat more than 2:1 ratio between the tensile strengths of wrought and recrystallized (annealed) electron beam melted metal at temperatures to 500°C (932°F) is revealed in Sections (1) and (2) of this table; these sections are based on the work of Holden, Schwartzberg, and Jaffee.[41] The wrought metal has a severalfold advantage in yield strength at the higher temperatures, but is much less ductile than annealed metal. The increase in tensile strength which occurs at about 300°C (572°F) is indicative of strain aging due to the presence of interstitials, even at the low level characteristic of electron beam melted tantalum. A similar effect is to be noted in Sections (3) and (4) which give the data of Pugh[79] and Bechtold[9] who worked with powder metallurgy metal having a much higher content of interstitials.

Using annealed powder metallurgy metal, Pugh,[79] Preston et al.,[78] and Glasier et al.[31] have determined the tensile properties at temperatures up to 1200°C (2192°F), 2760°C (5000°F), and 2818°C (5103°F), respectively,

as given in Sections (3), (5), and (6). Glasier et al. also worked with arc melted metal at temperatures up to 2782°C (5040°F), as given in Section (8).

The effects of cold working are shown in Sections (1) and (8) which tabulate the data of Holden et al.[41] on electron beam melted metal and of Myers[73] on powder metallurgy metal. Myers' study discloses the profound effect of cold working upon hardness as well as tensile strength.

The variation in tensile properties caused by annealing is given in Section (9) based on high purity arc melted metal.[95] This section also shows the grain growth caused by increasing the annealing temperature.

TABLE 25.8. TENSILE PROPERTIES

(1) **Effect of temperature on tensile properties**[41]

Material: wrought electron beam melted metal

Analysis: see Table 25.4 (Lot 2)

History: as-cast ingot cold rolled to 0.035 in. strip (95% reduction), stress-relief annealed in argon for ¼ hr at 750°C (1382°F)

Test atmosphere: air; strain rate: 0.05 in./min

Temperature		Ultimate tensile strength, 1000 psi	Yield strength (0.2% offset), 1000 psi	Elongation, %
°C	°F			
27	80	60.5	49.0	—*
150	302	48.3	45.0	6**
245	473	47.0	43.9	4**
310	590	49.7	48.0	5**
365	689	54.7	50.5	5**
490	914	45.7	45.1	5**

* fractured outside gage marks
** fractured through gage marks

(2) **Effect of temperature on tensile properties**[41]

Material: recrystallized electron beam melted metal

Analysis: see Table 25.4 (Lot 2)

History: as-cast ingot cold rolled 75% to 0.035 in. strip after intermediate anneal, and recrystallized by annealing 1 hr at 1200°C (2192°F)

Test atmosphere: air; strain rate: 0.05 in./min

Temperature,		Ultimate tensile strength, 1000 psi	Yield strength (0.2% offset), 1000 psi	Elongation, %
°C	°F			
27	80	29.4	26.3	36
230	446	27.9	8.5	23
325	617	31.1	6.7	30
390	734	30.1	—	25
425	797	28.1	6.4	23
490	914	27.0	6.4	20

TABLE 25.8. TENSILE PROPERTIES (*cont.*)

(3) Effect of temperature on tensile properties[79]

Material: annealed powder metallurgy strip
Analysis (in ppm): C 200, N 130, O 56, Cb 1000, W 100, Fe 150
History: ingot cold rolled to 0.05 in. sheet with intermediate anneals
Test atmosphere: vacuum; strain rate: 0.09 in./min

Temperature, °C	°F	Ultimate tensile strength, 1000 psi	Yield stress (0.2% offset), 1000 psi	Elongation, %
−195	−319	148	148	3.7
− 73	−100	73.2	72.5	23.1
27	80	67.1	57.4	25.3
98	200	59.3	42.5	24.6
205	400	56.1	35.4	12.7
316	600	73.9	37.9	18.0
427	800	65.3	33.4	24.3
538	1000	59.9	26.1	16.2
649	1200	44.7	18.9	17.3
760	1400	30.3	16.9	23.1
871	1600	22.2	12.1	32.8
982	1800	21.6	12.3	33.1
1093	2000	16.8	8.1	43.2
1204	2200	14.7	7.5	47.5

(data rounded and interpolated)

(4) Effect of temperature on tensile properties[9]

Material: annealed powder metallurgy rod
Analysis (in ppm): C 100, N 100, O not given
History: ingot swaged cold to 0.3 in. diameter with final anneal 1 hr at 1700°C (3092°F)
Test atmosphere: vacuum of 5 × 10⁻⁵ mm Hg; strain rate: 0.017 in./min

Temperature, °C	°F	Ultimate tensile strength, 1000 psi	Yield strength (linear depart.), 1000 psi	Elongation, %	Reduction in area, %
−195	−319	—	124	12.4	75
−180	−292	—	104.5	13.4	78
−130	−202	—	82.7	15	81
− 78	−108	58.7	60.3	37	89
− 30	− 22	55.7	56.5	34	86
25	77	49.8	39.3	45	86
200	393	46.8	26.2	31	86
400	752	52.2	22.4	27	84

(5) Effect of temperature on tensile properties[78, 95]

Material: annealed powder metallurgy strip
Analysis: "commercially pure"
History: sheet rolled to 0.064 in., annealed
Test atmosphere: argon

Temperature, °C	°F	Hold time, sec	Strain rate, in./min	Ultimate tensile strength, 1000 psi	Yield stress, (0.2% offset), 1000 psi	Elongation, %	Modulus of elasticity, 10⁶ psi
1649	3000	10	0.003	4.03	3.78	19.0	8.8
1927	3500	10	.003	0.915	0.611	—	—
1649	3000	90	.003	4.12	3.86	19.3	8.48

TABLE 25.8. TENSILE PROPERTIES (cont.)

Temperature,		Hold sec time,	Strain rate, in./min.	Ultimate tensile strength, 1000 psi	Yield stress, (0.2% offset), 1000 psi	Elongation, %	Modulus of elasticity, 10^6 psi
°C	°F						
1927	3500	90	.003	1.81	0.792	—	—
2204	4000	90	.003	0.415	0.42	—	—
1649	3000	10	6.0	10.7	7.49	29.7	9.8
2204	4000	10	6.0	3.69	1.76	43.5	1.4
2760	5000	10	6.0	2.34	1.29	47.8	—
1649	3000	90	6.0	10.78	6.96	30.2	10.7
2204	4000	90	6.0	3.95	1.61	46.0	1.5
2760	5000	90	6.0	2.06	1.17	50.8	—

(6) Effect of temperature on tensile properties[31]

Material: annealed powder metallurgy sheet
Analysis (in %): C 0.03 max, Fe 0.03 max, Si <0.005, Mo 0.24, and other impurities <0.05
History: sheet rolled to 0.050/0.060 in., annealed

Temperature,		Ultimate tensile strength, 1000 psi	Yield strength (0.2% offset), 1000 psi	E, 10^6 psi	Load rate, psi/sec	Elongation, %
°C	°F					
1882	3420	6.16	3.2	3.6	267	39
2022	3672	5.11	2.55	0.6	197	46
2180	3956	3.025	1.51	0.7	63	34
2180	3956	2.74	1.85	0.2	16	32
2417	4383	2.46	1.24	1.1	63	44
2417	4383	2.64	—	—	66	38
2467	4472	2.29	1.32	0.4	64	37
2497	4527	2.65	1.35	1.5	54	34
2497	4527	2.06	1.27	0.4	57	38
2752	4986	1.87	1.14	0.4	67	25
2767	5013	1.24	0.86	0.3	10	11
2817	5103	0.977	0.80	0.1	7.5	13

(7) Effect of temperature on tensile properties[31]

Material: arc melted sheet (annealed)
Analysis (in %): C 0.0015, Fe 0.0028, Cb 0.0062, H 0.0003–0.0008, N 0.002–0.003, O 0.0035–0.0059, and other impurities 0.0173
History: sheet rolled to 0.060 in., annealed

Temperature,		Ultimate tensile strength, 1000 psi	Yield strength (0.2% offset), 1000 psi	E, 10^6 psi	Load rate, psi/sec	Elongation, %
°C	°F					
1766	3211	4.37	1.95	1.0	59	35
2032	3690	3.8	1.55	0.3	146	47
2057	3725	2.78	1.26	0.2	63	43
2395	4343	2.38	0.60	0.04	92	47
2500	4532	1.73	0.64	0.07	62	35
2767	5013	0.705	0.36	—	9	26
2782	5040	1.17	0.35	0.07	35	31

(8) Effect of cold reduction on tensile properties[73]

Material: powder metallurgy wire
Analysis: "high purity" powder used to make sintered bar
History: 0.1 in. diameter wire annealed at 2600°C (4712°F) for ½ hr, cold drawn to final diameter 0.009 in. at 99% reduction
Tested at room temperature

TABLE 25.8. TENSILE PROPERTIES (*cont.*)

Area reduction by cold drawing, %	Ultimate tensile strength, 1000 psi	Elongation, %	Hardness, DPN
0*	33.5	50	90
20	49.5	—	130
80	65	—	180
90	75	—	190
99	105	—	—

* original material had lattice parameter of 3.296 Å and electrical resistivity of 13.1 microhm-cm

(9) Effect of annealing temperature on tensile properties[95]

Material: arc melted sheet and wire
Analysis (in %): O 0.008, C <0.0010, N 0.0015, Fe 0.0038, Cr <0.0010, Ni 0.0020, Si <0.0025
History: cold reduced and then annealed as indicated
Tested at room temperature

Form	Final thickness or diameter, in.	Cold reduction, %	Annealing temperature (½ hr), °C	Average grain size, mm	Ultimate tensile stress, 1000 psi	Yield stress (0.2% offset), 1000 psi	Uniform elongation, %
Sheet	0.010	—	(as rolled)	—	164	154	1
	.010	—	1350 (1 hr)	—	44	31	25
	.020	99	1150	0.007 r			
	.020	99	1200	.010			
	.020	99	1250	.015			
	.020	99	1300	.020			
	.125	97	1300	.030			
	.125	97	1350	.035			
	.125	97	1400	.05			
	.125	97	1450	.08			
Wire	.020	90	1150	.018	56		24
	.020	90	1200	.026	53		20
	.020	90	1250	.038	51		17
	.020	90	1300	.045	51		10

r = 75% recrystallized, all others 100%

Table 25.9 presents hardness data and indicates the effects of temperature in Sections (5) and (6); cold reduction in Sections (1) and (2); annealing temperature in Sections (3) and (4). The type of metal used, the purity, and the history of the sample are given where possible.

TABLE 25.9. HARDNESS

(1) Effect of cold reduction on hardness[95]

Material: arc melted sheet
Analysis (in %): O 0.0010, N 0.0020, C 0.0020, Fe 0.0016
History: sheet cold rolled from arc melted ingot

Reduction by cold rolling, %	Final thickness, in.	Superficial hardness, Rockwell 15T
0	0.125	70.5
20	.100	82.5
40	.075	86.0
60	.050	89.5
80	.010	90.5
97	.125	92.0

TABLE 25.9. HARDNESS (*cont.*)

(2) Effect of cold reduction on hardness[94]

Material: powder metallurgy sheet

Reduction, %	0	50	75	87.5	94
Hardness, DPN	95	150	170	175	183

(3) Effect of annealing temperature on hardness[80]

Material: powder metallurgy metal, 95% cold rolled
Analysis (in %): O 0.0056, N 0.013, Cb 0.10, W 0.01, Fe 0.015, C 0.02.
Annealing time: ½ hr

Annealing temperature, °C	Annealing temperature, °F	Knoop hardness number
200	392	260
600	1112	245
800	1472	240
1000	1832	215
1100	2012	190
1200	2192	130
1400	2552	110
1600	2912	133
2500	4532	130*

* extrapolated from plot of data

(4) Effect of annealing temperature on hardness[41]

Material: electron beam melted metal
Analysis: see Table 25.4 (Lot 2)
History: specimens cold reduced from as-cast ingot, then annealed 1 hr at indicated temperature in vacuum

Annealing temperature, °C	Annealing temperature, °F	Vickers hardness number (10 kg load) 50% cold reduced	75% cold reduced	85% cold reduced	75% cold reduced after intermediate anneal
25	77	150	150	156	137
200	392	125	172	145	130
400	752	132	175	152	143
600	1112	156	165	156	140
800	1472	140	135	142	128
1000	1832	120	105	102	111
1200	2192	100	80	83	80
1400	2552	80	92	85	86
1600	2912	85	88	90	90
1800	3272	83	83	90	86

(interpolated from smooth plots of data)

TABLE 25.9. HARDNESS (*cont.*)

(5) Hot hardness of tantalum[95]

Material: arc melted metal, as-cast condition

Testing done in vacuum, temperature stabilized 10 min before making hardness reading

Temperature, °C	25	200	400	600	800	900
°F	77	392	752	1112	1472	1652
Hardness, Rockwell A	57	44	41	37	25	10

(6) Hot hardness of tantalum[63]

Material: electron bombardment zone refined metal, arc melted to small ingot, ground and polished to 89 VPN. After test, hardness had risen to 100 VPN.

Temperature, °C	20	400	600	800	1000	1200
°F	68	752	1112	1472	1832	2192
Hardness, kg/mm²	89	82	73	37	29	21

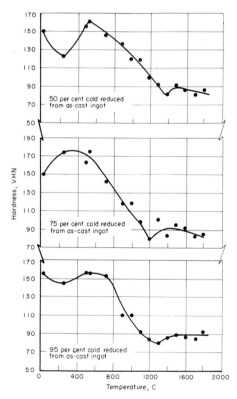

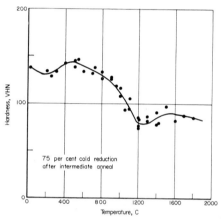

Figure 25.11. Hardness versus one-hour annealing temperature for high-purity tantalum cold rolled after intermediate annealing. (*From Holden, Schwartzberg, and Jaffee.*)[41]

Figure 25.10. Hardness versus one-hour annealing temperature for high-purity tantalum cold rolled from the as-cast ingot. (*From Holden, Schwartzberg, and Jaffee.*)[41]

Figures 25.10 and 25.11 show in graphical plots the effect of annealing temperature on the hardness of electron beam melted metal which has been cold reduced to varying degrees before annealing, as determined by Holden *et al.*[41]

The fatigue characteristics of powder metallurgy tantalum are given in Table 25.10, as determined by Bornemann and Gela,[10] on sheet and wire at room temperature and at −73°C (−100°F). The ratio of fatigue strength to ultimate strength has been found to be 0.63 at 27°C (80°F) and 0.59 at −73°C (−100°F); the fatigue strength at the lower temperature is greater than at room temperature. The study also concludes that the ductility and modulus of elasticity of tantalum are not impaired at the −73°C temperature; no evidence of brittleness is encountered; the metal can be used with safety at the low temperature.

TABLE 25.10. FATIGUE CHARACTERISTICS

Effect of temperature and annealing temperature[10]

(1) Material: 0.040 in. powder metallurgy sheet

Analysis (in %): C 0.028, Fe 0.015, traces of Mo, Cb, SiO_2, TiO_2

History: penultimate reduction in area approximately 33%, annealed at 1400°C (2552°F) for 1 hr

Tests made in roll direction on Sonntag SF–2 Universal Fatigue Machine

Ratio of fatigue strength to ultimate strength, 0.63 at 27°C (80°F) and 0.59 at −73°C (−100°F)

Temperature,		Stress, 1000 psi	Cycles to failure
°C	°F		
−73	−100	63	4×10^5
		50	8×10^5
		49	1×10^6
		43	4×10^6
		42	1×10^7
		41	2×10^7
		41	indefinitely large
27	80	55	1.6×10^5
		43	4×10^5
		37	1×10^6
		35	2×10^6
		35	2.5×10^7
		35	indefinitely large

(2) Material: 0.004 in. diameter powder metallurgy wire

History: annealed at 1400°C (2552°F) for 1 hr

Temperature,		Stress, 1000 psi	Cycles to failure
°C	°F		
−73	−100	90	4×10^4
		80	8×10^4
		77	1×10^5
		74	2×10^5
		70	6×10^5
		68	4×10^6
		68	1×10^7
		68	indefinitely large
27	80	99	2×10^4
		82	6×10^4
		78	1×10^5
		70	2×10^5
		65	4.5×10^5
		64	1×10^6
		64	1×10^7
		64	indefinitely large

TABLE 25.10. FATIGUE CHARACTERISTICS (*cont.*)

(3) Material: 0.004 in. diameter powder metallurgy wire
  History: annealed at 1140°C (2084°F) for 1 hr

Temperature,		Stress, 1000 psi	Cycles to failure
°C	°F		
28	80	106	2×10^4
		85	1×10^5
		65	8×10^5
		62	2×10^6
		62	5×10^7
		62	indefinitely large

(above values all from smoothed plots of data)

Impact strength data are given in Table 25.11 for annealed powder metallurgy metal.[10]

TABLE 25.11. IMPACT PROPERTIES

Effect of temperature on impact strength[10]
  Material: annealed 0.02 in. powder metallurgy sheet
  Tested in cross roll direction on Amsler PH–130
    Impact Testing Machine; approximate impact velocity, 15 ft/sec

Temperature,		Impact strength, ft-lb/in.²
°C	°F	
27	80	3850
−57	− 70	1670
−73	−100	1520

Creep and rupture properties of tantalum are given in Table 25.12. Using electron beam melted material, Holden *et al.*[41] have reported the results of their studies on recrystallized metal over the temperature range of 500–1400°C (932–2552°F), and on wrought tantalum over the range of room temperature to 750°C (77–1382°F). Stress-rupture data

TABLE 25.12. CREEP AND RUPTURE PROPERTIES

(1) **Material: annealed electron beam melted metal**[41]
  Analysis: See Table 25.4 (Lot 2)
  History: as-cast ingot cold reduced 75% after intermediate anneal, recrystallized by 1 hr vacuum anneal at 1200°C (2192°F)
  Test atmosphere: vacuum, at least 0.1 micron

Temperature, °C	Stress, 1000 psi	Elongation on loading, %	Total defor- mation, %	Time, hr	Creep, %	Time, hr	Minimum creep rate, %/hr	Rupture properties	
								Time, hr	Elongation, %
500									
(932°F)	25.3	—	—	—	—	—	—	0.0	28
	24.0	10.8	—	—	—	—	Nil	> 24.7	(a)
	22.0	10.2	—	—	—	—	Nil	>138.4	(a)

TABLE 25.12. CREEP AND RUPTURE PROPERTIES (*cont.*)

Temperature, °C	Stress, 1000 psi	Elongation on loading, %	Total deformation, %	Time, hr	Creep, %	Time, hr	Minimum creep rate, %/hr	Rupture properties	
								Time, hr	Elongation, %
750 (1382°F)	22.0	—	—	—	—	—	—	0.03	29
	16.0	5.70	—	—	1.0	0.06	9.8	1.1	33
					2.0	0.14			
					5.0	0.44			
	14.0	1.41	2.0	0.16	1.0	0.7	0.113	168.1	33
			5.0	13.6	2.0	4.0			
					5.0	23.7			
	12.0	0.57	1.0	0.5	0.5	1.5	0.0145	71.2(a)	2.2
			2.0	52.5	1.0	21.5			
					2.0	91.5(b)			
1000 (1832°F)	11.0	2.15	5.0	0.2	2.0	0.1	3.18	4.3	40
					5.0	0.64			
	10.0	1.70	2.0	0.03	0.5	0.05	1.40	12.0	43
			5.0	1.3	1.0	0.15			
					2.0	0.51			
					5.0	2.5			
	9.0	1.42	2.0	0.25	0.5	0.09	0.44	30.6	54
			5.0	5.0	1.0	0.6			
					2.0	2.3			
					5.0	8.0			
	8.0	1.02	2.0	1.1	0.5	0.2	0.34	55.3	58
			5.0	11.4	1.0	1.12			
					2.0	4.8			
					5.0	14.6			
1200 (2192°F)	7.0	3.62	5.0	0.01	2.0	0.015	85.5	0.38	61
					5.0	0.038			
	5.0	1.80	2.0	0.01	2.0	0.11	8.7	4.5	60
			5.0	0.21	5.0	0.36			
	3.5	0.29	0.5	0.02	0.5	0.05	0.48	55.8	59
			1.0	0.08	1.0	0.14			
			2.0	0.36	2.0	0.48			
			5.0	2.3	5.0	2.5			
	2.5	0.12	0.5	0.2	0.5	0.4	0.10	141.9(a)	16
			1.0	1.2	1.0	1.6			
			2.0	4.8	2.0	5.5			
			5.0	27.0	5.0	28.0			
1400 (2552°F)	2.5	0.48	2.0	0.07	0.5	0.01	2.6	7.3	35
			5.0	0.50	1.0	0.03			
					2.0	0.11			
					5.0	0.64			
	1.8	0.27	1.0	0.13	0.5	0.07	1.0	11.0	26
			2.0	0.65	1.0	0.25			
			5.0	3.40	2.0	0.85			
					5.0	3.65			
	1.5	0.13	0.5	0.10	0.2	0.04	0.58	22.4	33
			1.0	0.40	0.5	0.15			
			2.0	1.60	1.0	0.50			
			5.0	6.80	2.0	1.90			
					5.0	7.00			

(a) test discontinued before failure

(b) extrapolated value

TABLE 25.12. CREEP AND RUPTURE PROPERTIES (cont.)

(2) Material: wrought electron beam melted metal[41]

Analysis: see Table 25.4 (Lot 2)

History: as-cast ingot cold reduced 95%, stress relieved by ¼ hr anneal in argon at 750°C (1382°F)

Test atmosphere: vacuum, at least 0.1 micron

Temperature, °C	Stress, 1000 psi	Elongation on loading, %	Total deformation, %	Time, hr	Creep, %	Time, hr	Minimum creep rate, %/hr	Rupture properties	
								Time, hr	Elongation, %
27 (80°F)	54.0	0.48	1.0	0.05	0.5	0.05	0.29	5.6	8
			2.0	0.28	1.0	0.075			
					2.0	1.0			
	53.0	0.27	1.0	0.03	0.5	0.025	0.69	3.1	8
			2.0	0.10	1.0	0.033			
			5.0	3.0	2.0	0.16			
	52.5	0.42	0.5	0.006	0.5	0.035	0.86	0.6	6.4
			1.0	0.042	1.0	0.12			
	52.5	0.22	—	—	—	—	nil	>124.0	(a)
	50.0	0.19	—	—	—	—	nil	>146.0	(a)
500 (932°F)	47.0	—	—	—	—	—	—	0.0	5.1
	43.0	0.47	0.5	2.0	—	—	0.0004	>117.4	(a)
750 (1382°F)	32.5	0.27	0.5	0.10	0.2	0.10	2.3	0.6(c)	6.1
			1.0	0.34	0.5	0.23			
					1.0	0.46			
	27.5	0.25	0.5	0.85	0.1	0.16	0.11	19.4	7.7
			1.0	4.15	0.2	0.60			
			2.0	11.0	0.5	2.3			
					1.0	6.2			
					2.0	12.4			

(a) test discontinued before failure
(c) estimated value, failed at between 0.3 and 0.8 hours

(3) Material: powder metallurgy metal[2]

Test method: compression creep test in vacuum

Results: at 1000°C (1832°F) stress of 6000 to 8000 psi gives 1 per cent creep strain in 24 hours

(4) Material: cold rolled sheet 0.030 in. thick from arc melted ingot[95]

Analysis (in %): O 0.011, C 0.0015, N 0.0025, Fe 0.005, Cr <0.001, Ni 0.005, Si <0.0025, Ti <0.001, Mo <0.0025

Results: at 1649°C (3000°F) with stress of 4,000 psi the time to rupture = 3 min 6 sec; with stress of 2,500 psi the time to rupture = 18 min 37 sec

(5) Material: annealed powder metallurgy strip[78, 95]

Analysis: "commercially pure"

History: sheet rolled to 0.064 in., annealed

Test atmosphere: argon

Temperature, °C	Temperature, °F	Total elongation, %	Time under load, sec	Stress for indicated elongation in indicated time, psi			
				1% El.	2% El.	5% El.	Rupture
1649	3000	19.5–20	30	4700	5000	5400	5800
			60	4300	4600	5000	5400
			300	3500	3800	4200	4600

TABLE 25.12. CREEP AND RUPTURE PROPERTIES (*cont.*)

Temperature,		Total elongation, %	Time under load, sec	Stress for indicated elongation in indicated time, psi			
°C	°F			1% El.	2% El.	5% El.	Rupture
2204	4000	20	30	1170	1460	1860	2000
			60	1000	1360	1600	1700
			300	700	900	1150	—
2760	5000	22.5–25	30	510	620	770	—
			60	430	540	670	—
			300	300	390	480	600

(data interpolated and extrapolated from straight lines on log stress-log time graph)

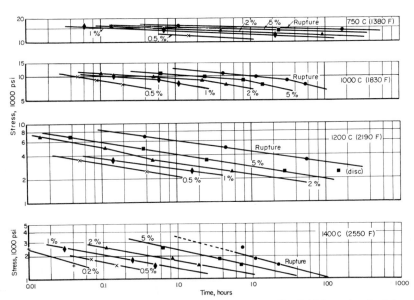

Figure 25.12. Creep and rupture curves for recrystallized high-purity tantalum cold reduced 75 per cent after intermediate anneal; recrystallized by one-hour anneal at 1200°C. (*From Holden, Schwartzberg and Jaffee.*)[41]

on arc melted metal are given by Torti[95] at 1649°C (3000°F). Working with powder metallurgy metal, Preston *et al.*[78] have determined creep-rupture properties at 1649°C (3000°F), 2204°C (4000°F), and 2760°C (5000°F). Allen and Carrington[2] have reported a compression creep test result at 1000°C (1832°F). The Holden *et al.*[41] results are illustrated in Figure 25.12.

Recrystallization behavior of electron beam melted metal is summarized in Table 25.13 which tabulates the results of Holden *et al.*[41] Other published results on this subject describe similar effects.

The effects of additions of nitrogen and oxygen on the tensile properties, hardness, annealing temperature, and the creep and rupture properties of high purity electron beam melted

TABLE 25.13. RECRYSTALLIZATION BEHAVIOR OF TANTALUM[41]

Material: electron beam melted metal
Analysis: see Table 25.4 (Lot 2)

	Temperature for indicated amount of recrystallization in 1 hr			
	50%		100%	
Condition	°C	°F	°C	°F
Cold reduced 50% from as-cast ingot	1100	2012	1400	2552
Cold reduced 75% from as-cast ingot	1000	1832	1200	2192
Cold reduced 95% from as-cast ingot	900	1652	1300	2372
Cold reduced 75% after intermediate anneal	1050	1922	1200	2192

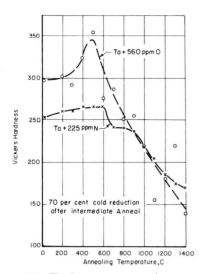

Figure 25.13. Hardness versus one-hour annealing temperature for Ta-N(225 ppm) and Ta-O(560 ppm) alloys. (*From Holden, Schwartzberg, and Jaffee.*)[41]

tantalum have been evaluated by Holden *et al.*[41] The interstitial alloys studied were Ta + 560 ppm O and Ta + 225 ppm N. While the hardness values of these alloys are approximately twice that of the original tantalum both before and after annealing, the recrystallization temperature is essentially the same for all three materials, i.e., 1200–1400°C (2192–

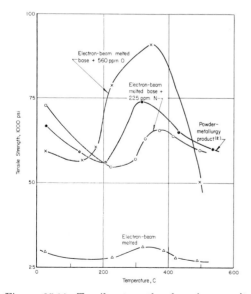

Figure 25.14. Tensile strength of various purity grades of tantalum. (2) = work of Pugh.[79] (*From Holden, Schwartzberg, and Jaffee.*)[41]

TABLE 25.14. EFFECT OF ADDITIONS OF NITROGEN AND OXYGEN ON TENSILE PROPERTIES OF TANTALUM[41]

Material: high purity electron beam melted metal converted to Ta-N and Ta-O interstitial alloys

Analysis: Ta-N alloy (in %), O 0.0006, N 0.0225, H 0.00032, C 0.0020
Ta-O alloy (in %), O 0.0560, N 0.0030, H 0.00032, C 0.0020.
In both alloys other elements as in Table 25.4 (Lot 2)

History: alloys cold rolled 70% and annealed 1 hr at 1200°C (2192°F) for Ta-N alloy and at 1300°C (2372°F) for Ta-O alloy

Tested in air at strain rate of 0.05 in./in./min

Alloy	Temperature, °C	°F	Ultimate tensile strength, 1000 psi	Yield strength,* 1000 psi	Elongation, %
Ta-N	27	80	73.4	67.5	25
	225	437	55.0	38.9	21
	300	572	57.7	35.8	21
	330	626	63.6	37.3	20**
	375	707	66.3	36.5	25
	415	779	64.2	37.0	18
	500	932	60.2	31.5	13
Ta-O	27	80	59.8	49.9	26
	135	275	57.1	41.9	22
	180	356	60.7	44.7	17
	225	437	79.2	50.8	14**
	350	662	91.6	44.2	27
	500	932	50.8	24.4	22

* at 0.2% offset.
** Failed outside gage length; elongation calculated from extension between shoulder gage marks. Relation between elongation and extension is 1.2/1.0.

2552°F) for one hour holding time. The effects of annealing temperature on the hardness of these alloys are shown in Figure 25.13. Similar findings on the original metal are shown in Figures 25.10 and 25.11.

Tensile properties of these Ta-O and Ta-N alloys are summarized in Table 25.14 over a temperature range to 500°C (932°F). The tensile strength of various purity grades of tantalum is illustrated in Figure 25.14, based on the work of Holden *et al.*[41] on electron beam melted metal and the work of Pugh[79] on powder metallurgy metal.

Deformation and rupture properties of the

Ta-N and Ta-O alloys at 750–1200°C (1372–2192°F) are given in Table 25.15.[41] The effects of nitrogen and oxygen on the rupture strength of tantalum are compared in Table 25.6. Although nitrogen has a pronounced strengthening effect on tantalum, the effect lessens both with increased time and temperature. Oxygen is a much less potent strengthener.

TABLE 25.15. EFFECT OF ADDITIONS OF NITROGEN AND OXYGEN ON
DEFORMATION AND RUPTURE PROPERTIES OF TANTALUM[41]

Material: same as in Table 25.14.
Analysis: same as in Table 25.14.
History: same as in Table 25.14.
Tested in vacuum of at least 0.1 micron

| Temperature, °C | Stress, 1000 psi | Elongation on loading, % | Deformation Properties | | | | Minimum creep rate, %/hr | Rupture properties | |
| | | | Total deformation | | Creep | | | | |
			Strain, %	Time, hr	Strain, %	Time, hr		Time, hr	Elongation, %
			Ta-N (225 ppm) Alloy (a)						
750 (1382°F)	18.0	0.06	0.2	0.02	0.2	0.03	<0.50	51.4	55
			0.5	0.10	0.5	0.12			
			1.0	0.22	1.0	0.24			
			2.0	0.43	2.0	0.44			
			5.0	1.5	5.0	1.5			
	20.0	0.72	1.0	0.06	0.5	0.10	4.7	5.9	62
			2.0	0.20	1.0	0.17			
			5.0	0.50	2.0	0.28			
					5.0	0.58			
	21.0	0.64	1.0	0.02	0.5	0.03	7.7	2.9	55
			2.0	0.13	1.0	0.10			
			5.0	0.40	2.0	0.19			
					5.0	0.45			
1200 (2192°F)	4.5	—	0.5	0.08			<1.0	24.3	68
			1.0	0.18					
			2.0	0.46					
			3.0	1.7					
	6.0	0.30	1.0	0.02	1.0	0.04	6.7	3.3	63
			2.0	0.08	2.0	0.10			
			5.0	0.33	5.0	0.36			
	10.0		No extensometer readings obtained				—	0.11	71
			Ta-O (560 ppm) Alloy (b)						
750 (1382°F)	13.0	0.96	2.0	1.0	0.2	0.03	0.03	>313	15(c)
			5.0	47.0	0.5	0.14			
					1.0	0.93			
					2.0	8.0			
					5.0	74.0			
	15.0	2.84	5.0	0.07	2.0	0.06	2.5	10	50
					5.0	0.37			
	17.5	4.38	5.0	0.02	2.0	0.04	20.4	10.2	61
					5.0	0.12			
	20.0	6.58	—	—	2.0	0.02	103.0	0.27	48
					5.0	0.05			

TABLE 25.15. EFFECT OF ADDITIONS OF NITROGEN AND OXYGEN ON
DEFORMATION AND RUPTURE PROPERTIES OF TANTALUM[41] (*cont.*)

| Temperature, °C | Stress, 1000 psi | Elongation on loading, % | Deformation Properties | | | | Minimum creep rate, %/hr | Rupture properties | |
| | | | Total deformation | | Creep | | | | |
			Strain, %	Time, hr	Strain, %	Time, hr		Time, hr	Elongation, %
1200									
(2192°F)	3.0	0.48	0.5	0.02	0.2	0.15	0.39	>86(d)	52
			1.0	0.60	0.5	0.55			
			2.0	3.3	1.0	1.8			
					2.0	4.2			
	5.0	0.84	2.0	0.04	1.0	0.03	4.2	3.6	38
			5.0	0.48	2.0	0.09			
					5.0	0.68			
	7.0	6.02	—	—	1.0	0.02	8.3	1.7	29
					2.0	0.06			
					5.0	0.28			

(a) Cold rolled 70% and annealed at 1300°C (2372°F) for 1 hour
(b) Cold rolled 70% and annealed at 1200°C (2192°F) for 1 hour
(c) Discontinued
(d) Temperature cycled after 86 hours; failure occurred in approximately 100 hours

Chemical Properties

Tantalum is one of the most inert of all metals to reaction with chemicals at temperatures below roughly 150°C (302°F). The only reagents which attack it rapidly are fluorine, hydrofluoric acid, acidic solutions containing fluoride ion, and free sulfur trioxide. Alkalis react with it slowly, the rate increasing with alkaline concentration.

As the temperature of exposure becomes higher tantalum begins to react slowly with a large variety of reagents, the rate of attack increasing with the temperature rise. The specific conditions under which reaction occurs will vary with the reactants involved, as is, of course, the case with any element. At temperatures of several hundred degrees Centigrade, tantalum becomes an extremely reactive element in most environments including air, with important exceptions noted hereafter.

The inertness of tantalum is caused by the presence on its surface of a thin, tenacious, self-healing film of tantalum oxide, Ta_2O_5; only as this film reacts with or is penetrated by a chemical reagent does attack on the metal occur. The film prevents the flow of current from tantalum to an electrolyte when the metal is made anodic, although it permits the flow of current when a metal-to-metal contact is present. This property makes tantalum valuable for rectifier and capacitor applications.

Tantalum becomes cathodic in galvanic cell circuit with almost all metals. Thus tantalum is in a high position toward the electropositive end of the electromotive series. Because of this cathodic behavior atomic hydrogen is liberated when tantalum is in galvanic circuit with most metals, and the atomic hydrogen liberated at the surface is rapidly absorbed with resultant embrittlement of the tantalum. Stray voltages can also cause the same effect. It is of the utmost importance, therefore, that tantalum present in chemical equipment, for example, be prevented from becoming cathodic so that the metal will not fail structurally.

Corrosion Resistance. The phenomenal corrosion resistance of tantalum over wide ranges of concentration and temperature has led to one of its main applications, a material of construction in chemical equipment. The resistance to a large variety of reagents is indicated in Table 25.16. Incidentally, when tantalum is attacked, corrosion is uniform without pitting.

Hydrochloric Acid. Tantalum is inert to hydrochloric acid at all concentrations at temperatures up to at least 110°C (230°F). This fact has been demonstrated by long industrial experience. For example, bayonet heaters fabricated of thin wall (0.013 inch) metal have

TABLE 25.16. CORROSION RESISTANCE OF TANTALUM

E = no attack up to about 150°C (302°F); V = variable depending on concentration and temperature; NR = not resistant.

E	Acetic acid	E	Hydrogen peroxide
E	Acetic anhydride	E	Hydrogen sulfide (see text)
E	Air, below 300°C (see text)	E	Hypochlorous acid
E	Aluminum chloride	E	Iodine, below 300°C (see text)
E	Aluminum sulfate	E	Lactic acid
E	Amines	E	Magnesium chloride
V	Ammonia	E	Magnesium sulfate
E	Ammonium chloride	E	Mercury salts
V	Ammonium hydroxide	E	Methyl sulfuric acid
E	Ammonium nitrate	E	Mixed acids (H_2SO_4–HNO_3) (see text)
E	Ammonium phosphate	E	Nickel salts
E	Ammonium sulfate	E	Nitric acid (see text)
E	Amyl acetate or chloride	E	Nitric acid, fuming (see text)
E	Aqua regia	E	Nitric oxides (see text)
E	Barium hydroxide	E	Nitrogen, below 300°C (see text)
E	Body fluids	E	Nitrous acid
E	Bromine, dry, below 300°C	E	Nitrosyl chloride
E	Bromine, wet	NR	Oleum (fuming sulfuric acid)
E	Calcium bisulfite	E	Organic chlorides
E	Calcium chloride	E	Oxalic acid
E	Calcium hydroxide	E	Oxygen, below 300°C (see text)
E	Calcium hypochlorite	E	Perchloric acid
E	Chloric acid	E	Phenol
E	Chlorinated brine	E	Phosphoric acid, <4 ppm F⁻ (see text)
E	Chlorinated hydrocarbons	E	Phosphorus, below 700°C (see text)
E	Chlorine, dry, below 250°C	E	Phosphorus chlorides
E	Chlorine, wet (see text)	E	Phosphorus oxychloride
E	Chlorine oxides	E	Pickling acids, except HNO_3–HF
E	Chloroacetic acid	E	Phthalic anhydride
E	Chromic acid	V	Potassium carbonate
E	Chrome plating solutions	E	Potassium chloride
E	Citric acid	E	Potassium dichromate
E	Cleaning solution	V	Potassium hydroxide, dilute (see text)
E	Copper salts	NR	Potassium hydroxide, concentrated
E	Ethylene dibromide	E	Potassium iodide-iodine
E	Ethyl sulfate	NR	Potassium pyrosulfate, molten
E	Fatty acids	E	Silver nitrate
E	Ferric chloride	NR	Sodium bisulfate, molten
E	Ferrous sulfate	E	Sodium bisulfate, solution
V	Fluoride salts (see text)	E	Sodium bromide
E	Formic acid	V	Sodium carbonate
E	Fuming nitric acid (see text)	E	Sodium chlorate
NR	Fuming sulfuric acid (see text)	E	Sodium chloride
E	Hydriodic acid	V	Sodium hydroxide, dilute (see text)
E	Hydrobromic acid	NR	Sodium hydroxide, concentrated
E	Hydrochloric acid (see text)	E	Sodium hypochlorite
NR	Hydrofluoric acid	E	Sodium nitrate
V	Hydrogen (see text)	NR	Sodium pyrosulfate, molten
E	Hydrogen bromide	E	Sodium sulfate
E	Hydrogen chloride	V	Sodium sulfide (see text)
NR	Hydrogen fluoride	E	Sodium sulfite
E	Hydrogen iodide	E	Sulfamic acid

TABLE 25.16. CORROSION RESISTANCE OF TANTALUM (cont.)

E	Sulfur, below 500°C (see text)			LIQUID METALS
E	Sulfur chlorides			(see text)
E	Sulfur dioxide	E	Bismuth to 900°C	
NR	Sulfur trioxide	E	Gallium to 450°C	
E	Sulfuric acid, to 175°C	E	Lead to 1000°C	
V	Sulfuric acid, over 175°C (see text)	E	Lithium to 1000°C	
E	Sulfurous acid	E	Magnesium to 1150°C	
E	Sulfuryl chloride	E	Mercury to 600°C	
E	Thionyl chloride	E	Potassium to 1000°C	
E	Tin salts	E	Sodium to 1200°C	
E	Zinc chloride	E	Sodium-potassium alloys to 1000°C	
E	Zinc sulfate	V	Zinc to 500°C	

been in continuous industrial use in distilling units for over twenty years without being attacked. Above the normal boiling point a temperature is reached for a given acid concentration at which point attack, accompanied by a degree of embrittlement, begins. Tests conducted at the Metals Research Laboratory of Union Carbide Metals Co.[5] at 190°C (374°F) under pressure have shown that the corrosion rate is less than 1 mil per year (0.001 inch per year or 0.001 ipy) for concentrations up to 25 per cent HCl. Some embrittlement due to hydrogen occurs in the 25 per cent acid. The rate of attack is 3.9 mils per year in 30 per cent acid, and 11.6 in 37 per cent acid, with increasing embrittlement as the concentration increases.

Nitric Acid. Tantalum is inert to nitric acid of all concentrations over a wide temperature range even in the presence of HCl or chloride salts. Numerous industrial installations of tantalum equipment in use for years verify this fact, as do many tests in industrial exposures.[30,33] Tests at 190°C (374°F) have shown corrosion rates of less than 1 mil per year with no embrittlement in concentrations up to 70 per cent HNO$_3$.[5] Others have shown nil corrosion at temperatures as high as 250–300°C (482–572°F) at 1200 psi.[33]

Red fuming nitric acid containing 6.5 per cent NO$_2$ does not attack tantalum at temperatures of 121–149°C (250–300°F).[43]

Sulfuric Acid. In 98 per cent H$_2$SO$_4$ a slow uniform attack begins on tantalum at about 175°C (347°F). At all concentrations below this temperature there is no corrosion. For this reason hundreds of tantalum heaters operating on 150–175 psig steam have been used for years in industrial sulfuric acid concentrators.

Taylor[90] has found that as the temperature of 98 per cent H$_2$SO$_4$ is increased above 175°C (347°F), the corrosion rate on tantalum increases. At 200°C (392°F) it is 1.5 mils per year, at 250°C (482°F) it is 29, and at 300°C (572°F) it is 342. (See Refs. 32, 33.) As the concentration of the H$_2$SO$_4$ is decreased the rate of corrosion at a given temperature tends to become less. A test in a chemical company concentrator showed a rate of 3.1 mils per year in 90 per cent H$_2$SO$_4$ at 250°C (482°F). This is about 1/10 that for 98 per cent H$_2$SO$_4$ at the same temperature.[33] The above exposures resulted in no embrittlement of the tantalum. The presence of HCl or chloride salts does not alter the resistance.

On the other hand, tests made at the boiling points of 80, 85, and 95 per cent H$_2$SO$_4$ are reported to cause some brittleness of the tantalum samples.[5] The respective corrosion rates and temperatures are 1.9 mils per year at 202°C (396°F), 19.3 at 225°C (437°F), and 192 at 290°C (554°F). At 190°C (374°F) the rate is less than 1 mil per year over the whole concentration range of 5–90 per cent H$_2$SO$_4$.[5]

Mixed acid prepared from 88 parts of 95 per cent HNO$_3$ and 12 parts of fuming H$_2$SO$_4$ (containing 20 per cent SO$_3$) has been reported to give a corrosion rate of 0.8 mil per year at 121–149°C (250–300°F).[43]

The attack of fuming sulfuric acid (containing 15 per cent SO$_3$) on tantalum is rapid. Taylor has found that while the corrosion rate is 0.3 mil per year at 23°C (73°F), it is 4 at 50°C (122°F), 9.2 at 70°C (158°F), and 3900 at 130°C (266°F).[33,90]

Phosphoric Acid. Tantalum is unaffected by 85 per cent H$_3$PO$_4$ at temperatures below about 180°C (356°F), but is attacked at higher temperatures, the rate increasing rapidly as the temperature rises. At 225°C (437°F) the rate is 3.5 mils per year, and at 250°C (482°F) it is 20 mils per year.[33] Another study has reported that the corrosion rate with phosphoric acid is less than 1 mil per year at the boiling point and at 190°C (374°F) over the concentration range of 1 to 85 per cent H_3PO_4.[5]

If the phosphoric acid contains hydrofluoric acid or more than a few ppm of fluoride ion, as frequently is the case with commercial acid, attack on the tantalum is likely to occur.

Effect of Fluoride Ion. Hydrofluoric acid (aqueous or anhydrous), gaseous HF, or acid solutions containing more than 2 or 3 ppm of fluoride ion all corrode and embrittle tantalum. However, this attack apparently does not occur in chromium plating baths containing fluorides. In one test a corrosion rate of 0.02 mil per year was observed on a sample placed in a chromium plating bath for 2½ months. The solution contained 40 per cent CrO_3 and 0.5 per cent fluoride ion at a temperature of 54–60°C (130–140°F). In another 4-day exposure a corrosion rate of 0.2 mil per year occurred in a bath containing 33 ounces per gallon CrO_3, 0.20 ounces per gallon H_2SO_4, and 0.40 ounces per gallon fluoride ion at 54°C (130°F). This negligible attack may be due to an inhibition caused by complex ion formation between chromium and fluoride ions.[33]

Other Reagents. Over the temperature range commonly used in solution processes, tantalum is inert to acids such as aqua regia, chromic acid, "cleaning solution" (concentrated H_2SO_4 + $K_2Cr_2O_7$ or CrO_3), perchloric acid, hypochlorous acid, nitrous acid, organic acids including monochloroacetic and methyl sulfuric acids, hydrobromic acid, bromic acid, etc. Chlorine oxides, nitrogen oxides, sulfur and phosphorous chlorides, $POCl_3$, $SOCl_2$, SO_2Cl, SO_2, hydrogen peroxide, phenol, hydrogen sulfide, and organic compounds of all sorts do not corrode tantalum. Salts which form acidic solutions, such as $ZnCl_2$, $NaHSO_4$, $AlCl_3$, $FeCl_3$, etc., have no effect on tantalum. It is also inert to all other salt solutions, unless HF or concentrated alkalis are present. Fused sodium or potassium pyrosulfate dissolves tantalum, however. Tantalum is completely inert to body fluids and can thus be used as surgical implants.

Alkalis. While tantalum is attacked by concentrated alkaline solutions even at room tem-

perature, and is dissolved by molten alkalis, it is quite resistant to dilute solutions. In a recent study[93] using change in electrical resistivity to measure corrosion rates, it was found that tantalum wire totally immersed in 10 per cent NaOH solution at room temperature for 210 days corroded at the rate of 9.3 x 10⁻³ mil per year. In 5 per cent NaOH solution at 100°C (212°F) for 60 days the rate was found to be 0.126 mil per year. A similar rate occurs in 10 per cent NaOH at 100°C (212°F). In the latter cases there was some local effect at the points where the wire left the solution and entered submerged rubber stoppers in the sides of the corrosion vessel; this accounts for most of the weight loss.

Halogens. Fluorine attacks tantalum at room temperature. Tantalum is totally inert to wet or dry chlorine, bromine, and iodine up to 150°C (302°F), and these elements dissolved in solutions of salts or acids likewise have no effect. Chlorine begins to attack tantalum at about 250°C (482°F); the reaction is violent after 35 minutes at 450°C (842°F), and at 500°C (932°F) occurs instantly. The presence of water vapor sharply decreases the corrosion by Cl_2 so that the maximum temperatures at which tantalum is satisfactorily resistant to Cl_2 containing 1.5 and 30 per cent H_2O are 375°C (707°F) and 400°C (752°F), respectively.[97] Bromine attacks tantalum at 300°C (572°F), and iodine at about the same temperature, forming $TaBr_5$ and TaI_5, respectively.

Sulfur. Tantalum reacts with sulfur or hydrogen sulfide at red heat forming tantalum sulfide, TaS_2. Tantalum disulfide is also formed when Ta_2O_5 is heated in H_2S or CS_2. Little or no data are available on the effect of solutions of sulfides such as those of the alkali and alkaline earth metals, but the highly alkaline nature of these compounds indicates that they probably corrode tantalum to some degree.

Selenium and Tellurium. Tantalum is attacked severely by selenium and tellurium vapors at temperatures of 800°C (1472°F) and higher. In contrast there is little or only slight attack on the metal by liquid selenides and tellurides of yttrium, the rare earths, and uranium at temperatures in the range of 1300–2100°C (272–3812°F), and tantalum is considered to be a satisfactory material in which to handle these intermetallic compounds.[69a]

Reactions with Gases. As mentioned previously, tantalum becomes quite reactive at higher temperatures. While completely stable in air at 250°C (482°F) and below, at 300°C (572°F) it shows a tarnish in 24 hours and at higher temperatures the reaction rate increases rapidly.[33,90] Similar effects are observed with other common gases.

Oxygen. While several oxides of tantalum have been reported or postulated, it is unlikely that others besides Ta_2O_5 exist as stable forms. Ta_2O_5 is formed by the direct union of oxygen with tantalum as well as by other chemical reactions whereby tantalum compounds are converted to the oxide, some of which have been described previously.

Numerous investigations have been made on the kinetics and results of the action of oxygen and air on tantalum. Miller[65] describes most of them in some detail. A more recent study by Albrecht, Klopp, Koehl, and Jaffee[1] on high purity electron beam melted metal shows that in the reaction of tantalum with air, no nitrides are formed, and that nitrogen has little effect, if any, on the reaction of tantalum with air. Bakish[6] also points this out. Oxidation at 400–800°C (752–1472°F) is initially parabolic and then becomes linear. At 800–1400°C (1472–2552°F) for the air reaction and at 500–1250°C (932–2282°F) for the oxygen reaction, only a linear rate is noted. Catastrophic oxidation occurs in 1 atmosphere of oxygen above 1250°C (2282°F). In air, where the partial pressure of O_2 is 0.2 of an atmosphere, the ignition temperature is above 1400°C (2552°F). The reac-

tion in oxygen at 1000°C (1832°F) follows a square root of pressure dependency. The oxide scale consists of a thin dark subscale of Ta_2O_5 with traces of Ta_2O_3, and an outer thick white scale of Ta_2O_5. The diffusion of oxygen ion through an adherent dark subscale is the rate determining reaction.

Varying the relative humidity from 0 to 100 per cent in the air entering the oxidation vessel does not affect the oxidation behavior with air at 600–800°C (1112–1472°F).

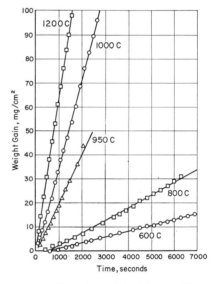

Figure 25.15. Reaction of tantalum with oxygen at various temperatures. (*From Albrecht, Klopp, Koehl, and Jaffee.*)[1]

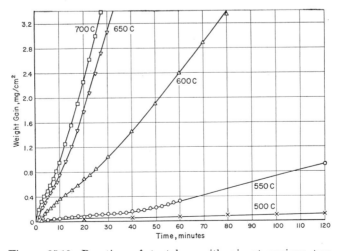

Figure 25.16. Reaction of tantalum with air at various temperatures. (*From Albrecht, Klopp, Koehl, and Jaffee.*)[1]

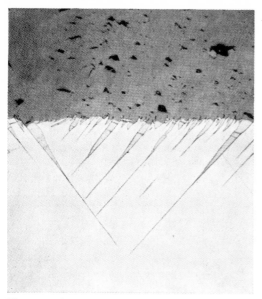

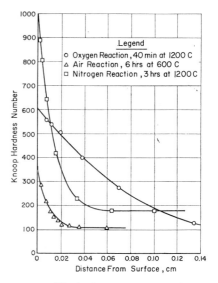

Figure 25.17. Tantalum reacted with air at 1000°C for 2.6 hours showing oxide penetration into base metal along (100) planes, 250×. (*From Albrecht, Klopp, Koehl, and Jaffee.*)[1]

Figure 25.18. Hardening of tantalum by oxygen and nitrogen. (*From Albrecht, Klopp, Koehl, and Jaffee.*)[1]

Figures 25.15 and 25.16 illustrate the reaction of tantalum with oxygen and air at various temperatures, and Figure 25.17 shows oxide penetration along the (100) crystallographic plane into tantalum reacted with air for 2.6 hours at 1000°C (1832°F).[1]

Figure 25.18 illustrates the effect on hardness at various depths from the surface after reaction in air, oxygen, and nitrogen.[1]

The presence of a few atomic per cent of oxygen in tantalum increases electrical resistivity, hardness, tensile strength, and modulus of elasticity, but it decreases elongation and reduction in area, magnetic susceptibility, and corrosion resistance to hydrofluoric acid.[27,29] Data on the effects on physical properties are listed in Table 25.17. When it is realized that 1 atomic per cent oxygen in tantalum is equal to only 892 ppm, the considerable effect of very small contents of oxygen on the properties of

TABLE 25.17. EFFECT OF OXYGEN ON PROPERTIES OF TANTALUM
(annealed gas free metal)

Atomic % O₂	Electrical resistivity,** microhm-cm		Hardness, Vickers, kg/mm²	Tensile strength, 1000 psi	Elongation, %	Modulus of elasticity, psi × 10⁶	Magnetic susceptibility, cgs units
	at 0°C	at 1000°C					
0	13.6	37.1	50	28.4	37	25.7	0.92
0.25				38.5	36		
0.5	16.6	40.1					
0.7				49*	10		
1.0	19.6	43.1	250			27.2	
1.5	22.6	46.1		128	8		
2.0	25.6	49.1	440		4.5	28	
2.5						28.2	0.87
2.9			583*				
4.5			633				0.82

* Curve breaks sharply

** A straight line relationship exists for the resistivity between 0–1000°C (32–1832°F) for each content of oxygen including zero content, i.e., all five curves are straight and parallel.

Data from Gebhardt and co-workers.[27,29] Above values interpolated from smoothed plots of data.

tantalum is evident. The tensile strength of 28,400 psi for pure tantalum in Table 25.17 closely approximates that of the high purity tantalum used by Holden et al.[41] in their work.

Nitrogen. Tantalum reacts directly with nitrogen to form nitrides, two of which are known to exist, TaN and Ta_2N. The reaction begins at about 300°C (572°F) and the rate increases with increasing temperature until at 1100°C (2012°F) TaN is formed. Absorbed nitrogen is removed at about 2000°C (3632°F) under high vacuum. Nitride formation also takes place by reaction between tantalum oxide or halide and nitrogen in the presence of hydrogen.

Several investigations of the action of nitrogen on tantalum have been made; Miller[66] discusses them in some detail. More recently Albrecht et al.[1] have studied the effect of nitrogen on high purity electron beam melted tantalum from 400–1475°C (752–2687°F). At 400–700°C (752–1292°F) the reaction follows a cubic rate law, and at 800–1475°C (1472–2687°F) the reaction follows a parabolic rate. The reaction is much slower than the oxidation reactions and TaN is the principal reaction product as an adherent film on the metal. Figure 25.19 shows the rate of weight gain at several temperatures. There is no effect of nitrogen pressure on the reaction, indicating that the reaction takes place through a nitride film.

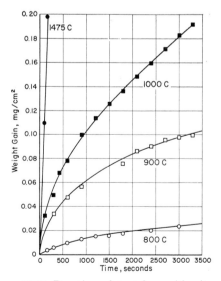

Figure 25.19. Reaction of tantalum with nitrogen at various temperatures. (*From Albrecht, Klopp, Koehl, and Jaffee.*)[1]

As in the case of oxygen in tantalum, the presence of nitrogen in only a few atomic per cent concentration increases hardness, tensile strength, and electrical resistivity, and decreases elongation and density. For example, hardness increases from about 75 VHN at zero atomic per cent N_2 to 300 at 1.25 atomic per cent and 600 at 4 atomic per cent. The ultimate tensile strength increases from about 20,000 psi at zero atomic per cent N_2 to about 168,000 psi at 2 atomic per cent, while elongation drops from 38 per cent to 16 per cent.[84] One atomic per cent N_2 in tantalum equals 780 ppm N_2.

Hydrogen. As indicated previously, tantalum absorbs hydrogen readily, and the Ta-H system has been investigated in some detail.[67] Tantalum will absorb hydrogen at room temperature during cathodic electrolysis or by heating the metal in a hydrogen atmosphere at temperatures above 250°C (482°F), forming an interstitial combination the maximum hydrogen ratio of which is $TaH_{0.74}$ or over 700 volumes per volume of metal. Absorption is accompanied by an expansion of the body-centered crystal lattice and an increase in the molecular volume so that the metal is embrittled. When such material is heated to about 800°C (1472°F) or more in a high vacuum it loses essentially all its hydrogen. Annealing or degassing at a higher temperature restores the metal to its original condition.

In addition to decreasing the ductility, strength, and density of tantalum, the presence of hydrogen increases the hardness and the electrical resistivity.

Water Vapor. While few published data have been found on the attack of steam on tantalum at high temperatures, it is known from industrial practice that tantalum is not affected adversely when heated with steam at pressures of up to 200 psig, corresponding to a temperature of 198°C (388°F). Andrews[4] has reported that at temperatures above 1127°C (2240°F) water is decomposed by tantalum with absorption of oxygen by the metal and evolution of hydrogen. At 927°C (1700°F) and lower temperatures the reaction is negligibly slow.

Carbon Dioxide. Tantalum is corroded by dry carbon dioxide at 8 atm pressure and 500°C (932°F).[75] In 10 days the weight gain is 6.7 mg/cm², in 60 days about 50 mg/cm². Tantalum reacts with carbon dioxide (presumably 1 atmosphere) at 1100°C (2012°F) to form Ta_2O_5, also with carbon monoxide at the same temperature to form TaO.[54] The latter reverts to Ta_2O_5 when exposed to oxygen.

Nitrogen Monoxide. Below about 1125°C (2057°F) the reaction rate of NO (as a 5 per cent mixture in argon) with tantalum cannot be detected. As the temperature is increased the reaction takes place with increasing rapidity, rising from 0.0065 per cent area loss per second at 1195°C (2183°F) to 0.076 at 1457°C (2672°F).[20]

Other Gases. While little published data appear to exist on the subject, it is expected that tantalum reacts at some elevated temperature with oxygen-containing gaseous compounds such as SO_2, NO_2, etc. With hydrocarbons such as benzene or naphthalene, tantalum reacts at temperatures between 1700–2500°C (3092–4532°F) to form tantalum carbide.[4] Tantalum is used as a getter in vacuum tubes at temperatures of 650–1000°C (1202–1832°F) to absorb gases and maintain a high vacuum.

Carbon, Boron and Silicon. Tantalum reacts at elevated temperatures directly with carbon, boron, and silicon to form Ta_2C and TaC, TaB and TaB_2, and $TaSi_2$, respectively, although other binary compounds of these elements have been reported. These compounds are characterized by metallic appearance and properties, high melting points, and high hardness.

Phosphorus. Tantalum phosphides, TaP and TaP_2, are formed by heating tantalum filings in phosphorus vapor at 750–950°C (1382–1742°F).

Liquid Metals. Tantalum exhibits remarkable resistance to liquid metals at high temperatures in the absence of oxygen or nitrogen. It is not affected by sodium at 1200°C (2192°F); by potassium, sodium potassium alloys (NaK), lithium, and lead at 1000°C (1832°F); by bismuth at 900°C (1652°F) or higher; by mercury at 600°C (1112°F); and by gallium at 450°C (842°F). Work at Argonne Laboratories shows that it is not attacked by magnesium or uranium-magnesium and plutonium-magnesium alloys at 1150°C (2102°F).[103]

Extensive tests at the Ames Laboratory on components for molten metal fuel reactors have revealed that tantalum is a satisfactory material for several thousand hours of service in high temperature circulating loops containing the following:[22,23]

(1) A molten magnesium-thorium alloy having a composition in the range of the magnesium-rich eutectic [63 weight per cent Mg–37 weight per cent Th, melting point 580°C (1076°F)] at 800°C (1472°F) in a helium atmosphere.

(2) Molten bismuth-uranium (5-10 weight per cent U) alloys at 1100°C (2012°F) in a helium atmosphere.

(3) Molten bismuth-uranium-manganese alloys (89.5-10.0-0.5 and 94.7-5.0-0.3 weight per cent) at 1160°C (2120°F) and 1050°C (1922°F), respectively, in a helium atmosphere.

Tantalum fails in a few days when used as containers for an alloy of aluminum-thorium-uranium (76-18-6 weight per cent) at 1000°C (1832°F), an alloy of uranium-iron (90-10 weight per cent) at 900°C (1652°F), and the eutectic alloy of uranium-chromium at similar temperatures.[22,23]

Liquid aluminum reacts rapidly with tantalum to form the stable compound Al_3Ta, aluminum tantalide.

Zinc is reported to wet and attack tantalum, the surface of which is abraded in zinc, at 440°C (824°F), but an industrial zinc producer has observed excellent corrosion resistance at 500°C (932°F).[33] The maintenance of the oxide film on the tantalum may account for the latter result.

The intermetallic compounds, YSb, ErSb, LaSb, and YBi have little effect on tantalum at 1800–2000°C (3272–3632°F), but antimony vapor severely attacks tantalum at temperatures of 1000°C (1832°F) and higher.[69a]

Corrosion Resistance of Tantalum Alloys. *Tantalum-Columbium Alloys.* These two corrosion resistant metals alloy in all proportions forming solid solutions. The question has often been raised, why effect a separation of the two sister metals from ores in which they occur together? Why not reduce them together and use the resultant alloy for fabrication of chemical equipment? The answer lies in the fact that the presence of even small amounts of columbium, say 5 per cent, in tantalum greatly reduces the corrosion resistance of the latter. Studies have been made on this subject by Murex, Ltd., wherein alloys of varying proportions of tantalum and columbium were tested in hot and cold concentrated hydrochloric and sulfuric acids. The corrosion rates increase roughly in proportion to the columbium content of the alloys, and even though the 95Ta-5Cb alloy shows excellent resistance in all exposures, the attack is three times that obtained on pure tantalum.[64]

Tantalum-Tungsten Alloys. A few corrosion test data have been reported by Kieffer *et al.*[46] for Ta-W alloys exposed to 50 per cent KOH, 20 per cent HF, and $KOH:3K_3Fe(CN)_6$ mixtures (concentration not given). Alloys containing more than 18 per cent tungsten show a nil corrosion rate in 20 per cent HF, an advantage over tantalum. Little improvement over tantalum is shown toward the other reagents by Ta-W alloys.

Other Alloys. It has been observed that the presence of a small amount of iron or nickel, for example, in a tantalum weld makes that site subject to about the same acid attack as would be experienced by iron or nickel alone. Galvanic action, as well as simple chemical attack, is undoubtedly involved in such situations. Little is known about the corrosion resistance of other tantalum alloys, but it is unlikely that the addition to tantalum of a metallic element, the corrosion resistance of which is less than that of tantalum in a given medium, will improve tantalum's corrosion characteristics.

However, it can be postulated that certain alloys of tantalum would have definite economic advantage in specific conditions where extraordinary corrosion resistance is required.

Alloys

Tantalum forms alloys with many other elements and reference should be made to Miller,[61] Hansen,[34] and the "Metals Handbook" of the American Society for Metals[59] for details and bibliographies. The systems which have been studied that form alloys with tantalum include:

Aluminum	Iron	Rhodium
Beryllium	Manganese	Ruthenium
Boron	Molybdenum	Silicon
Carbon	Nickel	Sulfur
Chromium	Nitrogen	Thorium
Cobalt	Osmium	Tin
Columbium	Oxygen	Titanium
Gallium	Palladium	Tungsten
Germanium	Phosphorus	Uranium
Hafnium	Platinum	Vanadium
Hydrogen	Plutonium	Zirconium
Iridium	Rhenium	

Tantalum apparently does not form alloys with the alkali metals, alkaline earth metals, magnesium, copper, silver, lead, bismuth, cadmium, mercury, zinc, yttrium, rare earth metals, and thallium.

Principal interest in alloys of tantalum lies in their formation to enhance the high temperature applications of tantalum and other metals having a high melting point. It is with the high melting point metals—columbium, molybdenum, hafnium, titanium (β phase), tungsten, vanadium, and zirconium—that tantalum forms a continuous series of solid solutions below the solidus. It also forms alloys with other high melting point metals: the platinum metals, chromium, and rhenium.

Among the objectives in forming alloys of these high melting point metals are strength, hardness, and ductility at high temperatures, good strength-weight ratios, and more economical products. Insofar as corrosion resistance in the temperature range used in industrial chemical processes is concerned, no tantalum alloy approaches pure tantalum in its breadth of usefulness in various corrosive media. However, resistance to attack by specific agents may be improved. Of great current interest is a high-strength high-temperature alloy with improved oxidation resistance in oxidizing atmospheres. Here, the lower density of columbium (one-half that of tantalum), its greater prevalency, and (for nuclear processes) its lower neutron absorption cross section give it great advantage over tantalum. Many studies have been made on this subject.[68]

Interestingly enough, an alloy of columbium containing 20 atomic per cent tantalum shows about $\frac{1}{8}$ the oxidation or scaling after 16 hours in air at 870–1090°C (1600–2000°F) as columbium over the whole range. This study by Michael[60] shows further that while the alloy retains the good room temperature properties of columbium, it also has superior high temperature mechanical properties. The 100-hour stress-rupture values at 1090°C (2000°F) are 17,000 psi for the alloy and 13,000 psi for columbium, and the fatigue life is 3×10^6 cycles at 30,000 psi for the alloy and 2.6×10^6 cycles at 20,000 psi for columbium. Among the tantalum-base alloys studied for oxidation resistance at 1090°C (2000°F), which show scaling rates 1/10 to 1/7 that of tantalum alone, are 30 Ti, 30 Fe, 10 Cr, 10 Ni, 33 Ti-18 Co, 33 Ti-18 Ni, 20 Cr-12 Ni, and 20 Cr-12 Co, all on an atomic per cent basis.

TABLE 25.18. TENSILE PROPERTIES OF TANTALUM—10% TUNGSTEN SHEET AT DIFFERENT TEMPERATURES[95]

Material: vacuum arc melted alloy sheet 0.060 in. thick

Analysis (in %): C 0.0010, O 0.0045, N 0.0015, Fe 0.0030, Cr <0.0010, Ni 0.0015, Mo <0.0025

(1) Test method: all specimens heated to test temperature within 10 sec and held 30 sec in argon before loading at a nominal strain rate of 0.01 in./in./min (a). Data from Southern Research Institute.

Temperature,		Ultimate strength, 1000 psi	Yield strength (0.2% offset), 1000 psi (a)	Elongation, % in 1 in.	Modulus of elasticity, 10^6 psi (b)
°C	°F				
Room temperature		161.5	160.5	9.0	20.6
816	1500	103.2	97.8	11.0	21.2
1371	2500	22.25	19.85	22.0	17.1
1649	3000	12.1	11.8	33.0	18.5
1927	3500	7.48	7.26	37.0	15.7
2204	4000	4.35	4.30	35.0	11.5
2482	4500	2.06	2.06	30.0(c)	5.0
2760	5000	0.645	0.645	20.0(c)	1.57

(a) strain measured from specimen grips
(b) modulus values are low because of method of measuring strain
(c) melted at fracture point

(2) Test method: short time tensile tests conducted on Marquardt Elevated Temperature Test Machine (Marquardt Corp.) employing strain rates of 0.001 in./in./sec to yield point, and 0.01 in./in./sec to fracture. Specimens heated to test temperature by resistance and held 5 min prior to pulling. Pure argon atmosphere maintained during testing.

Temperature,		Ultimate strength, 1000 psi	Yield strength (0.2% offset), 1000 psi (a)	Elongation, % in 1 in.	Modulus of elasticity, 10^6 psi (b)
°C	°F				
22	72	180.0	164.0	4.0(d)	26.5
982	1800	94.0	80.0	4.2	19.0
1204	2200	67.0	55.0	4.0	14.2
1427	2600	21.0	14.4	17.0	11.0

(a) strain measured from specimen grips
(b) modulus values are low because of method of measuring strain
(c) melted at fracture point
(d) elongation in 2 in.

TABLE 25.19. STRESS-RUPTURE PROPERTIES OF TANTALUM—10% TUNGSTEN ALLOY[95]

Material: cold rolled alloy sheet 0.030 in. thick made from vacuum arc melted ingots

Analysis (in %): O 0.0110, C 0.0015, N 0.0025, Fe 0.0050, Cr <0.0010, Ni 0.0050, Si <0.0025, Ti <0.0010, Mo <0.0025

Test atmosphere: argon

Material	Test Temperature,		Stress, 1000 psi	Time to rupture,	
	°C	°F		min	sec
Pure Ta	1649	3000	4.0	3	6
	1649	3000	2.5	18	37
Ta-10W	1092	2000	60.0	21	discontinued
	1649	3000	15.00	4	35
	1649	3000	12.5	26	15
	1649	3000	10.0	36	14
	2371	4300	5.0	2	13
	2371	4300	4.0	3	50
	2371	4300	3.0	9	14

Tantalum-Tungsten Alloys

One of the most interesting alloy systems that has received considerable attention is the one with tungsten. All compositions in the range up to 30 per cent tungsten have been vacuum arc melted into 3-inch ingots weighing 90 pounds. All can be sawed and machined effectively, and all have forgability in the range of 1482–1927°C (2700–3500°F). Hot hardness rises with increasing tungsten content. According to Torti[95] the Ta-10 per cent W alloy has received most attention. When double vacuum arc melted from good quality powders, it has high cold ductility as cast and hot tensile strengths approaching tungsten in the 1371–2482°C (2500–4500°F) range, i.e., values several times those of pure tantalum and about ⅔ those of tungsten. Ingots 3½ inches in diameter are hammer forged in air at 1093°C (2000°F) to sheet bar, vacuum annealed at 1600°C (2912°F), and cold rolled to sheet as thin as 0.010 inch.

The tensile properties of arc melted Ta-10 per cent W alloy at different temperatures are given in Table 25.18. The stress-rupture prop-

TABLE 25.20. HIGH TEMPERATURE HARDNESS VALUES OF TANTALUM AND TANTALUM-TUNGSTEN ALLOYS[95]

Materials: arc melted metals, as-cast condition
Test method: in vacuum, temperature stabilized 10 min.

Temperature,		Rockwell A Hardness Values			
°C	°F	Ta	Ta-10W	Ta-20W	Ta-30W
Room temperature		47	58	64.5	70
200	392	44	57	63.5	68
400	752	41	55.5	60.5	64
600	1112	37	54	56	61
700	1292	33	—	—	—
800	1472	25	51.5	54.5	58.5
900	1652	10	—	—	—
1000	1832	—	49	54	57.5

TABLE 25.21. PROPERTIES OF TANTALUM-TUNGSTEN ALLOYS
(powder metallurgy metal)[73]

Material: powder metallurgy metal wire
History: 0.1 in. diameter wire (as annealed) at 2600°C (4712°F),
0.009 in. diameter at 99% reduction

Tungsten content,*		Area reduction by cold drawing, %	Ultimate tensile strength, 1000 psi	Elongation, %	Hardness, DPN	Electrical resistivity, microhm-cm	Lattice parameter, Å
weight %	atomic %						
5.2	5.12	A	59	42	150	15.6	3.288
		20	86	12	220		
		80	112	5	270		
		90	125	—	280		
		99	180	—	—		
10.4	10.25	A	83	24	210	17.4	3.282
		20	115	10	290		
		80	142	4	340		
		90	158	3	350		
		99	210	—	—		
26.4	20.2	A	—	—	335	—	3.270

* An alloy containing 1.18 atomic per cent tungsten differed only slightly from the unalloyed tantalum [see Table 25.8, section (8)].

A—annealed ½ hr at 2600°C (4712°F). [Softening begins at 500–700°C (932–1292°F) and is substantially complete at 1600°C (2912°F)].

erties at temperatures above 1650°C (3000°F) are listed in Table 25.19. The hardness values at high temperatures of this alloy, as well as those of the 20 and 30 per cent tungsten alloys and pure tantalum, are given in Table 25.20.

Earlier work by Myers[73] on alloys prepared by powder metallurgy processes is summarized in Table 25.21. This table gives tensile strength and other data on various tantalum-rich Ta-W alloys at room temperature.

Data on electrical resistivity, hardness, and modulus of elasticity for the whole range of Ta-W alloys are listed in Table 25.22. The alloys used for these tests were prepared by sintering compacted powders of the two metals.[12,45,46] The lattice parameters of Ta-W alloys rise smoothly over the whole composition range from that of tungsten to that of tantalum.

TABLE 25.22. PROPERTIES OF TANTALUM-TUNGSTEN ALLOYS[12, 45]

Material: powder metallurgy alloys

Tantalum, atomic %	Electrical resistivity, microhm-cm	Hardness, VHN	Elastic modulus, 10^6 psi
0	6.5	375	58.8
20	10.5	525	46.5
40	22.5	560	42
60	31	525	42
80	27	405	39
100	13.6	120	27.2

(Above values interpolated from smoothed curves)

Tantalum-Molybdenum Alloys. Molybdenum, like tungsten, forms a continuous series of solid solution alloys with tantalum, and because of the high strength and melting point of molybdenum, its alloys with tantalum are of interest. The melting points of the Ta-Mo alloys lie on a smooth curve, without maximum or minimum, as indicated by the data in Table 25.23 for arc melted material; lattice parameters are also included.[26]

TABLE 25.23. MELTING POINTS OF TANTALUM-MOLYBDENUM ALLOYS[26]

Material: arc melted metals

Tantalum, atomic %	Melting point, °C	Melting point, °F	Lattice parameter, Å
0	2620	4748	3.1406
11.2	2630	4766	3.1541
25.2	2700	4892	3.1690
44.1	2760	5000	3.2007
53.8	2810	5090	3.2150
67.5	2850	5162	3.2372
80.0	2880	5216	3.2627
100	3000	5432	3.2973

Working with powder metallurgy products, Myers[73] has determined the physical and mechanical properties listed in Table 25.24. It will be noted that for the 5.2 per cent molybdenum alloy the tensile properties are quite similar to those of the 5.2 per cent tungsten alloy, also studied by Myers.

TABLE 25.24. PROPERTIES OF TANTALUM-MOLYBDENUM ALLOYS[73]

Material: powder metallurgy metal wire
History: ¼ in. bar alternately swaged and sintered at 2600°C (4712°F) to 0.1 in. diameter wire, reduced to 0.009 in. diameter at 99% reduction. [A = annealed ½ hr at 2600°C (4712°F)].

Molybdenum content,* weight %	Molybdenum content,* atomic %	Area reduction by cold drawing, %	Ultimate tensile strength, 1000 psi	Elongation, %	Hardness, DPN	Electrical resistivity, microhm-cm	Lattice parameter, Å
2.2	4.2	A	56	43	140	16.8	3.288
		20	80	13	210	—	—
		80	105	4	255	—	—
		90	120	—	270	—	—
		99	172	—	—	—	—
5.2	9.6	A	80	25	200	20	3.278
		20	110	10	275	—	—
		80	130	10	330	—	—
		90	147	2	335	—	—
		99	185	—	—	—	—
11.2	19.7	A	—	—	330	—	3.260

* An alloy of 0.78 atomic % Mo differed only slightly from pure tantalum

Fabrication

Mill forms of tantalum include plate, sheet, foil, rod, wire, and small diameter seamless tubing.

Tantalum has a strong tendency to seize, tear, and gall, somewhat like stainless steel, and this property must be considered in forming operations. Further, tantalum must be worked cold because of its reactivity with the common gases when heated; however, its high ductility and slow rate of work hardening permit all sorts of successful cold working.

Reductions of 60 per cent or more between vacuum anneals are standard practice. Heavy passes are used in the initial breakdown rolling of bars and ingots, and later rolling operations are usually kept at about 10 per cent reduction in thickness per pass. Sheet rolling is done with standard equipment such as 2-high and 4-high mills. The latter can produce sheet as thin as 0.002 inch. Pack rolling can also be used to make thinner sheets. Foil, such as that used in tantalum capacitors (less than 0.001 inch thick), is usually made in Sendzimir mills. Figure 25.20 shows rolling equipment used to make tantalum sheets.

The sheet size of tantalum is controlled by ingot size, mill size, and vacuum annealing furnace dimensions.

Rod and Wire. Rods can be formed cold by rod rolling and swaging. Standard equipment is used for wire drawing, but tools and guides are usually made of aluminum bronze, and dies are hard metal for sizes above 0.02 inch in diameter and diamond for smaller diameters. Beeswax is a suitable lubricant and a thin oxide coating on the tantalum (obtained by an anodizing operation) assists in holding the lubricant on the surface. Myers[72] recommends a hot aqueous solution of 5 per cent soft soap and 5 per cent tallow as a lubricant.

After annealing, tantalum wire is extremely ductile and can be bent 180° cold with practically zero radius of bend. It can be wound on a mandrel with a diameter equal to that of the wire. Screen and gauze can be woven from the wire by conventional methods.

Forming and Stamping. Tantalum allows blanking, punching, shearing, spinning, slitting, crimping, bending, and deep drawing to be done cold. Aluminum bronze dies and tools are preferred, although steel dies can be used if slippage is not too great. Rubber or pneumatic die cushions are used where required.

When punching or blanking tantalum, a clearance of about 6 per cent of the metal thickness should be maintained. A light oil or carbon tetrachloride is used to prevent scoring of dies. However, the toxicity of CCl_4 is such that it is much more advisable to use trichloroethane, which avoids this hazard.

In spinning operations aluminum bronze tools are recommended, with yellow soap or tallow

Figure 25.20. Rolling mill used to make large tantalum sheets.
(*Haynes Stellite Co.*)

as a lubricant. Peripheral speeds of 300 feet per minute are used with several light strokes rather than a few heavy ones.

Annealed sheet can be deep-drawn. If the drawn piece is to be made in one operation the depth of the draw can be equal to the diameter. If more than one drawing step is required the first draw should be about 40 to 50 per cent of the diameter in depth. A greater amount of reduction is possible with thicker than with thinner sheet.

Aluminum bronze dies should be used, but the punch may be of steel if slippage is not excess. Sulfonated tallow or drawing waxes are suggested as lubricants.

Seamless tubing is made by first drawing a deep small diameter cup. After the closed end has been cut off, this tube is drawn through dies of successively smaller size while a floating mandrel maintains the desired inner diameter. The dimensions of seamless tubing are limited by the volume of metal in the original disk used to make the initial cup. For this reason longer lengths of tubing are made by butt welding thick sheet longitudinally into a cylinder using inert gas arc welding. This cylinder is then drawn to the final desired dimensions. If the weld is made correctly, the final tubing will be equivalent of seamless tubing in quality. Intermediate anneals are made after approximately each 60 per cent reduction.

Tubing made from arc melted or electron beam melted metal is better than tubing made from powder metallurgy metal because of variations in porosity and density in the latter which tend to cause variations in the wall thickness when drawn.

Machining. Tantalum can be machined about as readily as copper or stainless steel if high speed steel tools with high cutting speeds and plenty of lubricant and coolant are used. Carbon tetrachloride is suitable, but trichloroethane is preferred because of the toxicity hazards of CCl_4.

In lathe operations tools must be kept sharp and should be ground with as much positive rake as possible. Rakes and angles similar to those used with soft copper are usually satisfactory. Surface speeds of 60 to 100 feet per minute are suggested, and heavy cuts with lighter feeds are better than the usual roughing and finishing cuts.

When milling, drilling, threading, and tapping tantalum, the same general procedures should be followed. Milling cutters of the staggered tooth type with a generous rake and clearance angle should be used. Screws can be made by thread rolling fully annealed rod; when threading larger diameters it is preferable to cut the threads on a lathe than to use a threading die. Drilling can be done with standard high speed steel drills the points of which are relieved to avoid rubbing the work. Drilling particles must be removed frequently and the drills resharpened often. Chips should also be cleaned frequently when dies and taps are used.

Grinding is not practical, partly because of the heavy loading of the wheel and the imbedding of abrasive particles into the tantalum surface. Polishing with fine emery paper or cloth is possible when these are kept flooded with CCl_4 or trichloroethane.

Annealing. Tantalum is annealed by heating in a vacuum of 10^{-5} mm Hg or less at 1300–1400°C (2372–2552°F) for 1 hour.

Cleaning. The inertness of tantalum to acids (except HF) permits it to be cleaned by immersion in hot hydrochloric acid, aqua regia, or sulfuric-chromic acid. Thorough washing in distilled water is essential after acid cleaning. CCl_4 or trichloroethane can be used for degreasing.

Welding. The high melting point and great reactivity of tantalum at elevated temperatures entail the use of special techniques for welding operations. Inert gas arc welding is the best method for obtaining welds of satisfactory properties, and is the same type applied to other high melting reactive metals such as titanium and zirconium. In fact, with very little change the equipment and techniques used for these metals can be used for tantalum welding.

Primary interest is in welding the thin sheet metal from which most fabricated products are made. Sheet ranging from 0.001 to 0.080 inch thick can be satisfactorily welded by use of tungsten electrodes whereby the parent metal is fused to make the joint. For thinner sheets, below about 0.020 inch, a folded or crimped mechanical joint is formed which extends about 1/16 inch out from the edges of the sheet. This is fused down to a bead. For thicknesses above about 0.020 inch, a butt joint can be made by fusing the edges of two mechanically formed mating sheets. The tightness of the mechanical joints is important for making good welds in both cases. Of extreme importance is the careful cleaning with CCl$_4$ of the surfaces to be joined.

The vital protective atmosphere of purified helium or argon must be present on both sides of the metal being welded. This can be provided by use of a purge chamber surrounding the work site through which the gas flows, or by use of a dry box which can be evacuated to a high vacuum and subsequently back-filled with inert gas. The material and the welding electrode are manipulated by use of gas-tight rubber gloves fitted through the sides of the chamber.

Figure 25.21 shows such a dry box chamber used for fabricating tantalum chemical equipment. Figure 25.22 is a view of the interior (from an opened end door) to illustrate the welding setup used for a tantalum vessel. The Heliarc welding gun is in the hands of the workman on the right. Inert gas flows out of the tools around the tungsten electrode tip. This gas flow can be used to cool the completed weld.

Although provisions can be made in both types of chambers for machine movement of the work or the electrode, in most cases manipulation is by hand.

While many factors affect exact welding conditions, the following pertinent conditions have been developed by workers at the Institute for Atomic Research, Ames, Iowa to obtain welds as good as or better than those produced in factory-fabricated material prior to 1958.[15,22,23,76] Using a 110-volt DC source with variable resistance in series to control current and stabilize the arc, 5 amperes are used for 0.003 inch *total* metal thickness to be fused, 8 amperes for 0.006 inch, 10 amperes for 0.009 inch, 14 amperes for 0.015 inch, and 50 to 60 amperes for 0.060 inch. These data are for a helium atmosphere. Using 40-volt open circuit, which drops to 20-volt closed circuit, straight polarity DC, 70 to 75 amperes are used for making a butt joint weld with 0.020 inch tantalum in argon. After the current is started by a foot switch with the tungsten electrode in contact with the work, the electrode is backed off a fraction of an inch to start the arc. One pass along the joint is used to fuse the metal, and a second quick pass removes any bubbles from the bead. After the arc is broken the torch is moved rapidly across the welded surface to cool the joint. Tantalum has a high surface tension, thus the tungsten electrode must have a sharp point to prevent wandering of the arc.

Figure 25.21. Exterior view of inert gas, tungsten electrode welding chamber used to weld tantalum equipment components. (*The Pfaudler Co., a division of Pfaudler Permutit Inc., Rochester, N.Y.*)

Figure 25.22. Interior view of inert gas welding chamber showing the welding of head and straight side of tantalum liner for 30-gallon reactor. (*The Pfaudler Co., a division of Pfaudler Permutit Co., Rochester, N. Y.*)

A welding current from a G.E. selenium-rectified 300-ampere DC welder is used. The work is negative (ground) and the torch is the positive electrode.

Most tantalum welds are made with no filler rod, but it is feasible to use tantalum wire or rod as the filler, either as a consumable electrode or fed from the side into the arc from the tungsten electrode.

Powder metallurgy tantalum, when welded by the arc method, frequently exhibits porosity in or near the weld, but arc melted tantalum does not.[36]

The weld bead and an area immediately adjacent to the weld become recrystallized during welding. Welds properly made under inert atmosphere in the absence of contaminating materials will not be otherwise affected. If the rest of the work has been work hardened by previous fabrication operations it will have a higher tensile strength than the recrystallized areas. Annealing subsequent to welding will bring all the tantalum to the same recrystallized state.

Resistance welding can be done under water to give essentially a continuous spot weld between the faying surfaces of two flat areas of tantalum. The two surfaces are held together by shaped tools, a current is passed between the tools through the tantalum while pressure is applied, and the tantalum at the interface (where the resistance is greatest) is heated and welded. Lap welded tubing can be made by this process, but the presence of a double thickness overlap area the length of the tube limits the use of such tubing in chemical equipment design.

Carbon arc welding, done while the weld site is submerged in CCl_4, has long been practiced in the fabrication of chemical equipment. Carbon introduced into the weld metal or adjoining areas causes embrittlement, making the weld unsound.[36] This has been responsible for many failures of tantalum equipment in industrial use. Tungsten arc inert atmosphere welding does not have this disadvantage, and welds made by it are far superior to the carbon arc welds made under CCl_4.

Electronic welding, conducted by focusing a beam of high velocity electrons on the weld site in a high vacuum, works admirably upon tantalum. Its use will undoubtedly increase in the future as more electronic welding equipment becomes available.

Ultrasonic welding is effective upon tantalum in thin sheet form. The absence of a fused state during the operation eliminates contamination and recrystallization.

In addition to welding to itself, tantalum can be welded to the metals with which it forms alloys, i.e., iron, steel, nickel, zirconium, titanium, columbium, molybdenum, tungsten, etc.

Applications

Applications of tantalum are based upon its high melting point, good strength and ductility, low vapor pressure, inertness to chemical attack at temperatures below about 150°C (302°F), gettering properties at elevated temperatures, and rectifying and dielectric properties of its oxide surface film.

Capacitors. At present the largest use of tantalum is in electrolytic capacitors. A tantalum electrolytic capacitor has four components: the tantalum anode, the tantalum oxide dielectric surface, the electrolyte which acts as the cathode, and the container or coating in contact with the electrolyte and chemically inert to it. The tantalum anode may be foil, wire, or powder sintered to produce strength without unduly decreasing porosity. The latter gives the highest surface area per unit volume (1000 to 2000 cm^2/cc) and thus the greatest capacitance per unit volume. The tantalum oxide dielectric is "formed" by anodic oxidation of the surface of the tantalum anode and is the heart of the capacitor.[92] The electrolyte is either liquid (solutions of sulfuric or phosphoric acid) or solid (semiconductors such as the higher oxides of Mn, Pb or Ni).[57,58,92,101]

Tantalum capacitors of the solid electrolyte type have the highest capacitance per unit volume of any capacitor, and their small size makes them very attractive for use in transistor circuits and other low voltage circuits requiring the ultimate in miniaturization.[92] They operate satisfactorily over a range of −80 to 180°C (−112 to 176°F), and have very low leakage properties. Porous-type tantalum capacitors with a liquid electrolyte are made with an operating range of −60 to 200°C (−76 to 392°F).[69] All types have a stable shelf life and a long service life.

Chemical Equipment. Fabrication of corrosion-resistant chemical equipment is perhaps the second largest application of tantalum. In addition to being strong and essentially inert to attack by nonalkaline highly corrosive media at ordinary temperatures (with the exception of F_2, HF, and free SO_3), tantalum is characterized by extremely high heat transfer coefficients. The latter is due to the thin wall of construction which can be used in equipment in the absence of corrosion, lack of a corrosion product scale on the surface, bubble-type vapor formation on the surface when heating most liquids, and dropwise condensate formation on the steam or condensing side in heat transfer operation. Of all the metals tantalum is the most like glass in corrosion resistance and is often used in conjunction with glass, glass-lined steel, and other nonmetallic materials of construction in chemical equipment.

Typical tantalum equipment items long used in the chemical industry are heat exchangers, bayonet heaters, condensers, U-coils, spiral coils, thermometer wells, dip pipes, orifices, and other miscellaneous items. Tantalum is used extensively in the repair of flaws and damage in glass-lined equipment.

Tantalum equipment is widely used for sulfuric acid concentrators, heaters and coolers for chromium plating baths, hydrogen peroxide concentrators, hydrochloric acid production and distillation, bromine heaters and stills, nitric acid heating and concentration, as well as in the production of fine chemicals and pharmaceuticals.[32,33,90] Because of its inertness tantalum does not contaminate the products exposed to it.

With the recent introduction of large size sheets (about 30 x 72 x 0.030 inch thick) made from arc melted metal and improved inert gas arc welding techniques for use on thin wall metal (0.012 to 0.015 inch), the use of tantalum as a liner for reactors, vessels, and towers has become feasible. The same factors have also resulted in the improved design and stability of tantalum bayonet heaters, heat exchangers, U-coils, condensers, etc. by elimination of lap-welded tubing and carbon arc welds. The larger sheets have reduced the number of welds needed for a given surface area. Reactors of several hundred gallons capacity have recently been lined with tantalum.

Tantalum is used to construct equipment for the preparation and handling of molten metals, such as the rare earth metals, and alloys containing fissionable materials, at elevated temperatures. For these uses tantalum must be protected from exposure to the atmosphere.[21,22,23]

Electronic Applications. Tantalum is used to form many components of vacuum tubes. Easily formed and welded into the desired shapes, tantalum can be cleaned thoroughly in strong, hot acids; has a high melting point, high temperature strength, and low vapor pressure; and acts as a good getter. Further, tantalum components, such as anodes and grids, can be outgassed at above 2000°C (3632°F) during the processing of the tubes.

A 92.5 tantalum–7.5 tungsten alloy has been applied in certain vacuum tubes as filament springs which retain elasticity at elevated temperatures. Tantalum-nickel alloys containing up to 30 per cent tantalum have also been used in vacuum tubes.

Rectifiers. The dielectric oxide film on tantalum makes the metal useful as a rectifier. This was one of its early uses, and many types of tantalum rectifiers are still made for use in battery chargers, signal devices, etc., wherein AC current is converted to DC current.

Surgical

The complete immunity of tantalum to body fluids and its non-irritating tolerance by body tissues have resulted in its wide use for surgical repairs. It is applied as plate and sheet in bone repair (especially in cranial sites), as wire for sutures, as foil and wire for nerve repair, and as plate, sheet, and woven gauze for abdominal muscle repair. A recent development involves covering the site of an excised brain tumor with tantalum powder, before the skull is closed. Here it serves as a focusing aid in subsequent x-ray examination and treatment, and the relative area of it as time passes indicates whether the tumor has been arrested or whether it is again growing.

Nuclear Energy Systems

While tantalum's thermal neutron absorption cross section is too high to permit it to be used in or near the core of most types of atomic reactors, it can be used in fast neutron reactors. However, it is of most interest for handling high temperature liquid metals, such as sodium or NaK, in heat transfer equipment, and in containing liquid metal systems such as the bismuth-uranium alloy.[22, 23]

Miscellaneous

Tantalum is used as components in high temperature furnaces operated under vacuum or in an inert gas atmosphere. Tantalum oxide is used as an ingredient in some kinds of high refractive index optical glasses. Tantalum carbide is present in many types of tungsten carbide cutting tools where it imparts shock resistance and a very low coefficient of friction.

References

1. Albrecht, W. M., Klopp, W. D., Koehl, B. G., and Jaffee, R. I., "Reaction of Pure Tantalum with Air, Nitrogen, and Oxygen," paper presented at AIME Meeting, Chicago, Nov. 2, 1959, to be published in *Transactions of the Metallurgical Society, AIME.*
2. Allen, N. P., and Carrington, W. E., *J. Appl. Phys.,* **82**, 525 (1952–1954).
3. American Institute of Physics, "Temperature, Its Measurement and Control in Science and Industry," p. 1309, New York, Reinhold Publishing Corporation, 1941.
4. Andrews, M. R., *J. Am. Chem. Soc.,* **54**, 1845–54 (1932).
5. Badger, F. S., personal communication, 1959; *Ind. Eng. Chem.,* **50**, 1608–1611 (1958); *Union Carbide Metals Review,* 18–21 (Winter/1960).
6. Backish, R., *J. Electrochem. Soc.,* **105**, 574–577 (1958).
7. Balke, C. W., U.S. Patent 1,754,453 (1929).
8. Balke, C. W., *Trans. Electrochem. Soc.,* **85**, 89–95 (1944).
9. Bechtold, J. H., *Acta Met.,* **3**, (3) 249 (1955).
10. Bornemann, A., and Gela, T., "Studies in the Behavior of Certain Non-ferrous Metals at Low Temperatures," **PB-111657**, Washington, U.S. Dept. Commerce (OTS), 1953.
11. Bridgman, P. W., *Proc. Am. Acad. Arts Sci.,* **77**, 187 (1949).
12. Braun, H., Kieffer, R., and Sedlatschek, K., "Beitrag Zur Technologie der Tantal-Wolfram-Legierungen," *Third Plansee Seminar Proceedings 1958,* pp. 264–276, New York, Pergammon Press, Inc., 1959.
13. Candidus, E. S., and Simons, J. C., Jr., "An Electron Bombardment Furnace for the Production of Vacuum Melted Metals," paper presented at Fifth National Symposium, American Vacuum Society, San Francisco, Oct. 22–24, 1958.
14. Chilton, C. H., *Chem. Eng.,* **65**, (22), 104–7 (Nov. 3, 1958; includes flow sheet).
15. Daane, A. H., *Rev. Sci. Instruments,* **23**, 245 (1952).

16. Driggs, F. H., U.S. Patent 1,815,054 (1931).
17. Driggs, F. H., and Lilliendahl, W. C., *Ind. Eng. Chem.*, **23**, 634 (1931).
18. Edwards, J. W., Speiser, R., and Johnston, H. L., *J. Appl. Phys.*, **22**, 424 (1951).
18a. Edwards, J. W., Johnston, H. L., and Blackburn, P. E., *J. Am. Chem. Soc.*, **74**, 172 (1951).
19. Espe, W., and Knoll, M., "Werkstoffkunde der Hochvakuumtechnik," Berlin, J. Springer, 1956.
20. Farber, M., Darnell, A. J., and Ehrenberg, D. M., *J. Electrochem. Soc.*, **102**, 446–53 (1955).
20a. Fieldhouse, I. B., Hedge, J. C., and Waterman, T. E., *WADC Tech. Report 55–495* (1956).
21. Fisher, R. W., and Fullhart, C. B., *U.S. Atomic Energy Commission Report, ISC–1039* (1958).
22. Fisher, R. W., and Fullhart, C. B., "Feasibility Studies on Molten Metal Reactor Components," *2nd United Nations International Conference on the Peaceful Uses of Atomic Energy, UN 1032,* Geneva, 1958.
23. Fisher, R. W., and Winders, G. R., "High Temperature Loop for Circulating Liquid Metals," *Chemical Engineering Progress Symposium Series,* (20), **53** (1957).
24. Foos, R. A., and Wilhelm, H. A., *U.S. Atomic Energy Commission Report, ISC–644,* 71 pp., 1954.
25. Friedrich, H. J., "Concerning the Production of Tantalum Metal," thesis, Technischen Hochschule, Hanover, 1955.
26. Geach, G. A., and Summers-Smith, D., *J. Inst. Metals,* **80**, 143 (1951–1952).
27. Gebhardt, E., and Preisendanz, H., *Z. Metallkunde,* **46**, 560 (1955).
28. Gebhardt, E., and Seghezzi, H. D., *Z. Metallkunde,* **48**, 430–435 (1957).
29. Gebhardt, E., and Seghezzi, H. D., *Z. Metallkunde,* **50**, 248–257, 521–527 (1959).
30. Gegner, P. J., Columbia-Southern Chemical Corp., personal communication, 1959.
31. Glasier, L. F., Jr., Allen, R. D., and Saldinger, I. L., "Mechanical and Physical Properties of the Refractory Metals, Tungsten, Tantalum and Molybdenum, above 4000°F," *Report No. M1826,* Aerojet-General Corp., Azusa, California (April, 1959).
31a. Goldsmith, A., Waterman, T. E., and Hirschhorn, H. J., *WADC Tech. Report 58–476* (1960).
32. Hampel, C. A., *Ind. Eng. Chem.,* **48**, 1979–1981 (1956).
33. Hampel, C. A., *Corrosion,* **14**, 557t–560t (1958).
34. Hansen, M., "Constitution of Binary Alloys," 2nd Ed., New York, McGraw-Hill Book Company, 1958.
35. Harrison, A. D. R., thesis, London University, 1950.
36. Haslip, L. R., and Payne, B. S., *Welding J. (N.Y.),* **38**, 1–10 (Dec. 1959).
37. Hatchett, C., *Phil. Trans. Roy. Soc. London,* Series A, **92**, 49–66 (1802).
38. Hidnert, P., *J. Research Nat. Bur. Standards,* **2**, 887 (1929).
39. Higbie, K. B., and Werning, J. R., *Bur. Mines Rept. of Investigation 5239,* 49 pp., 1956.
40. Hodge, W., Evans, R. M., and Hoskins, A. F., *J. Metals,* **7**, 824 (1955).
41. Holden, F. C., Schwartzberg, F. R., and Jaffee, R. I., "High Temperature Mechanical Properties of Tantalum," paper presented at ASTM Meeting, San Francisco, October, 1959; "Symposium on Newer Metals," *ASTM Spec. Tech. Publ. No. 272,* 1960.
42. Humphrey, G. L., *J. Am. Chem. Soc.,* **76**, 978 (1954).
43. Kaplan, N., and Andrus, R. J., *Ind. Eng. Chem.,* **40**, 1946 (1948).
44. Kieffer, R., and Benesovsky, F., *Planseeber. Pulvermetall.,* **5**, 56 (1957).
45. Kieffer, R., Sedlatschek, K., and Braun, H., *J. Less-Common Metals,* **1**, 19–33 (1959).
46. Kieffer, R., Sedlatschek, K., and Braun, H., *Z. Metallkunde,* **50**, (1), 18–24 (1959).
47. Klopp, W. D., Maykuth, D. J., Ogden, H. R., and Jaffee, R. I., "Purification Reactions of Tantalum During Vacuum Sintering," paper presented at AIME Meeting, Chicago, Nov. 2, 1959.
48. Klopp, W. D., Schwartzberg, F. R., Holden, F. C., Sims, C. T., Ogden, H. R., and Jaffee, R. I., *WADC Tech. Report 58–525* (1958).
49. Koc, S., *Czechoslov. J. Phys.,* **4**, 250 (1954).
50. Koerner, E. L., Jr., Smutz, M., and Wilhelm, H. A., *Chem. Eng. Progr.,* **54**, (9), 63–70 (1958).
51. Koster, W., *Z. Metallkunde,* **39**, 1–9 (1948).
52. Koster, W., *Appl. Sci. Research,* **A4**, 329 (1954).
53. Kriessman, C. J., Jr., *Rev. Mod. Phys.,* **25**, 122–126 (1953).
54. Lapotskii, A. V., Simanov, Y. P., and Artamonova, E. D., *Zhur. Neorg. Khim.,* **2**, 80 (1957).
55. Malter, L., and Langmuir, D. B., *Phys. Rev.,* **55**, (8), 743 (1939).
56. Marignac, J. C., *Ann. chim. phys.,* **8**, 5 (1866); *ibid.,* **9**, 249 (1866).
57. Martin, G. L., Fincham, C. J. B., and Chadsey, E. E., Jr., *J. Electrochem. Soc.,* **107**, 332–337 (1960).

58. McLean, D. A., and Power, F. S., *Proc. I.R.E.*, **44**, 872 (1956).
59. "Metals Handbook," Cleveland, American Society for Metals, 1948 (new edition now in preparation).
60. Michael, A. B., "Oxidation of Columbium-Base and Tantalum-Base Alloys," paper presented at Regional AIME Conference on Reactive Metals, Buffalo, 1958; see also Miller[61], pp. 510–511, 529–531.
61. Miller, G. L., "Tantalum and Niobium," pp. 67–178, New York, Academic Press, Inc., 1959.
62. *Ibid.*, pp. 179–243.
63. *Ibid.*, p. 422 (personal communication from O. P. Hartree, Associated Electrical Industries, Ltd.).
64. *Ibid.*, pp. 433–438.
65. *Ibid.*, pp. 486–499.
66. *Ibid.*, pp. 466–474.
67. *Ibid.*, pp. 445–457.
68. *Ibid.*, pp. 510–533.
69. *Ibid.*, pp. 45–59.
69a. Miller, J. F., Reid, F. J., and Himes, R. C., *J. Electrochem. Soc.*, **106**, 1043–46 (1959).
70. Morgan, F. H., and Danforth, W. E., *J. Appl. Phys.*, **21**, 112 (1950).
71. Myers, R. H., *Proc. Aust. Inst. Min. Eng.*, **144**, 297 (1946).
72. Myers, R. H., *Metallurgia*, **42**, 3 (June 1950).
73. Myers, R. H., *Metallurgia*, **39**, 7–10 (1948).
74. National Research Corp., *Chem. Week*, **83**, (3), 97–102 (July 19, 1958).
75. O'Driscoll, W. G., Tyzack, C., and Raine, T., "The Oxidation of Groups IVA, VA, and VIA Elements in Carbon Dioxide and the Development of Oxidation Resistant Zirconium Alloys," *2nd United Nations International Conference on the Peaceful Uses of Atomic Energy*, Geneva, 1958.
76. Peterson, D., Fisher, R. W., Dennison, D. H., and Daane, A. H., personal communications, 1958.
77. Placek, C., and Taylor, D. F., *Ind. Eng. Chem.*, **48**, 686–695 (1956).
78. Preston, J. B., Roe, W. P., and Kattus, J. R., *WADC Tech. Report 57–649, Part 1* (1958).
79. Pugh, J. W., *Trans. Am. Soc. Metals*, **48**, 677–688 (1956).
80. Pugh, J. W., and Hibbard, W. R., Jr., *Trans. Am. Soc. Metals*, **48**, 526 (1956).
80a. Rasor, N. S., and McClelland, J. D., *WADC Tech. Report 56–400* (1957).
81. Richardson, D., "Spectroscopy in Science and Industry, Proceedings of the Fifth Summer Conference on Spectroscopy and Its Applications," pp. 64–70, New York, John Wiley & Sons, Inc. (1938).
82. Rose, H., *Pogg. Ann. Physik. Chem.*, **63**, 317–341 (1844).
83. Rosenberg, H. M., *Phil. Trans.*, **A247**, 441 (1954–1955).
84. Seghezzi, H. D., "New Investigations into the Tantalum-Nitrogen System," *3rd Plansee Seminar*, Reutte, Austria, 1958.
85. Seraphim, D. P., Budnick, J. I., and Ittner, W. B., III, *Trans. Metallurgy Soc. of AIME*, **218**, 527–533 (1960).
86. Shelton, H., *Phys. Rev.*, **107**, (6), 1553–1557 (Sept. 15, 1957).
87. Smith, J. L., *Am. J. Sci.*, [3], **13**, No. 77 (May, 1877).
88. Smithells, C. J., "Metals Reference Book," Vol. II, London, Butterworths Scientific Publication, 1955.
89. Stull, D. R., and Sinke, G. C., "Thermodynamic Properties of the Metals," Washington, American Chemical Society, 1956.
90. Taylor, D. F., "Tantalum: Its Resistance to Corrosion," paper presented before Electrochemical Society (Chicago Section), May 4, 1956 (see also Reference 33).
91. Taylor, D. F., *Chem. Eng. Progr.*, **54**, (4), 47–50 (1958).
92. Taylor, R. L., and Haring, H. E., *J. Electrochem. Soc.*, **103**, 611–613 (1956).
93. Tingley, I. I., Department of Mines and Technical Surveys, Mines Branch, Ottawa, Canada, personal communication, 1959.
94. Titterington, R., and Simpson, A. G., *Iron & Steel Inst. Spec. Rep. No. 58* (1954).
95. Torti, M. L., personal communication giving National Research Corporation data of 1958–1959.
96. Torti, M. L., *J. Electrochem. Soc.*, **107**, 33–35 (1960).
97. Tseitlin, K. L., *Zhur. Proklad. Khim.*, **29**, 1281 (1956).
98. Werning, J. R., and Higbie, K. B., *Ind. Eng. Chem.*, **46**, 2491–2494 (1954).
99. Werning, J. R., Higbie, K. B., Grace, J. T., Speece, B. F., and Gilbert, H. L., *ibid.*, **46**, 644–652 (1954).
100. Whitehead, M., *Bell Labs. Record*, **28**, 448 (1950).
101. Wilhelm, H. A., and Kerrigan, J. V., *U.S. Atomic Energy Commission Report, ISC-220* (1952).
102. Winsch, I. O., and Burris, L., Jr., *Chem. Eng. Progr.*, **53**, (5), 237–242 (1957).
103. Yih, Stephan, Wah Chang Corp., personal communication, 1958; Carlson, C. W., and Nielson, R. H., *J. Metals*, **12**, (6), 472–475 (1960).

26. TELLURIUM

JOHN R. STONE and PETER E. CARBON*

American Smelting and Refining Company
New York, New York

INTRODUCTION

The interest in the metalloid tellurium has increased manyfold since the first edition of "Rare Metals Handbook" appeared. High-purity tellurium as a semiconductor is an important element in the thermoelectric devices now undergoing rapid development.

Tellurium was discovered by Muller von Richenstein in 1782 and was named by M. H. Klaproth in 1798 after the Latin word *tellus,* meaning earth. Present-day information lists tellurium as being about half as abundant as gold, with which it often occurs. Thus tellurium ranks about seventy-fifth in abundance in the crust of the earth, at a ratio of 0.002 part in a million parts of earth.

OCCURRENCE

Tellurium rarely occurs in the elemental state but usually is found as a telluride, especially as gold telluride.

The tellurides of gold are:[20,27]

calaverite	$AuTe_2$
sylvanite	$(Au,Ag)Te_2$
krennerite	$AuTe_2$
petzite	Ag_3AuTe_2
nagyagite†	$Au_2Pb_{10}Sb_2Te_6S$,

also given as $Pb_5(AuSb)_4S_5$ to $_8$.

The bismuth mineral is tetradymite [Bi_2Te_2S or $BiTeS$ or $Bi_2(TeS)_3$].

The tellurides of gold and silver are found in

* Revised by M. F. Perkins and Peter E. Caron.

† This leady mineral conveys tellurium to smelters operated to win lead.

Transylvania, Hungary, Mexico, New Zealand, Western Australia, and in the states of Colorado, California, North Carolina, and Virginia. A small town in San Miguel County, Colorado, is named Telluride. The mineral calaverite was named after Calaveras County of central California.

Although the most commercially important gold ores are the sulfides of gold, copper, arsenic, and antimony, the tellurides of gold are almost as important.

The foregoing facts indicate the strong affinity of tellurium for gold, silver, and copper and show why tellurium is a by-product from the metallurgy of copper. The tellurium-gold affinity is so strong that the fire-assay methods for analysis of gold ores must be drastically modified when more than trace amounts of tellurium are present.[4]

In North America the bulk of the tellurium is recovered from the copper and the lead refineries of the following companies:

American Metal Climax Co.
American Smelting and Refining Co.
Anaconda Co.
Canadian Copper Refineries, Ltd.
International Nickel Co.
United States Smelting, Refining and Mining Co.

DERIVATION

Tellurium is recovered from the anode mud or slimes produced during the electrolytic refining of impure copper, often called blister copper. Since tellurium is substantially insoluble in the electrolyte, it accompanies the other insoluble materials—including gold, silver, and the platinum metals—that fall from the dissolving anode to the bottom of the tank. Next in the slagging operations that concentrate the gold, silver, and platinum metals into an alloy or bullion, called *doré*, the tellurium and selenium are collected in the slags as sodium compounds.

When the slags are removed from the doré furnace, cooled, and dissolved in water, very little of the tellurium or selenium remains in the insoluble residue. The strongly alkaline solution is carefully neutralized with acid, usually sulfuric, to precipitate the tellurium. Local excesses of acid must absolutely be avoided to prevent any unwanted precipitation of selenium.

The precipitate of basic tellurium dioxide is allowed to settle and then is collected in a filter press. In some cases the well-washed and dried filter cake can be marketed directly. If excessive or objectionable impurities are in the filter cake, the cake must be dissolved, the solution purified if necessary, and the basic tellurium dioxide again carefully precipitated, filtered, washed, and dried.

Reduction of tellurium dioxide to metal is accomplished by heating with finely divided carbon. The liquid tellurium is cast as cakes or as stick for the market.

An electrolytic process for the conversion of impure tellurium dioxide into metal of good quality is described in U.S. Patent No. 2,258,963, issued in October, 1941. The electrolyte is an aqueous solution of tellurium in sodium hydroxide, and the tellurium is deposited on a cathode from which it can be stripped for subsequent melting and casting.

CONSUMPTION AND PRICES

Tellurium is presently being produced in the United States and Canada by six companies. In the past more tellurium was recovered than marketed, yielding a reserve stock as of January 1, 1960 among the producers totaling approximately 800,000 pounds of recoverable tellurium in crude form, and approximately 100,000 pounds as refined material.

Sales of tellurium in the United States as reported by the U.S. Bureau of Mines during the period 1954 through 1958 were between 100,000 and 170,000 pounds annually. Sales estimated by the U.S. Bureau of Mines for the year 1959 were in the neighborhood of 350,000 pounds.

During the last two years the demand for tellurium has materially increased and it is safe to assume that producers are able to dispose of their entire current intake in the form of refined metal. By improving recovery systems it is felt that the recovery of tellurium in both the lead and copper circuits can be increased to provide a maximum production in this hemisphere of between 500,000 and 750,000 pounds per year. However, forecasts of demand over the next few years indicate that there might not be enough tellurium available as by-products from copper and lead refining to satisfy the requirements of industry.

For many years commercial grade tellurium 99.5 per cent minimum in powder or ingot form was quoted in the trade journals at between $1.50 and $1.65 per pound. Price increases in May and July of 1959 and January and August of 1960 have brought the price up to $4.00 per pound.

In order to provide sufficient incentive for producers to increase recoveries, a higher price for tellurium will undoubtedly be necessary. One domestic producer, American Smelting and Refining Company, also has available on a commercial basis 99.99 per cent and 99.999 per cent tellurium in polycrystalline form.

PHYSICAL PROPERTIES[8,17,5,12]

Tellurium, atomic number 52, is a member of Group VI of the periodic arrangements of elements. Tellurium is more metallic than sulfur and selenium.

The atomic weight of tellurium was listed in 1916 as 127.5. In 1925 it was still listed as 127.5, but in 1956 the weight was placed at 127.61.

The isotopes of tellurium as of 1953 were listed at 20 in number. Isotopes 118 through 135 are quite definitely identified. Isotopes 117 and 137 are not completely established. The abundances of the tellurium isotopes 128 at 31.75 per cent and 130 at 34.27 per cent are sufficient to place the heavier tellurium of atomic number 52 before iodine of atomic number 53, despite the lower atomic weight of 126.91 for iodine.[14]

TABLE 26.1. PROPERTIES OF THE OXYGEN-TELLURIUM FAMILY[2, 12, 8]

	Oxygen	Sulfur	Selenium	Tellurium
Atomic weight (1956)	16.000	32.066	78.96	127.61
Specific gravity (solid)	1.426	Monoclinic 1.96	Vitreous 4.28	6.25
		Yellow amorphous 1.92	Hexagonal 4.79	
Temperature of sp gr value,				
°C	−252.5	20	20	20
°F	−422.5	68	68	68
Color	Blue	Yellow	Dark red, gray, metallic	Silver
Melting point,			Hexagonal	
°C	−218.4	119.25	217	449.5 ± 0.3
°F	−361.1	246.6	422.6	841.1 ± 0.54
Boiling point,				
°C	−182.96	444.6	684.9 ± 1.0	989.8 ± 3.8
°F	−297.32	832.28	1265.0 ± 1.8	1813.6 ± 6.8

Since tellurium at ordinary temperatures is believed to be diatomic, the molecular weight is 255.22.

Tellurium can be caused to exist as a solid, as a liquid, or as a vapor at temperatures easily handled in most metallurgical laboratories.

The Solid State

Since most tellurium is marketed in the crystalline state, that form will be described first.

Crystalline Tellurium. Crystalline tellurium is definitely metallic in appearance, crystallizing in the hexagonal system. It is brittle, hence is easily pulverized. In color, tellurium is silvery white; the purer grades exhibit a bright metallic luster. Tellurium shows few of the nonmetallic properties of the cogeners, sulfur and selenium.

Tellurium can be grown as a single crystal, using the Bridgman technique. Methods of crystallizing tellurium for use as a semiconductor are given on page 112 of "Semiconductors," by Hannay.[6]

HEXAGONAL. Hexagonal tellurium is the stable form below the melting point. In this form the atoms are arranged in spiral chains, each atom forming covalent bonds with the nearest neighbor so that each atom has an octet of valence electrons. The chains are held to adjacent chains by relatively weak van der Waals forces.

The c-axis of the hexagonal tellurium crystal is parallel to the axes of the helices. Additional details on the structure of the tellurium crystal are included in the description given on page 426 of "Semiconductors" by Hannay.[6]

The structure of hexagonal tellurium is shown diagrammatically on page 46 of "The Structure of Metals and Alloys" by Hume-Rothery and Raynor.[10]

Tellurium is unique in showing a remarkable mechanical property when subjected to hydrostatic pressure. Although the total volume decreases, the length in the direction of the c-axis increases. The phenomenon is discussed on pages 444 through 450 of the "Introduction to Chemical Physics" by Slater.[26]

Tellurium is easily fractured along the parallel well-defined cleavage planes. The resulting surfaces are mirror bright.

No information is at hand on the addition of trace elements to modify the mechanical properties of tellurium. Many of the intermetallic compounds of tellurium with other metals show much better mechanical properties.

Thermal conductivity for tellurium at room temperature is about one-tenth of the value reported for tin in the table on page 21 of "Metals Handbook."[19]

Amorphous Tellurium. Amorphous tellurium is said to be formed when tellurium is precipitated from a solution of tellurous or telluric acid by means of a suitable reducing agent. Whether or not the minute particles of precipitate are truly amorphous or are just minute crystals is open to question.

Colloidal Tellurium. This is prepared by the reduction of dilute aqueous solutions of tellurium compounds, such as tellurous or telluric acid, with such reducing agents as sulfur dioxide, hydrazine hydrate, etc. Elemental tellurium can be produced in the colloidal state by striking an electric arc between tellurium electrodes positioned below the surface of water. This is Bredig's method, devised in 1897.

The colloids, as produced above, may be stabilized by the use of typical protective colloids such as gelatin and gum arabic.

The Liquid State

The melting point of hexagonal tellurium is $449.5° \pm 0.3°C$ ($841.1° \pm 0.54°F$) and is a sharp transition from the solid state to the liquid state. Liquid tellurium pours as a mobile fluid, even when only a few degrees above the melting point.

Liquid tellurium is highly corrosive to iron, stainless steel, and copper but can be handled in "Pyrex" and quartz without much contamination.

The free surface of liquid tellurium is easily oxidized by air unless protected by reducing or inert gases. All melting operations should be conducted under a well-ventilated fume hood.

The Vapor State

The boiling point of pure tellurium is definitely much lower than the value of $1390°C$ ($2534°F$) that has appeared in the textbooks for years. Unpublished results of tests by the ASARCO Research Center in 1951 indicate a boiling point of slightly less than $1000°C$ ($1832°F$), a value substantiated by the extensive work reported by the United States Atomic Energy Commission.[2] The information reported by the AEC in the *Bulletin No. AECD-2546* indicate the following values:

Boiling point
at 760 mm Hg $989.8° \pm 3.8°C$ ($1813.64° \pm 6.8°F$)
Latent heat of
vaporization $27.26° \pm 0.07$ kg cal/mole

The vapor of tellurium at temperatures near the normal boiling point is believed to be mostly diatomic.

The vapor pressure–temperature relationship is shown in Figure 23.1 in Chapter 23.

Gaseous tellurium, like liquid tellurium, is strongly corrosive to metals.

Electrical Conductivity

Solid State. The electrical properties of tellurium are better understood than the properties of selenium, primarily because single crystals of tellurium are more easily prepared. The value reported by Horne for the electrical resistivity of vacuum cast tellurium is $(5.27 \pm 0.29) \times 10^{-2}$ ohm-cm[9].

Tellurium, like selenium, shows a greater electrical conductivity in the directions of the helices or chains forming the crystals than at right angles to the chains.[26] Electronically, tellurium is a semiconductor. The conductivity is only slightly increased by exposure to light.

Extrinsic tellurium is p-type. The introduction of impurities such as silver, copper, gold, iron, tin, arsenic, antimony, bismuth, bromine, and iodine provide acceptors. So far, no impurities have been found which act as donors.

Recently it has been reported that oxygen in tellurium, even in trace amounts, is a most insidious impurity. The following quotation is from a publication by Horne.[9]

". . . (b) TeO_2 is a p-type impurity in tellurium, small concentrations enormously increasing the thermoelectric power and is responsible for the lack of agreement among values previously reported. . . ."

The Hall coefficient for tellurium has been reported as being unusually large and subject to some unexpected changes at various temperatures. No values are given here because future tests in which oxygen is excluded should give more trustworthy values.

Liquid State. There is little information on the electrical conductivity of liquid tellurium. A probable reason is the violently corrosive action on metals that might be used as electrodes.

Electrical data suggest that the semiconducting properties of crystalline tellurium persist above the melting point, and that a gradual transition to metallic conduction takes place

TABLE 26.2. SOME PHYSICAL PROPERTIES OF HEXAGONAL TELLURIUM[17, 5, 12]

Atomic number	52
Atomic weight (1956)	127.61
Molecular weight (diatomic)	255.22
Isotopes: 20 are listed in the 1953 tables; the weights range from	117 through 135 and 137
Abundance by weight percentages:	
128	31.75%
130	34.27%
117 and 137 are not definitely established	
Electronic configuration K	2
L	8
M	18
N	18
O	6
Density, hexagonal at 25°C (77°F)	6.25 g/cc
Density, amorphous	6.00 g/cc
Atomic volume (hexagonal)	20.45 cc/g-atom
Melting point	449.5° ± 0.3°C (841.1° ± 0.54°F)
Boiling point (760 mm Hg)	989.8° ± 3.8°C (1813.6° ± 6.8°F)
Specific heat at 20°C (68°F)	0.047 cal/g/°C
Latent heat of fusion at melting point	32 cal/g
Latent heat of vaporization at boiling point	107 cal/g
Entropy crystal [25°C (77°F)]	11.88 cal/°C
Thermal conductivity (cal/sq cm/cm/°C/sec)	0.014
Coefficient of thermal expansion (μ in./°C)	16.75
Electrical resistivity (room temperature)	436,000 microhm-cm
Magnetic susceptibility (cgs at 18°C)	-0.31×10^{-6}
Hardness	2.3 Mohs' scale
Crystal structure	Hexagonal
Lattice constants	
a-axis	4.4570 Å
c-axis	5.9290 Å
Thermal neutron cross section (2,200 m/sec)	
Absorption (barns)	4.7 ± 0.1
Scattering (barns)	5.0 ± 1.0

with increasing temperature, as mentioned on page 430 of "Semiconductors."[6]

CHEMICAL PROPERTIES

The chemical properties of tellurium are as would be expected of a Group VI element. Chemically, tellurium is more basic than sulfur or selenium.

The oxidation states of tellurium are:

−2, in the tellurides (powerful reducing action).

0, zero for the elemental state.

+2, the +2 oxide, TeO, exists, and in cold hydrochloric acid it appears to form the salt tellurium dichloride, $TeCl_2$;

but, when the solution is warmed, the tellurium dichloride decomposes into the free element and a +4 complex chloride.

+4, in tellurium dioxide, TeO_2, and tellurium tetrachloride, $TeCl_4$.

+6, in tellurium trioxide, TeO_3, telluric acid, H_6TeO_6, and tellurium hexafluoride, TeF_6.

Oxidation states, including numerical values for potentials as well as extensive thermodynamic data, are given in the reference to Latimer.[13]

The chemical valences of importance in analytical procedures are six, four, and minus two, as given by Lundell and Hoffman.[15]

Oxygen

Vapors of elemental tellurium, if sufficiently hot when vented into air, ignite spontaneously, showing a blue flame and producing a finely divided oxide, TeO_2.

Tellurium dioxide, TeO_2, mol wt 159.61, as made under controlled conditions, is in the form of white odorless crystals containing 79.95 per cent by weight of tellurium. Yost and Russell[30] recommend the action of $6N$ nitric acid on elemental tellurium to prepare the tellurium dioxide by way of the basic nitrate. Only small amounts of tellurium dioxide are held in solution by water or by dilute acids.

Tellurous acid, H_2TeO_3, mol wt 177.63, contains 71.84 per cent tellurium. It exists in solid form as white crystals or crystalline powder that are slightly soluble in water, more soluble in dilute acids, and soluble in alkalis. Since tellurium dioxide is only sparingly soluble in water, only very dilute solutions can be prepared by adding the anhydride to water.[18]

Extensive information on the oxyacids of tellurium (also sulfur and selenium) is tabulated on page 326 et seq. of the reference to Yost and Russell.[30]

Tellurium trioxide, TeO_3, mol wt 175.61, contains 72.7 per cent tellurium. Tellurium trioxide results from heating telluric acid strongly enough to drive off the water, the final temperature being 300–360°C (572–680°F). The trioxide so prepared is an orange-yellow solid that does not dissolve in water, dilute acids, or dilute alkali. Hot concentrated alkalies dissolve tellurium trioxide to form tellurates.[30]

Telluric acid has several formulas listed in the literature. Telluric acid forms salts of the types Ag_6TeO_6 and Ag_2TeO_4. The acid, H_6TeO_6, is but sparingly soluble in water and is but weakly acidic. Upon heating, it loses water to form H_2TeO_4 and then TeO_3 as described under tellurium trioxide. Telluric acid is a good oxidizing agent.[14]

Telluric acid can be reduced by sulfur dioxide to elemental tellurium.

Hydrogen

The chemical reaction of hydrogen with tellurium is endothermic.

Hydrogen telluride, H_2Te, mol wt 129.63, contains 98.43 wt per cent tellurium. Its melting point is −51°C (−59.8°F), and its boiling point is −4°C (+24.8°F). The gas is colorless; the liquid is greenish yellow, and the solid crystallizes in lemon-yellow needles. The gas is generally believed to have a foul odor and is highly toxic.

Hydrogen telluride can be prepared by (1) the direct combination of the elements; (2) electrolysis of sulfuric acid, using a cathode of tellurium; or (3) action of dilute acids upon tellurides of zinc, aluminum, magnesium, etc.

Hydrogen telluride gas is soluble in water, producing weak acidity, but the values for solubilities are uncertain, since the solutions are unstable and absorb oxygen on exposure, causing the precipitation of metallic tellurium.

Solutions of hydrogen telluride precipitate metallic tellurides from solutions of the metals.

Halogens

The halogens combine with tellurium to form numerous compounds. Thirty-three halides and oxyhalides of Group VI, including melting points and boiling points, are tabulated on page 266 of the reference to Latimer and Hildebrand.[14]

Numerical values of the energies involved are given on page 87 of the book by Latimer.[13] Other facts on the properties of the halides of tellurium are given on page 297 et seq. of Yost and Russell.[30]

In general, the halogen compounds of tellurium hydrolyze with water to form hydrogen halide plus an acid of tellurium. The resulting tellurium compound is unstable under many conditions; hence, further decomposition is probable.

Fluorine. Fluorine combines with tellurium to give the tetrafluoride and the hexafluoride. Details for preparing the hexafluoride by passing fluorine over granular tellurium are given on page 121 of "Inorganic Syntheses" by Booth.[1] Tellurium hexafluoride, TeF_6, mol wt 241.61, contains 52.8 per cent by weight tellurium. Several different values are given at about −36°C (−32.8°F), for its melting point.

Chlorine. Chlorine combines with tellurium, even in the cold, to form a mixture of the dichloride, $TeCl_2$, and the tetrachloride, $TeCl_4$. Separation is by fractional distillation, probably at reduced pressures because the vapors decompose at higher temperatures. Tellurium dichloride and tellurium tetrachloride, when molten, are good conductors of electricity, indicating a saltlike character.

Tellurium dichloride, tellurous chloride, $TeCl_2$, mol wt 198.52, 64.28 per cent tellurium by weight, is an almost black mass or a greenish-yellow powder.

Tellurium tetrachloride, telluric chloride, $TeCl_4$, mol wt 269.44, 47.36 per cent tellurium by weight, is a white, hygroscopic, crystalline solid and is decomposed by water into oxychlorides and tellurous acid.

Bromine. Bromine can combine directly with tellurium to form the dibromide and the tetrabromide.

Tellurium dibromide, $TeBr_2$, mol wt 287.44, 44.04 per cent tellurium by weight, exists as a black-green crystalline mass or as black, very hygroscopic crystals.

Tellurium tetrabromide ($TeBr_4$), mol wt 447.27, 28.53 per cent tellurium by weight, exists as orange-colored crystals when cold, red when hot. It can be sublimed under vacuum without decomposition.

Iodine. The existence of tellurium diiodide, TeI_2, is uncertain. The tetraiodide has been reported as an iron-gray solid prepared by the reaction of tellurium dioxide with hydrogen iodide.

Sulfur. Tellurium and sulfur are miscible in all proportions in the liquid state.

The precipitate obtained by passing hydrogen sulfide into tellurous acid appears to be a mixture of the free elements and the sulfide, TeS_2.

The monosulfides, the disulfides, and the trisulfides of tellurium have all been reported but not established.

Nitrogen. The interaction of tellurium tetrachloride and ammonia, NH_3, at $-80°C$ ($-112°F$) is reported to yield tellurium nitride, Te_3N_4.

Acids. Tellurium is insoluble in hydrochloric acid but is soluble to a slight extent in nitric acid with the formation of the basic nitrate, $Te_2O_3(OH)NO_3$. Concentrated sulfuric acid dissolves tellurium, with the formation of a red solution.

The acidic reagents that are useful in dissolving analytical samples of tellurium are nitric acid, aqua regia, and concentrated sulfuric acid, as listed on page 26 of the reference to Lundell and Hoffman.[15]

Hydrobromic acid as well as hydrobromic acid plus bromine are used under reflux for the solution of tellurium in samples of rare elements (page 14 of the reference to Noyes and Bray).[21] Procedures for completing the analyses are given.

Alkalis. Elemental tellurium is listed as being soluble in a solution of potassium hydroxide and in a solution of potassium cyanide. Many of the compounds of tellurium are also soluble in these two solvents. Air should be excluded to prevent oxidation. Solutions of potassium cyanide have been used in leaching tellurium from some types of flue dusts.[16]

Fusion of tellurium and many of its compounds with sodium carbonate plus carbon, if needed, yields a sodium telluride. Fusion of tellurium dioxide with potassium nitrate forms tellurates.

Sodium peroxide as well as sodium carbonate plus potassium nitrate are suggested by Lundell and Hoffman as fusion reagents to dissolve tellurium and tellurium compounds.[15]

Carbon. Carbon telluride, CTe_2, is known only as produced by striking an electrical arc between tellurium electrodes in vaporous or in liquid carbon disulfide. Air must be excluded to prevent explosions, and the high vapor pressure of the carbon dioxide must be considered.

Metals. Tellurium, like sulfur and selenium, reacts with most metals. With tellurium the resulting compounds are tellurides. Some of the methods of producing tellurides are: (1) heating a mixture of tellurium and the chosen metal. (Only *small portions* of mixtures should be pulverized or heated, since large portions may produce dangerous explosions. An inert atmosphere is useful); (2) passing hydrogen telluride into a solution containing a soluble salt of the chosen metal; and (3) reduction of selected oxides, etc., with carbon in the presence of oxidic or elemental tellurium.

Metallic tellurides are all solid, have metallic luster, and show various colors. Their fusibilities range from low to higher temperatures, and some are volatile. All are insoluble in water, some are insoluble in dilute acids, but all are decomposed by nitric acid and aqua regia.

Some metallic tellurides are decomposed by heat alone (gold, mercury), by heating in a current of hydrogen (silver, gold, copper, zinc), or by heating in air, i.e., by an oxidizing roast.

Molten tellurium is either partially or completely miscible with most of the metals at

TABLE 26.3. EUTECTIC POINTS OF SOME BINARY SYSTEMS OF TELLURIUM[7]

System	Composition (% Te)	Temperature		Compounds formed
		°C	°F	
Aluminum-tellurium	3	621	1149.8	Al_2Te_3
	97	414	777.2	
Bismuth-tellurium	1.5	266	511	Bi_2Te_3
	85	413	775	
Copper-tellurium	83 (approx.)	340	644	Cu_2Te
Lead-tellurium	0.025	326.7	620	PbTe
	78	405	761	
Sulfur-tellurium	5.5	107	225	
Selenium-tellurium*				
Antimony-tellurium	30	540	1004	Sb_2Te_3
	89	424	795	
Tin-tellurium	85	405	761	SnTe

* Uninterrupted series of solid solutions.

elevated temperatures. Table 26.3 gives the values of the eutectic points, if present, of some of the binary systems of tellurium.

TOXICITY

Tellurium is reported to be less toxic than selenium. Tellurium, however, is more potent than selenium in generating the characteristic obnoxious breath. Workmen exposed to an atmosphere containing as little as 0.001 to 0.01 mg of tellurium/cu m of air have developed a tellurium breath. Fortunately, the malodorous breath vanishes in a few days.[3]

Methods for the determination of tellurium in air and in urine have been described by Steinburg.[29]

USES OF TELLURIUM

As is true in the case of selenium, the potential uses of tellurium are widely diversified. There is, however, one basic difference in the case of tellurium; although there are many potential applications, for one reason or another, very few actual uses have materialized.

Tellurium Additions to Iron, Copper, and Lead

The addition of selenium or tellurium to stainless steel acts not only as an excellent degasifier but also increases the machinability of the stainless steel. It is the general belief that the addition of tellurium is more effective than selenium; but, because of the fume prob-

lem created by tellurium, the majority of the steel companies avoid it.

Ductile cast iron, which combines the process advantages of gray cast iron, such as fluidity, castability, and machinability, with the product advantages of cast steel, is obtained by the introduction of magnesium and tellurium to the melt.

The "chill" on cast iron is said to be easier to control if between 0.1 and 0.005 per cent of tellurium is added to the liquid metal just before casting.

The addition of tellurium to pure copper, though not materially reducing the electrical conductivity, does greatly increase the machinability. Tellurium copper may be hot or cold worked, although it is slightly less ductile than pure copper.

Tellurium rectifiers operable at 300°C (626° F) have been developed, but the efficiencies at room temperatures are unsatisfactory.

In Europe the use of a lead alloy containing under 0.1 per cent of tellurium has found favorable acceptance. The use of tellurium in lead has been credited with decreasing the corrosive action of sulfuric acid upon the lead. Restricted grain growth, improved resistance to vibration and fatigue, and improved tensile strength (from cold working) also result from the addition of the tellurium.

Thermoelectric Devices

It is in the field of thermoelectricity that tellurium has made the best showing. It is an important component of many thermoelectric couples, and such couples can be used for both power generation and cooling.

The conversion of heat by a junction of dissimilar metals into electrical energy is called the Seebeck effect, after the discovery in 1826 by T. J. Seebeck.[24,28] Peltier, 8 years later in 1834, made an experiment of the opposite nature by directing an electric current from an external source through such a junction as had been studied by Seebeck. *Cooling* of the junction occurred when the applied current was in the same direction as the current the couple could generate if simply heated. Thus the device is a heat pump, free of moving parts, and is capable of effecting refrigeration.[22,11]

The requirements of a good thermoelement are: (1) high thermoelectric power, (2) low thermal conductivity, and (3) low electrical resistivity. A method of deriving a figure of merit based on the above three factors is shown by Shilliday.[25] Among the materials exhibiting high values for the figure of merit are: $PbTe$, Bi_2Te_3, and Bi_2Se_3. The compound Bi_2Te_3 can be made as an n-type or as a p-type semiconductor as desired.

Tellurium in Ceramics

Tellurium finds use in the ceramic industries for the production of blue, brown, red, and black glasses and porcelains.

Tellurium as a Catalyst

The use of an oxide of tellurium for the catalytic conversion of methyl and methylene groups to carbonyl groups is covered in U.S. Patent 2,653,138.

Tellurium has been suggested as a catalyst to replace selenium in the Kjeldahl digestions, in the oxidation of l-ascorbic acid, and to inhibit oxidation of polymethylsiloxanes. It has also been suggested in its tetrachloride form in the Friedel-Crafts synthesis of ketones.

References

1. Booth, H. S., "Inorganic Syntheses," Vol. 1, New York, McGraw-Hill Book Company, Inc., 1939.
2. Brooks, L. S., "The Vapor Pressure of Tellurium and Selenium," U.S. Atomic Energy Commission AECD-2546, Technical Information Branch, AEC, Oak Ridge, Tenn.
3. Elkins, H. B., "The Chemistry of Industrial Toxicology," New York, John Wiley & Sons, Inc., 1950.
4. Fulton, C. H., and Sharwood, W. J., "A Manual of Fire Assaying," 3rd Ed., New York, McGraw-Hill Book Company, Inc., 1929.
5. "Handbook of Chemistry and Physics," 40th Ed., Cleveland, Chemichal Rubber Publishing Co., 1958.
6. Hannay, N. B., "Semiconductors," New York, Reinhold Publishing Corp., 1959.
7. Hansen, M., "Constitution of Binary Alloys," New York, McGraw-Hill Book Company, Inc., 1958.
8. Hopkins, B. S., "Chemistry of the Less Familiar Elements," Champaign, Ill., Stipes Publishing Co., 1939.
9. Horne, R. A., *J. Appl. Phys.*, **30**, 393 (1959).
10. Hume-Rothery, W., and Raynor, G. V., "The Structure of Metals and Alloys," 3rd Ed., London, Institute of Metals, 1954.
11. Joffe, Abram F., *Sci. American*, **199**, 31 (1958).
12. Lange, N. A., "Handbook of Chemistry," 9th Ed., Sandusky, Ohio, Handbook Publishers, Inc., 1956.
13. Latimer, W. M., "The Oxidation States of the Elements and Their Potentials in Aqueous Solutions," 2nd Ed., Englewood Cliffs, N.J., Prentice-Hall, Inc., 1952.
14. Latimer, W. M., and Hildebrand, J. H., "Reference Book of Inorganic Chemistry," 3rd Ed., New York, The Macmillan Company, 1951.
15. Lundell, G. E. F., and Hoffman, J. I., "Outlines of Methods of Chemical Analysis," New York, John Wiley & Sons, Inc., 1938.
16. Lunge, G., "The Manufacture of Sulfuric Acid and Alkali," Vol. 1, Part 3, p. 1468, Princeton, N.J., D. Van Nostrand Company, Inc., 1913.
17. Mellor, J. W., "A Comprehensive Treatise on Inorganic and Theoretical Chemistry," Vol. 11, London, Longmans, Green & Co., Ltd., 1930.
18. "Merck Index of Chemicals and Drugs," Rahway, N.J., Merck & Co., Inc., 1952.
19. "Metals Handbook," Cleveland, American Society for Metals, 1948.
20. Moses, A. J., and Parsons, C. L., "Elements of Mineralogy, Crystallography, and Blowpipe Analysis," 5th Ed., Princeton, N.J., D. Van Nostrand Company, Inc., 1916.
21. Noyes, A. A., and Bray, W. C., "A System of Qualitative Analysis for The Rare Elements," New York, The Macmillan Company, 1927.
22. O'Brien, B. J., Wallace, C. S., and Landecker, K., *J. Appl. Phys.*, **27**, 820 (1956).
23. Pauling, L., "College Chemistry," 2nd Ed.,

San Francisco, W. H. Freeman & Co., 1955.

24. Pohl, R. W., "Physical Principles of Electricity and Magnetism," Princeton, N.J., D. Van Nostrand Company, Inc., 1930.

25. Shilliday, T. S., *J. Appl. Phys.*, **28**, 1035 (1957).

26. Slater, J. C., "Introduction to Chemical Physics," New York, McGraw-Hill Book Company, Inc., 1939.

27. Smith, O. C., "Identification and Qualitative Chemical Analysis of Minerals," 2nd Ed., Princeton, N.J., D. Van Nostrand Company, Inc., 1953.

28. Starling, S. G., "Electricity and Magnetism for Degree Students," London, Longmans, Green & Co., Ltd., 1941.

29. Steinburg, H. H., *et al.*, *Ind. Hyg. & Toxicol.*, **24**, 183 (1942).

30. Yost, D. M., and Russell, H., "Systematic Inorganic Chemistry," Englewood Cliffs, N.J., Prentice-Hall, Inc., 1944.

27. THALLIUM

Herbert E. Howe

Research Department
American Smelting & Refining Company
South Plainfield, New Jersey

INTRODUCTION

Thallium made its public debut in 1862 at the International Exhibition in London. The year before, Sir William Crookes, searching by spectroscopy for tellurium in the residues of a German sulfuric acid plant, noted an unaccountable green line in the spectrum. He concluded that the line represented a new element. With a poetic touch he compared the color of the spectrum line to the bright-green tint of new vegetation and named the element thallium from the Latin *thallus*—a budding twig. He was successful in obtaining a small quantity in metallic form for display at the 1862 exhibition.

Controversies have often arisen as to the priority of a discovery, and thallium was no exception. Professor A. Lamy, working independently of Crookes, observed this same spectrum line in the residues from another sulfuric plant and claimed credit for its discovery. Crookes probably was prior to Lamy in discovery and preparation by only a few months.

Crookes' assumption that thallium belonged to the sulfur family was soon disproved as the physical and chemical properties were investigated. Studies revealed that the element was closely associated with lead, mercury, potassium, and aluminum. Mendeleev, when publishing his atomic table, placed it in Group III under indium between mercury and lead, and this has been its accepted place ever since.

OCCURRENCE

Ahrens' estimate[9] of the abundance of thallium in the earth's crust (0.003 per cent) has increased previous estimates by a factor of 10, but this wide distribution does not represent its availability, for the major amount of the metal is found in potash minerals which have no commercial significance at the present time. Even the deposits of the main thallium minerals having 16 to 60 per cent thallium are so small as to be of no commercial importance.

The trace amounts of thallium found in sulfide ores, although small in quantity compared with the potash minerals, are, as in the time of Crookes, the major source of commercial thallium. The metal is recovered as a by-product from the roasting of pyrite ores in the production of sulfuric acid and from the smelting of lead and zinc.

PRODUCTION

The compounds of thallium, being volatile at the temperatures of the smelting operations, are collected in the flue dust, usually in the form of an oxide or sulfate. The extraction of thallium is largely dependent upon the difference in solubility in water of thallium salts and other metallic compounds associated with them in the flue dust. Thallium is soluble in acidified boiling water.[1,4]

The purification of thallium is also accomplished by taking advantage of the difference in solubility of certain thallium compounds and the same compounds of the impurities. For example, thallium sulfate's solubility in water permits its separation from lead sulfate; thallium sulfide is insoluble in alkaline solutions but soluble in acid solutions, permitting its separation from Group I elements; thallous chloride is only slightly soluble in cold water, permitting its separation from chlorides of cadmium, zinc, tellurium, and copper.

Thallium metal may be obtained from the compounds in several ways: (1) by electrolysis of carbonates, sulfates, or perchlorates; (2) by precipitation of metallic thallium with zinc; and (3) by reduction of thallous oxalate or chloride.[17]

A number of industrial processes for the recovery of thallium have been described in the literature. Several of them depend upon the extraction of thallium from the flue dust by boiling it in acidified water. The dissolved thallium in the filtrate is then precipitated with

TABLE 27.1. PHYSICAL PROPERTIES OF THALLIUM

Atomic number	81
Atomic weight	204.39
Density (g/cc)	
20°C (68°F)	11.85
306.5°C (584°F)	11.289
326.7°C (620°F)	11.254
330.0°C (626°F)	11.250
Density [lb/cu in., at 20°C (68°F)]	0.428
Atomic volume (cc/g-atom)	17.24
Melting point	303°C (577°F)
Boiling point	1457°C (2655°F)
Specific heat (20°C, cal/g/°C)	0.031
(303–500°C) (577–932°F)	0.0367
Heat of fusion (cal/g)	5.04
Latent heat of vaporization (cal/g)	189.9
Coefficient of linear thermal expansion (micro-in./°C)	28
Thermal conductivity (cal/sq cm/cm'/°C/sec)	0.093
Electrical resistivity (microhms/cm)	
0°C (32°F)	18
303°C (577.4°F)	74
Tensile strength (psi)	1300
Elongation in 5 in. (%)	40
Brinell hardness number (Pb–5)	2
Volume contraction on solidification (%)	3.23
Cubic compressibility [20°C (68°F), 100–500 megabars]	2.83×10^{-6}
Vapor pressure (845–900°K) (mm Hg)	

$$\log pmm = -\frac{8,927}{T} + 7.993$$

825°C (1517°F)	1.0
983°C (1801°F)	10.0
1196°C (2185°F)	100.0
1274°C (2325°F)	200.0
1364°C (2487°F)	400.0
1457°C (2655°F)	760.0
Crystal form	
Below 230°C (446°F)	a = 3.450 c = 5.514 close-packed hexagonal
Above 230°C	a = 3.874 body-centered cubic
Surface tension (dynes/sq cm) (327°C)	401
Thermal neutron absorption and activation cross section	

Isotope	Abundance	σ, abs	σ, act
Thallium 203	29.5%	11.4 ± 0.9	8 ± 3
Thallium 205	70.5%	0.8 ± 0.08	0.10 ± 0.03

zinc. Traces of metals such as zinc, copper, lead, cadmium, and indium are removed by dissolving the thallium in dilute sulfuric acid and precipitating the impurities with hydrogen sulfide. A saturated solution of thallous sulfate at 30°C (86°F) can be readily electrolyzed to yield thallium. An insoluble anode of platinum is suggested if a very pure metal is desired. The cathode may be of platinum, nickel, or stainless steel and is highly polished to allow easy removal of the thallium deposit. The metal is washed, compressed into blocks, melted in hydrogen, and cast into sticks.[17]

Another process handles it as a by-product in the recovery of cadmium.[18,19] The crude flue dust is leached with sulfuric acid, forming both cadmium and thallium sulfate. After the impurities are precipitated as sulfides and hydroxides, the purified solution is electrolyzed for deposition of cadmium. When the thallium content of the solution has reached a 1:10 ratio with that of the remaining cadmium, the cathodes are removed and replaced by new ones. The electrolysis is continued, depositing a cadmium-thallium alloy (5 to 20 per cent thallium).

The cadmium-thallium cathodes are treated with boiling water and steam. The solution contains the thallium as a hydroxide with very little cadmium. The small amount of cadmium in this solution is removed by precipitation with sodium carbonate, leaving a solution of thallium carbonate. Precipitation from this solution with sodium sulfide separates the thallium from any remaining impurities.

The sulfide is dissolved with sulfuric acid, producing pure thallium sulfate. This compound being the major commercial use for thallium, no further processing is necessary. If thallium metal is desired, the thallium sulfate solution is used as an electrolyte, and a thallium sponge is electrolytically deposited on aluminum cathodes, using "Duriron" anodes. The resulting thallium sponge is pressed, melted, and cast.

The estimated attainable yearly production is 15 tons/year. The only major producer in this country is the American Smelting and Refining Company.

The price of thallium has fluctuated over the last 30 years, at one time reaching a high of $22/lb. The present price, as of 1960, is $7.50/lb.

PHYSICAL PROPERTIES

When freshly cut, metallic thallium has a metallic luster which, upon exposure to air, dulls to a bluish-gray tinge resembling lead in appearance; but, unlike lead, if thallium is allowed to remain in contact with air for a few weeks, a heavy oxide crust will build up on the surface. As may be seen by comparing the properties of thallium (Table 27.1) with the physical properties of lead, they are very similar.

Investigations of the systems[2] of thallium and other elements reveal that thallium alloys readily with many other elements; the exceptions are copper, aluminum, zinc, manganese, nickel, and selenium, which have limited liquid solubility. Table 27.2 gives the eutectic points of binary, ternary, and quaternary alloys of thallium.

The resistance of various materials to attack by liquid thallium is given below:

Manganese—good resistance up to 1000°C (1832°F).

Austenitic stainless steel (18 chromium–8 nickel)—good resistance up to 649°C (1200°F).

Aluminum—good resistance up to 649°C (1200°F).

Armco iron—good resistance at m.p. 303°C (577.4°F).

Nickel and "Monel"—severely attacked at 649°C (1200°F).

Suggestions by Brewer[44] for containers for liquid thallium in order of decreasing preference are iron, tungsten, tantalum, molybdenum, columbium, and cobalt.

CHEMICAL PROPERTIES

Thallium is a member of the Group IIIB family along with boron, aluminum, gallium, and indium. The similarity between thallium's chemical properties and those of the alkali metals raised a question, for a time, as to the group to which it belonged.

The element forms two groups of compounds —the thallous and the thallic—with valences of one and three. The thallous are the most numerous and stable. Thallic salts are readily reduced to thallous salts by stannous chloride,

TABLE 27.2. EUTECTIC POINTS OF BINARY, TERNARY, AND QUATERNARY ALLOYS OF THALLIUM

System	Composition	Eutectic temperature
Ag-Tl	98.7Tl	289°C (552°F)
Au-Tl	73Tl	131°C (268°F)
Cd-Tl	83Tl	203°C (397°F)
Sn-Tl	43.5Tl	170°C (338°F)
Sb-Tl	80Tl	195°C (383°F)
Bi-Tl	52.5Tl	188°C (370°F)
Pb-Tl	No eutectic high solid solubility	
In-Tl	No eutectic high solid solubility	
Hg_5Tl_2-Tl	40.5Tl	0.6°C (33°F)
Hg_5Tl_2-Tl	8.5Tl	−60°C (−76°F)
Pb-Sn-Tl	—	No ternary*
Sn-Cd-Tl	19Cd, 42Sn, 39Tl	129.5°C (265°F)
Bi-Pb-Tl	55.2Bi, 33.3Pb, 11.5Tl	90.8°C (195.4°F)
	42.2Bi, 9.8Pb, 48.0Tl	186.4°C (367.5°F)
Bi-Sn-Tl	50Bi, 35.7Sn, 14.3Tl	124°C (255°F)
	44Bi, 31.0Sn, 2.5Tl	167.6°C (333.7°F)
Bi-Cd-Tl	43Bi, 40.8Cd, 16.2Tl	124°C (255°F)
	38.2Bi, 36.4Cd, 25.4Tl	146.6°C (296°F)
Cd-Pb-Tl	—	No ternary†
Pb-Sn-Bi-Tl	46.5Bi, 28Pb, 14Sn, 11.5Tl	93°C (199.4°F)
Pb-Cd-Bi-Tl	44.3Bi, 11Cd, 35.8Pb, 8.9Tl	81°C (177.8°F)
Bi-Cd-Sn-Tl	49.1Bi, 18.2Cd, 23.4Sn, 9.2Tl	94.6°C (202.3°F)

* A quasi-binary eutectic exists between $PbTl_2$ and Sn at 181.8°C (359°F), but no ternary eutectic occurs.[26]
† In the ternary system of Pb-Cd-Tl, an invariant point exists at 210°C (410°F) which is not a eutectic.[41]

sulfurous acid, metallic thallium, ferrous sulfate, and sodium arsenite, or by boiling water.

Thallium oxidizes slowly in air at 20°C (68°F) and more rapidly as the temperature increases. Thallium metal, exposed to air at ambient temperatures for a few weeks, will form a heavy oxide crust.

Some water-soluble thallous compounds are the acetate, nitrate, nitrite, perchlorate, hydroxide, carbonate, sulfate, and ferricyanide. The sulfide and chromate are insoluble, and the halides are moderately soluble in hot water.

Nitric acid will readily dissolve thallium. Dilute sulfuric will dissolve the metal slowly, but it is readily dissolved by concentrated sulfuric acid. Hydrochloric acid dissolves the metal very slowly.

Thallous oxide, Tl_2O, is formed by oxidizing the metal at low temperatures or heating thallous hydroxide, TlOH, at 100°C (212°F). It melts at 300°C (572°F) and will attack glass. It is easily oxidized to thallic oxide, Tl_2O_3, or reduced to thallium. Thallium tetraoxide, Tl_2O_4, must be prepared electrolytically. When thallous oxide is dissolved in water, it will form thallous hydroxide.

Thallous hydroxide is also formed when thallium contacts water containing oxygen. It reacts in water as a comparatively strong base, absorbing carbon dioxide and attacking glass and porcelain. Thallic hydroxide, $Tl(OH)_3$, is formed by adding alkali hydroxides or ammonia to a thallic solution.

The thallous halides resemble the lead salts and are formed by reaction of the acids on oxide, hydroxide, or carbonate. Thallium trichloride monohydrate, $TlCl_3·H_2O$, is formed by passing chlorine into water in which thallous chloride, TlCl, is suspended.

The action of fluorine on thallium was found to be so vigorous that the metal became incandescent.

Thallous sulfate, Tl_2SO_4, is soluble in cold water (4.87 g in 100 g water). Alums may also be made by combining the salt with trivalent sulfates.

Selenates and tellurates are formed with selenium and tellurium.

TOXICITY

When handling thallium, i.e., melting or just touching with the skin, a person must be protected against its poisonous effects. The **metal** readily forms soluble compounds when exposed to both air and water. Moisture on the skin may bring about this reaction, therefore the handling of thallium without protection should be prohibited. Although industrial poisoning from thallium is infrequent, many serious or fatal poisonings have resulted from accidental or therapeutic ingestion or external application of thallium. Signs of thallium poisoning are rapid loss of hair and gastrointestinal and nervous system disorders.[65,69,70,72]

FABRICATION TECHNIQUE

Thallium is a low-melting element with high malleability and low strength. It can be melted and fabricated by any one of the methods used for lead, i.e., cast, rolled, or extruded.

A smooth coherent deposit of thallium may be obtained with a perchlorate electrolyte, using peptone as an anodic depolarizer and cresylic acid as an addition agent.[11]

APPLICATIONS

The major commercial applications of thallium utilize it in the form of the compound thallium sulfate. It was first used as the active ingredient of a rodenticide in Germany about 1920, and since has been widely employed not only as a very effective rat killer but in destroying the troublesome little ant. Being odorless and tasteless, thallium sulfate may be mixed with starch, sugar, glycerin, and water, an appetizing treat for rats and ants, without giving the rodents or insects any warning of its presence.[57,66,67,73]

The unique photosensitivity of certain thallium salts has become important in its application in modern warfare. T. W. Case discovered, in 1917, that the electrical conductivity of oxidized thallium sulfide (thallofide cell) changed upon exposure to light. These cells are particularly sensitive to the long-wave, low-intensity light (infrared). Improvements on the thallofide cell have been made by Cashman, and his cell is used in war communication systems.[55,61,75]

Mixed thallium bromide–iodide crystals were used for an unusual application during World War II. These crystals can transmit infrared radiations of very long wavelength and were employed in military equipment designed for sniper detection, and signaling where visible radiation could not be used.[74]

Crystals of this type were first synthesized in Germany, but crystals of 42 mole per cent thallium bromide and 58 mole per cent thallium iodide have been synthesized in the United States by the Naval Research Laboratory. They have properties similar to the German crystals. A mixture of the required composition is melted in a platinum or "Pyrex" crucible with a conical bottom; an angle of 60 deg has been found satisfactory. The growth process is controlled by a temperature gradient in the furnace and the rate of movement of the crucible through the furnace. The temperature of the upper part of the furnace is 470°C (878°F). A lowering rate of 7 hr/in. gives excellent crystals 1 in. in diameter, and 32 hr/in. is used for 2-in. diameter crystals.

Increasing interest in lamps which will produce radiations in the erythemic (sun-tan) range has led to investigations of materials capable of converting primary ultraviolet radiation to radiation in the erythemic range. Several types of alkaline earth silicates and phosphates activated with thallium give not only a good initial erythemic emission but maintain a high per cent of this emission for several hundred hours.[56,60,62,63,68]

Thallium has shown some promise as a catalyst in the reduction of nitrobenzene by hydrogen.

The medicinal uses of thallium compounds are limited by the narrow margin between toxicity and therapeutic benefits. In the treatment of ringworm, it has been used to produce alopecia.

The applications of thallium in alloys are very limited, although alloys are formed with other elements which have unique properties.

The addition of lead to thallium raises the melting point above that of the components. These alloys have limited use in special types of fuses.

The most unique alloy of thallium is the mercury-thallium alloy which forms a eutectic at 8.5 per cent thallium and freezes at −60°C (−76°F), about 20°C (36°F) below the freezing point of mercury. Minus 60°C is the lowest temperature normally encountered in the arctic or stratosphere; therefore, this alloy has possibility in fulfilling the need for a substitute for mercury in switches and seals at these temperatures.

S. S. Flaschen and A. D. Pearson, of Bell Telephone Laboratories,[59] have produced a low-melting glass using thallium as one of the components (others—arsenic and sulfur). This glass has been used to coat semiconductors, capacitors, and other electronic devices to protect them from atmospheric oxidation, contamination, and humidity.

Although practically all the thallium now produced is used for rodenticides and insecticides, an increase in the commercial utilization of the unique properties of the metal and its compounds can be readily met with increased production.

Bibliography and References

Reference Books

1. DeMent, J., and Drake, H. C., "Rarer Metals," p. 43, New York, Chemical Publishing Company, Inc., 1946.
2. Hansen, M., "Der Aufbau der Zweistofflegierungen," pp. 160, 203, 265, 460, 651, 1001, 1078, 1087, Berlin, Verlag Julius Springer, 1936.
3. Haughton, J. L., "Bibliography of the Literature Relating to Constitutional Diagrams of Alloys," pp. 135, 138, 146, 157, London, Institute of Metals, 1942.
4. Hopkins, B. S., "Chapters in the Chemistry of Less Familiar Elements," Chap. 9, Champaign, Ill., Stipes Publishing Co., 1940.
5. Lyon, R. N., "Liquid Metals Handbook," Atomic Energy Commission, Department of the Navy, June, 1950.
6. Mellor, J. W., "A Comprehensive Treatise on Inorganic and Theoretical Chemistry," Vol. 5, p. 406, London, Longmans, Green & Co., Ltd., 1924.
7. "Metals Handbook," p. 20, Cleveland, American Society for Metals, 1948.
8. National Research Council, "International Critical Tables of Numerical Data, Physics, Chemistry and Technology," Vol. 2, pp. 416, 441, 474; Vol. 6, p. 196, New York, McGraw-Hill Book Company, Inc., 1927.

History, Occurrence, Recovery

9. Ahrens, L. H., *Science*, **106**, 268 (1947).
10. Andrieux, L., *Compt. rend.*, **190**, 925 (1930).
11. Brown, O. W., and McGlynn, Sister A., *Trans. Electrochem. Soc.*, **53**, 351 (1928).
12. Meyer, H. C., *Eng. Mining J.*, **121**, 94 (1926); **123**, 137 (1927); **125**, 136 (1928); **130**, 135 (1930).
13. *Mineral Ind.*, **39**, 661 (1930).
14. "Minerals Yearbook," U.S. Bur. Mines, **1942**, 829; **1943**, 829–830; **1944**, 820–1; **1945**, 824–5; **1946**, 1281.
15. Munch, J. C., *Chem. Trade J.*, **93**, 173, 195 (1933).
16. Petar, A., *U.S. Bur. Mines, Inform. Circ. No. 6453* (1941).
17. Sanderson, L., *Can. Mining J.*, **65**, 624 (1944).
18. Teats, R., U.S. Patent 2,011,882 (Aug. 20, 1935).
19. Teats, R., U.S. Patent 2,060,453 (Nov. 10, 1936).

Properties

20. Asahara, G., *Sci. Papers Inst. Phys. Chem. Research (Tokyo)*, **2**, 253 (1925).
21. Becker, K., *Z. Physik*, **42**, 479 (1927).
22. Coleman, F., and Egerton, E., *Trans. Roy. Soc. (London)*, **234A**, 177 (1935).
23. Einecke, E., *Z. anorg. u. allgem. Chem.*, **238**, 113 (1938).
24. Endo, H., *J. Inst. Metals*, **30**, 121 (1923).
25. Fajans, K., and Voigt, A., *Phys. Rev.*, **60**, 619 (1941).
26. French, S. J., *Metals & Alloys*, **7**, 64 (1936).
27. Jaeger, R., *Physik. Z.*, **41**, 398 (1940).
28. Janecke, E., *Z. Metallkunde*, **29**, 367 (1937).
29. Janecke, E., *Z. Metallkunde*, **31**, 170 (1939); *ibid.*, **26**, 153 (1934). See also *Z. Metallkunde*, **27**, 141 (1935) for correction.
30. Kirshnan, R., and Nahum, E. A., *Proc. Cambridge Phil. Soc.*, **36**, 490 (1940).
31. Köster, W., and Kam, K., *Z. Metallkunde*, **31**, 84 (1939).
32. Köster, W., and Kam, K., *ibid.*, p. 82.
33. Köster, W., and Wagner, E., *Z. Metallkunde*, **30**, 338 (1938).
34. Köster, W., and Wagner, E., *ibid.*, p. 335.
35. Kummakov, N. S., and Korenev, N. I., *Ann. inst. anal. phys. chim. (U.S.S.R.)*, **6**, 47 (1933).
36. Levi, G. R., *Z. Physik*, **44**, 603 (1927).
37. Lipsom, H., and Stokes, A. R., *Nature*, **148**, 437 (1941).
38. Meissner, W., Franz, H., and Westerhoff, H., *Ann. Physik*, **13**, 505 (1932).
39. Onnes, H. K., and Tuijn, W., *Arch. néerl. sci. (III)*, **6A**, 284 (1923).
40. Perlman, I., Goecherman, R. H., Templeton, R. H., and Howland, J. J., *Phys. Rev.*, **72**, 352 (1947).
41. Plank, J., and Urmanczy, A., *Korrosion u. Metallschutz*, **27**, 141 (1941).
42. Richards, T. W., and White, J. D., *J. Am. Chem. Soc.*, **50**, 3290 (1928).

Alloy Uses

43. Bray, J., and Morral, F. R., *Trans. Electrochem. Soc.*, **80**, 55 (1941).
44. Brewer, L., "The Thermodynamics of High

Vacuum—High Temperature Systems applied to Refractories," Metallurgical Project, cc-1802, June 8, 1944.

45. Ellis, O. W., *Am. Metal Market,* **35,** 1, 44 (1928).

46. Fink, C. G., and Conard, C. K., Jr., *Trans. Electrochem. Soc.,* **58,** 457 (1930); Scott, J. J., and Bana, W. P., U.S. Patent 2,236,840 (Apr. 1, 1941).

47. Hensel, F. R., *Am. Inst. Mining Met. Engrs., Metals Technol.,* **12,** (7), Oct. 1945, *Tech. Publ.* **1930,** 14 pp.

48. Hensel, F. R., U.S. Patents 2,180,845 (Nov. 21, 1939); 2,182,381 (Dec. 5, 1939); 2,375,224 (May 8, 1945); 2,379,434 (July 3, 1945); 2,379,435 (July 3, 1945); 2,393,905 (Jan. 29, 1946).

49. I. G. Farbenindustrie, A.-G., German Patents 494,153 (July 30, 1926); 496,348 (July 30, 1926); U.S. Patent 1,863,612 (June 21, 1932).

50. McDonald, J. C., *Trans. Am. Inst. Mining Met. Engrs.,* **137,** 430 (1940).

51. McDonald, J. C., U.S. Patents 2,233,954 (March 4, 1941); 2,302,968 (Nov. 24, 1943); 2,286,866 (June 16, 1942).

52. Meissner, W., Franz, H., and Westerhoff, H., *Ann. Physik,* **13,** 967 (1932).

53. Parks, W. G., and LeBaron, I. M., *Trans. Electrochem. Soc.,* **69,** 599 (1936).

Compound Uses

54. Asiatic Petroleum Co., Ltd., and Egerton, A. C., British Patent 279,560 (July 29, 1926).

55. Case, T. W., *Phys. Rev.,* **15,** 289 (1920).

56. Clapp, R. H., U.S. Patent 2,417,038 (Mar. 4, 1947); Clapp, R. H., and Ginther, R. J., *J. Opt. Soc. Am.,* **37,** 355 (1947).

57. Dieke, S. H., and Richter, C. P., *U.S. Public Health Repts.,* **61,** 672 (1946).

58. Emlen, T., and Stokes, A. W., *Am. J. Hyg.,* **45,** 254 (1947).

59. Flaschen, S. S., and Pearson, A. D., *J. Electrochem. Soc.,* **105,** 164C (1958). Abstract 116 of paper given at Electrochemical Society meeting, Ottawa, Canada (Sept. 28–Oct. 2, 1958).

60. Froelich, H. C., *Trans. Electrochem. Soc.,* **91,** 241 (1947).

61. Hewlett, C. W., *Gen. Elec. Rev.,* **50,** 22 (1947).

62. Kats, M. L., *Compt. rend. acad. sci. U.R.S.S.,* **32,** 178 (1941).

63. Klement, F. D., *Doklady Akad. Nauk S.S.S.R.,* **46,** 295; *Compt. rend. acad. sci. U.R.S.S.,* **46,** 270 (1945).

64. Kolomiets, B. T., *J. Tech. Phys. U.S.S.R.,* **17,** 195 (1947).

65. Munch, J. C., *J. Am. Med. Assoc.,* **102,** 1929 (1934).

66. Munch, J. C., and Silver, J., *U.S. Dept. Agr., Tech. Bull. No. 238,* 1 (1931).

67. Popence, C. H., *Science,* **64,** 525 (1926).

68. Pringsheim, P., *Rev. Modern Phys.,* **14,** 132 (1942).

69. Sessions, H. K., *U.S. Naval Med. Bull.,* **47,** 545 (1947).

70. Steidle, H., *Med. Welt,* **13,** 1557 (1939).

71. Sullivan, J. C., *U.S. Bur. Mines, Tech. Paper No. 381,* (1927).

72. Thibaut, S., *Ing. chim.,* **25,** 85 (1941).

73. Travis, B. W., *J. Econ. Entomol.,* **36,** 56 (1943).

74. Tuttle, O. F., and Egli, P. H., *J. Chem. Phys.,* **14,** 571 (1946).

75. Von Hippel, A., Chesley, F. G., Denmark, H. S., Uln, P. B., and Ritter, E. S., *J. Chem. Phys.,* **14,** 355 (1946).

28. THORIUM

HARLEY A. WILHELM

*Institute for Atomic Research and Ames Laboratory of the
United States Atomic Energy Commission
Iowa State University
Ames, Iowa*

INTRODUCTION

The discovery of thorium is attributed to Berzelius (1828), who reported the separation of a new earth from a mineral found near Brevig, Norway. The name thorium was derived from Thor, Scandinavian god of war.[35]

Interest in the metal and its oxide lagged until about 1884, when Auer von Welsbach patented the incandescent mantle, a lattice structure consisting of a mixture of thorium oxide and 1 per cent cerium oxide.[63] The subsequent growth of the mantle industry led to a search for deposits of thorium and to increased production of the oxide. During the early years of this century, the mantle industry was at a peak of activity, but, as electricity began to supplant gas for general lighting purposes, thorium demands dwindled and by 1925 were relatively unimportant to commerce.

The rare earths that were by-products of thorium ore treatment, however, soon began to find commercial applications, and after 1932 the processing of the ore for its rare earth content made thorium the by-product which was then in oversupply. In the United States this resulted in the building of a stockpile of thorium for the atomic energy project which was to come later. The nonenergy uses for thorium have, until recent years, remained largely in mantle manufacture;[56] as late as 1950, more than 90 per cent of the reported consumption of thorium for nonenergy purposes was still for mantles.

The use of a few per cent thorium in magnesium to give a low-density alloy with superior high-temperature properties has recently increased the consumption of thorium markedly in nonenergy applications. Table 28.1 lists the authorizations by the Atomic Energy Commission for thorium purchases for nonenergy consumption for the years 1952 to 1958.[56] These figures have little significance with respect to the total consumption of thorium, because

TABLE 28.1. AUTHORIZATIONS FOR THORIUM PURCHASES FOR NONENERGY PURPOSES IN THE UNITED STATES (POUNDS CONTAINED THORIUM DIOXIDE)

Uses	1952	1953	1954	1955	1956†	1957†	1958†
Magnesium alloys	—	3,600	4,647	23,944	50,000	100,000	120,000
Gas mantles	25,427	8,707	9,765	44,566	40,000	40,000	40,000
Refractories and polishing	1,157	236	24	105	200	—	5,000
Chemical and medical	11,064	5,179	3,738	3,898	4,000	4,000	6,000
Electronic products	277	1,222	2,016	926	1,000	1,000	1,000
Total (thorium dioxide)	37,925	18,944	20,190	73,439	95,200	145,000	172,000

† Estimate.

complete import and export data on ores, concentrates, metal, and alloys controlled by the Atomic Energy Commission are not disclosed.

Thorium is a source of fuel for atomic power.[77] Thorium 232, by capturing a neutron, can convert to fissionable uranium 233 in a manner similar to the conversion of fertile uranium 238 to fissionable plutonium 239. In the case of thorium, a neutron is captured by thorium 232 to form thorium 233, which decays radioactivity, as represented by the reaction

$$_{90}Th^{232} + _{0}n^{1} \rightarrow {_{90}Th^{233}} \xrightarrow{-\beta} {_{91}Pa^{233}} \xrightarrow{-\beta} {_{92}U^{233}}.$$

The uranium 233 product is capable of functioning in a fission chain reaction in a manner similar to that of uranium 235 or of plutonium 239 for the generation of nuclear energy. The interest in thorium for this application is increased owing to its abundance in the earth's crust as compared to uranium, the estimates[26] being uranium 0.0004 per cent and thorium 0.0012 per cent. These figures show that thorium is not a rare element but is as plentiful as lead and molybdenum. It has been estimated that in the earth's crust there is more energy possible from thorium than from the uranium and fossil fuels combined.

OCCURRENCE

Thorium occurs in a large number of minerals associated with uranium and the rare earths.[24] Those which contain a high percentage of the element, such as thorianite ($ThO_2 + UO_2$) and thorite ($ThSiO_4$), are scarce.

The major source of the oxide and metal is monazite, essentially a phosphate of the cerium earths. This mineral occurs associated with silica and other minerals in the so-called monazite sands. Concentrates from these sands yield varying enrichments of thorium oxide up to approximately 10 per cent.

Monazite deposits which have been worked for years are those in India and Brazil. Others are in Australia, Ceylon, Africa, and Canada. Domestic thorium mineral deposits are located in Idaho, Florida, Colorado, and the Carolinas. The most important proved source of monazite is the seacoast of Travancore, India. Concentrates from these sands average about 9 per cent thorium oxide and were for years the major source of oxide for domestic consumption, until

an embargo by India stopped export shortly after World War II. The Indian government, in 1952, entered into an agreement with two French firms for processing monazite. The plant is designed to produce 1,500 tons of concentrates annually; thorium and rare earth compounds are produced. Recent reports of preliminary surveys give indications that a larger and richer potential source for thorium exists in northeastern India.

The Brazilian deposits have been estimated at 150,000 tons of monazite, with the thorium oxide content of the concentrates averaging about 6 per cent. Since 1945 this monazite has been processed on a large scale in a plant at São Paulo, Brazil.

Domestic sources of monazite rarely exceed 4 per cent. The Union of South Africa has continued to supply much of the monazite for processing in the United States in recent years.

TREATMENT AND ORE PURIFICATION

The recovery of thorium compounds from monazite depends upon the separation of this element in rather low concentration from the cerium, lanthanum, and yttrium earths. This problem presents many technical difficulties.

There are, in general, two chemical processes commonly used for opening thorium ore. The sulfuric acid method has been in use for many decades, whereas the caustic soda process has received considerable attention only recently. In most commercial processes in the United States, the ground monazite is treated with hot sulfuric acid which dissolves the thorium and rare earths. The ratio of thorium oxide to rare earths in the solution is about 1:12. Caustic digestion of monazite is employed in the plants operating in India and Brazil. In general, the first step in the caustic process yields hydrated oxides of thorium and rare earths and soluble sodium triphosphate as a by-product. The washed oxides are dissolved in hydrochloric acid to give a solution containing the thorium and rare earths.

Since the product solutions from both the sulfuric acid and caustic digestion processes contain complex mixtures of many elements, including uranium, there are many variations in subsequent processing to yield thorium, rare earth, and uranium-rich fractions, followed by final purifications. Some commercial processes for thorium, employing the sulfuric acid treatment of the ore, depend on steps involving relative solubilities and selective precipitations. Sulfate, double sulfate, oxalate, double carbonate, iodate, nitrate and other compounds of thorium may be employed to effect the separations. The low solubility of thorium sulfate [$Th(SO_4)_2 \cdot 8H_2O$], as compared to the sulfates of cerium, neodymium, praseodymium, and lanthanum, gives a purification. The double sulfate of thorium and sodium can be precipitated from a dilute solution of thorium sulfate. In the use of carbonate, thorium forms a soluble double carbonate and cerium precipitates. The precipitation of thorium as the oxalate from highly acid solution separates this element from small quantities of the rare earths and common metals. The iodate separation involves the precipitation of thorium iodate from strong nitric acid solution and affords an excellent separation from the rare earths and common metals. It is expensive for commercial application, however.

Regardless of the variations, production by such processes generally conclude with a crystallization of the thorium as nitrate. Although greater purity can be obtained by extending the operations, the commercial product, prepared as oxide by one producer employing a process based on relative solubilities and selective precipitation, contains about 20 to 100 ppm of rare earths and is of adequate purity for preparation of mantle-grade thorium nitrate. For details of these general procedures, see Levy,[47] Spencer,[75] Urie,[78] Pilkington and Wylie,[62] Grimaldi and Marsh,[28] and Dickson and Kaufman.[18]

More recent developments[55] have evolved processing variations that give the greater purity generally required in nuclear applications and with some simplifications. A solution from either the sulfuric acid or caustic treatment of the ore is employed in chemical processing to yield a sulfate- and phosphate-free nitric acid solution of a thorium-enriched fraction. In these processes the final purification of thorium depends on a solvent-extraction treatment of the thorium fraction in a nitric acid solution.

One such variation of the sulfuric acid treatment of monazite sand employs 93 per cent sulfuric acid at a temperature of 210°C (410°F). The resulting monazite sulfate is dissolved in water, separated from the insolubles, and then treated with ammonium hydroxide to give a pH of 1.0. The addition of a solution of oxalic acid then precipitates thorium and rare earths from the sulfate, phosphate, and uranyl ions. The oxalate precipitate is separated and calcined to the oxides, which are then dissolved in nitric acid to give the aqueous-feed solution for solvent extraction with tributyl phosphate. Thorium and ceric cerium are extracted into the organic phase, while the other rare earths remain in the aqueous phase. Cerium may be stripped from the tributyl phosphate and its thorium by means of a 0.1 molar sodium nitrite solution, and the thorium is then subsequently stripped with 2 per cent aqueous sulfuric acid. Good separations and recoveries of high-purity thorium, as well as rare earths and uranium, can be effected.

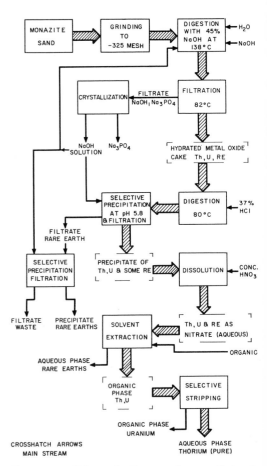

FIGURE 28.1. Schematic diagram of a caustic treatment of monazite sand with subsequent processing to yield pure thorium through solvent extraction.

A variation of caustic treatment in combination with solvent extraction, as shown in Figure 28.1, employs the reaction of finely ground monazite and a 45 per cent sodium hydroxide solution at 138°C (280°F) to open the ore. The products are water insoluble compounds of thorium, uranium, and rare earths that are filtered, washed, and then dissolved in 37 per cent hydrochloric acid at 80°C (176°F). Any unreacted ore or other insolubles, if present, should be separated from the solution, which is then treated with caustic to a pH of 5.8 in order to precipitate the thorium and uranium. This precipitate, which also contains a small percentage of some rare earths, is dissolved in nitric acid. (Any unreacted ore, etc., could be filtered out at this point as an alternative to filtering the hydrochloric acid solution.) The thorium and uranium are then removed from the residual rare earths in the nitric acid solution by a solvent extraction employing tributyl phosphate diluted with an inert organic solvent. The purified thorium is recovered from the solvent and from the uranium by selective stripping with an aqueous solution of nitric acid.

Recent and more detailed presentations of these and other processes for the recovery of thorium from monazite have been prepared by Barghusen and Smutz (see Reference 55) and by Cuthbert.[14]

THORIUM METAL PREPARATION

The metallurgy of thorium is, in some respects, similar to that of zirconium and titanium; i.e., the oxide is not reduced by hydrogen, and neither carbon nor silicon is a satisfactory reductant.

The effect of gases, particularly oxygen and nitrogen, on mechanical working of the metal is not as pronounced as in the case of zirconium and titanium; it is probable that the interstitial solution of these gases in thorium is small. Oxygen appears as thorium oxide, which is found dispersed at random. Such inclusions do not seriously impair mechanical fabrication in amounts even as high as 3 per cent oxide by weight.

Thorium metal has been prepared in small amounts and in various degrees of purity by a number of methods since it was first obtained by Berzelius[5] in 1829. His technique was to react thorium tetrachloride with an alkali metal (potassium). An impure powder metal product was obtained. This procedure was repeated by several experimenters, in particular, von Bolten,[80] Lely and Hamberger,[45] and Arsem.[1] The product metal generally contained large amounts of oxide and possibly carbide. The early failures to produce a relatively good product were more the result of impurities in reductants and lack of good equipment than of unsound metallurgical principles.

More recently, variations of the alkali metal reduction of thorium tetrachloride have yielded better quality metal. Block (see Reference 77) has reported briefly on a method for treating the tetrachloride with sodium metal under a helium atmosphere to yield a thorium-metal sponge that is arc melted to give thorium ingot.

The reaction between the tetrachloride and sodium metal is initiated by heating the mixed charge to about 525°C (977°F), and the treatment is continued with subsequent heating at 800°C (1472°F) for about 10 hr. The sodium chloride by-product and the excess sodium from the charge are removed from the thorium sponge by heating in a vacuum at 900°C (1652°F) for 16 hr. The sponge is then pressed in the form of bars that are subsequently arc melted to give solid ingot. The economic production of good-quality tetrachloride has been the main deterrent to the development of this and some other processes for thorium metal, such as the magnesium reduction of the tetrachloride.

Another variation of the alkali-thorium tetrachloride approach is the "Metallex" process reported in some detail by Dean (see Reference 77). In this case the tetrachloride is reacted with the sodium in a dilute sodium amalgam to give a thorium-mercury compound associated with the mercury phase. This makes possible a separation of the oxide impurity of the tetrachloride from the metal phase. The amalgam product contains about 1 per cent thorium as suspended compound, which is concentrated to about 15 per cent thorium by pressing out most of the excess liquid mercury from the solid intermetallic compound $ThHg_3$. Subsequent vacuum distillation yields a mercury-free thorium sponge, which may be prepared in the form of solid ingot by arc melting. Although this process has been reported to yield good-quality thorium metal, the required handling of large amounts of potentially toxic mercury (100 to 1 of thorium metal) is perhaps the least desirable feature of the process.

Commercial methods which have yielded metal of relatively high purity are (1) reduction of the oxide with calcium, (2) fused-salt electrolysis of thorium halide, and (3) bomb reduction of ThF_4 with calcium (addition of zinc chloride).

The primary product of either of the first two of these processes is thorium powder which is converted to solid massive metal by powder metallurgy techniques. Care should be exercised in handling thorium powder, since it can be pyrophoric. In the third process the primary product is a massive alloy that is subsequently treated to yield thorium sponge, which is then melted to solid ingot.

Thorium Powder

Production by Reaction of Thorium Dioxide with Calcium. The reduction of thorium oxide with calcium was investigated by Berger,[4] by Kuzel and Wedekind,[44] and by Kroll.[43] Although this basic method is capable of yielding a metal of relatively high purity, difficulties similar to those of the early chloride reduction were encountered also with the oxide.

A detailed investigation of the thorium dioxide–calcium process was made by Marden and Rentschler.[51] Their method involved the reduction of thorium oxide with calcium in the presence of calcium chloride, according to the following reaction:

$$ThO_2 + 2Ca + (2.4CaCl_2) \rightleftharpoons$$
$$Th + 2CaO + (2.4CaCl_2)$$

The actual charge includes 3 moles excess of calcium.

The mixed charge was heated in a closed steel bomb in a gas-fired furnace and held at 950°C (1742°F) for 1 hr. After cooling, the product was leached with water, then with 1:10 nitric acid, followed by washing with water, alcohol, and then ether. The resulting metal powder was dried *in vacuo*. After compacting and sintering, the solid metal was reported to assay 99.7 to

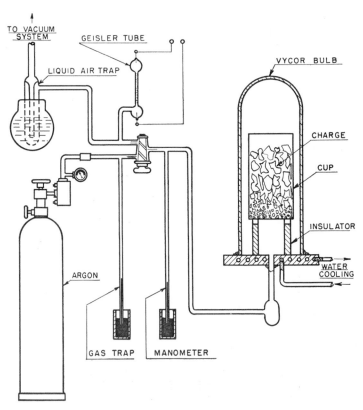

FIGURE 28.2. Reduction apparatus. (*Courtesy The Electrochemical Society.*)

99.8 per cent thorium. It was very ductile and easily fabricated into wire and sheet.

Improvements on this basic method were made by Rentschler, *et al.*[68] These included the elimination of calcium chloride in the reaction, and the use of a thin-walled cup in place of the older type of closed bomb. The reaction takes place under a static pressure of argon gas. A diagrammatic illustration of the apparatus is shown in Figure 28.2; details of the method are given in the reference. The charge is heated by high-frequency coils (not shown in the figure) which surround the "Vycor" cylinder. The reproducibility of this method, which is difficult to achieve with the earlier charge in the closed bomb, is excellent, and the metal is reported to assay 99.8 per cent thorium. The reaction is

$$ThO_2 + 2Ca \rightleftharpoons Th + 2CaO.$$

The actual charge of reactants includes 2 moles excess of calcium.

The thorium powder is recovered by leaching the charge with dilute acetic acid, water, alcohol, and ether, followed by vacuum drying.

A coarser metal is obtained by the substitution of $ThCl_4$ or $ThOCl_2$ for ThO_2.[49] A review of the production of thorium metal powder by calcium reduction of the oxide is given by Espe.[21] Meerson[53] has presented a report of his studies of the calcium reduction of thorium dioxide.

Production by Fused Salt Electrolysis. The electrolysis of anhydrous thorium chloride in a fused mixture of sodium and potassium chlorides was attempted by Moissan and Honigschmidt,[57] and by von Wartenberg.[81] The charge was heated in a carbon crucible which served as the cathode. The product assayed 87 to 88 per cent thorium metal.

The successful deposition of thorium metal powder from a fused salt electrolyte resulted from the work of Driggs and Lilliendahl.[19] The electrolyte was a mixture of equal parts by weight of sodium and potassium chlorides, to which was added the double fluoride, $ThF_4 \cdot KF$.

Thorium powder interspersed with salts was deposited on a molybdenum cathode suspended centrally in the bath which was contained in a carbon crucible. At the completion of the electrolysis, the cathode and deposit were slowly raised out of the electrolyte, which froze, forming on the deposit a coating that was protective against oxidation. Additional fluoride was then added to the bath, and the electrolysis continued. The type of cell which may be conveniently used is shown in Figure 28.3.

One disadvantage of this electrolysis is that the chloride-to-fluoride ratio in the fused bath changes, because fluoride is introduced and chlorine is electrolyzed out, and, as a result, the fused salt bath requires frequent compensating adjustments or changes. In order to get around this disadvantage, it would be necessary to electrolyze out of the bath only the elements introduced. The addition of thorium chloride

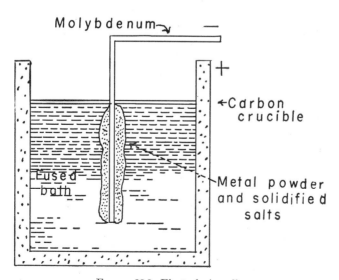

FIGURE 28.3. Electrolysis cell.

and the electrolytic deposition of thorium and chlorine should meet these requirements. The preparation of good quality anhydrous thorium tetrachloride, however, has been the main obstacle to its adoption in such an electrolysis. Raynes (see Reference 77) has referred to methods for preparing thorium chloride for use in electrolysis and to a process which is said to be completely integrated and produces thorium metal by the continuous fused salt electrolysis of thorium chloride in sodium chloride.

In the electrolytic processes for thorium, the recovery of the metal is accomplished by first stripping the deposit from the electrode and then crushing, leaching, and drying the metal to obtain a free flowing crystalline powder. This powder can be readily fabricated into solid shapes by powder metallurgy techniques.

Properties of Metal Powders. The purity of the final product in a powder metallurgy process is dependent not only on the thermodynamics of the process in the reduction step, but also on the activity of the metal powder in the recovery operation, particularly toward oxide formation. The large surface area of powders generally results in the formation of 0.1 to 0.2 per cent oxide, and, if this oxide cannot be removed in later operations, e.g., casting, it will contaminate the product. This is the case for such metals as thorium, titanium, and zirconium.

Powders produced by calcium reduction of thorium oxide differ in impurity content and particle size from those made by fused salt electrolysis. Electrolytic powders are coarser than those produced by calcium reduction. In powders prepared by electrolysis, 25 to 30 per cent may be +100 mesh (standard Tyler screen), whereas calcium reduced powders rarely show more than 1 to 2 per cent +100 mesh, the bulk passing through a 200-mesh screen.

All powders contain relatively large amounts of hydrogen, which may be removed by vacuum treatment at 1000°C (1832°F).

The chemical purity of thorium powder is dependent upon impurities in reactants and those introduced in processing. In the calcium-reduction process these include iron from charge containers, carbon from carbide in calcium, and calcium not removed in acid leaching.

The electrolytic powders are, in general, somewhat lower in impurity than those produced by calcium reduction of the oxide. Major contaminants are iron, carbon, silicon, and molybdenum, the latter being derived from the molybdenum cathode. Small amounts of fluorides also may be encountered.

Nitrogen contamination of powders is relatively low, because the nitride is unstable in the presence of water vapor at comparatively low temperatures.

Powder Compacts. FORMATION. The optimum procedure for compacting will depend upon the size and shape of the finished part. For rolling slabs where the sintered thickness is not over 0.5 in., the use of hardened steel dies with a hardness of Rockwell C 20 to 30 is satisfactory. Hydraulic pressures of 20 to 50 tons/sq in. are adequate. Steel dies should be designed to allow for 10 to 15 per cent shrinkage in the sintering operation to follow. Thorium powder has a tendency to seize to steel dies. This may be controlled by lubrication of the die parts with a compound such as "Sterotex." This should be used sparingly, however, because of possible contamination of the compact with carbon in the subsequent treating operation.

In the preparation of ingots of relatively large cross-sectional area, hydrostatic pressing is often desirable. In this operation the powder is enclosed in a rubber tube, stoppered at both ends, and hermetically sealed. The tube is then immersed in a pressure cylinder filled with water. Pressures of 10–15 tons/sq in. are applied by a suitable pump. This method of pressing produces a compact of more uniform density than is obtained in the usual vertical plunger type of die.

Meerson[53] has investigated the compacting of thorium powders prepared by electrolysis and by the calcium reduction of the oxide and has made the following observations:

(1) Thorium powder has a high plasticity and good compressibility.

(2) The compressibility of electrolytic powder is greater than that of the calcium reduced powder.

(3) The pressure required to obtain briquettes with a density of 10.5–11.0 g/cc at a height-to-diameter ratio of ~ 0.5, with pressure in one direction, or of ~ 1.0, with pressure in two directions, is 50–80 tons/sq in. for the calcium reduced powder and 40–60 tons/sq in. for the electrolytic.

SINTERING. The pressed compacts of metal

may be sintered to a relatively high density, *in vacuo*, of the order of 1×10^{-4} mm Hg or better, generally at 1200°C (2192°F) or higher. If the compacts are degassed *in vacuo* at 1000°C (1932°F), the final sintering may be performed in argon or helium gas.

Several types of equipment have been used in the sintering operation. Either porcelain or sillimanite tubes may be used, although resistance to thermal shock, particularly in tubes of more than 1-in. bore, has been found to be poor. These tubes are not impervious to diffusion of air at temperatures in excess of 1000°C (1832°F), and some pickup of oxygen by the metal will occur. The oxide increase in compacts sintered for 3–4 hr at 1300°C (2372°F) in carefully selected tubes should not exceed 0.2 per cent thorium dioxide by weight. The sintered density is 11.3–11.4, or approximately 98 per cent of the theoretical maximum density.

According to Meerson,[53] residual calcium oxide in metal powder can cause blistering and cracking of the briquettes on vacuum sintering at temperatures above 1150°C (2100°F) if the powder has been compacted to a density of greater than 10.3 g/cc. The residual calcium oxide tends to react with thorium to give calcium vapor, which develops internal pressure in the briquette on sintering. Less dense briquettes which contained greater porosity for escape of the calcium vapor were not observed to fail and contained less calcium in the final sintered metal. Blistering and cracking were not observed in sintering of highly compacted electrolytic powder briquettes.

MELTING AND EXTRUSION. Thorium powder may be melted by compacting and inductively heating *in vacuo*. The choice of a suitable refractory to hold the melt is a matter of compromise. Beryllia crucibles are the best choice; molten metal does not wet this oxide, and contamination is generally of the order of 100–200 ppm of beryllium. A diagrammatic sketch of a small-scale induction melting furnace for compacts is shown in Figure 28.4. The high-frequency coil surrounds the cylinder, composed of a glass such as "Vycor," which rests on the tubulated brass plate. The beryllia crucible is supported on an alundum crucible which contains a supporting bed of thorium oxide or other refractory oxide.

It is probable that some oxygen is dissolved in thorium melted in a beryllia crucible, as

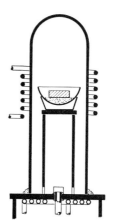

FIGURE 28.4. Small-scale vacuum induction melting furnace. (*Courtesy The Electrochemical Society.*)

Thompson,[76] investigating the melting point of thorium, states that molten thorium reacts with carbon, aluminum oxide, and thorium oxide. The solvent action of thorium on beryllium oxide, however, appears to be low.

Arc melting of pressed thorium powder compacts has been carried out on a small scale by Noland (see Reference 55), who employed a tungsten-tipped electrode in a nonconsumable electrode process, and by Raynes (see Reference 77), who employed pressed compacts as consumable electrodes.

Thorium powder has been converted to dense metal by extrusion at elevated temperatures. The metal compact must be protected from the air at temperatures sufficiently high for best results. Usually, the compacts are jacketed with a metal such as copper for this protection. Raynes (see Reference 77) states that warm extrusion can give metal of nearly 100 per cent theoretical density. He suggests warm extrusion followed by warm working as a means for fabrication of solid shapes from thorium powder.

Massive Thorium by Bomb Reduction

The only process operated continuously on a tonnage basis for thorium metal production in the United States is the calcium reduction of thorium tetrafluoride. The process, as described by Wilhelm (see Reference 55), employs a charge of thorium fluoride, anhydrous zinc chloride, and calcium metal which is mixed, packed, and closed in a refractory lined vessel— referred to as a bomb (Figure 28.5). The charged bomb is placed in a heat soaking pit

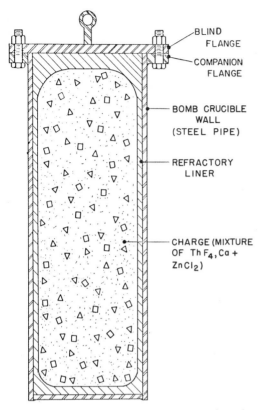

FIGURE 28.5. Sketch representing cross section of a charged bomb.

(furnace) maintained at a temperature of approximately 640°C (1185°F). The charge warms up to its ignition temperature in about ½ hr, and the reaction that ensues generates sufficient heat to fuse the products—a thorium-zinc alloy and a calcium chloride–calcium fluoride slag. The dense molten alloy collects at the bottom of the bomb and under the thick layer of fused slag. The bomb, with its contents, is removed from the furnace and allowed to cool.

A refractory liner material is employed in the bomb to protect the walls of the bomb from the molten metal and slag products and to prevent wall contamination of the thorium metal. Finely ground, electrically fused dolomitic oxide, jolt-packed in position, forms an effective liner for the bomb. The bomb crucible is of welded steel construction.

The thorium-zinc alloy is recovered after the products have solidified in position and cooled to room temperature. This alloy is one large massive piece of metal, referred to as a "biscuit," which is freed of adhering slag. The next

step involves removal of most of the zinc from the massive alloy by heating the biscuit in a vacuum. As the zinc is driven out, the thorium is left in a spongy condition as one piece. A number of dezinced biscuits are melted and cast to give an ingot.

Without the zinc chloride in the initial reduction charge, the products of the reaction would be only thorium metal and calcium fluoride which, by the reaction conditions employed, would not fuse or separate in the bomb. The zinc chloride in the initial charge, by reacting with calcium, serves three main purposes in promoting the separation of the metal and slag phases:

(1) The zinc metal reacts with the thorium metal to give a low-melting alloy.

(2) The calcium chloride formed in the reaction with calcium is a part of the slag, and, as a result, the slag is liquid at a lower temperature than is calcium fluoride alone.

(3) The heat of the auxiliary reaction between zinc chloride and calcium gives a thermal booster effect in the reaction, which effectively increases the temperature of the products to form the liquid state, allowing massive segregation of the metal and slag phases.

A typical charge for a bomb 12 in. in diameter by 45 in. in length consists of 166 lb of thorium fluoride, 60 lb of calcium metal (25 per cent excess), and 16 lb of anhydrous zinc chloride. These ingredients are prepared to pass 100-, 8-, and 60-mesh screens, respectively, before weighing. The thorium fluoride and calcium are allowed to mix for a short time before adding the zinc chloride. This charge yields a thorium–zinc alloy biscuit that weighs about 130 lb and contains roughly 6 weight per cent zinc. For smaller charges the ratio of zinc chloride to thorium fluoride should be somewhat increased. It should be pointed out that the zinc chloride picks up moisture readily from the air, so it must be prepared anhydrous and should then be handled with a minimum of contact with moist air.

Dezincing of Thorium-Zinc Alloy. Heating the alloy biscuit in a vacuum at a temperature of 1100°C (2010°F) removes the zinc. Holding the biscuit for 1 hr at this temperature leaves a fraction of a per cent of zinc in the sponge. Holding at this temperature for up to 8 hr removes essentially all of the zinc. Fast heating is permissible at temperatures up to 1000°C

(1832°F), since very little zinc is volatilized in this range. A fast heating rate at around 1035°C (1895°F) would evolve zinc at such a rate that excessive expansion or even explosion of the biscuit metal could occur; therefore, the alloy temperature is increased slowly between 1000–1100°C (1832–2012°F).

Production of Thorium Ingots from the Bomb Process. The spongy thorium biscuits obtained from the dezincing operation are converted to dense ingots by two methods: (1) by induction melting in a crucible and (2) by consumable electrode arc melting.

Experiences on large-scale induction melting and casting of thorium are described by Wilhelm (see Reference 55) and by Cuthbert.[14] Figure 28.6 is a diagrammatic sketch that represents one system used in this method for melting and casting thorium metal. The thorium sponge is placed in a beryllia crucible fitted with a valve for bottom pouring of the molten metal into a graphite mold. This crucible is contained in a graphite heater which is supported by a block of "Carbocell-60" which, in turn, rests on four tiers of insulation shaped from insulating firebrick. The graphite heater is surrounded by graphite powder thermal insulation which is

held in position by a silica cylinder. This heating assembly is covered by a bell-shaped silica tube, and the entire combination is supported on a water-cooled steel tub.

The hoist type induction coil is adjusted around the outside of the silica cover tube, and, when the pressure has been reduced to 1 μ or less, a fraction of the power from a 100-KW, 3,000-cps motor-generator unit is turned on. Progress of the heating is followed by columbium-tungsten thermocouples, and, after the charge has melted down completely, it is poured into the graphite mold. An upward thrust on the mold-lifting rod causes the beryllia valve to unseat and float to the top of the liquid thorium, thus allowing the metal to flow through the orifice and into the mold where it solidifies. A thorium ingot weighing from 250–300 lb and having a shape depending on the form of the mold can be obtained with the casting unit requiring the 19-in.-diameter silica cover tube. During the vacuum heating to temperatures above 1800°C (3270°F), most of the volatile impurities, including the residual zinc and some radioactive decay products from the thorium, collect on the inside wall of the silica cover tube.

Consumable-electrode arc melting for the preparation of thorum ingots has been described by Roberson and Beall (see Reference 55) and by Cuthbert.[14] The process resembles that used for the arc melting of titanium and zirconium. The thorium sponge should be dezinced to a greater extent than sponge for induction melting. The sponge biscuits may be sawed into narrow slabs that are welded together end to end to give a bar to serve as the primary consumable electrode.

The melting takes place in a reduced pressure of mixed helium and argon. Argon alone will produce a more stable arc, while helium assists in attaining a higher melting rate. The primary electrodes may be melted to give 4-in.-diameter ingots which are welded together to serve as secondary consumable electrodes for preparing larger-diameter ingots of arc-cast thorium. The larger diameter ingots could be recast by a third arc melting to give even larger diameter ingots if desired. Each remelting gives some purification, and the quality of the final metal by arc melting is considered to be equal to that obtainable by the vacuum induction melting described above.

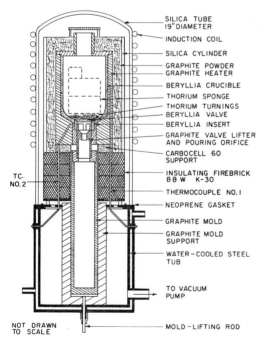

SILICA TUBE 19"DIAMETER
INDUCTION COIL
SILICA CYLINDER
GRAPHITE POWDER
GRAPHITE HEATER
BERYLLIA CRUCIBLE
THORIUM SPONGE
THORIUM TURNINGS
BERYLLIA VALVE
BERYLLIA INSERT
GRAPHITE VALVE LIFTER AND POURING ORIFICE
CARBOCELL 60 SUPPORT
INSULATING FIREBRICK B8W K-30
THERMOCOUPLE NO.1
NEOPRENE GASKET
GRAPHITE MOLD
GRAPHITE MOLD SUPPORT
WATER-COOLED STEEL TUB
TO VACUUM PUMP
MOLD-LIFTING ROD
TC. NO.2
NOT DRAWN TO SCALE

FIGURE 28.6. Diagrammatic sketch of vacuum induction melting and casting unit for thorium metal.

PURIFICATION OF THORIUM METAL

Van Arkel[79] has described a process that can be employed as a means for the refinement of thorium that has first been prepared in the metallic state by some means such as any one of those described above. This process, known as the *crystal bar* or *iodide process*, depends on the reaction of iodine vapor and impure thorium to form thorium iodide vapor at one temperature and, on subsequent decomposition of the iodide on contact with a higher-temperature surface, to give a deposit of purified thorium metal. Veigel, *et al.* (see Reference 55) have described in detail the refinement of small quantities of thorium by this process.

The apparatus and procedure are similar to those developed and used by van Arkel for zirconium and other metals. The operating conditions are different because of the difference in volatility and stability of the iodides. The feed thorium (impure) is held at a temperature of about 450°C (840°F), with a filament temperature of possibly 1300°C (2370°F) or higher for a rapid deposition rate.

The iodide process of purification of metals, in general, is particularly desirable where solid metals of very low oxygen, nitrogen, and carbon contents are required for the evaluation of properties in basic studies.

The Purity of Thorium Metal

In the methods for preparing thorium metal, the purity of the materials employed, the care in processing, and the protection of the product during operations bear heavily on the quality of the final metal. On laboratory-scale operations some exceptionally pure metal has been produced directly. The best approach to high-purity metal, however, seems to be to use good-quality metal as feed material and then to purify it further by the iodide, or crystal bar, process.

For the large-scale consumption of thorium metal, certain commercial processes for thorium can be properly controlled to supply metal of adequate quality directly, so the costly crystal bar purification is employed for preparing only experimental quantities. Table 28.2 gives data on the range of impurity content for commercial thorium and for iodide metal. It is to be

TABLE 28.2. COMPOSITION RANGES OF IMPURITIES IN COMMERCIAL AND IODIDE THORIUM METAL

Impurity	Bomb-reduced induction melt in beryllium oxide (%)	Bomb-reduced consumable-electrode arc melt (%)	Iodide (crystal bar) (%)
Oxygen	0.15 avg	0.18 avg	<0.03
Carbon	0.02–0.08	<0.03	0.02
Nitrogen	0.006–0.016	<0.030	0.002
Aluminum	<0.003	<0.020	<0.005
Silicon	<0.005	<0.005	<0.010
Iron	0.003–0.014	<0.050	<0.013
Zinc	<0.002	<0.050	<0.002

noted that the iodide metal generally contains much less carbon, nitrogen, or oxygen than does either commercial grade.

PHYSICAL, ELECTRICAL, AND THERMODYNAMIC PROPERTIES OF THORIUM METAL

Some of the properties of thorium metal are drastically affected by the presence of certain impurities in relatively small amounts. Since pure grades of thorium such as iodide (crystal bar) were not employed in many of the studies, and thorium of unspecified purity sometimes was used, disagreements between experimental values are to be expected in some areas.

Many of the experimental determinations on the properties of thorium and some of its alloys are treated in detail in chapters by Smith, by Berlincourt, and by Jetter and McHargue in the publication "The Metal Thorium."[55] The brief description which follows will serve to present some values that are believed to represent closely the true properties exhibited by thorium metal. Table 28.3 lists many of these values.

Typical of the variety of values that have been reported for a property of thorium is the range of melting-point temperatures for the metal. Evidently, the melting temperature is affected by small amounts of impurities, and the exact determination of the melting point of the metal is somewhat complicated by possibly a low heat of fusion and the fact that a restricting film tends to form on the surface of even the purest metal in high vacuum and prevents it from flowing at the melting temperature. Reported melting temperatures range from a low of 1120°C (2048°F) to a high of 1850°C

TABLE 28.3. PROPERTIES OF THORIUM[14, 55]

Atomic number	90
Atomic weight	232.05
Crystal structure[6, 10, 17, 37, 40, 58, 76]	
Face-centered cubic up to 1400°C (2552°F)	a_0 [25°C (77°F)] = 5.086 ± 0.001 Å
Body-centered cubic 1400°C (2552°F) to MP	a_0 [1450°C (2642°F)] = 4.11 ± 0.01 Å
Atomic diameter (CN12)	3.596 Å
Density [25°C (77°F)][52, 76, 79, 83]	
x ray	11.72 g/cc
Bomb-reduced (as-cast)	11.5–11.6 g/cc
Arc-melted iodide	11.66 g/cc
Electrical resistivity [25°C (77°F)][52, 54, 76]	
Bomb-reduced metal	18 microhm-cm
Pure thorium (estimated)	13–15 microhm-cm
Temperature coefficient	3.6–4.0 × 10⁻³ per °C
Elastic constants [25°C (77°F)][42, 69, 83]	
Young's modulus	10.3 × 10⁶ psi
Shear modulus	4.1 × 10⁶ psi
Poisson's ratio	0.27
Melting point[17, 52, 76, 79, 81]	1750°C (3182°F)
Boiling point[88, 90]	3500–4200°C (6332–7592°F)
Heat of vaporization[55]	130–145 kcal/mol
Heat of fusion[55]	<4.6 kcal/mol
Linear coefficient of expansion[52, 55, 76]	
25–1000°C (77–1832°F) (mean)	12.5 × 10⁻⁶/°C
Heat capacity at 25°C (77°F)[27]	6.53 cal (gm-atom)⁻¹ × deg⁻¹
Thermal conductivity at 200°C (392°F)[55]	0.09 cal × sec⁻¹ × deg⁻¹ × cm⁻¹
Hall coefficient[55]	−10 × 10⁻⁵ cc/coulomb
Thermal diffusivity at 150°C (302°F)[73]	0.28 cm²/sec
Emissivity (1000–1700°C) (1832–3092°F)[82]	0.38 at 6670 Å
Work function[32, 66, 89]	3.51 ± 0.05 ev
Radioactive half-life (α decay)	1.39 × 10¹⁰ years

(3362°F), with the more recent values for iodide thorium being in the neighborhood of 1750°C (3182°F).

The crystal structures and transformations in thorium metal have been studied by many workers. As discussed by Smith (see Reference 55), Chiotti, in 1950, established the transition of the room-temperature stable-form, face-centered cubic, to a body-centered cubic structure at about 1400°C (2552°F). There were earlier reports that indicated an allotropic change in thorium at 225°C (437°F), but considerable recent work has failed to show any evidence in this regard. Working with high pressures, Bridgman[8] obtained some data that might be interpreted as faint evidence for a transition under special conditions of pressure.

Further and detailed discussions and references to studies of the physical properties of thorium can be found in the treatments re-ferred to above (see Reference 55) and in "Thorium Production Technology" by Cuthbert.[14]

MECHANICAL PROPERTIES OF THORIUM METAL

Milko, Adams, and Harms (see Reference 55) have presented a rather detailed summary of studies made on the mechanical properties of thorium metal. These properties are generally dependent on both the purity of the metal and the previous treatment it received. The rate of fabrication, especially hot extrusion, has been shown by Jetter and McHargue (see Reference 55) to bear on the mechanical properties of the product. In hot [850°C (1560°F)] extrusion tests on thorium containing 0.12 per cent carbon, a tensile strength of 30,500 psi was found for fast-extruded rod, whereas the

TABLE 28.4. TENSILE PROPERTIES OF SOME THORIUM SPECIMENS

Condition	Tensile strength (psi)	0.2% yield strength (psi)	Elongation (2 in.) (%)	Reduction in area (%)
Iodide (sheet) wrought-annealed	17,300	6,900	36	62
Bomb-reduced (sheet)				
Wrought-annealed	39,600	30,300	—	52
Cold rolled 50%	65,400	61,600	—	16
Bomb-reduced (bar)				
Extruded-annealed	34,400	27,600	51	73
Cold rolled 37.5%	49,000	45,400	—	61

same metal, on slow extrusion, gave a rod with a tensile strength of 50,600 psi. Also, the textures of the final metals were found to differ; these effects are believed to be due to an increase in temperature of the rod on the fast extrusion.

Tensile Properties

Some typical values for the tensile properties of thorium are listed in Table 28.4. It is to be noted that the less-pure bomb-reduced sheet metal shows much higher strength than similarly treated iodide metal sheet. The extra carbon in the bomb-reduced metal accounts for only a part of this increase.

The strength of annealed bomb-reduced thorium metal drops in a somewhat regular fashion as its temperature is increased. The tensile and yield strengths at 500°C (932°F) are roughly half the values for the annealed metal at room temperature. The elongation drops to a minimum around 250°C (480°F), however, and then goes above the room temperature value at around 450°C (840°F).

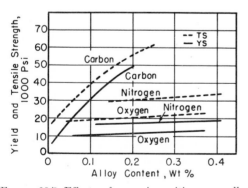

FIGURE 28.7. Effects of some impurities, normally found in thorium, on the tensile properties of annealed thorium.

The effects of carbon, oxygen, or nitrogen addition to iodide thorium on the room temperature yield and tensile strengths of the annealed metal are represented graphically in Figure 28.7. Carbon is much more effective in increasing the tensile strength of thorium than are oxygen and nitrogen.

Hardness

Similarly, the hardness of samples, as can be seen in Figure 28.8, increases for carbon additions at a greater rate than for oxygen or nitrogen. The effects of carbon on hardness and tensile properties are quite likely associated with the solid solubility which carbon, as carbide, has in thorium at room temperature. The VHN hardness of fully annealed thorium is about 38 for iodide metal and 65 for Ames metal.

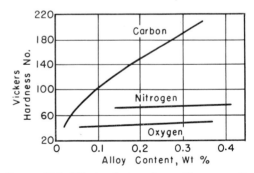

FIGURE 28.8. Effects of some impurities, normally found in thorium, on the hardness of annealed thorium.

Compressibility of Thorium

The compressibility of thorium has been studied by Bridgman.[9] At high pressures the volume varies inversely with pressure. The logarithm of the volume is linear with the logarithm of the pressure. Unit volume at 1 kg/sq cm becomes 0.886 at 10^5 kg/sq cm.

Further and more-detailed discussions of the physical and mechanical properties of thorium can be found in "The Metal Thorium"[55] and "Thorium Production Technology."[14]

THE FABRICATION OF THORIUM

Ingots of commercial-grade thorium metal can be readily worked either hot or cold by most mechanical fabrication processes. The face-centered cubic metal has low hardness, low strength, and high ductility at room temperature. Carbon in excess of 500 ppm and some other impurities, however, tend to impair the good working characteristics, especially for cold fabrication.

Early studies were made by Davenport[16] on the mechanical working of thorium; Cunningham (see Reference 55) has reported results of recent investigations. Most of the recent reports are based on studies employing two sources of thorium, viz., crystal bar (iodide) and commercial thorium which has often been referred to as "Ames (bomb-reduced)" thorium. The crystal bar metal is low in impurities, has low strength, and is the softest solid thorium metal prepared.

During cold rolling, drawing, and swaging of thorium without intermediate annealing, the metal increases in hardness only moderately up to about 40 per cent reduction in area. Further cold rolling up to 99 per cent reduction shows very little increase in hardness; however, Lowenstein[50] has shown that further cold drawing and swaging of extruded rod give definite decreases in hardness of bomb-reduced metal, indicating that this metal could be cold worked in this manner indefinitely without annealing.

The chemical reactivity of thorium must be considered when heating for hot working. The heating may be carried out in a fused salt bath[31] (mixed chlorides of barium and potassium and sodium), or the metal may be jacketed with another metal such as copper.[72] Most hot working operations, whether they are extrusion, forging, rolling, swaging, or combinations of these, are carried out on metal that is at a temperature in the range of 650–950°C (1200–1750°F). Also, because of the chemical reactivity of hot thorium with the oxygen and nitrogen of the air, it is necessary to have an inert gas protective atmosphere in welding thorium.

The metal can be machined easily by all standard operations such as turning, milling, grinding, drilling, and sawing. Its machining characteristics, however, because of its soft and ductile properties, are considered to be rather poor. Good finished surfaces are difficult to prepare by cutting operations; however, such surfaces are seldom required for thorium. The quality and history of the metal can affect its machinability drastically; cold working and some impurities give improved performance. Generally, cutting tools of high-speed steel are very satisfactory for most machining of thorium, but sintered-carbide tools are also used, especially when the thorium contains a sizable quantity of abrasive inclusions. Although the normal commercial grades of thorium can be machined dry, it is advisable to employ a coolant and good ventilation to protect operators from the intake of thorium dust.

ANNEALING AND RECRYSTALLIZATION

Studies at the Oak Ridge National Laboratory on the annealing and recrystallization behaviors of cold worked iodide thorium and of cold worked Ames thorium have been reported by Boyle (see Reference 55). Data on the annealing of cold worked iodide thorium and Ames thorium are represented in Figures 28.9 and 28.10, respectively. The metal was cold rolled to 80 per cent reduction in area before the annealing treatments at the various temperatures. It is to be noted that iodide thorium

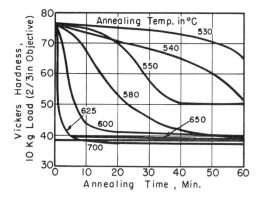

FIGURE 28.9. Isothermal annealing time-hardness curves for iodide thorium 80 per cent cold worked.

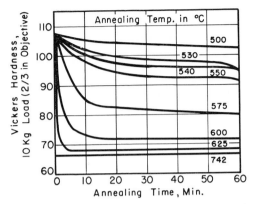

FIGURE 28.10. Isothermal annealing time-hardness curves for Ames thorium 80 per cent cold worked.

appears to anneal at a faster rate at the low temperatures than does the commercial metal, that the hardness range for the iodide is lower, and that both metals anneal completely in a very few minutes at a temperature of about 700°C (1292°F). The effect of subsequent annealing for 1 hr at various temperatures on the hardness of samples of iodide thorium having different degrees of cold working is shown by Figure 28.11. It is to be noted that 20 per cent

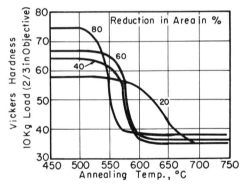

FIGURE 28.11. Annealing temperature effect on hardness of cold worked iodide thorium held at temperature for one hour.

reduction requires a higher temperature than 80 per cent reduction to anneal under these conditions.

Metallographic examination of specimens employed in obtaining hardness data on annealing of cold rolled metal revealed information on recrystallization behaviors. These are summarized in Table 28.5.

METALLOGRAPHY OF THORIUM

Representative microstructures of thorium metal specimens are not easily revealed. The very soft and ductile nature of the metal, coupled with its chemical activity, requires skill, patience, and adequate facilities for properly preparing a sample for best metallographic examination. Early work by Davenport[16] demonstrated that care was required in mechanical grinding and polishing and that an electrolytic etch was effective in revealing microstructures in thorium. Roth (see Reference 55) and Cuthbert[14] have reviewed and summarized much of the recent work of a number of laboratories on the metallography of thorium, and these references should be consulted for a more complete treatment of sample preparation and interpretation of microstructures.

Many variations in sample preparation have been developed for thorium, especially when alloy constituents are also considered. Hard inclusions in the soft matrix require extreme care in grinding and polishing to retain the true structure. It has been said that no one of the metallographic methods employed on thorium is a cure-all, each method leaving something to be desired.

Grinding

Mechanical grinding can be satisfactorily accomplished by any standard grinding tech-

TABLE 28.5. EFFECT OF COLD WORKING ON RECRYSTALLIZATION OF THORIUM*

Reduction in area (%)	Start of recrystallization (°C)		Recrystallization complete (°C)	
	Ames thorium	Iodide thorium	Ames thorium	Iodide thorium
80	520 (968°F)	500 (932°F)	625 (1157°F)	575 (1067°F)
60	520 (968°F)	510–520 (950–968°F)	625 (1157°F)	600 (1112°F)
40	540–550 (1004–1022°F)	520 (968°F)	650 (1202°F)	600 (1112°F)
20	550–575 (1022–1067°F)	550–575 (1022–1067°F)	650 (1202°F)	700 (1292°F)

* Samples held 1 hr at temperature.

nique. The final stage of the grinding may be done with 600-grit silicon carbide paper or 3/0 emery paper with water or kerosene as the lubricant. A grinding material with positive cutting action is desired for the finishing stages in order to reduce metal flow and structure distortion.

Mechanical Polishing

The mechanical polishing of properly ground surfaces is often accomplished by the use of diamond paste on a flat, nap-free type of cloth such as nylon. Although preference varies as to diamond particle sizes, polishing with 6 μ followed by the use of 1 μ is considered adequate for properly revealing inclusions. Alternate processes for mechanical polishing employ commercial levigated alumina. Two stages of polishing, using 15-μ-size and then 0.5-μ-size alumina on silk or broadcloth with water and liquid soap as a lubricant, have been used with and without additions of oxalic acid or very dilute nitric acid to the lubricant.

Electropolishing and Etching

The electrolytic polishing and etching of properly ground thorium specimens have been the subject of many investigations, and many variations in electrolyte composition, voltage, time, and other specifications are reported in the literature. Organic solutions as electrolytes have been found to be generally superior to aqueous solutions; however, some of the most satisfactory organic electrolytes involve a perchloric acid–organic solution which must be considered as a possible explosive. One recommended electrolytic bath which does not contain perchloric acid has the following composition limits (by volume):

100 parts of formic acid (98 per cent)

2 to 4 parts of hydrochloric acid (concentrated)

1 to 2 parts of hydriodic acid (50 per cent)

The use of this bath at a current density of 1.5 amp/sq in. on the sample as anode for 8 sec gives an excellent effect in preserving the inclusions and delineating the grain boundaries of cold worked and annealed thorium.

Inclusions in the Microstructures

Two common impurities in thorium are oxygen and nitrogen; these are combined chemically with thorium and, if present in amounts of more than a few parts per million, show as inclusions in mechanically polished samples. Likewise, carbon, which is a common contaminant, forms a compound, but there is some solid solubility in thorium and only in excess of this will small amounts of carbon show as an inclusion. The color of each of these inclusions by bright-field illumination of freshly polished specimens is for ThO_2, dark gray; for ThN, orange to yellow; and for ThC, an off-white. There is occasionally a "white phase" which shows in the grain boundaries of cast thorium. This phase is quite hard and is assumed to be due to iron or nickel as the compound $Th_7(Fe, Ni)_3$.

THORIUM CHEMISTRY

In the periodic table, thorium is the second element in the actinide series of elements, which includes natural actinium, thorium, protoactinium, and uranium, plus the recently synthesized neptunium, plutonium, and the other transuranic elements. This series of elements parallels in the periodic table the lanthanide series of the rare earths. Thorium is the first member of a radioactive decay series which in 10 successive disintegrations (a combination of 6 α and 4 β) terminates as lead 208. Thorium metal is chemically quite reactive but stands below magnesium in the electromotive force series. Its normal chemical valence is 4, although valences of 2 and 3 are said to be exhibited in a few cases. The heats of forma-

TABLE 28.6. ACTION OF COMMON REAGENTS OF THORIUM METAL

Reagent	Concentration (%)	Activity at 20°C (68°F)
Acetic acid	0–50	Nil
Hydrochloric acid	0–36	Attacked
Nitric acid	0–68	Nil*
Aqua regia	—	Attacked
Sodium hydroxide	0–100	Nil

* Traces of fluoride in the nitric acid solution cause dissolution of thorium metal.

tion for thorium compounds are generally greater than those for corresponding uranium compounds.[25]

The metal, when freshly cut or polished, has a bright, silvery luster. The surface, when exposed to the atmosphere, gradually tarnishes to give a thin, black, somewhat protective film. The rate of surface oxidation appears to be related to the amount of oxide in the metal. If the metal is in the form of sintered powder compacts and its oxide content is high, the metal may oxidize readily in air and disintegrate.

The metal is considered to be quite reactive but as indicated in Table 28.6, is not appreciably attacked by some acids.

Except for the rare gases, all of the nonmetallic elements form binary compounds with thorium. A brief treatment of some of the more important compounds of thorium is presented here. More detailed treatments and extended references, however, are given by Rollefson and Hagemann,[70] by Katzin,[41] and by Cuthbert.[14]

Thorium Oxides

The dioxide, ThO_2, has a fluorite structure,[87] is white, and is the oxide often referred to as "thoria." The residue of a burned mantle of a gas light is mainly thorium dioxide. Thoria can be prepared by thermal decomposition of compounds such as oxalate, hydroxide, and nitrate; also, heating the metal in air or oxygen to high temperatures gives the dioxide. The existence of a monoxide, ThO, having a sodium chloride crystal structure has been reported, but it is the dioxide that crystallizes out of the metal phase to form the oxide inclusions often found in thorium metal microstructures. A hydrated peroxide of thorium, $Th_2O_7 \cdot 4H_2O$, can be precipitated from a solution of a thorium salt by the addition of hydrogen peroxide. On heating $Th_2O_7 \cdot 4H_2O$ to ignition, it decomposes to ThO_2.

Thorium Carbides

Two carbides of thorium, ThC, having a face-centered-cubic structure,[16] and ThC_2, having a c-centered monoclinic structure,[38] are well known. They may be formed by reacting carbon with thorium; the dicarbide may be formed also by reaction of thorium dioxide with carbon. Both carbides hydrolyze readily, giving very

disagreeable odors and thorium oxide. ThC and thorium metal are completely miscible in the solid state at high temperatures.[12]

Thorium Nitrides

Thorium forms two nitrides, ThN and Th_2N_3. These may be prepared by heating thorium metal in an atmosphere of nitrogen. The thorium nitride, Th_2N_3, is dark red, and it reacts readily with water or moist air to give thorium dioxide. The crystal structure of the thorium nitride, Th_2N_3, is hexagonal,[85] whereas that of the other nitride, ThN, is face-centered cubic.[71]

Thorium Hydrides

Two hydrides are known for thorium.[61] The thorium hydride, ThH_2, has a density of 9.2 g/cc and a body-centered tetragonal structure with $a_0 = 4.10$ Å and $c_0 = 5.03$ Å. The other hydride, Th_4H_{15}, has a density of 8.33 g/cc and a cubic structure with 4 molecules per unit cell, and $a_0 = 9.11$ Å.[86] The dihydride is formed by heating the metal in an atmosphere of hydrogen to about 600°C (1110°F). The higher hydride forms when the dihydride is held in an atmosphere of hydrogen at about 250°C (482°F). The formation of these hydrides, followed by their thermal decomposition in a vacuum, gives the basic reactions in converting solid ingot metal to powder.[13] On forming the higher hydride, the charge expands and crumbles to a coarse powder; then complete thermal decomposition of both hydrides is carried out in a vacuum on heating to a temperature usually above 700°C (1290°F), but well below 900°C (1650°F), in order to reduce objectionable resintering of the powdered metal being formed.

The hydrides react with oxygen, the halides, the halogen hydrides, and water. The hydrides exhibit pyrophoricity.

Thorium Halides

Thorium readily forms tetrahalides, the tetrafluoride and tetrachloride being important to metal preparation and the tetraiodide being an intermediate in the crystal bar process for purifying thorium metal. Thorium tetrafluoride is commonly formed by the reaction of anhydrous hydrofluoric acid on thorium dioxide; the reaction is quite exothermic. Thorium tetrachloride can be prepared by passing chlorine gas over a heated mixture of thorium dioxide and carbon or by passing chlorine gas over heated thorium carbide. The thorium tetrachloride is quite hygroscopic, but the thorium tetrafluoride, ThF_4, is not. Thorium tetrachloride can be vacuum sublimed at a red heat, and this serves as a means for its purification.

ALLOYS OF THORIUM

Studies on thorium alloys have been rather extensive since 1940. The interest in thorium as a potential source for atomic fuel led to the development of processes that render the metal available on a relatively large scale for certain applications and, consequently, for studies of a number of the alloys of thorium. The high density, chemical reactivity, mediocre mechanical properties, and high cost of pure thorium metal rule it out as the major constituent of alloys for ordinary structural purposes. Improvement in its properties by alloying could increase its usefulness in atomic energy application.

Most of the alloys prepared and studied so far have exhibited no particularly important property applicable to nonnuclear engineering that is not duplicated or better satisfied by some more common metal or alloy. A sizable fraction of the nonnuclear consumption of thorium, however, goes into magnesium alloy manufacture. The effect of thorium on magnesium was first studied by McDonald,[51] who observed that additions of small amounts of thorium increased significantly both the strength and the ductility of magnesium rolled sheet. The alloys were amenable to precipitation hardening treatments indicating a range of solid solubility.

The addition of thorium up to 1 per cent in cast iron was studied by Baukloh and Meierling.[3] Such additions are claimed to exert a cleansing and desulfurizing action, resulting in increased fluidity of the melt, ductility in the casting, increased tensile strength, and graphitic refinement.

Frohlich and Barthel[23] investigated the addition of thorium to the alloy systems chromium-nickel-iron, chromium-nickel, and chromium-aluminum in the range 0.1 to 1.0

per cent. Life tests were made at 1150–1200°C (2100–2190°F). An increase in useful life of five to six times that of the normal alloys is reported. According to Hessenbruch and Horne,[34] the addition of thorium (0.015 to 2.0 per cent) to 80-20 nickel-chromium shows increased improvement in oxidation resistance at elevated temperatures.

An early review of some alloys of thorium with some of the common metals is given by Guertler.[29] It is reported that thorium acts as a scavenger in steel, similar to vanadium, molybdenum, and titanium, and that the mechanical properties of aluminum are improved by thorium additions.

Binary systems have been studied and diagrams presented for a number of thorium alloys. Many of the systems investigated show more than one intermetallic compound. Nickel and cobalt each form five such compounds with thorium. Iron and aluminum are reported to form four each, while three compounds are recorded for each of manganese, bismuth, silicon, and copper, with thorium. One and two compound systems have been reported for some other binary alloys. A number of the intermetallic compounds of thorium, especially those with copper, silver, gold, bismuth, and lead, are quite pyrophoric.

No compound has been observed in rather complete studies of thorium with each of titanium, vanadium, chromium, zirconium, columbium, hafnium, and uranium. Solid solutions in thorium metal have been observed for a very limited number of systems. Solid thorium exhibits some solubility for carbon, hafnium, and uranium, and extensive solubility for zirconium, cerium, and lanthanum.

For more extensive treatments and references on the constitution of thorium alloys, the reader is referred to summaries by Wilhelm[83] and by Rough, Bauer, and Saller. (See Reference 55.) The recently revised treatment of binary alloys by Hansen[33] also carries information on many thorium alloys.

HEALTH AND SAFETY ASPECTS

Some factors concerning toxicity and other hazards connected with thorium handling have not been thoroughly investigated. Although thorium has apparently been handled on a large scale under controlled conditions without incident, experience has shown that the hazards of thorium are real, they exist in a number of areas, and, for safety, they must be given due regard.

Voigt (see Reference 55) has reviewed the dangers connected with thorium under the headings of chemical toxicity, radiological toxicity, and fire and explosion hazards. In this treatment he presents much of the background material on which understandings of the nature of hazards, of the recommended safety measures, and of the establishment of limits are based. The radiological toxicity associated with thorium is due largely to its radioactive decay products, and, because of this, the waste materials often carry potentially hazardous radio isotopes. The reader is referred to the report by Voigt for details and references on the health and safety aspects of thorium handling.

APPLICATIONS

The major applications of thorium (its use in nuclear power, magnesium alloys, and mantles) have been discussed briefly in the introductory part of this chapter. The major impetus to recent expanded interest in thorium has been afforded by its potentialities in the atomic power area; however, interest in thorium-magnesium alloys is rapidly expanding, while the gas mantle industry seems to have stabilized somewhat and still represents a sizable fraction of total consumption. The mantle usage at present is principally in portable gas lights. There are many other fairly important uses of thorium that require relatively small amounts, either as oxide or as metal.

Nuclear Uses of Thorium

The form of the thorium for use in nuclear applications, discussed by Howe,[36] includes the metal, alloys, and compounds. It should be pointed out, however, that although very active large-scale developments are under way in the use of thorium to form uranium 233, no reactor has yet been operated on uranium 233,[77] so the future of thorium in atomic power has not yet been clearly established.* Thorium metal and

* Editor's note: The Indian Point, N.Y., plant of Consolidated Edison Co. of New York, rated at 275,000 KW and due to come onstream in 1961, uses a thorium breeder nuclear power plant. It will

thorium-uranium alloys clad with a protective metal such as zirconium or stainless steel are being tested, and metallic slurries of thorium-bismuth compound in liquid bismuth and aqueous slurries of thorium oxide are also being tested as practical approaches to the use of thorium in atomic power.

It is very desirable, in a long-range atomic power program, to be able to generate new atomic fuel atoms at a rate at least equivalent to that at which fuel atoms are consumed. On the average, at least 2 neutrons from each fissioning atom must find the proper targets (a fuel atom to keep the chain going, and a fertile atom to generate a new fuel atom) if the generated fuel is to be equivalent to that consumed.

There are numerous effects in any well-designed reactor that unavoidably cause losses of neutrons to the desired reactions. Absorption of neutrons by other components of a reactor as well as by impurities, escape of neutrons to the shield, absorption by fission and daughter products, and absorption resulting in side reactions are the main causes of the losses of neutrons. The number of neutrons liberated per atom that fissions must then actually be much greater than 2 if 100 per cent fuel regeneration is to become a reality.

An atomic furnace designed to operate on thermal neutrons and to give total regeneration of the fuel appears possible only with the thorium and uranium 233 cycle. A comparison of the three fission fuels in regard to the number of fission (liberated) neutrons per thermal neutron absorbed shows, for uranium 233, uranium 235, and plutonium 239, values of 2.28, 2.06, and 2.03, respectively. Because of the unavoidable losses of neutrons in a reactor, thermal neutron reactors in which plutonium 239 is the fuel have essentially no possibility

require an estimated 41,580 lb of thorium the first year of operation and 20,750 lb each succeeding year. Other nuclear power plants using thorium in the reactors are the Rural Cooperative Power Association plant, 22,000 KW, at Elk River, Minn., and the Enrico Fermi Plant of Power Reactor Development Co. and Detroit Edison Co., 100,000 KW, near Detroit, Mich. The Atomic Energy Commission estimates that some 10 tons/year of thorium metal will be required for atomic energy purposes during the next few years. (See *Chem. Week*, Sept. 19, 1959.)

of generating an equivalent amount of plutonium 239 from uranium 238. These data indicate, however, that once the thorium and uranium 233 cycle is primed, the generation of even more uranium 233 fuel than is burned and the complete utilization of all thorium for atomic power can be within the realm of possibility.

There are disadvantages as well as other advantages in the use of thorium in a reactor.[77] Perhaps the greatest weakness of thorium is the generation, through side nuclear reactions of highly radioactive materials that contaminate both the uranium 233 product and the residual thorium. Uranium 232, the major cause of this contamination, is formed directly by an (n, 2n) reaction on uranium 233 and indirectly following an (n, 2n) reaction on thorium 232. Intense and hard gamma activity of the contaminating isotopes and the toxicity of uranium 233 itself complicate the processing that is essential to the occasional recovery of purified fuel and thorium and to their subsequent fabrication. Remotely controlled and well-contained processing and fabrication operations appear to be necessary with thorium utilization for atomic power.

For fast neutron reactors the thorium and uranium 233 cycle should maintain its fuel regeneration potentialities, although here the uranium 238 and plutonium 239 cycle appears to be at least equally regenerative. Fast neutron power plants have not yet been put into operation, however.

The use of thorium in atomic power development in the United States has not at any time received the attention that uranium has because of the demand for plutonium. The explanation lies in the value placed on plutonium because of its military might. Because of certain nuclear effects associated with uranium 233, its value as a weapon does not compare favorably with plutonium. Consequently, there should then be less need for international inspection and security safeguards when thorium is used as the fertile element in power-fuel production.[77]

Nonnuclear Uses of Thorium

Thorium is an important alloying element in magnesium because it contributes high strength properties and creep resistance to magnesium at elevated temperatures. Although thorium metal has a density similar to lead, the amounts necessary to impart these desirable properties to magnesium are sufficiently low (about 3 per cent) to give lightweight alloys that are definitely advantageous for some airplane and missile construction. Leontis[46] has reviewed the magnesium alloys containing thorium, and the reader is referred to his report for further details.

Other nonnuclear uses of thorium have been reviewed by Lilliendahl.[48] The relatively low work-function and high electron-emissive properties of thorium find commercial application in several lamps of the gaseous-discharge type. Its use as an electrode material provides a lower starting potential, more uniform operating characteristics, and, in some cases, a longer life than is found with either oxide-coated electrodes or thoriated tungsten. In some applications the radioactive properties of thorium are utilized in the production of ionized particles, as described by Nottingham.[60]

The metal has been used in photoelectric tubes for the measurement of a wide band of the ultraviolet spectrum. The response of commercial tubes extends from 2000–3750 Å. The construction and operation of such tubes are described by Rentschler, et al.[67] The effect of gaseous impurities in the metal on the photoelectric response is reported by Rentschler and Henry.[65]

The advantage of thorium metal in lamps of the gaseous discharge type, such as a high-intensity mercury lamp, as described by Freeman,[22] may be demonstrated by use of the data in Table 28.7. The electrodes at opposite ends of the lamp tube consist of a thorium wire inserted in a tungsten helix. The operating characteristics of lamps containing a composite thorium electrode and those with alkaline earth

TABLE 28.7. THORIUM VERSUS ALKALINE EARTH OXIDE-COATED ELECTRODES*

Operating time (hr)	Lumens output	
	Thorium electrodes	Oxide-coated electrodes
0	3,610	3,450
100	3,260	3,180
500	3,090	2,680
1,000	3,030	2,320
2,000	2,620	1,430

* Courtesy of AIEE.

oxide-coated electrodes can be compared after various periods of operation. The superiority of thorium electrodes with increasing time of operation is apparent from these data.

Thorium metal has been used in germicidal lamps of the cold cathode type. These lamps generally have hollow, cylindrical nickel electrodes with a tab of thorium spot welded inside the electrode. Thorium is deposited by sputtering onto the nickel, providing a surface of lower work function and lower starting voltage. Other applications of thorium in lamps are described by Barnes[2] and by Gustin and Freeman.[30]

Nonnuclear Application of Thorium Oxide

The major consumption of thorium oxide is in the gas mantle industry, as referred to above. Although, in some uses, these mantles are gradually being replaced with tungsten or vapor lamp installations, their use in portable gas light sources has increased.

Another important application of thorium oxide in the lighting industry is in the control of grain size of tungsten filaments used as a source of radiant energy. Pure tungsten is unsatisfactory for filaments, because the rate of crystal growth is rapid at elevated temperatures and results in large, equiaxed grains subject to slip along grain boundaries. Such wires fail by "offsetting" and burn out. The addition of thorium oxide (0.8 to 1.2 per cent), which is added in the form of nitrate to the tungstic acid prior to reduction to metallic tungsten, results in a stabilized, relatively small grain size in the finished wire. This is not subject to "offsetting," and such wires have greater vibrational strength than do either pure tungsten or those doped with so-called volatile dopes, such as potassium chloride or silica. For details on this subject, reference should be made to Smithells.[74]

Special thorium composite systems are important, particularly those containing the oxide dispersed in a matrix of tungsten. These are used as a source of primary electron emission. The thorium oxide content is usually 1 to 2 per cent by weight.

The thermionic emission from thoriated tungsten is dealt with in numerous publications. A good industrial approach to this subject is found in "Industrial Electronics Reference Book."[39] Such emission results from the absorp-

tion of thermal energy by conduction electrons, sufficient to overcome the work function of a specific surface. The lower the work function, the greater the emission one can expect. Maximum emission occurs when approximately 70 per cent of the active surface is covered. The work function of thoriated tungsten has been determined by several experimenters. Some of the values are given in Table 28.8. These values compare with values of 3.36 obtained by Zwikker[88,90] and 3.51 shown in Table 28.3 for the thermionic work function of pure thorium.

TABLE 28.8. WORK FUNCTION OF
THORIATED TUNGSTEN

Work function (volts)	A*	Reference
2.63	3.0	Dushman[20]
2.64	3.2	Nottingham[59]
2.86	6.5	Brattain[7]
2.77	—	Reimann[64]

* Constant in Richardson-Dushman thermionic emission equation.

Thorium oxide has been used in electronic devices wherein the cathode is subjected to bombardment by charged particles, as in magnetrons. The thermionic emission obtained is comparable to that from thoriated tungsten at the same temperature of operation.[15,84]

A substantial amount of thorium oxide is being used in the fabrication of thoriated tungsten electrodes for welding operations, and also as nonconsumable electrodes in the arc melting of the transition metals. The role of the oxide is chiefly that of maintaining arc stability.

Thorium oxide is the most stable of the refractory oxides and has been used to a limited extent in crucibles for specialized melting operations.[11] Its resistance to thermal shock is poor, and it does not appear possible to melt the transition metals in thoria without some solution of the oxide in the metal matrix resulting.

References

1. Arsem, W. C., U.S. Patent 1,085,098 (1914).
2. Barnes, L. E., *Illum. Eng.*, **46**, 41 (1951).
3. Baukloh, W., and Meierling, J., *Giesserei*, **29**, 93 (1942).
4. Berger, K., Disserattioen Basel, "Gmelin Kraut Handbuch" (1907).
5. Berzelius, J. J., *Pogg. Ann.*, **16**, 385 (1829).
6. Bohlin, H., *Ann. Physik*, **61**, 421 (1920).

7. Brattain, W. H., and Becker, J. A., *Phys. Rev.*, **43**, 428 (1933).

8. Bridgman, P. W., *Phys. Rev.*, **48**, 825 (1935).

9. Bridgman, P. W., *Proc. Am. Acad. Arts Sci.*, **76**, 55 (1948).

10. Burgers, W. G., and van Liempt, J., *Z. anorg. u. allgem. Chem.*, **193**, 144 (1930).

11. Calderwood, W., *U.S. Atomic Energy Comm., Rept. No. 2736* (1945).

12. Chiotti, P., *U.S. Atomic Energy Comm., Rept. No. AECD-3072* (1950).

13. Chiotti, P., and Rogers, B. A., *Metal Progr.*, **60**, 60 (1951).

14. Cuthbert, F. L., "Thorium Production Technology," Reading, Mass., Addison-Wesley Publishing Company, 1958.

15. Danforth, W. E., *J. Franklin Inst.*, **248**, 449 (1949).

16. Davenport, E. S., *Am. Inst. Mining Met. Engrs., Tech. Publ. No. 226* (1929).

17. D'Eye, R. W. M., *U.S. Atomic Energy Comm., Rept. No. AERE-C/R-425* (1949).

18. Dickson, B. H., and Kaufman, D., *U.S. Atomic Energy Comm., Rept. No. AECD-2887* (1950).

19. Driggs, F. H., and Lilliendahl, W. C., *Ind. Eng. Chem.*, **22**, 1302 (1930).

20. Dushman, S., and Ewald, I., *Phys. Rev.*, **29**, 857 (1927).

21. Espe, W., *Powder Met. Bull.*, **4**, 17 (1949).

22. Freeman, G. A., *Elec. Eng.*, **59**, 444 (1940).

23. Frohlich, K. W., and Barthel, A., *Metallwirtschaft*, **21**, 103 (1942).

24. Frondel, Clifford, *U.S. Geological Survey, Bull. No. 1064* (1958).

25. Glassner, Alvin, *U.S. Atomic Energy Comm., Rept. No. ANL-5750* (1957).

26. Glasstone, S., "Source Book on Atomic Energy," Princeton, N.J., D. Van Nostrand Company, Inc., 1950.

27. Griffel, M., and Skochdopole, R. E., *J. Am. Chem. Soc.*, **75**, 5250 (1953).

28. Grimaldi, F. S., and Marsh, C. A., *U.S. Atomic Energy Comm., Rept. No. AECD 2818* (1947).

29. Guertler, W., *Metallwirtschaft*, **19**, 435 (1940).

30. Gustin, D. S., and Freeman, G. A., *U.S. Patents 2,241,345; 2,241,362* (1941).

31. Hamby, D. E., *U.S. Atomic Energy Comm., Rept., No. ORNL 1090* (1951).

32. Hamer, R. J., *J. Opt. Soc. Am.*, **9**, 251 (1924).

33. Hansen, Max, "Constitution of Binary Alloys," 2nd Ed., New York, McGraw-Hill Book Company, Inc., 1958.

34. Hessenbruch, W., and Horne, L., *Z. Metallk.*, **36**, 145 (1944).

35. Hopkins, B. S., "Chapters in the Chemistry of Less Familiar Elements," Champaign, Ill., Stipes Publishing Co., 1939.

36. Howe, John P., *Metal Progr.*, **71**, 97 (1957).

37. Hull, A. W., *Phys. Rev.*, **18**, 88 (1921).

38. Hunt, E. B., and Rundle, R. E., *J. Am. Chem. Soc.*, **73**, 4777 (1951).

39. "Industrial Electronics Reference Book," New York, John Wiley & Sons, Inc., 1948.

40. James, W. J., and Straumanis, M. E., *Acta Cryst.*, **9**, 376 (1956).

41. Katzin, L. I., "The Chemistry of Thorium," in "The Actinide Elements," by G. T. Seaborg and J. J. Katz, New York, McGraw-Hill Book Company, Inc., 1954.

42. Köster, W., *Z. Metallk.*, **39**, 1 (1948).

43. Kroll, W., *Z. Metallk.*, **28**, 30 (1936).

44. Kuzel, H., and Wedekind, E., U.S. Patent 1,088,909 (1914).

45. Lely, D., and Hamberger, L., *Z. anorg. u. allgem. Chem.*, **87**, 209 (1914).

46. Leontis, T. E., *Metal Progr.*, **72**, 97 (1957).

47. Levy, S. I., "The Rare Earths," London, Edward Arnold & Co., 1924.

48. Lilliendahl, W. C., *Metal Progr.*, **71**, 104 (1957).

49. Lilliendahl, W. C., U.S. Patent 2,537,067 (1951).

50. Lowenstein, P., *U.S. Atomic Energy Comm., Rept. No. MIT-1102*, p. 47 (1952).

51. McDonald, J. C., *Trans. Am. Inst. Mining Met. Engrs.*, **143**, 179 (1941).

52. Marden, J. W., and Rentschler, H. C., *Ind. Eng. Chem.*, **19**, 97 (1927).

53. Meerson, G. A., *Proc. Intern. Conf. Peaceful Uses Atomic Energy, Geneva, 1955, No. P/635*, **8** (1956).

54. Meissner, W., and Voigt, B., *Ann. Physik*, **7**, 892 (1930).

55. "The Metal Thorium," Proceedings of USAEC-ASM Conference on Thorium, Cleveland, American Society for Metals (1958).

56. "Minerals Yearbook (U.S. Bur. Mines)" Washington, D.C., Government Printing Office, 1956, 1957, 1958.

57. Moissan, H., and Honigschmidt, O., *Ann. chim. et phys.*, **8**, 182 (1905).

58. Neuberger, M. C., *Z. Krist.*, **93**, 1 (1936).

59. Nottingham, W. B., *Phys. Rev.*, **41**, 793 (1932).

60. Nottingham, W. B., *Rev. Sci. Instr.*, **11**, 2 (1940).

61. Nottorf, W., *U.S. Atomic Energy Comm., Rept. No. AECD-2984* (1945).

62. Pilkington, E. S., and Wylie, A. W., *J. Soc. Chem. Ind. (London)*, **66**, 387 (1947).

63. "The Rare Earth Industry," London, Crosby Lockwood & Son, Ltd., 1918.

64. Reimann, A. L., *Proc. Roy. Soc. (London)*, **A163**, 499 (1937).

65. Rentschler, H. C., and Henry, D. E., *J. Opt. Soc. Am.*, **26**, 30 (1936).

66. Rentschler, H. C., and Henry, D. E., *Trans. Electrochem. Soc.,* **87**, 289 (1945).
67. Rentschler, H. C., Henry, D. E., and Smith, K. O., *Rev. Sci. Instr.,* **3**, 794 (1932).
68. Rentschler, H. C., Lilliendahl, W. C., and Gray, J., U.S. Patent 2,446,062 (1948).
69. Reynolds, M. B., *U.S. Atomic Energy Comm., Rept. No. AECD-3242* (1951).
70. Rollefson, G. K., and Hagemann, F., *U.S. Atomic Energy Comm., Rept. No. CB-3717* (1947).
71. Rundle, R. E., *Acta Cryst.,* **1**, 180 (1948).
72. Schumar, J. F., and Macherey, R., *U.S. Atomic Energy Comm., Rept. No. CT-3731* (1946).
73. Sidles, P. H., and Danielson, G. C., *U.S. Atomic Energy Comm., Rept. No. ISC-761* (1956).
74. Smithells, C. J., "Tungsten," 3rd Ed., London, Chapman & Hall, Ltd., 1952.
75. Spencer, J., "The Metals of the Rare Earth," London, Edward Arnold & Co., 1918.
76. Thompson, J. G., *Metals & Alloys,* **4**, 114 (1933).
77. "Thorium-U233 Symposium," *U.S. Atomic Energy Comm., Rept. No. BNL 483(C-26)* (1958).
78. Urie, R. W., *J. Soc. Chem. Ind. (London),* **66**, 437 (1947).
79. van Arkel, A. E., "Reine Metalle," p. 212, Ann Arbor, Mich., Edwards Bros., Inc., 1943.
80. von Bolten, W., *Z. Elektrochem.,* **14**, 768 (1908).
81. von Wartenberg, H., *Z. Elektrochem.,* **15**, 866 (1909).
82. Whitney, L. V., *Phys. Rev.,* **48**, 458 (1935).
83. Wilhelm, H. A., Chapter on thorium in "Metallurgy and Fuels," by H. M. Finneston and J. P. Howe, New York, McGraw-Hill Book Company, Inc., 1956.
84. Wright, D. A., *Nature,* **160**, 129 (1947).
85. Zachariasen, W. H., *Acta Cryst.,* **2**, 288 (1949).
86. Zachariasen, W. H., *Acta Cryst.,* **6**, 393 (1953).
87. Zachariasen, W. H., *Phys. Rev.,* **73**, 1104 (1948).
88. Zwikker, C., *Physica,* **8**, 240 (1928).
89. Zwikker, C., *Physik. Z.,* **30**, 578 (1929).
90. Zwikker, C., *Proc. Acad. Sci. Amsterdam,* **29**, 792 (1926).

29. TITANIUM

H. R. Ogden

Battelle Memorial Institute
Columbus, Ohio

A decade ago titanium was considered a rare metal. Today, it is the basis of an entire industry. The element itself was first discovered in England by Gregor in 1790, although it did not receive its name until Klaproth found it in Hungary in 1795 and named it after the mythological first sons of the earth, the Titans. Gregor discovered titanium in iron-bearing sands of the type known today as ilmenite, and Klaproth found it in the more highly concentrated form in rutile sands. Neither Gregor nor Klaproth succeeded in isolating elemental titanium but, rather, isolated the oxide, TiO_2.

Although many investigators attempted to isolate titanium, it was not until 1910 that Hunter succeeded in preparing metallic titanium by the reduction of the tetrachloride with sodium in a steel bomb. This, however, was not the initiation of the titanium industry of today. Subsequent to Hunter's work, titanium remained a laboratory curiosity until Kroll, in 1946, working for the United States Bureau of Mines, proved that titanium could be produced on a pilot-plant scale by the magnesium reduction of titanium tetrachloride. This culminated many years of metallurgical research in Kroll's laboratory in Luxembourg. The E. I. du Pont de Nemours and Company converted this process to a commercial scale and became the first producer of metallic titanium for general sale in September, 1948.

Titanium is one of the transition elements, occupying a place in Group IV, Period 4, of Mendeleeff's periodic table. It has an atomic number of 22 and an atomic weight of 47.9. Being one of the transition elements, titanium has an incompletely filled d shell in its electronic structure and, like other transition elements, has a high modulus of elasticity to density ratio and a high melting point. The high melting point together with the high reactivity, particularly at elevated temperatures, have made titanium difficult to refine.

OCCURRENCE[2]

Titanium is the ninth-ranking element in abundance in the earth's crust. It is exceeded by oxygen, silicon, aluminum, iron, calcium, sodium, potassium, and magnesium. Practically all crystalline rocks, sand, clay, and other soils contain titanium; in fact, 98 per cent of all rocks examined in a study of the relative abundance of the elements contained titanium. It has been found in coal, oil, natural waters, vegetation, and animal flesh and bones, in volcanic ash and deep-sea dredging, and in meteorites and various stars. With this widespread distribution, it is not surprising to find numerous deposits of highly concentrated titanium minerals which are readily accessible and easily mined.

Of the many minerals containing titanium, only two are of prime commercial importance —ilmenite, a combined titanium-iron oxide, and rutile (TiO_2). The latter mineral is the richest in titanium content, but it is of lesser volume importance because it is usually so diluted with other rocks in scattered deposits and in beach or river sands that concentration is a big problem. Rutile forms tetragonal crystals. Two other minerals of the same composition (TiO_2) are brookite, which forms orthorhombic crystals, and anatase or octahedrite, which also

559

forms tetragonal crystals but of a higher hardness and a different ratio of the axes from rutile.

Ilmenite is of particular importance, since it frequently occurs as massive ore deposits where little or no concentration is needed. Commercially important deposits of ilmenite are found both in crystalline rocks, often with hematite or magnetite in massive lenses, and in secondary deposits of sands in beaches and rivers. Until recently, sand deposits of rutile and ilmenite were of greater commercial importance than rock, but, within the last decade, rock deposits have become the chief source. The composition of ilmenite varies considerably, since titanium and iron oxide form a series of compounds. Usually, it is expressed as a simple iron titanate ($FeO \cdot TiO_2$), but the term covers a family of ilmenites or titanium combined with various proportions of hematite or magnetite. Commonly, ilmenite contains about 32 per cent titanium and 37 per cent iron.

Probably the largest known titanium ore reserve is located in the Allard Lake district of eastern Quebec. Two large high-grade deposits of an ilmenite-hematite mixture are estimated to contain many hundreds of millions of tons of ore. Other major sources of titanium ore in North America are located in New York, Virginia, Florida, and North Carolina. Known deposits of possible future importance are in Minnesota, Rhode Island, Wyoming, Montana, California, Oklahoma, Colorado, and New Mexico. Among other areas in the world having known important ore bodies are Australia, Brazil, India, Federation of Malay, Norway, U.S.S.R., Sweden, Finland, Portugal, Manchuria, and various places in Africa. Almost all of these ore bodies are rich in titanium, having a titanium dioxide content between 40 and 60 per cent. Recovery of titania as a by-product in the treatment of residues or tailings in the treatment of bauxite and of copper ores is a possibility. Thus, in the strictest sense of the word, titanium is not a rare metal but a most abundant metal. The difficulties encountered in processing these ores into metal, however, have kept titanium for so long on the rare metal list.

PRODUCTION

Production of titanium in the form of sponge has increased steadily over the past several years, accompanied by a steady decrease in price. A decrease in demand for titanium in the latter part of 1957 and the early part of 1958 caused a slump in production of titanium mill products but did not alter the steady decrease in price. Titanium sponge and mill-product production and sponge prices for the period 1950 to 1959 are given in Table 29.1.

TABLE 29.1. TITANIUM PRODUCTION AND COST*

Year	Sponge production (short tons)	Mill production (short tons)	Sponge† price ($/lb)	Approximate price for mill products ($/lb)	
				Billet	Sheet‡
1950	75	—	5.00	9.00	15.00
1951	495	75§	5.00	9.00	15.00
1952	1,075	250§	5.00	9.00	15.00
1953	2,241	1,114	5.00	9.00	15.00
1954	5,370	1,299	4.72	9.00	15.00
1955	7,398	1,898	4.50–3.45	8.00	14.00
1956	14,595	5,166	3.45–2.75	7.00	13.00
1957	17,263	5,658	2.75–2.25	6.00	11.00
1958	4,585	2,594	2.25–1.82	4.50	9.00
1959	3,898	3,211	1.82–1.60	4.50	7.50

* Statistics to 1956 from "Mineral Yearbook (U.S. Bur. Mines)" (1956); 1957, 1958, and 1959 statistics from *Am. Metal Market.*

† Price for A-1 grade; A-2 grade has been 25 to 30 cents/lb less.

‡ Commercially pure, alloy grades are higher.

§ Estimated.

The decrease in demand for titanium in late 1957 was the direct result of a cutback in orders for military aircraft and jet engines. The decrease in demand, however, does not reflect a lack of interest in titanium and titanium alloys for military uses but, rather, is a reflection of the change in emphasis from aircraft to missiles that occurred at that time. Actually, the amount of titanium per unit aircraft has steadily increased, despite the 1957–58 slump. Present indications are that the production and use of titanium mill products is once again increasing steadily.

EXTRACTIVE METALLURGY

The reactivity of titanium at high temperatures has made its extraction from ores particularly difficult. By carbon reduction in an electric arc furnace, the oxide can be at least partially reduced, but the resultant product is a brittle carbide or, if done in air, a carbo- nitride, or a crude metal so contaminated with carbon, oxygen, and nitrogen as to be useless structurally. This ease of reaction at high tem- peratures is exemplified by the difficulty in handling molten titanium, since it reacts with every known refractory sufficiently to produce serious contamination. Special methods, conse- quently, have had to be devised to produce the relatively pure metal and to melt and cast it. Since the product of the present titanium- production plants is titanium sponge, and melt- ing and alloying is done largely by processing plants, melting and casting is considered under the heading "Processing and Fabrication."

Oxide Reduction[2]

Attempts to use carbon reduction of titanium dioxide have been unsuccessful in producing a satisfactory ductile metal. By using metal re- duction, as metallic calcium or sodium, some hot-ductile metal has been produced experi- mentally. Calcium has been most favored as a reducer of the oxide, but the relatively high cost of the metal, the need for it to be nitrogen free (since any nitrogen present reacts with the titanium), and the unsatisfactory purity of the metal obtained thus far have prevented this from becoming a commercially successful process.

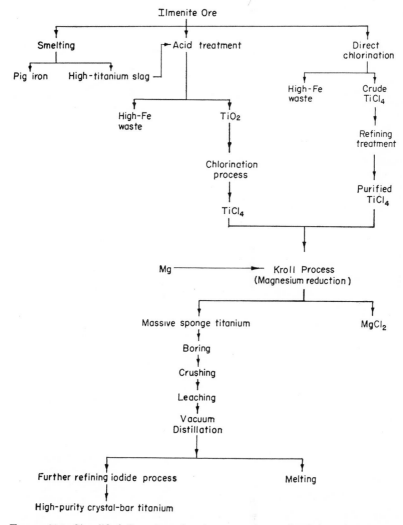

FIGURE 29.1. Simplified flow sheet for the extraction and refining of titanium.

Magnesium Reduction of Titanium Tetrachloride[7,10]

By going to the tetrachloride as a base for reduction, difficulties from excessive oxygen and nitrogen contamination can be avoided, as Kroll found in his experimental work. Titanium tetrachloride is easily purified. Since it is liquid at room temperature [b.p. 136.4°C (277.5°F)], it is readily handled. Magnesium forms a suitable reducing metal. It is comparatively inexpensive, and is largely recovered as magnesium chloride, which can be electrolytically reduced to metal and recycled. The reaction of molten magnesium with titanium tetrachloride is vigorous and exothermic, yet it is readily controlled. In early pilot plant operation, the resultant magnesium chloride was removed from the titanium powder dispersed through the melt by washing with cold hydrochloric acid. This gave a titanium powder that was consolidated to ductile metal by pressing and sintering, a normal powder metallurgy procedure. In commercial production the magnesium chloride and residual magnesium have been distilled off to leave a titanium sponge which can be crushed to a size suitable for arc melting or induction melting into ingot form. A general flow sheet of this method is shown in Figure 29.1.

Sodium Reduction of Titanium Tetrachloride[13]

The reduction of titanium tetrachloride with sodium as the reducing agent also is being used to produce titanium sponge. This process is similar to the magnesium-reduction process and follows the same general steps shown in the flow sheet of Figure 29.1, except that pure sodium is used in place of magnesium. Because of its lower valence, twice as much sodium as magnesium is required to produce a pound of titanium. Since the price of sodium is about one-half that of magnesium, the cost of the sodium is about the same as the magnesium. The titanium sponge produced by the sodium process is very similar in purity to the titanium sponge produced by the magnesium reduction process.

The Iodide Process

De Boer and Van Arkel,[13] working with the Phillips Gloelampenfabrik in the Netherlands, many years ago found an effective way to pre-

TABLE 29.2. TYPICAL ANALYSES OF TITANIUM

Type of titanium	Composition (%)											
	C	O	N	Al	Cu	Fe	Mg	Mn	Mo	Ni	Si	Sn
Iodide titanium	0.01–0.03	0.005–0.01	0.001–0.004	0.013–0.05	0.0015–0.002	0.0035–0.025	0.0015–0.002	0.005–0.013	0.0015	0.003	<0.03	<0.01
Magnesium reduced titanium	0.01–0.03	0.005–0.15	0.01–0.05	<0.005	<0.03	0.03–0.2	0.04–0.12	0.03–0.06	—	—	<0.01	<0.03

pare pure ductile titanium by thermally decomposing the tetraiodide. It consisted simply of (1) packing the periphery of a glass tube with crude titanium, such as that produced by sodium or calcium reduction of the oxide or tetrachloride, (2) evacuating and introducing a small amount of iodine into the system, (3) electrically heating to about 1300°C (2372°F) a tungsten filament that had been sealed into the center of the tube, and (4) warming the entire tube to about 150°C (302°F) to effect iodination of the crude titanium. Thenceforth, the operation was largely automatic, since the tetraiodide thus formed decomposed thermally

on the hot tungsten filament and released iodine, which completed the cycle by reacting with crude metal at the lower temperature.

In recent years this general procedure has been used to produce titanium in the United States on both an experimental and a small commercial scale. Metal tubes are used in conjunction with titanium starting wires, which are heated safely just below the melting point. This refining procedure has been comparatively expensive, chiefly because of the cost of the raw material, the low production rates obtained, and the small scale of operation. It has produced the best quality of titanium, since oxygen

TABLE 29.3. SUMMARY OF PHYSICAL PROPERTIES OF UNALLOYED TITANIUM*

Property	Value
Atomic number	22
Atomic weight	47.90 g/mole
Absorption cross section for thermal neutrons	5.8 ± 0.4 barns/atom
Crystal structure	
Alpha, hexagonal, close-packed	c = 4.6832 ± 0.0004 Å
	a = 2.9504 ± 0.0004 Å
Beta, cubic, body-centered	c/a = 1.5873
	a = 3.28 ± 0.003 Å
Density	4.54 g/cc
Compressibility	0.80×10^{-6} sq cm/kg
Surface tension	1,200 dynes/cm
Velocity of sound	16,320 ft/sec
Coefficient of thermal expansion, α, at 20°C (68°F)	8.4×10^{-6} in./in./°C
Thermal conductivity	0.041 cal/cm/sec/°C
Specific heat	0.125 cal/°C/g
Transformation temperature	882.5°C (1620°F)
Latent heat of transformation	1,050 cal/mole
Heat of fusion	5 kcal
Melting temperature	1668°C (3035°F)
Heat of vaporization	112,500 cal/mole
Boiling temperature, estimated	3260°C (5900°F)
Electrical resistivity	
High purity	42 microhm-cm
Commercial purity	55 microhm-cm
Superconductivity, critical temperature	0.38°K
Hall coefficient	$+ 1.82 \pm 0.2 \times 10^{-13}$ volt-cm/amp/oersted
Magneto-resistance coefficient, B_t	6.6×10^{-13}/oersted²
Magnetic susceptibility	3.17×10^{-6} ($\pm 0.03 \times 10^{-6}$) emu/g
Magnetic permeability	1.00005
Emissivity	
Alpha [810–870°C (1490–1598°F)]	0.459
Beta [1398.9°C (2550°F)]	0.42
Work function	4.17 ev
Band width (from soft x-ray spectra)	6.0 ± 0.5 ev
Electronic specific heat	8.00×10^{-4} cal/°C/mole
Modulus of elasticity	15.5×10^{6} psi

* Data from W. J. Lepkowski and J. W. Holladay, *TML Report No. 73*, July 25, 1957, Titanium Metallurgical Laboratory, Battelle Memorial Institute, Columbus, Ohio.

and nitrogen are kept to a very low contamination level. This method has been used particularly for making titanium for experimental purposes. A typical analysis is given in Table 29.2.

Electrolytic Production of Titanium[3,12]

The production of titanium by electrolysis has been largely limited to electrorefining of impure titanium or scrap, although considerable research has been conducted on various processes for electrowinning titanium. In all of these processes, a fused salt bath is used as the electrolyte. Usually, a subchloride of titanium, such as titanium dichloride or titanium trichloride or a fluotitanate, is dissolved in a low melting salt bath. For the electrowinning of titanium, the titanium salts are added to the bath, they are reduced, and titanium is deposited on the cathode. In the electrorefining process the impure titanium is the anode which dissolves in the fused salt bath as the divalent ion

and is subsequently deposited at the cathode as high-purity titanium.

The purity of titanium produced by these processes is excellent, particularly that made by the electrorefining process. The United States Bureau of Mines has electrorefined titanium scrap to a purity equal to or better than that produced by the iodide process.

PHYSICAL AND MECHANICAL PROPERTIES

The most promising properties of titanium are its low density, good strength, ease in fabrication, and excellent corrosion resistance. These properties, particularly strength and ease in fabrication, depend to a great extent on the purity of the metal. In general, the higher the purity of titanium, the easier it is to fabricate, but the lower is its strength. Also, titanium is a good base for alloying additions. Almost all of the metallic elements are soluble in solid titanium, thus improving the strength of titanium by solid-solution hardening. In addition,

TABLE 29.4. DESIGNATIONS FOR VARIOUS GRADES OF UNALLOYED TITANIUM

| Nominal composition (wt %) | Producers' designations | | | | Other designations | | |
	Crucible	Mallory-Sharon	Republic	TMCA	AMS	ASTM	Military
High purity (99.9%)*							
Commercial purity (99.2%)	A–40	MST–40	RS–40	Ti–55A†	4902	B–265–58T–Gr2	T–9047B–1
Commercial purity (99.0%)	A–55	MST–55	RS–55	Ti–65A	4900A	B–265–58T–Gr3	T–9047B–1
Commercial purity (99.0%)	A–70	MST–70	RS–70	(Ti–75A) (Ti–100A)	(4901B) (4921)	B–265–58T–Gr4	T–9047B–1

* This classification includes iodide process crystal bar and products from newer processes such as electrolysis of fused salt baths. Among producers recognized in the field from whom material may be available on a limited basis are National Distillers, Bureau of Mines, New Jersey Zinc, and Foote Mineral.

† Softer grades designated Ti–35A (35,000 psi yield strength) and Ti–45A (45,000 psi yield strength) also available.

TABLE 29.5. MECHANICAL PROPERTIES OF VARIOUS GRADES OF UNALLOYED TITANIUM

| Nominal composition (wt %) | Condition | Room temperature mechanical properties | | | 315°C (600°F) mechanical properties | | |
		Tensile ultimate (1,000 psi)	Tensile yield (1,000 psi)	Elongation (%)	Tensile ultimate (1,000 psi)	Tensile yield (1,000 psi)	Tensile elongation (%)
High purity (99.9%)	Annealed	34	20	54	16	—	52
Commercial purity (99.2%)	Annealed	59	40	28	28	13	—
Commercial purity (99.2%)	Annealed	79	63	27	33	19	33
Commercial purity (99.0%)	Annealed	95	80	25	43	27	28

TABLE 29.6. COMMERCIAL TITANIUM ALLOYS AND THEIR DESIGNATIONS

Nominal composition (wt %)	Producers' designations				Other designations		
	Crucible	Mallory-Sharon	Republic	TMCA	AMS	ASTM	Military
Alpha titanium alloys							
Ti-5Al-2.5Sn	A-110AT	MST-5Al-2.5Sn	RS-110C	Ti-5Al-2.5Sn	4926	B-265-58T-Gr6	(T-9047B-2) (T-9046B-3)
Ti-6Al-4Zr-1V	—	—	—	Ti-6Al-4Zr-1V			
Ti-8Al-1Mo-1V	—	—	—	Ti-8Al-1Mo-1V			
Ti-8Al-2Cb-1Ta	—	MST-821	—				
Ti-8Al-8Zr-1(Cb+Ta)	—	MST-881	—				
Ti-7Al-12Zr	A-120ZA						
Alpha-beta titanium alloys							
Ti-3Al-2.5V	—	MST-3Al-2.5V					
Ti-5Cr-3Al	—	MST-3Al-5Cr			4927	—	T-9047B-3
Ti-2Fe-2Cr-2Mo	—			Ti-140A	4923	—	(T-9046B-4) (T-9047B-4)
Ti-8Mn	C-110M	MST-8Mn	RS-110A	—	4908A	B-265-58T-Gr7	T-9046B-1
Ti-4Al-4Mn	C-130AM	MST-4Al-4Mn	RS-130	—	4925A	—	T-9047B-6
Ti-4Al-3Mo-1V	C-115AMoV	—	RS-115	Ti-4Al-3Mo-1V			
Ti-4Al-4Mo-4V	—	—	RS-140	Ti-4Al-4Mo-4V			
Ti-5Al-2.75Cr-1.25Fe	—	—	—				
Ti-5Al-1.5Fe-1.4Cr-1.2Mo	—	—	—	Ti-155A	4929	—	T-9047B-7
Ti-6Al-4V	C-120AV	MST-6Al-4V	RS-120A	Ti-6Al-4V	(4911) (4928)	B-265-58T-Gr5	(T-9046B-2) (T-9047B-5)
Ti-7Al-4Mo	C-135AMo		RS-135	Ti-7Al-4Mo			
Ti-16V-2.5Al	C-105VA	MST-16V-2.5Al					
Beta titanium alloys							
Ti-13V-11Cr-3Al	B-120VCA	—	RS-120B	Ti-13V-11Cr-3Al			

because titanium undergoes an allotropic transformation, many alloys of titanium are amenable to heat treatment.

A list of many of the physical properties of titanium is given in Table 29.3. Since the mechanical properties are dependent on the purity of the metal, several grades of titanium are being produced in mill product forms. These grades and their various designations, together with typical mechanical properties, are given in Tables 29.4 and 29.5. The differences in strength between the various grades of titanium can be attributed chiefly to the oxygen, nitrogen, and carbon contents of the metal.

Like most elements, the mechanical properties of titanium can be altered considerably by alloying, and many alloys are being produced commercially. Alloy designations and producers of titanium alloys are listed in Table 29.6. Properties of these alloys are given in Table 29.7. Of significance is the large increase in strength obtainable through alloying additions

TABLE 29.7. MECHANICAL PROPERTIES OF COMMERCIAL TITANIUM ALLOYS

Nominal composition (wt %)	Condition	Form	Room temperature mechanical properties			315°C (600°F) mechanical properties		
			Tensile ultimate (1,000 psi)	Tensile yield (1,000 psi)	Elongation (%)	Tensile ultimate (1,000 psi)	Tensile yield (1,000 psi)	Elongation (%)
Alpha titanium alloys								
Ti-5Al-2.5Sn	Annealed [718°C (1325°F) (4 hr) AC]	Sheet	125	120	18	82	65	17
Ti-6Al-4Zr-1V	Annealed [718°C (1325°F) (4 hr) FC]	Sheet	143	138	17	90	76	20
Ti-8Al-1Mo-1V	HT [982°C (1800°F) (5 min) AC; 593°C (1100°F) (8 hr) AC]	Sheet	147	135	16	112	88	16
Ti-8Al-2Cb-1Ta	Annealed [899°C (1650°F) (1 hr) AC]	Bar	126	120	17	100	81	25
Ti-8Al-8Zr-1(Cb+Ta)	Annealed [871°C (1600°F) (8 hr in vacuum); FC to 343°C (650°F)]	Bar	135	125	16	110	90	17
Ti-7Al-12Zr	Annealed	Bar	140	133	12	102	85	13
Alpha-beta titanium alloys								
Ti-3Al-2.5V	Annealed	Strip	100	85	15			
Ti-5Cr-3Al	Annealed	Bar	155	145	14	114	88	15
Ti-2Fe-2Cr-2Mo	Annealed	Bar	137	125	18	95	65	19
	HT [805°C (1480°F) (1 hr) WQ; 482°C (900°F) (2 hr) AC]	Bar	179	171	13	136	112	16
Ti-8Mn	Annealed	Sheet	138	125	15	103	83	13
Ti-4Al-4Mn	Annealed	Bar	148	133	16	110	90	17
	HT [760–815°C (1400–1500°F) (2 hr) WQ; 427–538°C (800–1000°F) (24 hr) AC]	Bar	162	140	9	125	100	11
Ti-4Al-3Mo-1V	HT [885°C (1625°F) (2½ min) WQ]	Sheet	140	95	15			
	HT [885°C (1625°F) (2½ min) WQ; 496°C (925°F) (12 hr) AC]	Sheet	195	167	6	152	113	7
Ti-4Al-4Mo-4V	HT [843°C (1550°F) (1–2 hr) WQ; 538°C (1000°F) (6 hr) AC]	Bar	170	150	6			

TABLE 29.7. MECHANICAL PROPERTIES OF COMMERCIAL TITANIUM ALLOYS (*cont.*)

Nominal composition (wt %)	Condition	Form	Room temperature mechanical properties			315°C (600°F) mechanical properties		
			Tensile ultimate (1,000 psi)	Tensile yield (1,000 psi)	Elongation (%)	Tensile ultimate (1,000 psi)	Tensile yield (1,000 psi)	Elongation (%)
Ti-5Al-2.75Cr-1.25Fe	Annealed	Bar	160	154	15	122	102	20
	HT [788°C (1450°F) (2 hr) WQ; 482°C (900°F) (5 hr) AC]	Bar	190	175	6	144	117	10
Ti-5Al-1.5Fe-1.4Cr-1.2Mo	Annealed	Bar	154	145	16	115	100	16
	HT [871°C (1600°F) (1 hr) WQ; 538°C (1000°F) (24 hr) AC]	Bar	195	184	9	150	125	14
Ti-6Al-4V	Annealed	Sheet	135	120	11	105	95	11
	HT [927°C (1700°F) (⅓ hr) WQ; 924°C (975°F) (8 hr) AC]	Sheet	170	150	7	130	105	7
Ti-7Al-4Mo	Annealed	Bar	160	150	15	125	117	17
	HT [899°C (1650°F) (⅓ hr) WQ; 482°C (900°F) (16 hr) AC]	Bar	190	175	12	155	120	15
Ti-16V-2.5Al	HT [749°C (1380°F) (⅓ hr) WQ]	Sheet	105	45	16			
	HT [749°C (1380°F) (⅓ hr) WQ; 516°C (960°F) (4 hr) AC]	Sheet	180	165	6	140	130	8
	Beta titanium alloys							
Ti-13V-11Cr-3Al	HT [760–815°C (1400–1500°F) (¼–½ hr) AC]	Sheet	135	130	16			
	HT [760°C (1400°F) (½ hr) AC; 482°C (900°F) Age, AC]	Sheet	180	170	6	175	145	8

AC = air cooled; FC = furnace cooled; HT = heat treated; WQ = water quenched.

with little loss in ductility. In addition, many titanium alloys can be further strengthened by heat treatment processes, discussed in a later section of the chapter.

CHEMICAL PROPERTIES

The most important chemical property of titanium is its excellent corrosion resistance under many conditions. As with stainless steel and aluminum, this can be attributed largely to the formation of a passive-oxide surface film. It is because of this film that titanium is resistant to attack in most oxidizing media. This oxide film is protective only up to moderate temperatures, since oxidation of titanium occurs very slowly at temperatures as low as 249°C (480°F), and the oxidation rate increases as the temperature is increased. It also reacts with nitrogen at somewhat higher temperatures than with oxygen.

Corrosion[5]

Chemical. In chemical media, titanium is resistant to moist chlorine gas, chloride solutions, and oxidizing acids such as nitric or aqua regia. It is resistant to dilute concentrations of sulfuric and hydrochloric acid and to most organic acids at room temperature. Hydrofluoric and phosphoric acids and moderate concentrations of the alkalies attack titanium. It is resistant to attack by dilute alkalies, however. Titanium has excellent resistance to either

TABLE 29.8. TYPICAL CORROSION RATE FOR UNALLOYED TITANIUM IN AQUEOUS SOLUTIONS

Media	Concentration (wt %)	Temperature °C	Temperature °F	Corrosion rate (mils/year)
HCl	1	60	140	0.11
HCl	1	100	212	18.5
HCl	5	Room		0.1
HCl	10	35	95	42.0
HCl	20	Room		20.4
HNO_3	5	35	95	0.08
HNO_3	5	100	212	0.61
HNO_3	10	35	95	0.16
HNO_3	10	100	212	1.29
HNO_3	20	35	95	0.18
HNO_3	Red fuming	Room		0.07
HNO_3	White fuming	Room		0.1
H_3PO_4	10	80	176	72.0
H_3PO_4	85	Room		8.4
H_2SO_4	1	Room		0.1
H_2SO_4	1	Boiling		360.0
H_2SO_4	10	Room		7.2
H_2SO_4	10	35	95	50.0
H_2SO_4	40	Room		60.0
H_2SO_4	40	35	95	341.0
NaOH	10	Boiling		0.84
NaOH	28	Room		0.1
NaOH	40	80	176	5.0
NH_4OH	28	Room		0.1
$AlCl_3$	10	100	212	0.09
NH_4Cl	10	100	212	0.5
$FeCl_3$	1–30	100	212	0.5
NaCl	Saturated	Boiling		0.05

general corrosion or to pitting attack by most salt solutions. It has good resistance to crevice corrosion, cavitation, erosion, corrosion fatigue, and galvanic attack. Its galvanic properties are such, however, that it often tends to accelerate corrosion of the other metal in the couple.

Titanium is corroded by hydrofluoric, hydrochloric, sulfuric, oxalic, and formic acids. In most cases, with the exception of hydrofluoric acid, the attack on titanium is inhibited in specific cases by suitable additions.

Table 29.8 summarizes actual corrosion rates in several media under various temperature conditions.

In general, the corrosion resistance of titanium-base alloys is considered comparable to unalloyed titanium, although very few data have been published on corrosion resistance of titanium alloys. The development of titanium-base alloys specifically for corrosion resistant applications has been secondary to the development of high-strength titanium alloys. Nevertheless, two types of titanium alloys have been developed specifically for corrosion resistance. An all-beta alloy containing 25 to 40 per cent molybdenum is reported to have excellent resistance to boiling sulfuric and hydrochloric acids. Another development utilizes small amounts of palladium or platinum to produce an alloy with excellent resistance to hydrochloric and sulfuric acids.

Marine. The corrosion resistance of titanium is outstanding in marine atmospheres and sea water. No noticeable corrosion or change in properties as a result of corrosion could be found on titanium specimens exposed for 18 months in both quiet and changing sea water or in salt air atmospheres. Titanium is not antifouling, but the presence of fouling organisms does not promote pitting or crevice corrosion. Titanium has been placed between "Inconel" (passive) and "Monel" in the galvanic series for various metals and alloys in sea water. Thus titanium is cathodic to most structural metals. Coupled with other metals, titanium is generally not attacked, but the corrosion of the more active metals is accelerated.

Oxidation

The oxidation of titanium follows the parabolic rate law with time at any given temperature. In addition to the oxidation reaction, there is also a diffusion of oxygen into titanium which enters into solid solution and hardens and embrittles the metal. The diffusion of oxygen into titanium is also temperature dependent so that, at the higher temperatures, both oxidation and diffusion take place. The use of titanium at elevated temperatures is restricted by its reactions with oxygen. For example, a 0.040-in. sheet becomes embrittled when exposed to air for several hours at 816°C (1500°F). The same sheet can be exposed to air at 566°C (1050°F) for at least 500 hr, however, with no significant change in properties. At the other extreme, 0.015-in. titanium sheet has withstood a 1093°C (2000°F) flame test for 15 min. The limitations of time and temperature for heating titanium in air are important when working or heat treating titanium. Other limitations, chiefly loss in mechanical properties at elevated temperatures, preclude its use as a high-temperature material.

By heating titanium with restricted access of air, it is possible to secure interference colors, as with steel. A brilliant blue surface can be formed, probably caused by titanium oxide formation, which is more resistant than titanium metal to some acids. The solution of oxygen, nitrogen, and carbon into titanium that is heated in gases containing these elements is a practical means of surface hardening.

Chemical Compounds

Titanium is a polyvalent reactive metal that forms many compounds—far too many to cover in this discussion of the metal. The metallurgy of titanium is plagued by the formation of subcompounds, as of the subhalides when reducing titanium halides by pyrolysis, by magnesium reduction, or by hydrogen. Likewise, there are three oxides (TiO, Ti_2O_3, and TiO_2) with corresponding hydroxides and salts. Complex titanates can be formed. The metal readily combines with hydrogen at elevated temperatures, as well as with oxygen and nitrogen, but, unlike the latter, much of the hydrogen can be removed by heating above about 800°C (1472°F) in vacuum. Chlorine, iodine, and bromine react with the heated metal to form the corresponding halides.

PHYSICAL METALLURGY[7]

Titanium technology has advanced very rapidly over the past decade. Less than 20 years ago, practically nothing was known about the physical metallurgy of titanium and its alloys. Through the concentrated efforts of many research organizations, companies, and universities, mostly in programs sponsored by the United States government, a thorough knowledge of titanium metallurgy has been obtained.

Alloying Principles

Of the several methods for classifying titanium-base alloys, perhaps the simplest is to classify the alloying additions according to their effects on the transformation temperature of titanium. Certain alloying additions have a high solubility in the beta phase (the high-temperature, body-centered cubic modification of titanium) and cause a lowering of the transformation temperature with increasing alloy content. These have been termed beta stabilizers. Conversely, the elements which have a high solubility in the low-temperature, hexagonal, close-packed alpha phase and raise the transformation temperature of titanium are called alpha stabilizers. Elements which have little or no solubility in either alpha or beta titanium and form compounds are called compound forming.

In general, it has been found that all of the transition elements are beta stabilizing. Of the nontransition elements, it is known that aluminum, tin, antimony, carbon, oxygen, and nitrogen are alpha stabilizers; hydrogen, beryllium, and silicon are beta stabilizers; and boron,

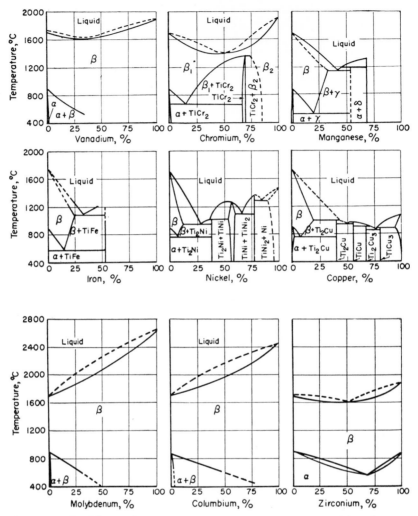

FIGURE 29.2. Equilibrium diagrams of titanium with some of the transition elements.

phosphorus, and sulfur are compound formers. The titanium-rich portions of the phase diagrams of the important alloying elements in titanium are shown in Figures 29.2 and 29.3.

Like other metals, the properties of titanium are greatly affected by alloying additions. Solid-solution strengthening is the most important strengthening mechanism involved in titanium metallurgy. Alpha stabilizers, when added to titanium, strengthen the base metal entirely by solid-solution strengthening, resulting in single-phase, nonheat-treatable alloys. In alpha-stabilized systems, the beta phase cannot be retained by quenching, nor is there any hardening action as a result of the beta-to-alpha transformation. Beta stabilizers, when added to

titanium, also strengthen the base metal through solid-solution strengthening. Because there is a very small solubility in beta titanium, however, it is predominately the beta phase that is strengthened by beta stabilizers. Compound formers, because of their low solubility in titanium, have little effect on the properties other than to embrittle the alloy, if they are present in excessive amounts.

Beta-stabilized titanium alloys are most versatile. When beta-stabilizing additions are added to titanium in small or medium amounts, a two-phase, alpha-beta alloy is obtained. When added in large amounts above about 10 per cent, the alloy addition stabilizes the beta phase to a sufficiently low temperature that the beta

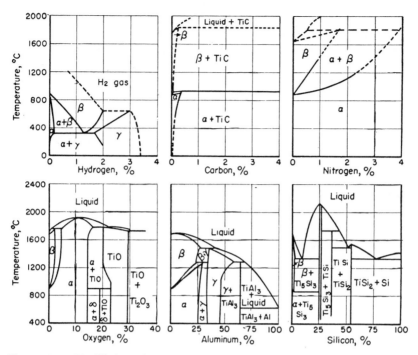

FIGURE 29.3. Equilibrium diagrams of titanium with some of the nontransition elements.

phase can be retained at room temperature by quenching. In this condition the beta phase is unstable and will transform partially to a transitory phase designated omega, a finely dispersed alpha phase, or, possibly, a compound phase when heated to slightly elevated temperatures. In certain systems, such as the titanium-molybdenum, titanium-columbium, titanium-tantalum, and titanium-vanadium systems, it is possible to stabilize the beta phase to room temperature and below by adding a very large quantity of a beta stabilizer. Thus in beta-stabilized systems there are three alloy types available: the alpha-beta, the unstable-beta, and the stable-beta alloys. Excluding heat treatment effects, the properties of the beta-stabilized alloys are governed by the quantity of alloying addition in solid solution. Since there is usually very little solubility of a beta stabilizer in alpha titanium, the properties of the alpha-beta alloys, as well as the unstable- or stable-beta alloys, can be attributed to the quantity of alloying addition in solution in the beta phase.

Because of the nature of beta-stabilized systems, the alpha-beta alloys are amenable to heat treatment. Simple quenching-type heat treatments can be used to alter the properties of the alloy considerably. Annealing at temperatures low in the alpha-beta field produces a relatively soft condition, because the quantity of the soft alpha phase present is quite large. Quenching from temperatures high in the alpha-beta field increases the quantity of the harder beta phase in the two-phase structure, and the hardness or strength of the alloy is increased. Quenching from the beta field results in either a martensitic type of structure or a retained beta structure, either of which is somewhat harder and less ductile than the alpha-beta-type structure. The beta phase in alpha-beta alloys is generally unstable when the alloys are quenched from a fairly high temperature in the two-phase field. This instability can result in embrittlement of the alloy if it is used in elevated-temperature service. The degree of instability increases as the quantity of beta phase in the alloy is increased. To overcome this possible embrittlement, alpha-beta alloys can be stabilized by heat treating at a low temperature in the alpha-beta field to reduce the quantity of the beta phase present through the formation of massive alpha phase. Alternatively, the alloy can be slow-cooled from the annealing temperature to cause transformation of the beta phase to massive alpha phase. Both methods reduce the strength of the alloy but ensure stability at elevated temperatures.

The instability of the beta phase can also be used to improve the strength of titanium alloys. It is possible, by proper adjustment of the initial alpha-beta condition so that the beta component will be sufficiently unstable, that subsequent aging will improve the strength without embrittlement. This is the type of heat treatment that is being used commercially in titanium alloys and is described more completely in a later section of this chapter.

Quenching from the beta field to form martensite does not appear to be practical for titanium alpha-beta alloys. The increase in hardness or strength caused by the formation of martensite is very small when compared to the strength increases obtainable in martensitic steels. Also, any heat treatment which involves heating titanium-base alloys at temperatures required to put the alloy into the beta field must be done in an inert atmosphere or in vacuum to avoid oxygen and nitrogen contamination and embrittlement.

With this understanding of the alloying behavior of the many elements which can be added to titanium, it is possible to classify the alloys of titanium into three basic types. These are alpha, alpha-beta, and beta alloys. The advantages and disadvantages of these alloy types are summarized in Table 29.9. This summary has been called the ABC's of titanium

TABLE 29.9. RELATION OF STRUCTURE TO PROPERTIES OF TITANIUM ALLOYS

Structure	Properties
Alpha	All-around performance; good weldability; good strength, hot or cold; good oxidation resistance; fair bendability
Beta	Best bendability; excellent bend ductility; good strength, hot or cold; vulnerable to contamination; large consumer of strategic metals
Combined alpha-beta	Combined performance; good cold strength; good bendability; excellent forgability; moderate contamination resistance; poor weldability

metallurgy. A is for alpha, all-around performance; B is for beta, best bendability; and C is for combined alpha-beta, compromise performance.

The Important Alloying Elements. In considering alloys of titanium, one cannot neglect the gaseous elements oxygen, nitrogen, and hydrogen. These, together with carbon and iron, are the chief impurities in commercial titanium ingot. As more and more is learned about the metallurgy of titanium, it becomes apparent that the gaseous elements should be avoided as much as possible. These elements dissolve in the interstices of the titanium crystals. Oxygen and nitrogen dissolve in the octahedral holes of the hexagonal close-packed lattice and have a higher solubility in alpha than in beta titanium. Hydrogen, on the other hand, dissolves preferentially in the tetrahedral holes of the body-centered-cubic lattice and has a high solubility in the beta phase. As pointed out previously, oxygen and nitrogen, in solid solution, increase the strength of titanium and, if present in excessive amounts, embrittle the metal. Although the tolerance for oxygen and nitrogen in titanium is quite high (about 0.5 per cent oxygen and 0.3 per cent nitrogen, maximum, before embrittlement occurs), their effect on other properties is detrimental. For example, when titanium is welded, the oxygen content should be kept below 0.15 per cent and the nitrogen content below 0.10 per cent to maintain useful ductility in welded joints. Evidence also shows that the presence of the interstitial elements causes a lowering in the toughness of titanium and should be avoided if titanium is to be used where its impact resistance must be high.

Hydrogen in unalloyed titanium or alpha titanium alloys has little effect on the tensile properties; however, it does have a profound effect on impact properties. Although hydrogen has a high solubility in titanium at elevated temperatures, at temperatures below about 300°C (572°F) the solubility decreases rapidly, with the result that a TiH phase precipitates at room temperature. The presence of this phase in the structure causes a lowering of the impact resistance of titanium which can be directly related to the quantity of hydrogen present. In alpha-beta titanium alloys the solubility for hydrogen is quite high. The presence of hydrogen in excess of about 150 to 200 ppm, however, causes slow strain-rate embrittlement in most alpha-beta alloys.

Carbon also dissolves interstitially in the octahedral holes of the hexagonal close-packed lattice. Its solubility, however, is very limited, being a maximum of about 0.45 per cent at the peritectoid temperature. When in solid solution, carbon strengthens titanium, but, if present as TiC, it has very little effect on properties other than to reduce ductility. Like the other interstitials, carbon in solid solution has an adverse effect on toughness. Also, for maintaining good-weld joint properties, the carbon content should not exceed about 0.2 per cent.

Of the many substitutional alloying elements that can be added to titanium, there are eight which appear to be most important: aluminum, tin, zirconium, chromium, iron, manganese, molybdenum, and vanadium. Of these, aluminum, tin, and zirconium are alpha stabilizers; the others are beta stabilizers. The basic strengths of alloys formed with these additions are dependent upon solid-solution strengthening. By comparing the properties of the annealed or stabilized alloys, it is possible to compare strengthening effects of each of the additions. The data given in Table 29.10 for binary alloys are approximate, since the properties of titanium alloys are influenced greatly by the impurities present in the base metal.

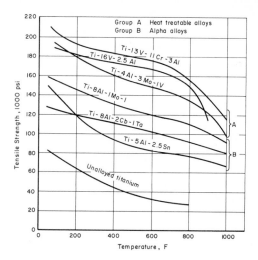

FIGURE 29.4. Effect of temperature on the tensile strength of several titanium alloys.

TABLE 29.10. TENSILE PROPERTIES OF TITANIUM-BASE ALLOYS

	Yield strength (1,000 psi)	Tensile strength (1,000 psi)	Elongation (%)	Reduction in area (%)
Titanium-5 zirconium	70	80	20	50
Titanium-5 tin	75	85	20	50
Titanium-5 aluminum	90	100	20	40
Titanium-5 vanadium	90	105	20	50
Titanium-5 molybdenum	95	110	20	50
Titanium-5 chromium	110	125	20	40
Titanium-5 manganese	110	125	20	40
Titanium-5 iron	130	140	10	25

Recently, the development of titanium alloys has followed two separate routes, resulting in two separate classes of alloys. Nonheat-treatable alpha alloys (alloys which have a single-phase hexagonal-close-packed structure) are being developed for applications which require good elevated-temperature creep strength and which can be welded. Heat-treatable alpha-beta or beta alloys are being developed which can be readily formed in the soft condition and then heat treated to high strength levels. The alpha alloys generally have medium strengths at room temperature but do not lose their strengths at high temperatures as rapidly as do the heat-treatable alloys. Also, the creep strength of the alpha alloys at high temperature is generally superior to the creep strength of heat-treatable alloys. Figure 29.4 shows the effect of temperature on the tensile strength of representative alloys of these two classes.

Heat Treatment of Titanium Alloys.[4,7,8,11]

Heat treatment of titanium alloys to obtain improved strengths can be accomplished by a process similar to precipitation hardening in other alloy systems. The strengthening mechanism is based on the metallurgical reactions which occur during the transformation of body-centered-cubic beta phase to hexagonal-close-packed alpha phase during a low-temperature aging cycle. The conditions which are required for this reaction to occur are illustrated in Figure 29.5 which shows the typical phase relations in a beta-stabilized titanium alloy system. The first requirement is that an alloy must contain a sufficient quantity of a beta-stabilizing element so that some beta phase is retained to

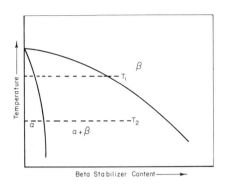

FIGURE 29.5. Typical diagram of the phase relations in a beta-stabilized titanium alloy system.

room temperature when the alloy is quenched from the solution treating temperature, temperature T_1 in Figure 29.5. After quenching, the alloy is reheated to an aging temperature T_2 for a sufficient length of time to cause precipitation of alpha phase, but not so long that the alpha phase agglomerates and overaging occurs. The properties obtainable in the heat treated condition are dependent on both the solution treating temperature and the aging treatment. Typical properties illustrating the effect of both solution treating temperature and aging temperature and time are given in Table 29.11.

All of the titanium-base alloys containing beta-stabilizing additions (the alpha-beta and beta alloys in Table 29.7) are amenable to

heat treatment. Some of these alloys were developed as annealed alloys, however, and, because of their compositions, they may not have as good combinations of strength and ductility in the heat treated conditions as those alloys which were developed as heat-treatable alloys. Also, no single alloy is capable of meeting all of the requirements called for by various industries. The selection of the alloy is based on many factors other than its simple mechanical properties. Thus many types of titanium alloys have been and are being developed. In the category of heat-treatable alloys, the types of titanium alloys available commercially can be illustrated by the data given in Table 29.12 for four heat-treatable sheet alloys. The Ti–6Al–4V alloy contains a large quantity of the alpha strengthener, aluminum, with only a small amount of beta stabilizer, vanadium. In the solution treated condition it is strong but is not amenable to many forming operations, and the increase in strength obtained by aging is small. The Ti–4Al–3Mo–1V alloy has less aluminum and more beta phase in the solution treated condition. (Molybdenum is a more effective beta stabilizer than is vanadium.) Thus, the solution treated strength is less than the Ti–6Al–4V alloy, and its aging response is greater. Also, its ability to be formed into parts in the solution treated condition is greater than that of the Ti–6Al–4V alloy. The Ti–16V–2.5Al alloy contains a large quantity of beta stabilizer

TABLE 29.11. TENSILE PROPERTIES OF TITANIUM–6 ALUMINUM–4 VANADIUM IN SEVERAL HEAT TREATED CONDITIONS

Heat treatment				Tensile strength (1,000 psi)	Yield strength (1,000 psi)	Elongation (%)
Solution treatment		Aging treatment				
Time (hr)	Temperature (°F)	Time (hr)	Temperature (°F)			
1	1500	—	—	149	92	14
1	1500	2	900	173	140	7
1	1500	8	1100	146	140	13
1	1600	—	—	155	122	16
1	1600	2	900	178	155	9
1	1700	—	—	170	150	7
1	1700	2	900	185	167	10
1	1700	2	1000	186	170	11
1	1700	8	1000	179	165	9
1	1800	—–	—	177	154	5
1	1800	8	900	183	167	4
1	1800	2	1100	170	156	12

TABLE 29.12. REPRESENTATIVE PROPERTIES OF HEAT-TREATABLE TITANIUM SHEET ALLOYS

Alloy	Solution treated properties					Aged properties				
	Solution treatment		Tensile strength (1,000 psi)	Yield strength (1,000 psi)	Elonga-tion (%)	Aging treatment		Tensile strength (1,000 psi)	Yield strength (1,000 psi)	Elonga-tion (%)
	Time (hr)	Tem-perature (°C)				Time (hr)	Tem-perature (°C)			
Ti–6Al–4V	1/3	927 (1700°F)	145	125	12	8	524 (975°F)	170	150	7
Ti–4Al–3Mo–1V	1/4	889 (1650°F)	140	95	15	12	496 (925°F)	195	167	6
Ti–16V–2.5Al	1/3	749 (1380°F)	105	45	16	4	516 (960°F)	180	165	6
Ti–13V–11Cr–3Al	1/2	788 (1450°F)	135	130	16	96	482 (900°F)	205	185	9

and only a small amount of alpha stabilizer. It is very soft and ductile in the solution treated condition and can be hardened to high strengths on aging. The fourth alloy in this group, Ti–13V–11Cr–3Al, is an all-beta alloy. Because of the large amount of beta-stabilizing elements (vanadium and chromium) present, it has a single-phase body-centered-cubic structure at room temperature when processed and annealed in a normal manner. The decomposition of the beta phase is very sluggish, so that long time aging treatments are required to obtain the very high strengths obtainable in this alloy.

The development of heat-treatable titanium alloys in commercial mill product forms has been accomplished through the cooperative efforts of the titanium mill product producers and the United States government.[8] Although the heat treatment potentialities of titanium alloys had been recognized for some time and proved in laboratory tests, the problems involved in production heat treatment appeared to prevent the rapid commercialization of heat-treatable alloys. Recognizing the need for the early commercialization of high-strength heat-treatable alloys, the Department of Defense initiated a three-phase program to accelerate the development of several new titanium alloys. Three phases of the program, which was started in 1956, are: Phase I, the production of uniform, reproducible sheet products from new heat-treatable titanium alloys; Phase II, the development of design data; Phase III, evaluation of formability and properties by airframe companies. As of April, 1959, the program had not been fully completed. The first objective, production of heat-treatable alloys, however, has largely been met. Phases II and III are under way, and early results indicate that the over-all program will successfully meet its objectives. The problems involved in the transition from the laboratory stage to the commercial stage centered around the methods of producing flat, uniform sheet having reproducible properties in the heat treated condition. The assistance provided by the Department of Defense has given the producers of titanium mill products the opportunity to gain the experience and know-how necessary to overcome these problems. One problem, in particular, that has been largely overcome is the quenching of large sheets of titanium (36 by 96 in.) without excessive warping. Three methods have been developed which are currently being used for this process. These are resistance heating of a full-sized sheet in a special jig and quenching by water spraying, quenching by dropping the sheet through a door in the bottom of the furnace, and quenching by spraying a sheet as it is rolled out of furnace on rollers containing a leveling device. Reproducibility of flatness and properties has been improved with each of these processes, and material suitable for airplane construction is now being produced.

Metallography

Titanium and its alloys can be polished for metallographic examination by the use of standard mechanical polishing and handling methods. Preliminary grinding may be done wet or dry, using a series of papers from 60 to 600 grit. After grinding, the samples are polished on a soft lap, using a fast wheel (1,750 rpm). The polishing abrasives vary considerably with the experience of the metallographer. Some of the more common abrasives used are jeweler's rouge, alumina, silica, and carborundum. Elec-

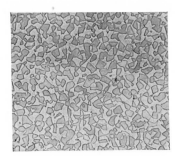

A. Structure of an alpha-beta alloy fabricated and annealed in the alpha-beta field.   250 ×

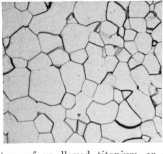

A. Structure of unalloyed titanium or an alpha alloy annealed in the alpha field.   100 ×

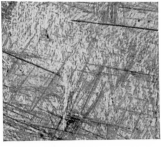

B. Structure of an alpha-beta alloy quenched from the beta field.   250 ×

B. Structure of unalloyed titanium or an alpha alloy quenched from the beta field.   250 ×

C. Structure of an unstable-beta alloy quenched from the beta field.   250 ×

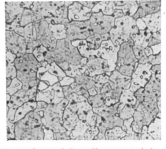

C. Structure of an alpha alloy containing carbides annealed in the alpha-carbide field.   250 ×

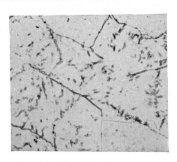

D. Structure of an unstable-beta alloy slow cooled from the beta field.   250 ×

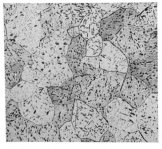

D. Structure of an alpha alloy containing hydrogen showing TiH precipitated as line markings. 100 ×

FIGURE 29.6. Typical microstructures of alpha-beta and beta titanium alloys.

FIGURE 29.7. Typical microstructures of alpha titanium alloys.

TABLE 29.13. ETCHANTS FOR TITANIUM AND ITS ALLOYS

Composition (volume)	Characteristics
1–10% hydrofluoric acid (48%), balance water	2.5% HF used most frequently; all-purpose etchant, tends to stain alpha phase
3% nitric acid (conc.), 1.5–2% hydrofluoric acid (48%), balance water	Most popular all-purpose etchant; very good for beta alloys as well as alpha and alpha-beta alloys; presence of HNO_3 minimizes staining
1–2% hydrofluoric acid (48%) plus a few crystals of ferric nitrate, balance water	Good all-purpose etchant; uses ferric nitrate in place of HNO_3
1 part hydrofluoric acid (48%), 1 part nitric acid (conc.), 2 parts glycerin	Good alpha etchant; reacts rapidly; does not stain
1 part hydrofluoric acid (48%), 1 part glycerin	Useful for two-phase alloys; tends to darken alpha but not beta or carbides

trolytic polishing is also used. The electrolyte is usually a perchloric acid–acetic anhydride mixture which reacts with organic materials; therefore, "Bakelite" or resinous mounts should not be used. Current densities of 20 to 30 amp/ sq dm at 40 to 60 volts have been found satisfactory for polishing titanium and some of its alloys. Because of the good corrosion resistance of titanium, all of the metallographic etches contain hydrofluoric acid. The more common etches for titanium are given in Table 29.13. Some typical microstructures of titanium and its alloys are given in Figures 29.6 and 29.7.

PROCESSING AND FABRICATION[1,8,9]

Melting

Starting with titanium sponge produced by the Kroll process or sodium-reduction process, the first step in processing is the consolidation of the metal into a form suitable for fabrication into mill products. Induction melting of titanium has not been satisfactory because all known crucible materials are attached by molten titanium. Arc melting is the standard method for consolidating titanium sponge. Practically all titanium alloys are now produced by double arc melting using consumable electrodes. Melting is done in vacuum at high currents and low voltages. Water-cooled copper molds, about 12 to 25 in. in diameter, contain the melted metal. Copper can be used as the mold material because the titanium solidifies on contact with the copper, providing an insulating shell. After the first melt, usually melting 12- to 16-in.-diameter ingots, two or more ingots are joined together and remelted as a consumable electrode into large ingots, 20 to 25 in. in diameter and weighing 4,000 to 5,000 lb.

Titanium castings are being produced using consumable electrode arc melting furnaces which are designed to permit casting within the evacuated chamber. Casting titanium requires a deep molten pool and a mold material that will not cause contamination. After the charge is melted, the furnace is tilted and the charge is poured into the mold. Castings of 165 lb of metal have been made using a 14- to 15-in.-diameter furnace. Graphite has been used as the mold material with fairly good success.

Fabrication

Once past the melting stage, the processing of titanium can be accomplished by conventional methods. The chief precaution necessary is not to overheat the metal during fabrication or heat treatment, so that oxygen contamination will be avoided and the desired microstructure will be obtained. Forging temperatures will depend on the alloy content. Generally, maximum temperatures are 1038°C (1900°F) for forging and 871°C (1600F°) for rolling. Titanium does have a tendency to seize and gall, so that special lubricants are required for wire drawing and extrusion. Bending and forming operations afford no difficulties if the stretch is limited to about 10 per cent. Titanium and, particularly, its alloys have a high spring-back tendency, so that many bending operations are done warm [about 260–316°C (500–600°F)] to eliminate spring back and cracking.

The seizing and galling tendencies of titanium

also affect machining characteristics. It has been noted that the machinability of titanium and its alloys is a function of its hardness or strength; the higher the strength, the more difficult it is to machine. The recommended practice for machining titanium is to use slow speeds with heavy cuts. The work should be kept as cool as possible, and this can be done by using cutting oils with added chlorinated solvents such as carbon tetrachloride. Grinding should also be done at slow speeds using sufficient cooling fluid to keep the work cold.

The joining of titanium to titanium can be accomplished by brazing, riveting, or welding. Rivets of stainless steel, "Monel," or titanium can be used. Stainless steel and "Monel" rivets require less driving force than do titanium rivets, and, since there is no galvanic action, they are recommended as rivet material. Welding of titanium can be accomplished by arc welding in a protective atmosphere. As long as contamination of the weld metal is eliminated, welds of commercially pure titanium are ductile and have about the same strength as the base metal. Alloys of titanium, however, do not respond so well to welding. The present commercial alloys, when welded, have brittle welds. The cause of this embrittlement may be attributed to transformation hardening caused by the rapid cooling after welding and segregation during freezing. The embrittlement caused by transformation hardening can be overcome by a postweld heat treatment below the beta-transformation temperature; however, the embrittlement caused by segregation cannot be overcome. Oxygen, nitrogen, and carbon adversely affect the ductility of welds and should be kept as low as possible. Alloys of moderately high strength that can be welded without embrittlement are being developed.

Titanium is rolled to strip and rod in the same general equipment as is used for stainless steel. In fact, there has been a tendency for titanium producing companies to join with companies processing stainless steel to utilize such equipment. Continuous titanium strip, 3 ft wide, 0.015 in. thick, and hundreds of feet long, is produced commercially.

Extrusion is used successfully in forming some titanium products, such as tubing. The drawing of titanium to wire and to thin wall tubing is done commercially, although it is more difficult than handling steel.

APPLICATIONS OF TITANIUM

The chief uses for titanium and titanium alloys are in defense applications, particularly aircraft and missiles where weight saving is important. The specific applications range from liquid-oxygen bottles for missile fuels to compressor-section parts in jet engines, covering the temperature range from -196–$482°C$ (-320–$900°F$). In between these two temperature extremes are a multitude of structural and nonstructural parts of airplanes including wing skins, engine shrouds, fasteners, spars, and other supporting members of an air frame. The selection of a titanium alloy for a specific part is based on strength-weight considerations and the ability of the alloy to meet the design considerations. Although the high strength and low density of titanium alloys are their chief attributes, some applications require special properties which titanium possesses. For example, titanium is used as a crack stopper in certain airplanes. Cracks do not propagate through titanium as rapidly as through other metals, and, as an added safety feature, titanium is used in places where cracks may form. Another safety feature takes advantage of the low heat conductivity of titanium, it being used to advantage in fire walls.

The nonmilitary uses of titanium are based primarily on its excellent corrosion resistance, and, although the percentage of titanium being used is small compared to military uses, there has been a steady increase in consumption of titanium in corrosion resistant applications. Pumps, filter cloths, heat exchange tubing, and valves are being used in equipment that handles moist chlorides or hypochlorate solutions. The resistance of titanium to moist chlorine is excellent. Titanium's resistance to oxidizing acids has found application in heat exchangers containing nitric acid (35 to 60 per cent nitric acid). It is not suitable, however, for use in contact with fuming nitric acid. Anodizing racks are being made from titanium because it is not attacked by the anodizing baths.

In marine applications titanium has excellent resistance to sea water. It has been used for propeller shafts, struts, bearings, anchor davits, rigging, and other parts exposed to sea water. A small but very important application for titanium is in the cathodic protection of ships' hulls. A small titanium anode, coated with platinum, provides cathodic protection from corrosion by sea water.

References

1. Abkowitz, S., Burke, J. J., and Hiltz, R. H., Jr., "Titanium in Industry," Princeton, N.J., D. Van Nostrand Company, Inc., 1955.
2. Barksdale, J., "Titanium, Its Occurrence, Chemistry, and Technology," New York, The Ronald Press Company, 1949.
3. *Chem. Eng.*, **65**, 124 (1958).
4. Frost, P. D., *Metal Progr.*, **75**, No. 3, p. 99; No. 4, p. 91 (1959).
5. Harris, W. J., Jr., *J. Metals*, **10**, 19 (1958).
6. Harris, W. J., Jr., Simcoe, C. R., and Ogden, H. R., "Department of Defense Titanium Sheet Rolling Program," Reports TML Nos. 46, 46A, 46B, 46C, 46D, 46E, and 46F, Defense Metals Information Center, Battelle Memorial Institute, Columbus, Ohio, 1955–1959.
7. Jaffee, R. I., *Modern Metals,* **14**, 46 (1948).
8. Jaffee, R. I., "The Physical Metallurgy of Titanium Alloys," "Progress in Metal Physics," Vol. 7, New York, Pergamon Press, 1958.
9. Kroll, W. J., *Metal Ind.*, 343 (May 2, 1952).
10. McQuillan, A. D., and McQuillan, M. K., "Titanium," New York, Academic Press, Inc., 1956.
11. Nittle, J. R., Baker, D. H., Jr., and Wartman, F. S., *U.S. Bur. Mines, Rept. Invest. No. 5315* (1957).
12. Sibert, M. E., and Steinberg, M. A., *J. Metals,* p. 1162–1168 (September, 1956).
13. Van Arkel, A. E., and DeBoer, J. H., *Z. anorg. Chem.*, **148**, 345 (1925).

30. TUNGSTEN

K. C. LI

Wah Chang Corporation
New York, New York

INTRODUCTION

Tungsten, also known by its European name, wolfram, is a metal with unique properties that lead to its use in cutting and forming other metals and in important high-temperature applications. It has the highest melting point [3410°C (6170°F)] and the lowest vapor pressure of any metal. It has the highest tensile strength, yielding tensiles of up to 600,000 psi in wire form. Its corrosion resistance is one of the highest. Its density is exceeded only by metals of the platinum group and rhenium. Properly worked, it is elastic and ductile. Its compound with carbon is the hardest known metallic substance.

The word "tungsten" is an adaptation of the Swedish *tung sten* (heavy stone) and was first applied to the mineral scheelite about 1758. The element was first identified in 1781 by a Swedish chemist, K. W. Scheele, for whom the calcium tungstate mineral, scheelite was later named. The iron-manganese-tungstate mineral, wolfram, was first described about 1574 and was originally believed to be a mineral of tin with which ores it is commonly associated. The name, of German origin and from which the chemical symbol W is derived, probably has reference to the "wolflike" characteristic of tungsten described by the early tin miners as "devouring tin" and causing low recoveries in the tin smelting operation. Wolfram was first identified as a mineral of tungsten about 1783 by the Spaniards J. J. and F. de Elhuyar, who are also credited with the first production of metallic tungsten in that same year.

The element did not find industrial application until early in the present century, but it has since become one of the most important of industrial metals.

OCCURRENCE

Tungsten is never found in the uncombined state in nature. With the exception of tungstenite, WS_2, tungsten always occurs in the form of tungsten trioxide combined with the oxides of iron, manganese, or calcium, and, to a limited extent, with the oxides of lead and copper. The most important ores are wolframite, the collective name given to a series of isomorphous ferrous-manganous tungstates, $(FeMn)WO_4$, and scheelite which is nearly pure calcium tungstate, $CaWO_4$.

The mineral wolframite varies in composition from $FeWO_4$ to $MnWO_4$ and contains from 76.3 to 76.5 per cent tungsten trioxide. Ferberite is the name given to those ores containing less than 20 per cent manganese tungstate, and hubnerite is the name for those with less than 20 per cent iron tungstate. The color varies from black to reddish brown, and the specific gravity from 7.1 to 7.5.

The mineral scheelite when pure, contains 80.6 per cent tungsten trioxide. It has an opaque, waxlike appearance and varies in color from white through pale yellow to black. The specific gravity varies from 5.9 to 6.1. A small part of the tungsten is frequently replaced by molybdenum. The mineral fluoresces when subjected to short wave ultraviolet light, the color varying from blue through white to yellow as the molybdenum content increases.

Tungsten makes up approximately 1×10^{-4}

part of the earth's crust, and its ores are widely distributed. Tungsten ore deposits are almost invariably associated with acid igneous intrusives. The wolframite series usually occurs in quartz veins and pegmatites, generally associated with cassiterite, small amounts of scheelite, and sulfide minerals, whereas scheelite is almost invariably found in tactite, a metamorphic rock formed by the alteration of calcareous rocks near intrusive granites. The tungstic oxide content of the ore deposits seldom exceeds 2 per cent, and the average of those in the United States is approximately 0.5 per cent.

The world's important tungsten deposits are found in China, the United States, Korea, Bolivia, Portugal, Burma, Australia, Siam, Spain, Argentina, Brazil, Russia, Peru, Belgian Congo, Rhodesia, and Malaya, in order of magnitude.[14] The most important producing states in this country are California, Nevada, North Carolina, Idaho, and Colorado.

Advantage is taken of their high specific gravity in concentrating tungsten minerals by means of jigs and tables. Flotation is extensively used in concentrating scheelite ores. The first concentrates are purified and further concentrated by magnetic and electrostatic separation, flotation, roasting, and leaching. Frequently, it becomes necessary to resort to chemical decomposition of the rough concentrates, with reprecipitation of the tungsten as calcium tungstate (known as synthetic scheelite) in order to produce a concentrate of marketable quality.

PRODUCTION AND ECONOMIC STATISTICS

For many years the major portion of the world's tungsten was produced in China, which still possesses the largest proved reserves. No nation today, however, dominates tungsten production. Stimulated by the high prices guaranteed by the United States government during the Korean hostilities, this country demonstrated its ability to produce 16 million lb of contained tungsten/year.[28] This compares with a normal annual national consumption of approximately 8 million lb and a maximum consumption reached, during World War II, of slightly over 19 million lb of tungsten.

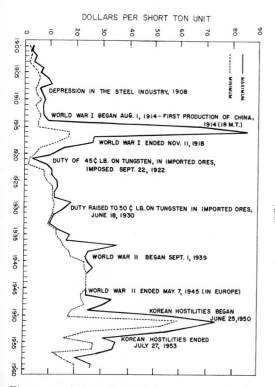

Figure 30.1. Prices of tungsten concentrates in the United States 1900-1959.

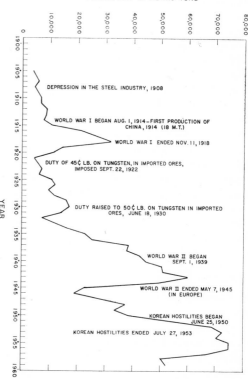

Figure 30.2. World production of tungsten concentrates containing 60 per cent WO_3 (metric tons).

Reflecting its critical importance in industrial production, tungsten production, consumption, and prices have always been very sensitive to changing economic conditions, and especially to increased demand in time of war. Thus tungsten's brief industrial history,[20] which coincides with the two major wars, three major depressions, and the unprecedented industrial development of the past 50 years, is characterized by widely fluctuating demand, production, and price levels. This is illustrated in Figure 30.1 which charts the price of tungsten concentrates in the United States for the years 1900 to 1959. Production statistics for the corresponding years are charted in Figure 30.2.

METALLURGY

Tungsten concentrates are reduced to three commercial products: ferrotungsten, tungsten chemicals, and pure tungsten.

Ferrotungsten

Commercial ferrotungsten contains from 70 to 80 per cent tungsten and is used almost exclusively in the manufacture of tungsten-containing steels and cast irons. It is prepared by reduction of one of the tungsten minerals with carbon or silicon in an electric furnace or with aluminum and silicon in the thermit process. With either method, recovery is good, and the impurity content can be controlled to a large extent. A relatively small weight of the reductant produces a large weight of tungsten, and the tungstic oxide is easily reduced at the high temperatures used. Owing to its high melting point, ferrotungsten is not tapped from the furnace; rather, the solid button is removed from the cold furnace, crushed, and graded into convenient size for addition to the steel baths.

Tungsten Compounds

Most of the chemical compounds of commerce (tungstic oxide, tungstic acid, calcium tungstate, ammonium paratungstate) are obtained as intermediate products in the process of preparation of pure tungsten metal described later.

Anhydrous sodium tungstate, Na_2WO_4, may be prepared by fusing tungsten trioxide with sodium hydroxide or carbonate. The dihydrate is obtained by crystallization from carbonate solutions at temperatures above 6°C (42.8°F).

The tungsten bronzes used as pigments are of the general type $M_{20}(WO_3)_x \cdot WO_2$, in which M is an alkali metal such as sodium or potassium. They are prepared by several methods, one of which is the reduction of alkali-metal acid tungstates with hydrogen or carbon monoxide at elevated temperatures.

Tungsten hexacarbonyl $W(CO)_6$, a volatile solid which shows promise for use in forming adherent metal coatings, may be formed by the interaction of tungsten powder and carbon monoxide at 225–300°C (437–572°F) under high pressure (200 atm). It is also produced through the interaction of carbon monoxide at high pressure with tungsten hexachloride dissolved in ether in the presence of magnesium.

Tungsten Metal

The high melting point of tungsten, its reactivity, and the nonavailability of refractories capable of containing molten tungsten, preclude the use of conventional smelting techniques. Consequently, tungsten is won from its ores by chemical decomposition and refining of the ore, isolation of the purified trioxide, reduction of the oxide to metal powder, and finally proceeding by powder metallurgical methods to the fabrication of metal products.

Of the many methods employed or proposed for the decomposition of tungsten ores, only three are of commercial importance today: (1) digestion with acids (usually hydrochloric), (2) digestion with alkalies, and (3) fusion with alkalies or alkali salts. The individual process schemes employed by different manufacturers vary widely, even when starting with similar raw material and producing metal for identical purposes. The chemistry underlying the decomposition and refining processes, however, is reasonably simple, as is illustrated by Figure 30.3, which presents a composite of current procedures.

It is noteworthy that the physical properties possessed by finished tungsten products are materially affected by the chemical and physical characteristics of the powder from which they are produced. These, in turn, are dependent on the chemical and physical properties of the oxide from which the metal is reduced, and the

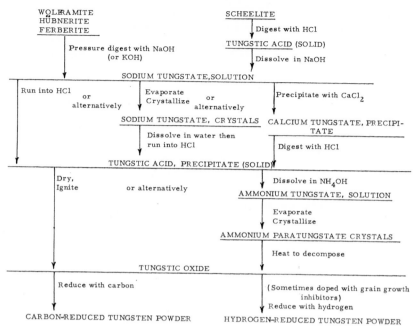

Figure 30.3. Composite of current industrial procedures for the processing of tungsten concentrates into metal powder.

conditions prevailing during reduction. Obviously, then, control of the properties of the final product begins almost with the inception of ore decomposition, and controlled variations are necessary throughout the process to yield the desired properties in the finished product.

Acid digestion is usually applied only to scheelite ores, since minerals of the wolframite series are comparatively resistant to attack by acid. The reaction is simply to form soluble calcium chloride and the insoluble hydrated tungstic oxide. After thorough washing (usually by decantation) the tungstic acid is dissolved in either ammonium hydroxide or alkali metal hydroxide, and the tungstate solution is filtered to remove insoluble material contained in the original ore.

Ores containing wolframite minerals are ordinarily decomposed by digestion with a strong (50 per cent) solution of alkali metal hydroxide, either under pressure or simply by boiling at atmospheric pressure. Alternatively, the ores may be mixed with alkali metal carbonate or hydroxide and sintered or carried to complete fusion to form the soluble alkali metal tungstate. This is followed by leaching with water. In either method the iron and manganese hydroxides, together with other insoluble materials contained in the ore, are separated by filtration and washing of the residue.

Ammonium tungstate solution, resulting from acid decomposition of high-grade scheelite and solution of the tungstic acid in ammonia, is frequently crystallized for use without further purification. Most tungsten concentrates of commerce, however, contain sufficient impurities such as soluble silica, arsenic, phosphorus, and particularly molybdenum as to require purification of the primary tungstate solution. Purification of the solution is accomplished by substantially the same procedures, regardless of whether it may consist of ammonium, potassium, or sodium tungstate, and regardless of the method used in decomposing the ore. Any or a combination of the following procedures may be used:

Arsenic and phosphorus are precipitated as magnesium arsenate and phosphate by vigorous agitation of the solution with small amounts of magnesium chloride. (Ammonium chloride is also added in the case of treatment of sodium or potassium tungstate solution.)

Molybdenum may be removed by (1) the addition of sodium sulfide followed by precipitation of the tungsten with calcium chloride. Molybdenum remains in solution as sulfomolybdate, and the precipitated calcium tungstate is again digested with acid as before. (2) The tungstate solution is acidified slightly, and molybdenum is precipitated as the sulfide by the addition, preferably under pressure, of H_2S or sodium sulfide. (3) Acidification of the tungstate solution, followed by crystallization as ammonium or alkali paratungstate, results in a concentration of molybdenum in the mother liquor.[16]

Following the removal of these impurities, the tungstate is usually further purified by precipitation as synthetic scheelite, redigestion with acid to form tungstic acid, solution in ammonium hydroxide, and finally crystallization of ammonium paratungstate. This is accomplished by evaporation of the ammonium tungstate solution to about one-eighth of its original volume. The mother liquor is returned to process, and the crystals are carefully washed and dried. The material obtained is ammonium paratungstate, $5(NH_4)_2O \cdot 12WO_3 \cdot 11H_2O$, pure stock from which various grades of tungsten may be prepared.

"Light oxide" may be prepared by digestion of the pure paratungstate crystals in boiling caustic solution, filtration, and precipitation of tungstic acid from the clear alkali tungstate solution by running it into boiling hydrochloric acid. Alternatively, sodium tungstate crystals may be dissolved in water and treated in the same manner. Concentrations of both acid and tungstate solution, temperature, and rate of mixing the solutions control the type of precipitate obtained. Too rapid addition of the tungstate produces a flocculent precipitate which is difficult to wash. Low temperatures result in a colloidal impure precipitate. After lengthy washing the tungstic acid is filtered and dehydrated by heating to approximately 350°C (662°F).

"Heavy oxide" is produced by simply igniting pure paratungstate crystals at a temperature of approximately 400°C (752°F) to drive off the ammonia.

The two forms of oxide obtained possess widely different physical properties and may be used to produce tungsten powders having equally widely different physical properties. The heavy oxide should have an average particle size of 4 to 5 μ and a packing density of 24 to 31 g/cu in., whereas the light oxide will have an average particle size of $\frac{1}{2}$ to 2 μ and a packing density of 15 to 18 g/cu in.

Curiously enough, it is only in the preparation of tungsten carbide products and a relatively few electronic applications that tungsten, in a state of great purity, has given best results. Thus, for many applications, "dope" is added to the purified oxide prior to reduction. These additives may consist of alkali chlorides and silicates, alumina, or thoria in amounts as small as a few hundredths of 1 per cent or as much as 5 per cent.

The alkali metals and silica additives are volatile and almost wholly eliminated in the subsequent sintering step, which takes place at over 3000°C (5432°F). Metal produced from oxide so treated shows a tendency to become large crystal metal upon sintering which, in turn, imparts the fibrous structure characteristic of "non-sag" filament wire. Transverse and longitudinal sections of such wire are illustrated in Figures 30.4 and 30.5.

The effect of nonvolatile additives such as thoria or alumina is to inhibit grain growth during the sintering operation, and during subsequent recrystallization.[3]

Figure 30.4. Tungsten wire, 0.007-inch transverse section etched electrolytically in NaOH (200X). (*Courtesy General Electric Co.*)

Figure 30.5. Tungsten wire, 0.007-inch longitudinal section etched electrolytically in NaOH (200X). (*Courtesy General Electric Co.*)

Reduction

The oxide may be reduced by carbon, carbonaceous gases, or hydrogen. The purest metal for use in electronic and carbide products is reduced by hydrogen. Carbon reduction leaves some residual carbon but is used to produce lower cost tungsten powder for melting. Other methods of reduction, such as electrolytic, have not attained industrial significance.

Hydrogen reduction is usually accomplished in gas fired or electrically heated tube furnaces, although both rotary tube and continuous belt types have been used to some extent. A typical tube furnace consists of a number of heat-resistant alloy tubes from 1½ to 3 in. internal diameter and 12 to 18 ft long, enclosed in a refractory frame. The furnace is heated in such manner as to provide several temperature zones, the first zone being maintained at 450–600°C (842–1112°F), and the final zone from 750–1100°C (1382–2012°F), depending upon the type of powder desired. The tungstic oxide is contained in heat resistant alloy boats, 12 to 18 in. long, which are introduced into the tubes at regular intervals. As a freshly loaded boat is introduced into the tube it moves a boat of re-

duced metal into the water-cooled discharge end of the tube. A large excess of dry, oxygen-free hydrogen is introduced at the discharge end of the tube and flows countercurrent to the movement of the oxide. The excess hydrogen is dried, deoxidized, and recirculated. Complete reduction may be effected in a single pass through the furnace, or, for special application, two-stage reduction may be used. The first stage is carried out at a low temperature [750°C (1382°F) maximum] to produce "brown oxide" WO_2, which is mixed with fresh yellow oxide for final reduction in the second stage. Oxide ready for charging into tube furnaces equipped for automatic loading, stoking, and unloading is shown in Figure 30.6.

The product is loosely sintered gray powder which is broken up by sifting through a 200-mesh sieve, blended into larger lots, and stored in airtight containers.

In summary, the particle size, particle size distribution, and physical properties of the final metal are controlled by:

(1) Particle size and method of production of the oxide.

(2) Impurities, intentionally or otherwise present in the oxide.

(3) Rate at which the oxide reaches minimum reduction temperature.

(4) Final temperature reached during reduction.

(5) The partial pressure of water vapor in the hydrogen.

Figure 30.6. Tungsten oxide being charged into automatic tube reduction furnace. (*Courtesy Wah Chang Corp.*)

(6) The depth of oxide in the boat.

(7) Whether reduction is completed in one or more stages.

Carbon Reduction. Melting grade tungsten for use in the manufacture of cast tungsten carbide and some alloys may be prepared by reduction of the oxide with carbon or hydrocarbon gases. In one practice, lampblack is mixed with the oxide in stoichiometric proportion, packed in graphite crucibles, and heated either in a gas fired kiln or an induction furnace. The lightly sintered product is furnace cooled, broken up, and screened, usually on a 65-mesh sieve. Usual trade specifications call for a minimum of 99 per cent W and a maximum of 0.15 per cent carbon.

Tungsten Carbide

Tungsten carbide, WC, is made in powder form by the chemical combination of pure tungsten metal powder and finely divided lampblack. What has been said regarding the importance of purity, particle size, and particle size distribution of tungsten powder for electronic purposes holds equally true for carbide powder. The properties of cemented carbide forms are dependent upon the purity and physical properties of the carbide powder used.

Pure tungsten powder is blended with the requisite amount of lampblack, placed in carbon boats or crucibles, and heated in a hydrogen atmosphere for about 2 hr at 1450–1550°C (2642–2822°F). Heating is accomplished either by induction furnaces or carbon tube furnaces, following which the product is cooled in a hydrogen atmosphere, broken up, and screened through a 200-mesh screen. Standard powder contains between 6.05 and 6.20 per cent total carbon with not more than 0.1 per cent uncombined carbon. Particle size is controlled by the particle size of the tungsten powder used and the temperature at which carburization is allowed to take place.

Macrocrystalline monocarbide, WC, is also produced by combined reduction of ore and carburization[15,17] and by carburization in a molten metal menstruum.[18]

Special purpose carbides or "hard metal" used for machining steels generally contain varying proportions of titanium, tantalum, and columbium, either individually or in combination. These elements are introduced by blending the requisite metal powder or oxide with the tungsten-lampblack mixture, or they may be produced as double carbides in the molten-metal menstruum process. The double carbide serves to lower the coefficient of friction and alleviates the "cratering" effect on the tool tip which is encountered in machining steel.

Tungsten subcarbide, W_2C, or more correctly, a mixture of WC and W_2C, is produced by fusion and casting. One process consists of packing carbon-reduced powder with the required amount of carbonaceous material in a carbon crucible and heating above the melting point [3000–3200°C (5432–5792°F)] by passing high amperage current through the crucible. A small hole in the bottom of the crucible allows the molten carbide to flow into molds, or it may be quenched in an oil bath, crushed, graded, and packed into metal tubes for use as hard facing electrodes.

PHYSICAL PROPERTIES

The most outstanding of the physical properties of tungsten are, of course, its high melting point [3410°C (6170°F)] and high modulus of elasticity, which are the highest of all metallic elements, and its low vapor pressure and low compressibility, which are the lowest of all metallic elements. Its density of 19.3 equals that of gold and is exceeded only by that of platinum, iridium, osmium, and rhenium. The high density and relatively high thermal neutron absorption cross sectional value make tungsten an effective shielding material.

The thermal conductivity of tungsten, though less than half that of copper, is much higher than that of iron or nickel. The electrical conductivity of tungsten, although roughly only one-third that of annealed copper, is higher than that of iron, nickel, mercury, platinum, or phosphor bronze.

Data on some of the physical properties are listed in Table 30.1.

MECHANICAL PROPERTIES

Tungsten exhibits high strength and high hardness at both room temperature and elevated temperatures. Fine tungsten wire has the highest reported tensile strength of all materials prepared by standard production techniques. The high-temperature strength is characterized

TABLE 30.1. PHYSICAL PROPERTIES OF TUNGSTEN
(Numbers in Parentheses Refer to References)

Atomic number	74	
Atomic weight	183.92	
Isotopes (natural)	180, 182, 183, 184, 186	(14)
Melting point	3410°C ± 20 (6170°F)	(21)
	3380°C (6116°F)	(27)
Boiling point	5900°C (10,652°F)	(14)
Density (g/cc) at 20°C	19.3	
	19.26 (calcd. from lattice constant)	(11)
Vapor pressure (mm Hg)		
1527°C (2780°F)	1.93×10^{-15}	
2127°C (3860°F)	7.9×10^{-9}	
2727°C (4940°F)	6.5×10^{-5}	
3227°C (5840°F)	4.68×10^{-3}	
Specific heat at 20°C (68°F) (cal/g/°C)	0.032	(14)
Thermal conductivity (cal/sq cm/cm/sec/°C)		(22)
20°C (68°F)	0.31	
927°C (1701°F)	0.275	
1127°C (2061°F)	0.268	
1327°C (2421°F)	0.260	
1527°C (2781°F)	0.253	
1727°C (3141°F)	0.245	
Lattice type	Body-centered cubic	
Lattice constant (Å)	3.1647 (25°C)	(12)
Coefficient of linear expansion [mean value 0–500°C (32–932°F)]		
Worked	4.98×10^{-6}	(21)
Annealed	4.45×10^{-6}	(21)
Atomic volume (cc/g-atom based on density 19.3)	9.53	
Heat of fusion (cal/g)	44	
Heat of vaporization (cal/g)	1,183	
Electrical resistivity (microhm-cm)		(14)
20°C (68°F)	5.5	
227°C (441°F)	10.5	
727°C (1341°F)	24.3	
1727°C (3141°F)	55.7	
2727°C (4941°F)	90.4	
3227°C (5841°F)	108.5	
Temperature coefficient of electrical resistivity per °C [20–100°C (68–212°F)]	0.00482	
Thermionic data		
Apparent electron work function (ev)	4.55	
Apparent positive ion emission (ev)	11.93	
Radiation emission coefficient	0.43	
First ionization potential	7.60	
Magnetic susceptibility (g-atom)	$+40 \times 10^{-6}$	
Thermal neutron absorption cross section (barns/atom)	19.2 ± 1.0	
Compressibility, per megabar, at 20°C (68°F)	0.28×10^{-6}, the smallest of any known metal	(14)
Young's modulus of elasticity at 20°C	59×10^{6} psi	

by the fact that the tensile strength of tungsten does not diminish sharply after it has been heated above recrystallization temperature, as do most other metals. In spite of its high density, the strength-weight ratio of tungsten at elevated temperature is superior to all other metals tested.

Sintered or as-cast polycrystalline tungsten has a relatively high ductile-brittle transition temperature of 150–450°C (302–842°F)[32] while single crystal tungsten is reported to have a transition temperature between −196 and −107°C (−320 and −160°F).[1] The effect of prior cold work, impurity content, grain size and strain rate on the change of transition temperature has not been fully established. It is generally believed that cold working lowers while impurity elevates the transition temperature of polycrystalline tungsten.

TABLE 30.2. TYPICAL MECHANICAL PROPERTIES OF TUNGSTEN AT ROOM TEMPERATURE

Form (in.)		Tensile strength (psi)	Hardness (Rockwell)
Sintered ingot		16,000	
Rod	0.250	70,000	37C
	0.100	150,000	40C
	0.050	200,000	44C
Wire	0.025	225,000	44C
	0.010	250,000	
	0.005	300,000	
	0.001	610,000	
Sheet	0.040	120,000	44C
	0.020	200,000	45C
	0.010	300,000	47C

Some room temperature tensile strength data of tungsten are given in Table 30.2. These data are typical only, since the strength of sintered and worked tungsten varies according to the particle size and purity of the metal used and according to the processing procedure in the manufacture. While sintered and cold worked tungsten shows little or no elongation at room temperature, annealing of the wire can give it as much as 15 per cent elongation at room temperature. Typical mechanical properties of tungsten at elevated temperatures are given in Table 30.3.

CHEMICAL PROPERTIES

Tungsten is one of the transition elements, a member of Group VI of the periodic table. The valence ranges from two to six. Compounds with the higher valence exhibit acidic properties, while those of lower valence have basic properties.

Tungsten has two oxides of definitely established compositions: the dioxide, which is brown in color, and the trioxide, which is yellow. Although the blue and violet oxides of tungsten, commonly encountered in the reduction of tungsten trioxide, have been identified by x-ray diffraction studies as two homogeneous intermediate oixde phases, their compositions, have yet to be established. From crystallographic considerations, the most likely compositions are $WO_{2.875}$ or W_8O_{23} for blue oxide and $WO_{2.75}$ or W_4O_{11} for violet oxide.[18a] Other intermediate oxides are merely mixtures of various identifiable oxides and metal phase[9a].

Elements such as carbon, boron, silicon, and sulfur combine directly with tungsten at elevated temperatures to form corresponding compounds. For example, tungsten carbide begins to form at 1200°C (2192°F) when carbon and tungsten are in contact.

TABLE 30.3. TYPICAL MECHANICAL PROPERTIES OF TUNGSTEN AT ELEVATED TEMPERATURES[23]

Treatment	Temperature		Yield strength 0.2% offset (psi)	Ultimate tensile strength (psi)	Elongation (per cent)
	°C	°F			
Swaged rod annealed	27	80		215,000	0.2
	326	600		103,000	24.5
	649	1200		76,579	16.0
	871	1600		66,200	13.5
	1093	2000		58,969	14.5
Swaged rod recrystallized	326	600	28,800	59,700	16.4
	649	1200	15,200	44,500	55.3
	871	1600	14,500	36,600	57.9
	1093	2000	12,900	33,500	52.0

Tungsten forms two carbides—ditungsten carbide, W_2C, and monotungsten carbide, WC, with the following properties:[26]

	Ditungsten Carbide, W_2C	Monotungsten Carbide, WC
Per cent C	3.16	6.13
Crystal structure	Hexagonal	Hexagonal, simple
Lattice constants	a = 2.98 Å c = 4.71 Å	a = 2.90 Å c = 2.83 Å
Theoretical density (g/cc)	17.34	15.77
Melting point	2730°C (4950°F)	2630°C (4770°F) decomposes
Hardness, Mohs	9+	9+

Tungsten carbonyl, $W(CO)_6$, may be sublimed and decomposed at low temperatures, and furnishes the means of vapor deposition of very high purity tungsten.

Borides and silicides of tungsten are characterized by their hardness and high melting point.

The metal is relatively resistant against acids.[8] It begins to oxidize in air at 400°C (752°F). The oxidation is rapid at red heat and in oxygen, forming the trioxide, which spalls easily. The trioxide begins to volatilize above 750°C (1382°F).

The chemical behavior of tungsten metal is outlined in Table 30.4.

TABLE 30.4. CHEMICAL BEHAVIOR OF TUNGSTEN

Substance	Reaction
Air or oxygen	Oxidation begins at 400°C (752°F)
Ammonia	None
Water	None
Steam	Oxidation above 700°C (1292°F)
Carbon	Carburization above 1200°C (2192°F)
CO	Carburization above 1700°C (3092°F)
CO_2	Oxidation above 1200°C (2192°F)
Hydrogen	None
Nitrogen	Nitriding at 1500°C (2732°F)
Fluorine	Forms fluoride at 20°C (68°F)
Chlorine	Forms chloride above 250°C (482°F)

Bromine	Forms bromide at red heat
Iodine	Forms iodide at red heat
Sulfur	Slow attack when molten
H_2S	Superficial attack at red heat
HCl (conc)	Slight attack at 100°C (212°F)
Aqua regia	Superficial oxidation to WO_3
HF	Slight attack at 100°C (212°F)
$HF + HNO_3$	Rapid solution
HNO_3 (conc)	Slight attack at 100°C (212°F)
H_2SO_4 (dilute)	Slight attack at 100°C (212°F)
H_2SO_4 (conc)	Slight attack at 20°C (68°F)
NaOH and KOH (aqueous)	None at 20°C (68°F)
NaOH and KOH (fused)	Slow attack, rapid solution with oxidizing agents

Tungsten has good resistance to attack by many liquid metals over extended periods of time. It can be used satisfactorily with sodium and sodium-potassium alloys to 900°C (1652°F), with mercury to 600°C (1112°F), with gallium to 800°C (1472°F), with bismuth to 980°C (1796°F), and with magnesium to 600°C (1112°F).[25] It has been found to be resistant to zinc at 700°C (1292°F) in a reducing atmosphere, whereas other metals and alloys are consumed rather rapidly.[10]

ALLOYS

Comprehensive data on binary alloys of tungsten have been presented by Hansen.[9] Some pertinent information from that work and other information are listed below:

Tungsten-Molybdenum, Columbium, Tantalum, Chromium

Tungsten forms continuous series of binary solid solutions only with molybdenum, columbium, and tantalum, and with chromium above 1400°C (2552°F). Ternary systems of tungsten with molybdenum, columbium, and tantalum are also continuous series of solid solutions. Additions of molybdenum, columbium, and tantalum decrease the hardness and tensile strength of tungsten at room temperature, but they show promise of improving the high-temperature strength of tungsten. With about 40 per cent Mo, maximum electrical resistivity and minimum temperature coefficient are reached. An alloy containing 3.7 per cent Ta has about one-third more resistivity than pure tungsten.[6]

Tungsten-Rhenium[3a]

Tungsten dissolves up to 37 per cent rhenium at 3000°C (5430°F) and rhenium up to 20 per cent tungsten at 2800°C (5070°F). Two intermediate phases have been found in the binary system. Sigma phase forms peritectically at 3000°C (5432°F), and χ-phase forms peritectoidally at 2125°C (3857°F). A eutectic occurs at 74 per cent rhenium between sigma phase and the rhenium-rich terminal solid solution. The eutectic horizontal extends from 71 to 80 per cent rhenium, and the eutectic temperature is 2825°C (5120°F). It has been reported that tungsten base alloys with 25 to 35 per cent rhenium can be rolled to thin strip from the arc cast condition at about 1000°C (1832°F). Less ductility has been observed with decreasing rhenium content while at higher rhenium contents excessive sigma phase results in a highly brittle structure. This seems to indicate a maximum ductility at maximum solid solution strengthening.

The solubility of tungsten in iron, cobalt, and nickel forms the basis of some of the powder-metal alloys of tungsten.

Tungsten-Iron

The solubility of tungsten in iron is about 33 per cent at 1538°C (2800°F), falling to about 8 per cent at ordinary temperatures.

Tungsten-Cobalt

Tungsten readily dissolves in molten cobalt. The eutectic, containing 45 per cent tungsten, occurs at approximately 1480°C (2696°F). The solid solubility drops rapidly with decrease in temperature.

Tungsten-Nickel

Tungsten readily dissolves in molten nickel. At 1495°C (2725°F) the eutectic composition containing 45 per cent tungsten is reached.

Tungsten-Nickel-Copper

Small additions of copper substantially reduce the sintering temperature of W-Ni powder to attain necessary density for heavy alloys. On sintering the powder mixture, the copper and nickel particles begin to alloy above 1000°C (1832°F). Although tungsten does not dissolve in copper, it is rapidly dissolved in the copper-nickel upon reaching the melting point of the alloy. As fine tungsten particles dissolve, the tungsten is reprecipitated on certain nuclei, forming large round particles. This progresses until all the fine tungsten particles have been dissolved, eliminating porosity in the process.

Tungsten Steels[27]

Tungsten is present in steel principally in the form of carbide. With low tungsten content, WC is present with iron carbide, Fe_3C, in varying proportions. Some of the tungsten may also dissolve in Fe_3C, replacing iron. With high tungsten content, double or complex carbides are probably formed which may be expressed as $(Fe-W)_6C$, or as $(Fe-W-Cr-V)_6C$. When additional tungsten is present, iron tungstides, Fe_2W and Fe_3W_2, may exist.

Miscellaneous

Tungsten is substantially soluble in aluminum, titanium, vanadium, zirconium, platinum, osmium, rhodium, and ruthenium. It is practically insoluble in mercury. Compounds of tungsten with beryllium and tellurium have been reported. Tungsten is slightly soluble in thorium and uranium, but it does not alloy with calcium, copper, magnesium, manganese, lead, zinc, silver, or tin.

ANALYSIS AND METALLOGRAPHY

The standard method for the chemical analysis of tungsten is the precipitation of cinchonine tungstate[29] with cinchonine from alkaline tungstate solutions that have been slightly acidified. The precipitate is decomposed to tungsten trioxide by igniting to 750°C (1382°F). Volumetric methods are not accurate.

For metallographic study, tungsten may be polished with emery paper followed with levigated alumina, then etched with an alkaline potassium ferricyanide solution. Tungsten ingot or rod may be polished electrolytically in a 4 per cent solution of sodium hydroxide at a current density of 20 to 45 amps/sq in. The same sample may also be etched electrolytically in the same solution, but at lower current density.

FABRICATION

Tungsten powder is converted to massive metal by hydraulically compressing it in a split mold at 10 to 40 tons/sq in. The pressed bars are next presintered in a hydrogen atmosphere at about 1200°C (2192°F) in order to give them sufficient strength for handling. In the final treatment the presintered bar is suspended vertically between a fixed water-cooled copper contact at its upper end and a slip clamp submerged in a water-cooled well of mercury at its lower end. The whole assembly is enclosed in a bell-type "treating bottle" through which dry hydrogen is circulated. Electric current is then passed through the bar to some 90 to 95 per cent of that required to melt the ingot. During this treatment the bar shrinks 15 to 20 per cent and attains a density of 17 to 18 g/cc. The current is applied in graduated steps, providing for the escape of volatile impurities and "dope" while the metal is still porous. In the case of a bar of, say, 1-in.-square cross section, the energy input is about 10,000 amp at 12 volts. The size of the ingots so prepared is limited by the problems of press construction and of handling the high amperages required. Practically, the ingots may vary from 8 to 30 in. in length, with cross sections of ½ to 4 sq. in.

Compared to other metals of body-centered-cubic lattice, tungsten has relatively low room-temperature ductility and is extremely brittle in the fully annealed (recrystallized) state. It can, however, be worked hot (but below the recrystallization temperature) and is subject to work hardening. The recovery of plasticity of worked tungsten by annealing below recrystallization temperature is essential to the successive stages in the fabrication of tungsten. The threshold temperature of recrystallization depends on microstructure, history of the metal, and the criteria used in establishing the point at which recrystallization begins. The amount of prior cold work, the impurity content and the annealing time are the principal factors that determine the lowest recrystallization temperature. Initial forging is accomplished at temperatures of 1500–1700°C (2732–3092°F). The working temperatures are progressively lowered, and the smaller sizes of wire are drawn at 300–400°C (572–752°F).

Ductile Rod and Wire

An ingot to be worked into small diameter rod or wire is first reduced by swaging. This operation is done between the two halves of a rotating split die which fly apart centrifugally to allow entry of the bar and then are forced together by impact of the back surfaces with a surrounding ring of rollers, thus effecting several thousand hammerlike blows per minute on the bar. The dies may be made of hardened high-speed steel, heat resistant alloy such as "Stellite" or "Tantung," or cemented carbide. Reduction in area may be as much as 30 per cent per pass. The density of the metal and the ductility are increased as the cross section is reduced, the density approaching the theoretical (19.3) at small rod diameters. As the size is reduced, the grains elongate to develop a tough, interlocking, fibrous structure.

In making wire the transition from swaging to drawing is largely determined by the limitations of the equipment used and economical considerations. Swaging is frequently continued to a rod diameter of 0.04 in.; however, bench drawing has been applied to 0.25-in.-diameter rod. Beyond about 0.04-in. diameter, the wire is sufficiently pliable to be coiled onto a reel. At about 0.01-in. diameter and under, drawing is done through diamond dies. Above this diameter, tungsten carbide dies are generally used.

Tungsten Sheet

Sheet is also produced by "hot-cold" working. One difference lies in the dimension of the original bar, which is pressed into flat sections instead of square bars. These sections are highly heated and forged before rolling. In working tungsten into sheet, the rolls are operated at a high rate of speed to prevent cooling of the metal. Pack rolling or protection by a metal envelope is practiced to prevent oxidation at the high rolling temperatures. As the metal is reduced to very thin sheet, rolling can be conducted at ordinary temperatures. The finished sheet has a high polish and can be punched and stamped into the various commercial forms.

With proper consideration being given to the brittle-ductile transition temperature of tungsten, the massive metal can be subjected to the usual forming operations such as forging, punching, shearing, and forming. Since tungsten oxidizes rapidly at fabrication temperatures, heating should be done in a protective atmosphere, preferably hydrogen, and the time of exposure of the work to the atmosphere should be held to a minimum. Oxidized surfaces may be removed in a bath of hot caustic soda solution or by firing in a hydrogen atmosphere at about 1000°C (1832°F).

Intricate parts of tungsten may be made by machining porous sintered tungsten pieces that have been infiltrated with copper. After machining, the copper is driven off by vacuum sintering which, at the same time, densifies the tungsten. This process,[13] however, can achieve only 90 per cent density. Tungsten tubing may be made by ultrasonic shaping of the rod.

Tungsten-to-tungsten joining can be made by spot welding or butting welding. The joint, however, is always recrystallized and is, therefore, brittle. Mechanical fastening, such as riveting, seems to be the most reliable. Tungsten is easily brazed with copper, silver, and nickel, provided the parts are clean and the brazing is carried out in nonoxidizing atmosphere. Resistance welding of tungsten to nickel is highly satisfactory in the manufacture of electronic parts.

Slip Casting

Special shapes of tungsten may be made by slip casting. Tungsten powder, of carefully selected particle size, is milled with dispersing agents to produce a slip of high apparent density and viscosity. This is cast into molds and fired according to ceramics technique. The product has mechanical properties comparable to those of swaged tungsten, except that the density is not much above 90 per cent.

Arc Casting

Tungsten may be arc cast in vacuum in the same manner as is done with molybdenum. This produces ingots of higher purity than can be made by the sintered powder method, particularly in respect to gaseous impurities. The large grain size of the ingot makes it extremely brittle.

Electron Beam Melting

Electron beam melting is conducted in a vacuum chamber where accelerated electrons are focused on the tungsten melt stock and the ingot surface, maintaining a molten pool. The pressure in the chamber must be maintained below one-half micron to avoid gas ionization and subsequent low-voltage discharge. The temperature achieved in the metal depends only on the input and the losses through conduction and radiation. For a unit of given capacity the melting rate is determined by the rate at which the melt stock is fed through the path of the electron beam. This is a decided advantage over other methods of melting because, with adequate time for volatilization of impurities, a purer product can often be made in a single melting. 6-in. diameter tungsten ingots have been produced by this method with total impurity level down to 150 ppm.

Provided with an appropriate driving mechanism, the electron beam furnace can be converted to a zone refining device to grow purified single crystals of tungsten. While substantial reduction of metallic impurities can be effected by repeated zoning, the gaseous impurities such as oxygen and nitrogen will be reintroduced into the molten zone by a higher external vapor pressure of these gases.[1] At present, the zone refining technique for tungsten is primarily a research tool.

Hydrostatic Compacting

Tungsten powder is easily consolidated by hydrostatic compacting. This technique is advantageous in producing very large pieces. Furnace sintering of such compacts can produce ingots comparable to resistance sintered ingots.

Flame Spraying

Tungsten may be flame sprayed onto steel or other metallic backing to give a coating of 0.01 to 0.05 in. thick per pass. The grains show a cast structure and can attain a density of 95 per cent.

Sintered Carbide

Tungsten carbide is hard and nonmalleable and is fabricated by cementing or bonding with

TABLE 30.5. TYPICAL GRADES OF CEMENTED TUNGSTEN CARBIDE*

Application	Designation	WC (%)	Co (%)	TaC (%)	TiC (%)	Hardness (RA)	Density (g/cc)	Transverse rupture strength (psi)	Compressive strength (psi)
Chip removal									
Cast iron, nonferrous and nonmetallic materials									
Roughing cuts	C-1	91.0	9.0	—	—	90.5	14.60	275,000	685,000
General purpose	C-2	94.0	6.0	—	—	91.5	14.95	240,000	700,000
Light finishing	C-3	96.0	4.0	—	—	92.0	15.10	160,000	750,000
Precision boring	C-4	97.0	3.0	—	—	92.8	15.15	160,000	815,000
Steel and steel alloys									
Roughing cuts	C-5	74.0	11.0	7.0	8.0	91.0	12.25	250,000	600,000
General purpose	C-6	82.0	10.0	—	8.0	90.8	12.45	225,000	625,000
Finishing cuts	C-7	76.0	9.0	—	15.0	91.7	11.20	160,000	650,000
Semifinish and finishing cuts, alloy steels	C-70	77.0	8.0	8.5	6.5	92.0	12.75	220,000	680,000
Precision	C-8	80.0	4.0	—	16.0	92.0	11.25	125,000	700,000
Wear resistant									
No shock	C-9	94.0	6.0	—	—	Same as C-2			
Light shock	C-10	91.0	9.0	—	—	Same as C-1			
Heavy shock	C-11	87.0	13.0	—	—	89.0	14.20	325,000	625,000
Impact resistant									
Light impact	C-12	87.0	13.0	—	—	Same as C-11			
Medium impact	C-13	85.0	15.0	—	—	88.0	14.00	375,000	600,000
Heavy impact	C-14	75.0	25.0	—	—	83.5	13.10	360,000	500,000

* Courtesy of Adamas Carbide Corporation.

another metal. Cobalt is commonly used in amounts from 5 to 30 per cent of the carbide. Increasing cobalt increases toughness but decreases hardness. The performance of the finished product depends upon the grain size of the material, the density, and surface condition, all of which are controlled by the method of production.

The "cold press" method makes use of standard techniques of powder metallurgy. Carbide powder and cobalt are ball milled to insure even distribution of the cobalt. The mixture is then pressed at 10 to 30 tons/sq in., and the molded articles are preheated in hydrogen to about 900°C (1652°F). They are next machined to final shape, packed in carbon black contained in graphite boxes, and sintered at 1300–1450°C (2372–2642°F). On sintering, the pieces shrink about 20 per cent linearly and attain their final size, density, and hardness.

The "hot press" method differs only in that pressing and sintering are carried out at the same time. The method is applied to produc-tion of large pieces and intricate shapes. Graphite molds are used. These are broken away from the finished piece after sintering.

The properties and general application of some typical grades of tungsten carbide and "hard metal" are shown in Table 30.5.

APPLICATIONS

Present Applications

The first important application of tungsten was in incandescent lamp filaments, which remains one of the most important uses today. This was followed by its application for high-speed tool steels. By 1941, 95 per cent of the total tungsten consumed went into steel production, and 5 per cent was used in the form of metal powder, chemical compounds, and related products. Since that time the consumption pattern has shifted, with only about one-quarter of the consumption going into ferroalloys. The probable distribution of the uses of tungsten, by percentage, in recent years is reported in the "Tungsten Materials Survey"[19] and "Minerals Yearbook"[20a] as follows:

Use	1949	1955	1956	1957	1958	1959	1960**
Ferro alloys	63	>33	40	35	31.5	32	30
Carbides	17	30	35	40.5	39	37.5	35
Hard-facing alloys	1	—	1	2	3	9	7
Co-Cr-W-Mo alloys	4	—	3.5	3.5	3	5	5
Electrical equipment	6	14	13	13.5	16	13.5	18
Chemicals	6	1	1.5	1.5	2.5	1.5	1
Miscellaneous	3	<22*	6	4	5	1.5	3.5

* Includes metal powder.
** Up to the end of July, 1960.

This shift may be explained by (1) the forced substitution of molybdenum compositions for tungsten high-speed steels, largely as a result of the fear of an anticipated tungsten shortage and government controls which were operative during the Korean crisis, and (2) the increased use of cemented carbide or "hard metal" for cutting tools.

Tungsten in Steel. Tungsten is an avid carbide former and combines with iron and carbon and other alloying elements to form complex carbides which are stable at high temperatures. It is also a mild ferrite strengthener and imparts some hardenability to steel. The grain refinement imparted to steel by small tungsten additions increases toughness.

The chief property of tungsten in steel is its ability to retain high hardness at elevated temperatures, called *red hardness*. This property is enhanced in the presence of chromium and still further by cobalt, though with some sacrifice in toughness. In addition to the high-speed steels for cutting tools, tungsten is used in hot-work steels, finishing and die steels, shock resisting steels, and nondeforming steels.

Tungsten Alloys. The development of jet aircraft and rockets since World War II has resulted in an ever-increasing need for alloys possessing high strength and oxidation resistance at high temperatures. High-temperature alloys, to date, have been developed largely on the basis of trial and error, and many compositions containing tungsten are in use.

Alloys of cobalt, chromium, and tungsten have been marketed under the name of "Stellite" since 1913. They maintain their hardness and strength at temperatures up to 600°C (1112°F) and have been used as cast cutting tools, lathe centers, knives, dies, wear strips, guide rollers, etc. A very important use of these alloys has been the hard facing of articles subject to extreme abrasion, such as crusher plates, bucket teeth, valve seats, and pump parts.

Nickel-base alloys such as the "Hastelloys"* are applied where strength at high operating temperature or resistance to corrosion and erosion are required.

Silver-tungsten alloys, or more properly, mixtures, made by powder metallurgical methods are useful as electrical contacts, switchgear, and motor starters subject to severe arcing.

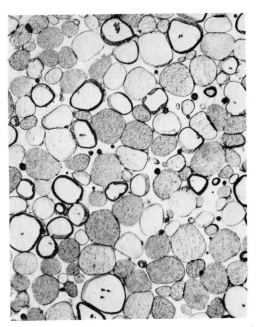

Figure 30.7. Heavy metal tungsten and matrix of W-Cu-Ni. (*Courtesy P. R. Mallory and Co.*)

Tungsten-nickel-copper alloys, composed of approximately 90 per cent tungsten, 6 per cent nickel, and 4 per cent copper, are extensively used as shields or containers for radioactive materials. The alloys generally referred to as "heavy metal" also find use as gyroscope rotors, counterweights in aircraft, and other applications where high density material is indicated. The microstructure of a typical heavy metal ("Mallory 1000") is illustrated in Figure 30.7.

* Trade name, Haynes Stellite Co.

Pure Tungsten. The high melting point and low vapor pressure of pure tungsten make it ideal for filaments in incandescent lamps and cathodes in electronic tubes. In pure rod or wire form, it is used in thermocouples for temperature measurements up to 3000°C (5432°F), electrodes in arc lamps, electrodes in gas shielded or atomic hydrogen welding, and electrochemical electrodes. Pure tungsten is employed for contact discs for the make-and-break type of electrical circuits and start-stop devices. X-ray machines use tungsten discs as targets because of the high penetrability of the tungsten x-rays. The high modulus of elasticity of tungsten wire suits it for use as cross hairs in telescopes, surgical stitching material, and springs in various instruments. Such springs will withstand temperatures up to 650°C (1202°F) with little permanent set.

Tungsten Carbide. The use of cemented tungsten carbide has assumed increasing importance in the past 10 years and has, to some extent, replaced tungsten alloys and high-speed steel in the tool-and-die industry. The extreme hardness of tungsten carbide at both ordinary and elevated temperatures makes it an excellent cutting material. In addition to its use as a cutting tool, tungsten carbide finds wide appli-

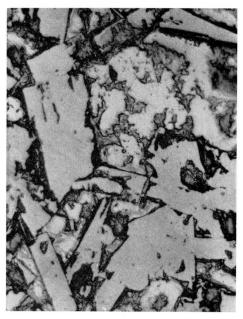

Figure 30.9. Cast tungsten carbide and cobalt (1500X). Twelve per cent Co; 84 per cent W and 4 per cent C (WC/W$_2$C). (*Courtesy Stoody Co.*)

cation in wear resistant parts and dies for hot and cold drawing of wire, rod, and tubing. Tungsten carbide reached great importance during World War II, when the Germans first used it to fabricate armor-piercing bullet cores.

Fused tungsten carbide finds extensive use in hard-facing applications to resist wear. The largest such use is, no doubt, the application to deep-well drilling tools. The fused carbide may also be cast into abrasion-resistant parts such as sandblasting nozzles, cutting tools, valve seats, etc. Figures 30.8 and 30.9 illustrate typical structures of cemented and cast tungsten carbides.

Phosphors. Phosphors are chemical compounds which, upon proper excitation by short wave rays, such as ultraviolet light, emit luminescent light which is more efficient than other light sources. The tungstates of calcium and magnesium are used extensively in fluorescent lighting.

Miscellaneous. Phosphotungstic acid, made by reacting sodium tungstate and phosphoric acid, is used as a mordant in the production of pigments. Tungsten trioxide finds use in oil and water colors. Tungsten bronzes are substituted for bronze powders in paints. Lead tungstates are used as substitutes for white

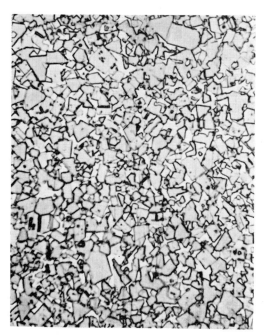

Figure 30.8. Cemented tungsten carbide with cobalt (1500X). (*Courtesy Adamas Carbide Corp.*)

lead. Tungsten compounds are used as opacifiers in glass, and one of the tungsten salts is reportedly used to raise the refractive index of optical glass, particularly in aerial photography. Sodium tungstate is used as a fire proofant.

Potential Applications

The uncertainty as to tungsten supply in the event of global warfare, price fluctuations, and the importance of tungsten to our economy, coupled with periodic governmental control of its use, have combined to stimulate metallurgical research toward satisfactory substitutions rather than expanded applications. As a result, the application of tungsten in the new high-temperature metals field has lagged behind other metals having even less potential application. Now, with a tremendous amount of tungsten in our national stockpile and with large tungsten reserves developed in the United States as well as abroad, it seems that extensive research on tungsten application can be pressed without hesitation or fear of a short supply, as has already been done with molybdenum.

The major impetus to the demand for materials capable of operating at higher temperatures and stresses and having greater corrosion resistance is due principally to the development of gas turbine and rocket engines. Further improvement in the efficiency of many industrial processes, however, particularly in the petroleum and chemical industries, depends largely upon the development of improved high-temperature creep resistant alloys. Tungsten will undoubtedly play an important part in the new alloys required in airframe and missile structural applications.

Alloys for high-temperature applications must exhibit high room- and high-temperature strength, creep resistance, toughness, fatigue strength, and corrosion and oxidation resistance. Furthermore, there must be a good relationship between these properties and density.

Tungsten appears to exhibit the best combination of properties for application at high temperatures of any of the refractory metals. The high rate of oxidation is, of course, intolerable for high-temperature application, but this is a fault common to all of the high-temperature metals. Encouraging results in improvement of oxidation resistance through alloying have been obtained. Of perhaps greater significance is the report of the extension of the molybdenum disilicide coating technique to tungsten.[19] Very little effort has been expended thus far on the development of tungsten for these applications, but it is now receiving more attention. Properties useful in determining a refractory metal's aptitude for high-temperature application are given for the common refractory metals in Table 30.6.[24]

Bibliography

1. Atkinson, R. H., and staff of Metals Research Group, Westinghouse Lamp Division, *WADD Tech. Rep. 60–37*, 1960.

TABLE 30.6. PROPERTIES OF REFRACTORY METALS

Property	W	Re	Ta	Mo	Cb
Melting point					
°C	3410	3180	2996	2610	2468
°F	6170	5656	5425	4730	4474
Density (g/cc)	19.3	21.0	16.6	10.2	8.57
Young's modulus (10^6 psi)	51	67	27	47	15.1
Structure	BCC	HCP	BCC	BCC	BCC
Recrystallization temperature [°C (1 hr)]	1565	1400	1275	1130	1050
Linear thermal expansion coefficient (10^{-6} per °C)	4.45	6.7	5.9	5.6	7.1
Thermal conductivity (cal/cm/sq cm/°C/sec)	0.31	0.17	0.13	0.35	0.125
Vapor pressure [μ at 2225°C (4037°F)]	1.38×10^{-4}	1.18×10^{-3}	7.9×10^{-4}	0.50	1.66×10^{-2}
Cost for powder ($/lb)	4.75	680.00	43.00	3.40	100.00

1a. Bechtold, J. H., and Shewmon, P. G., *Trans. Am. Soc. Metals,* **46,** 397–408 (1954).

1b. Brown, C. M., and Fountain, R. W., "New Metals Face the Future," *J. Metals,* **10,** 330 (May, 1958).

2. Buchle, H. Z., *Metallkunde,* **37,** 53–56 (1946).

3. Coolidge, W. D., British Patent 23,499 (1909); U.S. Patent 1,082,933 (1913).

3a. Dickinson, J. M., and Richardson, L., *Trans. Am. Soc. Metals,* **51,** 1055 (1959).

4. Erickson, C. G., *The Tool Engineer,* March, 1958.

5. Fitzer, E., "Materials of Maximum Creep and Oxidation Resistance Produced by Coating Tungsten and Molybdenum with Vapor Deposited Silicon," *Berg und Huttenmannische Monatahefte,* **97,** No. 5 (1952).

6. Goetzel, C. G., "Treatise on Powder Metallurgy," New York, Interscience Publishers Inc., 1950.

7. Gregg, J. L., "The Alloys of Iron and Tungsten," New York, McGraw-Hill Book Co., Inc., 1934.

8. Hampel, C. A., *Corrosion,* **14,** 557t–560t (1958).

9. Hansen, M., "Constitution of Binary Alloys," New York, McGraw-Hill Book Co., Inc., 1958.

9a. Hegedus, A. J., Miller, T., Heugebauer, J., and Sasvari, K., *Z. anorg. allgem. Chem.,* **281,** 64–82 (1955).

10. Hodge, W., Evans, R. M., and Hoskins, A. F., *Trans. AIME,* **203,** 824–32 (1955).

11. Kieffer, R., and Hotop, W., *Metal Ind.,* **66,** 332, 354, 378 (1945).

12. Kohl, W. H., "Materials Technology for Electron Tubes," New York, Reinhold Publishing Corp., 1951.

13. Levi, R., U.S. Patent 2,669,008 (1954).

14. Li, K. C., and Wang, C. Y., "Tungsten," 3rd Ed., New York, Reinhold Publishing Corp., 1955.

15. Li, K. C., and Dice, C. M., U.S. Patent 2,535,-217 (1950).

16. Loung, P. Y., Canadian Patent 552,462 (1958).

17. McKenna, P. M., U.S. Patent 2,525,778 (1950).

18. McKenna, P. M., U.S. Patent 2,113,355 (1938).

18a. Magneli, A., Anderson, G., Blomberg, B., and Kihlborg, L., *Anal. Chem.,* **24,** 1998 (1952).

19. "Materials Survey, Tungsten," U.S. Department of Commerce, Dec., 1956.

20. Mineral Statistics, American Metal Market, New York, 1958.

20a. "Minerals Yearbook," U.S. Bur. Mines, 1955, 1956, 1957, 1958, 1959.

21. National Bureau of Standards, "Mechanical Properties of Metals and Alloys," *Circular C447* (1943).

22. Osborn, R. H., *J. Opt. Soc. Amer.,* **31,** 428 (1941).

23. Pugh, J. W., Paper presented at Am. Soc. Testing Materials, Annual Meeting, June 16–21, 1957.

24. Pugh, J. W., "Refractory Metals: Tungsten, Tantalum, Columbium and Rhenium," *J. Metals,* **10,** 335 (May, 1958).

25. "The Reactor Handbook," Vol. 3, Section 1: "General Properties of Materials," *AECD-3647,* U.S. Atomic Energy Commission, 1955.

26. Schwartzkopf, P. and Kieffer, R., "Refractory Hard Metals," New York, The Macmillan Co., 1953.

27. Smithells, C. J., "Tungsten," London, Chapman and Hall, 1952.

28. U.S. Bur. of Mines, Mineral Industrial Surveys (1956).

29. Willard, H. H., and Diehl, H., "Advanced Quantitative Analysis," New York, D. Van Nostrand Co., Inc., 1943.

31. URANIUM

Saul Isserow

Nuclear Metals, Inc.
Concord, Massachusetts

INTRODUCTION

The element uranium was discovered by Klaproth in 1789.[112,113] Metallic uranium was first prepared successfully over a hundred years ago by Péligot, who showed that the substance discovered by Klaproth was the oxide and that reduction to metal was much more difficult than had previously been believed.[142,143] An interesting history of uranium metal production has been given by Wilhelm.[174] Uranium and its compounds have been of slight commercial interest, however, until the recent use of uranium in nuclear applications.

Uranium is the basic nuclear fuel, since it contains the only naturally occurring fissionable material. In these nuclear applications the element uranium is of interest because of its nuclear properties, providing energy, fission products, and more fissionable material. Uranium is not important as a metallic material except insofar as the metal is a convenient form for use in nuclear reactors because it can be fabricated like other metals and has attractive properties such as high density and thermal conductivity. Special problems arise in the processing of metallic uranium because of its chemical reactivity, radioactivity with conse-

quent health hazards, and anisotropy. Nevertheless, the advanced technology developed for the use of uranium as a nuclear fuel has yielded many tons of uranium, in various forms, by means of fairly conventional processing. No other metal has ever had its technology so intensively developed over such a short period of time. A large body of information is now available in the unclassified literature.

Isotopes and Nuclear Reactions

For nuclear applications, consideration must be given to the differences in nuclear reactions of the various uranium isotopes. These differences are important enough to justify large-scale separation of the isotopes, primarily to concentrate the fissionable uranium 235.

The properties of natural uranium tabulated below must be considered.

Artificial isotopes with mass numbers from 228 to 239 have been prepared. The most important of these is uranium 233, prepared from the reaction of neutrons with thorium 232 and amenable to fission (σ_f 525).

Uranium 235 is the only naturally occurring fissionable material. It captures a neutron to form uranium 236, which is most likely to

Mass number	Radiation			Abundance in natural uranium (%)	Reaction with thermal neutrons
	Type	Energy (mev)	Half life (years)		
234 (UII)	α	4.76	2.48×10^5	0.0056	$\sigma_f \lesssim 0.65$
235 (AcU)	α	4.39	7.13×10^8	0.718	Fission σ_f 590
238 (UI)	α	4.18	4.51×10^9	99.276	Formation of U 239, leading to Pu 239 $\sigma_f < 10^{-3}$

undergo fission into a pair of atoms with mass numbers between about 70 and 160. Depending on the pair of fission products, different numbers of neutrons are released. The corresponding energy release may be deduced from the mass loss found by comparison of the mass of the starting uranium 235 and neutron with the masses of the fission products and the released neutrons. Thus, e.g., taking for the most probable mass numbers 95 and 139[66,84] the nuclides $_{42}Mo^{95}$ and $_{57}La^{139}$, the mass loss is calculated to be 0.210 atomic mass unit. This mass loss is readily converted to energy release by the relation $E = mc^2$ and is found to be equivalent to 200 mev/fission or 2×10^{10} cal/g (10^7 kwh/lb). Comparison with a release of about 5×10^3 cal/g for the combustion of coal shows that a completely fissioned pound of uranium has the fuel value of over 1,500 tons of coal.

The more abundant uranium 238 is converted to the fissionable plutonium (plutonium 239, σ_f 729) by the following sequence of reactions:

$$_{92}U^{238} + _0n^1 \rightarrow {}_{92}U^{239} + \gamma$$
$$_{92}U^{239} \rightarrow {}_{93}Np^{239} + _{-1}\beta^0$$
$$_{93}Np^{239} \rightarrow {}_{94}Pu^{239} + _{-1}\beta^0$$

(In the notation $_aX^b$, a represents the atomic number or net nuclear charge; b is the mass. In this notation, a neutron is $_0n^1$ and an electron is $_{-1}\beta^0$.) The heavier uranium isotope initially formed by neutron capture thus undergoes two steps of beta radiation (electron emission) leading to the element plutonium, whose atomic number is higher by two. The conversion of thorium to the fissionable uranium 233 occurs by a similar set of reactions:

$$_{90}Th^{232} + _0n^1 \rightarrow {}_{90}Th^{233} + \gamma$$
$$_{90}Th^{233} \rightarrow {}_{91}Pa^{233} + _{-1}\beta^0$$
$$_{91}Pa^{233} \rightarrow {}_{92}U^{233} + _{-1}\beta^0$$

The plutonium and uranium 233 are separated from their respective precursors, uranium and thorium, by chemical means, since different chemical elements are involved. The separation of the fissionable uranium 235 from natural uranium requires other methods. The principal method for enrichment of uranium 235 is gaseous diffusion, originally carried out on a large scale at Oak Ridge, Tennessee, and now also at Paducah, Kentucky, and Portsmouth, Ohio.[5,13,166] These three plants involve a capital investment of nearly $3 billion and consume

7 per cent of the electrical power generated in this country.

OCCURRENCE AND SOURCES

Abundance data for uranium have to be revised upward, as a result of new discoveries stimulated by the incentives for more exploration. "Uranium geology, exploration, and development through the world are still very young, in spite of the tremendous effort that has been put into them in the past few years."[40] The data on uranium's concentration in the earth's crust, 2 to 4 ppm, show that it is about as abundant as beryllium, arsenic, molybdenum, and tantalum.[147] Uranium is more abundant than gold, platinum, silver, cadmium, bismuth, and mercury. Uranium is widely distributed geologically and also is dispersed, being less concentrated in ores than are other elements of comparable abundance. The bulk of uranium in the earth's crust is believed to be concentrated in a narrow surface zone.

Detailed listings of various uranium minerals are available.[39,60,62,91,139] Information on the minerals of major economic significance is summarized in Table 31.1. Some important uranium deposits are classified in Table 31.2. The significant uranium deposits of the world are shown

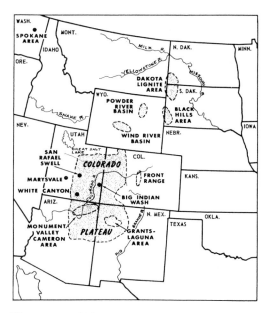

Figure 31.2. Principal uranium districts in the United States. (*From "Atomic Energy Facts," Figure 6, p. 58.*)[3]

TABLE 31.1. PRINCIPAL URANIUM MINERALS

Mineral	Composition	Color	Remarks	Occurrence
Uraninite	Essentially UO_2 with UO_3 present as result of oxidation	Black (grayish, greenish, brownish)	Massive or crystalline mineral; found in veins, pegmatites, and disseminated in sedimentary rocks	Norway
Pitchblende	Approximates U_3O_8	Black (grayish, greenish)	Term often used interchangeably with uraninite but usually applied to the massive form of uraninite found predominantly in veins usually with other metallic minerals and in unoxidized sedimentary deposits	Joachimsthal, Bohemia; Great Bear Lake, Canada; Athabasca Lake, Saskatchewan; Gilpin County, Colorado; Katanga, Congo
Coffinite	$U(SiO_4)_{1-x}(OH)_{4X}$	Black	Finely disseminated in sandstone; often intimately mixed with uraninite and carbonaceous material	Colorado
Carnotite	$K_2O \cdot 2UO_3 \cdot V_2O_5 \cdot nH_2O$ (n usually 1–3)	Canary yellow	Occurs in scattered deposits forming irregular lenses in sandstone beds; frequently associated with fossil logs and bonds	Colorado; Utah; South Australia; Katanga, Congo
Tyuyamunite	$CaO \cdot 2UO_3 \cdot V_2O_5 \cdot nH_2O$ (n usually 9–10)	Greenish-yellow	Most often formed in fractures in limestone or dolomite; also found with carnotite	Ferghana, Turkestan
Torbernite	$CuO \cdot 2UO_3 \cdot P_2O_5 \cdot nH_2O$ (n usually 8–12)	Green	Secondary mineral formed with other uranium minerals in fractures, especially where oxidation of primary deposits has occurred	Johanngeorgenstadt, Saxony
Autunite	$CaO \cdot 2UO_3 \cdot P_2O_5 \cdot nH_2O$ (n usually 8–12)	Lemon yellow to sulfur yellow, also green	Same mode of occurrence as torbernite	Utah; Autun, France
Uranophane	$CaO \cdot 2UO_3 \cdot 2SiO_2 \cdot 6H_2O$	Lemon yellow, pale greenish-yellow	Found in deposits with other secondary uranium minerals	Katanga, Congo
Schroeckingerite	$3CaO \cdot Na_2O \cdot UO_3 \cdot 3CO_2 \cdot SO_3 \cdot 10H_2O$	Yellow to greenish-yellow	A relatively minor secondary mineral found in certain gypsum-bearing clays and in the oxidized portions of some primary deposits	Joachimsthal, Bohemia
Davidite	$(Fe,Ce,U)(Ti,Fe,V,Cr)_3 (O,OH)_7$	Black	—	Radium Hill, Australia
Brannerite	$(U,Ca,Fe,V,Th)_3 Ti_5 O_{16}$	—	—	Custer County, Idaho

Adapted from "Atomic Energy Facts."[3]

TABLE 31.2. CLASSIFICATION OF SOME IMPORTANT URANIUM DEPOSITS

Typical mineral associations, depositional environments listed in descending order of their temperatures, left or right

Host rock	Davidite with ilmenite, quartz, and biotite	Uraninite with Cu, Mo, and Fe, and quartz, actinolite, and chlorite	Uraninite with Ni, Co, Ag, and Cu minerals, and carbonate (with minor quartz) gangue	Uraninite and/or brannerite with gold and iron sulfides	Uraninite with galena, pyrite, and silica minerals	Uraninite with Cu minerals (Cu–U deposits)	Uraninite and/or coffinite with Mo and As minerals	Uraninite and black minerals	"Carnotite ores" (or tyuyamunite)	Uranium phosphates and arsenate	Autunite-torbernite with limonite	Uraniferous lignite
Granite	—	Copiapo District, Chile*	Caribou, Colorado*	—	Urgeirica, Portugal	—	—	—	—	—	Spokane, Washington*	—
Rhyolitic rocks	—	—	—	—	—	—	—	—	—	—	Lakeview, Oregon*	—
Continental conglomerates, sandstones, mudstones, and shale	—	—	—	—	Los Ochos Mine, Colorado	Happy Jack Mine, Wyoming	Lucky Me Mine, Wyoming	Mi Vida Mine, Utah	Oxidized Uravan Belt Deposits, Colorado	Oxidized Wyoming Basin Deposits	—	North and South Dakota
Fresh-water limestone	—	—	—	—	—	—	—	—	Haystack Buttes, New Mexico	—	Pryor Mountains, Montana*	—
Altered conglomerates	—	—	—	Witwatersrand, South Africa, and Blind River, Ontario	—	—	—	—	—	—	—	—
Quartzite	—	—	Shinkolobwe, Congo	—	—	—	—	—	Eastern Pennsylvania*	—	—	—
Gneiss	Radium Hill, Australia	—	—	Colorado Front Range	Gunnar Deposit, Saskatchewan	—	—	—	—	—	—	—
Schist	—	—	Joachimsthal, Bohemia	—	Schwartzwalder Mine, Colorado	—	—	—	—	—	Cuneo District, Italy	—
Volcanics	—	—	—	—	Ace Mine, Saskatchewan	—	—	Ace Mine, Saskatchewan	—	—	—	—

* Nonproducer at present.

From Clegg, J. W., and Foley, D. D., "Uranium Ore Processing," Reading, Mass., Addison-Wesley Publishing Company, 1958.

Figure 31.1. Significant uranium occurrences in the world. (*From Clegg, J. W., and Foley, D. D., "Uranium Ore Processing," Figure 1.1, p. 2. Reading, Mass., Addison-Wesley Publishing Company, 1958.*)

in Figure 31.1. A more detailed representation of the principal uranium districts in the western United States is given in Figure 31.2.

Originally, the United States obtained its uranium from foreign sources, notably the Belgian Congo[43] and Canada.[42] In recent years, domestic sources have been developed to the point where the United States is probably the leading producer of the Western world. Another important source is the slime residue from gold production in the Union of South Africa (Witwatersrand).[44,55,79]

Uranium can also be recovered from other domestic materials such as phosphate rock, lignite, shale, and monazite sands.[41] Recovery processes have been developed for these marginal sources[45] but are not being applied. With the development of various sources of uranium, notably in the Colorado Plateau, the availability of uranium is not a limiting factor in the development of nuclear reactors.

PRODUCTION AND ECONOMIC STATISTICS

In prewar days, before the development of uranium as a source of energy or fissionable material, consumption of uranium compounds was discussed in pounds. This unit is still applicable in the discussion of nonenergy uses of this element. The market provided by these nonenergy uses was too low to justify mining operations primarily for uranium. Nuclear

TABLE 31.4. ORE PRODUCTION IN THE UNITED STATES
(Ore Receipts at All Private Plants and Government Purchase Depots)

Six-month period	Dry short tons
July–December, 1955	838,771
January–June, 1956	1,320,340
July–December, 1956	1,685,789
January–June, 1957	1,673,589
July–December, 1957	2,021,873
January–June, 1958	2,341,791
July–December, 1958	2,807,000

applications have made uranium important enough for its production, now considered in tons, to justify exploitations of deposits for uranium content.* Both open-pit and underground mining are applied. The rate of exploration and development has been helped by government incentives. Thus, bonus prices have been paid for uranium ore.[7] This incentive program has increased the known uranium reserves. The distribution of these reserves in the United States, as of December 31, 1959, is shown in Table 31.3. The rate of current domestic ore production may be seen from Table 31.4. The anticipated need for uranium as a fuel depends on projections of over-all power needs and the estimates of the fraction to be provided by nuclear energy. An estimate of 50,000 to 100,000 tons/year by 1970 or 1975 has been suggested.[3,48,87]

Several figures pertaining to the cost of uranium are worth noting. The Atomic Energy Commission has guaranteed a price of $8/lb of U_3O_8 concentrate. Its price for normal uranium metal billets of normal isotopic content (0.7115 per cent uranium 235) is $40/kg ($18.18/lb). Enriched uranium is distributed as the liquefied gas uranium hexafluoride (UF_6) in steel cylinders. The price per total uranium content or per uranium 235 content is a function of the enrichment, i.e., the weight fraction of uranium 235. Several examples of the prices are given in Table 31.5.[6,11] It is apparent that the cost of highly enriched uranium metal approaches $10,000/lb.

TABLE 31.3. MEASURED, INDICATED, AND INFERRED ORE RESERVES (DECEMBER 31, 1959)

Area	Thousand tons	% of total ore reserves	% U_3O_8
New Mexico	55,700	64.7	0.26
Wyoming	15,800	18.3	0.34
Utah	5,300	6.1	0.33
Colorado	4,500	5.3	0.30
Arizona	1,200	1.4	0.35
Washington, Oregon, Nevada	1,900	2.2	0.21
North and South Dakota	600	0.7	0.27
Others (Texas, California, Montana, Idaho, Alaska)	1,100	1.3	0.24
Total reserves	86,100	100.0	0.28 Avg.

* Processing of ores with minerals such as carnotite, containing a high proportion of vanadium, continues to provide a large source of vanadium, for which such ores were primarily processed originally.

TABLE 31.5. CHARGES FOR ENRICHED URANIUM IN
THE FORM OF URANIUM HEXAFLUORIDE

Per cent U-235	Dollars/kg U	Dollars/g U-235 contained
0.72	40.50	5.62
1.0	75.75	7.58
10.0	1,529.00	15.29
50.0	8,379.00	16.76
90.0	15,361.00	17.07

Adapted from "Atomic Energy Facts."[3]

CONCENTRATION FROM ORES

Uranium must first be separated from the bulk of diluents accompanying it in nature. The product obtained in this concentration step is a crude uranium compound (70 to 90 per cent U_3O_8) contaminated by some inert materials. Methods of ore beneficiation such as gravity separation and flotation have limited application. Principal reliance is placed on hydrometallurgical methods, which may be preceded by roasting. Acid or alkali converts uranium to a soluble compound.[31,34] The uranium is then recovered from the aqueous solution as oxide or a compound (for example, the salt $Na_2U_2O_7$) by a separation process such as precipitation. Because of the large volume of reagents needed for the leaching, inexpensive reagents are preferred. Regeneration of these reagents is sought in the subsequent steps.

The wide variety of uranium ores necessitates a diversity of mill flowsheets, adapted to the particular ore. The processing steps and the options available to the mill operator are summarized in Table 31.6. A simplified flow scheme is represented in Figure 31.3. Detailed information on the various steps is given in an authoritative work.[38] This volume also includes comprehensive descriptions of mills operating in the principal uranium ore-bearing regions of the United States, Canada, and South Africa.

Because of the small quantity of uranium in the ore, concentration is generally carried out near the source of the ore to minimize shipping costs. The capacity of a mill is from several hundred to several thousand tons of ore/day. Convenient tabulations of domestic mills, almost all privately owned, are available.[8,33,34,36b] (The only government-owned mill was closed at the end of the calendar year 1959).

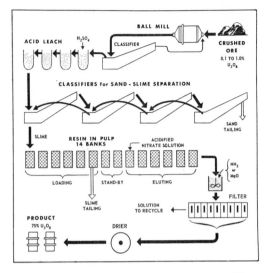

Figure 31.3. Simplified diagram of uranium milling. (*From "Atomic Energy Facts," Figure 7, p. 65.*)[3]

REFINING*

The uranium concentrate has to be refined to remove the remaining impurities and yield a pure oxide suitable for subsequent conversion through UF_4 to metal for reactor fuel or to UF_6 for an isotope separation plant. The concentrate is shipped to a feed material processing plant, where both the refining and final conversion to metal are carried out. Fairly conventional chemical operations are employed in the refining, but, since neutron-absorbing impurities are harmful even at the level of parts per million, the quality standards are more demanding than those usually encountered in metallurgical processing.

The concentrate is first dissolved in nitric acid to obtain a solution of uranyl nitrate, $UO_2(NO_3)_2$. This compound is soluble in various organic solvents[172] such as diethyl ether, methyl isobutyl ketone (hexone), and

* Attention is drawn to a recently published book that thoroughly covers the technology of producing uranium compounds and metal for nuclear applications: Harrington, C. D., and Ruehle, A. E., (Eds.), "Uranium Production Technology," Princeton, New Jersey, D. Van Nostrand Company, Inc., 1959. The reader is referred to this volume for more comprehensive treatment of items covered here to varying degrees. This volume includes numerous illustrations and references to the original work.

TABLE 31.6. PRINCIPAL STEPS IN MILLING URANIUM ORES

Feed: uranium-bearing ores containing 1.5 to 10 lb of U_3O_8/ton of ore.
Product: uranium oxide or salt concentrates assaying 70–90% U_3O_8 by weight.

Processing step	Methods	Notes
A. Ore preparation 1. Size reduction 2. Roasting	Crushing and grinding	Improves uranium solubility and ore handling; used infrequently
B. Leaching 1. Digestion	(a) Acid leaching: Generally with sulfuric acid; oxidant required; conventional equipment and techniques	Normally favored for low-lime ores ($\lesssim$12% lime content); high extraction efficiency
	(b) Alkaline leaching: Generally with a mixture of sodium carbonate and sodium bicarbonate; conventional equipment and techniques	Normally favored for high-lime ores
2. (a) Clarification	Decantation and filtration, yielding a clear leach liquor; flocculating agents sometimes required; conventional equipment and techniques	Used when clear solution is required for subsequent recovery operations, as in the case of the precipitation process (see C-1-a below)
(b) Sand-slime separation	Desanding, yielding sand and slime fractions; conventional equipment and techniques	Used in connection with the resin-in-pulp recovery process (see C-1-b below)
C. Product recovery 1. Recovery	(a) Chemical precipitation: Conventional process permitting use of standard solid-liquid separation equipment. Reagents and conditions vary, depending primarily on whether an acid or alkaline leach has been used	Limited to ores which yield a clear leach liquor; high reagent consumption when applied to acid-leach liquors (More recent mills using acid leach favor other recovery methods); product form is usually uranium oxide but may be sodium diuranate
	(b) Ion exchange: One method, using anion resins in conventional columns, requires a clear leach liquor. A recently developed method, known as the resin-in-pulp (RIP) process, can be used on leach pulp. In this process, perforated baskets containing anion resin beads are moved up and down through the pulp	Ion exchange used in many mills built since 1950; product form is ammonium diuranate or uranium oxide
	(c) Solvent extraction: Organic solvents (amines or phosphates) used in mixer-settler or column-type contacting equipment; applicable to clear liquors	Application of solvent-extraction techniques to uranium milling is a recent development; approximately one-third of uranium ore mined in the United States is now processed by solvent extraction[121]; work to date has been on acid-leach solutions and pulps
2. Final treatment	Filtration and drying of precipitate from recovery step	Final product contains 70–90 wt % uranium (as U_3O_8 or equivalent)

Adapted from "Atomic Energy Facts."[3]

tributyl phosphate (TBP). These solvents can be used to extract the uranyl nitrate, which is then re-extracted into water. The aqueous solution can be concentrated and evaporated to uranyl nitrate hexahydrate (UNH), which is calcined to uranium trioxide, UO_3. This oxide can also be obtained by calcination of $(NH_4)_2 U_2O_7$ precipitated from the uranyl nitrate solution. An alternate sequence involves direct precipitation of UO_4 with hydrogen peroxide. The UO_3 or UO_4 is then reduced by hydrogen or ammonia to (brown oxide) UO_2. This UO_2 may be the form in which uranium is used as fuel. Otherwise, it can be treated with hydrogen fluoride to obtain UF_4 (green salt). An alternative procedure involves reaction of UO_2 with NH_4HF_2 to obtain NH_4UF_5, which is decomposed to UF_4 and NH_4F, which can be recycled. The UF_4 is the uranium compound used for reduction to metal. It may alternatively be treated with fluorine to obtain UF_6 to be fed to a gaseous diffusion plant where the uranium isotopes are separated.

Feed material processing plants employing the above sequence involving purification of uranium nitrate and generation of pure UO_3 are operated by Mallinckrodt Chemical Works at St. Louis and Weldon Springs, Missouri, and by National Lead Co. at Fernald, Ohio. General Chemical Division of Allied Chemical Corp. is using, at Metropolis, Illinois, a process developed at Argonne National Laboratory for more direct preparation of UF_6 from the concentrate without going through nitrate and UO_3. The sequence of operations applied to the concentrate resembles that ordinarily applied to refined UO_3, obtained from purified uranyl nitrate: reduction to UO_2, hydrofluorination to UF_4, and fluorination to UF_6. Fluidization effects reaction between the solid and the gas in each step. Refining is achieved by fractional distillation of the crude UF_6.[88] It is also possible to precipitate UF_4 directly from an aqueous solution by catalytic reduction.[2]

Processes involving nitric acid and uranyl nitrate are used in scrap recovery, carried out mainly at Fernald[30] and in the aqueous processing of irradiated fuel (see page 622).

PREPARATION OF METAL

Pure uranium metal is difficult to prepare because of the element's affinity for other elements such as oxygen, halogens, nitrogen, and carbon. Drastic means of reduction are needed to obtain the metal from stable compounds such as oxides and halides. The reduction has to be performed in closed systems to avoid atmospheric contamination. Some of the problems involved in various reduction schemes are better understood with the help of tabulations of boiling points of the reactants, melting points of the products, and free energy and enthalpy changes for the reactions.[14,23,65,103,120,179]

The large negative free energy of formation of UO_2 [−123 kcal/g-atom of oxygen at 25°C (77°F)] shows the need for strong reducing agents if UO_2 is to be used as starting material in the preparation of the metal. Hydrogen would require a very high H_2/H_2O ratio in the gas and cannot be considered a practical reducing agent. Reduction with carbon requires vacuum and leads to contamination by carbide. Calcium is the most favorable reducing agent thermodynamically, but the heat generation is still so low as to render difficult the separation of the metal and the lime by-product. The resulting metal is therefore rather finely subdivided (globules or powder). A halide flux may be added to improve lime removal and thereby obtain coarser metal.[26,131,149] Calcium hydride can also be used for the reduction.[1,51] The metals magnesium, sodium, and potassium are so volatile as to distill from the reaction zone. Aluminum can reduce oxides but is likely to form alloys with uranium. Since uranium-aluminum alloys are used for nuclear fuels, reduction with excess aluminum offers a means of obtaining such alloys directly.[158]

Halides are more suitable than oxides as starting materials for metal preparation. Additional heat is evolved, and the halide by-product has a lower melting point. This halide therefore melts and permits the dense uranium metal to settle. Massive metal (biscuit or derby) is thus recovered in relatively high purity with low losses. In practice, UF_4 is preferred over the more hygroscopic UCl_4 as the starting material; Na_2UCl_6 has been used because it is less hygroscopic than UCl_4. In this country, magnesium is the standard reducing agent, being obtainable in high purity at low cost. It is also being used in England now.[32] The Ames process, developed by Spedding, Wilhelm, and co-workers at Iowa State College,[174] requires the use of a sealed bomb because of the magnesium's high vapor pressure at temperatures attained during the reaction. The steel bomb, 15 in. in diameter by 40 to 45 in. high for over 200 lb of uranium, is provided with a 1-in. refractory liner, thin enough to permit influx of heat during the preheating period that precedes the reaction, yet thick enough to prevent overheating of the steel by the heat of reaction.[12,173,175] Originally, electrically fused dolomitic lime (MgO, CaO) was used for the liner. It has been replaced by magnesium fluoride recovered as by-product of the reduction.[24] Reduction can be carried out on a large scale (e.g., 1½ tons) to give large castings (dingot = direct ingot) not requiring remelting before further fabrication.[58] The typical analysis of reactor grade massive metal (remelted derby) available from the Atomic Energy Commission is as follows:[144]

Impurity	Typical analysis (ppm)
Boron	0.25
Iron	150
Manganese	25
Nitrogen	100
Nickel	100
Magnesium	25
Carbon	150–750
Chloride	30
Silicon	65
Chromium	65
Silver	1
Cadmium	0.20

In Europe calcium is the preferred reductant for commercial production of uranium via halides.[71] More heat is evolved than with magnesium, and the volatility of calcium is low enough to permit reduction at atmospheric pressure. Calcium was used before magnesium in this country, at Ames and at the National Bureau of Standards. Calcium is also used in the United States with an iodine booster for enriched metal, where high yield is an over-riding consideration. Potassium was used in the first preparation of metallic uranium by Péligot, and sodium can also be used. Others have applied these reductants on a laboratory scale,[96] but they hardly lend themselves to large-scale operation because of their high vapor pressures.

Fused salt electrolysis at Westinghouse provided the first uranium metal used at the Metallurgical Laboratory.[165] (No evidence is available of feasibility of electrodeposition from an aqueous solution. Organic solvents have been studied with inconclusive results.[98]) The Westinghouse process involves electrolysis at 900°C (1652°F) of KUF_5 or UF_4 dissolved in molten 80:20 $CaCl_2$:NaCl.[53,54] The metal is deposited as powder on a molybdenum cathode and has to be leached to remove adhering electrolyte. This process provided 65 tons of metal by the fall of 1943, when it was superseded by the Ames process.[174] Bomb reduction has prevailed for commercial production, and electrolytic processes, with various modifications, are used only for special purposes. An electrolyte based on UCl_3 or UF_4 in LiCl-KCl eutectic has been developed at Argonne National Laboratory for the electrorefining of high-purity uranium near 400°C (752°F).[17]

Two other methods of obtaining uranium in special form are worth noting. The van Arkel-deBoer method involves thermal decomposition of a halide, usually iodide, on a hot filament and has been applied to other refractory metals.[170] This method has been applied to the preparation of high-purity uranium.[97] When fine uranium powder is needed, the reversible decomposition of UH_3 is a convenient source. Reduction of oxide by calcium or magnesium may be used to obtain nonpyrophoric powder directly.[22]

PHYSICAL PROPERTIES

The physical properties of uranium are summarized in Tables 31.7 to 31.10. The sensitivity of these properties to purity and metallurgical history accounts, in part, for discrepancies between values reported by different workers. The anisotropy of uranium always has to be borne in mind. The values listed here are based on the critical evaluations by Holden[72] and Klein.[114] References to the original work may be found in these compilations, which also include graphical representation and more detailed tabulation of these properties as a function of temperature. These compilations have also provided the information in the next section on mechanical behavior.

MECHANICAL AND METALLURGICAL BEHAVIOR

As is the case with the physical properties, mechanical properties require consideration of

TABLE 31.7. PHYSICAL PROPERTIES OF URANIUM

Density [25°C (77°F)]	19.07 g/cc
Melting point	1132°C (2070°F)
Boiling point (extrapolated)	3813°C (6895°F)
Vapor pressure (1630–1970°K)	log P(mm) = $-23{,}300/T$ + 8.583
Heat of vaporization	~100 kcal/g-atom
Heat of fusion	~4.7 kcal/g-atom
Thermal conductivity	
25°C (77°F)	270 milliwatts/cm-°C, 0.0645 cal/cm/°C/sec
600°C (1112°F)	380
700°C (1292°F) (β)	400
800°C (1472°F) (γ)	423
Electrical resistivity	
25°C (77°F)	30 microhm-cm
600°C (1112°F)	59
700°C (1292°F) (β)	55.5
800°C (1472°F) (γ)	54
Magnetic susceptibility	
25°C (77°F)	1.66 emu/g
600°C (1112°F)	1.85
700°C (1292°F) (β)	2.05
800°C (1472°F) (γ)	2.10
Thermoelectric potential versus platinum	
25°C (77°F)	~0.4 mv
600°C (1112°F)	13.8
700°C (1292°F) (β)	17.5
800°C (1472°F) (γ)	21.4
Thermionic emission	
Work function	3.27 volts
Richardson "A" value	~6
Photoelectric emission	
Work function	3.63 volts
Threshold wavelength	3600 Å
Optical emissivity (λ = 6700Å)	0.51

the purity and metallurgical history of the metal, as well as its anisotropy.

Hardness

The Vickers hardness number (Vhn, or DPH for diamond pyramid hardness) is commonly used as the scale for hardness of uranium, since it is applicable to the broad range of hardness encountered from alpha at room temperature to gamma above 900°C (1652°F). Tables developed empirically for conversion to other scales for other metals are not applicable because of differences in work-hardening and elastic properties.

At room temperature, a hardness of about 220 Vhn is found for uranium which has been either cast, gamma extruded, or alpha rolled and annealed. The hardness falls sharply as the temperature increases. The rate of decrease becomes more rapid after a break in the hardness-temperature curve between 350–400°C (662–752°F). A sharp rise in hardness accompanies the transformation from alpha to beta, so that the hardness of beta at the transformation temperature 663°C (1225°F) approximates that of alpha at 500°C (932°F). The hardness of beta decreases gradually with temperature. The transformation to gamma gives a very soft phase, comparable to lead at room temperature.

TABLE 31.8. CRYSTALLOGRAPHY OF URANIUM

	Structure	Space group	Lattice constants (Å)	Number of atoms per cell	Calculated density (g/cc)	Linear coefficient of expansion	Volume coefficient of expansion
Alpha	Orthorhombic	Cmcm	25°C (77°F)	4	19.07	0–662°C (32–1224°F)	
	(Stacked corrugated sheets of atoms; binding within sheets largely covalent)		a_0 2.853 b_0 5.865 c_0 4.954			$a_0 + 36.1 \times 10^{-6}/°C$ $b_0 - 8.7 \times 10^{-6}/°C$ $c_0 + 31.3 \times 10^{-6}/°C$	$+58.8 \times 10^{-6}/°C$
Beta	Tetragonal	P4/mnm	700°C (1292°F)	30	18.14	662–772°C (1224–1422°F)	
			a_0 10.75 c_0 5.65			$a_0 + 22.8 \times 10^{-6}/°C$ $c_0 + 5.6 \times 10^{-6}/°C$	$+51.2 \times 10^{-6}/°C$
Gamma	Body-centered cubic		800°C (1472°F)	2	17.91	772–1000°C (1422–1832°F)	
			a_0 3.534			$+21.7 \times 10^{-6}/°C$	$+65.2 \times 10^{-6}/°C$

TABLE 31.9. PHASE TRANSFORMATIONS IN URANIUM

Transformation					
Low-temperature phase	High-temperature phase	Temperature (°C)	$\Delta V/V\%$	$\Delta L/L\%$	ΔH, kcal/g-atom
Alpha	Beta	667 (1233°F)	+1.06	+0.35	0.7
Beta	Gamma	775 (1427°F)	+0.736	+0.245	1.15
Gamma	Liquid	1132 (2070°F)	~5		~4.7

TABLE 31.10. THERMODYNAMIC FUNCTIONS FOR URANIUM

Temperature		Specific heat, C_p (cal/g-atom/°C)	Enthalpy, H_T (cal/g-atom)	Entropy, S (cal/g-atom/°C)
°K	°C			
300	27	6.649	1,539	12.052
400	127	7.072	2,203	13.941
500	227	7.606	2,935	15.601
600	327	8.227	3,725	17.056
700	427	8.952	4,583	18.387
800	527	9.863	5,520	19.646
900	627	11.107	6,567	20.882
941 (α)	668	11.737	7,066	21.436
941 (β)	668	10.147	7,740	22.152
1000	727	10.147	8,337	22.760
1047	774	10.147	8,816	23.236
1047 (γ)	774	9.147	9,947	24.316
1100	827	9.147	10,430	24.761
1200	927	~ 9.2	11,350	25.38
1300	1027	~ 9.2	12,260	26.12
1375	1102	~ 9.2	13,000	26.8

TABLE 31.11. ELASTIC PROPERTIES OF URANIUM AT 25°C (77°F)*

	As cast	Alpha rolled at			Alpha swaged and recrystal- lized	Beta treated	Gamma extruded	"Hot" rolled
		480°C (896°F)	550°C (1022°F)	630°C (1166°F)				
Young's modulus (10⁶ psi)	29.8	26.8	27.3	27.9	29.1	25.5–29.1	29.8	25.5
Shear modulus (10⁶ psi)	12.1	11.0	10.9	11.4	11.1	12.1	12.0	10.6
Bulk modulus (10⁶ psi)	17.6	14.7	14.9	15.2	17.3	17.0	16.8	14.2
Poisson's ratio	0.23	0.19	0.20	0.20	0.22	0.19	0.21	0.20

* All data from ultrasonic measurements except for the last column, which was obtained from compression tests.

Elastic Properties

Table 31.11 summarizes the elastic properties at 25°C (77°F) of uranium with different metallurgical histories. In going from 25°C (77°F) to 300°C (572°F), Young's modulus decreases from 27.0 to 23.4 x 10⁶ psi and Poisson's ratio increases from 0.20 to 0.24. The most reliable data are obtained by sonic measurements, since uranium's low proportional limit leads to inaccurate elastic data from tensile tests.

Tensile Properties

Typical values for the tensile properties of uranium at room temperature are given in Table 31.12. Since these properties are sensitive to factors which are not included in the description of the material's history, it must be recognized that the tabulated values are indicative, being near the middle of the range of

likely values. Since beta treated uranium is the most common condition for reactor use, data for its properties versus temperature are given in Table 31.13 to illustrate the effect of temperature. Evidence is available of a brittle transition near room temperature, but the metal does not become completely brittle below this transition temperature. Hydrogen at the parts per million level shifts this temperature upward.

Notched-bar impact data do not provide conclusive evidence of the nature of the brittle-to-ductile transition from −73 to 149°C (−100 to 300°F). The impact strength at room temperature is about 10 ft-lb and at 149°C (300°F) is 30 to 50 ft-lb.[140]

Creep

In addition to the factors introducing uncertainty in values for other properties, thermal cycling effects and anelastic behavior introduce

TABLE 31.12. TYPICAL ROOM TEMPERATURE TENSILE PROPERTIES OF URANIUM
HAVING DIFFERENT FABRICATION HISTORIES

Fabrication history	Yield strength 0.2% offset, in 1,000 psi	Ultimate tensile strength in 1,000 psi	Elongation in 2 in. (%)	Reduction of area (%)
As cast	30	65	5	10
Alpha rolled at				
300°C (572°F) ⎫	110	170	7	14
500°C (932°F) ⎬ as rolled	60	130	20	
600°C (1112°F) ⎭	40	110	20	
Annealed after alpha rolling at				
300°C (572°F) ⎫	50	110	5	
500°C (932°F) ⎬ then annealed	40	100	15	
Beta treated after alpha rolling				
Water quenched	35	85	10	12
Slow cooled	30	60	7	
Alpha extruded [600°C (1112°F)]	30	90	20	15
Beta rolled	30	85	12	
Gamma extruded	25	80	10	12

TABLE 31.13. VARIATION OF TENSILE PROPERTIES OF BETA TREATED URANIUM WITH TEST TEMPERATURE

Test temperature		Yield strength, 0.2% offset, in 1,000 psi	Ultimate tensile strength in 1,000 psi	Elongation in 2 in. (%)	Reduction of area (%)
°C	°F				
−73	−99	42	88	4	5
−45	−49	40	92	5	6
25	77	35	85	10	12
100	212	31	76	28	21
200	392	26	58	31	34
300	572	22	42	32	40
400	752	17	28	33	50
500	932	12	16	34	60
600	1112	7	8	34	72
666 (α)	1230	4	4	35	79
666 (β)	1230	7	9	35	79
700	1292	6	9	35.5	85
776 (β)	1429	5	9	36	94
776 (γ)	1429	< 1	< 1	36	94
800	1472	< 1	< 1	36	99

further uncertainty in data on creep behavior. Data obtained at Battelle[164] with precise temperature control are shown in Figure 31.4. The sharp reduction in stress for a given creep rate in the 300–400°C (572–752°F) range should be noted; other mechanical properties change sharply in this range. (See "Hardness," p. 608.)

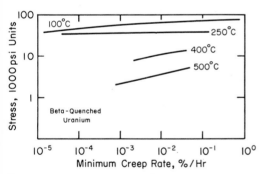

Figure 31.4. Relationship between creep stress and creep rate for uranium tested at several temperatures. (*From Holden, A. N., "Physical Metallurgy of Uranium," Figure 5.12, p. 73, Reading, Mass., Addison-Wesley Publishing Company, 1958.*)

Fatigue

Data obtained above the elastic limit are shown in Figure 31.5.[46] These data were obtained for uranium rolled in the high-alpha range. The wider scatter for transverse specimens is attributed to the distribution of stringers and impurities as a result of the rolling process.

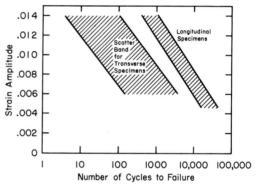

Figure 31.5. Strain-cycling fatigue of uranium at room temperature. (*From Holden, A. N., "Physical Metallurgy of Uranium," Figure 5.15, p. 75, Reading, Mass., Addison-Wesley Publishing Company, 1958.*)

Earlier measurements[145] of ⅜-in. extruded bars on a Krouse 10,000 rpm cantilever machine established an endurance limit of 25,000 psi for over 10^6 cycles, and 35,000 psi for 120,000 to 250,000 cycles.

Deformation and Textures

The rather unusual structure of alpha uranium introduces problems in the metal's plastic deformation. These problems are of great practical importance in use of the metal as fuel. In addition, they are of fundamental interest because of corrugated planes, covalent bonding, and anisotropy.

At room temperature the predominant deformation mechanism is twinning. The strong covalent bonds are not broken but are sheared and readjusted. The (130) twin system occurs primarily, but the (172) and (176) systems are also involved. The other two reported twin systems (112) and (121) are much less important. As the temperature increases, slip becomes more important as the deformation mechanism. The most important slip system is (010)–[100]. Slip on the (010) plane does not involve the strong covalent bonds. The critical resolved shear stress for (010) slip, 0.34 kg/sq mm (480 psi), helps account for the low yield strength. Kinking and cross-slip have also been observed.

As metal is worked, it develops a preferred orientation reflecting the equilibrium orientation reached by each grain in its deformation systems. The preferred orientation or texture depends on the method and temperature of working and on any subsequent heat treatment. The texture manifests itself in the anisotropy of important properties such as thermal expansion and irradiation growth. Working high in the alpha temperature range produces a texture with the (110) poles predominating parallel to the working direction, whereas cold working causes (010) poles to predominate parallel to the working direction. At all temperatures the (001) poles become aligned perpendicular to the working direction. Much of the preferred orientation is eliminated by heat treatment in the beta region.

Recovery, Recrystallization, and Grain Growth

In its general features, uranium resembles other metals in the sequence of recovery, recrystallization, and grain growth after cold work. The details are affected by the predominance of twinning as the deformation mechanism. The pronounced line broadening in the x-ray diffraction pattern of the cold worked metal indicates very large lattice distortions. The critical strain for recrystallization is only about 1 per cent elongation, compared to values closer to 3 per cent for other metals. The specific recrystallization behavior and subsequent grain size of a metal sample depend on its working history and impurities (nature, volume, size, dispersion). Recrystallization occurs in the range of 400–600°C (752–1112°F). As the cold work increases, i.e., higher reductions, recrystal-

lization starts and ends at a lower temperature. The time needed for completion of recrystallization decreases as the annealing temperature increases.

RADIATION DAMAGE[73,146,178]

Exposure to high-energy radiation changes the properties of any engineering material. For a fissionable material exposed to neutrons, the changes are marked enough to justify the term *radiation damage* in discussing the effects. The fission event generates highly energetic fragments which displace the uranium atoms from their original lattice sites. (It has been estimated[77] that, in the exposure of normal uranium to 0.1 per cent burnup, every part of the specimen will have been heated to above 3000°C (5432°F) for a period of 10^{-11} sec about 15,000 times.) In addition, the fission products not only act as impurities in a metal but are sufficiently lower in density than uranium to cause a significant volume increase. Thus the conversion of 1 per cent of the uranium to fission products can be calculated to cause a volume increase of 3.4 per cent.[18] Particular attention must be paid to the inert gas fission products (xenon, krypton). These gases constitute 12 per cent of the fission products, 1 atom of gas being obtained for every 4 atoms fissioned. The diffusion of this gas is slow, and the effect of the gas atoms remains slight as long as these atoms are isolated. If these atoms can diffuse and coalesce, they can generate high gas pressures, depending on the volume of voids, e.g., microcracks. The resulting pressures can easily exceed the metal's yield point or creep strength and lead to fracture or porosity, respectively.

Irradiated uranium undergoes anisotropic dimensional changes, depending on the texture and hence on the fabrication history of the metal (plus any subsequent heat treatment). The anisotropic growth has been observed for single crystals, contraction occurring in the [100] direction. (Single crystals do not grow on thermal cycling.)[74] The growth depends on temperature, reaching a maximum near 250°C (482°F) but being reduced almost to zero at or above 500°C (932°F). Growth can be reduced by either a random structure or a balanced structure in which the (010) lengthening and the (100) shortening offset each other. Even with reduced growth, the problem of surface roughness persists because of the different behavior of different grains. This problem can be minimized by refining the grain structure, notably through alloy additions (chromium, silicon, zirconium).[70]

From an engineering point of view, swelling of uranium metal is the most serious problem in its use as a reactor fuel. The metal undergoes a density decrease which may exceed the 3.4 per cent per atom per cent burnup, calculated on the basis of conversion of uranium to fission products. One of the purposes of cladding nuclear fuel elements is to restrain the resultant swelling. Aside from anisotropic dimensional change and swelling, the metal also experiences further dimensional instability because of the varying thermal stresses to which it is subjected during startup, shutdown, and power fluctuations. It should be noted that, even during stable reactor operation, a severe temperature gradient exists in the fuel, depending on various reactor parameters such as fuel geometry, coolant temperature and flow rate, and neutron flux.

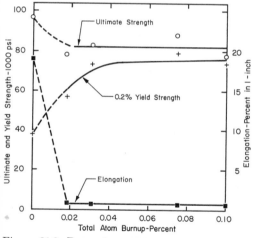

Figure 31.6. Room temperature properties of irradiated uranium—effect of exposure. (*From Bush, S. H., Figure 1, United States Atomic Energy Commission, Report No. HW–51444*.)

The mechanical properties of uranium are changed by irradiation, probably as a result of the production of interstitials and vacancies. The changes resemble those introduced by severe cold working, and some recovery can be achieved by postirradiation annealing. The effect of burnup on room temperature properties is shown in Figure 31.6. Loss of ductility is already observed at a burnup of 4×10^{-5} atom per cent. The loss of ductility is marked even in gamma uranium. Fortunately, the decrease in thermal conductivity is slight.

CHEMICAL BEHAVIOR: REACTIONS AND COMPOUNDS

The chemistry of uranium has been thoroughly reviewed by Katz and Rabinowitch.[90] The following summary is based largely on their book, which should be consulted for references to the original work, including the wartime project literature. A more recent book is also a very valuable source of information.[104]

Uranium is a very reactive metal, combining readily with both nonmetallic and metallic elements. The neutral atom may be represented as having 86 "inner electrons" and 6 valence electrons, probably distributed in the states $5f^3 6d7s^2$. Uranium thus acts as a strong reducing agent, reaching a valence as high as six. In aqueous systems hexavalent uranium is likely to be present as a complex cation such as UO_2^{++}. The common uranyl salts and their solution are yellow. Uranium (IV) solutions are deep green, and uranium (III) solutions are reddish violet. Uranium is also capable of forming complex anions (e.g., $U_2O_7^=$) amenable to anion exchange. The only known oxygen-free hexavalent compounds of uranium are the hexafluoride and the hexachloride.

Latimer[119] has summarized the electromotive force relationships for the various oxidation states of uranium as follows:

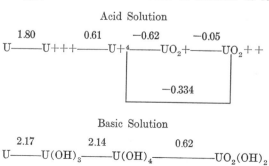

Acid Solution

$$U \xrightarrow{1.80} U^{+++} \xrightarrow{0.61} U^{+4} \xrightarrow{-0.62} UO_2^+ \xrightarrow{-0.05} UO_2^{++}$$

$$-0.334$$

Basic Solution

$$U \xrightarrow{2.17} U(OH)_3 \xrightarrow{2.14} U(OH)_4 \xrightarrow{0.62} UO_2(OH)_2$$

In the following summary of reactions with various chemical reagents, notably gases, it will be obvious that the rate and initiation temperature strongly depend on the metal's state of subdivision. Statements of reaction temperature should be qualified in this light.

Reactions with Nonmetallic Elements; Binary Compounds

Hydrogen. The uranium-hydrogen system has received considerable attention.[92,155] The solubility of hydrogen in solid or liquid metal depends on the metal phase, the temperature, and the pressure, being increased by transformation from a low temperature phase to a high temperature phase, by a temperature increase, and by higher hydrogen pressure. The solubility is proportional to the square root of hydrogen pressure for any of the three solid phases, indicating that hydrogen dissolves as free atoms.[129,133] The stoichiometric compound UH_3 is most readily formed in the range of 225–250°C (437–482°F). At higher temperatures, decomposition of this hydride becomes significant. The decomposition pressure has been represented by the equation

$$\log P, mm = \frac{-4480}{T, °K} + 9.20$$

based on data below atmospheric pressure. This equation gives a decomposition pressure of 760 mm at 436°C (817°F). Data now available to 650°C (1202°F) give the equation[123]

$$\log P, atm = \frac{-4410}{T, °K} + 6.26$$

The hydride is a convenient starting material for finely divided (and therefore reactive) uranium. It is also a convenient source for pure hydrogen or deuterium.

The usual form of UH_3, designated as β, is ferromagnetic below 174°K.[67,124,169] Another form, designated as α, can be obtained by hydriding uranium at low temperatures, either with gaseous hydrogen or by electrolysis at a uranium cathode in an aqueous electrolyte.[27,135]

Nitrogen. Uranium reacts slowly with nitrogen at about 400°C (752°F). The reaction becomes more rapid with increasing temperature, proceeding quite rapidly above 800°C (1472°F), presumably because the metal is in the gamma phase. The compounds UN, U_2N_3, and UN_2 are known, but the system is homo-geneous between U_2N_3 and UN_2, the U_2N_3 transforming without discontinuity into the UN_2 structure. These two higher nitrides dissociate above 700–800°C (1292–1472°F) to give UN, which remains stable in vacuum to 1700°C (3092°F). The mononitride UN is a light-gray powder isomorphous with the monocarbide UC. It melts at about 2630°C (4766°F).[37]

Oxygen. The surface of uranium begins to oxidize in air even at room temperature, forming first a light yellowish tarnish film and then a dark, nonprotective oxide. The oxidation rate depends on the temperature and the form of the metal. Massive metal oxidizes slowly below 700°C (1292°F), but at higher temperatures oxidation is rapid. At low temperatures the oxide formed is the brown to black UO_2, but at higher temperatures U_3O_8 is likely to be produced. Consideration has to be given to the possible decomposition of U_3O_8 to UO_2 as an example of the complex phase relations in the uranium-oxygen system.[94,105,156] The oxide phases include fairly broad ranges of nonstoichiometric compositions. Uranium dioxide is being used as fuel in nuclear reactors.[10,36,122,136,143a] It melts at about 2700°C (4892°F).

Sulfur. Uranium reacts slowly with molten sulfur at 250–300°C (482–572°F) but burns at 500°C (932°F) in sulfur vapor. The ratio of US_2 and U_2S_3 formed depends on the conditions. US is formed by the interaction of fine uranium powder (from the hydride) with hydrogen sulfide or US_2. US melts considerably above 2000°C (3632°F) and is quite stable, being suitable for use as a refractory.

Halogens. Fluorine reacts vigorously with uranium at room temperature, forming the volatile hexafluoride UF_6 [sublimation point, 56.5°C (133.7°F)]. This compound is used in the gaseous-diffusion process for isotope separation. (See page 602.) Uranium tetrafluoride, obtained by reduction of UF_6 or by conversion of UO_2 with hydrofluoric acid or "Freons," is the usual starting material for reduction to metal. (See page 606.) Fluorides are also considered in nuclear reactors where the fuel is a fused salt.[116]

The reaction of uranium with chlorine depends on the state of subdivision of the metal. Finely divided metal burns at 150–180°C (302–356°F). Massive metal may require temperatures near 500°C (932°F) for chlorination. The chlorides obtained are UCl_3, UCl_4, and

UCL$_5$. The reduction of UCl$_4$ with hydrogen or metals gives UCl$_3$. With increasing valence of uranium, the chlorides have higher volatility and a lower melting point.

The different temperatures (from 210–650°C) (410–1202°F) reported for the reaction of uranium with bromine probably reflect different states of subdivision and surface of the metal. The usual reaction product is UBr$_4$, but control of the quantity of bromine can lead to UBr$_3$. Different temperatures are also reported for the reaction of uranium with iodine. The tetraiodide is much less stable than the other tetrahalides. Its existence as well as its direct formation from the elements require a sufficient iodine pressure to reverse the thermal decomposition to UI$_3$. Without excess iodine, the triiodide is likely to be the principal product.

The existence of mixed halides, e.g., UCl$_2$F$_2$, UBrCl$_3$, UIF$_3$, of tetravalent and trivalent uranium should be noted.[95]

Reactions with Simple Compounds of Nonmetallic Elements

Water. Uranium is oxidized quite readily by water, forming UO$_2$ and hydrogen. Thus the corrosion rate in boiling water is 3mg/sq cm/hr (about 2 mils/day). In pressurized water above 200°C (392°F), the rate is in the range of 1 g/sq cm/hr or higher. Similar rates are observed in steam. In each case the hydrogen formed by the initial reaction of metal with water can accelerate corrosion through the formation of hydride.

The considerable interest in the use of uranium as fuel in water-cooled reactors has led to a substantial body of work on uranium alloys with much better resistance to aqueous corrosion. In spite of the protection of the uranium by cladding materials, the behavior of uranium is of concern because of its possible exposure to the coolant in case of any imperfection in the cladding. Uranium alloys have been developed with corrosion rates in 350°C (662°F) water similar to the rate for unalloyed uranium in boiling water. The corrosion resistant alloys fall into three categories: (1) metastable gamma-phase alloys, such as those containing about 10 per cent columbium or molybdenum, or about 50 per cent zirconium; (2) supersaturated alpha-phase alloys, obtained by a martensitic transformation of more dilute alloys such as 3 per cent columbium or 1.5 per cent columbium plus 5 per cent zirconium (these alloys suffer the serious disadvantage of requiring incompatible heat treatments for corrosion resistance and radiation stability); and (3) new phases, such as U$_3$Si[81,82,106] or U$_6$Ni.[47] Such phases introduce problems in achieving stoichiometric composition. In addition, they are likely to be difficult to fabricate. The U$_3$Si has received considerable attention; it can be fabricated at high temperature and has been successfully coextruded with Zircaloy. More brittle intermetallics, such as U$_6$Ni, may be fabricated by dispersion in a suitable matrix material such as an aluminum alloy.[52]

Another class of alloys receives consideration, although the improvement in corrosion resistance is much less striking. A slight reduction of corrosion rate is achieved by the addition of small amounts of zirconium, e.g., 2 per cent. The magnitude of fuel element failure is consequently reduced in case of exposure of the fuel through a defect in the cladding.[83]

Hydrogen Halides. Hydrogen fluoride and hydrogen chloride attack uranium metal to give halides of intermediate valence, UF$_4$ and UCl$_3$, respectively. The reactions are likely to be slowed by the caking of the relatively nonvolatile halides. Hydrogen facilitates the reactions by forming the hydride UH$_3$, which reacts more readily with the hydrogen halide.

Little is known about the reaction of uranium metal with hydrogen bromide or iodide. These hydrogen halides react with uranium hydride, apparently giving the uranium trihalides.

Carbon Monoxide and Dioxide. Uranium turnings react at 750°C (1382°F) with carbon monoxide or dioxide to give a mixture of oxides and carbides. No success has been achieved in attempts to prepare a uranium carbonyl.[102] Reaction with carbon dioxide is of particular interest because of use of this gas as a coolant in nuclear reactors. Finely divided metal has been reported to ignite spontaneously.

Ammonia. Uranium reacts with ammonia to form nitride, the rate and temperature of formation depending on the metal's state of subdivision.

Methane and Other Organic Compounds. Uranium monocarbide is formed by the reaction of finely divided uranium with methane at 635–900°C (1175–1652°F).[125]

Other low molecular weight hydrocarbons may be presumed to react similarly. At suitable temperatures, hydrocarbons of higher molecular weight may yield some of their hydrogen to the metal, forming hydride. Thus, decalin and tetralin form UH_3 at 210–270°C (410–518°F).[101] The hydride may then react with the hydrocarbon to give uranium monocarbide and release more hydrogen. Such a reaction cycle, initiated by decomposition of the hydrocarbon, is of interest in connection with the use of polynuclear aromatics (biphenyl, terphenyl) as coolants for nuclear reactors. Failure of the cladding is not expected to lead to severe corrosion damage.[19,141,168]

The affinity of uranium for halogens has to be considered when chlorinated hydrocarbons (carbon tetrachloride, trichloroethylene) are brought in contact with the metal, as for cleaning. The likelihood of reaction is greatest with vapors and increases as the temperature and metal's subdivision increase.[100]

Reactions with Aqueous Solutions

Acids. The reaction of uranium with hydrofluoric acid is retarded by the formation of an insoluble coating of uranium tetrafluoride. Hydrochloric acid attacks the metal very rapidly. The degree of oxidation depends on various factors such as acid concentration and temperature.[171] At the outset, the reddish-violet color of the hydrated trivalent uranium ion is seen. This color is soon masked by a voluminous, black, insoluble compound, presumably a hydrated dioxide, which tends to remain suspended. This compound can be dissolved with a suitable oxidizing agent. Its formation can be minimized by the presence of fluosilicic acid (0.05 M). Hydrobromic acid and hydriodic acid resemble hydrochloric acid in their effects on uranium. The rate becomes slower in going from hydrochloric to hydrobromic to hydriodic.

Nitric acid dissolves the metal slowly to form uranyl nitrate. The slow rate of this reaction permits the use of nitric acid to remove oxide film or scale from the metal. Special care is required with some alloys, notably uranium-zirconium, which leave an explosive residue when attacked by nitric acid.[117,151,159]

Sulfuric acid is slow in its attack on metallic uranium, forming uranium (IV) acid sulfate and reduction products of the acid (SO_2,S,H_2S). In the presence of oxidizing agents such as hydrogen peroxide, dilute sulfuric acid will dissolve uranium.

Warm phosphoric acid can react rapidly with metallic uranium, giving a green solution of uranium (IV) acid phosphate.

Dilute perchloric acid has little effect on uranium, but as it becomes concentrated, e.g., by boiling off water, a vigorous reaction can ensue. The dilute acid can be caused to attack the metal smoothly with the aid of oxidizing agents such as peroxides or chlorates.

Organic acids do not react with metallic uranium, but the formation of their salts can be effected by the presence of hydrogen chloride or hydrochloric acid.

Alkali Solutions. The metal is hardly affected by solutions of alkali metal hydroxides, but, if these solutions contain oxidizing agents such as hydrogen peroxide (or sodium peroxide), the metal is dissolved to give soluble peruranates.

Heavy Metal Salt Solutions.[99] The reducing power of uranium, i.e., its ease of oxidation, permits it to displace from their aqueous solutions metals such as mercury, silver, copper, tin, platinum, and gold. Displacement of less active metals by uranium also occurs in fused salt solutions, e.g., halides.[64,132]

CHEMICAL ANALYSIS

The analytical chemistry of uranium has been intensively developed. It is thoroughly reviewed by Rodden,[150] who discusses the principles of the various methods and also provides detailed procedures. Two features of uranium chemistry which are often exploited in these procedures are worth noting. First, the oxidation potential for U(IV)–U(VI) is fairly small (see page 613), permitting ready interconversion between these two valence states. The compounds in these two valence states may differ widely in solubility and extractability. Second, uranium readily forms complexes with both inorganic and organic compounds, which can be used either to keep uranium in solution (e.g., carbonate) or to remove it from solution (e.g., cupferron).

Uranium metal is generally dissolved in nitric acid, with suitable modifications for any alloying elements. Several methods can be used to separate the uranium. In precipitation methods, likely forms of the precipitate are ammonium diuranate, uranium tetroxide ($UO_4 \cdot 2H_2O$), sodium uranyl acetate, uranium (IV) oxalate, and uranium (IV) cupferrate. In the separation as cupferrate, the same reagent can first be used to remove other metals while uranium is kept in the hexavalent state. Uranium can also be kept in solution by complexing, e.g., with carbonates. It can be separated by extraction, notably the ether extraction of uranyl nitrate or uranium (IV) cupferrate. Uranium can also be separated by volatilization as UF_6.

The method of determining uranium is governed by the amount present. When it is the predominant material, it is determined gravimetrically or volumetrically. Smaller amounts are determined colorimetrically. Below the microgram range, a fluorometric method is suitable. For gravimetric determination, the weighing form is normally U_3O_8, obtained from any one of various precipitates, including those from organic reagents, by ignition at 800–1050°C (1472–1922°F) under oxidizing conditions. Usually, volumetric determination involves reduction to U (IV) which is then titrated to U (VI) with a standard oxidizing solution, such as potassium permanganate, potassium dichromate, ceric sulfate, or ferric sulfate. The most common inorganic reagent for colorimetric determination of uranium is alkaline peroxide. Various organic reagents are also available. The fluorescence of trace quantities of uranium in ultraviolet light is intensified by fusion with a solid such as sodium fluoride. As little as 10^{-11} g of uranium can be detected by this method, which has been developed to a high degree of accuracy.[29] A commercial instrument is available for the fluorometric analysis.[85]

Other elements present in uranium are determined by conventional methods, but, in some cases, the bulk of uranium first has to be removed to avoid interference.

URANIUM ALLOYS

The use of uranium as nuclear fuel may involve alloying to overcome various limitations in the properties of metallic uranium. This alloying may go so far as to eliminate solid metal and use a liquid metal in which uranium may either predominate or be present as a solute of low concentration. In all cases the choice of alloying elements is also influenced by their nuclear properties; i.e., the alloying elements should have low neutron absorption cross sections. Low cross section is one of the reasons for the popularity of aluminum and zirconium as alloying elements.

Data on alloy systems are given below. Klein has summarized information regarding the properties of alloys containing aluminum, beryllium, chromium, molybdenum, columbium, silicon, and zirconium.[114]

Nonmetals: Carbon, Boron, and Silicon[93,152,160]

Carbon, boron, and silicon show limited solubility in metallic uranium. Compounds are formed with established structures. The compounds can be formed by direct reaction of the elements (or using UH_3 instead of elemental uranium). The carbides UC and UC_2 are known. Evidence is also available for the compound U_2C_3; its formation requires residual stress.[128,154] The stability of these compounds prevents preparation of metal by reduction of oxide with carbon.[128,161] Uranium carbides are receiving serious attention as potential reactor fuels.[157a,166a] Three uranium borides have been reported: UB_2, UB_4, and UB_{12}.[153,162] More compounds have been reported in the uranium-silicon system: U_3Si, U_3Si_2, USi, α-USi_2, β-USi_2, and USi_3.[106,163,180] Particular attention has been paid to the U_3Si (epsilon) phase because of its high density, corrosion resistance, and amenability to fabrication like a metal.[81,82]

METALS

Liquid Metals

Uranium may be contacted with liquid metals in applications where solubility is desirable or undesirable. Solubility is sought for use of dissolved uranium in a liquid metal fuel reactor. Here bismuth is used as the solvent to contain 0.1 per cent uranium compared to solubilities of 0.21 per cent at 400°C (752°F) and 0.97 per cent at 550°C (1022°F).[116] The solubility of uranium may also be exploited for processing schemes.[57] In other applications a metal in which uranium has very slight solubility is used either as coolant or as liquid metal bond. The alkali metals are suited for this application.

Phase Diagrams

The binary phase diagrams of uranium have been the subject of intensive study and are now available in several compilations,[69,78,152] where information is also given regarding the structure of the intermediate phases. The principal features of the phase diagrams are summarized in Table 31.14, where the elements are grouped

TABLE 31.14. ALLOYING BEHAVIOR OF URANIUM

Element	Eutectic temperature (°C)	Terminal solid solubility element in γ U,a/o	U phase stabilized	Compound
Na				None
Be	~1100 (2012°F)	Small	—	UBe_{13}
Mg		0	—	None
Ca	—	—	—	None
Al	640; 1105 (1184°; 2021°F)	~ 3	γ	UAl_2; UAl_3; UAl_4
Ce	~1000 (1832°F)	—		None
Ti	—	Complete	(α); γ	U_2Ti
Zr	—	Complete	α; γ	Delta (UZr_2)
Th	—	0.3		None
V	1040 (1904°F)	12	β; γ	None
Cb	—	Complete	γ	None
Ta	—	~ 3	—	None
Cr	859 (1578°F)	~ 4	β; γ	None
Mo	—	42	β; γ	None (ordered gamma)
W	—	~ 0.5	—	None
Mn	716; 1035 (1321°; 1895°F)	~ 4	β; γ	U_6Mn; UMn_2
Re		~ 6	β; γ	URe_2
Fe	725; 1080 (1337°; 1976°F)	~ 1	—	U_6Fe; UFe_2
Co	740; 1120 (1364°; 2048°F)	Small	—	U_6Co; UCo; UCo_2; UCo_3; UCo_4; U_2Co_{11}
Ni	740; 1100 (1364°; 2012°F)	~ 2	γ	U_6Ni; U_7Ni_9; U_5Ni_7; UNi_2; UNi_5
Ru	885 (1625°F)	~ 9	β; γ	U_2Ru; URu; U_3Ru_4; U_2Ru_3; U_3Ru_5; URu_3
Rh	885 (1625°F)	9	γ	URh_3
Pd	998 (1828°F)	5	γ	UPd; U_5Pd_6; UPd_3
Os	—	—	β; γ	UOs_2
Ir	—	~ 3	—	UIr_2
Pt	1005; 1340 (1841°; 2444°F)	6.5	β; γ	UPt; UPt_2; UPt_3; UPt_5
Cu	950 (1742°F)	0	—	UCu_5
Ag	950 (1742°F)	~ 0	—	None
Au	852; 1105 (1566°; 2021°F)	6	β; γ	(U_2Au_3); (UAu_3)
Zn	944; 1050 (1731°; 1922°F)	0	—	UZn_9
Hg		—	—	UHg_2; UHg_3; UHg_4
Ga	~1100 (2012°F)	0	—	UGa_2; UGa_3
In		—	—	UIn_3
Tl	—	—	—	UTl_3
Ge	—	—	—	UGe_3
Sn	—	0	—	(U_5Sn_4); (U_3Sn_5); USn_3
Pb	—	0	—	UPb; UPb_3
As	—	—	—	UAs; U_3As_4; UAs_2
Sb	—	—	—	USb; U_3Sb_4; USb_2
Bi	—	0	—	UBi; U_3Bi_4; UBi_2
Pu	—	Complete	β; γ	

on the basis of location in the periodic table. It should be noted that the rather unusual structures of the alpha and beta phases limit the solubility of other elements. The body-centered cubic gamma phase more readily dissolves other elements, but only a few (columbium, molybdenum, zirconium) are so soluble as to permit retention of the (metastable) gamma phase to room temperature. The constitution of the alloys has been discussed on the basis of alloy theory.[80]

METALLOGRAPHY[76]

Preparation of metallographic specimens requires consideration of several properties of uranium. The soft metal is likely to contain hard inclusions. The metal oxidizes easily, and its surface is readily deformed, making a final electropolish advisable. The toxicity of fine uranium powders necessitates the use of hoods and/or wet polishing media. The final surface preparation of any specimen is determined by the objective of its examination: grain structure, inclusions, diffusion layers. Each metallographer probably has his or her favorite recipe and can be expected to introduce a modification in published procedures. Klein[114] has tabulated the more common techniques for both electrolytic polishing and etching. Cathodic vacuum etching is a valuable technique, especially for electron microscopy.[15,16,16a,138]

The anisotropy of uranium permits examination by polarized light to reveal grain structure. The specification of grain size is made ambiguous by subgraining or faceting. Thus a group of alpha grains derived from the same beta grain may have slightly different orientations. Yet, when irradiated or deformed mechanically, this group may act essentially as a single grain. Polarized light may help somewhat in the examination of inclusions. In contrast to uranium, they are likely to be isotropic, notably the cubic isomorphs, UN, UC, and UO, which form solutions with each other, U(C,N) or U (O,C,N). Bright light is relied upon for examination of these compounds, but their identification is difficult. An ultrasonic jack hammer has been used to remove these inclusions and provide material for x-ray examination.[110,111] An electroplating technique differentiates these compounds on the basis of their cathodic behavior in copper deposition.[109]

FABRICATION

Melting and Casting[9,24,28,86]

The reactivity of uranium with atmospheric gases necessitates the use of closed systems with inert atmosphere (e.g., vacuum) for the melting of uranium, except in cases where a low-melting alloying element, e.g., aluminum, permits considerable reduction of the melting temperature. Reactivity is also a problem in the choice of the crucible material. On chemical grounds, preference is given to stable oxides such as thoria, magnesia, and beryllia. Their poor resistance to thermal shock limits their usefulness. Metallic yttrium offers promise as a crucible material because of its low solubility in liquid uranium.[157] Where possible, graphite is likely to be used for the crucible and stopper rod. Carbon contamination of the melt is minimized not only by shortening the heating time but also by keeping the metal pouring temperature not much higher than 1300°C (2372°F), where the solubility of carbon is several hundred parts per million. An alternative approach is necessary when melting an alloy having a liquidus temperature significantly higher than the melting point of uranium. The stable oxides are used individually or in combination as crucible washes. Possible washes, applied as aqueous suspensions by brushing or spraying, include the following: beryllia, magnesium zirconate, magnesium zirconate followed by thoria, and a mixture of thoria and zirconia. Protection of the graphite is not as important when the graphite is used for the mold. Graphite offers means of controlling the rate of cooling in the mold by increasing its thickness or by heating it by induction. Water-cooled copper molds can be used for chill casting. Fuel element rods can be obtained directly by centrifugal casting.[50]

Heating of the crucible and charge is generally by induction. For alloys, stirring of the melt may also be obtained at the same time, except with graphite crucibles, which act as susceptors and limit the effect of the electromagnetic field on the metal. Stirring may be promoted by the evolution of volatile material present in the metal charge, e.g., magnesium in uranium biscuit or in zirconium sponge. Such volatile material may be deliberately added to the charge. The use of master alloys is sometimes desirable. Prior arc melting can be used to prealloy uranium with a high-melting metal and thereby lower the temperature required in induction melting.[20]

Uranium scrap has been consolidated by melting in an open furnace under protective salt cover.[50]

Forging[58,59]

Press forging is preferred over hammer forging in order to avoid splattering of the salt coating the metal. This salt is carried over from the salt bath (e.g., potassium carbonate–lithium carbonate) used for heating the metal and serves to prevent the formation and dispersal of uranium oxide. As in other hot-working operations, a temperature in the vicinity of 600°C (1112°F) is chosen, to be fairly high in the alpha range but safely below transformation to beta. At the end of forging, the metal is quenched in water to prevent oxidation. The initial forging operations eliminate the coarse dendritic structure of the casting by upsetting and cross forging. Later forging operations are determined by the shapes needed for subsequent use.

Rolling[50,68]

Rolling of uranium to obtain sheet is likely to combine hot rolling near 600°C (1112°F) followed by warm rolling near 300°C (572°F). The respective heating media are a fused salt bath (e.g., carbonate) and an oil bath. The mechanical properties and metallography (grain size, orientation) of the final sheet depend on the rolling schedule, including per cent reduction before annealing as well as time and temperature of annealing.

With suitably grooved rolls, uranium can be rolled to obtain other shapes such as squares, rounds, and ovals.

Extrusion[58,126]

Uranium can be extruded to produce rod, tubing, ovals, and other shapes having uniform cross section. As in the previously mentioned hot working operations in the high alpha range, heating with protection against oxidation requires special attention. In addition, the more drastic working of the metal and uranium's

tendency to gall make the problem of lubrication more critical. Copper is used as a can or as a thin plate for lubrication as well as for protection against oxidation. It can then be removed chemically in a nitric acid bath. Uranium can also be extruded in the gamma phase, where it is very soft. In spite of its use for uranium slugs used in the first piles, gamma extrusion is not as well developed as alpha extrusion, which has been used on a large scale. (The gamma uranium alloys with columbium or molybdenum are much stiffer than unalloyed uranium and have been extruded successfully.) Extrusion is applicable for the cladding of uranium as it is being reduced.[61,107,134] Thin and uniform cladding can be applied not only to the outside diameter but also to the inside diameter, if tubular fuel elements are sought. The ends can also be sealed at the same time. Zirconium is particularly suitable for cladding uranium, because the two metals have approximately the same resistance to plastic deformation by extrusion and do not form brittle intermetallic compounds.

Swaging and Drawing[50,167]

Uranium may be swaged either hot or cold. It can also be cold drawn to small diameters if suitable lubrication is used. Advantage should be taken of the transition to more ductile behavior between 100°C (212°F) and 150°C (302°F).

Machining[50]

Standard machine-shop practice is applicable to uranium with allowance for its work hardening and its pyrophoricity. Fast cutting is necessary. The coolant should flow rapidly enough to swamp the chips and turnings and prevent them from igniting. Ventilation is strongly advised. Provision must be made for storage of scrap in small batches under mineral oil to minimize the fire hazard.

Welding[21]

Uranium can be arc welded with standard commercial equipment if the metal surface is adequately cleaned and an inert gas blanket is maintained above the weld area to prevent oxidation of the metal. The fluidity of the molten uranium requires that the weld area be kept close to a horizontal position. Preheating of the metal offers no advantage, and stress relieving after welding is unnecessary.

Other methods of joining uranium (brazing, soldering) are limited by the formation of brittle, intermetallic compounds with the joining metal.

Powder Metallurgy[50,176,181]

Powder metallurgy permits the preparation of metal with uniform composition, controlled porosity (0 to 40 per cent) and grain size, and a minimum of preferred orientation. Alloys with high melting metals can be prepared. Metal losses can be kept very low, a particular advantage when dealing with expensive materials such as enriched uranium.

The uranium powder may be obtained directly by reduction, e.g., of the oxide by calcium or magnesium. A common method of converting massive metal or chips to powder is by hydriding at about 225°C (437°F) and then decomposing the hydride under vacuum near 400°C (752°F). The pyrophoric nature of the powder necessitates handling in an inert atmosphere. Surface oxide can prevent sintering. It should be broken up during compacting. Uranium powder is compacted either cold (with organic lubricants) or hot. For maximum densification, sintering should be carried out just below the melting point. The sintering time must be minimized to avoid grain coarsening.

The preparation of homogeneous alloys is particularly difficult in the uranium-aluminum system because of the large density differences between the phases. Chips blended from segregated castings can be compacted, e.g., by extrusion, to obtain a homogeneous alloy.[118]

Powder metallurgy processes, resembling those used for ceramics, are used to prepare dispersion type fuel elements, e.g., UO_2 in stainless steel.[49,115]

USE OF URANIUM

In Nuclear Reactors

Preparation of Metallic Fuel Elements.[4,75,108,177] Uranium is not used as a structural metal. When used in reactors, the element may be present in one of many forms, not necessarily metallic. Thus the fuel for a nuclear reactor may be uranium as a solid compound (notably UO_2), as a compound dissolved in water or in a fused salt, or as a liquid metal solution. The predominant form of nuclear fuel remains, however, metallic uranium, unalloyed or alloyed.

The form of the fuel element is determined by the options exercised by the reactor designer for the specific reactor. Depending on the size and purpose of the reactor, he makes his choices for the following variables in fuel design: geometry, enrichment, coolant, and cladding. The geometry determines the temperature gradient through the fuel. Various shapes have been or can be used: plates, rods, tubes, wire, and ribbon. The choices of reactor coolant (and moderator) and of fuel cladding are closely related, since one of the main purposes of the cladding is protection of the uranium against the coolant. The cladding also prevents the entry of fission products from the fuel into the coolant. The cladding may be required to be strong enough at reactor temperatures to restrain distortion of the fuel under irradiation. Several considerations guide the choice of cladding. In a thermal reactor, neutron economy attaches a premium to metals with a low neutron absorption cross section: aluminum, zirconium (free of hafnium), magnesium, beryllium. The cladding and fuel are compatible (no interaction forming liquid or brittle intermetallic phase) or a barrier is provided. If the cladding and fuel cannot be directly bonded, other means must be provided for transmittal of the heat outward from the fuel to the cladding for transfer to the coolant; thus direct contact between steels and uranium is avoided because of the formation of low melting eutectics between uranium and iron [m.p. 725°C (1337°F)] or alloying elements in the steel. The thermal bond can then be provided by a highly conductive molten metal, e.g., sodium.

The various fabrication techniques mentioned above are used in the preparation of fuel elements. These techniques can be modified to obtain the composite fuel element. Thus, zirconium can be bonded to uranium by coextrusion as the uranium is being reduced in diameter.[61,107,134] Fuel element fabrication requires special handling techniques because of the fuel's radioactivity and the high cost of the components. In some cases designs and processes are preferred, which lend themselves to remote handling of highly active materials.

Figure 31.7. A variety of fuel elements: (1) Slugs of uranium such as are used in the Oak Ridge and Brookhaven research reactors and the Hanford production reactors. (2) The Brookhaven slugs are contained in a long aluminum can, finned to speed the dissipation of heat to the cooling air. (3) A Materials Testing Reactor fuel element and (4) the similar Argonne Research Reactor element. (5) A fuel element of the first Boiling Reactor Experiment in Idaho, also of aluminum-clad plates. (6) An Experimental Boiling Water Reactor fuel element, made up of thick plates clad with zirconium. (7) One 10-in. section of a blanket element of the Shippingport Pressurized Water Reactor is superimposed on a board to show the element's full length. (8) A shortened fuel cluster for the Sodium Reactor Experiment—uranium in stainless steel tubes. (9) Somewhat similar, smaller element of Experimental Breeder Reactor No. 1. (10) Element for Experimental Breeder Reactor No. 2, clusters of many small stainless steel tubes containing uranium pins. (*Courtesy Museum of Science and Industry, Chicago.*)

Fuel element specifications are quite rigid and are usually checked by a series of rigorous, nondestructive tests before use of the elements in a reactor.

Some examples of fuel elements are illustrated in Figure 31.7.

Processing of Irradiated Fuel. The length of time for which fuel can be left in a reactor is limited by irradiation damage and the accumulation of fission products, causing, respectively, loss of the fuel's integrity and reactivity. When the fuel is removed from the reactor, only a small fraction of the fissionable material (generally less than 1 per cent) has been consumed. Recovery of the unburned balance is then advisable for fuel economy. In addition, newly generated plutonium is also recovered.

The established method of processing irradiated fuel involves dissolution with nitric acid; the solution of nitrates is then processed in a manner resembling that applied to ore concentrates. (See page 606.) The fuel is dissolved by 55 per cent (11.7 M) nitric acid in a reaction approximated by the following equation:

$$U + 4.5\ HNO_3 \rightarrow UO_2(NO_3)_2 + 1.56\ NO + 0.84\ NO_2 + 0.0005\ N_2O + 0.043\ N_2 + 2.25\ H_2O$$

The uranyl nitrate solution is subjected to solvent extraction. Pure uranyl nitrate solution is recovered from the organic solvent and thermally decomposed to UO_3, which is then reduced to UO_2. The radioactivity of the irradiated fuel necessitates remote operation and shielding, at least in the early stages of processing. The over-all process leads to complete decontamination, permitting direct handling. Depending on the composition of the fuel and the cladding, prior treatments ("head end") are applied to obtain fairly standard nitrate solutions from various fuels for the solvent extraction. These treatments may be chemical or mechanical.

Various nonaqueous methods, generally involving high temperatures, have been studied as alternatives, perhaps giving lower decontamination than the nitric acid methods but having compensating advantages, such as the avoidance of radiation-sensitive organic extractants and the reduction of volumes and criticality problems through the elimination of water.[56] The processes may exploit physical or chemical differences between uranium and the fission products (or their compounds). An attempt is made to keep the fuel in the metallic state, avoiding the oxidation-reduction cycle of aqueous processes and thus eliminating the cost of regenerating metallic fuel.

Other Uses

When its nuclear properties cannot be exploited, the use of uranium as a metal is severely limited by its chemical and mechanical properties. The development of another application for the metal would be welcomed as a means of consuming supplies of depleted uranium. (Uranium 235 has been separated, leaving material rich in uranium 238.) For nonnuclear applications, this change in isotopic composition is quite unimportant. The depleted material can be considered safer because of lower radioactivity. When used as a target in an x-ray tube, its high atomic number causes the production of high energy x-rays (very short length).[130,148] The high atomic number makes uranium an outstandingly effective shielding material. The use of uranium instead of lead effects a considerable saving in the weight of shielding. This saving can be of particular value in a mobile reactor system.

The affinity of uranium for gases makes it a very effective means of purifying inert gases. For this purpose it is heated to about 600°C (1112°F).[63] A polished metal surface can be used to indicate the purity of a gas stream.[127,137]

The Atomic Energy Commission has released depleted uranium hexafluoride for commercial use, but its licensing restrictions still cover the sales of uranium products. An incentive for other applications is the very low price of highly depleted material. This material is being used in the resumed manufacture of uranium pigments for high-temperature glazes.[35] No major market exists yet for depleted uranium; new uses are being sought.[19a,31a,136a]

References

1. Alexander, P. P., *Metals & Alloys*, **8**, 263 (1937).
2. Allen, R. J., Petrow, H. G., and Magno, P. J., *Ind. Eng. Chem.*, **50**, 1748 (1958).
3. "Atomic Energy Facts," U.S. Atomic Energy Commission, Nuclear Technology Series, Chap. 5, Washington, D.C., Government Printing Office, 1957.
4. *Ibid.*, Chap. 6.
5. *Ibid.*, p. 68.
6. *Ibid.*, Table 6, p. 14.
7. *Ibid.*, Table 17, p. 61.
8. *Ibid.*, Table 19, p. 66.
9. Baird, J. E., and Carson, N. J., "Melting and Casting of Uranium, Zirconium, Niobium Alloys," in "Nuclear Metallurgy," Vol. 4, p. 31, New York, Institute of Metals Division, The Metallurgical Society, American Institute of Mining, Metallurgical, and Petroleum Engineers, 1957.
10. Belle, J., and Lustman, B., "Properties of Uranium Dioxide," in "Fuel Elements Conference, Paris, Nov. 18–23, 1957," *U.S.Atomic Energy Comm., Rept. No. TID-7546*, Book 1, p. 442, 1958; *No. WAPD-184*, Westinghouse Atomic Power Division (1957).
11. Benedict, M., and Pigford, T. H., "Nuclear Chemical Engineering," Figs. 10, 11, p. 404, New York, McGraw-Hill Book Company, Inc., 1957.
12. Benedict, M., and Pigford, T. H., *ibid.*, p. 157.
13. Benedict, M., and Pigford, T. H., *ibid.*, p. 472.
14. Benedict, M., and Pigford, T. H., *ibid.*, Table 4.9, p. 153.
15. Bierlein, T. K., *U.S. Atomic Energy Comm., Rept. No. HW-32676*, Hanford Atomic Products Operation (1955).
16. Bierlein, T. K., *U.S. Atomic Energy Comm., Rept. No. HW-34390*, Hanford Atomic Products Operation (1955).
16a. Bierlein, T. K., and Mastel B., *Rev. Sci. Instr.*, **30**, 832 (1959).
17. Blumenthal, B., and Noland, R. A., "High Purity Uranium," in "Progress in Nuclear Energy, Series 5, Metallurgy and Fuels," H. M. Finniston and J. P. Howe (Eds.), p. 62, New York, McGraw-Hill Book Company, Inc., 1956.
18. Bowen, D., "Survey of Radiation Effects on

Fuel Materials," in "Symposium on Radiation Effects on Materials," Vol. 1, *ASTM Special Technical Publication No. 208,* Philadelphia, American Society for Testing Materials, 1957.

18a. Breese, J. C., *et al., U.S. Atomic Energy Comm., Rept. No. CRNL-2889,* Oak Ridge National Laboratory (1960).

19. Boyd, W. K., *et al., U.S. Atomic Energy Comm., Rept. No. BMI-1160,* Battelle Memorial Institute (1957).

20. Britton, W. H., and Haynes, W. V., "Arc Melting of Uranium-Rich Alloys," in "Nuclear Metallurgy," Vol. 4, p. 63, New York, Institute of Metals Division, The Metallurgical Society, American Institute of Mining, Metallurgical, and Petroleum Engineers, 1957.

21. Brundige, E. L., Doll, D. T., Hanks, G. S., and Taub, J. M., "Fusion Welding of Uranium," in "Nuclear Metallurgy," Vol. 4, p. 107, New York, Institute of Metals Division, The Metallurgical Society, American Institute of Mining, Metallurgical, and Petroleum Engineers, 1957.

22. Buddery, J. H., "Production of Uranium Metal by Calcium and Magnesium Reduction of its Oxide," in "Progress in Nuclear Energy, Series 5, Metallurgy and Fuels," H. M. Finniston, and J. P. Howe, (Eds.), p. 24, New York, McGraw-Hill Book Company, Inc., 1956.

23. Buddery, J. H., and Hedger, H. J., "Fundamental Considerations," in "Progress in Nuclear Energy, Series 5, Metallurgy and Fuels," H. M. Finniston, and J. P. Howe, (Eds.), p. 3, New York, McGraw-Hill Book Company, Inc., 1956.

24. Buntz, B. J., "Uranium Ingot Production at Atomic Energy Commission Feed Material Production Centers," in "Nuclear Metallurgy," Vol. 4, p. 17, New York, Institute of Metals Division, The Metallurgical Society, American Institute of Mining, Metallurgical, and Petroleum Engineers, 1957.

25. Bush, S. H., *U.S. Atomic Energy Comm., Rept No. HW-51444,* Hanford Atomic Products Operation (1957).

26. Cachemaille, A., British Patent 238,663 (July 7, 1924).

27. Caillat, R., Coriou, H., and Pério, P., *Compt. rend.,* **237,** 812 (1953).

28. Carson, N. J., Jr., "Induction Melting of Uranium Base Alloys," in "Nuclear Metallurgy," Vol. 4, p. 23, New York, Institute of Metals Division, The Metallurgical Society, American Institute of Mining, Metallurgical, and Petroleum Engineers, 1957.

29. Centanni, F. A., Ross, A. M., and DeSesa, M. A., "Fluorometric Determination of Uranium," *Anal. Chem.,* **28,** 1651 (1956).

30. *Chem. Eng.,* **65,** No. 20, 50 (Oct. 6, 1958).

30a. *Chem. Eng.,* **67,** No. 14, 70 (July 11, 1960).

31. *Chem. Eng. News,* **34,** 2968 (June 18, 1956).

31a. *Chem. Eng. News,* **38,** No. 18, 53 (May 2, 1960).

32. *Chem. Eng. News,* **37,** No. 6, 78 (Feb. 9, 1959).

33. *Chem. Week,* **81,** No. 10, 83 (Sept. 7, 1957).

34. *Chem. Week,* **81,** No. 17, 87 (Oct. 26, 1957).

35. *Chem. Week,* **84,** No. 1, 24 (Jan. 3, 1959).

36. *Chem. Week,* **84,** No. 13, 30 (Mar. 28, 1959).

36a. *Chem. Week,* **87,** No. 2, 4 (July 9, 1960).

36b. *Chem. Week,* **87,** No. 11, 95 (Sept. 10, 1960).

37. Chiotti, P., *J. Am. Ceram. Soc.,* **35,** 123 (1952).

38. Clegg, J. W., and Foley, D. D., "Uranium Ore Processing," Reading, Mass., Addison-Wesley Publishing Company, 1958.

39. Clegg, J. W., and Foley, D. D., *ibid.,* Chap. 4.

40. Clegg, J. W., and Foley, D. D., *ibid.,* p. 7.

41. Clegg, J. W., and Foley, D. D., *ibid.,* p. 12.

42. Clegg, J. W., and Foley, D. D., *ibid.,* p. 14.

43. Clegg, J. W., and Foley, D. D., *ibid.,* p. 18.

44. Clegg, J. W., and Foley, D. D., *ibid.,* p. 354.

45. Clegg, J. W., and Foley, D. D., *ibid.,* p. 372.

46. Coffin, L. F., Jr., *U.S. Atomic Energy Comm., Rept. No. KAPL-1019,* Knolls Atomic Power Laboratory (1953).

47. Creslicki, M. E., and Nelson, B. J., U.S. Patent 2,692,823 (Oct. 26, 1954); *C.A.* **49,** 826i (1955).

48. Cronan, C. S., *Chem. Eng.,* **65,** No. 11, 72 (June 2, 1958).

49. Cunningham, J. E., Beaver, R. J., and Waugh, R. C., "Fuel Dispersion in Stainless-steel Components for Power Reactors," in "Fuel Elements Conference, Paris, Nov. 18–23, 1957," *U.S. Atomic Energy Comm., Rept. TID-7546,* Book 1, p. 243, 1958.

50. Cuthbert, F. L., "Casting and Fabrication of Natural Uranium," in "Fuel Elements Conference, Paris, Nov. 18–23, 1957," *U.S. Atomic Energyy Comm., Rept. No. TID-7546,* Book 1, p. 29, 1958.

51. Decroly, C., and Van Impe, J., *Bull. tech. A. I. Br.,* **3,** (5), 1 (1950).

52. Draley, J. E., private communication, Argonne National Laboratory.

53. Driggs, F. H., and Lilliendahl, W. C., *Ind. Eng. Chem.,* **22,** 516 (1930).

54. Driggs, F. H., *et al.,* U.S. Patents 1,821,176; 1,842,254; 1,861,625 (1932).

55. *Eng. Mining J.,* **154,** No. 5, 72-76 (1953).

56. Feder, H. M., "The Chemistry of Pyrometallurgical Processes: A Review," in "Symposium on the Reprocessing of Irradiated Fuels Held at Brussels, Belgium, May 20–25, 1957," *U.S. Atomic Energy Comm., Rept. No. TID-7534,* Book 2, p. 690, 1957.

57. Feder, H. M., and Teitel, R. J., "Purification of Reactor Fuels and Blankets by Crystallization from Liquid Metal Solvents," *Geneva Conference Paper, P 540* (1958).

58. Fellows, J. A., "Bomb Reduction, Forging, and Extrusion of Uranium and Uranium Alloys," in "Fuel Elements Conference, Paris, Nov. 18–23, 1957," *U.S. Atomic Energy Comm., Rept. No. TID-7546,* Book 1, p. 46, 1958.

59. Fellows, J. A., and Schaffer, H. J., "Press Forging of Dingot Uranium," in "Nuclear Metallurgy," Vol. 4, p. 67, New York, Institute of Metals Division, The Metallurgical Society, American Institute of Mining, Metallurgical, and Petroleum Engineers, 1957.

60. Frondel, J. W., and Fleischer, M., *U.S. Geol. Survey, Bull. No. 1009-F* (1955).

61. Gardner, N. R., *Materials in Design Eng.,* No. **7, 48,** 91 (Dec. 1958).

62. George, D. R., *U.S. Atomic Energy Comm., Rept. No. RMO-563* (1949).

63. Gibbs, D. S., Svec, H. J., and Harrington, R. E., *Ind. Eng. Chem.,* **48,** 289 (1956).

64. Gibson, A. R., and Murray, P., *U.K. Atomic Energy Authority, Report AERE-M/M-72* (1954).

65. Glassner, A., *U.S. Atomic Energy Comm., Rept. No. ANL-5750, Argonne National Laboratory* (1957).

66. Glasstone, S., "Sourcebook on Atomic Energy," 2nd Ed., p. 395, Princeton, N.J., D. Van Nostrand Company, Inc., 1958.

67. Gruen, D. M., *J. Chem. Phys.,* **23,** 1708 (1955).

68. Hanks, G. S., Taub, J. M., and Doll, D. T., "Rolling of Uranium," in "Nuclear Metallurgy," Vol. 4, p. 73, New York, Institute of Metals Division, The Metallurgical Society, American Institute of Mining, Metallurgical, and Petroleum Engineers, 1957.

69. Hansen, M., and Anderko, K., "Constitution of Binary Alloys," New York, McGraw-Hill Book Company, Inc., 1958.

70. Hayes, E. E., "Grain Refinement of Uranium by Heat-treatment and Alloying," in "Fuel Elements Conference, Paris, Nov. 18–23, 1957," *U.S. Atomic Energy Comm., Rept. No. TID-7546,* Book 1, p. 75, 1958.

71. Hedger, H. J., "Production of Uranium Metal by the Reduction of Uranium Tetrafluoride," in "Progress in Nuclear Energy, Series 5, Metallurgy and Fuels," H. M. Finniston, and J. P. Howe, (Eds.), p. 16, New York, McGraw-Hill Book Company, Inc., 1956.

72. Holden, A. N., "Physical Metallurgy of Uranium," Reading, Mass., Addison-Wesley Publishing Company, 1958.

73. Holden, A. N., *ibid.,* Chap. 11.

74. Holden, A. N., *ibid.,* Chap. 12.

75. Holden, A. N., *ibid.,* Chap. 13.

76. Holden, A. N., *ibid.,* Chap. 14.

77. Holden, A. N., *ibid.,* p. 168.

78. Holden, A. N., *ibid.,* pp. 237f.

79. Hull, W. O., and Pinkney, F. T., *Ind. Eng. Chem.,* **49,** 1 (1957).

80. Hume-Rothery, W., *et al., J. Inst. Metals,* **83,** 535 (1955).

81. Isserow, S. *J. Metals,* **9,** 1237 (1957).

82. Isserow, S., *U.S. Atomic Energy Comm., Rept. No. NMI-1145,* Nuclear Metals, Inc. (1956).

83. Isserow, S., *U.S. Atomic Energy Comm., Rept. No. NMI-4364,* Nuclear Metals, Inc. (1958).

84. *J. Am. Chem. Soc.,* **68,** 2437 (1946).

85. Jarrell-Ash Company, *Bulletin No. FL 5-58,* Newtonville, Mass.

86. Jaynes, G. E., Taub, J. M., and Doll, D. T., "Development of Casting Techniques for Uranium and Uranium Alloys," in "Nuclear Metallurgy," Vol. 4, p. 1, New York, Institute of Metals Division, The Metallurgical Society, American Institute of Mining, Metallurgical, and Petroleum Engineers, 1957.

87. Johnson, J. C., *Chem. Eng. News,* **35,** No. 48, 70 (Dec. 2, 1957).

88. Jonke, A. A., Levitz, N. M., Litty, A., and Lawroski, S., *Ind. Eng. Chem.,* **50,** 1739 (1958).

89. Kalish, H. S., *Trans. Am. Soc. Metals,* preprint No. 63 (1958).

90. Katz, J. J., and Rabinowitch, E. (Eds.), "The Chemistry of Uranium, Part 1, The Element, Its Binary and Related Compounds," National Nuclear Energy Series, Div. 8, Vol. 5, New York, McGraw-Hill Book Company, Inc., 1951.

91. Katz, J. J., and Rabinowitch, E. (Eds.), *ibid.,* Chap. 3.

92. Katz, J. J., and Rabinowitch, E. (Eds.), *ibid.,* Chap. 8.

93. Katz, J. J., and Rabinowitch, E. (Eds.), *ibid.,* Chap. 9.

94. Katz, J. J., and Rabinowitch, E. (Eds.), *ibid.,* Chap. 11.

95. Katz, J. J., and Rabinowitch, E. (Eds.), *ibid.,* Chap. 15.

96. Katz, J. J., and Rabinowitch, E. (Eds.), *ibid.*, p. 124.

97. Katz, J. J., and Rabinowitch, E. (Eds.), *ibid.*, p. 126.

98. Katz, J. J., and Rabinowitch, E. (Eds.), *ibid.*, p. 127.

99. Katz, J. J., and Rabinowitch, E. (Eds.), *ibid.*, p. 170.

100. Katz, J. J., and Rabinowitch, E. (Eds.), *ibid.*, p. 172.

101. Katz, J. J., and Rabinowitch, E. (Eds.), *ibid.*, p. 197.

102. Katz, J. J., and Rabinowitch, E. (Eds.), *ibid.*, p. 557.

103. Katz, J. J., and Rabinowitch, E. (Eds.), *ibid.*, Table 4.1, p. 127.

104. Katz, J. J., and Seaborg, G. T., "The Chemistry of The Actinide Elements," New York, John Wiley & Sons, Inc., 1957.

105. Katz, J. J., and Seaborg, G. T., *ibid.*, pp. 138f.

106. Kaufmann, A. R., Cullity, B., and Bitsianes, G., *J. Metals*, **9**, Sec. 2, 23 (1957).

107. Kaufmann, A. R., Klein, J. L., Loewenstein, P., and Sawyer, H. F., "Zirconium Cladding of Uranium and Uranium Alloys by Coextrusion," in "Fuel Elements Conference, Paris, Nov. 18–23, 1957," *U.S. Atomic Energy Comm., Rept. No. TID-7546*, Book 1, p. 157, 1958; *No. NMI-TJ-8*, Nuclear Metals, Inc. (1957).

108. Kaufmann, A. R., (Ed) "Nuclear Reactor Fuel Elements, Metallurgical Fabrication," New York, Interscience Publishers, Inc., 1961.

109. Kehl, G. L., Mendel, E., Jaraiz, F. E., and Mueller, M. H., *Trans. Am. Soc. Metals*, **51**, preprint No. 100 (1958).

110. Kehl, G. L., Steinmetz, H., and McGonnagle, W. J., *Metallurgia*, **4**, (1957).

111. Kehl, G. L., Steinmetz, H., and McGonnagle, W. J., *U.S. Atomic Energy Comm., Rept., No. ANL-5545*, Argonne National Laboratory (1956).

112. Klaproth, M. H., *Chem. Ann. (Crell) II*, **12**, 387 (1789).

113. Klaproth, M. H., *Mem. Akad. Wiss. Berlin*, 273 (1789).

114. Klein, J. L., "Uranium and Its Alloys," in Kaufmann, A. R., (Ed) "Nuclear Reactor Fuel Elements, Metallurgical Fabrication," New York, Interscience Publishers, Inc., 1961.

115. Kopelman, B., "Recent Developments in Dispersion Type Fuel Elements," in "Fuel Elements Conference, Paris, Nov. 18–23, 1957," *U.S. Atomic Energy Comm., Rept. No. TID-7546*, Book 1, p. 231, 1958.

116. Lane, J. A., MacPherson, H. G., and Maslan, F. (Eds.), "Fluid Fuel Reactors," Reading, Mass., Addison-Wesley Publishing Company, 1958.

117. Larsen, R. P., *et al.*, *U.S. Atomic Energy Comm., Rept. No. ANL-5135*, Argonne National Laboratory (1954).

118. Larson, W. L., and Klein, J. L., *U.S. Atomic Energy Comm., Rept., No. NMI-1168*, Nuclear Metals, Inc. (1956).

119. Latimer, W. M., "The Oxidation States of the Elements and Their Potentials in Aqueous Solutions," 2nd Ed., p. 304, Englewood Cliffs, N.J., Prentice-Hall, Inc., 1952.

120. Lemmon, A. W., *et al.*, *U.S. Atomic Energy Comm., Rept. No. BMI-550*, Battelle Memorial Institute (1952).

121. Lewis, C. J., and Probnick, J. L., *Ind. Eng. Chem.*, **50**, No. 12, 53A (1958).

122. Lewis, W. B., "Uranium Dioxide," Atomic Energy of Canada, Ltd., *Report No. DL-34*, December, 1958.

123. Libowitz, G. G., and Gibb, T. R. P., Jr., *J. Phys. Chem.*, **61**, 793 (1957).

124. Lin, S. T., and Kaufmann, A. R., *Phys. Rev.*, **102**, 640 (1956).

125. Litz, L. M., Garrett, A. B., and Croxton, F. C., *J. Am. Chem. Soc.*, **70**, 1718 (1948).

126. Lowenstein, P., "Extrusion of Uranium," in "Nuclear Metallurgy," Vol. 4, p. 87, New York, Institute of Metals Division, The Metallurgical Society, American Institute of Mining, Metallurgical, and Petroleum Engineers, 1957.

127. Mallett, M. W., *Ind. Eng. Chem.*, **42**, 2095 (1950).

128. Mallett, M. W., Gerds, A. F., and Vaughan, D. A., *Trans. Electrochem. Soc.*, **98**, 505 (1951).

129. Mallett, M. W., and Trzeciak, M. J., *Trans. Am. Soc. Metals*, **50**, preprint No. 36 (1957).

130. Marden, J. W., *Trans. Electrochem. Soc.*, **66**, 39 (1934).

131. Marden, J. W., U.S. Patent 1,659,209 (Feb. 14, 1928).

132. Martin, F. S., and Miles, G. L., "The Processing of Irradiated Uranium by High-Temperature Oxidation Reactions," in "Progress in Nuclear Energy, Series 3, Process Chemistry," F. R. Bruce, *et al.* (Eds.), Vol. 1, p. 338, New York, McGraw-Hill Book Company, Inc., 1956.

133. Mattraw, H. C., *J. Phys. Chem.*, **59**, 93 (1955).

134. Montagne, R., and Meney, L., "Coextrusion Applied to the Fabrication of Solid or Disperse Fuel Elements," in "Fuel Elements Conference, Paris, Nov. 18–23, 1957," *U.S.*

Atomic Energy Comm., Rept. No. TID-7546, Book 1, p. 142, 1958.

135. Mulford, R. N. R., Ellinger, F. H., and Zachariasen, W. H., *J. Am. Chem. Soc.,* **76,** 297 (1954).

136. Murray, P., Pugh, S. F., and Williams, J., "Uranium Dioxide as a Reactor Fuel," in "Fuel Elements Conference, Paris, Nov. 18–23, 1957," *U.S. Atomic Energy Comm., Rept. No. TID-7546,* Book 1, p. 432, 1958.

136a. Nelson, H. W., and Carmichael, R. L., *U.S. Atomic Energy Comm., Rept. No. TID-8203* (1960).

137. Newton, A. S., *U.S. Atomic Energy Comm., Rept. No. MDDC-724* (Jan. 1, 1947).

138. Padden, T. R., and Cain, F., *U.S. Atomic Energy Comm., Rept. No. WAPD-83* (Del.), Westinghouse Atomic Power Division (1953).

139. Palache, C., *et al.,* "Dana's System of Mineralogy," 7th Ed., Vols. 1 and 2, New York, John Wiley & Sons, Inc., 1951.

140. Paprocki, S. J., and Saller, H. A., *U.S. Atomic Energy Comm., Rept. No. BMI-753,* Battelle Memorial Institute (1952).

141. Pearlman, H., "Corrosion of Uranium, Thorium, and Uranium Alloys in Sodium and Organics," in "Fuel Elements Conference, Paris, Nov. 18–23, 1957," *U.S. Atomic Energy Comm., Rept. No. TID-7546,* Book 1, p. 565, 1958.

142. Péligot, E., *Ann. Chem. Phys. (3),* **5,** 5 (1842).

143. Péligot, E., *J. prakt. Chem.,* **24,** 442 (1841).

143a. Placek, C., and North, E. D., *Ind. Eng. Chem.,* **52,** 458 (1960).

144. Price, H. L., "Declassification of Typical Analyses for Normal Uranium Metal," Director, Division of Civilian Application, U.S. Atomic Energy Commission, Memorandum of July 19, 1957.

145. "Progress Report on Metallurgy of Tubaloy," to University of Chicago from Battelle Memorial Institute, *Rept. No. CT-1795,* p. 159 (June 1, 1944).

146. Pugh, S. F., "Radiation Damage in Fissile Materials," in "Progress in Nuclear Energy, Series 5, Metallurgy and Fuels," H. M. Finniston, and J. P. Howe (Eds.), p. 652, New York, McGraw-Hill Book Company, Inc., 1956.

147. Rankama, K., and Sahama, T. G., "Geochemistry," Chicago, University of Chicago Press, 1950.

148. Rentschler, H. C., and Marden, J. W., U.S. Patent 1,625,427 (1927).

149. Rich, M. N., U.S. Patent 1,738,669 (Dec. 10, 1929).

150. Rodden, C. J. (Ed.), "Analytical Chemistry of the Manhattan Project," National Nuclear Energy Series, Div. 8, Vol. 1, New York, McGraw-Hill Book Company, Inc., 1950.

151. Roth, H. P., *U.S. Atomic Energy Comm., Rept. No. MIT-1105,* Massachusetts Institute of Technology (1952).

152. Rough, F. A., and Bauer, A. A., *U.S. Atomic Energy Comm., Rept. No. BMI-1300,* Battelle Memorial Institute (1958).

153. Rough, F. A., and Bauer, A. A., *ibid.,* p. 17.

154. Rough, F. A., and Bauer, A. A., *ibid.,* p. 19.

155. Rough, F. A., and Bauer, A. A., *ibid.,* p. 30.

156. Rough, F. A., and Bauer, A. A., *ibid.,* p. 49.

157. Rough, F. A., and Bauer, A. A., *ibid.,* p. 75.

157a. Rough, F. A., and Dickerson, R. F., *Nucleonics,* **18,** No. 3, 74 (1960).

158. Saller, H. A., *Geneva Conference Paper P/562,* 9, 214 (1955).

159. Schulz, W. W., Scott, F. A., and Voiland, E. E., *U.S. Atomic Energy Comm., Rept. No. HW-32410,* Hanford Atomic Products Operation (1954).

160. Schwarzkopf, P., and Kieffer, R., "Refractory Hard Metals," New York, The Macmillan Company, 1953.

161. Schwarzkopf, P., and Kieffer, R., *ibid.,* p. 165.

162. Schwarzkopf, P., and Kieffer, R., *ibid.,* p. 309.

163. Schwarzkopf, P., and Kieffer, R., *ibid.,* p. 344.

164. Shober, F. R., Marsh, L. L., and Manning, G. K., *U.S. Atomic Energy Comm., Rept. No. BMI-1036,* Battelle Memorial Institute (1955).

164a. Smith, R. B., *U.S. Atomic Energy Comm., Rept. No. TID-8011* (1956).

165. Smyth, H. D., "A General Account of the Development of Methods of Using Atomic Energy for Military Purposes Under the Auspices of the United States Government, 1940–1945," p. 67, Washington, D.C., Government Printing Office, 1945.

166. Smyth, H. D., *ibid.,* p. 112.

166a. Strassa, A., *Nuclear Eng.,* **5,** 353 (1960).

167. Taub, J. M., Doll, D. T., and Hanks, G. S., "Cold Working of Uranium," in "Nuclear Metallurgy," Vol. 4, p. 95, New York, Institute of Metals Division, The Metallurgical Society, American Institute of Mining, Metallurgical, and Petroleum Engineers, 1957.

168. Troutner, V. H., *U.S. Atomic Energy Comm., Rept. No. HW-58146,* Hanford Atomic Products Operation (1958).

169. Trzebiatowski, W., Sliwa, A., and Stalinski, B., *Roczniki Chem.,* **28,** 12 (1954); *C.A.,* **48,** 11131a (1954).

170. van Arkel, A. E., "Reine Metalle," Berlin, Verlag Julius Springer, 1939; Ann Arbor, Mich., Edwards Bros., Inc., 1943.

171. Warf, J. C., "Some Reactions of Uranium Metal," *U.S. Atomic Energy Comm., Report MDDC-1391*, declassified Oct. 9, 1947.

172. Warner, R. K., *Australian J. Appl. Sci.,* **4,** 581 (1953).

173. Wilhelm, H. A., *Geneva Conference Paper P 817,* **8,** 162 (1956).

174. Wilhelm, H. A., *J. Chem. Ed.,* **37,** 56 (1960).

175. Wilhelm, H. A., *Metal Progr.,* **69,** 81 (1956).

176. Wilkinson, W. D., and Murphy, W. F., "Nuclear Reactor Metallurgy," Chap. 7, Princeton, N.J., D. Van Nostrand Company, Inc., 1958.

177. Wilkinson, W. D., and Murphy, W. F., *ibid.,* Chaps. 9 and 10.

178. Wilkinson, W. D., and Murphy, W. F., *ibid.,* Chap. 11.

179. Wilkinson, W. D., and Murphy, W. F., *ibid.,* p. 21.

180. Zachariasen, W. H., *Acta Cryst.,* **2,** 94 (1949).

181. Zambrow, J. L., "Powder Metallurgy of Uranium and Uranium Alloys," in "Nuclear Metallurgy," Vol. 4, p. 117, New York, Institute of Metals Division, The Metallurgical Society, American Institute of Mining, Metallurgical, and Petroleum Engineers, 1957.

32. VANADIUM

H. E. Dunn and D. L. Edlund

Vanadium Corporation of America
New York, New York

INTRODUCTION

Vanadium was discovered in the year 1801 by Manuel del Rio, Professor of Mineralogy at the School of Mines, Mexico City, in lead ore from Zamapan in the State of Hidalgo, and named "erythronium" by him, because of the property of its salts of becoming red when heated with acids. In 1805 a French chemist, Collet-Descostils, declared that erythronium was nothing but impure chromium, which statement was accepted by the discoverer. In 1830 Sefström found what he thought was an unrecognized metal in the iron ores of Taberg, Sweden, and named it "vanadium," in honor of the Scandinavian goddess Vanadis, because of its beautiful multicolored compounds. Wöhler, in 1830, demonstrated that erythronium and vanadium were the same element.

In 1831 Berzelius published a description of the compounds, but the chemistry of the metal was not thoroughly worked out until Roscoe made extensive studies of vanadium and its compounds in the 1860's, placing it properly in the fifth periodic group with phosphorus.

Roscoe's silvery-white powder, first produced in 1867 by hydrogen reduction of the chloride, VCl_2, was probably the first nearly pure vanadium metal. Efforts of other workers, notably Moissan, Helouis, Goldschmidt, Weiss and Aichel, Prandtl and Bleyer, and Ruff and Martin, to produce the pure metal by electro-thermic carbon reduction or aluminothermic reduction of vanadium pentoxide or trioxide, during the interim until 1920, were not successful, in that the metal product always contained either substantial residual quantities of the re-ducer or lower oxides of vanadium, and physical properties of the pure metal were derived by extrapolating a diminishing series to zero per cent impurity after the manner of Ruff and Martin. Thus, Weiss and Aichel, who reduced the pentoxide with misch-metal in 1904 to obtain a 10-g regulus of silvery-white rhombohedral crystals of a hardness of 7, were inadvertently led to place vanadium in Periodic Group VA, with arsenic, antimony, and bismuth, rather than in Group VB where it stands currently with columbium and tantalum. It is now known to be likewise a ductile metal when of high purity, 99.0+ per cent, although recently revised periodic charts are currently extant that include Group VB under "brittle, heavy metals."

In 1923 Hunter and Jones reduced vanadium trichloride with sodium in a steel bomb, obtaining a fine gray powder analyzing 99.5 to 100 per cent vanadium, but no coherent grains were formed that could well be utilized in physical research.

In order to stimulate such research, the major producer of master alloys of vanadium began, about this time, to distribute free or at nominal charge 100-g reguli of 95 per cent vanadium metal containing impurities of the order of 0.45 per cent carbon, 0.19 per cent silicon, 0.06 per cent iron, 1.00 per cent maximum aluminum, with the balance as oxygen. From these brittle metal buttons, produced by aluminothermic reduction of pure vanadium tetroxide with high-purity aluminum, such research tools as x-ray targets and electrode tips could be fashioned.

In 1927 Marden and Rich[13] announced the

629

production of 99.3 to 99.8 per cent vanadium metal in the form of ductile globules or shot, $\frac{3}{8}$ in. and smaller in diameter, by means of the reaction

$$V_2O_5 + 5Ca + 5CaCl_2 \rightarrow 2V + 5CaO \cdot 5CaCl_2$$

conducted in a heated steel bomb at 900–950°C (1652–1742°F) for 1 hr, thus providing, for the first time, metal of very high purity in a ductile form which could be worked and shaped in sufficient quantities to determine its physical properties, and, moreover, finally proving that the metal is not like arsenic or bismuth but resembles tantalum.

Though Van Arkel[23] produced metal of slightly higher purity by thermal decomposition of the iodide, the method was not practical, and for the next two decades the process of Marden and Rich[13] was the source of the few hundred grams of metal produced annually.

OCCURRENCE

The real impetus to the commercial development of the vanadium alloy industry came as a consequence of the metallurgical investigations of Choubley (1896), Helouis (1897), Arnold (1900), and Guillet (1904). In 1896 the Firminy Steel Works in France made three armor plates in which vanadium was used, which showed striking superiority over plates without vanadium. In 1900 Arnold at Sheffield made a series of tests to investigate the effect of vanadium on plain carbon tool steels, finding remarkable improvement in physical properties, but there was still no adequate supply of vanadium in sight.

At this critical time (1905) Riza Patron, a prospector, discovered the first really large deposit of rich vanadium ore in the Peruvian Andes, at an altitude of 16,000 ft, which was to place the hitherto rare or semirare metal within the reach of commercial manufacture, and to furnish the bulk of world requirements for many years.

Vanadium has been found by geologists, mineralogists, and geochemists to be one of the more abundant trace elements, ranking twenty-second among the elements in the earth's crust, but, although widely spread in minute quantities, it is found in few places sufficiently concentrated to be economically mined and processed for use. Data on 47 minerals are

given in the Appendix (Tables 32.13 and 32.14).

Most rocks and meteorites carry from a trace to a few hundredths of a per cent expressed usually as vanadium pentoxide, V_2O_5. Coal ash may carry a similar order of content, and petroleum ash from some sources carries sufficient to warrant processing for recovery of vanadium. Likewise, the ash of certain asphaltites, notably those of Peru and Argentina, warrant processing where utilization of the fuel value of the raw materials can be realized economically.

Magnetite iron ores may carry upwards of 1.0 per cent vanadium pentoxide and, where necessity dictates, blast furnace, converter, and/or open hearth furnace operations may be so integrated as to concentrate the vanadium in a type of slag amenable to vanadium extractive processes.

Ilmenite and other titanium minerals commonly carry 0.1 to 0.3 per cent vanadium pentoxide which is currently being removed as impurity residues in processing such mineral concentrates for production of titanium dioxide pigments and pure titanium metal.

The phosphate rocks of Idaho and Montana contain from 0.11 to 0.45 per cent vanadium pentoxide, which has for some years been separated as an impurity residue and recovered as vanadium pentoxide in the sulfuric acid process for manufacture of phosphoric acid and phosphate fertilizers.

Mineralogy

More than 65 vanadium minerals have been identified, but only 5 original primary minerals are known.

Primary Minerals. PATRONITE. Patronite ($V_2S_5 + nS$) is found only at Mina Ragra, Peru, where it has formed the largest known vanadium deposit. It is a greenish-black, amorphous mineral, usually carrying some iron, nickel, molybdenum, phosphorus, and carbon.

BRAVOITE. In bravoite, $(Fe,Ni)S_2$, cobalt or vanadium substitutes for nickel and iron. As found in small quantities in Mina Ragra, it occurs in brassy cubes of metallic luster carrying 25 per cent iron, 15 per cent nickel, 5 per cent vanadium, and 45 per cent sulfur.

SULVANITE. Sulvanite, $3Cu_2S \cdot V_2S_5$, a bronze-yellow, crystalline sulfide found only in small quantities in Burra, South Australia, and in

TABLE 32.1. X-RAY CHARACTERISTICS OF VANADIUM OXIDES[6]

Compound	System, type of structure	Space group	Lattice constants	Molecule per unit cell
V_2O_2	Cub,NaCl		4.08	4
V_2O_3	Hex.,Fe_2O_3	D_{3d}^6	5.43 α, 53°53'	2
VO_2	Tet.,SnO_2	D_{4th}^{14}	4.54, —, 2.88	2
V_2O_5	—		11.48, 4.36, 3.55	2

Utah. It contains 51 per cent copper, 14 per cent vanadium, and 35 per cent sulfur.

DAVIDITE. Davidite is a titanium-iron mineral from Mt. Painter, South Australia, carrying some vanadium.

ROSCOELITE. Roscoelite, $2K_2O \cdot 2Al_2O_3(Mg, Fe)O \cdot 3V_2O_5 \cdot 10SiO_2 \cdot 4H_2O$, is a vanadium-bearing mica found as a vein mineral in a number of rich gold-bearing veins; it occurs in important quantity as a secondary mineral in the sandstones of Colorado and Utah. It carries 20 per cent V_2O_5, 7.5 per cent K_2O, 14 per cent Al_2O_3, 2 per cent MgO, 1.5 per cent FeO, and 47.5 per cent SiO_2.

Other Minerals. All other known vanadium minerals are products of the oxidizing zone of the upper lithosphere and may be classified as follows:

Metallic veins of Mexico, New Mexico, Arizona, Nevada, Argentina, Spain, Turkestan, and Rhodesia:

Vanadinite $[Pb_4(VO_4)_3 \cdot PbCl]$
Descloizite $[4(Zn,Cu,Pb)O \cdot V_2O_5 \cdot H_2O]$
Cuprodescloizite $[4(Cu,Zn,Pb)O \cdot (V,As)_2O_5 \cdot H_2O]$
Mottramite $[4(Cu,Zn,Pb)O \cdot V_2O_5 \cdot H_2O]$
Endlichite $[Pb_4(V,AsO_4)_3 \cdot PbCl]$
Psittacinite $[4(Pb,Cu)O \cdot V_2O_5 \cdot 2H_2O]$

Patronite deposit of Peru:
Hewettite $(CaO \cdot 3V_2O_5 \cdot 9H_2O)$
Melanovanadite $(2CaO \cdot 2V_2O_4 \cdot 3V_2O_5)$
Minasragrite $(V_2O_4 \cdot 3SO_3 \cdot 16H_2O)$
Fernandinite $(CaO \cdot V_2O_4 \cdot 5V_2O_5 \cdot 14H_2O)$
Sincosite $(CaO \cdot V_2O_4 \cdot P_2O_5 \cdot 5H_2O)$
Pascoite $(2CaO \cdot 3V_2O_5 \cdot 11H_2O)$

Uranium-bearing sandstones of Colorado, Utah, and Arizona:
Carnotite $(K_2O \cdot 2UO_3 \cdot V_2O_5 \cdot 3H_2O)$
Uvanite $(2UO_3 \cdot 3V_2O_5 \cdot 15H_2O)$
Tyuyamunite $(CaO \cdot 2UO_3 \cdot V_2O_5 \cdot 4H_2O)$
Roscoelite $[2K_2O \cdot 2Al_2O_3(Mg,Fe)O \cdot 3V_2O_5 \cdot 10SiO_2 \cdot 4H_2O]$
Hewettite
Metahewettite $\Big\}$ $(CaO \cdot 3V_2O_5 \cdot 9H_2O)$

Vanoxite $(2V_2O_4 \cdot V_2O_5 \cdot 8H_2O)$
Volborthite $[6(Cu,Ca,Ba)O \cdot V_2O_5 \cdot 15H_2O]$
Fervanite $(2Fe_2O_3 \cdot 2V_2O_5 \cdot 5H_2O)$
Rossite $(CaO \cdot V_2O_5 \cdot 4H_2O)$

Fergana Valley (Central Asia) Siberia:
Tyuyamunite $(CaO \cdot 2UO_3 \cdot V_2O_5 \cdot 4H_2O)$
Alaite $(V_2O_5 \cdot H_2O)$
Ferghanite $(3UO \cdot V_2O_5 \cdot 6H_2O)$
Turanite $(5CuO \cdot V_2O_5 \cdot 2H_2O)$

The x-ray characteristics of four vanadium oxides are tabulated in Table 32.1.

ORE PROCESSING

The principal ores[8] of vanadium at the present time are roscoelite, mottramite, carnotite, and vanadinite; formerly, the major source was the patronite deposit of Mina Ragra, Peru. The vanadium is most generally extracted by roasting with common salt to convert it to water-soluble sodium vanadate, followed by a releach with dilute acids to obtain a combined extract which can be precipitated variously with sulfuric acid to obtain an oxide concentrate. This concentrate, when sufficiently pure to carry 80 per cent or better V_2O_5, is commercially known as "vanadium pentoxide," although it may carry sufficient sodium monoxide and/or calcium oxide to be actually a sodium and/or calcium hexavanadate. When such concentrates are redissolved in soda solution and maintained in the pentavalent state, the vanadium may be precipitated by the addition of ammonium chloride in the form of ammonium metavanadate, NH_4VO_3, a white crystalline powder of high purity. This, in turn, may be calcined to remove the ammonia and combined water to give a vanadium pentoxide of high purity suitable for reduction to vanadium metal.

The wide variety of vanadium minerals to be found even in a given ore body; the remote location of the major ore bodies, such as the patronite deposit in the high Andes of Peru;

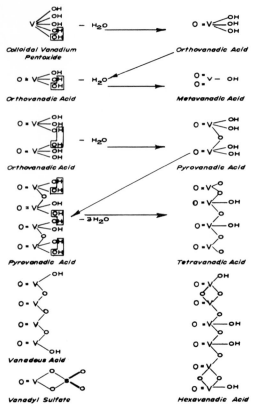

Figure 32.1. Typical structural formulas illustrating the interrelation of vanadium acids. From Alexander, Jerome, "Vanadium and Some of Its Industrial Applications," *J. Soc. Chem, Ind.*, **46**, 36-37 (1929).

the enormous number and complexity of the compounds of vanadium formed because of its ability (1) to exist in five states of valence, (2) to serve either as a metal or a nonmetal, (3) to form several radicals, and (4) to enter into a great variety of complex compounds by way of its poly acids, graphically shown by Figure 32.1—all these are major factors to be dealt with in the chemical and metallurgical processing of the ores (Figure 32.2) to provide the chemical compounds and ferroalloys or master alloys needed for industrial use as well as in the successful development of these applications.

DERIVATION

With the military demand for materials with unique physical and chemical properties and as a result of the accelerated activity in the study

of neutron bombardment of pure metals, a great many attempts have been made to produce pure massive ductile vanadium. The currently used technique of reducing vanadium oxide with calcium to make pure vanadium was first reported by Gregory[7] and McKechnie and Seybolt[12] at an Electrochemical Society symposium on rare metals in 1950.

The Method of Gregory

Gregory[7] has modified the Marden and Rich[13] process by substituting vanadium trioxide for the pentoxide to control the heat of reaction at about 1900°C (3452°F), a little above the melting point of the metal, so that the product would be a metal powder rather than metal shot. The reaction, according to the equation

$$V_2O_3 + 3Ca \rightarrow 2V + 3CaO$$

with 1 molecule of calcium chloride and 3 molecules excess calcium, is thermally initiated at 1000°C (1832°F) under an argon atmosphere. The powder product, after leaching the slag, is fabricated by powder metallurgy into ductile rod, sheet, and wire, using a vacuum sintering furnace to prevent reaction with oxygen, nitrogen, and hydrogen. The typical analysis given for the sintered product is 99.7 to 99.8 per cent vanadium, 0.05 per cent calcium, 0.05 per cent carbon, 0.01 per cent iron, 0.1 to 0.25 per cent oxygen, and 0.01 to 0.015 per cent nitrogen.

The Method of McKechnie and Seybolt

Although the procedures of Marden and Rich,[13] Van Arkel,[23] and Gregory[7] are capable of producing high-purity metal, the limited capacity and the high cost of the product inherent in these methods have not been conducive to development of the metal on a broad scale. With the procedure of McKechnie and Seybolt,[12] massive ductile vanadium can be produced on a scale heretofore impossible, thereby removing vanadium metal from practically a laboratory curiosity to a metal of high industrial potential.

Whereas Gregory[7] modified the Marden and Rich type of reaction by substituting vanadium trioxide to control the heat of reaction, McKechnie and Seybolt[12] improved the energy relationships by substituting iodine for the cal-

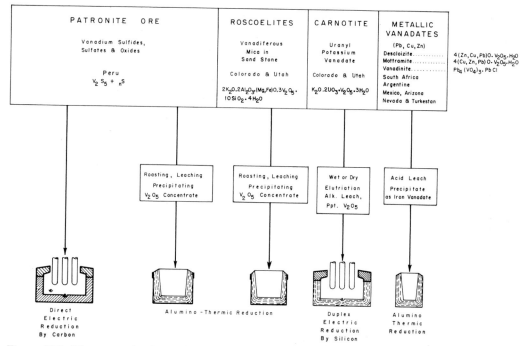

Figure 32.2. Diagrammatic chart of metallurgical processes used to convert vanadium ores to ferro-alloys and master alloys. From *Vancoram Rev.*, 1, 3 (1930).

TABLE 32.2. PURITY OF DUCTILE VANADIUM REGULI

V	Fe	Si	Ca	C	H₂	N₂	O₂
99.9	0.06	0.01	<0.005	0.24	0.002	0.05	0.089
99.1	<0.01	0.01	0.011	0.23			
99.0	<0.01	0.04	0.023	0.21	0.002	0.01	0.029
99.0	<0.01	0.0001	0.014	0.20	0.002	0.01	0.020
99.6	—	—	0.015	0.29			
99.8	—	—	0.022	0.15	0.010	0.02	0.070
99.5	—	—	0.016	0.21	0.003	0.005	0.029

cium chloride on the basis of 0.1 mole of iodine for every mole of vanadium produced. According to McKechnie and Seybolt,[12] the iodine combines with calcium at about 425°C (797°F) to form calcium iodide with the release of about 100 kcal/mole which is sufficient to initiate the main reaction. The alteration in slag composition by the presence of calcium iodide permits the metal to collect as a solid regulus.

The reaction is carried out in a covered magnesite crucible fitted inside a steel bomb which is sealed by means of a copper gasket and a steel cover plate. The bomb is fired by heating in a high-frequency furnace. A typical bomb charge consists of 300 g vanadium pentoxide, 552 g calcium, and 150 g iodine. This corre-

sponds to 60 per cent excess calcium and 0.2 mole of iodine for each 2 molecules of vanadium. The average yield from this mix is about 125 g of vanadium, or 74 per cent of the theoretical yield. The purity of the metal produced under these conditions is shown in Table 32.2.

PRODUCTION AND ECONOMIC STATISTICS

Ductile vanadium metal is being regularly produced by Union Carbide Metals Co. and by Vanadium Corporation of America by the calcium-iodine or modified calcium-iodine method in quantities of hundreds of pounds per day, and is available in reguli, ingots up to about 6-in. diameter, and wrought shapes. The range in chemical composition of the as-reduced metal is

V	C	Fe	Si about	Ni about	Cr about	O_2	N_2	H_2
99.6+	0.02/0.10	0.01/0.08	0.01	0.01	0.01	0.04/0.15	0.02/0.06	0.002/0.006

After remelting to ingot form, the metal will usually analyze 99.8+ per cent vanadium.

At the present time, pure, as-reduced vanadium metal is selling for $30 to $50/lb, depending upon size and quantity. Although the present price of $30 to $50/lb is in sharp contrast to the $1,800/lb obtained as late as 1950 for the metal produced by the Marden and Rich process, the current price is still relatively high as compared with other pure commercially available metals. Though lower costs can possibly be obtained by producing the metal in larger units, the price of the metal must necessarily remain high as long as expensive raw materials and close supervision are required for its production. It seems likely, therefore, that,

whatever its application in the engineering field, its cost will have to be justified by its unique properties.

PHYSICAL PROPERTIES

All the known physical properties of pure vanadium are listed in Table 32.3. The mechanical properties available at this time are tensile and hardness data for both the hot rolled and annealed, and the cold rolled states; short time elevated temperature strength; and transition from ductile to brittle fracture as measured by notched bar impact tests. Typical values for these mechanical properties are shown in Tables 32.4 to 32.10. The corrosion resistant properties

TABLE 32.3 PHYSICAL PROPERTIES OF VANADIUM METAL
(Superscript numbers refer to references)

Atomic number	23[21]
Atomic weight	50.95[21]
Reported isotopes	46, 47, 48, 49, 50, 51, 52, 53, 54[21, 22]
Crystal structure (to 1550° ± 10°C) (2822°F)	Body-centered cubic[19]
Lattice constant	3.034 Å[21]
Density (g/cc)	6.11[17]
Melting point	1900° ± 25°C (3452°F), 1919 ± 2°C (3486°F)[14]
Boiling point	3000°C (5432°F)[21]
Vapor pressure [1393–1609°C (2539–2928°F)]	$R \ln p = 121.95 \times 10^3 T^{-1} -$ $5.123 \times 10^{-4}T + 36.29^5$ R = gas constant (cal mol^{-1} deg^{-1}) p = pressure in atmosphere $\ln$ = logarithm to base e T = absolute temperature (°K)
Volatility at melting point	Very low[13]
Specific heat [20–100°C (68–212°F)] (cal/g)	0.120[13]
Latent heat of fusion	4 kcal/mole[16]
Latent heat of vaporization	106 kcal/mole[16]
Enthalpy [25°C (77°F)] (kcal/mole)	1.26[16]
Entropy [25°C (77°F)] (cal/mole/°C)	7.05[16]
Thermal conductivity (cal/sq cm/°C/cm)	
100°C (212°F)	0.074[18]
500°C (932°F)	0.088[18]
700°C (1292°F)	0.084[24]
Electrical resistance [20°C (68°F)] (microhm-cm)	24.8[17]
30.6°C (87°F)	25.2[3]
58.9°C (138°F)	27.4[3]
Temperature coefficient of resistance (microhm-cm/°C)	
0–100°C (32–212°F)	0.0034[17]
0–200°C (32–392°F)	0.0033[17]

TABLE 32.3. PHYSICAL PROPERTIES OF VANADIUM METAL (*cont.*)
(Superscript numbers refer to references)

Thermal emf versus platinum cold junction [0°C (32°F)] (mv)	
100°C (212°F)	0.63[3]
200°C (392°F)	1.56
400°C (752°F)	3.97
700°C (1292°F)	9.26
900°C (1652°F)	13.97
1000°C (1832°F)	16.71
Magnetic susceptibility	1.4×10^{-6} (cgs)[21]
Superconductive transition temperature	5.13°K[25]
Coefficient of linear thermal expansion	$9.7 \pm 0.3 \times 10^{-6}$/°C x-ray (20–720°C) (68–1328°F)[18] 8.95×10^{-6}/°C dilatometer (200–1000°C) (392–1832°F)
Thermal expansion (μ in./in./°C)	
23–100°C (73–212°F)	8.3[17]
23–500°C (73–932°F)	9.6[17]
23–900°C (73–1652°F)	10.4[17]
23–1100°C (73–2012°F)	10.9[17]
Recrystallization temperature	700–800°C (1292–1472°F) (for 70% cold-rolled sheet)[18]
Modulus of elasticity	18 to 19×10^6 psi[14, 17]
Shear modulus	6.73×10^6 psi[10]
Poisson ratio	0.36[10]
Thermal neutron-absorption cross section (barns/atom)	4.98 ± 0.02[16]

of high-purity vanadium are shown in Table 32.11. A few of the properties which may influence the further utility of the metal are discussed below.

Crystal Structure

From room temperature to 1550° ± 10°C (2822°F) the crystal structure of vanadium is body-centered cubic. At 1550°C, Seybolt and Sumsion[19] have found evidence for a polymorphic transformation, but as yet they have no information on the structure of the new phase.

Recrystallization Temperature

The recrystallization temperature for vanadium has been reported by Seybolt[18] to be 700–800°C (1292–1472°F) for 70 per cent cold rolled sheet.

Density and Modulus of Elasticity

The density of vanadium is 6.11 g/cc and its modulus of elasticity is 18 to 19×10^6 psi. This combination of density and modulus of elasticity indicates that vanadium could be used as a structural material.

Electrical Properties

At room temperature the resistivity of vanadium is 24.8 microhm-cm, and the temperature coefficient of resistance from 0–200°C (32–392°F) is 0.0033 microhm-cm/°C. This value of resistivity is considerably higher than the resistivity of copper or aluminum; conversely, the conductivity of vanadium is much lower than that of copper or aluminum. Vanadium metal is a poor conductor of a magnetic flux, its magnetic susceptibility being 1.4×10^{-6} cgs units.

Thermal Properties

Compared to other metals, vanadium is a poor conductor of heat, its thermal conductivity being 0.074 to 0.088 cal/sq cm/cm/°C/sec between 100–500°C (212–932°F). The value of this property [in the same units at 20°C (68°F)] for iron is 0.18 and for copper is 0.94. The specific heat of vanadium from 20–100°C (68–212°F) is 0.120 cal/g/°C. Vanadium's

TABLE 32.4. TENSILE PROPERTIES OF HOT OR COLD WORKED AND ANNEALED VANADIUM METAL

Composition (%)				Condition	Yield strength (drop of beam) (psi)	Tensile strength (psi)	Elongation (% in 1 in.)	Reduction of area (%)	Hardness (Rockwell)	Reference
C	O	H	N							
0.024	<0.010	0.001	0.005	a	13200(c)	28700	38.3	95.0	A21	11
0.08	0.015	0.006	0.02	b	23000(c)	37600	33.7	36.7	A38	11
0.05	0.08	0.008	0.04	d	42000	55000	32	72	B71	2
0.07	0.08	0.004	0.04	d	63000	69600	32	66	B78	2
0.09	0.06	0.006	0.04	d	56000	63600	36	68	B75	2
0.06	0.08	0.004	0.05	d	52000	60300	34	69	B79	2
0.06	0.10	0.005	0.05	d	64000	66400	38	82	B81	2
0.10	0.09	0.007	0.07	d	64000	74600	26	68	B77	2
0.047	0.07	0.0043	0.052	e	55400(c)	68000	34	68	—	4
0.045	0.048	0.0028	0.047	e	43000(c)	83400	24	50	—	4
0.13	0.045	0.0043	0.0072	f	47800(i)	56000	44.5	78.5	—	10
0.17	0.031	0.0021	0.026	g	55100(i)	61700	37.0	79.0	—	10
0.075	0.032	0.0025	0.0009	h	48600(i)	58400	33.0	80.5	—	10

(a) ¾-in.-diameter arc welded iodide vanadium ingot cold swaged to 7/16-in.-diameter 1100°C (2012°F), 48 hr, furnace cool.

(b) Arc welded calcium reduced vanadium ingot rolled at 400°C (752°F) to 45% reduction + 900°C (1652°F), 5 hr, furnace cool.

(c) 0.2% offset.

(d) Calcium reduced vanadium hot rolled from 2-in.-square ingot + 800°C (1472°F), ½ hr, furnace cool.

(e) Arc welded calcium reduced vanadium ingot (2-in.-square, hot-worked + 800°C (1472°F) furnace cool.

(f) Hot extruded 1100–1150°C (2012–2100°F), cold swaged 63%, anneal for 1 hr at 900–950°C (1650–1740°F).

(g) Same as (f) except 50% cold swaging.

(h) Same as (f) except 47% cold swaging.

(i) Upper yield point.

TABLE 32.5. EFFECT OF ANNEALING TEMPERATURE ON TENSILE STRENGTH AND DUCTILITY OF COLD ROLLED AND ANNEALED VANADIUM METAL[2]

Thickness of strip (in.)	Composition (%)				Condition	Tensile strength (psi)	% elongation in 2 in.
	C	O	H	N			
0.06	0.14	0.15	0.001	0.08	A	112,900	5.0
	"	"	"	"	B	103,500	14.5
	"	"	"	"	C	76,400	25.0
	"	"	"	"	D	71,900	28.0
0.025	0.12	0.10	0.003	0.13	B	102,500	8.0
	"	"	"	"	C	78,700	22.0
	"	"	"	"	D	74,500	24.0
0.014	"	"	"	"	B	111,200	4.0
	"	"	"	"	C	70,700	22.0
	"	"	"	"	D	67,800	24.0

A = As cold rolled 75%.

B = Cold rolled and heated in vacuum 15 min at 600°C (1112°F).

C = Cold rolled and heated in vacuum 15 min at 800°C (1472°F).

D = Cold rolled and heated in vacuum 15 min at 915°C (1679°F).

linear coefficient of thermal expansion is low for a metal, being 8.95×10^{-6} in./in./°C from 200–1000°C (392–1832°F). The value of this property [in the same units at 20°C (68°F)] for iron is 11.7 and for copper is 16.5.

Mechanical Properties

The mechanical properties of commercially pure (unalloyed, calcium reduced) ductile vanadium are materially influenced by variations in interstitial nonmetallic elements such as oxygen, nitrogen, hydrogen, and carbon. The higher interstitial content of the calcium reduced metal produces about double the tensile strength of the iodide metal in the annealed condition. This is shown in the tensile and hardness data of Table 32.4 for several heats of hot or cold worked and annealed or homogenized vanadium. The total oxygen and nitrogen contents should not exceed about 0.25 per cent if a hot or cold workable metal is required; however, for commercial satisfactory processing, this content should be held below 0.15 per cent.

Vanadium work hardens to a minor degree and has a very high capacity to withstand cold reduction without intermediate annealing. It is not unusual to cold work over 90 per cent without intermediate annealing. Table 32.5 lists the tensile strength and elongation values for several heats after cold rolling and annealing, at various temperatures.

Metallographic examination of these strips (75 per cent cold work) showed that recrystallization took place at 800°C (1472°F). Vanadium metal recrystallizes at temperature of about 800–1000°C (1472–1832°F), depending upon the degree of cold work.

Since vanadium has a strong tendency to react with oxygen and nitrogen, elevated temperature tests must be made in an inert atmosphere. The results of elevated temperature tensile tests made in a helium atmosphere are shown in Table 32.6. Brown[2] calls attention to the fact that the data show a slight increase in strength up to 400°C (752°F). The author also points out that up to 600°C (1112°F) the strength of vanadium is slightly higher than the strength generally ascribed to Type 304 stainless steel over the same temperature range. From 600–1000°C (1112–1832°F), the strength of vanadium is about the same as Type 304.

Loomis and Carlson[11] have investigated the brittle-ductile transition temperature range of unalloyed vanadium by tension tests on iodide vanadium (carbon 0.024, nitrogen 0.005, oxygen <0.010, hydrogen 0.001, chromium, iron, silicon <0.02) and calcium reduced vanadium (carbon 0.08, nitrogen 0.02, oxygen 0.015, hydrogen 0.006, and chromium, iron, silicon <0.02) at test temperatures of 20 to −179°C (68 to −290°F) and reported −110°C (−166°F) for the former and −65°C (−85°F) for the latter heats of vanadium. The data are given in Table 32.7.

The effect of deliberate additions of hydrogen, oxygen, nitrogen, or carbon on the ductile-brittle transition of vanadium has been reported by Loomis and Carlson[11] as the result of tensile or bend (0.25 in. by 0.375 in. by 2.25 in. tested on 2-in. span) tests and is given in Table 32.8.

Clough and Pavlovic[4] have likewise reported tension (0.200 to 0.252 in. diameter by 1-in. gauge) and Charpy (standard V notch) tests on two lots of calcium-reduced vanadium ingots [2-in.-square ingots hot worked and annealed at 800°C (1472°F) in argon atmosphere] to determine the brittle-ductile transition temperature. The results are shown in Tables 32.9 and 32.10.

TABLE 32.6. ELEVATED TEMPERATURE TENSILE TEST DATA AS HOT ROLLED VANADIUM METAL*

Composition (%)					Tensile strength (psi)	% Elongation in 1 in.	% Reduction in area
C	O	H	N	Test temperature			
0.062	0.085	0.0068	0.11	22°C (72°F)	91,200	22	48
				400°C (752°F)	99,200	19	58
				600°C (1112°F)	40,000	38	87
				800°C (1472°F)	23,100	36	89
				1000°C (1832°F)	7,120	50	99+

* Tests conducted in atmosphere of helium.

TABLE 32.7. TENSILE PROPERTIES OF IODIDE AND CALCIUM REDUCED VANADIUM
AT ROOM AND LOW TEMPERATURES

Test temperature		Elongation in 1 in. (%)	Reduction of area (%)	Yield strength (0.2% offset) (psi)	Ultimate strength (psi)	Type fracture
°C	°F					
Iodide vanadium*						
20	68	38.3	95.0	13,200	28,700	Ductile
0	32	37.1	95.0	15,800	29,600	"
− 20	− 4	38.7	95.0	21,000	32,000	"
− 40	− 40	35.2	95.0	16,300	29,500	"
− 60	− 76	32.9	95.0	21,300	35,900	"
− 80	−112	38.6	95.0	19,800	36,400	"
−100	−148	39.2	95.0	25,000	40,700	"
−110	−166	23.0	18.8	39,200	43,400	Semiductile
−120	−184	2.0	8.7	30,700	58,700	Cleavage
−140	−220	4.2	14.9	38,900	59,400	"
−150	−238	13.4	18.8	55,700	61,200	Semiductile
−179	−290	17.4	30.2	58,100	62,700	"
Calcium reduced vanadium†						
22	72	35.3	51.0	23,000	37,600	Ductile
− 32	− 26	33.7	36.7	27,000	49,900	"
− 55	− 67	34.4	26.3	28,100	49,700	"
− 71	− 96	2.9	1.2	23,000	45,500	Cleavage
− 90	−130	1.7	1.6	31,000	51,300	"
−105	−155	2.4	3.2	54,500	61,100	"
−132	−206	1.3	0.8	—	66,900	"

* ¾-in.-diameter ingots, swaged to ⁷⁄₁₆-in.-diameter and recrystallized at 1100°C (2012°F), 48 hr, in vacuum—Rockwell A21.

† 400-g ingots warm rolled [at 400°C (752°F)] 45%, recrystallized in vacuum furnace at 900°C (1652°F) for 5 hr—Rockwell A38.

TABLE 32.8. THE EFFECTS OF HYDROGEN, OXYGEN, NITROGEN, AND CARBON
ON THE DUCTILE-BRITTLE TRANSITION OF VANADIUM METAL

Type metal	Transition temperature		Type test	Rockwell A
	°C	°F		
Iodide vanadium + 0.001% hydrogen	−110	−148	Tensile	21
Calcium reduced vanadium + 0.006% hydrogen	− 70	− 94	Bend	38
Iodide vanadium + 0.010% hydrogen	23	73	Bend	
Iodide vanadium + 0.027% hydrogen	23	73	Bend	
Iodide vanadium + 0.010% oxygen	−110	−148	Tensile	21
Calcium reduced vanadium + 0.015% oxygen	− 70	− 94	Bend	38
Calcium reduced vanadium + 0.065% oxygen	− 40	− 40	Bend	45
Calcium reduced vanadium + 0.115% oxygen	− 25	− 13	Bend	46
Calcium reduced vanadium + 0.215% oxygen	105	221	Bend	55
Iodide vanadium + 0.005% nitrogen	−110	−148	Tensile	21
Calcium reduced vanadium + 0.021% nitrogen	− 70	− 94	Bend	38
Calcium reduced vanadium + 0.23% nitrogen	25	77	Bend	58
Calcium reduced vanadium + 0.44% nitrogen	315	599	Bend	68
Iodide vanadium + 0.024% carbon	−110	−148	Tensile	21
Calcium reduced vanadium + 0.09% carbon	− 70	− 94	Bend	38
Calcium reduced vanadium + 0.10% carbon	− 80	−112	Bend	43
Calcium reduced vanadium + 0.19% carbon	− 47	− 53	Bend	44
Calcium reduced vanadium + 0.29% carbon	− 45	− 49	Bend	42

TABLE 32.9. THE TRANSITION TEMPERATURE OF DUCTILE VANADIUM METAL
AS DETERMINED BY TENSILE TESTS

Bar number	Test temperature		Yield point (0.2% offset) (psi)	Ultimate strength (psi)	Elongation in 1 in. (%)	Reduction of area (%)
	°C	°F				
A	200	302	37,000	57,200	39	75
A	RT	RT	55,400	68,000	34	68
A	0	32	60,000	71,200	30	65
A	− 40	− 40	67,600	77,200	26	57
A	− 78	−108	79,000	85,600	20	45
A	−140	−220	110,000	114,000	8	18
A	−196	−321	178,000	178,000	0	0
B	RT	RT	43,000	59,600	40	74
B	− 78	−108	70,000	83,400	24	50

TABLE 32.10. TRANSITION TEMPERATURE OF DUCTILE VANADIUM AS DETERMINED BY CHARPY TESTS

Test temperature		Charpy (V notch) on Bar B, (ft-lb)
°C	°F	
150	302	207–215
140	284	207–215
135	275	207–215
130	266	17, 15, 215
125	257	15
100	212	12
30	86	12
− 80	−112	5

Chemical Composition		
	Bar Number	
	A	B
Carbon	0.047	0.045
Nitrogen	0.052	0.047
Oxygen	0.07	0.048
Hydrogen	0.0043	0.0028

The tension test indicates a transition temperature below about −78°C (−108.4°F) for bar No. A, and about 125°C (257°F) for bar No. B by V notch Charpy tests.

CHEMICAL PROPERTIES

The element vanadium, atomic number 23, currently stands vertically in Group VA of the periodic table with columbium and tantalum, while its atomic weight of 50.95 places it horizontally between titanium and chromium. Pearson[15] states that the reactivity of the element is a mean between that of titanium and chromium. Characteristically, it shares the property of both divisions of the active Group V in functioning in different valencies and forming basic as well as acid radicals, which includes the power of functioning as the central atom in polyacids, in common with most of the elements of Groups IV, V, VI, and VIII. The two subgroups resemble each other particularly in their chemical properties, with all elements of the group forming an oxide R_2O_5 which is strongly acidic in the cases of lower atomic weight but decreasing in acidity as atomic weight increases; thus, modern chemistry of aqueous solution teaches the following order of decreasing acidity: P_2O_5, SiO_2, MnO_3, Cr_2O_3, MoO_3, V_2O_5, WO_3, Cb_2O_5, Ta_2O_5, U_3O_8.

When the metal is heated in air, it is oxidized showing various colors—brownish-black V_2O_3, blue-black V_2O_4 and red to orange V_2O_5. When heated in chlorine at 180°C (356°F) it combines directly to form vanadium tetrachloride VCl_4, and at high temperature it combines directly with nitrogen to form vanadium nitride, VN, and with carbon to form vanadium carbide, VC. The metal is not soluble in hydrochloric acid or in dilute sulfuric acid, but it dissolves in nitric acid, hydrofluoric acid, and concentrated sulfuric acid. Solutions of alkalis have little action, but fused alkalis react readily to form water-soluble vanadates, liberating hydrogen.

Vanadium pentoxide or vanadic anhydride, V_2O_5, is the most important oxide from which nearly all vanadium compounds are derived. In its commercial form it normally ranges from 85 to 94 per cent vanadium pentoxide, with a sodium oxide content of 6 to 11 per cent, with 2 to 3 per cent of other impurities carried through from the ores, usually by alkaline and/ or acid extraction, and sulfuric acid precipitation by the following reaction:

$$6NaVO_3 + 2H_2SO_4 \rightarrow Na_2H_2V_6O_{17}$$

sodium metavanadate   sodium hexavanadate
(water soluble)   (precipitated at
                                 2 to 3 pH)

$$+ 2Na_2SO_4 + H_2O.$$

If conducted in stages, as e.g., according to U.S. Patent No. 2,551,733, formation of the complex sodium vanadate can be avoided, and vanadium pentoxide can be precipitated as follows:

$$6NaVO_3 + 3H_2SO_4 \rightarrow 3V_2O_5 + 3Na_2SO_4 + 3H_2O.$$

vanadium
pentoxide
(precipitated at
1 to 3 pH)

In its freshly precipitated condition, more properly termed sodium hexavanadate, it is readily redissolved by alkaline solutions from which it may be precipitated as ammonium metavanadate, NH_4VO_3, upon the addition of an excess of ammonium chloride, NH_4Cl. When filtered, washed, and carefully dried and calcined to remove the ammonia, a vanadium pentoxide of very high purity results. The reaction for the precipitation is as follows:

$$2NaVO_3 + 2NH_4Cl \rightarrow (NH_3)_2 \cdot H_2O \cdot V_2O_5 +$$
2NaCl or $2NH_4VO_3.$

(solubility 3% in cold water,
10% in boiling water)

The theoretical composition of ammonium metavanadate is

77.74% V_2O_5

14.56% NH_3

7.70% H_2O

By fusing vanadium pentoxide with molecular proportions of caustic soda, a series of water-soluble sodium vanadates can be made as follows:

(1) $V_2O_5 + 2NaOH \rightarrow 2NaVO_3 + H_2O$
sodium
metavanadate

(2) $V_2O_5 + 4NaOH \rightarrow Na_4V_2O_7 + 2H_2O$
sodium
pyrovanadate

(3) $V_2O_5 + 6NaOH \rightarrow 2Na_3VO_4 + 3H_2O$
sodium
orthovanadate

When vanadium pentoxide is treated with sulfuric acid while gassing with sulfur dioxide,

the following reaction occurs to produce vanadyl sulfate, which can be crystallized from solution in beautiful blue crystals:

$$V_2O_5 + H_2SO_4 + H_2O + SO_2 \rightarrow V_2O_2(SO_4)_2 + 2H_2O.$$

vanadyl sulfate

Application of this reaction, more often using ferrous ammonium sulfate as reducer, is made in the analytical determination of vanadium. The excess of reducer is then destroyed with ammonium persulfate, and the vanadyl sulfate is titrated with potassium permanganate, thus:

$$5V_2O_2(SO_4)_2 + 2KMnO_4 + 22H_2O \rightarrow 10H_3VO_4 + K_2SO_4 + 2MnSO_4 + 7H_2SO_4.$$

orthovanadic acid

Vanadium pentoxide can be chlorinated at red heat when mixed with carbon to give

$$V_2O_5 + 3C + 3Cl_2 \rightarrow 2VOCl_3 + 3CO.$$

vanadium
oxytrichloride
(BP 127.2°C) (261°F)

Vanadium acetate, citrate, linoleate, oleate, oxalate, palmitate, phenolate, resinate, and stearate are examples of vanadyl organic compounds that can be formed, while metal vanadates such as those of bismuth, cadmium, calcium, chromium, cobalt, copper, iron, lead, magnesium, manganese, molybdenum, nickel, potassium, silver, sodium, tin, and zinc have been produced for special purposes—mostly as catalysts or interprocess materials in purification of ore concentrates.

Corrosion Resistance

Table 32.11 lists the corrosion rate of vanadium metal in various corrodents. Kinzel[9] summarizes the general corrosion resistance of vanadium in this manner: the metal is highly resistant to reducing acids in moderate concentrations but is not resistant to oxidizing acids. Unalloyed vanadium is resistant to pitting and corrosion by salt spray and sea water.

Schlain, Kenahan, and Acherman[17a] have reported the corrosion of pure vanadium metal in simulated ocean water and in various concentrations of sulfuric, hydrochloric, and nitric acids. They have also given data on galvanic corrosion of vanadium metal in simulated ocean water when coupled and uncoupled with second metals such as stainless steel, copper, aluminum, magnesium, and SAE 4130. These data are sum-

TABLE 32.11. CORROSION RESISTANCE OF VANADIUM METAL

Corrodent*	Corrosion rate (inches penetration per month)		
	As-cast	As-rolled	Annealed†
10% hydrochloric acid, 70°C (158°F), aerated	—	0.00072	0.00073
20% hydrochloric acid, 70°C, aerated	0.0075	0.0056	0.0045
20% hydrochloric acid, 70°C, air free	—	0.0123	0.0055
37% hydrochloric acid, RT, nonaerated	—	0.0029	0.0026
10% sulfuric acid, 70°C, aerated	—	0.00065	0.00059
10% sulfuric acid, 70°C, air free	—	0.00036	0.00036
10% sulfuric acid, boiling	0.0048	0.0031	0.0036
85% phosphoric acid, boiling	—	Dissolved	Dissolved
Dilute or concentrated nitric acid, RT	Dissolved	Dissolved	Dissolved
5% ferric chloride + 10% sodium chloride, RT	—	0.072	0.075
20% sodium chloride, spray, RT	—	No effect	No effect
Sea water	—	—	0.00038
Sea water potential (against calomel half-cell)	—	—	0.21 volts
Industrial atmosphere	—	—	Some staining

* Aerated = air bubbled through solution.
Air free = nitrogen bubbled through solution.
Nonaerated = quiet solution, not saturated with either air or nitrogen.
† Annealed = as-rolled metal heated ½ hr at 900°C (1652°F) in vacuum.

TABLE 32.11A. CORROSION RESISTANCE OF VANADIUM METAL

Corrodent	Corrosion Rate (Mils per Year)		
	Air	Natural Aeration	Helium
Simulated ocean water, 35°C (95°F), 30 Days	0.2	0.4	0.0
Sulphuric acid, 1.0 N (4.8%), 35°C (95°F), 6 Days	0.6		0.6
Sulphuric acid, 3.1 N (13.9%), 35°C (95°F), 6 Days	1.2		1.1
Sulphuric acid, 17.8 N (58.8%), 35°C (95°F), 6 Days	3.9		3.9
Sulphuric acid, 17.8 N 35°C (95°F), 6 Days	3.0		3.2
Sulphuric acid, 17.8 N 35°C (95°F), 6 Days	4.5		4.4
Hydrochloric acid, 1.0 N (3.6%), 35°C (95°F), 6 Days	0.6		0.5
Hyldrochloric acid, 2.0 N (7.1%), 35°C (95°F), 6 Days	1.1		1.0
Hydrochloric acid, 6.1 N (20.2%), 35°C (95°F), 6 Days	5.5		5.5
Hydrochloric acid, 6.1 N 35°C (95°F), 6 Days	5.1		4.3
Hydrochloric acid, 6.1 N 35°C (95°F), 6 Days	4.8		5.8
Nitric acid, 0.5 N (3.1%), 35°C (95°F), 6 Days	1.0		0.8
Nitric acid, 2.0 N (11.8%), 35°C (95°F), 6 Days	2.7		18.6
Nitric acid, 3.0 N (17.2%), 35°C (95°F), 6 Days	98.0, 20.4		19, 4470
Nitric acid, 3.0 N 35°C (95°F), 6 Days	2270		2010
Nitric acid, 3.0 N 35°C (95°F), 6 Days	11, 40		1350

marized in Tables 32.11A and 32.11B. Vanadium is resistant to corrosion in (a) simulated ocean water at 35°C (95°F), and (b) 60 per cent sulfuric acid and 20 per cent hydrochloric acid at 35°C (95°F). Vanadium resists corrosion in 3 per cent nitric acid solution, corrodes slowly in 12 per cent acid, and corrodes very rapidly in 17 per cent acid. Vanadium is less noble than stainless steel and copper in simulated ocean water, and is more noble than aluminum, magnesium, and SAE 4130. Coupled with these metals, vanadium behaves as a sacrificial metal for copper, but is protected by aluminum, magnesium, and SAE 4130.

The available data on the liquid metal corrosion resistance of ductile vanadium are sum-

TABLE 32.11B. CORROSION OF VANADIUM METAL COUPLES IN SIMULATED OCEAN WATER, FLOW OF AIR, 35°C (95°F), 15 DAYS

Second metal	Anodic metal	Galvanic corrosion, MPY, (calc. from current)	Corrosion rate, Vanadium, MPY (based on weight loss)		Corrosion rate, second metal MPY (based on weight loss)	
			Coupled	Uncoupled	Coupled	Uncoupled
Stainless steel, Type 316		0.0	0.8	0.8	0.0	0.0
Stainless steel, Type 316		0.0	0.2	0.1	0.0	0.0
Copper	Vanadium	2.0	1.2	0.5	0.0	0.9
Copper	Vanadium	2.0	0.7	0.2	0.0	0.5
Aluminum	Aluminum	0.3	0.0	0.5	0.1	0.0
Steel, SAE 4130	Steel, SAE 4130	3.0	0.05	0.7	9.5	4.7
Magnesium	Magnesium	353	0.0	0.3	727	35.2
Magnesium	Magnesium	378	0.0	0.9	920	41.5

TABLE 32.12. CORROSION RESISTANCE OF VANADIUM TO LIQUID METALS

Liquid metal	Test temperature		Remarks	Reference
	°F	°C		
Sodium	932	500	Good resistance; corrosion rate of 0.2 mg/(sq cm) (mo)	16
55.5 Bismuth, 44.5 lead,	1200	649	Good resistance, static test, 500 hr	16
52 Bismuth, 32 lead, 16 tin	1200	649	Good resistance, static test, 500 hr	16
52.3 Bismuth, 21.9 indium, 25.8 lead	1200	649	Good resistance, static test, 500 hr	16
49.5 Bismuth, 11.6 tin, 17.6 lead, 21.3 indium	1200	649	Good resistance, static test, 500 hr	16
57.5 Bismuth, 25.2 indium, 17.3 tin	1200	649	Good resistance, static test, 500 hr	16
55.5 Bismuth, 44.5 lead	900	482	Dynamic test, 1008 hr; sample gained weight; generally good resistance	16
52 Bismuth, 32 lead, 16 tin	1200	649	Dynamic test, 1008 hr; 20 mg/(sq cm) (mo) attack	16
Sodium (Na_2O ?)	1135	613	Static test, satin-gray tarnish; −0.2 mg/(sq cm) (mo)	20
	1476	802	Static test, dull-gray tarnish; −1.3 mg/(sq cm) (mo)	20
Sodium (Na_2O, 0.001%)	1292	700	Static test for 288 hr; 0.10% gain weight; not attacked	20

marized in Table 32.12. The data indicate that vanadium has considerable promise as a container material.

FABRICATION

The metal button resulting from either the direct reduction of the vanadium oxides or from remelted vanadium metal is a suitable form from which working may begin. The exception to the utilization of the as-reduced metal would be a reduction technique which produced metal shot. Pure vanadium metal lends itself to common fabricating methods such as forging, rolling, extruding, swaging, drawing, bending, stamping, pressing, machining, and welding. Of course in hot working or welding pure vanadium, special precautions must be taken to prevent the reaction with and absorption of gases.

Remelting

The as-reduced metal button of vanadium metal may be remelted to produce an ingot, which is a more convenient starting form if the end product is to be bar, tube, wire, sheet, or foil. Vanadium can be remelted in a water-

Appendix

TABLE 32.13. DESCRIPTIVE MINERALOGY OF VANADIUM MINERALS[6]

Mineral	Location	Color	Texture	Associates
		SULFIDES		
1. Patronite (VS_4 or V_2S_5)*	Mina Ragra, Peru	Greenish-black	Massive with conchoidal fracture	Quisquesite, gypsum; alters to vanadates
2. Sulvanite ($3Cu_2S \cdot V_2S_5$)	Burra-Burra, South Australia; Utah	Bronze yellow	Massive and crystalline	
		OXIDES		
3. Doloresite ($3V_2O_4 \cdot 4H_2O$)	Southwestern Colorado	Reddish-brown	Very fine fragments	
4. Alaite ($V_2O_5 \cdot H_2O$)	Alai Mountains, Turkestan	Bluish-red	Mosslike masses	
5. Navajoite ($V_2O_5 \cdot 3H_2O$)	Monument Valley, Arizona	Dark brown	Soft, fibrous silky luster	In sandstone with tyuyamunite, rauvite, hewettite, steigerite, and limonite
6. Duttonite [$VO(OH)_2$]	Montrose, Colorado	Light brown	Vitreous luster	In sandstone with montrosite, paramontrosite, vanadiferous silicate, uraninite, and coffinite
7. Vanoxite ($2V_2O_4 \cdot V_2O_5 \cdot 8H_2O$)	Western Colorado; Arizona; New Mexico	Black to dark brown	Crystalline aggregates, dark-brown velvety coating	In sandstone, replaces sand grains and V mica, gypsum
8. Corvusite ($V_2O_4 \cdot 6V_2O_5 \cdot nH_2O$)	Western Colorado; Utah	Blue-black	Massive with conchoidal fracture	In sandstone with vanoxite, gypsum
		SULFATES		
9. Minasragrite ($V_2O_4 \cdot 3SO_3 \cdot 16H_2O$)	Mina Ragra, Peru	Blue	Granular aggregate and mammillary masses	Alteration product of patronite
		VANADATES		
10. Barnesite ($Na_2O \cdot 3V_2O_5 \cdot 3H_2O$)	Grand County, Utah	Deep red, brownish-red		
11. Steigerite ($Al_2V_2O_8 \cdot 6\frac{1}{2}H_2O$)	Gypsum Valley, Colorado	Yellow	Powder, waxy luster	With corvusite in fractures of sandstone
12. Brackebuschite [$2(Pb,Mn,Fe)O \cdot V_2O_5 \cdot H_2O$]	State of Cordoba, Argentina	Black		

TABLE 32.13. DESCRIPTIVE MINERALOGY OF VANADIUM MINERALS[6] (*cont.*)

Mineral	Location	Color	Texture	Associates
13. Cuprodescloizite† [4(Cu,Zn,Pb)O·(V,As)$_2$O$_5$·H$_2$O]	Rhodesia, Africa; Mexico; New Mexico; Arizona	Greenish-brown	Crystalline, massive or as radial fibers	With lead minerals, descloizite, and sandstone
14. Descloizite† [4(Zn,Cu,Pb)O·V$_2$O$_5$·H$_2$O]	Rhodesia, Africa; Mexico; New Mexico; Arizona	Cherry red to brown and black	Crystalline, massive fibers with mammillary surface	With lead minerals, quartz, and cuprodescloizite
15. Pyrobelonite (4PbO·7MnO·2V$_2$O$_5$·3H$_2$O)	Langban, Sweden	Bright to deep red	Small acicular crystals	Possibly related to descloizite
16. Dechenite§	Nieder-Schlettenbach, Bavaria, Germany	Red, brownish-red	Massive, nodular botryoidal	
17. Vanadinite [Pb$_4$(VO$_4$)$_3$·PbCl]	Zimipan, Mexico; Arizona; New Mexico; Argentina; Africa	Red, yellow, brown	Crystalline, compact fibrous crusts	With lead minerals, descloizite, and quartz
18. Endlichite [Pb$_4$(V,AsO$_4$)$_3$·PbCl]	New Mexico; South Dakota	Yellow	Small crystals	With lead minerals, descloizite, and quartz
19. Huegelite (Hydrated Zn,Pb Vanadate)	Reichenbach, Baden, Germany	Yellow to brown	Microscopic crystals	
20. Turanite (5CuO·V$_2$O$_5$·2H$_2$O)	Russian Turkestan	Olive green	Radial aggregates	With copper minerals
21. Uzbekite (3CuO·V$_2$O$_5$·3H$_2$O)	Uzbekistana District, Ferghana, Russian Turkestan	Green	Dark-green crusts of needles	With copper minerals
22. Volborthite [6(Cu,Ba,Ca)O·V$_2$O$_5$·15H$_2$O]	Ural Mountains, Russia; Colorado	Yellow to green	Globular masses	With copper minerals
23. Calciovolborthite [(Cu,Ca)$_3$V$_2$O$_8$·(Cu,Ca)(OH)$_2$]	Colorado; Southeastern Utah; Baku City, Russia	Yellow to green	Fine masses and aggregates, crystalline and granular	With copper minerals and calcium vanadates
24. Tangeite (2CaO·2CuO·V$_2$O$_5$·H$_2$O)	Alai Mts, Ferghana, Russian Turkestan	Dark olive green	Fine fibrous and botryoidal masses	With copper minerals
25. Gamagarite [Ba$_4$(Fe,Mn)$_2$V$_4$O$_{15}$(OH)$_2$]	Postmasburg District of Cape Province, S. Africa	Very dark brown	Needles and prisms aggregates	Sitaparite and ephesite
26. Hewettite (CaO·3V$_2$O$_5$·9H$_2$O)	Mina Ragra, Peru; Paradox Valley, Montrose Co., Colorado	Deep red	Fibrous aggregates, luster	In patronite, with other vanadates, and in sandstone

	Color	Habit	Occurrence
27. Metahewettite ($CaO \cdot 3V_2O_5 \cdot 9H_2O$)	Deep red	Fibrous aggregates	On patronite
28. Pascoite ($2CaO \cdot 3V_2O_5 \cdot 11H_2O$)	Orange	Granular aggregates, efflorescent coatings	On sandstone; with other vanadates and oxides
29. Pintadoite ($2CaO \cdot V_2O_5 \cdot 9H_2O$)	Green		On sandstone; with other vanadates
30. Rossite ($CaO \cdot V_2O_5 \cdot 4H_2O$)	Light yellow	Granular aggregates, efflorescent coatings	On sandstone; vanoxite and corvusite with pascoite
31. Metarossite ($CaO \cdot V_2O_5 \cdot 2H_2O$)	Light yellow	Granular aggregates, efflorescent coatings	On sandstone with rossite and pascoite; dehydration of rossite
32. Delrioite ($CaO \cdot SrO \cdot V_2O_5 \cdot 3H_2O$)	Pale yellow to green	Fibrous acicular crystals	On sandstone with metarossite
33. Simplotite ($CaO \cdot 2V_2O_4 \cdot 5H_2O$)	Black to yellow-green	Platy crystals	On sandstone associated with duttonite, melovanadite, native selenium, montrosite, paramontrosite, vanadiferous silicate, uraninite, coffinite
34. Fernandinite ($CaO \cdot V_2O_4 \cdot 5V_2O_5 \cdot 14H_2O$)	Dull green	Massive or fibrous aggregates	After patronite with other calcium vanadates
35. Melanovanadite ($2CaO \cdot 3V_2O_5 \cdot 2V_2O_4$)	Black		After patronite with other calcium vanadates
36. Sincosite ($CaO \cdot V_2O_4 \cdot P_2O_5 \cdot 5H_2O$)	Leek green		
37. Fervanite ($2Fe_2O_3 \cdot 2V_2O_5 \cdot 5H_2O$)	Brown	Fibrous with silky luster	With oxides, gypsum and vanadates in sandstone
38. Nolanite (?)	Black	Small opaque hexag. plates with sub-metallic luster	
39. Pucherite ($Bi_2O_3 \cdot V_2O_5$)	Reddish-brown		
40. Uvanite ($2UO_3 \cdot 3V_2O_5 \cdot 15H_2O$)	Brownish-yellow	Fine granular aggregates	With carnotite and V mica in sandstone; with calcium vanadates
41. Ferghanite ($3UO \cdot V_2O_5 \cdot 6H_2O$)	Sulfur yellow	Yellow scales	

	Locality
27.	Mina Ragra, Peru; Paradox Valley, Montrose Co., Colorado; California
28.	Mina Ragra, Peru; Colorado
29.	Canyon Pintado, Colorado
30.	Montrose Co., Colorado
31.	Montrose Co., Colorado
32.	Montrose Co., Colorado
33.	Montrose Co., Colorado
34.	Mina Ragra, Peru
35.	Mina Ragra, Peru
36.	Sincos, Peru
37.	Montrose Co., Colorado
38.	Fish Hook Bay (Beaver Lodge Region), Saskatchewan
39.	Saxony, Germany; San Diego Co., California
40.	Temple Rock, Utah
41.	Province of Ferghana, Russia

TABLE 32.13. DESCRIPTIVE MINERALOGY OF VANADIUM MINERALS[6] (cont.)

Mineral	Location	Color	Texture	Associates
42. Carnotite $(K_2O \cdot 2UO_3 \cdot V_2O_5 \cdot 3H_2O)$	Western Colorado; Eastern Utah; South Australia; Pennsylvania	Yellow	Earthy aggregates	Disseminated in sandstone with tyuyamunite
43. Tyuyamunite $(CaO \cdot 2UO_3 \cdot V_2O_5 \cdot 4H_2O)$	Western Colorado; Eastern Utah, Ferghana Province, Russia	Yellow	Very fine crystals	In pores and fractures of sandstone, with carnotite
44. Rauvite $(CaO \cdot 2UO_3 \cdot 6V_2O_5 \cdot 20H_2O)$	Temple Mountain, Utah	Purple	Crystalline aggregates	In pores of sandstone with carnotite, hewettite, etc.
45. Sengierite $(2CuO \cdot 2UO_3 \cdot V_2O_5 \cdot 10H_2O)$	Belgian Congo			
		SILICATES		
46. Roscoelite $[2K_2O \cdot 2Al_2O_3 \cdot (Mg \cdot Fe)O \cdot 3V_2O_5 \cdot 10SiO_2 \cdot 4H_2O]$	Western Colorado	Brown, greenish-brown	Micaceous	In sandstone with vanadium oxides
47. Ardennite $[8MnO \cdot 4Al_2O_3 \cdot (As \cdot V)_2O_3 \cdot 8SiO_2 \cdot 5H_2O]$	Ala Valley, Italy; Salm Chateau, Belgium	Yellow to brown		

* Probably $V_2S_5 + nS$.
† Ramirite of Mexico; mottramite of Cheshire, England, and Tanganyika Territory, Africa; and psittacinite of Montana, United States have been identified as cuprodescloizite.
‡ Eusynchite of Baden, Germany, is probably identical with descloizite.
§ Composition usually given as PbV_2O_6. The composition, most probably, is similar to that of descloizite but also contains arsenic. May be identical with aroeoxene from same locality.

TABLE 32.14. OPTICAL AND OTHER PHYSICAL PROPERTIES OF VANADIUM MINERALS[6]

Mineral	Hardness specific gravity fusibility	Crystal structure	Cleavage	Optical group	Indices of refraction Alpha	Indices of refraction Gamma	Indices of refraction Beta	Axial angles dispersion	Optical orientation	Remarks
SULFIDES										
1. Patronite* (VS_4 or V_2S_5)	H = 2.5 G = 2.65–2.71	Amorphous								
2. Sulvanite ($3Cu_2S \cdot V_2O_5$)	H = 3.5 G = 4.0	Isometric	Cubic							
OXIDES										
3. Doloresite ($3V_2O_4 \cdot 4H_2O$)	G = 3.27–3.33	Monoclinic								
4. Alaite ($V_2O_5 \cdot H_2O$)										
5. Navajoite ($V_2O_5 \cdot 3H_2O$)	G = 2.56	Monoclinic	(Bi- ?)		1.905	About 2.02	Slightly above 2.02		Z‖ fiber	X = Yellowish-brown Y = Yellowish-brown Z = Dark brown
6. Duttonite [$VO(OH)_2$]	H = 2.5 G = 3.24	Orthorhombic	Bi+		1.810	1.900	>2.01	2V = 60° R < V	X = a Y = c Z = b	X = Pale pinkish-brown Y = Pale yellowish-brown Z = Pale brown
7. Vanoxite ($2V_2O_4 \cdot V_2O_5 \cdot 8H_2O$)		Rhomboidal sections				Opaque				
8. Corvusite ($V_2O_4 \cdot 6V_2O_5 \cdot nH_2O$)	H = 2.5–3 G = 2.82									
SULFATES										
9. Minasragrite ($V_2O_4 \cdot 3SO_3 \cdot 16H_2O$)	Easily fusible	Fibers, mono, rhombs	010 Perf	Bi(−)	1.518	1.542	1.530	Large	X = B Z ∧ fibers 12°	Pleo = strong, X = deep blue, Y = pale blue, Z = colorless
VANADATES										
10. Barnesite ($Na_2O \cdot 3V_2O_5 \cdot 3H_2O$)										
11. Steigerite ($Al_2V_2O_8 \cdot 6\frac{1}{2}H_2O$)		Flat plates and fibers				Mean of indices 1.71				
12. Brackebuschite [$2(Pb,Mn,Fe)O \cdot V_2O_5 \cdot H_2O$]	F = 1.5	Monoclinic prisms		Bi(+)	2.28	2.48	2.32	Large R > V		Pleo = strong, X = colorless, Y + Z = reddish-brown

TABLE 32.14. OPTICAL AND OTHER PHYSICAL PROPERTIES OF VANADIUM MINERALS⁶ (cont.)

Mineral	Hardness specific gravity fusibility	Crystal structure	Cleavage	Optical group	Indices of refraction			Axial angles dispersion	Optical orientation	Remarks
					Alpha	Gamma	Beta			
13. Cuprodescloizite† [4(Cu,Zn,Pb)O.(V,As)₂O₅.H₂O]	H = 3-4 G = 6.1	Orthorhombic	No	Bi(−)	2.21	2.33	2.31	2V = 47° ± 2E = 134° ± R > V	X = fibers	Pleo = strong in yellow
14. Descloizite‡ [4(Zn,Cu,Pb)O·V₂O₅·H₂O]	H = 3.5 G = 5.1-6.2	Orthorhombic short prisms	No	Bi(+) Bi(−)	2.18 2.18	2.35 2.35	2.27 2.26	2V = 90° R > V	X = c, Z = a	
15. Pyrobelonite (4PbO.7MnO.2V₂O₅.3H₂O)	H = 3.5 G = 5.377	Orthorhombic prisms	No	Bi(−)	2.32	2.37	2.36	2V = 29° 2E = 73° R > V	X = a, Y = c	Pleo = strong red to brown
16. Dechenite§	G = 5.6-5.8									
17. Vanadinite [Pb₄(VO₄)₃·PbCl]	H = 2.75-3 G = 6.66-7.10 F = 1.5	Hexagonal prisms	Good	Uni(−)	E = 2.299 W = 2.354					
18. Endlichite [Pb₄(V,AsO₄)₃·PbCl]	H = 3 G = 7 F = 1.5	Hexagonal prisms		Uni(−)	W = 2.25 E = 2.20					
19. Huegelite (Hydrated Zn, Pb Vanadate)	H = 5	Monoclinic laths		Bi(+)		B = .01	1.915	2V = 0° for red and orange	Y near c Z ⊥ lath	
20. Turanite (5CuO.V₂O₅.2H₂O)	H = 5	Ortho (?) radial fibers		Bi(−)	2.00	2.02	2.01	Medium R > V	Elongation (+) ∥ extinction	Pleo = strong, X + Y = brown, Z = green Slightly Pleo
21. Uzbekite (3CuO.V₂O₅.3H₂O)				Bi(−)	2.01	2.07	2.04	2V = Large R < V		
22. Volborthite [6(Cu,Ba,Ca)O·V₂O₅·15H₂O]	H = 3 G = 3.5-3.9 F = 1.5-3	Six-sided tablets		Bi(+) Bi(−)	2.02 2.02	2.00 2.00	2.01 2.01	2V = 0-90° R > V	X nearly ∥ to plate for Bi(+) Z nearly ∥ to plate for Bi(−)	X = colorless Y + Z = pale green
23. Calciovolborthite [(Cu,Ca)₃V₂O₈·(Cu,Ca)(OH)₂]	H = 3.5 G = 3.5-3.8 F = 1.5-3	Green tablets		Bi(+)	2.01	2.10	2.05	2V = 83°		
24. Tangeite (2CaO.2CuO.V₂O₅.H₂O)				Bi(−)	2.00	2.02	2.01	Large	Elongation (+) ∥ extinction	Pleo = strong, X + Y = brown, Z = green
25. Gamagarite [Ba₂(Fe,Mn)₂V₄O₁₅(OH)₂]	H = 4.5-5 G = 4.62	Monoclinic	001 100 101	Bi(−)	2.016	2.130	2.040	2V = 46-62°	Y = b X ∧ C = 41° ±	R < V Pleo, red-brown to light salmon—buff
26. Hewettite (CaO·3V₂O₅·9H₂O)	G = 2.55 F = 1.5	Ortho needles and blades		Bi(−)	1.77	2.35	2.18	Medium	Z = elongation	X + Y = light orange-yellow, Z = deep red

No. & Name (Composition)	H, G, F	Crystal system / habit	Cleavage	Optic	α	β	γ	2V / 2E	Orientation	Remarks
27. Metahewettite ($CaO \cdot 3V_2O_5 \cdot 9H_2O$)	G = 2.51, F = 1.5	Ortho tablets and blades	010 Poor	Bi(−)	1.70	2.23	2.10	2V = 52°, 2E = 134°	X ⊥ to blades, Z = elongation	Z = deep red, X + Y = light orange-yellow
28. Pascoite ($2CaO \cdot 3V_2O_5 \cdot 11H_2O$)	H = 2.5, G = 2.46, F = 1.5	Monoclinic	010 Poor	Bi(−)	1.775	1.825	1.815	2V = 50°, 2E = 100°, R = strong	Z = elongation, X = b	Pleo = strong, X = yellow, Y = cadmium yellow, Z = orange
29. Pintadoite ($2CaO \cdot V_2O_5 \cdot 9H_2O$)										
30. Rossite ($2CaO \cdot V_2O_5 \cdot 9H_2O$)	H = 2.3, G = 2.45, F = 1.5	Triclinic prisms	010 Good	Bi(+)	1.710	1.840	1.770	Large	Z = c	Tubular twinning 100
31. Metarossite ($CaO \cdot V_2O_5 \cdot 2H_2O$)	H = 2.3, F = 1.5	Plates	One Perf	Bi(+)	1.84	B = high		Large		Optic axes emerge from cleavage
32. Delrioite ($CaO \cdot SrO \cdot V_2O_5 \cdot 3H_2O$)	H = about 2, G = 3.1		One Perf	Bi(−)	1.783	1.866	1.834	2V = 78¾°		Readily sol. in H_2O, X = Colorless, Y = Pale yellow, Z = Slightly deeper yellow
33. Simplotite ($CaO \cdot 2V_2O_4 \cdot 5H_2O$)	G = 2.64	Monoclinic	Micaceous on 010		1.705	1.767	1.769	R > V, 2V about 25°	X = b, Z ∧ C = +58°	X = Yellow, Y = Green, Z = Green
34. Fernandinite ($CaO \cdot V_2O_4 \cdot 5V_2O_5 \cdot 14H_2O$)		Fibers				2.05 B = strong				
35. Melanovanadite ($2CaO \cdot 3V_2O_5 \cdot 2V_2O_4$)	H = 2.5, G = 3.48	Monoclinic prisms	010 Perf	Bi(−)	1.73	1.98	1.96	Medium	Z = b, Z ∧ C = 15°	Pleo = strong, X = yellow-brown, Y = red-brown, Z = red-brown
36. Sincosite ($CaO \cdot V_2O_4 \cdot P_2O_5 \cdot 5H_2O$)	H = 2.3, G = 2.84	Tetrag. basal pseudotetrag.	001 Good	Uni(−) Bi(−)	E = 1.655, 1.657	1.693	W = 1.680, 1.690	Small		Twinning on 110. Pleo, gray-green to colorless
37. Fervanite ($2Fe_2O_3 \cdot 2V_2O_5 \cdot 5H_2O$)		Monoclinic tablets	None	Bi(−)	2.186	2.224	2.22	Small		
38. Nolanite (?)				Bi						
39. Pucherite ($Bi_2O_3 \cdot V_2O_5$)	H = 4, G = 6.25, F = 2	Ortho tablets 001 acicular	001 Perf	Bi(−)	2.41	2.51	2.50	2V = 20°, 2E = 52°, R < V	X = c, Y = a	Sol HCl with evolution of Cl
40. Uvanite ($2UO_3 \cdot 3V_2O_5 \cdot 15H_2O$)		Orthorhombic	Two Pinacoidal	Bi(+)	1.817	2.057	1.879	2V = 52°, 2E = 110°		Pleo = strong, X = yellow, Y = dark brown, Z = green-yellow
41. Ferghanite ($3UO_3 \cdot V_2O_5 \cdot 6H_2O$)	H = 2, G = 3.3		One Perf	Bi	Low			2V = large		

TABLE 32.14. OPTICAL AND OTHER PHYSICAL PROPERTIES OF VANADIUM MINERALS[6] (cont.)

Mineral	Hardness specific gravity fusibility	Crystal structure	Cleavage	Optical group	Indices of refraction			Axial angles dispersion	Optical orientation	Remarks
					Alpha	Gamma	Beta			
42. Carnotite $(K_2O \cdot 2UO_3 \cdot V_2O_5 \cdot 3H_2O)$	$H = 1.2$ $G = 4.1$	Ortho plates	001 Basal	Bi(−)	1.75 2.06	1.92 1.95 2.08	1.895 1.925	$2V = 39$–$48°$ $2F = 79$–$91°$ $R < V$	$X = c$ Y bisects acute angle of plates	Colorless to yellow in section
43. Tyuyamunite $(CaO \cdot 2UO_3 \cdot V_2O_5 \cdot 4H_2O)$	Soft	Ortho plates tabular	001	Bi(−)	1.670 1.77	1.895 1.97	1.870 1.93	$2V = 36°$	$X = c$	Pleo = strong, X = colorless, Y = canary yellow, Z = darker yellow
44. Rauvite $(CaO \cdot 2UO_3 \cdot 6V_2O_5 \cdot 20H_2O)$							1.87 1.90			
45. Sengierite $(2CuO \cdot 2UO_3 \cdot V_2O_5 \cdot 10H_2O)$	$H = 2.5$ $G = 4\pm$	Rhombic plates	001 Perf	Bi(−)	1.77	1.97	1.94	$2V = 37$–$39°$ $R < V$	$X = c$ $Y = b$ $Z = a$	Pleo strong, X = bluish-green, Y = olive green, Z = yellowish-green
SILICATES										
46. Roscoelite $[2K_2O \cdot 2Al_2O_3 \cdot (Mg,Fe)O \cdot 3V_2O_5 \cdot 10SiO_2 \cdot 4H_2O]$	$H = 3$ $G = 2.97$ $F = 3$	Monoclinic plates	001 Plates	Bi(−)	1.610	1.704	1.685	$2V = 10$–15 $R < V$	$Z = b$ $X \wedge C = 0$–$4°$	Y + Z = green-brown X = olive green
47. Ardennite $[8MnO \cdot 4Al_2O_3 \cdot (As,V)_2O_3 \cdot 8SiO_2 \cdot 5H_2O]$	$H = 6$–7 $G = 3.6$ $F = 2$–2.5	Ortho prismatic crystals	010 Perf	Bi(+)	1.739	1.760	1.740	$2V = 0°$ to small	$Z = a$ X or Y = c	X = deep yellow, Y = golden yellow, Z = pale yellow
47A. Ardennite $[8MnO \cdot 4Al_2O_3 \cdot (As,V)_2O_3 \cdot 8SiO_2 \cdot 5H_2O]$	$H = 6$–7 $G = ?$ $F = 2$–2.5	Ortho prismatic crystals	010 Perf	Bi(+)	$B = 0.020$		1.79	$2V = 36°$ $2E = 67°$ $R > V$	$X = b$ $Z = a$ or b	X = deep yellow, Y = golden yellow, Z = pale yellow
47B. Ardennite $[8MnO \cdot 4Al_2O_3 \cdot (As,V)_2O_3 \cdot 8SiO_2 \cdot 5H_2O]$	$H = 6$–7 $G = ?$ $F = 2$–2.5	Orthorhombic	010 Perf	Bi(+)	$B = 0.015$		$1.8\pm$	$2V = 0$–$50°$ $2E = 99°$ $R > V$	$Z = b$ $X = c$	X = deep yellow, Y = golden yellow, Z = pale yellow
47C. Ardennite $(8MnO \cdot 4Al_2O_3 \cdot V_2O_5 \cdot 8SiO_2 \cdot 5H_2O)$	$H = 6$–7 $G = 3.62$ $F = 2$–2.5	Orthorhombic prisms	010 Perf	Bi(+)	$B = 0.015$		$1.9\pm$	$2V = 0$–$50°$ $2E = 0.107°$ $R > V$	$Z = b$ $X = c$	X = deep yellow, Y = golden yellow, Z = pale yellow
47D. Ardennite $(8MnO \cdot 4Al_2O_3 \cdot V_2O_5 \cdot 8SiO_2 \cdot 5H_2O)$	$H = 6$–7 $G = 3.6$ $F = 2.25$	Ortho prismatic crystals	010 Perf	Bi(+)	$B = 0.015$		2.0	$2V = 0$–$50°$ $2E = 0.116°$ $R > V$	$Z = b$ $X = c$	X = deep yellow, Y = golden yellow, Z = pale yellow

* Probably $V_2S_5 + nS$.

† Ramirite of Mexico; mottramite of Cheshire, England, and Tanganyika Territory, Africa; and psittacinite of Montana, United States, have been identified with cuprodescloizite.

‡ Eusynchite of Baden, Germany, is probably identical with descloizite.

§ Composition usually given as PbV_2O_6. The composition, most probably, is similar to that of descloizite but also contains arsenic. May be identical with aroeoxene from same locality.

33. YTTRIUM

A. H. Daane

Ames Laboratory, Atomic Energy Commission, Iowa State University
Ames, Iowa

INTRODUCTION

Yttrium was discovered in 1794 by the Scandinavian chemist Gadolin; he named it after the small town of Ytterby in Sweden, which also bears the honor of having given names to the elements terbium, erbium, and ytterbium. Yttrium always occurs with the rare earth elements and is very similar to them in both chemical and metallurgical respects. The first element of the second transition group, it is in Group 3B of the periodic table, and resembles the rare earth elements more than it resembles scandium. A few early experimental preparations of yttrium metal were made in the 1800's, but they were of a quality that did not permit characterization of the metal. Recently, newly developed separations processes for the rare earths have made yttrium much more available, and it has been prepared and studied in many laboratories. Interest in the use of yttrium metal in nuclear reactor programs prompted support of a research program by the U.S. Atomic Energy Commission, and a detailed description of the development of large scale processes for the separation of yttrium from its ores, the preparation and purification of the metal, and the analytical methods associated with such work has been described in a report of the Ames Laboratory of the U.S. Atomic Energy Commission.[1] Also, the proceedings of a 1959 symposium on "The Rare Earths and Related Metals," sponsored by the American Society for Metals and the U.S.

Atomic Energy Commission,[18] and a recent paper by J. A. McGurity and C. R. Simmons[12] include many additional details on the preparation, properties, fabrication, and uses of yttrium. Gschneidner[8a] has recently made an extensive and critical review of rare earth metal alloy systems. Interest in this metal has been heightened by its low neutron cross section, its melting point 1509°C (2748°F), its density (4.47 g/cc), and its behavior with other metals.

CHEMISTRY

The chemistry of yttrium is very like that of the rare earths except that only a trivalent state is known for this element whereas about half the rare earths exhibit other valences in addition to their normal valence of three. In aqueous solutions yttrium forms an insoluble hydroxide, oxalate, and fluoride, all of which may be used for gravimetric analytical procedures. The chloride, bromide, iodide, nitrate, and sulfate are all soluble. Because of the absence of "d" and "f" electrons, the Y^{+3} ion is colorless in solutions, and direct spectrophotometric determination of this species is not possible. The Y^{+3} ion is so nearly the same size as the heavy rare earth ions that it behaves as one of them in solutions; in many chemical separations and reactions yttrium falls between gadolinium and erbium in order of reaction. Because of its occurrence with, and similarity to, the heavy rare earths, and because of its greater abundance, this group of elements is

653

often called the "yttrium earths." As will be seen later, this similarity of yttrium to the heavy rare earths extends to the metallic state.

OCCURRENCE

In the geochemical processes in which the earth's crust was formed, yttrium and the rare earth elements remained together. Today we find them together as phosphates in xenotime and monazite, as silicates in gadolinite, as columbates in samarskite, as well as in other important minerals such as fergusonite, apatite, blomstrandite, and euxenite. Norway has been a rich source of supply of many of these minerals, and more recently, mining operations have been carried out in this hemisphere in the Fair Valley, Idaho; Blind River, Ontario; Aiken, South Carolina, and Brazilian areas. Yttrium is present in the earth's crust to the extent of 40 ppm compared to concentrations of 46 ppm for cerium, 24 ppm for neodymium, 18 ppm for lanthanum, and less than 10 ppm for the other rare earths and scandium. For comparison, the concentration of copper is 45 ppm. This is somewhat misleading, as the copper deposits are much more concentrated.

ORE TREATMENT AND SEPARATION

Development of pilot plant scale processing of ores for their yttrium and rare earth content has been carried out by Spedding and Powell,[1, 13, 14, 18a] and a typical treatment by their process follows. Starting with electromagnetically concentrated xenotime (36 per cent Y_2O_3, 24 per cent RE_2O_3 as phosphates), the ore is broken down with a high temperature sulfuric acid treatment. The leachate from this digestion is then loaded onto cation exchange resin beds, which are then eluted with an ammonia buffered ethylenediaminetetraacetic acid (EDTA) solution containing cupric ion which prevents precipitation of the insoluble EDTA on the resin bed. Yttrium and the rare earths are obtained in separate fractions of the eluent and are precipitated as their oxalates and ignited to their oxides. Other complexing agents have been studied for this process, but EDTA appears to be most suited for this separation. This process is operated using 30-in. diameter columns containing 10-ft beds, and with 12 such columns a throughput of about 500 pounds

of 99.9 per cent pure Y_2O_3/cycle is achieved; a cycle consists of two months. Several companies have constructed separation plants based on the above process. Solvent extraction has been used as a pretreatment in at least one case.

PREPARATION

Metallic yttrium was first prepared by Wöhler[20] in 1828; he reduced the anhydrous chloride, and since that time metallothermic reductions of yttrium halides have been employed by several workers. The largest scale application of this type of reaction has been that recently described by Spedding, Carlson, and Daane,[1, 18b] who have reduced yttrium trifluoride with calcium in several variations as described below. The halides are the only yttrium compounds that have been successfully reduced to the metal on any scale of operations. Their preparation is described below.

PREPARATION OF HALIDES

Yttrium Fluoride. The preparation of yttrium fluoride may be carried out by the same procedures described in this book for scandium fluoride: (1) ammonium hydrogen fluoride may be mixed with yttrium oxide and heated to 400°C (752°F) in a stream of dry air or helium; (2) yttrium oxide may be heated to 750°C (1382°F) in a stream of anhydrous hydrogen fluoride. The latter method is preferable for large scale operations. In preparing yttrium fluoride on a pilot plant scale by this method, a 50-pound batch of yttrium oxide is heated in an "Inconel" lined furnace to 150°C (302°F), and a stream of anhydrous hydrogen fluoride is then passed into the furnace. The charge is heated for 6 hours at 750°C (1382°F) in a stationary position, and the furnace tube is then slowly rotated for 1 hour. After cooling, the product is stored in polyethylene bags until used. A 300 per cent excess quantity of hydrogen fluoride is consumed by this process.

Yttrium Chloride. The very hygroscopic nature of yttrium chloride, as well as the bromide and iodide, makes it necessary to handle these salts under dry conditions. Yttrium chloride may be prepared by mixing 9 moles of ammonium chloride and 1 mole of yttrium oxide together, and adding 4 moles of hydroxylamine hydrochloride. This mixture is heated to 400°C

(752°F) in a stream of dry air or helium to effect the conversion to the trichloride.

Yttrium Bromide. Yttrium oxide is dissolved in hydrobromic acid and the solution is evaporated to near dryness. Absolute alcohol is added and the solution is evaporated to dryness. This is repeated 3 times, and in the last evaporation a quantity of ammonium bromide equal to the original weight of yttrium oxide is added. The resulting granular mass is heated slowly to 600°C (1112°F) in a "Vycor" tube under a stream of dry air or helium.

Yttrium Iodide. Yttrium oxide is dissolved in redistilled 47 per cent aqueous HI. Three moles of ammonium iodide are added per mole of yttrium; the solution is evaporated to dryness and then very slowly heated to 300°C (572°F) over a 72-hour period in a vacuum.

PREPARATION OF YTTRIUM METAL

Calcium Reduction of Yttrium Fluoride. Yttrium fluoride prepared by the methods described above has a relatively large surface area and a tendency to adsorb atmospheric gases. A vacuum sintering or melting operation is helpful in eliminating some of the adsorbed gases before the actual reduction. This may be done by heating the salt in a tantalum, molybdenum, or titanium crucible to 1000°C (1832°F) in a vacuum of 1×10^{-4} mm Hg or better. This temperature is near the 1152°C (2106°F) melting point of the salt, and the treatment results in a considerable amount of shrinking and sintering. The fluoride is then mixed with 10 per cent more than the stoichiometric amount of redistilled calcium required to reduce the salt by the reaction:

$$2YF_3 + 3Ca \rightarrow 2Y + 3CaF_2.$$

The charge is then placed in a tantalum crucible that is capped with a perforated lid and placed in a silica tube induction furnace and evacuated. The furnace is heated slowly to 600°C (1112°F) to outgas the charge, and purified argon gas is then bled into the system to a pressure of 500 mm Hg. As the temperature rises the charge reacts at about 1000°C (1832°F), as evidenced by the rapid rise in the temperature of the reaction crucible. Heating is continued to 1600°C (2912°F) to allow complete separation of slag and metal, and the furnace is allowed to cool. The slag may easily

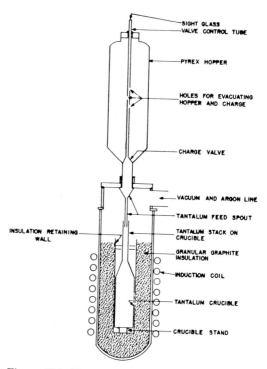

Figure 33.1. Furnace for 500-gram scale preparation of yttrium.

be broken away, leaving the solid metal ingot in yields of 98.5 to 99 per cent. Vacuum melting the ingot in the crucible reduces the calcium content to less than 150 ppm, and leaves tantalum (0.5 to 2 per cent) and oxygen (500 to 2000 ppm) as the major impurities. Using a crucible 2 inches in diameter and 8 inches high, 150 grams of metal may be prepared. This type of reduction is scaled up to produce 500 grams of metal by use of the furnace shown in Figure 33.1. The charge is contained in the hopper while the tantalum crucible is outgassed by heating to 1400°C (2552°F) in a vacuum. Argon is then admitted to the furnace, and the charge is added to the hot crucible until it is filled with molten metal and slag at a temperature of 1600°C (2912°F). This allows the full volume of the crucible to be utilized, whereas the packed charge permits only the lower third of the crucible to contain the slag and metal layers.

To extend this method of preparing the metal to a scale of from 32 to 40 kg per charge, the furnace shown in Figure 33.2 has been devised. In this unit the stainless steel charge hopper is discharged into the reaction

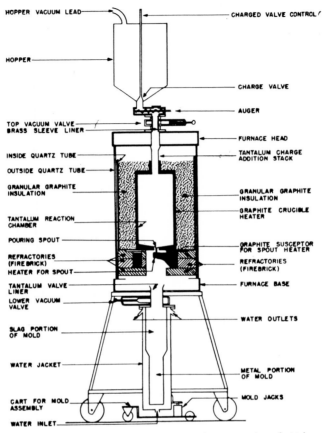

HOPPER VACUUM LEAD

CHARGED VALVE CONTROL

HOPPER

CHARGE VALVE

AUGER

TOP VACUUM VALVE
BRASS SLEEVE LINER

FURNACE HEAD

INSIDE QUARTZ TUBE

TANTALUM CHARGE
ADDITION STACK

OUTSIDE QUARTZ TUBE

GRANULAR GRAPHITE
INSULATION

GRANULAR GRAPHITE
INSULATION

GRAPHITE CRUCIBLE
HEATER

TANTALUM REACTION
CHAMBER

POURING SPOUT

GRAPHITE SUSCEPTOR
FOR SPOUT HEATER

REFRACTORIES
(FIRE BRICK)

HEATER FOR SPOUT

REFRACTORIES
(FIREBRICK)

TANTALUM VALVE
LINER

FURNACE BASE

LOWER VACUUM
VALVE

WATER OUTLETS

SLAG PORTION
OF MOLD

WATER JACKET

METAL PORTION
OF MOLD

CART FOR MOLD
ASSEMBLY

MOLD JACKS

WATER INLET

Figure 33.2. Furnace for 40-kilogram scale preparation of yttrium.

chamber by means of an auger feed. The temperature of the reaction chamber is maintained at 1500–1550°C (2732–2822°F), and the charge is fed in intermittently as each previous addition melts down. The tantalum reaction chamber is 9 inches in diameter and 16 inches high, with 35-mil (0.035 of an inch) walls, and as indicated in Figure 33.2, is contained in a graphite crucible surrounded by a 2-inch layer of granular graphite insulation.*

* This graphite insulation is prepared from lathe turnings of high purity graphite stock (such as result from turning the graphite crucible above) and is sieved to remove particles larger than ⅛ of an inch in diameter. It is then air classified to remove the fines. The resulting material has the consistency of ground coffee, and after vacuum outgasing is extremely effective inert atmosphere insulation. A less pure grade of graphite containing an appreciable quantity of sulfur was found to release vapors that severely attack tantalum in one heating.

A bottom pour spout on the crucible extends out of the heated zone and stays at a sufficiently low temperature for the first metal running into it to freeze and seal the chamber.

Figure 33.3. Forty kilogram scale furnace in operation.

Figure 33.4. Mold contents after casting; slag and metal on left, metal ingot on right.

A graphite bottom heater surrounds the pouring spout. To tap the heat the induction coil is lowered to generate heat around the spout by means of the heater. This melts out the plug, and the metal flows into the water-cooled copper mold, followed by the slag. Vacuum valves seal the top and bottom of the furnace while the charge hopper is being reloaded and flushed with argon, and a new mold is set in place; this allows another heat to be run through immediately on a schedule of 80 minutes per heat.

Figure 33.3 is a photograph of the furnace in operation. Figure 33.4 shows the mold contents of a run on the left, the yttrium ingot after the slag has been broken away on the right. These ingots contained 1 per cent calcium, 0.5 to 2 per cent tantalum, 1000 to 2000 ppm oxygen, 200 ppm carbon, and 50 ppm nitrogen. Vacuum melting the ingots in an arc melting furnace or an induction furnace eliminates the calcium, leaving the other impurities essentially unchanged.

Magnesium Alloy Process. To carry out the preparation of yttrium metal at a lower temperature than in the above process, several modifications in the general metallothermic reduction of yttrium halides have been studied. These include the use of yttrium chloride and bromide with lithium and sodium as the reductants. In each case the halide slag melts at a lower temperature than calcium fluoride, and promotes collection of the yttrium. However, the high melting point of yttrium metal itself 1509°C (2748°F), means that the product of

these lower temperature reductions is a sintered mass of metal full of fused slag, and if higher temperatures are employed to try to consolidate the metal as a separate phase, in most cases very poor yields result.

The most successful application of the metallothermic reaction to the preparation of yttrium has been that of Spedding and Carlson.[1,18b] This process utilizes a lower melting magnesium alloy of yttrium and operates with a lower melting slag by the addition of calcium chloride to the reaction mixture. In a typical run the process is operated as follows: A mixture of 83 pounds of redistilled calcium and 35 pounds of redistilled magnesium are placed in a 20-inch diameter titanium vessel 48 inches high; this in turn is placed in a 24-inch diameter mild steel retort 54 inches long having ½-inch walls. After evacuating, the retort is lowered into a furnace at 750°C (1382°F), as shown in Figure 33.5, and when the calcium-magnesium mixture is molten, 1 atmosphere of helium is admitted to the system. A sealed hopper system is attached to the retort, as shown in Figure 33.6, and a mixture of 180 pounds of YF_3 and 160 pounds of $CaCl_2$ is added as the temperature is raised to 800°C (1472°F). After 3 hours at

Figure 33.5. Retort entering furnace; 110 pound scale, magnesium alloy process.

Figure 33.6. Sealed hopper on retort discharging reactants.

800°C the temperature is increased to 960°C (1760°F) to finish the reaction. The retort is then cooled in an inclined position, as shown in Figure 33.7; this allows the slag and metal to freeze in a configuration that may be easily broken out of the container. The resulting 150

Figure 33.7. Retort cooling in inclined position.

Figure 33.8. Vacuum induction furnace for "demaging" yttrium alloy.

pounds of 27 weight per cent magnesium alloy, is quite brittle, and is crushed to ½-inch diameter chunks with as little exposure to atmospheric moisture as possible. These chunks are loaded into a titanium container and heated in a vacuum in an induction furnace or a resistance furnace for 6 hours at 900°C (1652°F), followed by 24 hours at 950°C (1742°F).

An induction furnace for this operation (called "demaging") is shown in Figure 33.8. During the operation the magnesium and residual calcium are slowly sublimed from the alloy, leaving behind a porous, soft, slightly sintered mass of metal called "sponge," which has a calcium and magnesium content of about 100 ppm each. In Figure 33.9 the alloy chunks are shown in the center, a "de-maged" charge in the titanium container on the left, and the magnesium condensate on the right. To arc melt this material into ingots the granular sponge particles are pressed into 12 x 1½ x 1½ inch sticks which are welded end-to-end to make an

Figure 33.9. Yttrium-magnesium alloy chunks in center, "demaged" yttrium in titanium container on left, and magnesium condensate on right.

electrode. This is consumably arc melted into a 4-inch diameter ingot in an arc of 22 to 24 volts and 1000 to 1200 amperes in a vacuum. The resulting 4-inch diameter ingots are welded together to make a 60-inch long electrode which may be arc melted in a vacuum at a rate of 4.5 pounds per minute, requiring 20 to 24 volts at 2800 to 3200 amperes. A typical ingot of such a run will have the following analysis: Ca less than 10 ppm, Mg 30 ppm, oxygen 500 to 1650 ppm, titanium 0.5 to 1 per cent. Such an ingot is shown at the left in Figure 33.10, with 4-inch ingots in the center and pressed sponge electrodes on the right.

Dennison[4] has attempted the preparation of yttrium metal by the hot wire decomposition of yttrium iodide, but under a variety of conditions has never been able to obtain yttrium metal. These attempts have included conditions under which excellent yields of zirconium could be obtained by the same process. The failure of yttrium metal to form appears to be related to the extreme stability of the iodide as well as the high vapor pressure of the metal at temperatures necessary to effect a decomposition of the iodide. These findings have been corroborated in work reported by Huffine and Williams.[18c]

Figure 33.10. Six-inch diameter arc melted ingot at left, four-inch diameter ingots in center, and pressed "sponge" electrodes on right.

PURIFICATION OF YTTRIUM METAL

As the fabricability of yttrium appears to improve with lower oxygen content, much effort has been expended by several laboratories to achieve lower oxygen content in the metal. At the Ames Laboratory of the U.S. Atomic Energy Commission some of the approaches have involved high-vacuum high-temperature distillation of the metal, purification of the reactants by distilling them into the reaction chamber, and extraction of oxygen from the metal into a YF_3-$CaCl_2$ or YCl_3 fused salt bath. From this work samples of metal with oxygen contents of only 120 ppm (by distillation of the metal) and 150 ppm (by fused salt extraction) have been obtained, and these specimens show greatly improved fabricability. Huffine and Williams[18c] have described a number of additional methods that have been attempted for the purification of yttrium metal at the laboratories of the General Electric ANP Department, Oak Ridge National Laboratory, U.S. Bureau of Mines, Corwith Corporation, Lunex Company, Michigan Chemical Company, and others. These methods include zone melting, solid state electrolysis, electrorefining in a fused salt bath, amalgam separation and vacuum melting. Solid state electrolysis has been proved to be effective in removing oxygen from yttrium, but this and other techniques are only partially successful in obtaining pure metal; the most fruitful approach for improving the quality of the metal appears to be to achieve purer reactants and conditions in the preparation and handling of the metal.

PROPERTIES

In many of its physical properties yttrium is quite similar to the heavy rare earth metals, and if properties are plotted against atomic number for the heavy rare earths, yttrium would have an apparent atomic number of

TABLE 33.1. PHYSICAL PROPERTIES OF YTTRIUM

Atomic number	39
Atomic weight	88.92 (100% isotope 89)
Melting point	1509°C (2748°F)
Boiling point	3200°C (5792°F)
Density	4.472 g/cc
Crystal structure	
Room temperature to 1490°C (2714°F)	Hexagonal close packed a = 3.6457 Å, c = 5.7305 Å
1490–1509°C (2714–2748°F)	Body centered cubic, a = 3.90 Å
Atomic volume	19.86 cc/mole
Metallic radius	1.802 Å
Heat capacity (25°C)	6.50 cal/mole/°C
Heat of fusion	(4.1 kcal/mole)
Heat of vaporization at 25°C	(93 kcal/mole)
Thermal conductivity	0.0240 cal/sec/cm/°C
Linear coefficient of expansion	10.8×10^{-6}/°C
Compressibility	2.09×10^{-6} cm²/kg
Young's modulus	6.63×10^{11} dynes/cm², 9.62×10^6 psi
Shear modulus	3.8×10^6 psi
Poisson's ratio	0.265
Hardness	Brinell 32
Ultimate tensile strength	22,000 psi (24,000 after 10% reduction in area)
Yield strength	9,800 psi (21,000 after 10% reduction in area)
Elongation	25% (7% after 10% reduction in area)
Thermal neutron absorption cross section	1.31 ± 0.08 barns/atom
Electrical resistivity, microhm-cm	
25°C (77°F)	65
100°C (212°F)	83.5
400°C (752°F)	133.5
700°C (1292°F)	169.5
1000°C (1832°F)	190.6

TABLE 33.2. ENTHALPY AND INSTANTANEOUS SPECIFIC HEAT VALUES
FOR YTTRIUM METAL AS A FUNCTION OF TEMPERATURE

°C	°F	Enthalpy, H_o^t, cal/g	°C	°F	Specific heat	
					cal/g/°c	cal/mole/°C
0	32	0	50	122	0.074	6.57
177.0	350.6	13.4	100	212	.076	6.75
177.2	351	13.2	200	392	.077	6.84
242.5	468.5	18.2	300	572	.078	6.93
243.4	470	18.4	300	752	.081	7.20
343.1	649.5	24.8	500	932	.084	7.46
353.0	667.4	26.6	600	1112	.088	7.82
357.7	676	26.1	700	1292	.096	8.54
354.4	670	27.6	800	1472	.105	9.33
375.8	708.4	29.2	900	1652	.115	10.22
379.7	715.4	29.6	1000	1832	.124	11.02
397.6	747.6	31.2				
403.9	759	31.6				
536.3	997	41.8				
538.2	1001	42.2				
721.7	1331	58.8				
722.0	1331.6	58.8				
933.8	1821	88.5				
996.2	1825	89.4				

Enthalpy data H^t (total heat content between the temperature and the ice point) were obtained by ice calorimetric measurements for GE–ANPD at the Battelle Memorial Institute. Instantaneous specific heats were measured graphically as slopes of H_o^t vs. T°C plots. The error in specific heats reportedly did not exceed ±1 per cent.

from 64.5 to 67.5 (i.e., between gadolinium and erbium).

Table 33.1 gives the physical and mechanical properties of yttrium, and Tables 33.2 to 33.5 give data on some of the properties of yttrium that have been studied over a temperature range at the General Electric ANP Department and the Battelle Memorial Institute Laboratories as reported by Simmons.[1sd] Much of the data on physical properties has been obtained with quite pure specimens, particularly where only small specimens are involved, and is not

likely to require much modification in the future; uncertain measurements are enclosed in parentheses. Mechanical properties and other properties requiring bulk specimens have gen-

TABLE 33.3. LINEAR THERMAL EXPANSION
COEFFICIENT OF YTTRIUM METAL AS A
FUNCTION OF TEMPERATURE

°C	°F	Coefficient, alpha × 10⁻⁶
25–300	77–572	7.6
25–600	77–1112	9.3
25–900	77–1652	9.9
25–1000	77–1832	10.1

Most probable values for polycrystalline metal of random grain orientation.

From paper submitted to *J. Inorganic & Nuclear Chem.*, entitled "The Preparation and Properties of High Purity Yttrium Metal," by H. J. Nolting and C. R. Simmons of GE–ANPD and J. J. Klingenberg of Dept. of Chemistry, Xavier University.

Data obtained by dilarometric measurements

TABLE 33.4. THERMAL CONDUCTIVITY OF YTTRIUM
AS A FUNCTION OF TEMPERATURE

°C	°F	Thermal conductivity	
		BTU/hr/ft²/°F/ft	cal/sec/cm/°C
−18	0	5.6	0.0231
0	32	5.7	.0236
38	100	6.0	.0248
93	200	6.3	.0260
149	300	6.7	.0277
204	400	7.1	.0293
260	500	7.6	.0314
315	600	8.1	.0334
371	700	8.7	.0359
427	800	9.5	.0392
482	900	10.3	.0425
538	1000	11.3	.0466

Measurements made on longitudinal rod specimen. Results are average of GE–ANPD measurements and those made for GE–ANPD at the Battelle Memorial Institute.

These and specific heat data are from "Chemistry and Metallurgy of Yttrium," APEX 475 (deleted) by C. R. Simmons, C. B. Magee, J. A. McGurty, E. S. Funston, and V. P. Calkins, GE–ANPD, now in process of being issued from the Technical Information Service Extension (TISE), Oak Ridge National Laboratory, Oak Ridge, Tenn.

erally been determined with production grade yttrium, and these figures, given in Table 33.1, will undoubtedly have to be modified when purer metal is available in quantity to permit examination of these properties. This is already apparent in the hardness studies of Carlson and General Electric ANP workers, presented by Simmons[18d]: hardness increases with increasing oxygen content, and there is some indication of a variation with heat treatment and degree of working. There is also a distinct decrease in hardness with increasing temperature. Tensile data given by Simmons[18d] show an increasing strength and decreasing ductility with increasing oxygen content, and a decreasing strength and increasing ductility with increasing temperature.

ALLOYS

Alloying Behavior. Yttrium is a large atom among metal atoms; there are only a few metals with which it can form substitutional solid solutions. As might be expected, yttrium forms nearly complete solid solutions with the rare earths and thorium. Yttrium and magnesium show significant solid solubility in one another. Other metals appear to have a very restricted solubility relationship with yttrium, but Collins et al.[18e] have reported very striking effects when yttrium is added to iron, chromium, vanadium, columbium, and some of their alloys.

Yttrium is slightly soluble in iron-base alloys, yet it appears to have very striking effects in that it improves workability, causes grain refinement, promotes resistance to high temperature recrystallization, and, most of all, enhances high temperature oxidation resistance of the alloys. A specific example is a Type 446 stainless steel (25 per cent Cr) which withstands atmospheric oxidation to 1100°C (2200°F); the addition of 1 per cent yttrium extends this temperature to 1370°C (2498°F). This is essentially the same corrosion resistance which results when 5 per cent aluminum is added to these steels, but yttrium prevents the undesirable grain growth caused by aluminum. This enhanced oxidation resistance appears to be the result of a more adherent oxide coating in which the Y_2O_3 combines with iron and chromium oxides to provide a less permeable coating. By adding either thorium (1 per cent) or aluminum (3 per cent) to this

1 per cent yttrium alloy, an enamel-like oxide coating is formed that is non-spalling and thermally shock-resistant to temperatures of 1425°C (2600°F). This resistance to oxidation is not evident in typical austenitic stainless steels of the 18-8 composition, and is seen only slightly in the higher alloy austenitics such as the 310 series.

Yttrium and the rare earths are only slightly soluble in chromium, but addition of these metals shows a marked effect on the oxidation resistance of this metal. Collins et al.[18e] report 0.07 per cent yttrium soluble in chromium, an amount sufficient to convert the chromium oxide of surface oxidation from a nitrogen-porous layer to a nitrogen-impervious layer capable of withstanding 100-hour exposures at 1260°C (2300°F). Since chromium is ordinarily severely penetrated and embrittled by nitrogen at this temperature, this constitutes a significant accomplishment in chromium technology; yttrium, however, does not eliminate the room temperature brittleness of chromium though it does prevent excessive grain growth at high temperatures.

Yttrium is only slightly soluble in vanadium (less than 0.1 per cent), but when it is added to vanadium it scavenges the oxygen, removing it as an insoluble layer and leaving behind a room temperature ductile vanadium that may be cold rolled to sheet and foil. Evidence for the scavenging action of yttrium is apparent in alloys made up with 1 per cent yttrium; after removing the segregated Y_2O_3 which floats to the surface from the scavenging action, the vanadium was found to contain 0.5 per cent yttrium.

These alloying additions of yttrium to iron-, chromium-, and vanadium-base alloys represent very significant improvements in the technology of these metals, and the exploitation of these findings will undoubtedly bring these alloys into new uses. In particular, Jaffee,[11] commenting on the air corrosion resistance conferred on chromium by the addition of yttrium, states that this combination may be considered one of our most stable refractory metals for elevated temperature service.

In cases where an yttrium alloy system has not been investigated but information exists on the corresponding system with a rare earth metal, it appears reasonable to assume, as a first approximation, similar behavior with yttrium.

Alloy Systems. Some of the more important features found in alloy systems of yttrium with other metals are given in the following paragraphs. A more detailed review of yttrium alloy systems has been given by Lundin.[18f]

Group 1A (Alkali metals). Lithium, sodium, and potassium, used as reductants for the preparation of yttrium, do not form stable intermetallic compounds and have little affinity for yttrium.

Group 2A (Alkaline earth metals). The yttrium-magnesium system has been investigated by Gibson and Carlson[8] who found three peritectic compounds to exist. The maximum solubility of yttrium in magnesium is 9 weight per cent at 567°C (1053°F), while 15 weight per cent magnesium is soluble in beta yttrium (body centered cubic) at 935°C (1715°F); this latter phase may be quenched to room temperature. The possibility of heat treating the terminal solutions is suggested in this work. Calcium does not alloy readily with yttrium and appears to form immiscible liquids like those found in the lanthanum-calcium system.

Group 3B (Rare earth metals). Valletta[19] has found yttrium and gadolinium to form a nearly perfect solid solution at all compositions. With lanthanum, cerium, praseodymium, and neodymium, however, yttrium forms terminal solid solutions that are quite extensive, with an intervening solid solution that appears to have the unusual samarium structure.

Group 4B (Ti, Zr, Hf). The yttrium-titanium system has a simple eutectic with less than 1 weight per cent yttrium soluble in titanium and about 0.5 per cent titanium soluble in yttrium.[2] The yttrium-zirconium system is similar.

Group 5B (V, Cb, Ta). Vanadium and columbium form a eutectic near the yttrium side of these systems. Tantalum is soluble in liquid yttrium to the extent of about 2 per cent at 1550°C (2822°F). There is no solid solubility of these metals in one another.

Group 6B (Cr, Mo, W). Yttrium and chromium form a simple eutectic system. Molybdenum and tungsten are only slightly soluble in liquid yttrium; tungsten less so than tantalum.

Group 7B (Mn, Tc, Re). Yttrium and manganese form a Laves phase YMn_2 and other compounds.

Group 8B (Fe, Co, Ni, Ru, Rh, Pd, Os, Ir, Pt). Yttrium and iron form several intermetallic compounds and show little solid solubility in each other. The yttrium-nickel system has been found to contain 9 intermetallic compounds.[3] The yttrium cobalt system is similar.

Group 1B (Cu, Ag, Au). Yttrium and copper form several intermetallic compounds and have little solid solubility in each other. In this system a eutectic is the limiting factor in choosing the soaking temperature for copper clad yttrium for hot fabrication.

Group 2B (Zn, Cd, Hg).—

Group 3A (B, Al, Ga, In, Tl). Yttrium forms several borides that are quite refractory; yttrium dissolves in boron to stabilize a new phase of boron.[15] Yttrium is soluble in solid aluminum to the extent of about 0.2 weight per cent and forms at least one compound.

Group 4A (C, Si, Ge, Sn, Pb). Yttrium forms three carbides, Y_3C, Y_2C_3, and YC_2, all of which hydrolyze to form hydrocarbons.[17] Silicides of yttrium are refractory.

Group 5A (N, P, As, Sb, Bi). Yttrium forms a nitride, YN, that is unstable to water vapor.

Group 6A (O, S, Se, Te). Y_2O_3 is the only reported stable oxide of yttrium. YS and YSe have been observed.

Group 7A (F, Cl, Br, I). The halides of yttrium have the following melting points: YF_3, 1152°C (2106°F); YCl_3, 709°C (1308°F); YBr_3, 913°C (1675°F); YI_3, 964°C (1767°F).[5]

Actinides. Yttrium and thorium form a complete solid solution in the beta (body centered cubic) forms of these metals, with extensive solid solubility in the room temperature close packed forms.[6] Yttrium is immiscible with uranium in the liquid and solid states,[10] and Scheinhartz[16] has suggested the use of uranium metal dispersions in yttrium as nuclear reactor fuel elements to alleviate the problem of radiation damage. The use of yttrium to contain liquid uranium alloys has been mentioned previously.

Compositions of yttrium and hydrogen have also occasioned much interest in nuclear reactor circles in that the hydrogen is held tightly by the yttrium at high temperatures and provides a very effective neutron reflector and shield. Anderson[18g] has described work done at several laboratories (GE-KAPL, GE-ANP, Denver Research Institute) in which pressure-temperature-composition measurements were made on yttrium-hydrogen samples showing that at approximately a 1:1 atom ratio, a hydrogen pressure of less than 1 atmosphere is generated at 1300°C (2372°F). Significantly higher hydrogen contents (between 1 and 2 atoms of hydrogen/yttrium) were achieved having hydrogen pressures of 1 atmosphere at temperatures between 900–1200°C (1652–2192°F). Samples of these materials are found to be compatible with stainless steel jackets which permits exposure of the clad specimens to the atmosphere at high temperatures. These compositions represent some of the most stable hydrogen containing materials available for this type of reactor application; further study and consideration of this material is in order.

FABRICATION

Yttrium may be conveniently arc melted into ingots as described previously. Ingots of round and irregular cross section may be obtained by casting the metal from a tantalum or molybdenum crucible into a water-cooled copper mold.

As has been mentioned, attempts to work the first quantities of yttrium available for this type of study were quite discouraging. Oxygen, fluorine, and other impurities were present in amounts which suggested that these elements might be responsible for the poor workability observed for yttrium, and concerted efforts were made to eliminate these impurities. It was found that as the oxygen content was lowered the metal became much more ductile; since this high purity metal was obtainable only in small amounts, however, detailed studies of the mechanical properties and the fabricability could not be made. Consequently, as Bohlender[18h] has indicated in his paper on the fabrication of rare earths, much of the information on fabricating yttrium is the result of observations of the less pure (and less workable) metal. That higher purity metal requires less stringent conditions for its fabrication has been confirmed by the development of the salt extraction process for purifying yttrium, which has made larger quantities of low oxygen yttrium available.

Ingot Breakdown

Extrusion and Forging. The ingots resulting from consumable arc melting operations exhibit very large grains that have undergone extreme directional growth; most of the non-metallic impurities in the metal are observed as precipitated phases along the grain boundaries as well as within the grains. These conditions lead to very poor workability of the metal in the "as-melted" condition. A preliminary working operation at this stage improves the grain size and redistributes the inclusions, achieving a more workable condition in yttrium. This preliminary working may be either an extrusion or forging process, as described by Bohlender[18h] and Guidoboni et al.[9] The 6-inch diameter ingots are sealed in copper cans and after soaking, are extruded into a 0.6 to 3.6-inch diameter rod at 700°C (1292°F) at a ram speed of 13 inches per minute. After decladding, the extrusion is turned smooth and may be further extruded at 480°C (896°F) using an oil dag lubricant. By boring out the ingots, tubing 1 to 4 inches in diameter may also be extruded. Because there is a tendency for the copper jacket to react with the yttrium at temperatures as low as 510°C (950°F) the soaking should not be prolonged. Guidoboni[9] reports an extrusion constant of 20 to 30,000 psi in these operations. Bohlender[18h] reports work in which it was found that low oxygen yttrium (500 ppm O_2) may be extruded at 260°C (500°F) into complex shapes having smooth surfaces.

To carry out the initial breakdown of arc melted billets by forging, a 3-hour soaking at 870°C (1600°F) in an inert atmosphere brings a 6-in. diameter specimen to working temperature. This may then be pressed on 90° faces, $\frac{1}{8}$ inch at a time, the corners of the resulting square ingot being rounded by a press after every second or third axial press to prevent interior cracking and opening of the billet. When a 4 x 4 inch billet is obtained by this process, breakdown is sufficient for it to be pressed into a 2 inch slab for flat rolling. Drop or hammer forging is feasible if the ingot is given an initial breakdown as described above. Bohlender[18h] reports work done at Battelle Memorial Institute in which a 4 x 4 inch billet, first formed from a 6-inch diameter billet as described above, was then hammer forged into a 1.5-inch diameter rod at 700°C (1292°F), with 10-minute heatings in an argon atmosphere in a 870°C (1600°F) furnace between forgings.

Rolling. Yttrium may be cold rolled with much better results on low oxygen metal. Guidoboni[9] reports that a 4 to 5 per cent reduction per pass works well with an anneal between each 25 per cent reduction; below a 0.030 inch thickness a 50 per cent reduction per pass is practical. On metal containing less than 1000 ppm oxygen, reductions of 50 per cent per pass appear to give better results than 5 per cent reductions per pass, and sheet 0.009 inch thick has been made.

Yttrium may be hot rolled at 760–870°C (1400–1600°F) in air, with reductions of 10 to 25 per cent per pass to obtain 0.125-inch material from 2-inch stock.

Swaging. As with many other metals, swaging yttrium seems to be a more satisfactory method of obtaining some shapes than rolling. Hot swaging at 788°C (1450°F) gives a smooth finish 0.022-inch wire from ¼-inch rod. Bohlender[18h] and Guidoboni[9] find that in swaging to 0.02-inch diameter, a 5 to 10 per cent reduction per pass serves well with 25 per cent reduction between anneals. In work performed at the GE-ANP described by Bohlender,[18h] a comparison was made between rod rolling and swaging as a method of reducing yttrium stock. After annealing at 982°C (1800°F), identical samples were rod rolled and swaged to cracking failure; rod rolling resulted in a 15 per cent reduction, and swaging 42 per cent.

Drawing. Yttrium rod and tube may be drawn using a MoS_2 calcium stearate lubricant with 25 per cent reduction between anneals.

Machining. Yttrium may be machined by conventional operations such as sawing, milling, drilling, tapping, grinding, etc. In these operations a generous bath with an oil coolant is essential; water-base coolants must not be used. Tool surface speeds of 150 to 200 feet per minute may be expected to give finishes of 30 to 60 RMS. A typical milling operation uses a ⅛-inch cut on a 1¼-inch diameter end mill with feeds of 1 to 12 inches per minute and a tool speed of 93 to 153 rpm. Drilling may be done with points of 90–130° and a speed of 200 to 250 surface feet per minute with a medium feed. Chips from yttrium machining operations are a distinct fire hazard and should be stored with care and processed for remelting or chemical recovery as soon as possible.

Joining. Yttrium may be fusion or spot welded to itself by conventional methods that provide an inert atmosphere. Fusion butt welds show some tendency to crack, but better results are obtained by use of a filler rod. Yttrium may be welded to most other metals, but the quality of the joint is dependent on the nature of the particular alloy system represented by the metals in the welded zone. Fisher and Fullhart,[7] in their study of welded yttrium loops through which liquid uranium alloys have been circulated to simulate fluid fueled nuclear reactors, have described the need for a clean atmosphere in the welding of yttrium. To prevent porosity in the yttrium welds it was necessary to eliminate the film from the liquid weld bead by "chasing" it off onto a piece of yttrium adjacent to the weld; otherwise the film produced a porosity in the weld which occasioned failure of the apparatus.

CORROSION

Yttrium is quite stable to normal atmospheres, acquiring a slight tarnish but never losing its metallic sheen. It oxidizes at higher temperatures, and turnings must be handled carefully since they burn vigorously if ignited. In water vapor at 750°C (1382°F), an oxide coating 10^5 Å thick is formed which protects the metal from further attack.

As mentioned above, yttrium is not rapidly attacked by a 1:1 mixture of concentrated nitric acid and 48 per cent hydrofluoric acid; it is, however, rapidly attacked by other acids.

TOXICITY

Although extensive data on the toxicity of yttrium are not available, no apparent toxic effects have been reported despite considerable exposure of workers to this element.

THE FUTURE OF YTTRIUM

Yttrium promises to have an interesting future. It is the most abundant of the heavy rare earths, and methods of producing it in large quantity have been devised. In the field of nuclear reactor technology, the low cross section of yttrium for neutron capture and the high temperature stability of yttrium-hydrogen compositions have already occasioned much interest and study. The relatively high melting point of yttrium and its inertness toward liquid uranium metal and many liquid uranium alloys have been demonstrated; should further tests confirm the results of preliminary experiments, yttrium will most certainly be considered seriously as a prime material for some nuclear reactors involing bolder approaches to economic nuclear power.

Although yttrium is too large an atom to form solid solution alloys with many of our more useful metals, it has shown promise in the case of magnesium. Perhaps the most striking application of yttrium may be as an additive to some of the more refractory metals and alloys, where its ability to form stable adherent oxide coatings on high temperature alloys has been demonstrated. Further developments in this area are likely.

References

1. Ames Laboratory Staff, *U.S. Atomic Energy Commission Report, IS-1* (1959).
2. Bare, D., and Carlson, O. N., paper accepted for publication in *Trans. Am. Soc. Metals,* 1960.
3. Beaudry, B. J., Master of Science Thesis, Iowa State University, Ames, Iowa, 1959.
4. Dennison, D. H., *U.S. Atomic Energy Commission Report, ISC-617* (1955).
5. Dennison, D. H., Unpublished data, Ames Laboratory, Ames, Iowa, 1960.
6. Eash, D. T., and Carlson, O. N., *Trans Am. Soc. Metals,* **52,** 1097 (1960).
7. Fisher, R. W., and Fullhart, C. B., *Second United Nations Conference on Peaceful Uses of Atomic Energy, Geneva,* **7,** 216 (1958).
8. Gibson, E. D., and Carlson, O. N., *Trans. Am. Soc. Metals,* **52,** 1084 (1960).
8a. Gschneidner, K. A., "A Critical Review of Rare Earth Alloy Systems," U.S. Atomic Energy Commission, 1961.
9. Guidoboni, E. S., Huntress, A. M., and Lowenstein, P., *U.S. Atomic Energy Commission Report, NMI-1223* (1959).
10. Haefling, J. F., and Daane, A. H., *Trans. AIME,* **215,** 336 (1959).
11. Jaffee, R. I., "High Temperature Technology," chapter on "Refractory Metals," New York, McGraw-Hill Book Company, Inc., 1960.
12. McGurty, J. A., and Simmons, C. R., paper presented at National Western Mining and Engineering Conference, Dever, 1960.
13. Powell, J. E., and Spedding, F. H., *U.S. Atomic Energy Commission Report, ISC-617* (1955).
14. Powell, J. E., and Spedding, F. H., *Chem. Eng. Progr. Symposium Ser.,* **55,** 101 (1959).
15. Seybolt, A. U., *Trans. Am. Soc. Metals,* **52,** 971 (1960).
16. Sheinhartz, I., Sylvania-Corning Nuclear Corporation, Quarterly Progress Reports, 1959.
17. Spedding, F. H., Gschneidner, K. A., and Daane, A. H., *J. Am. Chem. Soc.,* **80,** 4499 (1958).
18. Spedding, F. H., and Daane, A. H., editors, "The Rare Earths and Related Metals," Novelty, Ohio, American Society for Metals, 1960.

CHAPTERS IN REFERENCE 18

18a. Powell, J. E., "The Separation of Rare Earth by Ion Exchange."
18b. Carlson, O. N., and Schmidt, F. A., "Metallothermic Preparation of Yttrium Metal."
18c. Huffine, C. L., and Williams, J. M., "Refining and Purification of Rare Earth Metals."
18d. Simmons, C. R., "The Mechanical Properties of Yttrium, Scandium, and The Rare Earths."
18e. Collins, J. F., Calkins, V. P., and McGurty, J. A., "Application of Rare Earths to Ferrous and Non-Ferrous Alloys."
18f. Lundin, C. E., "Rare Earth Metal Phase Diagrams."
18g. Anderson, W. K., "Nuclear Applications of Yttrium, Scandium, and The Lanthanons."
18h. Bohlender, K. M., "Mechanical Fabrication of Rare Earth Metals."
19. Valletta, R. M., Doctoral Thesis, Iowa State University, Ames, Iowa, 1959.
20. Wöhler, F., *Pogg. Ann. chim. phys.,* (2), **39,** 77 (1828).

34. ZIRCONIUM

A. W. Schlechten

Missouri School of Mines and Metallurgy
Rolla, Missouri

INTRODUCTION

Zirconium occurs in Group IVA of the periodic system; it has an atomic weight of 91.22, and its atomic number is 40.

Older references describe zirconium and the other members of the same subgroup as being hard and brittle metals of relative unimportance. Modern developments, however, have shown that zirconium, if sufficiently pure, is soft and ductile, and that it has valuable properties which have given rise to a spectacular increase in its production and an intensive study of the metal and its alloys. The reason for this great interest is the combination of corrosion resistance and low absorption capacity for thermal neutrons that makes zirconium alloys of particular value as constructional material in nuclear reactors. The United States output of zirconium has risen from 21 lb of high-grade ductile metal in 1945 to an estimated 1,370 tons of sponge metal in 1959.

It was in 1789 that Klaproth discovered the presence of a new metal oxide in the mineral zircon. This compound was given the name zirconia, and was recognized to contain a new element. Subsequent chemical studies were made by de Morveau, Vauquelin, and Trommsdorff.

Berzelius is given credit for first producing metallic zirconium in 1824 by the reduction of K_2ZrF_6 with potassium metal. The resulting product must have been quite impure, because he reported that it was in the form of a black powder that could not be compressed or polished like a metal.

In the following years a series of research workers used various methods for the production of zirconium, all of which gave a brittle material because of contamination, usually with oxygen, carbon, nitrogen, or hydrogen.

Lely and Hamburger[35] were the first to produce a metal sufficiently pure so that it showed ductility. They reduced resublimed zirconium chloride with high-purity sodium in a pressure vessel. The same method was used later in the United States by Cooper[10] and by Hunter and Jones.[21]

During World War I there were rumors that the Germans had developed zirconium steels with wonderful properties for ordnance use. This instigated research on the part of several government bureaus and private companies into the production of zirconium and the properties of zirconium alloys. The results were not particularly encouraging.

In 1925 van Arkel and de Boer,[67] and in 1926, de Boer and Fast[14] published the first of a series of papers describing the thermal decomposition of metal halides as a means of producing a pure metal. Zirconium deposited from zirconium iodide onto a hot filament is very ductile and can readily be drawn into fine wires or rolled into thin sheets. This method is actually a refining process because it requires a fairly good grade of metal as a starting material.

Some years later the Foote Mineral Company of Philadelphia started the production of iodide zirconium in this country. Meanwhile the Titanium Alloy Manufacturing Company and the Metal Hydrides Company were producing a nonductile metal suitable for use as a getter, an alloying addition, or in flash powders.

In 1944 the United States Bureau of Mines started research at Albany, Oregon, to develop a practical large-scale method for producing high-purity zirconium. This investigation used, as a raw material, zircon sand found along certain parts of the Oregon coast; some zircon sand concentrate had been made as a by-product in the separation of chromite from the beach sands.

The investigation, under the direction of W. J. Kroll, soon developed a successful method based on the reduction of zirconium tetrachloride with magnesium.[32] This process is similar to the Kroll process for the production of titanium, with the exception of several important variations. Zirconium tetrachloride is a solid at room temperature; it reacts readily with the moisture of the air, and the resulting oxides and oxychlorides are retained in the chloride. If this chloride is added directly to molten magnesium, an oxygen-contaminated metal will be produced and it will be in the form of a powder, as described in the patents of von Zepplin.[69] To avoid this difficulty, the zirconium tetrachloride is heated in a separate portion of the reduction vessel, and the resulting vapors come in contact with molten magnesium and are reduced. Most of the oxygen-bearing material remains unvolatilized. An intermediate step of volatilizing the chloride in a hydrogen atmosphere is effective in reducing iron contamination.

When the Kroll process for large-scale production of titanium was first developed by the Bureau of Mines, the sponge metal was ground and leached to remove magnesium chloride and any excess magnesium metal. This procedure did not work well with zirconium, and a vacuum distillation method was developed which avoided the necessity of grinding the sponge and reduced the opportunity for oxygen and hydrogen contamination encountered in leaching.

The zirconium plant of the Bureau of Mines at Albany, Oregon, evolved through several stages and reached a tonnage basis by virtue of the demands of the Atomic Energy Commission; this plant was subsequently closed and dismantled. In 1960 four companies produced zirconium in the United States. Carborundum Metals Corp. operated a plant of 163 tons

annual capacity at Akron, New York, and a new 600-ton plant near Parkersburg, West Virginia. Wah Chang Corp., which at one time leased the Bureau of Mines plant, has built a new plant, also at Albany, Oregon, estimated at over 300 tons annual capacity. Mallory-Sharon Metals had a 1,000-ton/year plant at Ashtabula, Ohio, and Columbia-National Corp. near Pensacola, Florida, had a 350-ton plant.

The production of zirconium sponge in 1959 was 1,370 tons, of which about 10 tons were commercial grade. Some 165 tons of reactor grade sponge were imported from Japan during 1957 and 1958.

Open market prices for reactor grade sponge in 1959 averaged $6/lb. Atomic Energy Commission contracts purchased sponge at an adjusted, weighted-average price of $6.25/lb.

SOURCES OF ZIRCONIUM

According to the well-known paper of Clarke and Washington,[9] the occurrence of zirconium in the earth's crust is greater than the total percentage of copper, lead, and zinc. It ranks twentieth in order of prevalence and is about as prevalent as chromium. (See Chapter 1.) Certainly the supply, both domestic and foreign, seems to be more than sufficient for any demands made by the production of metal.

Domestic production is entirely in the form of zircon sand, chiefly from the beach sand deposits of Florida and South Carolina, which are worked also for their titanium minerals and which are very extensive. Zircon has also been separated on a small scale from Oregon beach sands, and is found in the gold-monazite gravels of central Idaho and the gold gravels of central California.

Zircon production amounted to 30,443 tons in 1958.

Foreign imports of zircon come chiefly from Australia and, to a much lesser extent, from India. The tonnage obtained from both of these sources has decreased because of better domestic supply and because of restrictions set up by both India and Australia to avoid the shipment of any monazite content of the beach sands. In 1958 about 17,300 tons of zircon were imported.

Zirconium oxide, baddeleyite, is imported from Brazil. This ore, when it contains some zircon, is often called zirkite. Baddeleyite imports have been only a fraction of total zircon imports and domestic zircon production. Brazilian shipments have also been affected by government export restrictions on radioactive ores.

ORE CONCENTRATION AND TREATMENT

Beach sands are readily concentrated by gravity methods; the use of shaking tables has been abandoned in this country in favor of spiral concentrators, which are simpler and use less power. Final cleaning of the concentrate is accomplished with magnetic and electrostatic separators.

Zircon concentrates, when heated in an arc furnace with additions of carbon, yield an impure carbide; the silica content is largely driven off as fume. If nitrogen from the air is allowed to reach the charge or is deliberately introduced as a gas, a mixed zirconium carbide-nitride (cyanonitride) of golden-yellow color is obtained. These furnace products chlorinate readily with evolution of heat, and a relatively pure zirconium chloride is obtained, although no hafnium has been eliminated.

The above procedure is used by the Bureau of Mines, Carborundum, and Wah Chang, but both acid and alkali decomposition methods have been proposed. The new Columbia-National plant fuses zircon with caustic soda, and then separates zirconium from silicon as sodium zirconate.

Separation of Zirconium and Hafnium

Zircon ores contain 0.5 to 2.0 per cent hafnia, and the hafnium has chemical properties so similar to zirconium that no separation is achieved in the usual chemical processes such as those mentioned above. Reactor grade zirconium, however, is limited to a maximum of 0.01 per cent hafnium, because the latter metal has such a high thermal neutron absorption cross section. Zirconium has a cross section of 0.18 barns, whereas hafnium has a cross section of 115 barns—more than 500 times as great. For this reason, hafnium is used for control rods in reactors.

Many methods have been developed for the separation of zirconium and hafnium, such as fractional distillation, ion exchange, fractional crystallization, disproportionation, and liquid-liquid extraction. The last named procedure is

the most widely used. In one process, crude zirconyl chloride is brought into contact with a countercurrent stream of thiocyanate-rich methyl isobutyl ketone. The solvent extracts the hafnium, and the zirconyl chloride is mixed with sulfuric acid and ammonium hydroxide. Zirconium sulfate is precipitated and then agitated with ammonium hydroxide to produce zirconium hydroxide, which is subsequently heated to produce pure zirconium oxide. Other solvents and procedures of precipitation are used. Increased interest has been shown in a process wherein zirconium tetrachloride is selectively reduced to trichloride; the hafnium tetrachloride is then sublimed and a separation is achieved.

PRODUCTION OF DUCTILE ZIRCONIUM METAL

The production of high-purity zirconium metal has almost the same problems as the production of titanium, and the immense sums spent on the latter metal have not developed any startling new procedures. As far as is generally known at present, the only practical process for large-scale production of zirconium is the reduction of zirconium tetrachloride with magnesium or sodium. The iodide decomposition process can be used to purify this metal further.

Various possible methods of production and their limitations are listed below.

Reduction of ZrO_2

The great stability of this compound resists complete reduction by even the strongest reducing agents. Reactions of the oxide with Ca,[26] with Al,[40] with Mg,[39] or with calcium hydride[2] can produce a high-grade metal, but the equilibrium is such that sufficient oxygen is left to impair the ductility. The use of carbon or zirconium carbide[30] as a reducing agent is equally unsuccessful in producing a soft and workable metal.

Reduction of Zirconium Halides

It would appear that the fluorides, bromides, and iodides have no great advantages for regular reduction processes that outweigh their high cost and difficulties of preparation. This leaves, then, zirconium chloride; its reduction with any

of several alkali and alkaline earth metals is possible, but magnesium and sodium are the only
ones that seem economically feasible.

Reduction with magnesium—the Kroll process—is most widely used and will be described
later. Reduction with sodium is used in one of
the new plants. It has certain advantages in
that its low melting point [97.5°C (207.5°F)]
makes it possible to handle it in liquid form;
this facilitates purification, handling, and feeding to the reactor. The reaction product of
zirconium and NaCl can be leached with water
or weak acids, although there is a definite danger
in leaching zirconium, and precautions must be
taken.

The use of sodium also has certain disadvantages. Nearly twice as much monovalent
sodium must be used per pound of zirconium
as compared to divalent magnesium. On the
same basis there is a greater quantity of by-
product chloride to be disposed of. The reactivity of sodium causes certain safety hazards.

The reduction of zirconium chloride with
hydrogen at high temperatures has been investigated, but the resulting metal is finely divided,
it is difficult to collect, and large quantities of
pure hydrogen are needed. The hydrogen reduction of zirconium iodide would have no
advantage over straight thermal decomposition
because the formation of hydriodic acid is endothermic.

The reduction of sodium or potassium zirconium fluoride with sodium or potassium
metal[13] produces a very fine colloidal metal.

Reduction of Other Compounds

A series of zirconium sulfides have been reported.[43,64] It is possible that these could be
reacted with calcium to produce metal, but
there have been no reports of such experiments.

Zirconium nitride is such a stable compound
that it is very unlikely that it can be used
directly as a source of metal.

Reduction of ZrCl₄ with Mg—the Kroll Process

It has already been pointed out that the
reduction of zirconium tetrachloride with magnesium produces a high-purity metal and that
it can be carried out on a large scale.

The method, as developed by Kroll and his

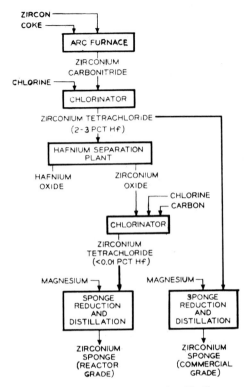

Figure 34.1. Typical flow sheet for Kroll process.

co-workers[27,31,32,33] at the United States Bureau
of Mines, Albany, Oregon, is outlined in Figure
34.1. Some variations from this basic scheme
have been made, such as the use of a resistor
furnace for producing the carbide, or the direct

Figure 34.2. Zirconium sponge as it is removed from
a Kroll process reactor. After the reduction of
ZrCl₄ with magnesium is completed, a vacuum
distillation removes excess magnesium and magnesium chloride to leave zirconium sponge. (*Courtesy
Carborundum Metals Co.*)

chlorination of a zirconium oxide feed; and for melting, a resistance furnace has been used. Other changes have been suggested[29] and might be improvements.

As mentioned before, the unique feature of this process is the heating of the zirconium chloride so that only the vapors come in contact with the magnesium which is the reducing agent.

Zirconium sponge, as it comes from a Kroll process reactor, is shown in Figure 34.2.

The extensive research on the Kroll process for titanium may bring developments that can be transferred to the zirconium process, particularly with respect to simplifying the equipment and operation and increasing the unit size.

Iodide Decomposition Process

Iodide decomposition is a highly effective method for refining zirconium, particularly with respect to oxygen and nitrogen, which are the chief sources of hardness. High-purity feed metal is preferable, because the carry-over of certain metallic impurities is in proportion to their percentage in the original metal.

Essentially, the procedure is to place the crude zirconium in an evacuated vessel which contains a filament of tungsten or zirconium and a means of introducing iodine. The iodine reacts with the zirconium at a moderate temperature to form volatile zirconium iodide. The iodide diffuses to the filament, which is heated to 1200–1300°C (2192–2373°F), and is decomposed so as to deposit zirconium on the filament and release iodine which is available to repeat the cycle. The resulting crystal bar is usually 0.25 to 0.4 in. in diameter in lengths up to 24 in. Westinghouse and Battelle, however, have produced bars as large as 1.7 in. in diameter and 50 ft in over-all length.

Experiments have been made at Battelle on a straight-flow iodide process wherein the crude sponge is iodinated in a separate vessel and then the iodide vapors are passed through a deposition chamber. This would permit purification of the vapors, if necessary, and would give a positive movement to the vapors rather than depending on diffusion.

Investigations to determine whether or not a compound such as zirconium carbide can be used as the source of zirconium in an iodide or bromide decomposition process have not been encouraging.

In the early days of large-scale production of zirconium, it was necessary to refine by the iodide process all of the metal intended for the Atomic Energy Commission; improvements in the Kroll process soon produced a metal of such high purity that the refining step was eliminated.

Electrodeposition of Zirconium

The deposition of a very thin silvery deposit from an aqueous solution containing zirconyl sulphate was reported by Bradt and Linford,[6] but subsequent work by Holt[20] and by Senderoff

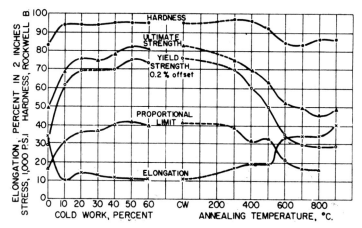

Figure 34.3. Effect of cold work and annealing temperature on the tensile properties of arc melted Kroll process zirconium. (*From Hayes.*)[16]

TABLE 34.1. PHYSICAL AND MECHANICAL PROPERTIES OF ZIRCONIUM

Thermal properties

Property	Value	Remarks	Reference
Atomic number	40		
Atomic weight	91.22		
Density, 20° (g/cc)	6.45		
Melting point	1852 ± 10°C (3366 ± 18°F)		3, 23
Boiling point	3580–3700°C (6476–6692°F)	Estimated	7, 37
Allotropic transition HCP to BCC	862 ± 5°C (1584 ± 9°F)	O, N, C, Al, Hf, and Sn raise the transition temperature; most other alloying elements lower it	44, 45, 68
Thermal expansion linear coefficient	$6.39 \times 10^{-6}/°C$ $\parallel$ c-axis $5.64 \times 10^{-6}/°C$ $\perp$ c-axis $5.89 \times 10^{-6}/°C$ random [all at 20°C (68°F)]	Mean value 298–1143°K = $7.2 \times 10^{-6}/°K$ Mean value β zirconium = $9.7 \times 10^{-6}/°C$	51, 52, 53, 60
Thermal conductivity	0.04 cal/°C/sq cm/cm/sec [at 25°C (77°F)]		5
Specific heat	0.0659 cal/g-°C [at 25°C (77°F)]		59
Molal heat capacity	Zr (α) $C_p = 6.83 + 1.12 \times 10^{-3}T - 0.87 \times 10^{5}T^{-2}$ (298–1135°K) Zr (β) $C_p = 7.27$ (1135–1400°K)		11
Heat content	Zr (α) $H°_T - H°_{298} =$ (298° – 1135°K) = $6.83T + 0.56 \times 10^{-3}T^2 + 0.87 \times 10^{5}\,T^{-1} - 2378$ Zr (β) $H°_T - H°_{298} =$ (1135–1400°K) = $7.27T - 1163$		11
Entropy	9.29 ± 0.04 cal/mole-deg (at 298°K)		59
Heat of fusion	5.5 kcal/mole		7
Heat of vaporization	$\Delta H°_o = 142{,}150 \pm 350$ cal/mole	Estimated	58
Vapor pressure	$\log P \text{ (atm)} = \dfrac{-31{,}066}{T} + 7.3351 - 2.415 \times 10^{-4}T$ (1949–2054°K)		58
Thermal neutron absorption cross section	0.180 ± 0.004 barns/atom		

Electrical properties

Property	Value	Remarks	Reference
Electrical resistivity	High-purity crystal bar-44.1 Regular crystal bar -45 Mg reduced, melted -54 [microhm-cm at 20°C (68°F)]	Wide variation in literature indicates great sensitivity to impurities; 38.8×10^{-6} ohm-cm indicated for zero oxygen[40]	50, 65, 66

Property	Value	Notes	References
Temperature coefficient of resistivity	$43.5 \times 10^{-4}/°C$ (0–200°C) (32–392°F)	Higher purity gives higher coefficient values	1, 13, 66, 73
Pressure coefficient of resistivity	$29.3 \times 10^{-4}/°C$ (0–800°C) (32–1472°F)		8

Pressure kg/sq cm	$\dfrac{\text{R at pressure}}{\text{R at 0 pressure}}$
0	1.0000
40,000	0.9914
80,000	0.9836

Property	Value	Notes	References
Superconductivity	$Tc = 0.546–0.68°K$		34, 44
Electrochemical equivalent	0.2363 mg/coulomb for valence of four		
Thermoelectric power	Zr versus constantan (0–600°C) (32–1112°F) $$\frac{dE}{dt} = 0.05725 - 109.4t \times 10^{-8} \text{ mv/°C}$$ Zr versus alumel (0–600°C) (32–1112°F) $$\frac{dE}{dt} = 0.02881 - 336t \times 10^{-7} \text{ mv/°C}$$		57

Optical and thermionic properties

Property	Value	Notes	References
Emissivity coefficients	$0.46(\alpha)–0.50(\beta)$ (5410Å) $0.43(\alpha)–0.48(\beta)$ (6520Å) $0.49(\alpha)–0.51$ (liq) (6500Å)		12, 71
Photoelectric threshold	3200 Å	Increases to 3400 Å by additions of oxygen	47
Work function	4.1 volts to 3.7 volts		4, 72

Magnetic properties

Property	Value	Notes	References
Susceptibility	200°K 1.28×10^{-6} cgs; 400°K 1.32×10^{-6} cgs; 600°K 1.41×10^{-6} cgs	Zr is paramagnetic and the susceptibility increases linearly with temperature to the transformation temperature	24, 61

Mechanical properties

Property	Value	Notes	References
Modulus of elasticity	$12.8–14.2 \times 10^6$ psi; 13.7×10^6 for pure annealed Zr		1, 48, 55
Poisson's ratio	0.32–0.35		48, 56
Hardness	As low as 60–70 Brinell and Vickers or 20–30 R_B for highest purity Zr		36
Tensile strength	As low as 25×10^3 psi for high purity annealed		41

and Brenner[54] indicates quite conclusively that there is no prospect of producing pure zirconium by the electrolysis of aqueous or organic solutions.

Electrodeposition of zirconium from fused baths has been investigated by many persons. The most recent work on a sizable scale has been reported by Steinberg, Sibert, and Wainer,[62] who had the best success with a bath containing 100 parts of sodium chloride and 25 parts of potassium zirconium fluoride. The essential parts of the cell are constructed of graphite, and an atmosphere of argon is maintained over the bath. Chlorine is evolved at the anode, so the bath builds up with NaF and KF. A dendritic deposit of zirconium impregnated with electrolyte is obtained on the cathode; upon leaching and washing, a zirconium powder is obtained.

Despite claims for economy and purity of product, the electrowinning of zirconium does not seem promising, because of the complexity of the cells, the requirements of high-purity feed, and the powder form of the metal produced.

PHYSICAL AND MECHANICAL PROPERTIES

The physical and mechanical properties of zirconium are given in Table 34.1, in tabular

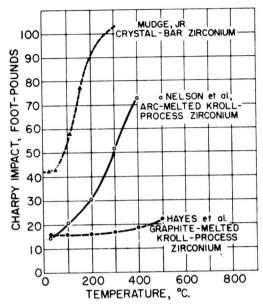

Figure 34.5. Effect of temperature on impact strength of zirconium (*From Hayes.*)[16]

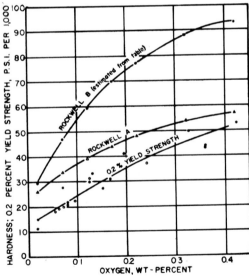

Figure 34.6. Effect of oxygen on hardness and yield strength of zirconium. (*From Hayes.*)[16]

form, in the following order: thermal, electrical, optical and thermionic, magnetic, and mechanical.

Additional information on the variation of mechanical properties with cold work, oxygen content, and temperature, as assembled by Hayes,[16] is given in Figures 34.3 to 34.7.

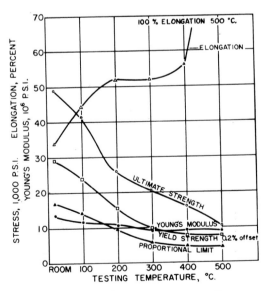

Figure 34.4. Effect of temperature on tensile properties of arc melted Kroll process zirconium. (*From Hayes.*)[16]

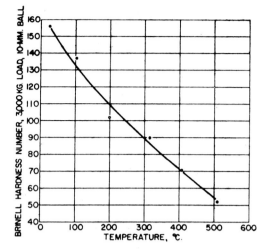

Figure 34.7. Hot hardness of arc melted Kroll process zirconium. (*From Hayes.*)[16]

CHEMICAL PROPERTIES

Reaction with Gases

Oxygen. Zirconium reacts readily with oxygen, the rate of reaction varying with particle size, temperature, presence of impurities, and the nature of the surface. Gulbransen and Andrew[14b] found a measurable rate of oxidation of massive zirconium as low as 200°C (392°F) at 7.6 mm oxygen pressure. After 120 min the film thickness at 200°C was 150 Å and at 425°C (797°F) it was 5000 Å. They did not find any single rate law to fit their data at all temperatures.

Various workers have found that large amounts of oxygen, up to 60 atomic per cent, can be dissolved in solid solution in zirconium without showing any zirconium dioxide structure.

The equilibrium vapor pressure of saturated solutions of oxygen in zirconium are so low that there is no possibility of removing oxygen by vacuum treatment. Lilliendahl and Gregory[35a] removed from 50 to 90 per cent of the oxygen content of zirconium by heating in molten calcium or in calcium vapor.

Bureau of Mines workers found that samples heated in air gained weight faster than those heated in pure oxygen. Samples heated to 1000°C (1832°F) ignited spontaneously. Zirconium powder ignites at much lower temperatures, and its preparation and handling involve considerable risk of explosion and fire.

Nitrogen. The reaction of nitrogen and zirconium occurs very slowly at 400°C (752°F) according to Gulbransen and Andrews[14b] but increases rapidly at 800°C (1472°F) and above; the reaction is insensitive to pressure. Amounts up to 20 atomic per cent form solid solutions; above this ZrN is formed. Nitrogen cannot be removed by vacuum pumping and is not removed by treatment with calcium.

Hydrogen. Hydrogen is absorbed rapidly by zirconium at temperatures between 300–1000°C (572–1832°F). Some absorption has been reported at room temperature for specimens previously heated in vacuum to remove surface contamination which would prevent hydrogen penetration.

In contrast to oxygen and nitrogen, hydrogen can be completely removed by prolonged heating in vacuum above 1000°C (1832°F). The absorption of hydrogen embrittles zirconium to the extent that it can be crushed, thus providing one method for making zirconium powder.

CO_2, CO, and H_2O. Zirconium reacts rapidly with CO_2 above 800° (1472°F) and with CO and with H_2O vapor above 1000°C (1832°F). ZrO_2 is formed by all three gases and at high temperatures the CO and CO_2 also lead to zirconium carbide formation. Lack of resistance to CO and CO_2 attack limits the use of zirconium for gas-cooled reactors to 500°C (932°F) or less.

Reaction with Halogens

Zirconium reacts readily with all of the halogens in the range 200–400°C (392–752°F) to form volatile halides.

Miscellaneous

Zirconium reacts with sulfur, carbon, silicon, phosphorus, boron, and aluminum at elevated temperatures. It also reacts with all metal oxides and other refractory materials, thus making it impossible to use refractory crucibles for melting without contamination of the metal.

CORROSION RESISTANCE

Corrosion in Various Media

Corrosion properties of zirconium, as compared with titanium, tantalum, "Stellite No. 6,"

TABLE 34.2. CORROSION PROPERTIES OF ZIRCONIUM AND OTHER METALS*

The tabulated data include solution concentration, in per cent; temperatures, in degrees F; and resistance to attack, graded as follows:

Excellent: Less than 0.0005 in. penetration per year   Fair: 0.005–0.010 in. penetration per year
Good: 0.0005–0.005 in. penetration per year   Poor: More than 0.010 in. penetration per year

[NOTE.—5, 10% indicates 5% and 10%; 5–10% indicates 5 to 10%]

	Zirconium	Titanium	Tantalum	"Stellite No. 6" Cr = 30%; W = 4.5%; C = 1.10%; Co = remainder	Stainless steel Type 316
Acetic acid	5, 99.5% 140°, 212°F Excellent	5, 10% 68°F Excellent	All % 68–735°F Excellent	10%–conc. Boiling Good	5% glacial 95–390°F Good
Aluminum chloride	20, 30% Room–boiling Excellent	10% 95°, 212°F Excellent	—	—	—
Ammonium hydroxide	28% Room–212°F Excellent	28% Room Excellent		—	All % Good
Aqua regia	65–140°F Poor	65–140°F Excellent	65–140°F Excellent	—	
Calcium chloride	20, 30, 50% 68°, 120°, 212°F Excellent	10, 25% 95°, 212°F Excellent	—	—	5%–saturated 95–212°F Poor
Chlorine-saturated H₂O	Room Excellent	Room Excellent	—		95–212°F Poor
H₂O-saturated chlorine	Room Poor	Room Excellent	—	Room Poor	
Citric acid	10% Room–212°F Excellent	—	—	—	5%–conc. 95–212°F Poor
Chromic acid	10, 20, 30% 68°, 120°, 212° Excellent	10% Boiling Good	—	—	10–50% 95°, 212°F Fair to poor
Phosphoric acid	10–85% Room–212°F Excellent—fair	1–85% 65–212°F Excellent in dilute at room temp., otherwise poor	85% 290–410°F Excellent	38% Boiling Good	10–85% 68°F–boiling Poor
Sodium chloride	3% 95°F Excellent	3% 95°F Excellent	—	—	5% 68°F Good
Sodium hydroxide	10, 50% Room–212°F Excellent	10, 40% 175°F–boiling Good	5, 40% 212°, 230°F 40%–poor	10% Boiling Poor	All % 175–600°F Excellent, except in dilute, boiling
Sulfuric acid	10–96% 65–212°F Excellent in dilute, poor in hot conc.	5–65% 65–95°F Good in dilute, poor in conc.	20%–conc. 65–570°F Excellent	10% Room–boiling Excellent at room temp., poor at boiling	25%–conc. Good at 68°F Poor at high temp.
Carbon tetrachloride	100% Room–120°F Excellent	1–99% Boiling Excellent	—	—	Room Good
Ferric chloride	2.5–30% 65–212°F Poor	1–20% 65–212°F Excellent	5–30% 65°F–boiling Excellent	10, 30% Room–boiling Poor	1–5% 70°F–boiling Poor
Hydrochloric acid	Dilute—excellent at all temps. Conc. at room—excel., conc. at boiling—poor	5%–conc. 95–212°F Poor	19%–conc. 65–212°F Excellent	10%–conc. Room–boiling Poor	Dry, moist 68°F Poor
Lactic acid	5–85% Boiling Excellent	85% 95°F–Boiling Excellent	—	—	5, 10% 95°F–boiling Poor
Mercuric chloride	1%–saturated 95–212°F Excellent	1%–saturated 95–212°F Excellent	Saturated at 212°F Excellent	— —	0.5%–2% 70°F–boiling Poor

TABLE 34.2. CORROSION PROPERTIES OF ZIRCONIUM AND OTHER METALS* (*cont.*)

	Zirconium	Titanium	Tantalum	"Stellite No. 6" Cr = 30% ; W = 4.5% ; C = 1.10% ; Co = remainder	Stainless steel Type 316
Nitric acid	10%–conc. 65–212°F Excellent	5%–conc. 95–212°F Good	Conc. 65–185°F Excellent	Dilute—excellent Conc.—poor	Dilute—excellent Conc. poor Boiling
Potassium hydroxide	10, 20, 30, 40% Room–212°F Excellent	— — —	230°F 5%–excellent 40%–poor	— —	20, 30% 68°F–boiling Good
White-fuming nitric acid	Room–160°F Good	Room–160°F Excellent			

* Corrosion data from "*Zirconium, Its Production and Properties.*" Bulletin 561, Bureau of Mines, U.S. Government Printing Office, 1956.

and No. 316 stainless steel, are given in Table 34.2.

Corrosion in Gases

Hayes, Roberson, and Robertson[18] tested zirconium in CO, CO_2, SO_2, H_2, C_3H_8, and steam at temperatures from 300–1000°C (572–1832°F) with the results shown in Table 34.3.

Corrosion data in air, oxygen, and nitrogen have been reported by Hayes and Roberson,[19] as shown in Table 34.4.

Jaffee and Campbell[22] have reported that zirconium is stable in NH_3 up to 1000°C

TABLE 34.3. WEIGHT GAINS OF ZIRCONIUM IN VARIOUS GASES[18]
(mg/sq dm)

Temperature		Carbon monoxide		Carbon dioxide		Sulfur dioxide		Hydrogen		Propane		Steam	
°C	°F	1 hr	24 hr	1 hr	24 hr	1 hr	24 hr	1 hr	24 hr	1 hr	24 hr	1 hr	24 hr
300	572	—	—	—	—	—	—	95	93	—	—	—	—
400	752	—	—	—	—	—	1.1	95	95	—	—	—	—
500	932	—	—	—	—	20	40	95	95	15	—	—	72
600	1112	30	200	37	220	4,000	Decomposed	93	2,540	39	—	73	107
700	1292	115	275	150	864	5,500	do	95	—	50	193	284	860
750	1382	—	—	—	790	—	—	—	—	—	—	—	—
800	1472	150	600	265	740	—	—	—	—	85	760	385	—
900	1652	90	500	365	1,325	—	—	—	—	143	420	464	—
1000	1832	60	120	900	2,700	—	—	—	—	205	2,080	1,496	—

TABLE 34.4. CORROSION OF ZIRCONIUM IN GASES[19]
(mg/sq dm)

Temperature		Air			Dry air (1 hr)	Oxygen (1 hr)	Nitrogen	
°C	°F	1 hr	4 hr	24 hr			1 hr	24 hr
425	797	7.6	11.4	36	—	—	—	—
500	932	36.0	63.0	159	35	19	—	—
600	1112	95.0	179.0	740	63	38	—	—
700	1292	169.0	286.0	3,515	160	75	4.7	—
800	1472	326.0	565.0	5,930	287	222	7.2	—
900	1652	6,500.0	—	—	2,170	310	15.0	65
1000	1832	—	—	—	—	—	27.0	149
1100	2012	—	—	—	—	—	65.0	304
1200	2192	—	—	—	—	—	102.0	572

TABLE 34.5. CORROSION OF ZIRCONIUM IN
VARIOUS LIQUID METALS

Liquid metals	Temperature (°C)		
	300 (572°F)	600 (1112°F)	800 (1472°F)
Bi	Unknown	Poor	Poor
Bi–In–Sn	do.	do.	Unknown
Bi–Pb	Good	Limited	do.
Bi–Pb–In	Unknown	Poor	do.
Bi–Pb–Sn	Good	Limited	do.
Ga	Limited	Poor	do.
Hg	Poor	do.	do.
Te	Good	Limited	Limited
Mg	Poor at m.p. of 651°C		
Na, K or NaK	Good	Good	
Pb	do.¹	Limited	do.

¹ At its melting point, 327°C (621°F).

(1832°F), and that it reacts with all halides at temperatures of 200–400°C (392–752°F).

Corrosion in Liquid Metals

The work of Koenig,[25] as summarized by Hayes in Table 34.5, shows the corrosion of zirconium in liquid metals and alloys.

Corrosion in Other Media

More detailed data for corrosion behavior in common acids are given in Tables 34.6, 34.7, and 34.8.

MELTING ZIRCONIUM

Ingots for subsequent working are produced from sponge or platelets by arc melting in vacuum or in an inert gas atmosphere.

TABLE 34.6. THE CORROSION RESISTANCE OF ZIRCONIUM IN
HYDROCHLORIC, SULFURIC, PHOSPHORIC, AND NITRIC ACIDS*

Corrosion rate (IPY)	Acid concentration (% by weight)					
	Atmospheric conditions**			High-pressure conditions sealed "Pyrex" containers†		
	Less than 38°C (100°F)	38–80°C (100–175°F)	Boiling temperatures	80–121°C (175–250°F)	121–163°C (250–325°F)	163–204°C (325–400°F)
Hydrochloric						
Less than 0.005	0–37	0–20	0–20	0–37	0–25	0–15
Less than 0.020	0–37	0–20	0–20	0–37	0–37	0–18
Greater than 0.020						18–37
Sulfuric						
Less than 0.005	0–75	0–72	0–66	0–70	0–70	0–15
Less than 0.020	0–78	0–76	0–72	0–70	0–70	0–32
Greater than 0.020	78–95	76–95	72–95			32–70
Phosphoric						
Less than 0.005	0–80	0–61	53	0–60	0–60	0–80
Less than 0.020	0–85	0–63	65	0–60	0–60	0–82
Greater than 0.020		63–80	65–70			82–85
Nitric						
Less than 0.005	0–70	0–70	0–70	0–70	0–70	0–70
Less than 0.020	0–70	0–70	0–70	0–70	0–70	0–70
Greater than 0.020						

* From the Research and Development Division of the Carborundum Metals Co.
** Specimens 2 in. × ½ in. × 0.045 in. with 120-grit silicon carbide finish for 144 hr at atmospheric pressure.
† Specimens 2 in. × ½ in. × 0.045 in. with 120-grit silicon carbide finish 60 ml of CP acid solution. Tubes sealed containing air. Duration of test 48 hr.

TABLE 34.7. SUMMARY OF LONG DURATION CORROSION TESTS IN BOILING 20% HCL*

Surface treatment	Duration of test hours	Iron content of solution (ppm) (IPY)	Corrosion rate for 144 hr exposure (IPY)	Corrosion rate for 2,000 hr exposure (IPY)
As rolled and pickled surface	1,892	5	0.0011	0.003
As rolled and pickled surface	1,892	0	0.0007	0.002
Surface finished with 120-grit abrasive	1,892	5	0.0001	0.002
Surface finished with 120-grit abrasive	1,892	0	0.00006	0.001
Electrolytic polish	1,728	5	0.001	0.0004
Electrolytic polish	1,728	0	0.001	0.0007

* From the Research and Development Division of the Carborundum Metals Co.

TABLE 34.8. RATE CONSTANTS FOR THE CORROSION OF ZIRCONIUM IN HIGH-TEMPERATURE WATER

Temperature		Pressure (psi)	K (mg/ sq cm)	n
°F	°C			
500*	260	2,000	1.5	0.264
550	287	1,048	2.4	0.270
600*	315	2,000	2.6	0.315
600	315	1,553	3.5	0.301
680	360	2,705	5.9	0.330

K and n refer to the oxidation rate law $\Delta_m = Kt^n$.
* Pressurized.

TABLE 34.9. EFFECT OF TEMPERATURE ON CORROSION OF ARC MELTED CRYSTAL BAR ZIRCONIUM Steam at 1 atm*

Temperature		Exposure time (hr)	Weight gain (mg/ sq dm)	Specimen appearance
°F	°C			
1500	816	48	870	Gray-black. White on edges
1150	621	42	205	Gray-black. White on edges
950	510	70	67	Gray. White areas
850	454	72	411	Gray. White spots
750	399	84	2	Black

* From D. E. Thomas, **WAPD–T–186**, June 6, 1954.

TABLE 34.10. CORROSION OF ZIRCONIUM IN FLOWING SODIUM
(Flow rate 5.5 ft/sec)*

Specimen temperature (°C)	Filter temperature (°C)	Oxygen level in Na (ppm)	Exposure time (weeks)	Mean corrosion wt. gain (mg/sq in.)	Mean penetration of Zr (0.001 in.)	Mean corrosion rate (mg/sq cm/ month)	Mean penetration rate (0.001 in./ month)
600	340	260	2	1.65	0.28	3.30	0.57
600	130	23	2	1.70	0.29	3.40	0.59
400	120	21	2	0.045	0.008	0.09	0.016

* From C. Tyzack, *Nuclear Engineering*, 3 (24), 102–114 (1958).

TABLE 34.11. CORROSION RESISTANCE—ZR IN OTHER MEDIA*

Type of media	% Concentration	Temperature (°C)	Corrosion rate (IPY)
Mineral acids			
Hydrofluoric acid			Not recommended
Miscellaneous acids			
Aqua regia	3 HNO_3 to 1 HCl	Room temperature	Poor
Sulfurous acid 6% SO_2	6 (SO_2)	100	0.00017
Chromic acid	10	Boiling	Completely resistant
Chlorine saturated water		Room temperature	0.0006
Red fuming nitric acid	92 HNO_3	Room temperature	0.00002

TABLE 34.11. CORROSION RESISTANCE—ZR IN OTHER MEDIA* (cont.)

Type of media	% Concentration	Temperature (°C)	Corrosion rate (IPY)
Metal chlorides			
Ferric chloride	1	Boiling	0.0009
Ferric chloride	5	Boiling	0.07
Ferric chloride	10	Boiling	0.152
Cupric chloride	1	35	0.0009
Cupric chloride	5	35	0.074
Cupric chloride	10	35	0.35
Cupric chloride	1	Boiling	0.037
Mercuric chloride	Saturated solution	100	Completely resistant
Stannic chloride	24	100	0.00024
Manganous chloride	20	100	0.00024
Nickel chloride	20	100	0.00024
Sodium chloride	Saturated solution		0.00024
Other chlorides			
Ammonium	Saturated solution	100	0.00024
Calcium	25	100	0.00024
Magnesium	42	100	0.00024
Barium	20	100	0.00024
Zinc	20	100	0.00024
Aluminum	25	100	0.00024
Substitute sea water		Room temperature	Completely resistant
Substitute sea water		Boiling	Completely resistant
Organic compounds			
Formic acid	10–90	35–100	<0.0005
Formic acid	90	Boiling	Nil
Acetic acid	5–99.5	35–100	<0.0005
Acetic acid	99.5	Boiling	Nil
Monochloracetic acid	100	35–100	<0.0005
Dichloracetic acid	100	Boiling	0.0085
Trichloracetic acid	100	Boiling	0.445
Lactic acid	10–85	35–100	0.00001
Lactic acid	85	Boiling	Nil
Tannic acid	25	35–100	<0.0005
Oxalic acid	0.5–25	35–100	<0.0005
Tartaric acid	10–50	35–100	<0.0005
Citric acid	10–50	35–100	<0.0005
Acetic anhydride	99.5	Boiling	Nil
Citric acid	50	Boiling	Nil
Carbon tetrachloride	50	Boiling	0.0001
Chloroform	50	Boiling	0.0001
Ethylenechloride	50	Boiling	0.00012
Trichlorethylene	50	Boiling	0.00012
Tetrachlorethylene	50	Boiling	0.00012
Tetrachlorethane	50	Boiling	0.00012
Alkaline solutions and fused caustics			
Sodium hydroxide	10–50	35–100	Excellent
Fused sodium hydroxide	28	35–100	Excellent
Ammonium hydroxide	28–40	35–100	Excellent
Potassium hydroxide	10–40	35–100	Excellent
Liquid sodium		600	Good
Fused potassium hydroxide			Slight attack
Trisodium phosphate	5–20	35–100	Excellent
Uranyl sulphate	U, 40g/liter	250	Excellent

* From the work of Lane, Golden, and Ackerman.[84a]

Earlier work refers to melting zirconium in graphite crucibles by induction heating[42] or by heating with a split-tube graphite resistance element;[28] but it was found that about 0.2 per cent carbon was picked up from the graphite crucibles, and no refractory oxide crucible was practical.

Figure 34.8. A zirconium ingot, weighing 6,700 lb, formed by the arc melting process under argon atmosphere from zirconium sponge. After the rough surface has been removed by machining, the ingot is suitable for use in a continuous blooming mill to make strip and sheet forms. (*Courtesy Mallory-Sharon Metals Corp.*)

The next development was that of tungsten electrode arc furnaces[46] using a water-cooled copper ingot mold similar in principle to experimental furnaces that had been used for other refractory metals. The contamination from the electrode ruled this furnace out in favor of the consumable electrode arc furnace.[63] Double melting procedures are used for alloying, purification, and eliminating porosity. Ingots weighing over 6,000 lb have been made. (See Figure 34.8.)

Other methods such as drip melting[38] auto-crucible melting,[38] and levitation melting[70] have been performed on a small scale in commercial operations.

FABRICATION

The commercial producers of zirconium have the following to say about fabrication.

Rolling and Forging

The stresses and temperatures required for primary working are far lower than for stainless steel and are even lower than for mild steel. Zirconium ingots can be heated to 850°C (1562°F) in ordinary furnace atmospheres and rolled or hammer cogged without difficulty; "Zircaloy II" and III must be heated to about 1000°C (1832°F).

Zirconium billets are sandblasted or pickled in HNO_3-HF, then are heated to 780°C (1436°F) for the same period of time. Annealing in air followed by sandblasting is satisfactory during conversion operations, but vacuum annealing is recommended for finished sizes of fabricated parts, in order to meet final dimensional and finish specifications.

Extrusion

Seamless tubing is made by extruding billets coated with glass or encased in copper. Salt-bath heating permits extrusion temperatures up to 1000°C (1832°F). At 760°C (1400°F) the extrusion constant is greater than that for copper but less than that for mild steel.

Cold Working

Rod, tube, and wire are cold-drawn, and sheet can be deep-drawn in conventional equipment, but the surface of the zirconium or "Zircaloys" must be slightly oxidized unless a copper coating remains from the extruding operation. When the oxidation method is used, reductions must be kept low to prevent rupture of the oxide skin.

Machining

Machining zirconium requires care and a knowledge of the metal, but it does not involve any limitations in terms of design or type of machining operation.

The metal is abrasive and tends to gall. Furthermore, zirconium work-hardens quite rapidly. These characteristics suggest the use of carbide-tipped tools, and fairly heavy cuts.

Zirconium chips can burn if heated, so that care should be exercised to prevent overheating at the cut. Sharp, polished tool edges, adequate coolant, and reasonable cutting speeds will minimize fire hazards.

Power Brake Forming

Unalloyed zirconium, "Zircaloy III," and "Zircaloy II" can be fabricated by techniques similar to those used for unalloyed titanium. In fabricating these grades in their dead-soft, annealed condition—forming 90-deg angle, permanent set—on a power brake, a die adjustment to bend the material 95 to 110 deg before spring-back is required. Planished or temper-rolled material will probably require 100 to 120-deg bending before spring-back. Warming facilitates the forming of zirconium.

Surface Finishing

Zirconium can be finished by conventional mechanical means. Grinding-wheel speeds must be very low, as compared with those for other metals, to prevent burning and excess wheel wear.

Zirconium oxides cannot be removed in pickling baths. Therefore, sand- or metal-grit blasting is substituted at those stages of fabrication where another metal might be pickled—after hot rolling and air annealing, for instance. After mechanically descaling, a HNO_3-HF acid solution dip is recommended.

Welding

Zirconium must be welded in an inert atmosphere to prevent harmful contamination by atmospheric gases. Often, it is advisable to perform the operation with the work inside a vessel that has been evacuated, then filled with argon, as shown in Figure 34.9. More generally, conventional argon-shielded, tungsten-tipped or consumable electrode arc welding equipment is used without a special enclosure. Flash butt welds can be made in an argon atmosphere.

Zirconium's tendency to gall or weld during machining suggests an advantageous joining

Figure 34.9. Zirconium is welded under an inert atmosphere in this closed chamber through which the inert gas is flushed to prevent atmospheric contamination of the metal. (*Courtesy Carborundum Metals Co. and Pfaudler Co.*)

method. Pressure welds with aluminum, e.g., have been made readily and successfully.

ZIRCONIUM-ALLOY SYSTEMS

Many zirconium-alloy systems have been investigated recently, but no systematic investigation has been made of the mechanical properties of such alloys. Hayes[15] believes that no vast improvements will be made by alloying such as those found in titanium-alloy metallurgy. He points out that most alloying elements show only limited solubility in beta zirconium and even less in alpha; solubility of these same elements in titanium is several times greater.

The alpha to beta transition is raised by O, N, Sn, and Al. The transition is lowered by Ta, Cb, Th, and U. Systems showing a eutectic and a eutectoid are obtained with H, W, V, Ag, Be, Co, Cr, Cu, Fe, Mn, Mo, and Ni. Complete solid solubility is found in the Zr-Hf and Zr-Ti systems.

TABLE 34.12. ROOM-TEMPERATURE TENSILE PROPERTIES OF ALPHA ANNEALED ZIRCONIUM ALLOYS

Zr–alloy analysis (wt %)	Strength, lb/sq in.		Elonga- tion in 1 in. (%)	Melting method and base*	Zr–alloy analysis (wt %)	Strength, lb/sq in.		Elonga- tion in 1 in. (%)	Melting method and base*
	Yield (0.2% offset)	Tensile				Yield (0.2% offset)	Tensile		
Iodide Zr[10]	14,000	29,200	34	A–C	0.14 N[10]	72,600	98,600	40	A–C
					0.08 O[4]	37,500	58,000	30	A–C
Sponge Zr[11]	35,800	56,400	33	I–S	0.5 Si[19]	57,600	92,300	16	I–S
					0.3 Ag[19]	42,900	68,100	22	I–S
0.8 Al[18]	49,600	70,000	33	I–C	5.9 Ta[22]	52,000	74,000	26	I–C
1.4 Al[19]	84,800	121,400	9	I–S	9.7 Ta[19]	92,000	124,800	9	I–S
1.6 Cb[18]	54,000	68,800	38	I–C	5.4 Th[19]	54,400	82,500	18	I–S
5.1 Cb[19]	79,800	104,700	14	I–S	2.5 Sn[4]	37,900	51,300	39	A–C
0.9 Cr[19]	44,000	74,600	20	I–S	3.9 Sn[10]	42,000	51,800	33	A–C
0.6 Co[19]	46,500	71,500	14	I–S	5.6 Sn[19]	64,600	100,000	9	I–S
0.4 Cu[4]	26,600	55,300	33	A–C	8.0 Ti[22]	57,800	77,500	6	I–C
1.6 Hf[4]	16,500	38,000	47	A–C	35.0 Ti[23]	110,000	138,800	3	A–C
0.02 H[20]	17,400	39,500	27	A–C	0.4 W[4]	32,600	60,300	23	A–C
0.4 Fe[19]	51,900	72,100	16	I–S	0.5 W[23]	32,600	67,700	17	A–C
0.6 Mn[19]	62,600	93,400	2	I–S	3.4 U[10]	29,700	57,300	35	A–C
0.4 Mo[19]	71,500	100,400	17	I–S	9.7 U[24]	103,000	121,000	18	A–C
1.3 Mo[21]	101,900	124,500	8	I–C	0.004 V[4]	22,500	51,800	26	A–C
0.5 Ni[19]	42,900	73,500	17	I–S	0.8 V[19]	74,500	107,600	12	I–S

* A, arc melted; I, induction melted; S, sponge-zirconium base; and C, crystal bar base.
By permission of the U.S. Atomic Energy Commission, from the "Metallurgy of Zirconium," by Lustman and Kerze, copyright, 1955, by McGraw-Hill Book Company, Inc. (Superscript numbers in above table are reference numbers in this book.)

TABLE 34.13. TYPICAL CHEMICAL ANALYSIS OF ZIRCONIUM AND "ZIRCALOYS"

Element	Zirconium Sponge	"Zircaloy II" Ingot	"Zircaloy III" Ingot
Sn	—	1.460%	0.250%
Fe	0.150%	0.124%	0.250%
Cr	0.020%	0.104%	0.050%
Ni	0.007%	0.050%	0.050%
Al	75 ppm	75 ppm	75 ppm
B	0.5	0.5	0.5
Co	20	20	20
Hf	100	200	200
Pb	100	130	130
Mn	50	50	50
O_2	1400	—	—
N_2	50	80	80
Cl_2	1300	—	—
Si	100	100	100
Ti	50	50	50
V	50	50	50
Cd	0.5	0.5	0.5
C	500	500	500
Cu	50	50	50
Mg	600	20	20
Mo	50	50	50
W	50	100	100
Na	50	—	—
Ca	30	—	—

Tensile Properties of Alloys

The room-temperature tensile properties of alpha annealed zirconium alloys as assembled by Chubb are shown in Table 34.12.

Zircaloy

Two alloys, "Zircaloy II" and "Zircaloy III," have been developed specifically for nuclear applications because of their superior resistance to corrosion especially as influenced by small amounts of oxygen, nitrogen, and hydrogen in the metal.

Typical analyses of commercial zirconium and the two "Zircaloy" alloys are given in Table 34.13 and a comparison of the mechanical properties of the "Zircaloys" is given in Table 34.14.

APPLICATIONS

The chief consumption of zirconium metal has been for nuclear energy applications. This results from its excellent corrosion resistance combined with a low absorption cross section for neutrons. The cross section for zirconium is 0.18 barns (1 barn = 10^{-24} sq cm/ nucleus)

TABLE 34.14. MECHANICAL PROPERTIES OF "ZIRCALOYS"*

	Tensile strength 1,000 psi		0.2% yield strength 1,000 psi		Reduction of area- per cent		Hardness	
	Long.	Trans.	Long.	Trans.	Long.	Trans.	DPH†	Rockwell B
"Zircaloy II"								
Room temperature	66.1	64.6	45.1	55.4	40	40	156–200	90
260°C (500°F)	32.5	32.1	18.9	24.2	62	61		
"Zircaloy III"								
Room temperature	60.3	61.9	37.0	51.3	34	39	144–189	85
260°C (500°F)	26.4	26.3	14.1	19.2	48	38		

* Base annealed.
† 30 kg, ⅔ objective.

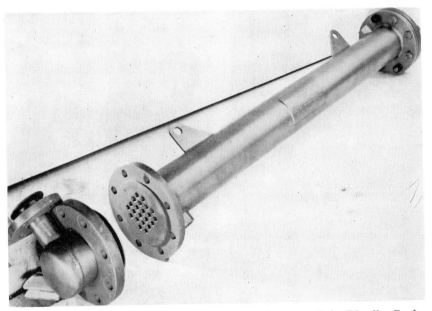

Figure 34.10. Zirconium tube and tube sheet heat exchanger made by Pfaudler Co. for Carborundum Metals Co. as a joint development.

as compared with 0.22 barns for aluminum, about 3 barns for stainless steel, and 120 barns for hafnium.

As a result, zirconium can be used in the core of a reactor as a cladding material for the fuel elements, as an alloying metal with the uranium, or as the material for the structure of the core.* Almost 44 miles of "Zircaloy II," ⁹/₁₆-in.-diameter tubing is installed in the Dresden reactor near Chicago.

* Editor's note: Of 18 nuclear powered vessels that have been authorized, 17 will have reactor cores of zirconium and only one will have stainless steel.

An economic comparison of zirconium and stainless steel for fuel cladding and for permanent parts in a reactor has been made by Benedict.[4a] For slightly enriched fuels zirconium has a great advantage, but as the degree of fuel enrichment increases the economic advantage shifts to the stainless steel. Zirconium has a higher break-even price when used for permanent parts than it does for fuel cladding.

The general commercial application of zirconium depends chiefly on its corrosion resistance. It combines outstanding resistance to both mineral and organic acids as well as to strong alkaline solutions. As the price of commercial grade zirconium is reduced and better knowledge is gained concerning fabrication methods, it will be used in a variety of ways. Pumps, valves, heat exchangers, filters, piping, and other components are already being made. The availability of such parts in a metal with outstanding corrosion resistance will undoubtedly encourage processes never attempted before; this, in turn, will encourage greater use. There are examples of chemical plant installations that failed with every known material until zirconium was used.

Figure 34.11. All-zirconium valve for acid and caustic service. (*Courtesy Powell Valve Co. and Carborundum Metals Co.*)

For chemical industry use, zirconium combines extreme resistance to corrosion in both alkaline and acids exposures. Its low corrosion rates in nitric, hydrochloric, and sulfuric acids, dry chlorine [below about 200°C (412°F)], sodium and potassium hydroxides, sea water, halide salts, and sodium hypochlorite are outstanding. These factors, combined with its fine mechanical properties, make its use attractive in chemical equipment. Figures 34.10 and 34.11 show typical equipment items made of zirconium.

Other uses, such as in vacuum tubes, in photoflash bulbs, and for surgical use, will undoubtedly increase as the new sources of supply make the metal more generally available.

References

1. Adenstedt, H. K., *Trans. Am. Soc. Metals*, **44**, 949 (1952).
2. Alexander, P. P., U.S. Patent 2,038,402 (1936).
3. Armour Research Foundation, *Summary Rep. COO-89*, (1951–52).
4. Becker, J. G., *Review of Modern Physics*, **7**, 95, 128 (1935).
4a. Benedict, M., *Metal Progress*, **75**, 76 (1959).
5. Bing, G., Fink, F. W., and Thompson, H. B., *Rept. BMI-65* (April 16, 1951).
6. Bradt, W. E., and Linford, H. B., *Trans. Electrochem. Soc.*, **70**, 431 (1936).
7. Brewer, L., "Chemistry and Metallurgy of Miscellaneous Materials," edited by L. L. Quill, p. 13, McGraw-Hill, New York, (1950).
8. Bridgeman, P. W., *Proc. Am. Acad. Arts Sci.*, **81**, (4), 165 (1952).
9. Clarke, F. W., and Washington, H. S., *U.S. Geol. Survey Profess. Paper* **127** (1924).
10. Cooper, H. S., *Trans. Electrochem. Soc.*, **43**, 215 (1923).
11. Coughlin, J. P. and King, E. G., *J. Am. Chem. Soc.*, **72**, 2262 (1950).
12. Cubicciotti, D., *J. Am. Chem. Soc.*, **73**, 2032 (1951).
13. de Boer, J. H., *Z. anorg. chem.*, **187**, 177 (1930).
14. de Boer, J. H., and Fast, J. D., *Z. anorg. chem.*, **153**, 1 (1926).
14a. Golden, L. B., A.S.M. Symposium on "Zirconium and Zirconium Alloys," pp. 305–326 (1953).
14b. Gulbransen, E. A., and Andrew, R. F., *Trans. Am. Inst. Mining Met. Engrs.*, **185**, 515 (1949).
15. Hayes, E. T., *Metal Progress*, **63**, 109 (1953).
16. Hayes, E. T., *U.S. Bur. Mines, Bull.* **561**, (1956).
17. Hayes, E. T., Dilling, E. D., and Roberson, A. H., *Trans. Am. Soc. Metals*, **42**, 619 (1950).
18. Hayes, E. T., Roberson, A. H., and Robertson, R. H., *J. Electrochem. Soc.*, **97**, 316–323 (1950).
19. Hayes, E. T., and Roberson, A. H., *J. Electrochem. Soc.*, **96**, 142–151 (1949).
20. Holt, M. L., *J. Electrochem. Soc.*, **98**, No. 3, 33C (1951).
21. Hunter, M. A., and Jones, A., *Trans. Electrochem. Soc.*, **44**, 23 (1923).
22. Jaffee, R. I., and Campbell, I. E., "The Properties of Zirconium," Battelle Memorial Inst., AEC file *NP-266*, (June 18, 1947) 24 pp.
23. Keeler, J. H., *G. E. Research Lab. Rep. SO-2512*, (Oct. 5, 1953).
24. Klemm, W., *Z. Elektrochem.*, **45**, 354 (1939).
25. Koenig, R. F., "Corrosion of Zirconium and Its Alloys in Liquid Metals," Knolls Atomic

Power Lab., Schenectady, N.Y. (Oct. 1, 1953) 14 pp.

26. Kroll, W. J., *Z. anorg. chem.*, **234**, 42 (1937).

27. Kroll, W. J., Anderson, C. T., et al., *J. Electrochem. Soc.*, **94**, 1 (1948).

28. Kroll, W. J., Anderson, C. T., and Gilbert, H. L., *Am. Inst. Mining Met. Engrs., Tech. Publ.*, **2310** (1948).

29. Kroll, W. J., Hergert, W. F., and Yerkes, L. A., *J. Electrochem. Soc.*, **97**, 305 (1950).

30. Kroll, W. J., and Schlechten, A. W., *J. Electrochem. Soc.*, **93**, 247 (1948).

31. Kroll, W. J., Schlechten, A. W., et al., *Trans. Electrochem. Soc.*, **92**, 99 (1947).

32. Kroll, W. J., Schlechten, A. W., and Yerkes, L. A., *Trans. Electrochem. Soc.*, **89**, 263 (1946).

33. Kroll, W. J., Stephens, W. W., and Holmes, H. P., *Trans. Am. Inst. Mining Met. Engrs.*, **188**, 1445 (1950).

34. Kurti, N. and Simon, F., *Proc. Roy. Soc. London*, **151A**, 610 (1935).

34a. Lane, I. R., Golden, L. B. and Ackerman, W. L., *Ind. Eng. Chem.*, **45**, 1067 (1953).

35. Lely, D., and Hamburger, L., *Z. anorg. chem.*, **87**, 209 (1914).

35a. Lilliendahl, W. C. and Gregory, E. D., *J. Electrochem. Soc.*, **99**, 187 (1952).

36. Lilliendahl, W. C., Wroughton, D. M., and Gregory, E., *Trans. Electrochem. Soc.*, **93**, 235 (1948).

37. Loftness, R. L., *Rept. NAA-SR-132* (July 10, 1952).

38. Magel, T. T., Kulin, S. A., and Kaufman, A. R., *Rept. MIT 1080, AECD 3320* (Jan. 1952).

39. Marden, J. W., U.S. Patent 1,602,542 (1926).

40. Marden, J. W., and Rich, M. N., *U.S. Bur. Mines, Bull.* **186** (1921).

41. Mudge, W. L., *Rept. WAPD-T-46* (June 1953).

42. National Lead Co., *Steel*, **128** (5), 77 (1951).

43. Picon, M., *Compt. rend.*, **196**, 2003 (1933).

44. Pfeil, P.C.L., *Rept. AERE-M/TN-11* (June 9, 1952).

45. Pfeil, P.C.L., *Rept. AERE-M/R-960* (June 27, 1952).

46. Radtke, S. F., Scriver, R. M., and Snyder. J. A., *J. Metals*, **3**, 620 (1951).

47. Rentschler, H. C., and Henry, D. E., *Trans. Electrochem. Soc.*, **87**, 289 (1945).

48. Reynolds, M. B., *Trans. Am. Soc. Metals,* **45**, 839 (1953).

49. Roberts, L. D., and Dabbs, J. W. T., *Phys. Rev.*, **86**, 628 (1952).

50. Roberts, L. D., Sartain, C. C., and Dabbs, J. W. T., *Rept. ORNL-1365* (June 20, 1952).

51. Russell, R. B., *Rept. MIT-1073* (Oct. 1951).

52. Russell, R. B., *Rept. MIT-1102* (Dec. 1952).

53. Russell, R. B., *Trans. Am. Inst. Mining Met. Engrs.*, **200**, 1045 (1954).

54. Senderoff, S., and Brenner, A., *J. Electrochem. Soc.*, **97**, 361 (1950).

55. Schwope, A. D. and Muehlenkamp, G. T., *Rept. BMI-T-23* (April 1950).

56. Schwope, A. D. and Stockett, S. J., *Rept. BMI-T-32* (July 1, 1950).

57. Schoens, C. J. and Shortall, J. W., *Rept. LRL-62* (Dec. 1953).

58. Skinner, G. B., Edwards, J. W., and Johnston, H. L., *J. Am. Chem. Soc.*, **73**, 174 (1951).

59. Skinner, G. B. and Johnston, H. L., *J. Am. Chem. Soc.*, **73**, 4549 (1951).

60. Skinner, G. B. and Johnston, H. L., *J. Chem. Phys.*, **21**, 1383 (1953).

61. Squire, C. F. and Kaufmann, A. R., *J. Chem. Phys.*, **9**, 673 (1941).

62. Steinberg, M. A., Sibert, M. E. and Wainer, E., *J. Electrochem. Soc.*, **101**, 63 (1954).

63. Stephens, W. W., Gilbert, H. L., and Beall, R. A., *Trans. Am. Soc. Metals,* **45**, 862 (1953).

64. Strotzer, E. R., Biltz, W., and Meisel, K., *Z. anorg. chem.*, **242**, 249 (1939).

65. Treco, R. M., "Zirconium and Zirconium Alloys", p. 254, American Society for Metals, Cleveland (1953).

66. Udy, M. C., Shaw, H. L., and Boulger, F. W., *Rept. BMI-711* (Feb. 20, 1952).

67. Van Arkel, A. E., and de Boer, J. H., *Z. anorg. chem.*, **148**, 345 (1925).

68. Vogel, R., and Tonn, W., *Z. anorg. u. allgem. Chem.*, **202**, 293 (1931).

69. von Zepplin, H., U.S. Patent 2,214,211 (1940).

70. Wroughton, D. M., et. al., *J. Electrochem. Soc.*, **99**, 205 (1952).

71. Zwikker, C., *Proc. Acad. Sci. Amsterdam*, **29**, 792 (1926).

72. Zwikker, C., *Physik. Z.*, **30**, 578 (1929).

73. Zwikker, C., "Physical Properties of Solid Materials", p. 250, New York, Interscience (1954).

35. PHYSICAL PROPERTIES OF METALS

CLIFFORD A. HAMPEL

Consulting Chemical Engineer
Skokie, Ill.

This chapter is devoted to the presentation, in tabular form, of many of the data on the physical properties of the metals described in this book, as well as corresponding data for the more common metals. Such a summary will enable the user to compare directly the properties of several metals and to locate conveniently the pertinent values desired. Also included is a list of metal prices that prevailed in early 1960.

With respect to the rare metals the values listed have been taken, when available, from those selected by the contributors of the individual chapters of this book. Properties of the more common metals have been obtained from a variety of sources, chiefly the well-known critical surveys such as those of the U.S. Bureau of Mines, the National Bureau of Standards, the American Society for Metals, and the Atomic Energy Commission. More complete bibliographic information is given in the reference list for this chapter.

The compiler of physical data is always faced with the problem of choosing the most probable and accurate value for any one property of a specific material from a variety of reported values which in many instances are only of the same order of magnitude. This dilemma is even greater in the case of metals that are in general more difficult to obtain in pure or uncontaminated form than most compounds or nonmetallic elements. Many factors contribute to this difficulty. Most metals exist in the solid state at ordinary temperatures and are not soluble in common solvents. Thus they are not amenable to the variety of manipulations related to purification and handling that

are possible with many other materials. Data on physical properties in the liquid and gaseous states are often quite difficult to obtain simply because of the physical problems of working at the high temperatures associated with these states while maintaining a high degree of purity in the metals. Nonreactive containers for use at elevated temperatures are not easy to find, and the increased chemical reactivity engendered by the high temperatures needed to maintain the liquid or gaseous state increases the pickup of impurities.

The effect of even minute amounts of impurities on the properties of metals is widely appreciated, of course, and the discrepancies in reported values for such properties are not surprising in view of the twin problems of obtaining and maintaining metals in a highly pure form.

In recent years techniques and equipment have been developed for the preparation and handling of metals at elevated temperatures in highly purified form. These have resulted in more accurate measurement of physical properties. Among such developments have been the arc melting and electron beam melting of metals under high vacuum or inert atmospheres, the improved vacuum equipment, and the attainment of greater purity in the raw materials from which uncontaminated metals are made.

In addition to the matter of purity, variations in physical properties are caused by the way in which the solid state is reached. For instance, the thermal history of a sample profoundly affects the crystal size and the state and distribution of impurities present in the metal. The nature of the prior mechanical treatment

TABLE 35.1. PHYSICAL PROPERTIES

(Elements in italics not

Name	Symbol	Atomic number	Atomic weight	Density, 20°C,		Melting point,	
				g/cc	lb/cu in.	°C	°F
Aluminum	Al	13	26.98	2.7	0.0975	660	1220
Antimony	Sb	51	121.76	6.68	0.241	630.5	1167
Arsenic	As	33	74.91	5.727	0.207	814	1497
Barium	Ba	56	137.36	3.5	0.126	710	1310
Beryllium	Be	4	9.013	1.845	0.0665	1284	2345
Bismuth	Bi	83	209	9.8	0.354	271.3	520
Boron	B	5	10.82	2.34	0.0808	2300	4172
Cadmium	Cd	48	112.41	8.65	0.312	320.9	610
Calcium	Ca	20	40.08	1.54	0.0556	851	1564
Cerium	Ce	58	140.13	6.66	0.241	795	1463
Cesium	Cs	55	132.91	1.873	0.0676	28.5	83.3
Chromium	Cr	24	52.01	7.19	0.259	1875	3407
Cobalt	Co	27	58.94	8.90	0.321	1493	2719
Columbium	Cb	41	92.91	8.57	0.309	2468	4474
Copper	Cu	29	63.54	8.94	0.321	1083	1981
Dysprosium	Dy	66	162.51	8.536	0.309	1407	2565
Erbium	Er	68	167.21	9.051	0.327	1497	2730
Europium	Eu	63	152.0	5.259	0.190	826	1519
Gadolinium	Gd	64	157.26	7.895	0.285	1312	2394
Gallium	Ga	31	69.72	5.907	0.212	29.75	85.55
Germanium	Ge	32	72.60	5.32	0.191	936	1717
Gold	Au	79	197.2	19.32	0.698	1063	1945
Hafnium	Hf	72	178.50	13.29	0.480	2150	3902
Holmium	Ho	67	164.94	8.803	0.318	1461	2662
Indium	In	49	114.82	7.31	0.264	156.6	314
Iridium	Ir	77	192.2	22.42	0.808	2410	4370
Iron	Fe	26	55.85	7.87	0.284	1535	2795
Lanthanum	La	57	138.92	6.174	0.224	920	1688
Lead	Pb	82	207.21	11.34	0.410	327.4	621
Lithium	Li	3	6.940	0.534	0.0193	179	354
Lutetium	Lu	71	174.99	9.842	0.356	1652	3006
Magnesium	Mg	12	24.32	1.74	0.063	651	1204
Manganese	Mn	25	54.94	7.44	0.268	1244	2271
Mercury	Hg	80	200.61	13.55	0.489	−38.87	−37.96
Molybdenum	Mo	42	95.95	10.22	0.369	2610	4730
Neodymium	Nd	60	144.27	7.004	0.253	1024	1875
Nickel	Ni	28	58.69	8.9	0.321	1452	2646
Osmium	Os	76	190.2	22.5	0.812	3000	5432
Palladium	Pd	46	106.4	12.02	0.434	1552	2826
Platinum	Pt	78	195.09	21.40	0.772	1769	3216
Plutonium	Pu	94	239.11	19.84	0.714	639.5	1183
Potassium	K	19	39.10	0.87	0.0313	63.7	147
Praseodymium	Pr	59	140.92	6.782	0.245	935	1715
Promethium	Pm	61	145	—	—	1035	1895
Rhenium	Re	75	186.22	21.02	0.76	3180	5756
Rhodium	Rh	45	102.91	12.44	0.449	1960	3560
Rubidium	Rb	37	85.48	1.53	0.0552	38.5	101.3
Ruthenium	Ru	44	101.1	12.4	0.448	2250	4082
Samarium	Sm	62	150.35	7.536	0.273	1072	1962
Scandium	Sc	21	44.96	2.99	0.108	1539	2802
Selenium	Se	34	78.96	4.79	0.173	217	423
Silicon	Si	14	28.09	2.33	0.0843	1410	2570
Silver	Ag	47	107.873	10.49	0.379	960.5	1761
Sodium	Na	11	22.991	0.97	0.035	97.9	207.5
Strontium	Sr	38	87.63	2.6	0.094	770	1418
Tantalum	Ta	73	180.95	16.6	0.600	2996	5425
Tellurium	Te	52	127.61	6.25	0.226	449.5	841
Terbium	Tb	65	158.93	8.272	0.299	1356	2473
Thallium	Tl	81	204.39	11.85	0.428	303	577
Thorium	Th	90	232.05	11.66	0.421	1750	3182
Thulium	Tm	69	168.94	9.332	0.338	1545	2813
Tin	Sn	50	118.7	7.3	0.263	232	449
Titanium	Ti	22	47.90	4.54	0.164	1668	3035
Tungsten	W	74	183.92	19.3	0.697	3410	6170
Uranium	U	92	238.07	19.07	0.688	1132	2070
Vanadium	V	23	50.95	6.11	0.221	1919	3486
Ytterbium	Yb	70	173.04	6.977	0.252	824	1515
Yttrium	Y	39	88.92	4.472	0.162	1509	2748
Zinc	Zn	30	65.38	7.133	0.258	419.5	787
Zirconium	Zr	40	91.22	6.45	0.233	1852	3366

of Metals

included in this book)

Symbol	Boiling point, °C	Boiling point, °F	Latent heat of fusion, cal/g	Latent heat of vaporization, cal/g	Specific heat, cal/g/°C
Al	2450	4442	96	3050	0.214 (20°)
Sb	1440	2624	38.3	383	0.0504 (20°)
As	615	1139 (sublimes)	88.5	102 (subl.)	0.078
Ba	1500	2732	13.3	262	0.068 (20°)
Be	2507	4545	250–275	5917	0.425 (20°)
Bi	1627	2960	12.5	204.3	0.0294 (20°)
B	2550	4622	489	8300	0.307 (25°)
Cd	767	1413	13.2	286.4	0.055 (28°)
Ca	1482	2700	55.7	918	0.149 (20°)
Ce	3468	6265	15.7	679	0.049 (20°)
Cs	705	1301	3.766	146	0.052 (20°)
Cr	2199	3990	61.5	1474	0.1068 (20°)
Co	3100	5610	62	1500	0.1056 (20°)
Cb	4927	8900	69	1782	0.0642 (20°)
Cu	2595	4703	48.9	1150	0.092 (20°)
Dy	2600	4712	25.2	412	0.0413 (0°)
Er	2900	5252	24.5	401	0.0398 (0°)
Eu	1439	2614	15.15	276	0.0395 (0°)
Gd	3000	5432	23.6	459	0.0713 (0°)
Ga	1983	3601	19.16	1014	0.0977 (29°)
Ge	2700	4892	111.5	1200	0.086 (25°)
Au	2966	5371	14.96	415	0.0312 (18°)
Hf	5400	9752	29.1	885	0.0352 (20°)
Ho	2600	4712	24.8	405	0.0391 (0°)
In	2075	3767	6.8	484	0.058 (20°)
Ir	5300	9572	32.6	790	0.032 (20°)
Fe	3000	5432	66.2	1515	0.107 (20°)
La	3469	6277	17.3	690	0.048 (20°)
Pb	1737	3159	5.89	204.6	0.031 (20°)
Li	1317	2403	158	4680	0.784 (0°)
Lu	3327	6021	26.3	515	0.0368 (0°)
Mg	1103	2017	82.2	1337	0.25 (25°)
Mn	2097	3806	63.7	977.6	0.114 (20°)
Hg	357	674.4	2.8	69.7	0.03325 (20°)
Mo	5560	10,040	69.8	1222	0.066 (0°)
Nd	3027	5481	18.0	479	0.0499 (0°)
Ni	2900	5252	73.8	1487	0.105 (20°)
Os	5500	9932	36.9	790	0.039 (20°)
Pd	3980	7196	37.8	88.3	0.0584 (20°)
Pt	4530	8186	24.1	625	0.0314 (20°)
Pu	3235	5855	~3	336.6	0.034 (25°)
K	760	1400	14.6	496	0.18 (14°)
Pr	3127	5661	17.0	560	0.0458 (0°)
Pm	2730	4946	—	415	
Re	5900	10,652	42.4	815	0.03262 (20°)
Rh	4500	8132	50.5	1150	0.059 (20°)
Rb	688	1270	6.1	212	0.080 (0°)
Ru	4900	8852	60.3	1340	0.057 (20°)
Sm	1900	3452	17.3	306	0.0431 (20°)
Sc	2727	4941	85.3	1743	0.1332 (20°)
Se	685	1265	16.5	79.6	0.081 (20°)
Si	2480	4496	395	2530	0.1597 (0°)
Ag	2212	4014	25	556	0.056 (20°)
Na	883	1621	27.05	1005	0.295 (20°)
Sr	1380	2516	25	383	0.176 (20°)
Ta	6100	11,012	41.5	995	0.034 (0°)
Te	990	1814	32	95	0.047 (20°)
Tb	2800	5072	24.5	440	0.041 (0°)
Tl	1457	2655	5.04	189.9	0.031 (20°)
Th	4200	7592	19.8	560	0.0282 (20°)
Tm	1727	3141	26.0	348	0.0381 (0°)
Sn	2270	4118	14.5	573	0.0542 (20°)
Ti	3260	5900	104.5	2350	0.125 (20°)
W	5900	10,652	46	1038	0.032 (20°)
U	3813	6895	19.75	420	0.028 (20°)
V	3000	5432	82.5	2150	0.120 (0°)
Yb	1427	2601	12.71	220	0.0347 (0°)
Y	3200	5792	46.2	1045.8	0.074 (50°)
Zn	906	1663	24.4	419.5	0.0925 (20°)
Zr	3580	6476	60.3	1360	0.0659 (20°)

(hot or cold working) has similar and additional effects. Furthermore, the allotropy of many metals, whereby different crystal forms may exist at a given temperature, influences the physical characteristics of a metal. In this respect the prior thermal and mechanical treatments are major factors in determining what crystal form or forms will exist in a sample whose physical properties are being measured.

Because of all these variables the comparison and choice of values for the physical properties of metals become quite involved. However, the data listed in this chapter can be considered representative of the properties of metals even if they are not absolutely precise and reproducible.

Incidentally, not all the elements regarded as metals are included in the tabulations of this chapter. In addition to those metals covered in this book, aluminum, antimony, arsenic, copper, gold, iron, lead, magnesium, mercury, nickel, potassium, silver, sodium, tin, and zinc are included in the following tables.

Table 35.1

Values for atomic number, atomic weight, density, melting point, boiling point, latent heat of fusion, latent heat of vaporization, and specific heat near room temperature for both rare and common metals are listed in Table 35.1 insofar as they are available. Data for the

TABLE 35.2. DENSITIES OF METALS IN ASCENDING ORDER

(Elements in italics not included in this book.)

Element	Atomic number	Density, g/cc	Element	Atomic number	Density, g/cc
Lithium	3	0.534	Samarium	62	7.536
Potassium	19	0.87	*Iron*	26	7.87
Sodium	11	0.97	Gadolinium	64	7.895
Rubidium	37	1.53	Terbium	65	8.272
Calcium	20	1.54	Dysprosium	66	8.536
Magnesium	12	1.74	Columbium	41	8.57
Beryllium	4	1.845	Cadmium	48	8.65
Cesium	55	1.873	Holmium	67	8.803
Silicon	14	2.33	*Nickel*	28	8.9
Boron	5	2.34	Cobalt	27	8.90
Strontium	38	2.6	*Copper*	29	8.94
Aluminum	13	2.7	Erbium	68	9.051
Scandium	21	2.99	Thulium	69	9.332
Barium	56	3.5	Bismuth	83	9.8
Yttrium	39	4.472	Lutetium	71	9.842
Titanium	22	4.54	Molybdenum	42	10.22
Selenium	34	4.79	*Silver*	47	10.49
Europium	63	5.259	*Lead*	82	11.34
Germanium	32	5.32	Thorium	90	11.66
Arsenic	33	5.727	Thallium	81	11.85
Gallium	31	5.907	Palladium	46	12.02
Vanadium	23	6.11	Ruthenium	44	12.4
Lanthanum	57	6.174	Rhodium	45	12.44
Tellurium	52	6.25	Hafnium	72	13.29
Zirconium	40	6.45	*Mercury*	80	13.55
Cerium	58	6.66	Tungsten	74	19.3
Antimony	51	6.68	Uranium	92	19.07
Praseodymium	59	6.782	Tungsten	74	19.3
Ytterbium	70	6.977	*Gold*	79	19.32
Neodymium	60	7.004	Plutonium	94	19.84
Zinc	30	7.13	Rhenium	75	21.02
Chromium	24	7.19	Platinum	78	21.40
Tin	50	7.3	Iridium	77	22.42
Indium	49	7.31	Osmium	76	22.5
Manganese	25	7.44			

metals covered in this book have been taken from the individual chapters, if given there, and supplemented by such values as could be obtained from other sources which are also sources of data for the more common metals.

With few exceptions, all information concerning aluminum, antimony, lead, magnesium, mercury, potassium, sodium, tin, and zinc has been taken from the "Liquid Metals Handbook" sponsored by the Atomic Energy Commission and the Department of the Navy, and edited by R. N. Lyon. For the other metals, principal sources of data on melting and boiling points, latent heats, and specific heats include critical compilations by K. K. Kelley of the U.S. Bureau of Mines, Stull and Sinke, and "The Reactor Handbook" of the U.S. Atomic Energy Commission. Density values have also been taken from the National Bureau of Standards Circular C447, "Mechanical Properties of Metals and Alloys," and the "Metals Handbook" of the American Society for Metals. All these publications include references to the original articles from which data were derived.

Table 35.2

In this table the metals are arranged in ascending order of densities. Included are the atomic numbers of the metals to indicate that the atomic number or atomic weight of a metal bear little relationship to its density, or rather, its density relative to those of other metals. The table offers a convenient method of comparing the densities of metals and reveals the wide spread in metal densities, from 0.534 g/cc for lithium to 22.5 for osmium, the heaviest element.

A number of interesting relationships are disclosed in this table. While lead has always been regarded as a heavy metal, it actually stands at the midpoint of the tabulation. It is, however, one of the heavier of the common metals, exceeded by mercury and gold. All the metals that are heavier than lead, with the exception of mercury, are uncommon according to any criterion of measurement. By and large the metals long known and used by man are those whose densities lie in the range of about 6 to 11 g/cc. Of the lighter metals, sodium, magnesium, and aluminum have been in tonnage production for many years, sodium chiefly for chemical applications, the other two for structural uses. In the past few years beryllium and titanium, among the metals with densities below 5, have also been used for structural purposes.

Table 35.3

Table 35.3 lists melting and boiling points in ascending order of melting points.

The length of the liquid range of many of the metals is most interesting. While tin has long been regarded as having one of the longest, its range is exceeded by those of the fissionable metals: uranium, plutonium, and thorium; by the rare earth metals: cerium, lanthanum, and

TABLE 35.3. MELTING AND BOILING POINTS OF METALS IN ASCENDING ORDER OF MELTING POINTS
(*Elements in italics are not included in this book.*)

	Melting point,		Boiling point,	
	°C	°F	°C	F°
Mercury	−38.87	−38	357	675
Cesium	28.5	83.3	705	1301
Gallium	29.75	85.5	1983	3601
Rubidium	38.5	101.3	688	1270
Potassium	63.7	147	760	1400
Sodium	97.9	208	883	1621
Indium	156.6	314	2075	3767
Lithium	179	354	1317	2403
Selenium	217	423	685	1265
Tin	232	449	2270	4118
Bismuth	271.3	520	1627	2960
Thallium	303	577	1457	2655
Cadmium	321	610	767	1413
Lead	327.4	621	1737	3159
Zinc	419.5	787	906	1663
Tellurium	449.5	841	990	1814

TABLE 35.3. MELTING AND BOILING POINTS OF METALS IN ASCENDING ORDER OF MELTING POINTS (*cont.*)
(*Elements in italics are not included in this book.*)

	Melting point,		Boiling point,	
	°C	°F	°C	F°
Antimony	630.5	1167	1440	2624
Plutonium	639.5	1183	3235	5855
Magnesium	651	1204	1103	2017
Aluminum	660	1220	2450	4442
Barium	710	1310	1500	2732
Strontium	770	1418	1380	2516
Cerium	795	1463	3468	6265
Arsenic	814	1497	615	1139 (sublimes)
Ytterbium	824	1515	1427	2601
Europium	826	1519	1439	2614
Calcium	851	1564	1482	2700
Lanthanum	920	1688	3470	6278
Praseodymium	935	1715	3127	5661
Germanium	936	1717	2700	4892
Silver	960.5	1761	2212	4014
Neodymium	1024	1875	3027	5481
Promethium	1035	1895	2730	4946
Gold	1063	1945	2966	5713
Samarium	1072	1962	1900	3452
Copper	1083	1981	2595	4703
Uranium	1132	2070	3813	6895
Manganese	1244	2271	2097	3806
Beryllium	1284	2345	2507	4545
Gadolinium	1312	2394	3000	5432
Terbium	1356	2473	2800	5072
Dysprosium	1407	2565	2600	4712
Silicon	1410	2570	2480	4496
Nickel	1452	2646	2900	5252
Holmium	1461	2662	2600	4712
Cobalt	1493	2719	3100	5610
Erbium	1497	2730	2900	5252
Yttrium	1509	2748	3200	5792
Iron	1535	2795	3000	5432
Scandium	1539	2802	2727	4941
Thulium	1545	2813	1727	3141
Palladium	1552	2826	3980	7196
Lutetium	1652	3006	3327	6021
Titanium	1668	3035	3260	5900
Thorium	1750	3182	4200	7592
Platinum	1769	3216	4530	8186
Zirconium	1852	3366	3580	6476
Chromium	1875	3407	2199	3990
Vanadium	1919	3486	3000	5432
Rhodium	1960	3560	4500	8132
Hafnium	2150	3902	5400	9752
Ruthenium	2250	4622	4900	8852
Boron	2300	4172	2550	4622
Iridium	2410	4370	5300	9572
Columbium	2468	4474	4927	8900
Molybdenum	2610	4730	5560	10,040
Tantalum	2996	5425	6100	11,012
Osmium	3000	5432	5500	9932
Rhenium	3180	5756	5900	10,652
Tungsten	3410	6170	5900	10,652

praseodymium; by the platinum metals: palladium, platinum, rhodium, ruthenium, osmium, iridium; and by the refractory metals: hafnium, molybdenum, tantalum, rhenium, and tungsten. Hafnium apparently has the longest liquid range of any element, about 3250°C (5850°F).

It is to be emphasized that the temperatures reported for melting and boiling points over about 2200°C (3992°F) contain a degree of inaccuracy which increases with increasing temperature. Not only are temperature-measuring devices increasingly unreliable, but their use becomes more difficult as the temperature becomes higher. The platinum/platinum-rhodium thermocouple can be used with good results to about 1700°C (3092°F), the iridium/iridium-rhodium to about 2000°C (3632°F),

the tungsten-iridium to about 2200°C (3932°F) in the absence of oxygen, and the iridium/iridium-10 per cent ruthenium to 2300°C (4112°F), according to Steven.[12] Rhenium-tungsten and rhenium-molybdenum thermocouples can be used to over 2200°C (3932°F) in the absence of oxygen.

Optical pyrometers, based on radiation methods, are relied on for measuring higher temperatures and can be used with an accuracy of ±25°C at temperatures considerably above 3000°C (5432°F). They are applied with corrections in the theoretical expressions of radiation relationships, with filters, and with corrections for sight-glass absorption.

Many of the temperatures given in the literature for the boiling points of metals are

TABLE 35.4. ELECTRICAL RESISTIVITY OF METALS

(Elements in italics are not included in this book.)

	Resistivity (microhm-cm)		Resistivity (microhm-cm)
Aluminum	2.66 (20°)	Neodymium	64 (25°)
Antimony	41.7 (20°)	*Nickel*	7.8 (20°)
Arsenic	33.3 (20°)	Osmium	9.5 (0°)
Beryllium	4.2 (20°)	Palladium	10.3 (20°)
Bismuth	106.8 (0°)	Platinum	10.58 (20°)
Boron	650 × 10⁹ (27°)	Plutonium	146.45 (0°)
Cadmium	6.83 (0°)	*Potassium*	6.1 (0°)
Calcium	4.6 (20°)	Praseodymium	68 (25°)
Cerium	75 (25°)	Rhenium	19.14 (0°)
Cesium	36.6 (30°)	Rhodium	4.7 (0°)
Chromium	12.8 (20°)	Rubidium	11.6 (0°)
Cobalt	5.68 (0°)	Ruthenium	7.16–7.6 (0°)
Columbium	14.6 (20°)	Samarium	92 (25°)
Copper	1.692 (20°)	Scandium	66 (25°)
Dysprosium	91 (25°)	Selenium	12 (0°)
Erbium	86 (25°)	Silicon	15 × 10⁶ (300°)
Europium	81.0 (25°)	*Silver*	1.59 (20°)
Gadolinium	134.0 (25°)	*Sodium*	4.3 (0°)
Gallium	56.8 (20°)	Strontium	23 (20°)
Germanium	60 × 10⁶ (25°)	Tantalum	13.6 (25°)
Gold	2.44 (20°)	Tellurium	52,700 (25°)
Hafnium	35.5 (20°)	Terbium	116 (25°)
Holmium	94 (25°)	Thallium	18 (0°)
Indium	8.8 (22°)	Thorium	18 (25°)
Iridium	5.3 (0°)	Thulium	90 (25°)
Iron	10.7 (20°)	*Tin*	11.5 (20°)
Lanthanum	57 (25°)	Titanium	42 (20°)
Lead	22 (20°)	Tungsten	5.5 (20°)
Lithium	8.55 (0°)	Uranium	30 (25°)
Lutetium	68 (25°)	Vanadium	24.8 (20°)
Magnesium	4.46 (20°)	Ytterbium	28 (25°)
Manganese	185 (20°)	Yttrium	65 (25°)
Mercury	95.78 (20°)	*Zinc*	5.75 (0°)
Molybdenum	5.78 (27°)	Zirconium	44 (20°)

based on extrapolations of vapor pressure or heat capacity data as deduced from thermodynamic calculations. If the material being considered were to act as a perfect liquid or gas, such extensions obviously would be entirely valid, but there are deviations from perfect behavior that cannot always be determined. However, as more basic data become available about such deviations, the determination of elevated temperature properties becomes more reliable.

There are several techniques for determining high temperature data for metals. One is the use of the rate of vaporization at elevated temperatures, as from an electrically heated filament. By the appropriate use of thermodynamic relationships the vapor pressure at various temperatures can be calculated and thus the boiling point defined. The methods are explained in detail by Jones, Langmuir, and Mackay.[2]

Spectroscopic data can be utilized to calculate vapor pressures; results are based on obtaining the expression for the free energy of a gas from the spectroscopically determined energy levels. Kelley presents the methods in the first part of his summary of values for the free energies of vaporization and vapor pressures of inorganic substances.[3]

Still another method for estimating boiling points, devised by Richardson,[11] utilizes the vaporization of a mixture of six or more elements in the arc of a spectrograph. The order of appearance of the elements in the arc is the same as the order of their boiling points, and the exact time of appearance is determined by locating the beginning and end of the spectrum lines of each element on a moving photographic plate driven at a constant rate. By including in the charge at least three elements with known boiling points, the boiling points of the others can be read from a time-temperature plot. The Richardson technique is capable of much refinement through study of the actual charge temperatures obtained with an optical pyrometer, since its accuracy depends on the accuracy of

TABLE 35.5. THERMAL CONDUCTIVITY OF METALS
(Elements in italics not included in this book.)

	Thermal conductivity, cal/cm/cm²/sec/°C		Thermal conductivity, cal/cm/cm²/sec/°C
Aluminum	0.503 (25°)	Neodymium	0.031
Antimony	0.045 (25°)	*Nickel*	0.215 (25°)
Beryllium	0.35	Palladium	0.17
Bismuth	0.020	Platinum	0.17
Cadmium	0.222 (18°)	Plutonium	0.020 (25°)
Calcium	0.3	*Potassium*	0.232 (21°)
Cerium	0.026	Praseodymium	0.028
Cesium	0.044 (28.5°)	Rhenium	0.17
Chromium	0.16 (20°)	Rhodium	0.36
Cobalt	0.165 (0–100°)	Rubidium	0.07 (39°)
Columbium	0.125 (0°)	Selenium	0.0007–0.00183
Copper	0.934 (20°)	Silicon	0.20
Dysprosium	0.024	*Silver*	0.934 (100°)
Erbium	0.023	*Sodium*	0.317 (21°)
Gadolinium	0.021	Tantalum	0.13 (20°)
Gallium	0.08 (30°)	Tellurium	0.014 (25°)
Gold	0.707 (25°)	Thallium	0.093
Hafnium	0.0533 (50°)	Thorium	0.09 (200°)
Indium	0.06	*Tin*	0.1528 (0°)
Iridium	0.35	Titanium	0.041
Iron	0.175	Tungsten	0.31 (20°)
Lanthanum	0.033	Uranium	0.0645 (25°)
Lead	0.0827 (18°)	Vanadium	0.074 (100°)
Lithium	0.17 (0°)	Yttrium	0.024
Magnesium	0.376 (20°)	*Zinc*	0.2653 (18°)
Mercury	0.020 (0–100°)	Zirconium	0.04 (25°)
Molybdenum	0.298 (204°)		

the boiling points of the internal standards used.

Table 35.4

The electrical resistivities of metals are given in Table 35.4, the values being those at or near room temperature. As with other properties the electrical resistivity of a metal is affected by the amounts and nature of impurities and by the temperature. It is especially sensitive to the presence of the interstitial elements O, N, H, and C, which tend to segregate at grain boundaries. In general the resistivity increases with increasing temperature; impurities may

lower or raise the value, depending on their nature.

The effect of temperature on boron is especially pronounced: at 27°C (81°F) the resistivity is 775,000 ohms; it decreases with rising temperature to a value of 4 ohms at 600°C (1112°F). Semiconductors such as germanium and silicon, as well as alloys containing such elements as gallium, tellurium, and indium, supply unusual electrical resistivity relationships; selenium's resistivity is altered by light. These factors make such metals most useful for a growing variety of applications.

Among the metals commonly considered to be conductors, the range of electrical resistivity is

TABLE 35.6. COEFFICIENT OF LINEAR THERMAL EXPANSION
(Elements in italics not included in this book.)

	Coefficient/°C × 10⁻⁶		Coefficient/°C × 10⁻⁶
Aluminum	23.86 (20–100°)	Neodymium	6.7 (25°)
Antimony	10.8 (0–100°)	*Nickel*	13.3 (25°)
Arsenic	5.6 (40°)	Osmium	4.6 (50°)
Barium	19	Palladium	11.67 (20°)
Beryllium	12	Platinum	8.9 (20°)
Bismuth	13.3	Plutonium	55 (21–104°)
Boron	8.3 (20–750°)	*Potassium*	83 (20°)
Cadmium	29.8 (25°)	Praseodymium	4.8 (25°)
Calcium	22.0	Rhenium	6.6
Cerium	8.5 (25°)	Rhodium	8.5 (20°)
Cesium	97 (20°)	Rubidium	90 (20°)
Chromium	6.2 (20°)	Ruthenium	9.1 (20°)
Cobalt	12.36 (40°)	Scandium	12 (25–100°)
Columbium	7.1 (20°)	Selenium	37 (40°)
Copper	16.6 (20°)	Silicon	4.68
Dysprosium	8.6 (25°)	*Silver*	19.68 (0–100°)
Erbium	9.2 (25°)	*Sodium*	71 (20°)
Europium	32 (50°)	Strontium	23 (20°)
Gadolinium	6.4 (25°)	Tantalum	6.6 (25°)
Gallium	18 (0–30°)	Tellurium	16.75 (40°)
Germanium	6	Terbium	7.0 (25°)
Gold	14.2 (20°)	Thallium	28 (20°)
Hafnium	5.9 (0–1000°)	Thorium	12.5 (20°)
Holmium	9.5 (400°)	Thulium	11.6 (400°)
Indium	24.8	*Tin*	20 (20–163°)
Iridium	6.5	Titanium	8.4
Iron	11.7 (20°)	Tungsten	4.45 (0–500°)
Lanthanum	4.9 (25°)	Uranium	a₀ +36.1
Lead	29.1 (20°)		b₀ −8.7
Lithium	56		c₀ +31.3
Lutetium	12.5 (400°)	Vanadium	8.95
Magnesium	25.8 (20°)	Ytterbium	25.0 (25°)
Manganese	22 (20°)	Yttrium	10.8 (25–1000°)
Mercury	182 (20°) (cubical coeff.)	*Zinc*	29.2 (40°)
Molybdenum	5.44 (20°)	Zirconium	5.89

great, from 1.59 microhm-cm for silver to 95.8 for mercury to 185 for manganese. Long appreciated but nonetheless surprising is the small number of really good conductors: silver, copper, gold, and aluminum with resistivities of 1.59, 1.692, 2.44, and 2.66, respectively, followed by beryllium, sodium, magnesium, calcium, and rhodium, in that order.

Table 35.5

Table 35.5 lists the thermal conductivities of metals, showing values at or near room temperature. This property is affected by impurities or additives and by temperature. The change with temperature may be positive or negative, differing in this respect from electrical resistivity which generally rises with increase in temperature.

It is of interest that the four metals with the highest thermal conductivity—silver, copper, gold, and aluminum—also rank in that order with respect to electrical conductivity,

and that the same elements are in the first ten in each listing of these two properties. Mercury, plutonium, and the rare earth metals are at the low end of the list of thermal conductivities.

Table 35.6

The coefficients of linear thermal expansion, defined as the change in length per unit length per degree centigrade temperature change, are given in Table 35.6. According to this tabulation the alkali metals have the greatest coefficients of expansion, ranging from cesium to lithium in order of decreasing atomic weight, followed by plutonium, selenium, europium, cadmium, zinc, and lead, in that order. Of the metals listed, tungsten has the lowest coefficient, with osmium and silicon second and third from the bottom of the list.

The value actually varies with the crystal axis along which the measurement is made, but since the crystal orientation is random for most

TABLE 35.7. MODULUS OF ELASTICITY OF METALS

(Elements in italics not included in this book.)

	Modulus of elasticity, million psi		Modulus of elasticity, million psi
Aluminum	10.3	*Nickel*	30
Antimony	11.3	Osmium	80
Beryllium	44.2	Palladium	16
Bismuth	4.6	Platinum	22
Boron	64	Plutonium	14.5
Cadmium	8	Praseodymium	5.11
Calcium	3–4	Rhenium	67
Cerium	4.35	Rhodium	41.2
Chromium	42	Ruthenium	60
Cobalt	30	Samarium	4.95
Columbium	15.2	Selenium	8.4
Copper	17	Silicon	15.5
Dysprosium	9.15	*Silver*	11
Erbium	10.63	Tantalum	27
Gadolinium	8.15	Tellurium	6
Gold	10.8	Terbium	8.34
Hafnium	20	Thorium	10.3
Holmium	9.7	*Tin*	5.9
Indium	1.57	Titanium	15.5
Iridium	74	Tungsten	59
Iron	30	Uranium	27
Lanthanum	5.6	Vanadium	18–19
Lead	2.6	Ytterbium	2.58
Magnesium	6.5	Yttrium	9.62
Molybdenum	47	*Zinc*	12
Neodymium	5.5	Zirconium	13.7

TABLE 35.8. THERMAL NEUTRON CROSS SECTIONS OF ELEMENTS IN
ASCENDING ORDER OF ABSORPTION CROSS SECTION

(for 2200 m/sec neutron velocity)

Element	Atomic number	Absorption cross section, barns/atom	Element	Atomic number	Absorption cross section, barns/atom
D	1	0	Th^{232}	90	7.56
O	8	<0.0002	U	92	7.68
C	6	0.0034	Pd	46	8.0
He	2	0.005	Pt	78	8.8
F	9	<0.010	La	57	9.3
Be	4	0.010	Pr	59	11.6
Bi	83	0.034	Se	34	12.3
Mg	12	0.063	Mn	25	13.2
Si	14	0.16	Os	76	15.3
Pb	82	0.170	W	74	19.2
Zr	40	0.180	Ta	73	21
P	15	0.20	Tc	43	22
Al	13	0.23	Sc	21	24
H	1	0.332	Th^{230}	90	27
Ca	20	0.44	Cs	55	29
Na	11	0.505	Kr	36	31
S	16	0.52	Cl	17	33.6
Sn	50	0.625	Co	27	37
A	18	0.66	Yb	70	37
Rb	37	0.73	Tb	65	46
Ce	58	0.73	Nd	60	46
Zn	30	1.10	Ag	47	63
Cb	41	1.15	Ho	67	65
Ba	56	1.2	Li	3	71
Sr	38	1.21	Re	75	86
Y	39	1.31	Au	79	98.8
N	7	1.88	Hf	72	105
K	19	2.07	Lu	71	112
Ge	32	2.45	Tm	69	127
Fe	26	2.53	Rh	45	156
Ru	44	2.56	Np^{237}	93	170
Mo	42	2.7	Er	68	173
Ne	10	<2.8	In	49	196
Ga	31	2.8	Pu^{240}	94	295
Cr	24	3.1	Hg	80	380
Tl	81	3.4	Ir	77	440
Cu	29	3.77	Ac	89	510
As	33	4.3	B	5	755
Te	52	4.7	Dy	66	950
Ni	28	4.8	Pu^{239}	94	1026
V	23	4.98	Pu^{241}	94	1400
Sb	51	5.7	Cd	48	2450
Ti	22	5.8	Eu	63	4300
Br	35	6.7	Sm	62	5600
I	53	7.0	Gd	64	46,000

(From: Hughes, D. J., and Schwartz, R. B., "Neutron Cross Sections," BNL–325, 2nd Ed., U.S. Government Printing Office, Washington, D.C., July 1, 1958).

metals, the average thermal expansion is the one obtained in all except a few cases, such as uranium.

Table 35.7

The modulus of elasticity, or Young's modulus of metals, is given in Table 35.7. Values presented are those given in the individual chapters of this book plus those listed in the "Metals Handbook."[9] Because of the difficulty of summarizing in a brief tabulation the values of other mechanical properties, such as tensile strength, yield point, elongation, etc., no attempt has been made to present data for these properties.

The demands of the atomic energy and missile programs have resulted in an outpouring of data on the mechanical properties of metals in the last few years which is most gratifying. Especially to be mentioned are the valuable data on properties at elevated temperatures.

Tables 35.8 and 35.9

Neutron absorption cross sections of all elements in ascending order of value are listed in Table 35.8, and the absorption cross sections of possible structural materials in ascending order are given in Table 35.9. The values refer to thermal neutrons the velocity of which is 2200 meters per second or the energy level of which is 0.025 ev. They are expressed in barns, an area of 10^{-24} square centimeter.

These data, of the utmost importance in the design of atomic reactors, reveal why certain elements are in demand for this purpose. In general the materials of construction of atomic reactors must not absorb enough neutrons to bring the multiplication factor, k, below unity and thus stop the chain reaction. At the same time resistance to corrosion, and chemical reactivity with coolants, for example, must be considered, as must mechanical properties such as strength and modulus of elasticity. Sacrifices must be made with respect to one property or another in order to attain a practical device. Unfortunately the common metals of construction—iron, copper alloys, and steel alloying elements—have rather high neutron absorption cross sections. This explains why a scarce material like zirconium is so useful. It is strong, corrosion resistant, not attacked appreciably by liquid metal coolants such as sodium, and has a relatively low cross section.

For the reverse reason metals like hafnium,

TABLE 35.9. THERMAL NEUTRON ABSORPTION CROSS SECTIONS OF POSSIBLE STRUCTURAL MATERIALS IN ASCENDING ORDER OF ABSORPTION CROSS SECTION

(for 2200 m/sec neutron velocity)

Element	Absorption cross section, barns/atom	Element	Absorption cross section, barns/atom	Element	Absorption cross section, barns/atom
C	0.0034	Ni	4.8	Ag	63
Be	0.010	V	4.98	Ho	65
Bi	0.034	Sb	5.7	Re	86
Mg	0.063	Ti	5.8	Au	98.8
Si	0.16	Th^{232}	7.56	Hf	105
Pb	0.170	U	7.68	Lu	112
Zr	0.180	Pd	8.0	Tm	127
Al	0.23	Pt	8.8	Rh	156
Sn	0.625	La	9.3	Np^{237}	170
Ce	0.73	Pr	11.6	Er	173
Zn	1.10	Se	12.3	In	196
Cb	1.15	Mn	13.2	Pu^{240}	295
Y	1.31	Os	15.3	Ir	440
Ge	2.45	W	19.2	B	755
Fe	2.53	Ta	21	Dy	950
Ru	2.56	Sc	24	Pu^{239}	1026
Mo	2.7	Th^{230}	27	Pu^{241}	1400
Cr	3.1	Co	37	Cd	2450
Tl	3.4	Yb	37	Eu	4300
Cu	3.77	Tb	46	Sm	5600
Te	4.7	Nd	46	Gd	46,000

TABLE 35.10. PRICES OF METALS (1960)

(Elements in italics not included in this book.)

Alphabetical order, $/lb		Increasing price order, $/lb		Increasing price order, $/cu in.	
Aluminum	0.26	*Iron*	0.062	*Sodium*	0.006
Antimony	0.29	*Lead*	0.118	*Iron*	0.018
Arsenic	0.60	*Zinc*	0.13	*Magnesium*	0.022
Barium	6.00	*Sodium*	0.165	*Aluminum*	0.025
Beryllium	47.00	*Aluminum*	0.26	*Zinc*	0.034
Bismuth	2.25	*Antimony*	0.29	*Lead*	0.048
Boron	318.00	*Copper*	0.33	*Potassium*	0.06
Cadmium	1.40	*Magnesium*	0.35	*Antimony*	0.07
Calcium	2.05	Manganese	0.45	*Copper*	0.106
Cerium	100.00	*Arsenic*	0.60	Calcium	0.114
Cesium	100.00	*Nickel*	0.74	Manganese	0.12
Chromium	1.15	*Tin*	1.00	*Arsenic*	0.124
Cobalt	1.50	Chromium	1.15	Lithium	0.19
Columbium	36.00	Cadmium	1.40	*Nickel*	0.24
Copper	0.33	Cobalt	1.50	*Tin*	0.263
Dysprosium	275.00	*Potassium*	2.00	Chromium	0.30
Erbium	275.00	Calcium	2.05	Cadmium	0.44
Europium	1300.00	Bismuth	2.25	Cobalt	0.48
Gadolinium	275.00	*Mercury*	2.84	Strontium	0.75
Gallium	1362.00	Tungsten	3.50	Barium	0.76
Germanium	136.00	Tellurium	3.50	Tellurium	0.79
Gold	510.00	Barium	6.00	Bismuth	0.80
Hafnium	30.00	Selenium	6.50	Selenium	1.12
Holmium	275.00	Thallium	7.50	Titanium	1.25
Indium	18.25	Titanium	7.65	*Mercury*	1.39
Iridium	1090.00	Molybdenum	8.00	Tungsten	2.44
Iron	0.062	Strontium	8.00	Zirconium	2.56
Lanthanum	100.00	Lithium	10.00	Molybdenum	2.95
Lead	0.118	Zirconium	11.00	Beryllium	3.12
Lithium	10.00	*Silver*	13.30	Thallium	3.21
Lutetium	1300.00	Uranium	18.18	Indium	4.82
Magnesium	0.35	Indium	18.25	*Silver*	5.05
Manganese	0.45	Thorium	23.00	Rubidium	5.52
Mercury	2.84	Hafnium	30.00	Cesium	6.76
Molybdenum	8.00	Vanadium	35.00	Vanadium	7.75
Neodymium	100.00	Tantalum	35.00	Thorium	9.68
Nickel	0.74	Columbium	36.00	Silicon	10.95
Osmium	1160.00	Beryllium	47.00	Columbium	11.13
Palladium	235.00	Cerium	100.00	Uranium	12.50
Platinum	1210.00	Cesium	100.00	Hafnium	14.40
Plutonium	12,700.00	Lanthanum	100.00	Tantalum	21.00
Potassium	2.00	Neodymium	100.00	Lanthanum	22.40
Praseodymium	100.00	Praseodymium	100.00	Cerium	24.10
Rhenium	780.00	Rubidium	100.00	Praseodymium	24.50
Rhodium	2000.00	Silicon	130.00	Neodymium	25.30
Rubidium	100.00	Germanium	136.00	Boron	25.69
Ruthenium	800.00	Yttrium	200.00	Germanium	26.00
Samarium	275.00	Palladium	235.00	Yttrium	32.40
Selenium	6.50	Dysprosium	275.00	Ytterbium	69.25
Silicon	130.00	Erbium	275.00	Samarium	75.00
Silver	13.30	Gadolinium	275.00	Gadolinium	78.40
Sodium	0.165	Holmium	275.00	Dysprosium	84.98
Strontium	8.00	Samarium	275.00	Holmium	87.40
Tantalum	35.00	Ytterbium	275.00	Erbium	90.00

Table 35.10. Prices of Metals (1960) *(cont.)*

(Elements in italics not included in this book.)

Alphabetical order, $/lb		Increasing price order, $/lb		Increasing price order, $/cu in.	
Tellurium	3.50	Boron	318.00	Palladium	102.00
Terbium	1300.00	*Gold*	510.00	Europium	247.00
Thallium	7.50	Rhenium	780.00	Gallium	289.00
Thorium	23.00	Ruthenium	800.00	*Gold*	356.00
Thulium	1300.00	Iridium	1090.00	Ruthenium	358.00
Tin	1.00	Osmium	1160.00	Terbium	389.00
Titanium	7.65	Platinum	1210.00	Thulium	440.00
Tungsten	3.50	Europium	1300.00	Lutetium	462.50
Uranium	18.18	Lutetium	1300.00	Rhenium	594.00
Vanadium	35.00	Terbium	1300.00	Iridium	881.00
Ytterbium	275.00	Thulium	1300.00	Rhodium	898.00
Yttrium	200.00	Gallium	1362.00	Platinum	935.00
Zinc	0.13	Rhodium	2000.00	Osmium	942.00
Zirconium	11.00	Plutonium	12,700.00	Plutonium	9068.00

cobalt, and several of the rare earth metals with high absorption cross sections are valuable for control purposes. Here too, properties of good strength and corrosion resistance are desired.

Prices of Metals

The current prices of both the common and the rare metals are given, with few exceptions, in Table 35.10. Three listings have been prepared: the first is an alphabetical sequence for convenience in locating any particular one; the second is a sequence arranged by increasing price per pound of metal; the third is an arrangement according to increasing price per cubic inch of metal. This last list has been prepared to emphasize the volume basis of considering metal costs. For many reasons the volume and the area covered by a definite thickness of metal are of more importance than the weight. This is especially true if the costs of fabricated parts of similar dimensions are to be evaluated, or if corrosion resistant coatings are under consideration.

The prices given in Table 35.10 have been obtained chiefly from the individual chapters in this volume and from quotations given in *Oil, Paint and Drug Reporter, Chemical and Engineering News,* and *Engineering and Mining Journal.* The *Mineral Market* and other reports of the U.S. Bureau of Mines are another source. Naturally, a considerable range of prices is found for any given metal, depending on purity, form, and quantity ordered, but in general the prices listed are for quantity lots of the highest grade metals in commercially available forms. The price for boron, columbium, and tungsten is for powder; for arsenic, chromium, and manganese is for lumps or chips; for barium, rhenium, and strontium is for rod; for cesium, gallium, mercury, and rubidium is for containers for liquids; for hafnium is for crystal bar; for tantalum is for melting stock; for iron is the composite price of steel in 1959; for titanium is the composite price for mill forms in 1960; and all other prices are for ingots or billets.

A word about the prices for rare earth metals —these have been obtained as $100–180/lb for cerium, lanthanum, neodymium, and praseodymium; $275–300/lb for dysprosium, erbium, godolinium, holmium, samarium, and ytterbium; and $1300–3000/lb for europium, lutetium, terbium, and thulium. These prices pertain to metals of highest purity and reflect quantity factors as well as the balance of demand for any metal relative to others which must be separated from sources that contain all of these elements in more or less fixed ratios. In Table 35.10 the lower price in each range has been given.

Although it was not realized at the time that the selection was made of the metals to be covered in this book, examination of the listing by order of increasing cost on a per pound basis reveals that price alone apparently warrants the choices made. Of the first twelve metals in that list, all except manganese are not included in this book. Moreover, only three metals long known and used by man and not covered in this book, namely, mercury, silver, and gold, appear further down the cost list.

It is evident that price is a good reason for designating any metal as either "rare" or "common."

The market price of any metal is controlled by one or more of many factors. Availability and cost of raw materials, ease of processing, and scale of operation are among the most important. Many metals are affected by strategic demands that create shortages and raise prices, or create over-capacity and lower prices. Titanium has been affected by the last situation. Dependence upon foreign sources of ores sometimes causes major fluctuations in cost in an uncontrollable manner. International and domestic political influences affect some, like copper, tin, lead, and zinc. The price of gold, uranium, and plutonium is set by government decree.

As has been the experience with aluminum and magnesium, it is to be expected that the price of other metals, notably titanium, zirconium, vanadium, columbium, and the rare earth metals, will continue to decrease as greater rates of production (and application) are attained. Many of the rare metals are now produced in such small quantities that their prices are not indicative at all of what they might be if larger scales of operation are reached. This is the situation with respect to boron, gallium, and the higher priced rare earth metals.

By and large, however, the prices given in Table 35.10 for most of the rare metals probably will remain for some time much as they are now due to limited and costly raw materials, inherently expensive processes for obtaining raw materials in the desired purity and form, small demands for raw materials with special properties, or combinations of these and other factors. Of course, as has been indicated, greater consumer demands will allow the initiation of the cheaper production rates reached only at greater output levels. Nor is the all-important influence of continuing technological improvements to be overlooked, whereby a metal now selling for many dollars per pound may become available for a fraction of that cost.

References

1. Everhart, J. L., Lindlief, W. E., Kanegis, J., Weissler, P. G., and Siegel, F., "Mechanical Properties of Metals and Alloys," *National Bureau of Standards Circular C447* (1943).
2. Jones, H. A., Langmuir, I, and Mackay, M. F., *Phys. Rev.*, **30**, 201 (1927).
3. Kelley, K. K., *U.S. Bur. Mines Bull. 383* (1935).
4. Kelley, K. K., *U.S. Bur. Mines Bull. 371* (1934).
5. Kelley, K. K., *U.S. Bur. Mines Bull. 393* (1936).
6. Kelley, K. K., *U.S. Bur. Mines Bull. 476* (1949).
7. Kelley, K. K., *U.S. Bur. Mines Bull. 477* (1950).
8. Lyon, R. L., "Liquid Metals Handbook," Washington, Atomic Energy Commission and Department of the Navy, 2nd Ed., 1952.
9. "Metals Handbook," Cleveland, American Society for Metals, 1948 (new edition now in preparation).
10. "Reactor Handbook," Vol. 3, "General Properties of Materials," U.S. Atomic Energy Commission, *AECD-3647*, 1955.
11. Richardson, D., "Spectroscopy in Science and Industry, Proceedings of the Fifth Summer Conference on Spectroscopy and Its Applications," pp. 64–70, New York, John Wiley & Sons, Inc., 1938.
12. Steven, G., chapter on "Temperature Measurement," p. 335, in "High-Temperature Technology," I. E. Campbell, editor, New York, John Wiley & Sons, Inc., 1956; also personal communication.
13. Stull, D. R., and Sinke, G. C., "Thermodynamic Properties of the Elements," Washington, American Chemical Society, 1956.

INDEX